ELECTRONIC DESIGN

From Concept to Reality

FOURTH EDITION

MARTIN S. RODEN
California State University, Los Angeles

GORDON L. CARPENTER
California State University, Long Beach

WILLIAM R. WIESERMAN
University of Pittsburgh at Johnstown

Discovery Press
Los Angeles, CA

Includes bibliographical references
ISBN 0-9646969-1-6
Library of Congress Catalog Card Number:
97-65044

Production Supervisor: **Raymond B. Landis**
Cover Design: **David McNutt**
Cover Photos: **Courtesy of NASA**
Editorial Consultant: **Dennis J. E. Ross**
Distribution: **Legal Books Distributing: (800) 200-7110**

Printed in the United States of America.

10 9 8 7 6 5 4 3 2 1

0-9646969-8-3

PREFACE

Electronic Design, Fourth Edition is written for use in the core electronics courses in undergraduate programs in electrical engineering. The book provides coverage of three areas: discrete devices, linear integrated circuits, and digital integrated circuits. A practicing engineer looking for a current reference for self-study will also find this book valuable. The only prerequisite for understanding the material in this text is a basic knowledge of circuit analysis.

Why This Book?

With many books in the field of analog and digital electronics to choose from, you may wonder why we have written yet another book on the subject. Our principal goal in writing this text is to relieve our frustrations. We had attempted to teach electronics to undergraduates using traditional texts. These other texts look at the field from a theoretical point of view, emphasizing analysis and the physics of semiconductors, but paying little attention to the important and exciting design applications. Dealing only with fundamentals detracts from the excitement of the subject, and, indeed, the student may never develop the design skills required for a career position in electronics. While our book covers the fundamentals in a thorough and direct fashion, it goes one step further toward a balanced approach to designing electronic systems. The requirements of the Accreditation Board for Engineering and Technology (ABET) and the industry demand that this type of approach be taken.

It is our hope that this book will inspire the imaginations of tomorrow's engineers. These professionals will be called upon to *design*, not just to analyze, electronic systems.

Features of This Text

As this text enters its fourth edition, we have maintained many positive features of the previous editions will enhancing important areas. These include:

- Heavy emphasis on design.
- Numerous design *Examples* that provide a real-world flavor. These are taken from the years of engineering experience of the authors.
- A readable writing style that results from class teaching and student evaluation of the earlier editions.
- A proper balance among the three areas of the text.
- Extensive use of *Exercises*. Unlike the examples, these exercises contain only the answers (not solutions). They allow students to reinforce the concepts.
- Both the analog and digital portions of the text have been thoroughly updated. Data sheets are taken from current references.
- Computer simulations using PSPICE have been added to many sections of the text. Extensive discussion of computer models is included.
- Each chapter begins with a list of objectives and ends with a summary.

- Many of the design approaches taught in the book have been enhanced to help the student understand the reasons leading to various design decisions. Although design problems are under-specified (i.e., fewer equations than number of unknowns), the student must not get the impression that any decisions are arbitrary.
- Any hints of the dreaded "cook book approach" have been removed from design discussions.
- MOSFET coverage has been expanded.
- All diagrams in the text have been redrawn for improved clarity.

Uniqueness of the System Design Approach

Contacts with practicing engineers and engineering recruiters have encouraged us to place significant emphasis on *design* of electronic *systems*. The new engineer will be asked to design systems using an ever-increasing inventory of new linear and digital ICs, discrete components, and electromechanical devices. Thus, we attempt to teach engineering students to *think* as system designers, rather than to mimic just a few design approaches. Our goal is to "educate" rather than to "train."

Elementary design procedures are introduced early in the text to motivate the student. It is our experience that electronic design is best comprehended through a "learn by doing" approach. Thus, topics such as small-signal analysis have been presented immediately following *dc* analysis to allow for presentation of some early meaningful and realistic design problems.

Appendices

The book includes appendices covering:

- Standard Component Values
- Manufacturers' Data Sheets for selected devices
- Answers to Selected Problems

Micro-Cap 7, Student Edition

Included with this text is a CD with the most recent version of the very popular electronic circuit analysis program, Micro-Cap. This program, from Spectrum Software, adapts a SPICE engine to a user-friendly input and output format. A brief manual is included on the CD.

Accuracy of the Book

Nobody likes errors! As authors, we have nightmares about them. Every effort has been made to write and publish an *accurate* book. Many reviewers have picked through the earlier editions of the text, and users of the first three editions were often vocal in pointing out typographical errors. This new edition evolved out of extensive use in the classroom environment. It has been thoroughly checked and class-tested with students.

Instructional Adjuncts

The following materials are available to instructors:

•An **Instructor's Manual** containing complete solutions to all the exercises and end-of-chapter problems in the book. The manual includes design case studies.

•Problem sets on computer disk.

•Overhead projector **Transparency Masters** of the important figures in the text

•A **Laboratory Manual** is available separately from the publishers. It is keyed to sections of the book.

Guide for Classroom Use

The material in this book can be presented in a series of two or three one-semester courses or three one-quarter courses in the junior and/or senior years.

Earlier versions of this book have been successfully used in both individual courses (e.g., analog electronics or digital electronics), and comprehensive sequences of courses. Examples of some approaches are given in the following table:

One quarter course in basic electronics	Chapters 1, 3, 4, 5 and 6
One semester course in basic electronics	Chapters 1, 3, 4, 5, 6, and 7.
Two-quarter sequence in basic electronics	Chapters 1, 3, 4, 5, 6, 7, 10, 11, 12
Two-semester sequence in basic electronics	Chapters 1 through 12
One quarter or one semester course in digital electronics	Chapters 14, 15 and 16

Acknowledgments

We express our appreciation to the students in the various electronic design classes the authors have taught while using the earlier versions of this text. Sincere thanks are extended to our colleagues, Professor Hassan Babaie, Lou Balin, Roy Barnett, Fred Daneshgaran, Ed Evans, Mike Hassul, Ken James, George Killinger, and Sid Soclof for their comments and assistance with various portions of the manuscript.

A very special acknowledgment to the late Dr. C. J. Savant, Jr. Sixteen years ago, Dr. Savant had a dream of authoring a core electronics book that "broke the mold" and prepared graduates for the real world in a way no other books were doing. We are pleased that he lived to see his dream fulfilled with a text whose first two editions were used and enjoyed by students at well over 100 major universities in the United States. His influence stretched around the world with the many translations of those texts. This book would not have been possible without the pioneering vision of this outstanding professor and unique human being.

Every book is the result of a number of iterations and revisions based on classroom experience and the expert advice of reviewers. We were fortunate to have fifty seven readers review all or part of the manuscripts for the first, second and third and fourth editions. We hereby thank the following reviewers, and the many others who are not mentioned by name, for their efforts:

H. Jack Allison, Oklahoma State University

Kay D. Baker, Utah State University
W. L. Beasley, Texas A&M University
Robert L. Bernick, Cal Poly Pomona
Raymond Black, New Mexico State University
T. V. Blalock, University of Tennessee
Frank Brands, Washington State University
John Churchill, UC Davis
R. G. Deshmuckh, Florida Institute of Technology
Mahmoud El Nokali, University of Pittsburgh
E. L. Gerber, Drexel University
Ward Helms University of Washington
George W. Hoyle, Northern Arizona University
Alfred T. Johnson, Jr., Widener University
B. Lalevic, Rutgers University
Hung Chang Lin, University of Maryland
John Lowell, Texas Tech University
Edward W. Maby, Rensselaer Polytechnic
Eugene Manus, Virginia Polytechnic Institute and State University
Donald C. Moore, South Dakota State University
Richard Morris, University of Portland
David A. Navon, University of Massachusetts, Amherst
Harry Neinhaus, University of South Florida
Charles Nelson, California State University, Sacramento
David Perlman, Rochester Institute of Technology
William Sayle, Georgia Institute of Technology
Bernhard Schmidt, University of Dayton
Deborah Sharer, University of North Carolina at Charlotte
Barry Sherlock, University of North Carolina at Charlotte
Paul Van Halen, Portland State University
Darrell L. Vines, Texas Tech University
J. L Yeh, Rutgers University
Carl R. Zimmer, Arizona State University
Reza Zoughi, Colorado State University

We also acknowledge Dr. Bradley Clymer of The Ohio State University, who participated in many discussions regarding the philosophy of the third edition and made numerous valuable suggestions.

We truly hope that all of the people who contributed to this book and had a hand in its development are as pleased with the finished product as we are.

Gordon L. Carpenter
Martin S. Roden
William R. Wieserman

Introduction to the Student

You are embarking on an exciting adventure in your undergraduate education. Electronics is the backbone, and the driving force behind much of Electrical Engineering.

When many of your (more senior) professors were undergraduates, very few students could say they specialized in *electronics*. An Electrical Engineering major claiming to be specializing in electronics was similar to a Math major claiming to specialize in *addition*. Each "specialization" was viewed as a necessary tool on the way toward a particular application such as communications, computers, or power. The passage of time has dramatically altered the situation! The rapidly accelerating pace of electronic developments has been the necessary catalyst for most of the newer technologies, from high-speed personal computers to cellular telephones. While electronics *must* be understood and appreciated by all Electrical Engineers, the need for specialists has never been greater.

We sincerely hope this book serves both purposes–to lay the foundation for use by all specializations within Electrical Engineering, and to motivate some of you to specialize in electronics.

This is not an easy task, since the field is changing at a rapid pace. You must be careful to concentrate upon *education* rather than *training*. Those who were *trained* in vacuum tube electronic design during the 1950s found their training to be useless a decade later when transistors replaced vacuum tubes in all but a few high-power or high-frequency applications. Likewise, those who were *trained* in transistor design during the 1960s and early 1970s found that training to be obsolete with the advent of integrated circuits and op-amp systems. It is therefore important that you prepare yourself for the next revolution by both learning the fundamentals and "learning how to learn."

Many texts approach this challenge by overemphasizing the theory and completely avoiding applications. This is certainly not the case with our text! A sterile theoretical presentation could leave you with some basic knowledge that you could *someday* apply. However, you would probably not experience the excitement of applying this knowledge to practical situations as you learn. Indeed, you would not even know if you are capable of it.

For that reason, this text is *design oriented*. You will be guided through many practical applications of the theory–and we do mean *practical!* We emphasize that the practical design procedures presented in this text represent *one way* of reducing the theory to practice. True design requires many tradeoff decisions, and there is more than one correct answer given the system constraints. For this reason, the procedures we illustrate are **not** the only ways in which the theory can be applied to practical situations. You are encouraged to seek other procedures, either independently or with the help of your professor. We hope you will be motivated to construct some of the systems you will design on paper, for that will truly "close the loop" and make your education more meaningful.

Some of the problems at the back of the chapters might seem overwhelming at first glance. Learning design is a gradual process, so don't become discouraged. You will find you are capable of making progress on even the most complex design problems.

Most of all, enjoy the subject material. You have chosen an exciting career, but the same factors that make it exciting also make it challenging. You must sometimes strain to the limits of your mental abilities if you are to succeed, but the rewards of success will be fine compensation.

If you have any comments or suggestions about the text, please feel free to communicate them to either of the authors. Because we take a genuine interest in engineering education, we welcome all your comments and suggestions.

Gordon Carpenter
email: WPCOL2813@cs.com
Martin S. Roden
email: mroden@calstatela.edu
William Wieserman
email: k3zyk@pitt.edu

TABLE OF CONTENTS

CHAPTER 14 - PULSED WAVEFORMS AND TIMING CIRCUITS

CHAPTER 15 - DIGITAL LOGIC FAMILIES

CHAPTER 16 - DIGITAL INTEGRATED CIRCUITS

APPENDICES

Chapter 1

Basic Concepts

Part of this introductory chapter is a review of the circuit concepts that you should have learned in your prerequisite course(s). These concepts will be viewed in a way slightly different from that you have already done–a way that will make it easier to develop the circuit models for solid state devices. In addition to this review, we discuss the differences between design and analysis and give you an idea of what you will learn in this course. After reading this chapter, you will:

- Know and appreciate the history of modern electronics.
- Learn circuit analysis techniques for developing solid state mathematical models.
- Appreciate the difference between linear and nonlinear elements.
- Know the essential contrasts between analog and digital systems.
- Develop the mathematical model for different frequency ranges.
- Appreciate the essential difference between analysis and design.
- Know the important role played by computer simulations in design and analysis.
- Appreciate the essential components in the design process.

1.0 INTRODUCTION

The study of electronic circuits is a continuation of electric circuit analysis – probably your first Electrical Engineering course. It uses *nonlinear devices* in contrast with the linear devices with which you are already familiar: resistors, capacitors, inductors, voltage sources, and current sources. The nonlinear devices in which we are most interested are diodes and transistors. You will become familiar with new operations that can be performed on signals using these nonlinear devices. These include amplification, clipping, thresholding, and digitizing.

1.1 HISTORY

The field of electronics had its beginning in 1906 when Henry Dunwoody developed the simplest nonlinear device, the diode. He placed a piece of electric furnace carborundum between two brass holders. Later that year, Greenleaf Pickard put this device to practical use by developing a crystal radio detector in the form of a cat's whisker in contact with a crystal. Studies conducted during the period from 1906 to 1940 indicated that silicon and germanium were excellent materials to use in the construction of these devices.

Although William Shockley has been credited with the discovery of the *transistor*, it was really John Bardeen and Walter Brattain who discovered it on December 16, 1947. When Bardeen identified *carrier injection* with a current, the transistor era began. The first "instant-on" oscillator-amplifier was designed in 1949 using point contact transistors – it is still operating at the University of Illinois Museum. This was a crude device without much practical application. It was intended primarily for laboratory use. Meanwhile, in industry, the *vacuum tube* dominated in applications ranging from consumer goods to advanced military hardware. But there were many applications that the vacuum tube could not fulfill without a great deal of expense. Even worse, certain applications were impossible using vacuum tubes.

Soon after the invention of the transistor, engineers saw its advantages for lightweight electronic hardware with very low power consumption and high reliability. Initially, it was difficult to manufacture these devices. It wasn't until the late 1950s that many earlier manufacturing problems were overcome. The need for low power, light weight, high reliability devices for intercontinental missiles and space vehicles forced the government and industry to place a lot of effort into solving these manufacturing problems. This resulted in a technology explosion in solid state development.

During this time, John Moll became a dominant figure in the development of different types of transistors and the analysis of the resultant devices. The *Ebers-Moll transistor model* is still used today to evaluate transistor performance.

William Shockley is credited with developing the *field effect transistor* during the early 1950s. These early solid state devices were separately made and then wired to the other circuit elements (e.g., resistors, capacitors and inductors) to make up electronic circuits such as amplifiers or logic circuits. The resulting circuits were much smaller and lighter in weight than the conventional vacuum tube circuits. These circuits are known as *discrete circuits* in contrast to *integrated circuits* that have all the components fabricated on one single silicon chip. In 1960, Fairchild Semiconductor Corporation introduced a family of monolithic transistor logic gates that contained a number of transistors and resistors on a single chip. Improvement in fabrication techniques led to further advances and the integration of more and more components on a single chip. We can now place millions of components on a single chip. Advances in the electronic technology will result in improvement of power handling capability, number and types of components on a single chip, and performance at higher and higher frequencies. In the future, new materials will be developed which can be even more useful for circuit design.

1.2 SOLID STATE CIRCUIT MODELS

A *model* is a copy or imitation of something. In electrical engineering, we use models to help us analyze and design complex systems. The model represents an attempt to take a complex real-life system and reduce it to a theoretical abstract made up of ideal components. For example, when you draw a zigzag line on a piece of paper and apply Ohm's law, you are dealing with an ideal model of what we call a *resistor*. If you go into the lab and work with a practical resistor, you realize that the idealized pencil and paper model is simply a first approximation. You can improve the approximation by adding to the model. For example, you can model the real resistor with an ideal resistor in parallel with a capacitor. This yields an improved model. As more and more components are added to the model, its behavior more closely matches that of the practical device.

The observations we just made about modeling a resistor apply equally to more complex devices and systems. The goal is to devise an ideal model that closely matches the terminal behavior of the real system. That is, if you enclosed the real system in a box with only the terminals exposed, you could not tell whether the box contained that real system or the ideal model.

In your earlier electrical engineering studies, you learned to analyze electric circuits composed of capacitors, inductors, resistors, and power sources. Our goal is therefore to take complex electronic devices and *model* them with the ideal components you have already studied. How closely the behavior of the model matches the actual operation of the device being modeled is dependent on how complex the model is.

Solid state devices are not simple electric circuits. We will therefore have to develop models for each solid state device. The complexity of the model will be determined by the application of the solid state device and what results we want from the device. For example, we may sometimes simply need an approximate solution to determine the overall behavior of a system. In such cases simple models will be sufficient, even if they only approximately agree with the real device behavior.

The complexity of the model will also depend on what resources we have available for the analysis. Simple models permit quick "paper and pencil" analysis. However, if computers are available to perform the analysis and simulation, we can use far more complex models.

We will also find that the choice of model depends on operating conditions. We will explore non-linearities in the following section. This will lead us to conclude that the choice of model depends on the actual form of the input signals. Larger signals require different models than do small signals.

Signal frequencies also affect our choice of model. Looking back at the resistor, we saw that a more accurate model includes a parallel capacitance. However, if the resistor is operated at *dc*, the capacitor behaves as an open circuit and there is no need to include it in the model. For this reason, we will develop special models for transistors operating at high frequency.

1.3 LINEAR AND NONLINEAR CIRCUIT ELEMENTS

Up to now in your electric circuit studies, you have examined resistors, capacitors, inductors, and independent current and voltage sources. These elements are *linear.* If the input is scaled (multiplied or divided by a constant) the output is scaled by the same amount. A system is linear when it exhibits the properties of *homogeneity* and *superposition.*

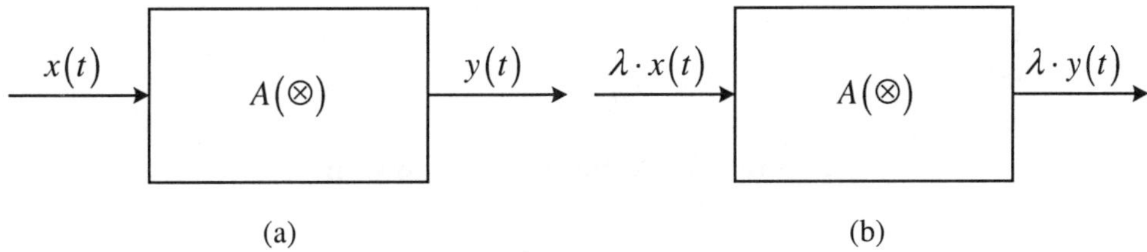

Figure 1.1 - Homogeneity

The property of *homogeneity* is shown in Figure 1.1 where $A(\otimes)$ is defined as "convolved with *h(t)*". We show an input of *x(t)* and an output of *y(t)* with *y(t)* equal to *h(t)* convolved with *x(t)*. If the input is now scaled by $\lambda > 0$, the output is also multiplied by λ. That is,

$$\lambda x(t) \otimes h(t) = \lambda\left[x(t) \otimes h(t)\right] = \lambda y(t) \quad (1.1)$$

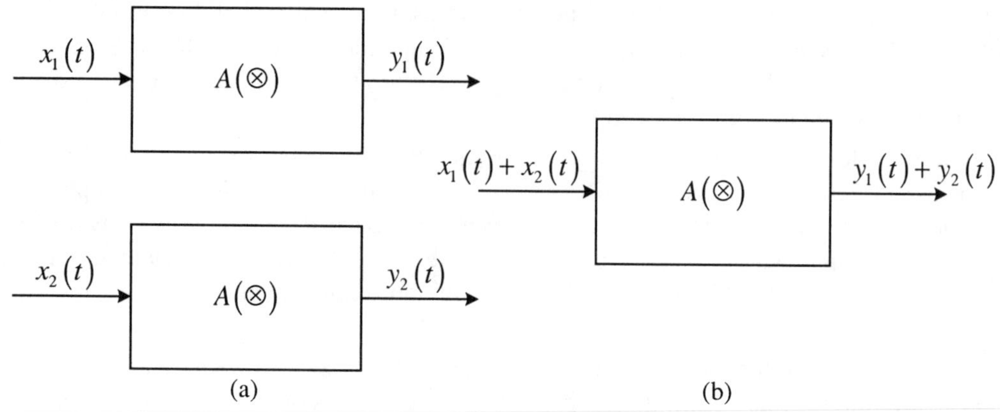

Figure 1.2 - Superposition

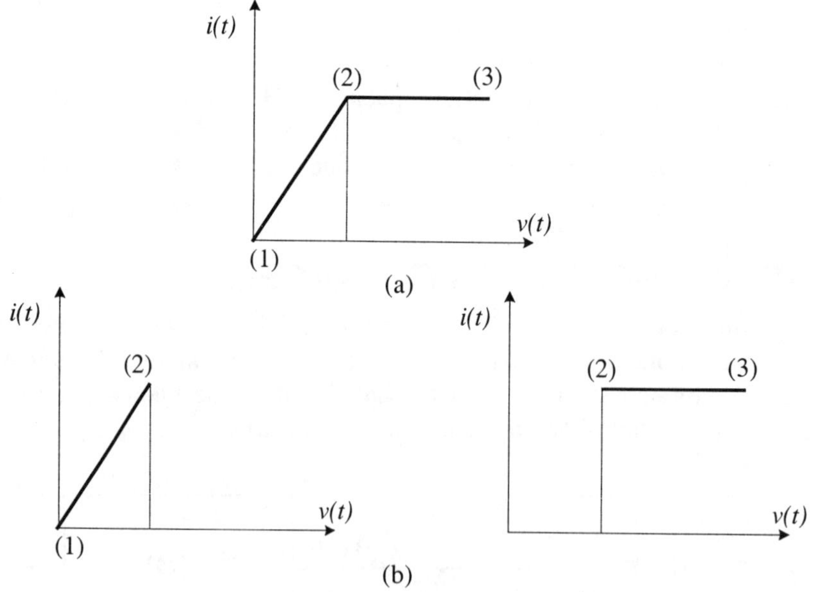

Figure 1.3 – Nonlinear relationship

The property of *superposition* is an important function of linear systems. It allows you to characterize a system using a single input-output pair (i.e., the impulse response). Figure 1.2 shows that a linear system can be analyzed piece by piece. We break down the input into smaller increments and then sum the corresponding outputs. This permits simpler analysis, particularly when the component pieces can be easily analyzed.

If

$$h(t) \otimes x_1(t) = y_1(t)$$
$$h(t) \otimes x_2(t) = y_2(t) \tag{1.2}$$

then

$$h(t) \otimes [x_1(t) + x_2(t)] = h(t) \otimes x_1(t) + h(t) \otimes x_2(t) = y_1(t) + y_2(t) \equiv h(t) \otimes x_3(t)^1.$$

As an example of the usefulness of this property, suppose you know how a system behaves when the input is a sinusoidal waveform. You can then infer the behavior for complex periodic inputs. This is true since the periodic input can be expressed as a Fourier series expansion.

In most cases, we attempt to "break down" the circuit into sections, each of which is linear. In this manner, we can use the superposition principle since it is a powerful tool to analyze circuits. When we develop the models, we try to use linear systems as the building blocks so that these analytical tools are available to us. As an example, refer to Figure 1.3 where we show a nonlinear relationship between current and voltage.

The nonlinear system of Figure 1.3 (a) can be broken down into two linear segments, as shown in Figure 1.3 (b). The horizontal line can be considered one linear segment and the sloped line can be considered another linear segment. This approach allows us to make different models for different circuit conditions or limitations.

1.4 ANALOG VS. DIGITAL SIGNALS

An *analog signal* can be viewed as a waveform which can take on a continuum of values for any time within a range of times. Although a measuring device may be limited in resolution (e.g., It may not be possible to read an analog voltmeter more accurately than the nearest 1/100 of a volt), the actual signal can take on an infinity of possible values. For example, you might read the value of a voltage waveform at a particular time to be 13.45 (V). If the voltage is an analog signal, the actual value would be expressed as an extended decimal with an infinite number of digits to the right of the decimal point.

Just as the ordinate of the function contains an infinity of values, so does the time axis. Although we may conveniently resolve the time axis into points (e.g., every microsecond on an oscilloscope), the function has a defined value for any of the infinity of time points between any two resolution points.

Suppose now that an analog time signal is defined only at discrete time points. For example, suppose you read a voltage waveform by sending values to a voltmeter every microsecond. The resulting function is only known at these discrete points in time. This results in a *discrete time function*, or a *sampled waveform*. It is distinguished from a continuous analog waveform by the manner in which we specify the function. In the case of the continuous analog waveform, we

---

[1] Convolution is commutative. We may write $h(t) \otimes x(t) = x(t) \otimes h(t) = y(t)$. Convolution of h with x yields the same result as the convolution of x with h.

must either display the function (e.g., graphically, on an oscilloscope), or give a functional relationship between the variables. In contrast to this, the discrete signal can be thought of as a list, or sequence of numbers. Thus, while an analog voltage waveform can be expressed as a function of time, $v(t)$, the discrete waveform is a sequence of the form, v_n or $v[n]$, where n is an integer, or index.

A *digital signal* is a form of sampled or discrete waveform, but each number in the list can now only take on specific values. For example, if we were to take a sampled voltage waveform and round each value to the nearest tenth of a volt, the result is a digital signal.

We can use a thermometer as an example of all three types of signals. If the thermometer has a dial or a tube of mercury, the output is an analog signal. We can read the temperature at any time, and to any desired degree of accuracy (limited, of course, by the resolution of the reader – human or mechanical).

Suppose now that the thermometer consists of a dial, but that it is only updated once every minute. The result is an analog sampled signal.

If the thermometer display now takes the form of a numerical readout, the thermometer becomes digital. The readout is the result of sampling the temperature (perhaps every minute), and then displaying the sampled temperature to a predetermined resolution (perhaps the nearest 1/10 degree).

Digital signals result from many devices. For example, dialing a telephone number results in one of 12 possible signals depending on which button is pressed. Other examples include pressing keys on a bank automated teller machine (ATM), or using a computer keyboard. Digital signals also result from performing analog to digital conversion operations.

1.5 DEPENDENT SOURCES

Circuit courses concentrate on independent voltage and current sources. In the electronics models we will be developing, we will need to use dependent current and voltage sources.

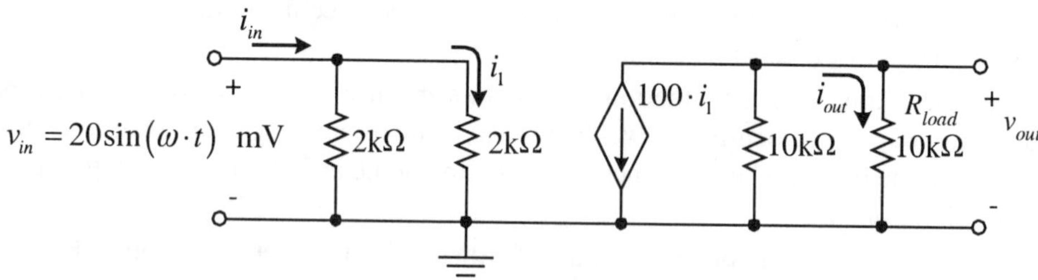

Figure 1.4 – Dependent source

Dependent sources (also known as *controlled* sources) produce a voltage or current whose value is determined by a voltage or current existing *in some other location* in the circuit. Note that passive devices produce a voltage or current whose value is determined by a voltage or current existing at the *same* location in the circuit. Both dependent and independent sources are *active* elements[2]. That is, they are capable of delivering power to some external device. *Passive* elements are not capable of generating power, although they can store finite amounts of energy for delivery at a later time as is the case with capacitors and inductors.

Figure 1.4 illustrates a simple model developed for a solid state device which we will use to illustrate the analysis techniques. Don't worry about where this comes from at this time. For now, we are simply illustrating a dependent source. We will find the voltage and current gain of the system. *Voltage gain* is defined as the ratio of the output to input voltage. Similarly, *current gain* is the ratio of the output to input current. The input current is

$$i_{in} = \frac{v_{in}}{R_{in}} = \frac{20\sin\omega t \quad mV}{1k\Omega} = 20\sin\omega t \quad \mu A \tag{1.3}$$

A current divider relationship can be used to find i_1.

$$i_1 = \frac{2000(20\sin\omega t) \quad \mu A}{2000+2000} = 10\sin\omega t \quad \mu A \tag{1.4}$$

The output voltage is then given by

$$v_{out} = -100 i_1 (10k\Omega \| 10k\Omega) = -(5\times10^5) i_1 = -5\sin\omega t \quad \text{V} \tag{1.5}$$

In Equation (1.5), $\|$ indicates a parallel combination of resistors.

Using a current divider relationship, the output current is

$$i_{out} = \frac{10^4(-100 i_1)}{10^4+10^4} = -50\cdot i_1 \tag{1.6}$$

The voltage gain is then

$$A_v = \frac{v_{out}}{v_{in}} = \frac{-5\sin\omega t}{0.02\sin\omega t} = -250 \tag{1.7}$$

The current gain is

$$A_i = \frac{i_{out}}{i_{in}} = \frac{-50(10\times10^{-6})}{20\times10^{-6}} = -25 \tag{1.8}$$

1.6 FREQUENCY EFFECTS

In Section 1.5, we examined a circuit which was a simple model of a solid state device. Note that this model did not include any capacitors or inductors. A more accurate model of the real device would include these elements.

---

[2] Strictly speaking, dependent sources might not be active elements. For example, a dependent source can be used to model a transformer (a non-active device). However, as we will use them in this text, dependent sources will always be active elements.

There are usually two types of capacitors in a real circuit. The first type consists of large capacitors that are included for a variety of reasons that will become clear later in this text. Since capacitive impedance is inversely proportional to the value of the capacitor, we often assume that all the large capacitors act as short circuits for the signals of interest. That is, the impedance is considered small compared to other impedances in the circuit. The second type of capacitor found in more complete circuit models consists of small capacitors that are part of the detailed solid state model. These have relatively high impedance, so we often assume that these small capacitors act as open circuits for the signals of interest. That is, the impedance is considered high compared to other impedances in the circuit.

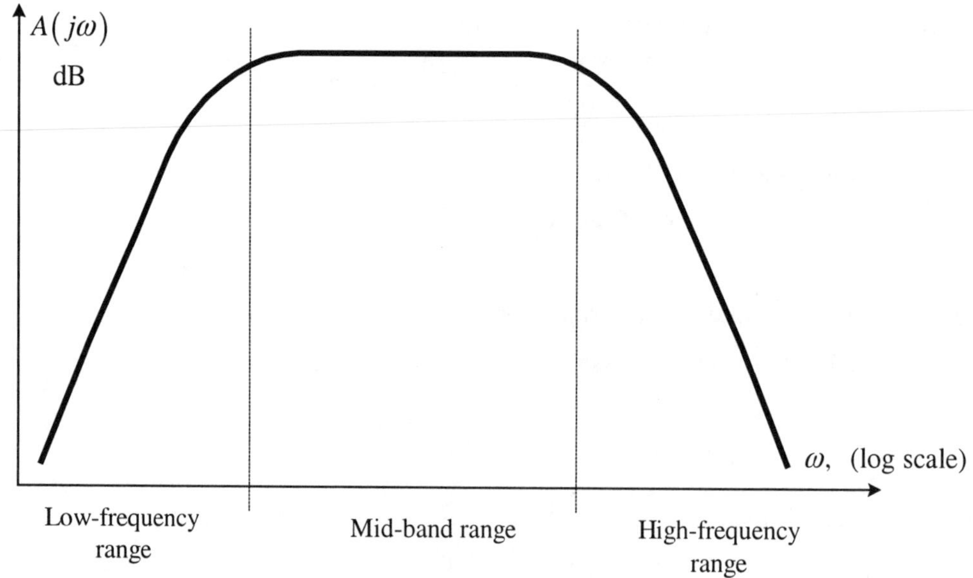

Figure 1.5 Frequency response

The approximations we just described apply for the *mid band frequency range*. If we can work in this range of frequencies, our models can be made simple. For more thorough analysis, we normally subdivide the frequency spectrum into three ranges: low frequencies, mid band frequencies, and high frequencies. The exact definitions of these frequency bands are determined by the location of the poles and zeros of the circuit. These poles and zeros are determined by the values of the resistors, capacitors, and other components in the circuit.

For the low-frequency band, the impedance of a large series capacitor becomes significant. The capacitor can no longer be assumed to be a short circuit. The small shunt capacitors (those in the models) present no problems at these frequencies as they can be assumed to be open circuits.

For the high-frequency band, the impedance of the large series capacitors approaches zero but the small shunt capacitors become the predominant factor. These small capacitors must be included in the model.

When the effects of the three frequency bands are combined, we find performance curves that resemble that of Figure 1.5. You can think of this as the transfer function $A(j\omega)$ of the overall system. Note that there is a flat portion in the mid range of frequencies. Then the performance falls off at both low and high frequencies due to the effects of the capacitors.

Amplifiers are often designed to have a flat frequency response over a preferred range of input frequencies. In the initial chapters of this text, we will concentrate on the flat frequency range or mid band frequency. This allows us to concentrate our efforts on learning the characteristics of different amplifiers without having to evaluate the poles and zeros of the circuits. The models will not include series and shunt capacitors.

1.7 ANALYSIS AND DESIGN

When a complete circuit is presented (perhaps including models), we can determine the input-output characteristics. These include voltage gain, current gain, power gain, and input and output impedance. This process is one of *analysis* as it determines how the circuit reacts to a particular input. But engineers would not be in much demand if all they did was examine existing systems and circuits and make observations about the behavior of these systems and circuits. The real challenge of engineering is to change things around us. Therefore, rather than simply analyze systems, the engineer must make new systems to achieve desired results. This is the essence of *design*.

1.7.1 Comparison of Design and Analysis

In *analysis*, all parameters are given and a specific question is asked. For example, you may be given a complex circuit and asked to find the ratio of output voltage to input voltage (i.e., the voltage gain). In developing the circuit, solid state devices may have been replaced by their circuit models.

Design starts with a requirement and a list of constraints. For example, you might be asked to design a circuit with a particular voltage gain. The constraints might include costs, component counts, power utilization, input impedance, or time required to do the design and testing. This process is termed design as you know what you want but need to determine the type of circuit that would meet these requirements.

In analysis, we find that there is a single solution. In design, there can be many solutions that all meet the given requirements.

The first step in design is to identify the circuit type or circuit types that are needed to achieve the stated requirement. Using the analytical equations defined for the circuit selected, we can determine the number and sizes of the components needed.

1.7.2 Origin of Design Requirements

Design requirements are really *specifications*. These might be *system specifications*. If so, they can usually be broken down to the subsystem and then to the equipment level. The systems engineering group in a company starts with the system level requirements given by the customer or by the product design organization. These requirements are broken up and reduced to the subsystem and equipment levels, as shown in Figure 1.6.

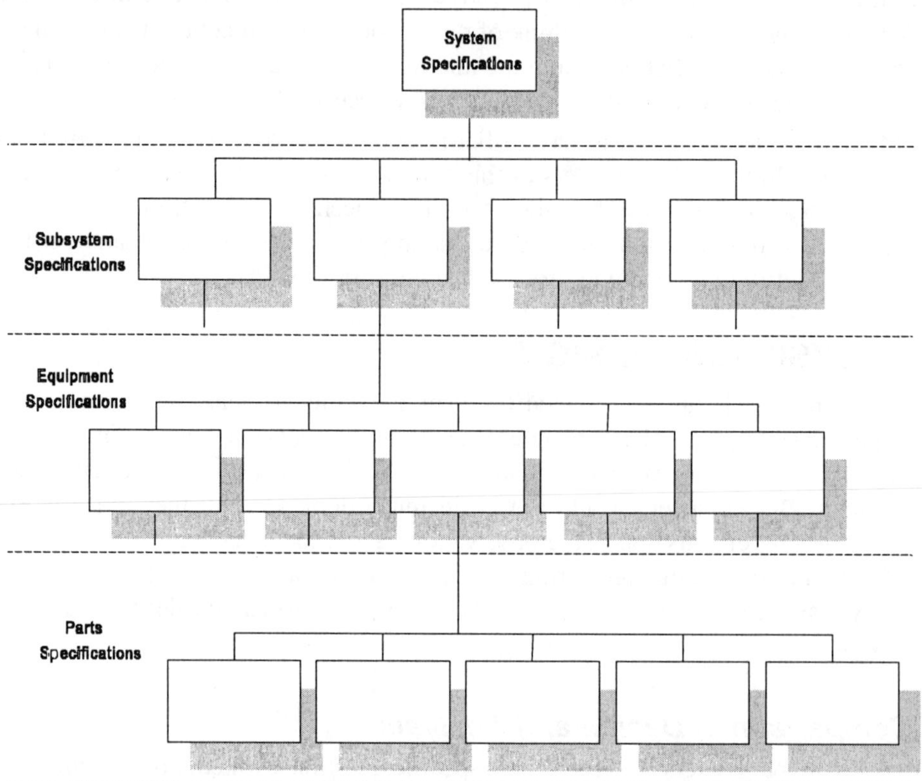

Figure 1.6 – System and subsystems specifications

Systems engineers are responsible for breaking down the requirements for the system and allocating the contributions of each subsystem to the overall requirements. These engineers determine the interface between subsystems so that each subsystem will be compatible with all the other subsystems and with the outside environment.

As a simple example, consider the constraint of the weight of a system. The systems engineer allots specified weights to each subsystem so that the overall weight will not exceed the requirements of the system. The subsystems engineer would then divide the specified subsystem weight into portions allocated to each component of the subsystem. Each subsystem component is made up of different circuits. The *circuit level design engineer* takes the equipment specifications and designs circuits that meet these specifications. Clearly we are describing a complex team effort.

In this text, we concentrate on giving the circuit level design engineer tools to use to meet the requirements defined by the system and subsystem level engineers.

1.7.3 What Do "Open-Ended" and "Trade Off" Mean?

When people talk about real life design problems, two terms often appear: *open-ended* and *trade offs.* These terms are important to the design process.

Real life design is unlike most of the textbook end-of-chapter problems you have dealt with in your earlier courses. These text problems typically carefully define the problem, and specify enough so that your answer is either right or wrong. There is only one correct answer, and you lose points on an exam if your answer doesn't match this.

The first thing you find in the real world is that even the question is not defined. As an engineer, your first job is to define the problem and identify constraints - you must decide what question to ask.

The idea of trade offs can be traced to the early history of civilization. Its recent manifestations probably date to the early part of the 20th century when Werner Heisenberg developed the *Heisenberg uncertainty principle*. This principle says that the position and velocity of an electron in motion cannot simultaneously be measured with high precision. As you do a better job measuring position, you do a worse job on velocity, and vice versa. The version you are probably most familiar with forms part of a linear systems course. That is the relationship between rise time and bandwidth (i.e., time-bandwidth product). The faster you want a signal to change in time, the wider the range of frequencies must be. There is an inverse relationship between time and frequency. You may also have learned that in synthesizing a filter (for example, a low-pass filter), the closer you get to the ideal amplitude characteristic, the worse the phase characteristic. In less technical terms, as one thing gets better, another gets worse. You can find examples of trade offs throughout your experiences, both technical and non-technical.

Let's begin with a "non-electrical" example. Suppose you were an automotive engineer working for a large car company. Your job is to design a "safe" car. Clearly you could design cars that are safer than those presently on the road. For example, if you drove the highways in a military tank, you probably would not have to worry about being injured in an (nonmilitary) accident. Why don't the engineers design cars to be like military tanks? The answer rests in trade off decisions. Safety is *not* the only consideration. Generally, as cars are made safer they are probably going to be more expensive, less attractive, heavier (i.e., need more fuel), larger, and slower. So as the automotive engineer, you must settle for a less safe car in order to balance safety against the other criteria for good design.

Looking now at an example from recent Electrical Engineering, let's look at the cellular telephone. There are many trade off decisions required in its design. At the system level, engineers had to choose power levels and signal formats. The higher the power, the further the distance a telephone can transmit. However, with increasing power, the device becomes heavier, batteries do not last as long, and the public gets more nervous about physiological effects of the transmitted signal on the human body. Additionally, the further the device transmits, the fewer people can simultaneously use one band of the channel. Choice of signal format also contains trade offs. Some formats are easier to implement and lead to increased user capacity, but they can interfere with hearing aids. Other formats contain desirable features, but are balanced against noisier signals.

At the circuit level, decisions must be made regarding batteries and electronic circuitry. Some forms of circuitry require less power and are lighter, but lead to increased noise in the system. Increasing battery capacity leads to higher weight, larger size, and potential dangers of battery explosion.

Clearly the engineer must balance all of the conflicting requirements and come up with a design that satisfies the need. There is not just a single correct solution to this design problem.

The concept of *open-ended* is closely related to the trade off considerations. Going back to the textbook problem, once you solve it, you *know* that you are finished. The open-ended problem has no well-defined ending. You may come up with a design that must be later modified due to changing requirements. Another design engineer may come up with a totally different way to approach the design specifications.

An overused word in design is *optimum.* Specifications sometimes call for the "optimum solution." In real life, there is no "best" solution. There are only solutions that meet the various design specifications.

The legendary Norbert Wiener (the father of cybernetics) was once asked if a particular solution he proposed was optimum. Folklore has it that he shrugged his shoulders, looked at the person who asked the question, and replied, "I did the best I could." Indeed, if we add to the list of constraints the limited ability of the particular engineer solving the problem, then all solutions are optimum. The optimum solution to a particular problem might do a terrible job meeting specifications if one constraint is that the problem be solved completely in five minutes.

1.8 COMPUTER SIMULATIONS

Throughout this text, we present computer simulations as an augmentation to the theoretical approach to design and analysis. A computer is capable of using detailed models of various components in the performance of circuit analysis. It can factor in such physical conditions as temperature dependence and device tolerances.

One of the earliest and most widely used circuit analysis programs is *SPICE* (Simulated Program with Integrated Circuit Emphasis). This program was developed at the University of California, Berkeley and first released in 1973. It has been continuously refined since that time, and is still accepted as the standard in analog network simulation programs. We include a thorough discussion of SPICE in Appendix A. Several derivatives of SPICE having wide use include Micro-Cap, Capture/PSpice, from Cadence (merger of MicroSim Corporation and OrCAD Corporation), and Electronic Workbench are readily available for use with personal computers (PCs). Experience with high-level simulation software represents a window into the future - a window that is very clear and very bright. At the turn of the century, nearly all electronic design, development, testing, and troubleshooting may be *simulated* on a computer. All components and processes exist only as databases and mathematical operations. Only at the very end of the product development is the design turned into a real device.

Micro-Cap is a SPICE-based computer simulation program. A copy of the Student Version of Micro-Cap VII is included with this text. We refer to this program in several of the examples throughout this text. A major difference between the various simulation programs is in the method of drawing circuits. SPICE typically requires that the user specify components in terms of the nodes to which they are connected (i.e. a *netlist*). [An option known as the *Design Center* provides a graphical input interface of SPICE.] Alternatively, Micro-Cap allows the user to draw the circuit directly on the computer display screen. Both programs use the same models, and Micro-Cap can accept SPICE file listings as input. PSpice uses an input file and is written in C-language while Micro-Cap uses a schematic input and is written in Microsoft Basic. Although this gives Micro-Cap some advantages regarding circuit alterations (e.g. a new run with modified file is not required each time something is changed), it does give PSpice an overall speed advantage. Such a speed advantage becomes significant when simulations are used for design rather than analysis (on relatively slow PCs).

The computer results vary from our calculated results because of the use of more detailed models. For example, in many of our calculations, we assume that parameters of electronic devices remain constant at their nominal values. In contrast, the computer simulation varies these parameters according to operating point. If the computer simulation yields a far-different result from the "paper solution," we have to reconcile these discrepancies. Perhaps a mistake was made in the paper solution, or an error was made in the input to the computer.

Computer simulation is popular on PCs. The capacity and speed of the PC are such that we are usually using the simulation for *analysis* rather than *design*. That is, we usually *verify the performance* of a circuit in which the various components have *already been selected.*

Simulation programs can be used for design by employing an *iteration* technique. For example, if we wish to choose a resistor value, we can analyze the circuit for various resistor values and choose the one that achieves the desired results.

The computer simulation is also useful in performing *worst case* and temperature analysis. The programs assign a tolerance to each parameter. In a *Monte Carlo* analysis, the computer runs the simulation many times, and between runs it randomly varies parameters within their specified ranges. This produces a family of performance curves. The program can also step the temperature through a specified range, thereby developing another family of output curves. These results are critical to the circuit designer. Even though a particular design may nominally meet specifications, it may not do so in actual application due to temperature variations and tolerances. It is important for the designer to know this and to make appropriate adjustments.

1.9 COMPONENTS OF THE DESIGN PROCESS

Problems facing the electronics engineer can involve material from every chapter in this text. Electronic system design draws from a good portion of your past knowledge. This makes design extremely challenging - indeed it has the potential to be discouraging. It is important to keep in mind that good design skills are acquired over a long period of time. You should not expect to be an expert electronic circuit designer having just taken your first course covering this material.

1.9.1 Principles of Design

The orderly approach to problem solving consists of five major steps. We briefly state the steps here, and expand on the discussion in the following sections.

1. ***Define the problem:*** State what your product is supposed to accomplish, including any special requirements and specifications.

2. ***Subdivide the problem:*** To simplify and speed the design process, break up the main problem into several smaller problems. It is difficult for even the most experienced engineer to solve a large, complex problem in one operation.

3. ***Create documentation:*** The essence of engineering is to generate drawings or plans so that the system can be manufactured and sold on the market. The best piece of engineering design

work is useless unless others are aware of it. It would not be satisfying or profitable if all your work had to be repeated each time the product is produced.

4. *Build a prototype:* We like to think that our theory and equations represent good models of real life behavior. In practice, this is not always the case. Until a prototype is built and tested, the designer cannot be sure that all contingencies have been considered and that the design specifications have been met. This step may include computer simulations.

Since the prototype is not built until we have some confidence that the "paper" design is complete, we include a section entitled "Design Checklist." We suggest that you develop such a checklist just before constructing the prototype.

5. *Finalize the design:* Once the prototype is working to your satisfaction, test it under the conditions in which it will be used. Then complete any documentation that may be required beyond the drawings that have already been generated.

This concludes the design cycle. However, it is valuable to consider other options or methods of designing the product. A discussion with several of your engineering colleagues can often lead to valuable improvements. A flowchart of the process is shown in Figure 1.7.

Once the design process is complete, the finished documents are sent to the appropriate departments and construction of the product begins. If your job has been done properly, you have generated a clear set of plans, instructions, and additional information needed to build, service and update the design.

1.9.2 Problem Definition

The first step in the design process is to *define the problem.* In this stage of the design, the engineer faces one of two possibilities. A fully specified design may be available or the design may be a vague idea in the mind of a customer. The engineer will often be faced with a combination of these two where part of the design must perform certain precise functions, while the other part of the design is in the form of a hazy sketch.

In the case of the fully specified design, the engineer's job is to analyze and understand the specifications given by the customer. After reviewing the requirements, the engineer will often meet with the customer to make sure that they both understand and agree on what the product is supposed to do. It is now the engineer's task to design a product that will meet the specifications. If a product does not measure up to these requirements, the manufacturer will be forced to modify the design in order to make the product meet the standards or face loss of money, reputation and time. The consequences of this course of action for the design engineer are open to speculation. It is an opportunity for activity by the design engineer.

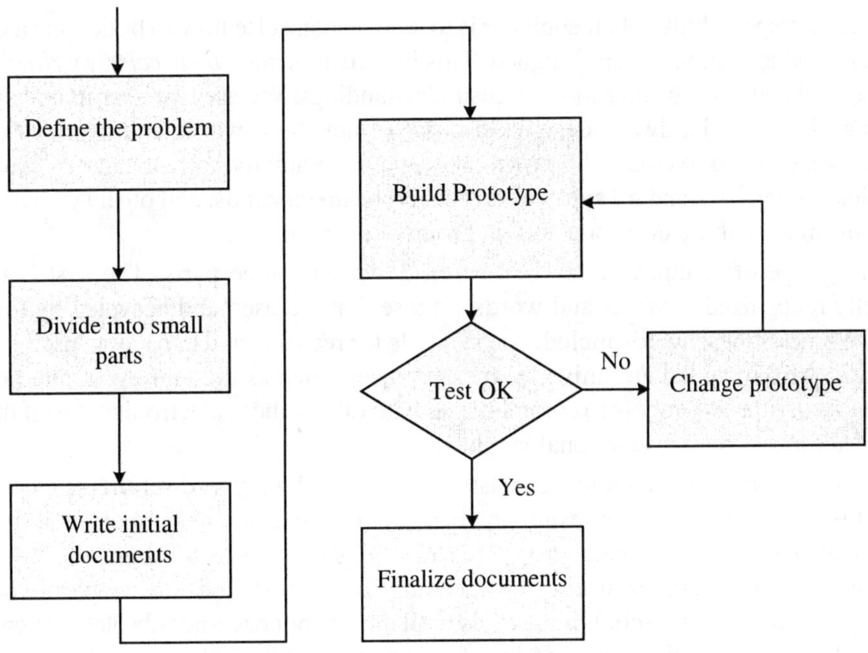

Figure 1.7 – Design process flowchart

In cases where the design is not fully specified, the customer may have only a general idea of what the product should accomplish. It is then the job of the engineer to define the product for the customer. This will usually require that the engineer and customer work together until both sides have agreed upon the product definition. Once again, the engineer must exercise care in determining special customer requirements. If the product fails to perform to expectations, the customer may decide to take future business elsewhere.

1.9.3 Subdividing the Problem

Once the product has been defined and specified, the problem is usually broken into a series of smaller designs. The number of smaller designs depends on the complexity of the product.

As an example, consider the design of an electronically controlled toaster. One design group could be working on the toaster mechanism, while another group works on the electronic control portion. In this case, the product design is broken into two parts. Even with such a simple example, there are other ways to divide the problem. It is the project engineer's job to divide the problem into the best subsets so that the design can be rapidly and inexpensively implemented. Frequently, an engineering department is divided into groups that specialize in the various disciplines - for example, power supplies, electronic circuits, and control electronics.

1.9.4 Documentation

A primary responsibility of an engineer is to tell someone else how to build, service, use and update the product that has been designed. This information *must be precisely written* so it will not be lost and there will be no room for misunderstandings. We use many terms and symbols in specifying electronic hardware design. In order to put these words and symbols on paper, engineers were forced to create their own language. Like any living language, the language of electronics has certain standard symbols that everyone understands, and other symbols that have come to mean something else for a certain group of users.

The language of electronics can be broken down into three parts. The first is the set of universally recognized symbols and words - those that are used and accepted by most of the industry. Some of these words include the symbols for resistors and capacitors used in drawing schematics. Also included are universal measurements such as the ohm, volt, and henry. The engineer can use these symbols to communicate with others about electronics even if the readers do not speak the same conversational language.

The second part of the language consists of the symbol and word set that is recognized by most, but is not standardized. For example, there are several different symbols used for the field effect transistor (FET), all of which mean the same thing but they look different from each other. This subset will be recognized and the meaning understood, but the people involved will continue to use their own symbols and words until the symbol becomes obsolete or nonstandard. Many "jargon" words such as *bus* and *interface* can be used in several ways and mean various things to different people.

The final portion of this language is composed of the special forms that each separate business uses to communicate internally. Many of these forms are specialized for use only by the company in question. Others are semi-standard forms that are variants on industry standards. Every time an engineer moves to a new company, a new dialect must be learned so that documents can be generated in acceptable form. Examples of these forms include schedules, requisitions, and product change requests - information that the company must know but outsiders need not know.

1.9.5 The Schematic Diagram

The *schematic* or *circuit diagram* is a plan of an electronic device that is drawn using standard and nonstandard symbols. This diagram shows the interconnections and components used to build the circuit. A schematic usually shows only the electrical connections needed to build a circuit, and not the physical layout and construction of the circuit.

The schematic is one of the most important documents that an engineer must draw. Most of the other documents needed for production and servicing are derived from the schematic drawing.

In order to draw a clear and understandable schematic of the entire system, it is usually desirable to first draw individual schematics for each of the blocks in a subdivided system. The complete schematic is then drawn using the smaller ones and combining them in appropriate ways.

The master schematic is arranged to put related modules next to each other so that the interconnecting signal lines traverse the shortest path. The master schematic is drawn so that each of the modules occupies a separate part of the plan. As a rule of good design, modules should be shown as a whole and not scattered over the drawing. Related stages that have inputs and outputs in common should be drawn next to each other.

1.9.6 The Parts List

Anyone who has ever used a list for grocery shopping understands the concept behind the parts lists. This is a compendium of all of the parts needed to construct the product. The list shows the component tolerances, power ratings, voltage levels, and type of component (e.g., if a capacitor is electrolytic, paper, or mica). This list is often subdivided into modules so that it is easier to read. Components of the same type are listed together for ease of reference. Parts lists are used by both engineers and managers for cost evaluation and as a checklist for building the prototype. There is no standard way in which to make a parts list since each manufacturer has its own ideas on what should be included. A sample list with some of the possibilities is shown below. Such a parts list is often produced and updated using a computer simulation program.

In addition, the following may also be listed:

1. Alternate parts
2. Parts manufacturer
3. Serial numbers if applicable.
4. Other information deemed necessary by the engineering, marketing, and production departments.

Schematic Symbol	Value in appropriate units	Additional descriptive information	Manufacturer's or in-house part number	Quantity Required
R_1, R_2	10 k, 1/4 W	carbon film 5%	R10353	2
R_3	12 k, 1/4 W	carbon composition 10%	R12310	1
C_1	0.01 μF	50 (V) disc ceramic	C18201	1

1.9.7 Running Lists and Other Documentation

In addition to the schematic and the parts list, other lists are used at the prototype production stages. These lists are assigned various names and can be arranged in several different ways. The purposes of these lists are to keep track of wiring, maintain a list of signals, and to ease the construction of the prototype. Typical lists, including running, wrapping, signal and wiring lists, are shown below:

Signal	Location	X	Y
CE	10C12	1119	110
CE	5B6	509	90
CE	3D2	330	130
CE	2D3	220	120

The **X** and **Y** entries in the table indicate pin location according to a grid system.

These lists, in combination with the parts lists and the assembly drawings, are used by engineers to build and test the prototype and generate the paperwork that the production department needs in order to build the unit. Computer simulation programs provide a great tool for the engineer to generate and update these lists.

1.9.8 Using Documents

There are different types of documents and paperwork used throughout the engineering profession. Many of these documents are for company use in accounting, advertising, or management. We have covered a few types of documents used for building and planning a unit. To keep track of what changes have been made to a unit, schematics and lists must be constantly updated and changed. Whenever changes are made to the unit, all of the appropriate documents should be changed as soon as possible. Trusting to memory is a sure way to create errors in the documents, and to waste time for everyone who must use these documents in order to test and build the unit.

1.9.9 Design Checklist

We are almost ready to build and test the prototype. However, since the transition from paper design to hardware represents a major step in the design process, we recommend a pause at this point to double check the previous work.

Some problems that may occur include the following: outputs that are inadvertently tied together assuming different states, floating IC terminals, ground loop problems, inter-coupling between circuits, and false triggering.

Most engineers who design electronic circuitry have a checklist that they run through in their minds while they are designing the circuits. Unfortunately, these lists are usually developed as a result of making design errors. They represent attempts to avoid repeating the same mistake twice.

A short version of a typical checklist might contain the following four steps. If some of these seem obscure at this point, be patient. As you progress through the text, the various precautions will take on more meaning.

1. ***Input and output precautions***: Make sure that all unused inputs are tied to either an output, a ground, or a power supply. Inputs that are left floating can assume incorrect levels and "fool" the circuit into thinking that another logic level has been applied. Another input related item is to check that the number of inputs connected to any one output does not exceed the specifications

for the device. If the number is too large, additional buffers must be added so that the circuit can properly feed the load.

2. ***Timing problems***: Many troubles occur in circuits when events are expected to happen simultaneously but do not. These problems can be traced back to propagation delays. This causes an integrated circuit with several outputs to change state at different times, even though the design calls for the events to happen at the same time. Another problem that can occur is when several inputs require data at the same time and the inputs are delayed by first going through other circuitry. Although compensating time delays can be added, often the only sure way to cure time related problems is to redesign the circuit.

3. ***Special requirements***: This category includes any special quirks that must be considered. For example, certain memory ICs cause spikes to appear on their power inputs. In order for these pulses not to interfere with other devices, the power input pins must be bypassed with a capacitor that is located close to the power input pin. In addition, some chips must have their outputs tied to the supply voltage through a resistor for proper operation.

4. ***Power requirements***: The designer must make sure that the power supply can deliver the required current and voltage. Additionally, the supply must be adequately filtered and there must be sufficient bypass capacitors on the supply leads. Provision must be made for the escape of excess heat.

1.9.10 Prototyping the Circuit

While this text is not intended as a guide to circuit construction, a few words on the subject are in order. Engineers, experimenters, and hobbyists require fast, economical means of constructing circuits. None of these people need to construct large numbers of circuits. Production methods of building circuits are not usually warranted because of cost and complexity. Mass-produced circuits use printed circuit boards (often double sided). These boards are plated and processed at a printed circuit board fabricating facility. It is difficult to rectify mistakes on such a board, or to make changes. When changes are required, traces are cut and lifted from the board and/or jumper wires are added. To avoid this problem, several methods have been developed that permit easy alteration of circuits.

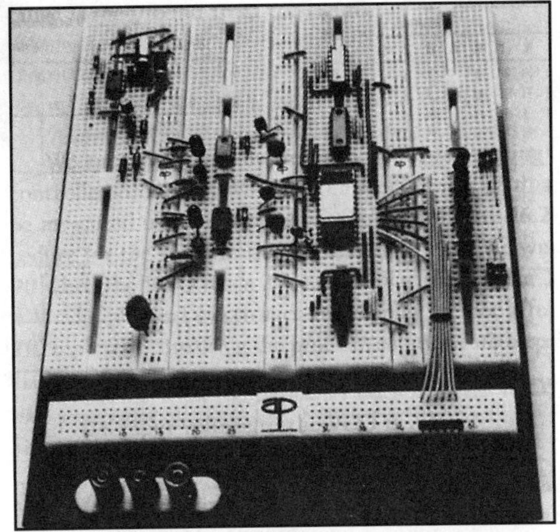

Figure 1.8 - Proto-Board*(Courtesy of AP Products)*

One device that is commonly used for simple circuits goes under a variety of trade names including *Proto-Board* and *Circuit Board*. A representative board is shown in Figure 1.8. It consists of a plastic base with a grid of interconnected holes that can be used to connect components together. These boards are designed to accept standard integrated circuits and component leads so that any element may be used. They are fast to use, and components may be reused. There are some disadvantages associated with using these boards. Because of their layout, they suffer from high inter-lead capacitance and, after much use, develop intermittent lead contacts.

Another popular method for prototyping and small production runs is *wirewrap*, as illustrated in Figure 1.9.

Connections are made using a special tool and socket combination that permits fast and reliable circuit interconnections. The special socket consists of a top portion that allows the insertion of an integrated circuit while the bottom portion consists of square posts around which the wire is wrapped. The tool is designed to wrap neat, compact coils around the posts. These wires are run by the assembler from post to post for interconnections within the circuit. Wirewrap boards have several advantages. The connections are secure, circuits are easy to change, and the boards are inexpensive for small production runs. Among their disadvantages are that they are susceptible to noise from other circuits and cross-talk. They can be miss-wired and they are bulkier than a printed circuit board.

Figure 1.9 Wire Wrap

No matter which method of prototyping is used, it is important to test the circuit as you go along. An inexperienced engineer often builds an entire circuit only to find that it fails to operate properly when tested. In constructing a new circuit, build a portion of it and immediately test this portion. Do not go further until the first section is working as you have designed it. Once this circuit works properly, build the next part and test it together with the first part (which you already know is working properly). If there is a problem in the design or the wiring, it is easier to check the smaller part of the circuit than to check out the entire circuit at one time.

SUMMARY

This chapter was intended to be a broad introduction to the textbook. We began with a brief history of electronics highlighting the invention of the transistor, the integrated circuit, and large scale integrated circuits.

We then examined the contrast between linear and non-linear circuit elements. This is important since the solid-state devices that form the building blocks of electronic circuits are non-linear devices.

Since the models of many electronic devices include dependent sources, we devoted a section to the study of these sources and the required analysis techniques. This was followed by an examination of the essential differences between analog and digital signals.

We next examined the effect of frequency on circuit design. In the discussion, we justified splitting analysis and design problems into bands of frequencies and then integrating the results into a single analysis or design.

The chapter then explored the differences between analysis and design. We saw examples of this difference, and highlighted the meaning of "open-ended" and "trade-offs."

Next, we introduced you to computer simulations as a tool in circuit and system design.

Finally, we carefully traced the steps of an effective engineering design.

You should now be in a position to follow the development of the various aspects of electronic analysis and design. You should have a greater appreciation for the approaches taken in the remainder of this text.

Chapter 2

Ideal Operational Amplifiers

The operational amplifier is an important electronic device that serves as a building block for relatively complex circuits.

In this chapter, you will learn:

- The characteristics of ideal operational amplifiers as circuit elements.
- How to use operational amplifiers to build inverting and non-inverting amplifiers.
- Input and output characteristics of operational amplifier circuits.
- Circuit models used to represent operational amplifiers.
- Design approaches applied to multiple-input amplifiers.
- How to design more complicated operational amplifier circuits to perform a variety of functions.

2.0 INTRODUCTION

The rapid expansion of requirements for smaller, lighter and more complex circuits resulted in the need to place *hundreds* of transistors on a single chip. Whenever more than one element is placed on a single chip, the resulting device is known as an *integrated circuit (IC)*.

Integrated circuits are classified according to their complexity. The term, *small scale integration (SSI)* is used to describe those chips composed of less than about 50 elements. If a chip contains over 50 but less than about 300 elements, the term *medium scale integration (MSI)* is used. If the number of elements is over 300 but less than about 1000, the circuit is known as *large scale integration (LSI). Very large scale integration (VLSI)* refers to those chips with more than one thousand elements but less than about one million elements. Circuits with more than one million devices per chip are known as *ultra large scale integration (ULSI). Linear integrated circuits (LIC)* can replace standard circuits, and these *LIC*s are then used as building blocks for more complex systems. Integrated circuits can be analog or digital depending on the forms of the input and output waveforms. One of the most utilized analog integrated circuit is the *operational amplifier (op-amp). Ideal* operational amplifiers have infinite gain, infinite input impedance and zero output impedance. *Practical* operational amplifiers have performance characteristics that closely approach those of ideal operational amplifiers.

In this chapter, we consider the ideal op-amp and explore its use in circuit design. In Chapter 9, we explore the non-ideal op-amp. The reason we treat ideal op-amps this early in the text is that they can be considered similar to basic circuit elements (resistors, capacitors, inductors). We will see later that the simplified model of the ideal amplifier behaves very much like the actual device, so we are justified in taking this early, simplified approach toward using op-amps as circuit building blocks.

2.1 IDEAL OP-AMPS

This section uses a *systems* approach to present the fundamentals of ideal operational amplifiers. As such, we consider the op-amp as a block with input and output terminals. We are not currently concerned with the individual electronic devices within the op-amp.

An op-amp is an amplifier that is often powered by both positive and negative supply voltages. This allows the output voltage to swing both above and below ground potential. The op-amp finds wide application in many linear electronic systems.

The name *operational amplifier* is derived from one of the original uses of op-amp circuits; to perform mathematical *operations* in analog computers. This traditional application is discussed later in this chapter. Early op-amps used a single inverting input. A positive voltage change at the input caused a negative change at the output.

To understand the operation of the op-amp, it is necessary to first become familiar with the concept of controlled (dependent) sources since they form the basis of the op-amp model.

2.1.1 Dependent Sources

Dependent (or controlled) sources produce a voltage or current whose value is determined by a voltage or current existing in another location in the circuit. In contrast, *passive devices* produce a voltage or current whose value is determined by a voltage or current existing at the *same* location in the circuit. Both independent and dependent voltage and current sources are *active* elements. That is, they are capable of delivering power to some external device. *Passive* elements are not capable of generating power, although they can store energy for delivery at a later time, as is the case with capacitors and inductors.

Figure 2.1 illustrates an equivalent circuit configuration of an amplifying device often used in circuit analysis. The rightmost 20 kΩ resistor is the *load.* We will find the voltage and current gain of this system. *Voltage gain,* A_v is defined as the ratio of output voltage to input voltage. Similarly, *current gain,* A_i is the ratio of output current to input current.

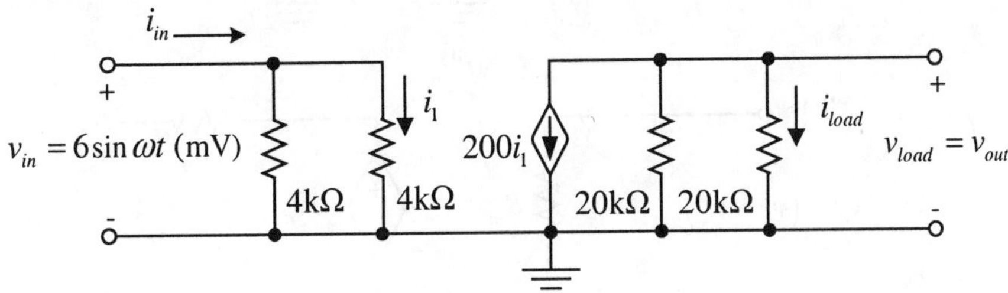

Figure 2.1 - Equivalent circuit of a solid-state amplifying device

The input current is

$$i_{in} = \frac{v_{in}}{R_{in}} = \frac{6\sin(\omega t)}{2}\left(\frac{\text{mV}}{\text{k}\Omega}\right) = 3\sin\omega t \quad \mu\text{A} \tag{2.1}$$

The current in the second resistor, i_1, is found directly from Ohm's law.

$$i_1 = \frac{v_{in}}{4000} = 1.5 \sin \omega t \quad \mu\text{A} \tag{2.2}$$

The output voltage is then given by

$$v_{out} = -200 i_1 \times \left(20\text{k}\Omega \| 20\text{k}\Omega\right) = -3 \sin \omega t \quad \text{V} \tag{2.3}$$

In Equation (2.3), $\|$ indicates a parallel combination of resistors. The output current is found directly from Ohm's law.

$$i_{out} = \frac{v_{out}}{20000} = -0.15 \sin \omega t \quad \text{mA} \tag{2.4}$$

The voltage and current gains are then found by forming the ratios:

$$\frac{v_{out}}{v_{in}} = -500 \tag{2.5}$$

$$\frac{i_{out}}{i_{in}} = -50 \tag{2.6}$$

2.1.2 Operational Amplifier Equivalent Circuit

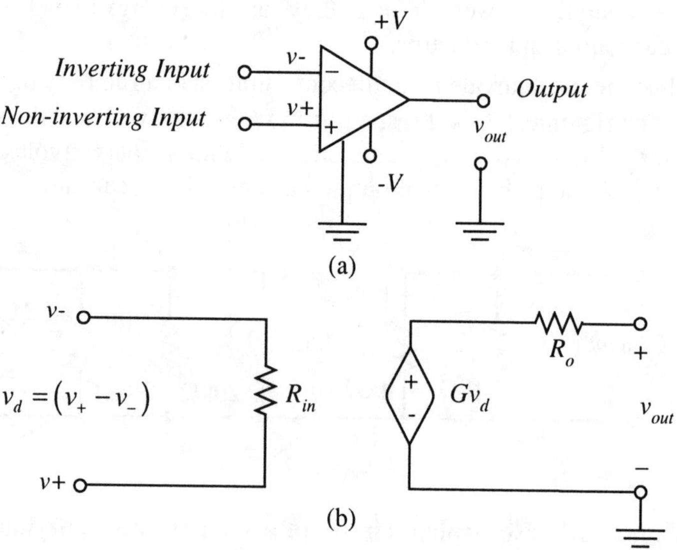

Figure 2.2 - Operational amplifier and equivalent circuit

Figure 2.2(a) presents the symbol for the operational amplifier, and Figure 2.2(b) shows its equivalent circuit. The input terminals are v_+ and v_-. The output terminal is v_{out}. The power supply connections are at the $+V$, $-V$ and ground terminals. The power supply connections are often omitted from schematic drawings. The value of the output voltage is bounded by $+V$ and $-V$ since these are the most positive and negative voltages in the circuit.

The model contains a dependent voltage source whose voltage depends on the input voltage difference between v_+ and v_-. The two input terminals are known as the *non-inverting* and *inverting* inputs respectively. Ideally, the output of the amplifier does not depend on the magnitudes of the two input voltages, but only on the difference between them. We define the *differential input voltage,* v_d, as the difference,

$$v_d = (v_+ - v_-) \tag{2.7}$$

The output voltage is proportional to the differential input voltage, and we designate the ratio as the open-loop gain, G. Thus, the output voltage is

$$v_{out} = G \cdot (v_+ - v_-) = G \cdot v_d \tag{2.8}$$

As an example, an input of $E \sin \omega t$ (E is usually a small amplitude) applied to the non-inverting input with the inverting terminal grounded, produces $+G(E \sin \omega t)$ at the output. When the same source signal is applied to the inverting input with the non-inverting terminal grounded, the output is $-G(E \sin \omega t)$.

The input impedance of the op-amp is shown as a resistance in Figure 2.2(b). The output impedance is represented in the figure as a resistance, R_o.

An *ideal* operational amplifier is characterized as follows:

Input resistance, $R_{in} \to \infty$.

Output Thevenin resistance, $R_o = 0$.

Open Loop Voltage Gain, $G \to \infty$.

These are usually good approximations to the parameters of real op-amps. Typical parameters of real op-amps are:

Input resistance, R_{in}, on the order of 1 MΩ.

Output Thevenin resistance, R_o, on the order of 100 Ω or less.

Open Loop Voltage Gain, G, is typically 10^5 at low frequencies.

Using ideal op-amps to approximate real op-amps is therefore a valuable simplification for circuit analysis.

Let us explore the implication of the open-loop gain being infinite. If we rewrite Equation (2.8) as follows:

$$v_+ - v_- = \frac{v_{out}}{G} \tag{2.9}$$

and let G approach infinity, we see that

$$v_+ - v_- \cong 0 \tag{2.10}$$

Equation (2.10) results by observing that the output voltage cannot be infinite. The value of the output voltage is bounded by the positive and negative power supply values.

Equation (2.10) indicates that the voltages at the two terminals are the same:

$$v_+ = v_- \tag{2.11}$$

The equality of Equation (2.11) leads us to say there is a *virtual short circuit* between the input terminals.

Since the input resistance of the ideal op-amp is infinite, *the current into each input, inverting terminal and non-inverting terminal, is zero.*

When real op-amps are used in a linear amplification mode, the gain is very large, and Equation (2.11) is a good approximation. However, several applications for real op-amps use the device in a nonlinear mode. The approximation of Equation (2.11)is not valid for these circuits. We will investigate nonlinear op-amp circuits in detail in Chapter 14.

Although practical op-amps have high voltage gain, this gain varies with frequency. For this reason, an op-amp is not normally used in the form shown in Figure 2.2(a). This configuration is known as *open loop* because there is no feedback from output to input. We see later that, while the open-loop configuration is useful for *comparator* applications, the more common configuration for linear applications is the *closed-loop* circuit with *feedback.*

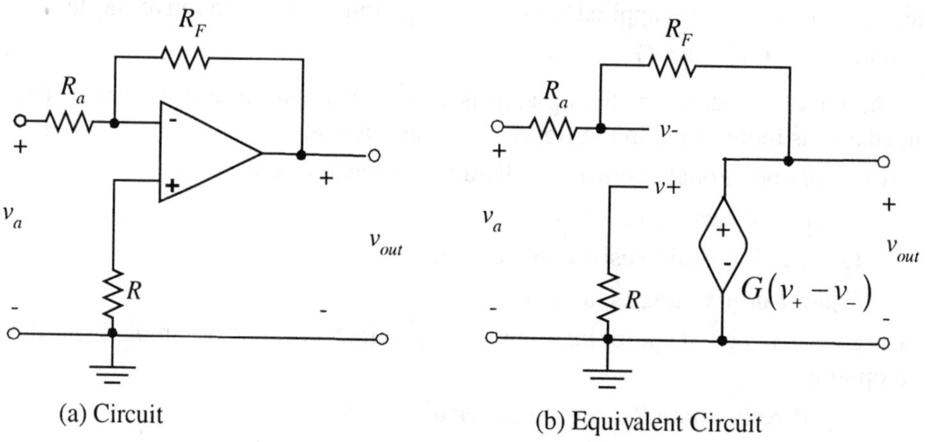

(a) Circuit (b) Equivalent Circuit

Figure 2.3 - The inverting op-amp

External elements are used to "feedback" a portion of the output signal to the input. If the feedback elements are placed between the output and the inverting input, the *closed-loop gain* is decreased since a portion of the output subtracts from the input. We will see later that feedback not only decreases the overall gain, but it also makes that gain *less* sensitive to the value of G. With feedback, the closed-loop gain depends more on the feedback circuit elements, and less on the basic op-amp voltage gain, G. In fact, the closed-loop gain is essentially *independent* of the value of G–it depends only on values of the external circuit elements. A rigorous treatment of feedback theory is presented in Chapter 12, where we explore several op-amp feedback configurations using classical feedback theory. We wait until Chapter 12 for this discussion since we can use the ideal op-amp approximations (infinite input impedance, and the virtual short circuit between the input terminals) to solve linear amplifier circuits without using the classical feedback theory.

Figure 2.3 illustrates a single stage negative feedback op-amp circuit. We will analyze this circuit in the next section. For now, note that a single resistor, R_F, is used to connect the output voltage, v_{out} to the inverting input, v_-. Another resistor, R_a is connected from the inverting input, v_-, to the input voltage, v_a. A third resistor, R is placed between the non-inverting input and ground.

Circuits using op-amps, resistors and capacitors can be configured to perform many useful operations such as *summing, subtracting, integrating, differentiating, filtering, comparing,* and *amplifying*.

2.1.3 Analysis Method

We analyze circuits using the two important ideal op-amp properties:

- **The voltage between v_+ and v_- is zero, or $v_+ = v_-$.**
- **The current into both the v_+ and v_- terminal is zero.**

These simple observations lead to a procedure for analyzing any ideal op-amp circuit as follows:

- **Write the Kirchhoff current law node equation at the non-inverting terminal, v_+.**
- **Write the Kirchhoff current law node equation at the inverting terminal, v_-.**
- **Set $v_+ = v_-$ and solve for the desired closed-loop gains.**

When applying Kirchhoff's laws, remember that the current into both the v_+ and v_- terminal is zero.

2.2 The Inverting Amplifier

Figure 2.3(a) illustrates an inverting amplifier with feedback, and Figure 2.3(b) shows the equivalent circuit for this ideal inverting op-amp circuit. We have used the properties of the ideal op-amp to model the op-amp input as an open circuit. The controlled source is Gv_d, but under the given assumptions, we will not have to use this information explicitly. We wish to solve for the output voltage, v_{out}, in terms of the input voltage, v_a. We write equations for v_+ and v_- and then set these expressions equal to each other. Since the current through R is zero,

$$v_+ = 0 \tag{2.12}$$

Kirchhoff's node equation at v_- yields,

$$\frac{v_- - v_a}{R_a} + \frac{v_- - v_{out}}{R_F} = 0 \tag{2.13}$$

Since $v_+ = v_-$ and $v_+ = 0$, then v_- is also zero. Therefore, we have one equation in two unknowns, v_a and v_{out}, so we can solve for the closed-loop gain as,

$$\frac{v_{out}}{v_a} = \frac{-R_F}{R_a} \tag{2.14}$$

Notice that the closed-loop gain, v_{out}/v_a, is negative (inverted) and is dependent only on the ratio of two resistors, R_F/R_a. It is independent of the very high open-loop gain, G. This desirable result is caused by the use of feedback of a portion of the output voltage to subtract from the input voltage. The feedback from output to input through R_F serves to drive the differential voltage, $v_d = v_+ - v_-$, close to zero. Since the non-inverting input voltage, v_+, is zero, the feedback has the effect of driving v_- to zero. Hence, at the input of the op-amp,

$$v_+ = v_- = 0 \tag{2.15}$$

No matter how complex the ideal op-amp circuit, by following this simple procedure the engineer can quickly analyze (and soon design) op-amp systems.

We may now expand this result to the case of multiple inputs. The amplifier shown in Figure 2.4 produces an output which is a negative weighted summation of several input voltages.

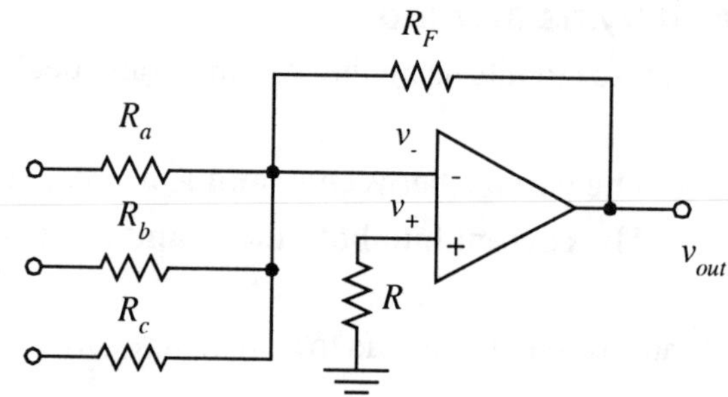

Figure 2.4 – Op-amp circuit

Since the current through R is zero, $v_+ = 0$. The node equation at the inverting input terminal is given by Equation (2.16).

$$\frac{v_- - v_a}{R_a} + \frac{v_- - v_b}{R_b} + \frac{v_- - v_c}{R_c} + \frac{v_- - v_{out}}{R_F} = 0 \tag{2.16}$$

Since $v_+ = v_-$, then $v_+ = 0 = v_-$ and we find v_{out} in terms of the inputs as follows:

$$v_{out} = -R_F\left(\frac{v_a}{R_a} + \frac{v_b}{R_b} + \frac{v_c}{R_c}\right) = -R_F \sum_{j=a,b,c}^{c} \frac{v_j}{R_j} \tag{2.17}$$

The extension to n inputs is straightforward.

EXERCISES

Analyze the following circuits to determine v_{out} in terms of the input voltages. (The answers are shown within each problem).

E2.1 Single inverting amplifier (Figure E2.1). *answer*: $v_{out} = -\frac{R_F}{R_a} v_a$

E2.2 Voltage divider amplifier (Figure E2.2). *answer*: $v_{out} = -\frac{R_F}{R_b} v_b$

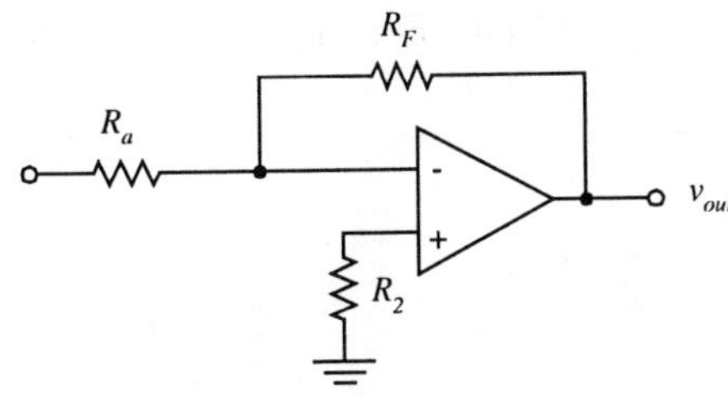

Figure E2.1

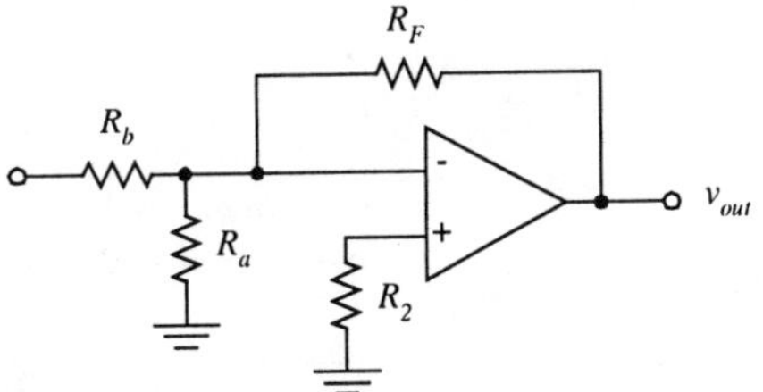

R_F

R_b

R_a

R_2

v_{out}

Figure E2.2

E2.3 Inverter (Figure E2.3).

$$answer: \quad v_{out} = -\frac{R_F}{R_a} v_{in}$$

E2.4 Summing inverter (Figure E2.4).

$$answer: \quad v_{out} = -\left(\frac{R_F}{R_a} v_a + \frac{R_F}{R_b} v_b + \frac{R_F}{R_c} v_c \right)$$

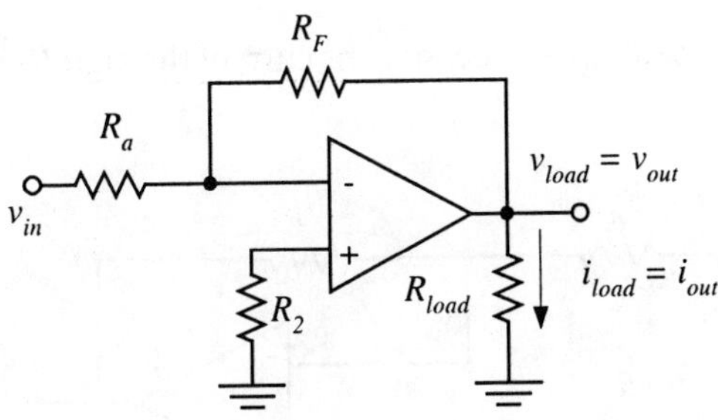

Figure E2.3

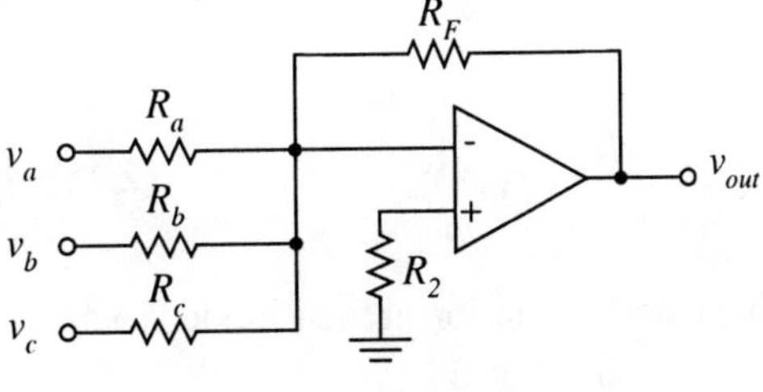

Figure E2.4

E2.5 Equal gain summing inverter (Figure E2.5).

$$answer: \quad v_{out} = -(v_a + v_b)$$

E2.6 Dual inverted summer with gain (Figure E2.6).

$$answer: \quad v_{out} = -10(v_a + v_b)$$

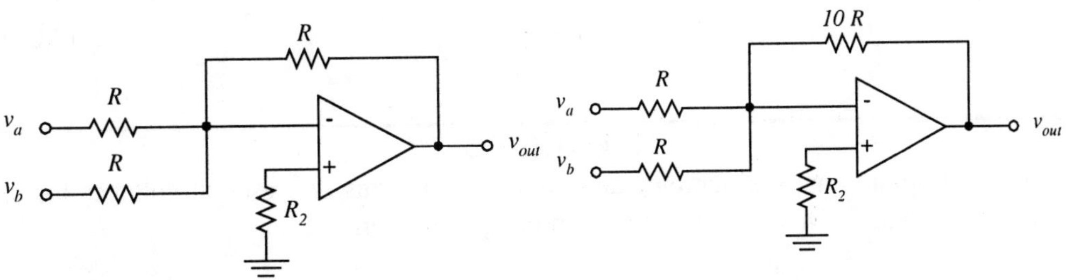

Figure E2.5

Figure E2.6

E2.7 Dual inverted weighted summer (Figure E2.7).

answer: $v_{out} = -(v_a + 10v_b)$

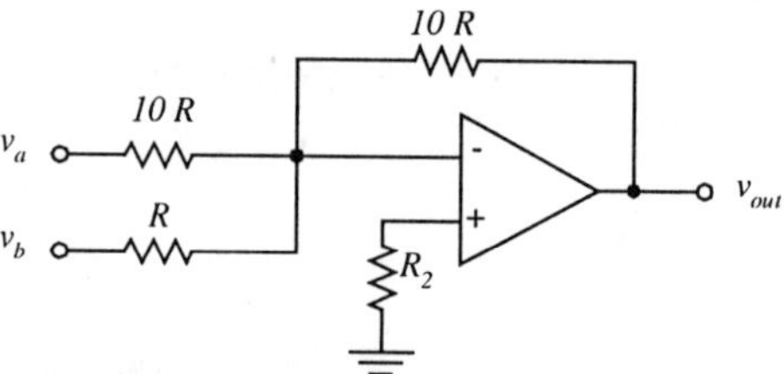

Figure E2.7

2.3 THE NON-INVERTING AMPLIFIER

The op-amp can be configured to produce either an inverted or non-inverted output. In the previous section we analyzed the inverting amplifier. We now repeat the analysis for the non-inverting amplifier, as shown in Figure 2.5.

We analyze this using the basic properties of the ideal op-amp. Since the current through R_1 is zero,

$$v_+ = v_{in}. \quad (2.18)$$

Writing a node equation at the v_- node yields,

$$\frac{v_-}{R_A} + \frac{v_- - v_{out}}{R_F} = 0. \quad (2.19)$$

We set $v_+ = v_-$, and substitute for v_- to obtain,

$$\frac{v_{in}}{R_a} + \frac{v_{in} - v_{out}}{R_F} = 0. \quad (2.20)$$

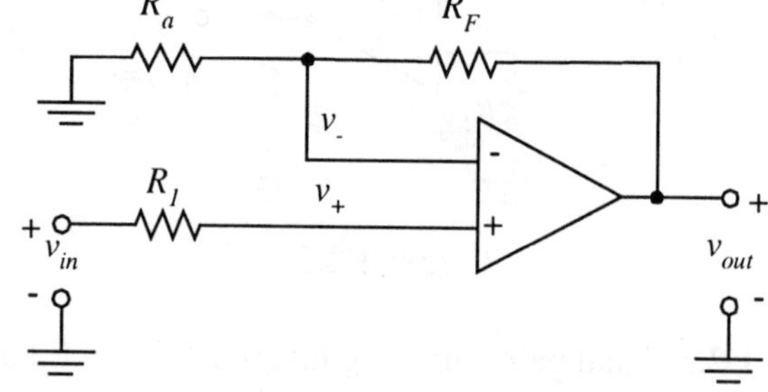

Figure 2.5 – Non-inverting amplifier

The non-inverting gain is then given by,

$$\frac{v_{out}}{v_{in}} = 1 + \frac{R_F}{R_a}. \quad (2.21)$$

EXERCISES

Using the ideal op-amp approximations, determine v_{out} in terms of the input voltages for the following four circuits. (The answers are shown in each problem).

E2.8 Non-inverting amplifier (Figure E2.8). *answer*: $v_{out} = \left(1 + \frac{R_F}{R_a}\right) v_{in}$

E2.9 Non-inverting buffer (Figure E2.9). *answer*: $v_{out} = v_{in}$

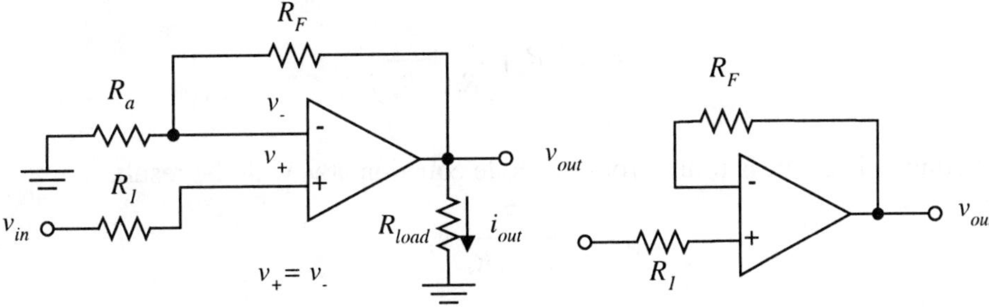

Figure E2.8 **Figure E2.9**

E2.10 Non-inverting input with voltage divider (Figure E2.10).

answer: $v_{out} = \left(1 + \frac{R_F}{R_a}\right)\left(\frac{R_2}{R_1 + R_2}\right) v_{in}$

E2.11 Less than unity gain (Figure E2.11).

answer: $v_{out} = \frac{R_2}{R_1 + R_2} v_{in}$

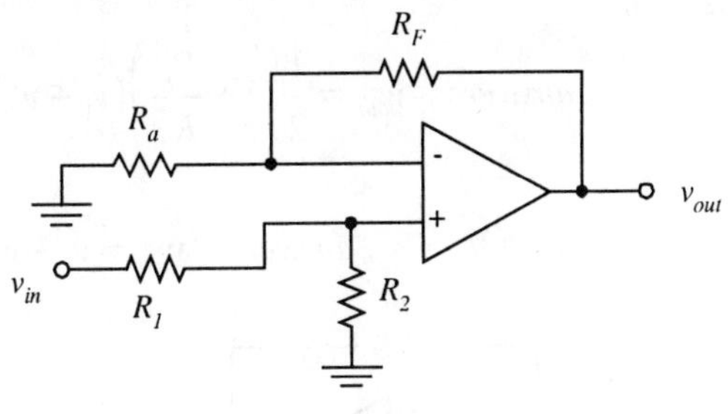

Figure E2.10

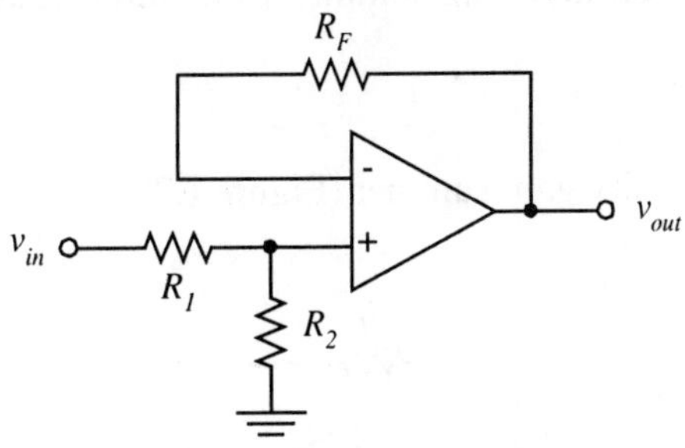

Figure E2.11

We analyzed multiple-input inverting op-amps in Section 2.2. We now analyze non-inverting op-amps with multiple inputs. Figure 2.6 illustrates a circuit with two input voltages.

To find v_+, we apply Kirchhoff's current law to the non-inverting input terminal to yield (recall that the input current to the op-amp is zero),

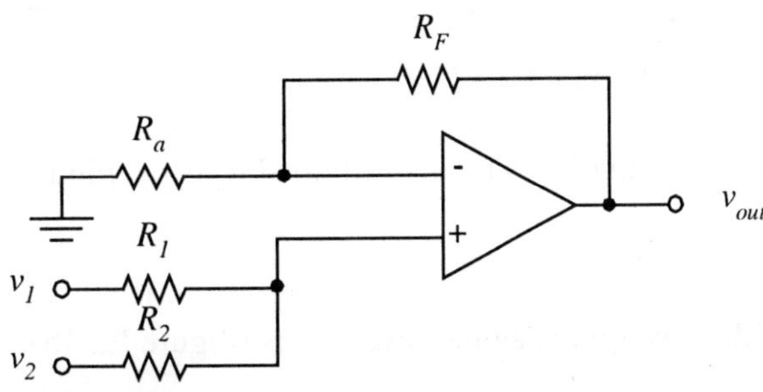

Figure 2.6 – Two non-inverting inputs

$$\frac{v_+ - v_1}{R_1} + \frac{v_+ - v_2}{R_2} = 0. \tag{2.22}$$

Solving for v_+, we obtain

$$v_+ = (R_1 \| R_2)\left(\frac{v_1}{R_1} + \frac{v_2}{R_2}\right). \tag{2.23}$$

The inverting voltage, v_-, is found from the node equation at v_- with the result,

$$v_- = \frac{R_a}{R_a + R_F} v_{out}. \tag{2.24}$$

Setting v_+ equal to v_-, we obtain

$$v_{out} = (R_1 \| R_2)\left(\frac{v_1}{R_1} + \frac{v_2}{R_2}\right)\left(1 + \frac{R_F}{R_a}\right). \tag{2.25}$$

EXERCISES

Determine v_{out} in terms of the input voltages for the following circuits. (The answers are shown in each problem).

E2.12 Non-inverting summer with gain (Figure E2.12).

answer: $v_{out} = \frac{1}{2}\left(1 + \frac{R_F}{R_a}\right)(v_1 + v_2)$

E2.13 Unity gain summer (Figure E2.13).

answer: $v_{out} = v_1 + v_2$

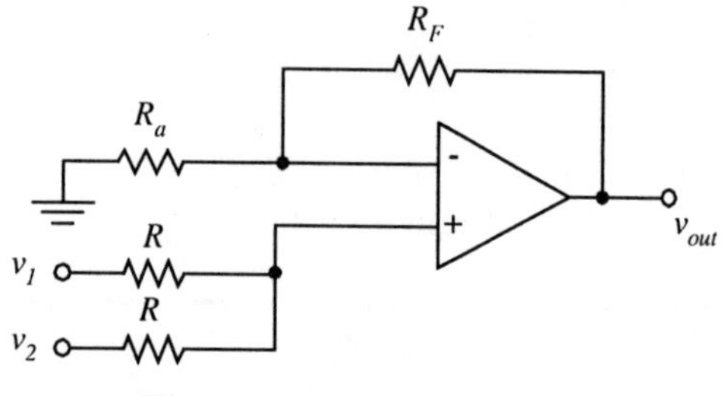

Figure E2.12

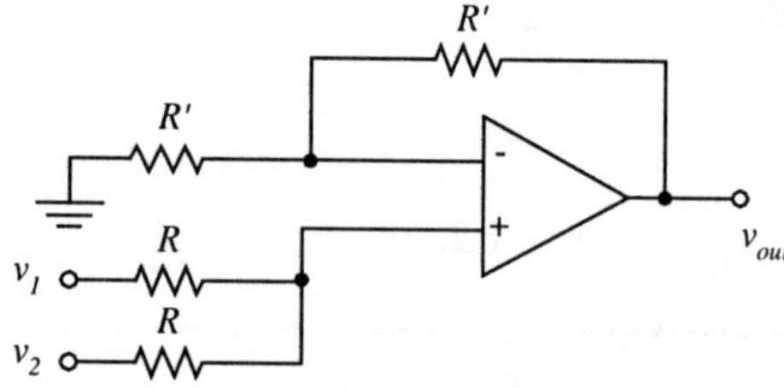

Figure E2.13

E2.14 Sum of two inputs with load resistor (Figure E2.14).

answer: $v_{out} = \left(1 + \frac{R_F}{R_a}\right)\frac{v_1 + v_2}{2}$

E2.15 Weighted sum of two inputs (Figure E2.15).

$$answer: \quad v_{out} = \left(1+\frac{R_F}{R_a}\right)\frac{10v_1+v_2}{11}$$

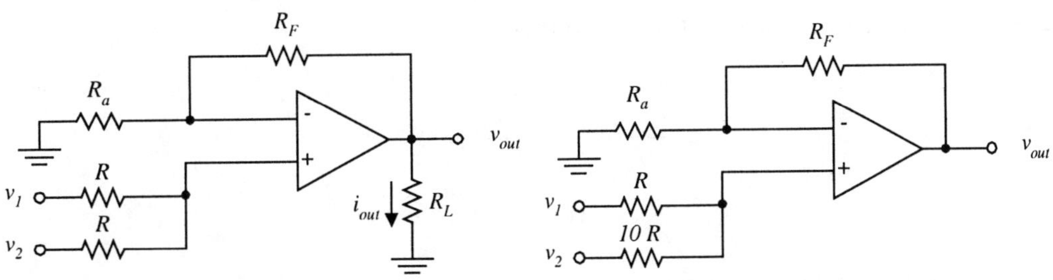

Figure E2.14 **Figure E2.15**

E2.16 Sum of three inputs (Figure E2.16).

$$answer: \quad v_{out} = \left(1+\frac{R_F}{R_a}\right)\frac{v_1+v_2+v_3}{3}$$

E2.17 Voltage divider weighted sum of two inputs (Figure E2.17)

$$answer: \quad v_{out} = \left(1+\frac{R_F}{R_a}\right)\left(R_1\|R_2\|R_3\right)\left(\frac{v_1}{R_2}+\frac{v_2}{R_2}\right)$$

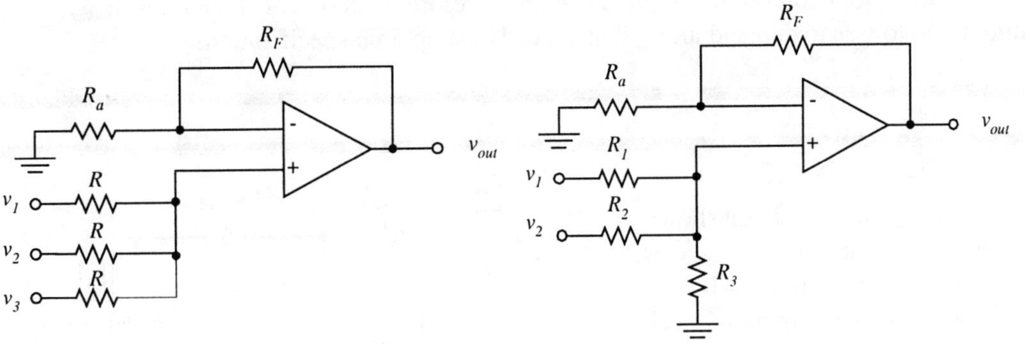

Figure E2.16 **Figure E2.17**

In a practical sense, it is important to briefly consider the effects of *loading* on the op-amp. The method we have been using for analysis yields the correct voltage gain, v_{out}/v_{in} based on the assumption that the current required from the dependent source of the *ideal* op-amp model is within the range set forth by the manufacturer's data sheet for a *real* op-amp. Although we explore the practical considerations in later chapters, the next two examples illustrate the concept.

Example 2.1

Find v_{out} and i_{out} for the circuit for Figure E2.3.

Solution: We write the node equations as follows:

$$v_+ = 0$$

$$\frac{v_- - v_{in}}{R_a} + \frac{v_- - v_{out}}{R_F} = 0$$

$$v_+ = v_-$$

Solving these three equations, we obtain

$$v_{out} = -\frac{R_F}{R_a} v_{in}$$

The output current, i_{out}, is found from v_{out} by applying Ohm's law to the load resistor.

$$i_{out} = \frac{v_{out}}{R_{load}} = -\frac{R_F}{R_a R_{load}} v_{in}$$

Notice that the value of R_{load} does not appear in the expression for the gain, v_{out}/v_{in}. However, R_{load} does control the output current. Therefore, with practical op-amps, R_{load} cannot be so low as to demand an i_{out} that exceeds the op-amp specifications.

Example 2.2

Find v_{out} and i_{out} for the circuit shown in Figure 2.7. The input voltage is sinusoidal with amplitude of 0.5 V, as indicated on the diagram. Check your result using a computer simulation.

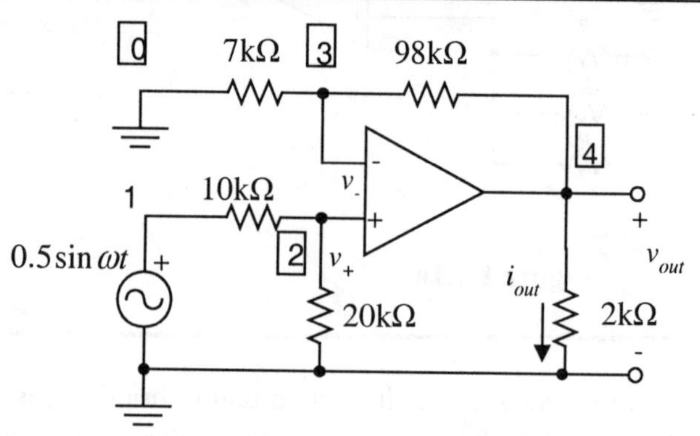

Figure 2.7 - Circuit for Example 2.2

Solution: We begin by writing the KCL equations at both the + and - terminals of the op-amp.

For the negative terminal,

$$\frac{v_- - v_{out}}{9.8\times10^4} + \frac{v_- - 0}{7000} = 0.$$

Therefore,

$$15v_- = v_{out} .$$

For the positive terminal,

$$\frac{v_+ - v_{in}}{10^4} + \frac{v_+ - 0}{2\times10^4} = 0 .$$

This yields two equations in three unknowns, v_{out}, v_+, and v_-. The third equation is the terminal relationship for the ideal op-amp,

$$v_+ = v_- .$$

Solving these equations, we find

$$v_{out} = 10v_{in} = 5\sin\omega t \quad \text{V} .$$

Since the 2-kΩ resistor forms the load of the op-amp, then by Ohm's Law we have

$$i_{out} = \frac{v_{out}}{R_{load}} \times 2.5\sin\omega t \quad \text{mA} .$$

We now verify the result using the computer simulation program. Given the input signal is 0.5V peak, we expect the output voltage to be 10 times the input voltage, i.e., output voltage should be 5.0 V peak. The node numbers are labeled in Figure 2.7. We first need to input the data representing the circuit of Figure 2.7. This is done in a straightforward manner using either MICRO-CAP or PSPICE provided you load the library containing the op-amp model (i.e., the EVAL.LIB in PSPICE has the LM324 and µA741 op-amp models).

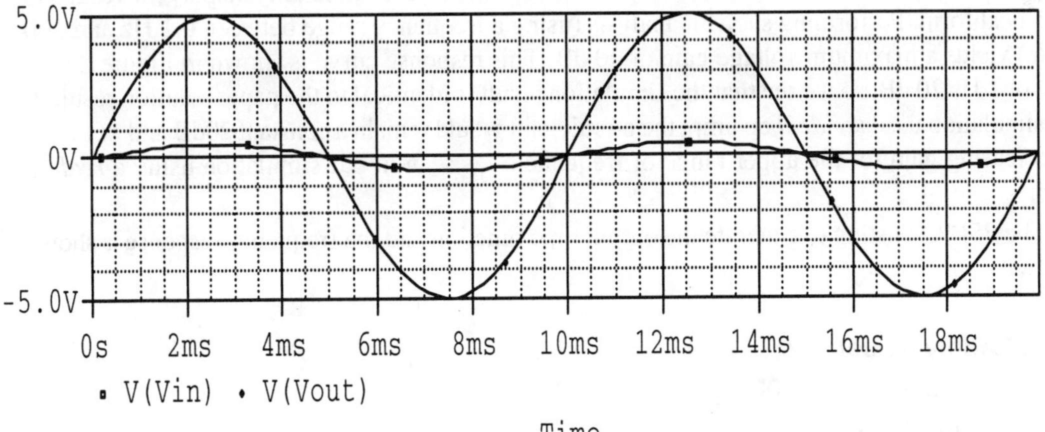

Figure 2.8 - Simulated input and output waveforms

The only questions that may come up during the input process are related to the op-amp and to the source. The current chapter deals with *ideal* op-amps, yet the simulation programs model *practical* op-amps. However, we shall find that practical op-amps behave very much like their ideal counterparts as long as input frequencies are relatively low. The specified input frequency for this example is only 100 Hz (or 628.2 rad/sec), which is fairly low. We therefore can choose a practical op-amp and expect results very close to ideal. Suppose we choose the μA741 op-amp, a model that traditionally was very common. We can then input the 0.5V peak signal voltage by choosing a voltage source from the library with that particular waveform. After running the simulation with a 100 Hz input signal of 0.5V peak, we are very satisfied with the simulation results shown in Figure 2.8. The output voltage at node 4 is 10 times the input voltage.

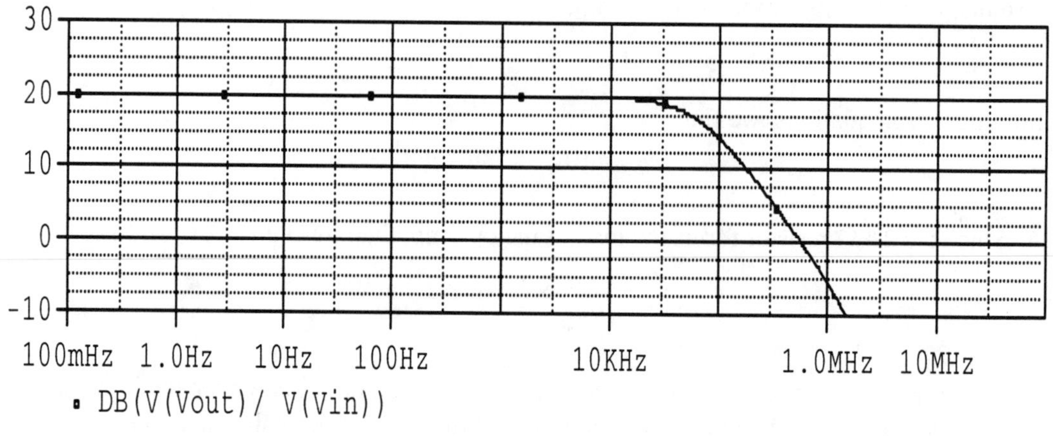

Figure 2.9 - Frequency response of the real op-amp

Instead of simulating the specific frequency of 100 Hz of the input signal source, there is a way to simulate the behavior of this circuit for many frequencies, low to high frequencies. Since the specified input is sinusoidal, we can perform an *ac* analysis and readily display the results in graphical form. Performing such an analysis (using a frequency range between 0.1 Hz and 100 MHz) yields a maximum voltage gain of 20 dB. This response curve is shown in Figure 2.9. A gain of 10 is 20 dB, so we see that the simulation result is identical to the paper solution result. If the simulation used an *ideal* op amp, the circuit gain would remain a constant 20dB and not show a decreasing gain for the upper range of frequencies as seen in our simulation using a *real* op amp.

The PSPICE listing to generate the output time function and the frequency response is shown below:

```
** Analysis setup **
.ac DEC 101 .10 100Meg
.tran 0ns 20ms
.OP
.lib "nom.lib"
.INC "Schematic1.net"
```

```
R_Rload      Vout 0  2k
V_V1       Vin 0 DC 0V AC 0.5V
+SIN 0V 0.5Vpeak 100Hz 0 0 0
R_R3       Vin Node-2  10k
R_R4       Node-2 0  20k
V_V2       VCC 0 15V
V_V3       0 VDD 15V
R_R1       0 Node-3  7k
X_U2       Node-3 Node-2 VCC VDD Vout uA741
R_R2       Node-3 Vout  98k
.probe
.END
```

Example 2.3

Find v_{out} and i_{out} for the circuit of Figure E2.8.

Solution: We write node equations,

$$v_+ = v_{in},$$

$$v_- = \frac{R_a}{R_a + R_F} v_{out},$$

and

$$v_- = v_+ .$$

Solving these three equations yields

$$v_{out} = \left(1 + \frac{R_F}{Ra}\right) v_{in} .$$

The current through the load resistor, R_{load}, is then

$$i_{out} = \frac{v_{out}}{R_{load}} = \frac{1}{R_{load}} \left(1 + \frac{R_F}{R_a}\right) v_{in} .$$

Again, R_{load} does not affect the equations used to find v_{out}/v_{in} provided that R_{load} is not so low as to overload the op-amp. However, if the design requires more current than can be provided by the op-amp, it may be necessary to include a power amplifier, as discussed in Chapter 8, between the op-amp and the load, R_{load}.

When analyzing both the inverting and the non-inverting configurations, we must be certain that the op-amp is capable of supplying sufficient current to drive the load resistor.

2.4 INPUT RESISTANCE OF OP-AMP CIRCUITS

The input resistance of the ideal op-amp is infinite. However, the input resistance to a circuit composed of an ideal op-amp connected to external components is not infinite. It depends on the form of the external circuit.

We first consider the *inverting* op-amp. The equivalent circuit for the inverting op-amp of Figure 2.3 is shown in Figure 2.10(a). Figure 2.10(b) shows the same circuit rearranged for simplicity of analysis. Note that we have attached a "test" voltage source to the input in order to calculate the equivalent resistance. Since the circuit contains a dependent voltage source, we can't find the input resistance by simply combining resistors. Instead, we find the input resistance by replacing the input signal source and its associated resistance with a test source of specified voltage, v_{test}, and then calculate the current delivered by the test source to the circuit, i_{test}. Alternatively, we could use a current test source, i_{test}, and solve for the voltage delivered to the circuit, v_{test}. Using either technique, the resistance is found from Ohm's law.

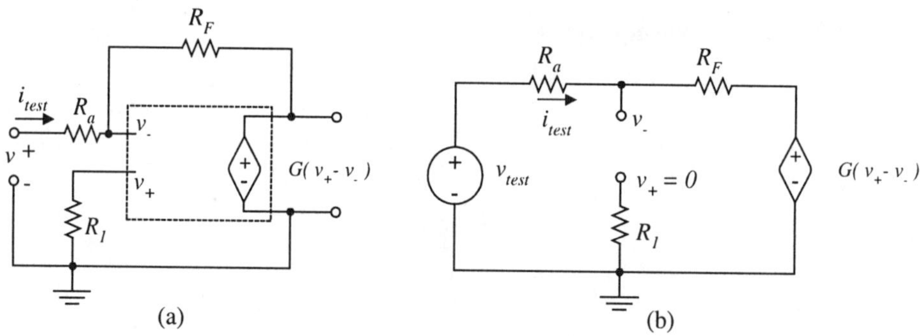

Figure 2.10- Input resistance, inverting amplifier

The loop equation is given by,

$$\begin{aligned}(R_a + R_F)i_{test} &= v_{test} - G(v_+ - v_-) \\ &= v_{test} - G(iR_a - v_{test})\end{aligned} \tag{2.26}$$

The equivalent input resistance is then

$$R_{in} = \frac{v_{test}}{i_{test}} = \frac{R_a + R_F}{1+G} + \frac{GR_a}{1+G} \tag{2.27}$$

As the loop gain, G, approaches infinity, the first term in Equation (2.27) approaches zero and the input resistance approaches R_a. Thus, the input resistance seen by the source is equal to the value of the external resistance, R_a. This verifies the virtual ground property since the result indicates that the inverting input is equivalent to a ground.

We now consider the inverting amplifier with two inputs. This is shown in Figure 2.11. It is a special case of the circuit of Figure 2.4.

Since the voltage at the inverting input to the op-amp is zero (virtual ground), the input resistance seen by v_a is R_a, and that seen by v_b is R_b. The "grounded" inverting input also serves to isolate the two inputs from each other. That is, a variation in v_a does not affect the input v_b, and vice versa.

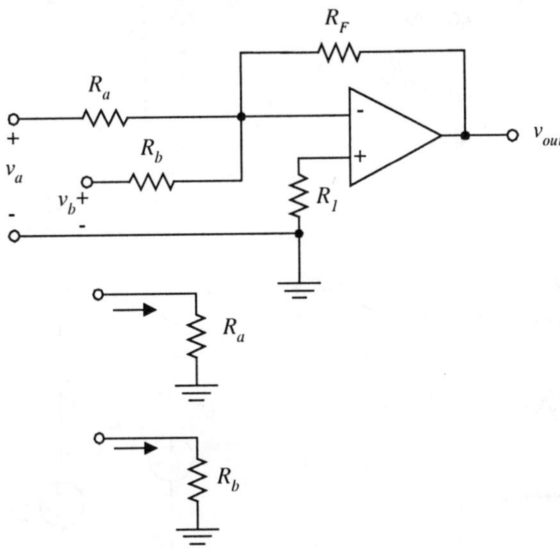

Figure 2.11 - Two-input inverting amplifier

The input resistance for the *non-inverting amplifier* can be determined by referring to the circuit configuration of Figure 2.5. The equivalent circuit is shown in Figure 2.12(a). No current passes through R_1 since the v_+ input to the op-amp has infinite resistance. As a result, R_{in} to a non-inverting terminal is infinity. If a design needs a large input resistance, we often use a single-input non-inverting op-amp. Such a configuration is called a *non-inverting buffer* if it has a voltage gain of unity. This is shown in Exercise 2.9.

The situation changes when we go to a multiple input non-inverting op-amp, as shown in Figure 2.12(b). The equivalent circuit is shown in Figure 2.12(c). We are assuming that the resistance associated with each source, (r_1, r_2 and r_3) is zero ohms. When applying the test source to calculate the input resistance for multiple-input circuits, we use superposition. We therefore apply the test source at each input separately while disabling the other inputs (short circuits for voltage sources and open circuits for current sources in accordance with the principle of Superposition). The various input resistances are then

$$R_{in1} = R_1 + R_2 \| R_3$$
$$R_{in2} = R_2 + R_1 \| R_3 \quad (2.28)$$
$$R_{in3} = R_3 + R_1 \| R_2$$

This concept can easily be extended to n inputs.

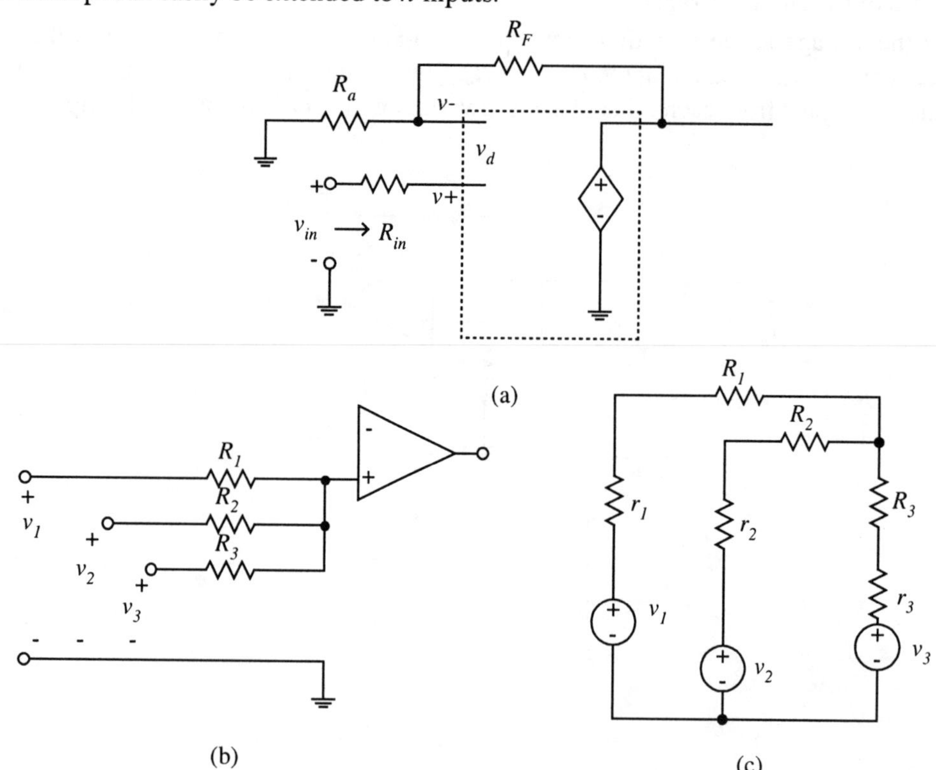

Figure 2.12 - Input resistance of a non-inverting amplifier

2.5 COMBINED INVERTING AND NON-INVERTING INPUTS

The general case of input configuration is a combination of the previous two cases. That is, we allow for both inverting and non-inverting inputs. The general configuration is shown in Figure 2.13.

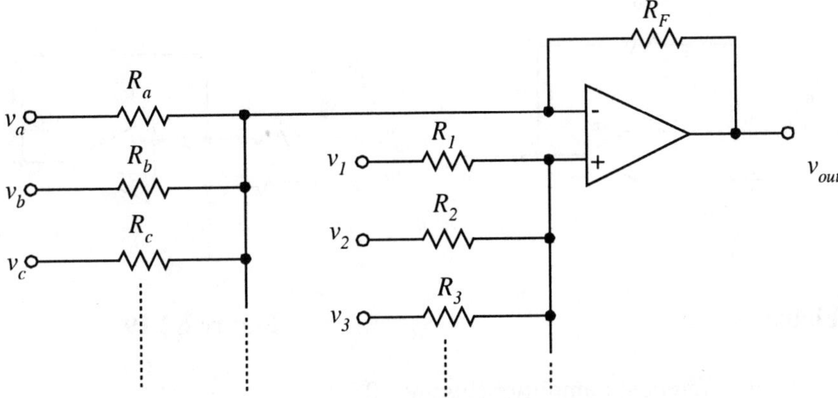

Figure 2.13 – Inverting and non-inverting inputs

The previous circuits can be considered as special cases of this general problem. The output relationship is found by applying superposition as follows. Equation (2.29) is derived by combining Equation (2.17) with Equation (2.25).

$$v_{out} = \left[1 + \frac{R_F}{R_a \| R_b \| R_c \| \ldots}\right]\left(R_1 \| R_2 \| R_3 \| \ldots\right)\left[\frac{v_1}{R_1} + \frac{v_2}{R_2} + \frac{v_3}{R_3} + \ldots\right] - \left[\frac{R_F}{R_a}v_a + \frac{R_F}{R_b}v_b + \frac{R_F}{R_c}v_c + \ldots\right] \tag{2.29}$$

Equation (2.29) represents a general result which will prove useful in analyzing a wide variety of circuits. With equations this complex, it is always a good idea to verify that the units on each side of the equality match. Indeed, the units on both sides of the equality are "volts".

EXERCISES

Determine in terms of all input voltages for the 'ollowing configurations. (The answers are shown within each problem.)

E2.18 Positive and negative gain (Figure E2.18).

answer: $v_{out} = \left(1 + \frac{R_F}{R_a}\right)v_1 - \frac{R_F}{R_a}v_a$

E2.19 Differencing amplifier configuration (Figure E2.19).

answer: $v_{out} = v_1 - v_a$

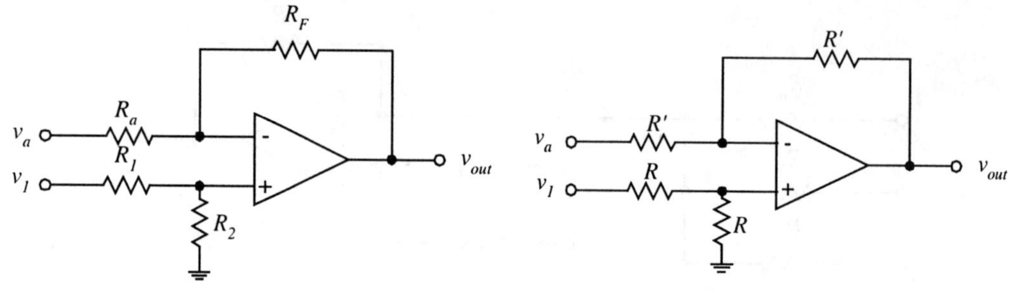

Figure E2.18 **Figure E2.19**

E2.20 Weighted differencing amplifier (Figure E2.20).

$$answer: \quad v_{out} = \left(1 + \frac{R_F}{R_a}\right)\left(\frac{R_2}{R_1 + R_2}\right)v_1 - \frac{R_F}{R_a}v_a$$

E2.21 Differencing amplifier with gain (Figure E2.21).

$$answer: \quad v_{out} = \frac{R'}{R}(v_1 - v_a)$$

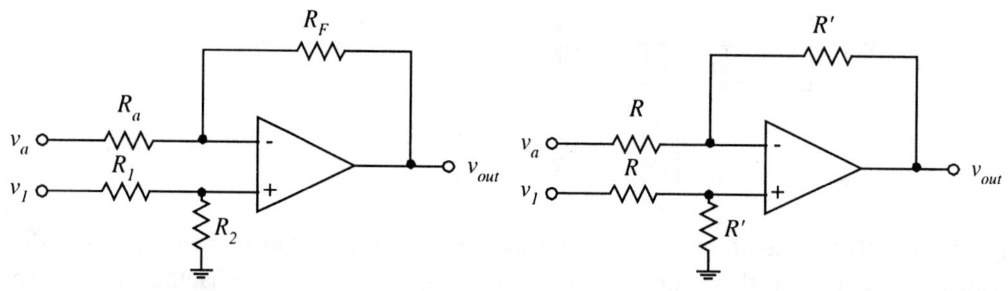

Figure E2.20 **Figure E2.21**

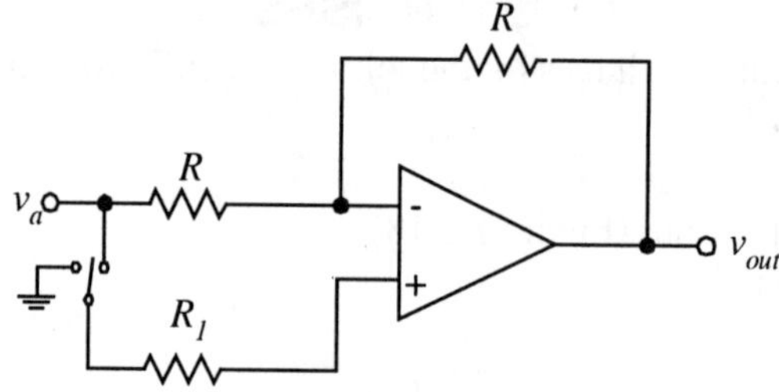

Figure E2.22

E2.22 Sign switcher (Figure E2.22). "Plus" for switch up, "minus" for switch left (i.e., connected to ground).

$$answer: \quad v_{out} = \pm v_{in}$$

2.6 DESIGN OF OP-AMP CIRCUITS

Once the configuration of an op-amp system is given, we can *analyze* that system to determine the output in terms of the inputs. We perform this analysis using the procedure discussed earlier in this chapter.

If you now wish to *design* a circuit that combines both inverting and non-inverting inputs, the problem is more complex. In a design problem, a desired linear equation is given, and the op-amp circuit must be designed. The desired output of the operational amplifier summer can be expressed as a linear combination of inputs,

$$v_{out} = X_1x_1 + X_2x_2 + X_3x_3 + ... + X_nx_n - Y_av_a - Y_bv_b - Y_cv_c - ... - Y_mv_m \quad (2.30)$$

where $X_1, X_2 ... X_n$ are the desired gains at the non-inverting inputs and Y_a, $Y_b ... Y_m$ are the desired gains at the inverting inputs. Equation (2.30) is implemented with the circuit of Figure 2.14.

This circuit is a slightly modified version of the circuit of Figure 2.13. The only change we have made is to include resistors between the op-amp inputs and ground. The ground can be viewed as an additional input of zero volts connected through the corresponding resistor (R_y for the inverting input and R_x for the non-inverting input). The addition of these resistors gives us flexibility in meeting any requirements beyond those of Equation (2.30). For example, the input resistances might be specified. Either or both of these additional resistors can be removed by letting their values go to infinity.

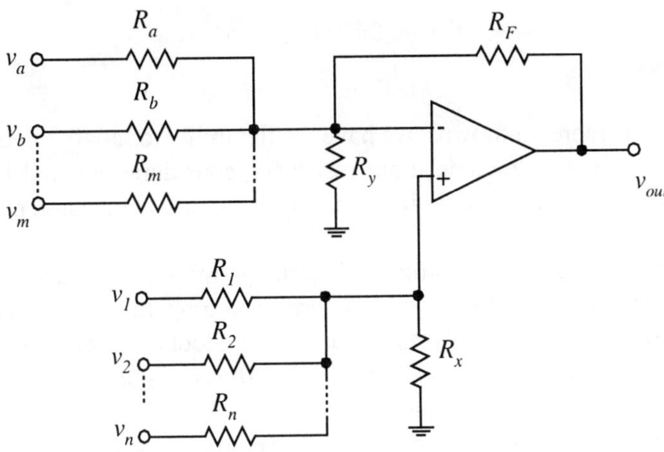

Figure 2.14 – Multiple input summer

Equation (2.29) from the previous section shows that the values of the resistors, R_a, R_b, ...R_m and R_1, R_2, ...R_n are inversely proportional to the desired gains associated with the respective input voltages. In other words, if a large gain is desired at a particular input terminal, then the resistance at that terminal is small.

When the open loop gain of the operational amplifier, G, is large, the output voltage may be written in terms of the resistors connected to the operational amplifier as in Equation (2.29).

Equation (2.31) repeats this expression with slight simplification and with addition of the resistors to ground.

$$v_{out} = R_{eq}\left[\frac{v_1}{R_1} + \frac{v_2}{R_2} + \frac{v_3}{R_3} + \ldots + \frac{v_n}{R_n}\right] - R_F\left[\frac{v_a}{R_a} + \frac{v_b}{R_b} + \frac{v_c}{R_c} + \ldots + \frac{v_m}{R_m}\right] \tag{2.31}$$

We define two equivalent resistances as follows:

$$\begin{aligned} R_A &= R_a \| R_b \| R_c \| \ldots \| R_m \| R_y \\ R_{eq} &= \left(1 + \frac{R_F}{R_A}\right)\left(R_1 \| R_2 \| \ldots \| R_n \| R_x\right) \end{aligned} \tag{2.32}$$

We see that the output voltage is a linear combination of inputs where each input is divided by its associated resistance and multiplied by another resistance. The multiplying resistance is R_F for inverting inputs and R_{eq} for non-inverting inputs.

The number of unknowns in this problem is $n+m+3$ (i.e. the unknown resistor values). We therefore need to develop $n+m+3$ equations in order to solve for these unknowns. We can formulate $n+m$ of these equations by matching the given coefficients in Equation (2.30). That is, we simply develop the system of equations from Equations (2.30), (2.31) and (2.32) as follows:

$$\begin{aligned} \frac{R_{eq}}{R_i} &= X_i \qquad \text{for} \quad i = 1 \quad \text{to} \quad n \\ \frac{R_F}{R_j} &= Y_j \qquad \text{for} \quad j = 1 \quad \text{to} \quad m \end{aligned} \tag{2.33}$$

Since we have three more unknowns, we have the flexibility to satisfy three more constraints. Typical additional constraints include input resistance considerations and having reasonable values for the resistors (e.g., You would not want to have to use a precision resistor for R_1 equal to 10^{-4} ohms!).

Although not required for design using ideal op-amps, we will use a design constraint that is important for non-ideal op-amps. For the non-inverting op-amp, the Thevenin resistance looking back from the inverting input is usually made equal to that looking back from the non-inverting input. We will see the reason for this in Chapter 9. For the configuration shown in Figure 2.14, this constraint can be expressed as follows:

$$R_1 \| R_2 \| R_3 \| \ldots \| R_n \| R_x = R_a \| R_b \| R_c \| \ldots \| R_m \| R_y \| R_F \equiv R_A \| R_F \tag{2.34}$$

The last equality results from the definition of R_A from Equation (2.32). Substituting this result into Equation (2.31) yields the constraint,

$$R_{eq} = \left(1 + \frac{R_F}{R_A}\right)\left(R_A \| R_F\right) \tag{2.35}$$

so

$$R_{eq} = R_F \tag{2.36}$$

Substituting this result into Equation (2.33) yields the simple set of equations,

$$\frac{R_F}{R_i} = X_i \qquad \text{for} \quad i = 1 \quad \text{to} \quad n$$
$$\frac{R_F}{R_j} = Y_j \qquad \text{for} \quad j = a \quad \text{to} \quad m \tag{2.37}$$

The combinations of Equation (2.34) and Equation (2.37) give us the necessary information to design the circuit. We select a value of R_F and then solve for the various input resistors using Equation (2.37). If the values of the resistors are not in a practical range, we go back and change the value of the feedback resistor. Once we solve for the input resistors, we then use Equation (2.34) to force the resistances to be equal looking back from the two op-amp inputs. We select values of R_x and R_y to force this equality. While Equations (2.34) and (2.37) contain the essential information for the design, one important consideration is whether or not to include the resistors between the op-amp inputs and ground (R_x and R_y). The solution may require iterations to obtain meaningful values (i.e. you may perform the solution one time and come up with negative resistance values). For this reason, we present a numerical procedure which simplifies the amount of calculations[1]

Equation (2.34) can be rewritten as follows:

$$\frac{1}{R_x} + \sum_{i=1}^{n} \frac{1}{R_i} = \frac{1}{R_F} + \frac{1}{R_y} + \sum_{j=a}^{m} \frac{1}{R_j} \tag{2.38}$$

Substituting Equation (2.37) into Equation (2.38) we obtain,

$$\frac{1}{R_x} + \frac{1}{R_F} \sum_{i=1}^{n} X_i = \frac{1}{R_F} + \frac{1}{R_y} + \frac{1}{R_F} \sum_{j=a}^{m} Y_j \tag{2.39}$$

Recall that our goal is to solve for the resistors values in terms of X_i and Y_j. Let us define summation terms as follows:

$$X = \sum_{i=1}^{n} X_i$$
$$Y = \sum_{j=a}^{m} Y_j \tag{2.40}$$

We can then rewrite Equation (2.39) as follows:

$$\frac{1}{R_x} + \frac{1}{R_F} X = \frac{1}{R_F} + \frac{1}{R_y} + \frac{1}{R_F} Y \tag{2.41}$$

This is a starting point for our design procedure. Recall that R_x and R_y are the resistors

---

[1]This technique was devised by Phil Vrbancic, a student at California State University, Long Beach, and presented in a paper submitted to the IEEE Region VI Prize Paper Contest.

between ground and the non-inverting and inverting inputs, respectively. The feedback resistor is denoted R_F and a new term, Z, is defined as

$$Z = X - (Y + 1) \tag{2.42}$$

Case	Z	R_y	R_x	R_i	R_j
I	>0	R_F/Z	∞	R_F/X_i	R_F/Y_j
II	<0	∞	$-R_F/Z$	R_F/X_i	R_F/Y_j
III	0	∞	∞	R_F/X_i	R_F/Y_j

Table 2.1 - Summing Amplifier Design

We can eliminate either or both of the resistors, R_x and R_y, from the circuit of Figure 2.14. That is, either or both of these resistors can be set to infinity (i.e., open-circuited). This yields three design possibilities. Depending on the desired multiplying factors relating output to input, one of these cases will yield the appropriate design. The results are summarized in Table 2.1.

Example 2.4-Op Amp Summer (Design)

Design an op-amp summer to yield the following input/output relationship.

$$v_{out} = 10v_1 + 6v_2 + 4v_3 - 5v_a - 2v_b$$

Solution: We begin by solving for Z. This yields,

$$Z = X - (Y + 1) = 20 - (7 + 1) = 12$$

$$R_1 = \frac{R_F}{X_1} = 12\text{k}\Omega$$

$$R_2 = \frac{R_F}{X_2} = 20\text{k}\Omega$$

$$R_3 = \frac{R_F}{X_3} = 30\text{k}\Omega$$

$$R_a = \frac{R_F}{Y_a} = 24\text{k}\Omega$$

$$R_b = \frac{R_F}{Y_b} = 60\text{k}\Omega$$

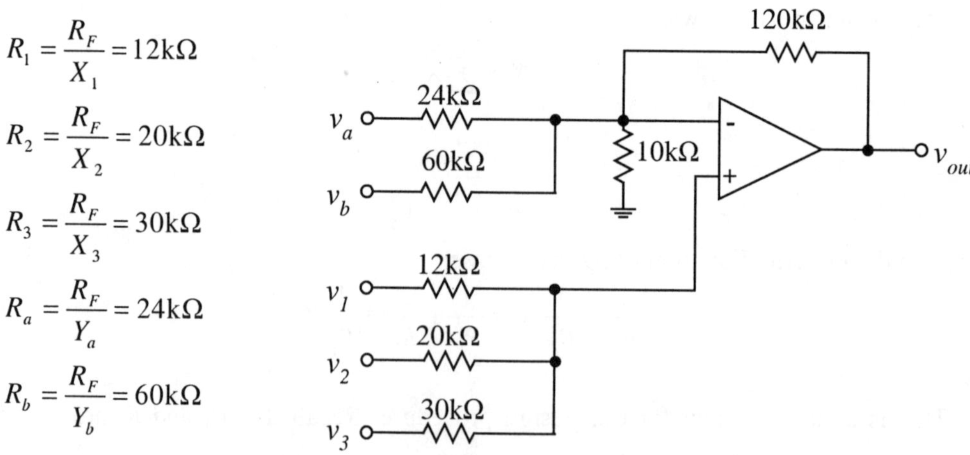

Figure 2.16 – Amplifier for Example 2.5

Since Z is greater than zero, we are dealing with Case I, so R_x is open-circuited. A suitable value of feedback resistor must first be chosen. Once this is determined, all other resistor values are easily found. Because there is one more unknown variable than the number of equations, the R_F can be selected to be any value we wish. We choose a value that will enhance the final design. If a poor choice is made, unrealistic values of the other resistors might result.

Suppose we want the minimum resistance at any of the input to be 10 kΩ. The various resistor values are given in the table (see Case I). The smallest resistor corresponds to the largest value among Z, X_i and Y_j. In this case, Z (which is 12) is larger than any of the coefficients. Therefore, R_y will be the smallest resistance. Setting this resistor to 10 kΩ yields a value of R_F equal to 120 kΩ. Now the remaining resistances can be found, as shown to the right.

The resulting amplifier is shown in Figure 2.15.

Example 2.5 - Op-Amp Summer (Design)

Design an op-amp circuit to implement the following equation:

$$v_{out} = 4v_1 + v_2 - 8v_a - 6v_b$$

Solution: We approach this in the same manner as the previous problem. The value of Z is given by,

$$Z = X - (Y+1) = 5 - (14+1) = -10$$

$$R_1 = \frac{R_F}{X_1} = 37.5\text{k}\Omega$$

$$R_2 = \frac{R_F}{X_2} = 150\text{k}\Omega$$

$$R_a = \frac{R_F}{Y_a} = 18.75\text{k}\Omega$$

$$R_b = \frac{R_F}{Y_b} = 25\text{k}\Omega$$

$$R_x = -\frac{R_F}{Z} = 15\text{k}\Omega$$

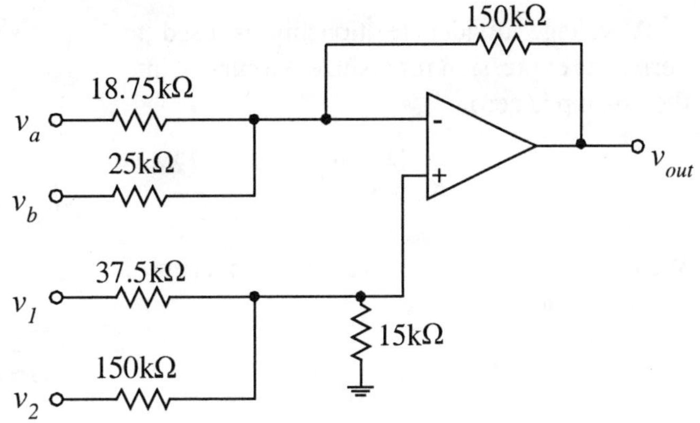

Figure 2.16 –Amplifier for Example 2.5

This is an example of Case II, and R_y is open-circuited. While we could use the same constraint as in the previous example, we present a *different* constraint here based on the equivalent resistance at the inverting and non-inverting terminals *(note that the previous derivation forced these to be equal).* Suppose we set this to 10 kΩ. If you examine the rules for parallel combinations of resistances, you see that the feedback resistance must be 150 kΩ (Y+1 multiplied by the specified terminal equivalent resistance). The remaining resistance values are then easily found using the equations in the table.

The complete circuit is shown in Figure 2.16. Note that at each input terminal, the equivalent resistance is 10 kΩ. The initial selection of R_F is not critical since if we are not happy with the resulting resistor values, they can all be multiplied by the same constant without changing the voltage relationships.

2.7 OTHER OP-AMP APPLICATIONS

We have seen that the op-amp can be used as an amplifier, or as a means of combining a number of inputs in a linear manner. We now investigate several additional important applications of this versatile linear IC.

2.7.1 Negative Impedance Circuit

The circuit shown in Figure 2.17 produces a negative input resistance (impedance in the general case).

This circuit can be used to cancel an unwanted positive resistance. Many oscillator applications depend on a negative resistance op-amp circuit. The input resistance, R_{in}, is the ratio of input voltage to current.

$$R_{in} = \frac{v_{in}}{i_{in}} = \frac{v_+}{i_{in}} \tag{2.43}$$

A voltage divider relationship is used to derive the expression for v_- since the current into the op-amp is zero.

$$v_- = \frac{R_A}{R_A + R_F} v_{out} \tag{2.44}$$

We now let $v_+ = v_-$ and solve for v_{out} in terms of v_{in}, which yields,

$$v_{out} = \left(1 + \frac{R_F}{R_A}\right) v_{in} \tag{2.45}$$

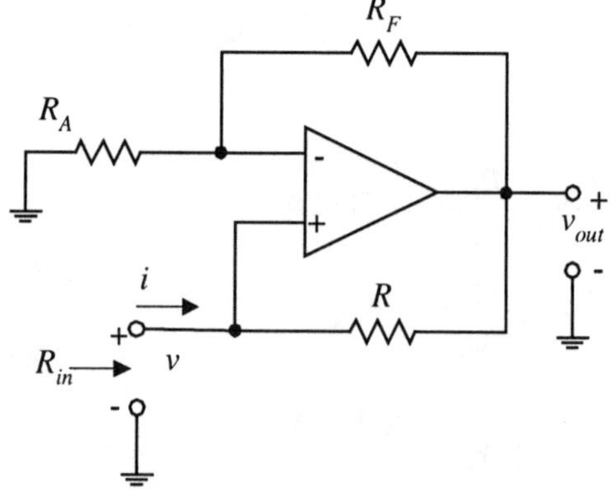

Figure 2.17 – Negative impedance circuit

Since the input impedance to the v_+ terminal is infinite, the current in R is equal to i_{in} and can be found as follows:

$$i_{in} = \frac{v_{in} - v_{out}}{R} = -\frac{R_F v_{in}}{R_A R} \tag{2.46}$$

The input resistance, R_{in}, is then given by

$$R_{in} = \frac{v_{in}}{i_{in}} = -\frac{R_A R}{R_F} \tag{2.47}$$

Equation (2.47) shows that the circuit of Figure 2.17 develops a negative resistance. If R is replaced by an impedance, Z, the circuit develops a negative impedance.

2.7.2 Dependent-Current Generator

A dependent-current generator produces a load current which is proportional to an applied voltage, v_{in}, and is independent of the load resistance. It can be designed using a slight modification of the negative-impedance circuit. The circuit is shown in Figure 2.18(a).

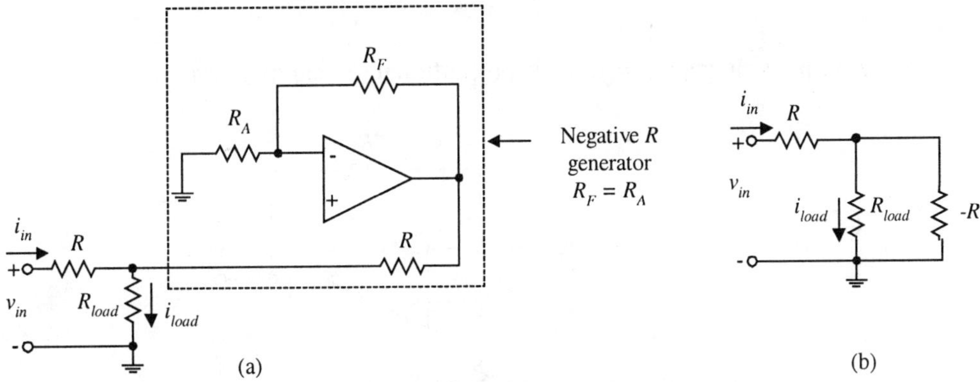

Figure 2.18 – Dependent current generator

Suppose we let $R_F = R_A$. Equation (2.47) then indicates that the input resistance to the op-amp circuit (enclosed in the dashed box) is $-R$. The input circuit can then be simplified as shown in Figure 2.18(b). We wish to calculate i_{load}, the current in R_{load}. Although the resistance is negative, the normal Kirchhoff's laws still apply since nothing in their derivations assumes positive resistors. The input current, i_{in}, is then found by combining the resistances into a single resistor, R_{in}.

$$i_{in} = \frac{v_{in}}{R_{in}} = \frac{v_{in}}{R - (R \cdot R_{load})/(R_{load} - R)} = \frac{v_{in}(R_{load} - R)}{-R^2} \tag{2.48}$$

We then apply a current-divider ratio to the current split between R_{load} *and* $-R$ *to* obtain

$$i_{load} = \frac{-i_{in}R}{R_{load} - R} = \frac{-v_{in}(R_{load} - R)}{R^2}\frac{-R}{R_{load} - R} = \frac{v_{in}}{R} \tag{2.49}$$

Thus the effect of the addition of the op-amp circuit is to make the current in the load proportional to the input voltage. It does not depend upon the value of the load resistance, R_{load}. The current is therefore independent of changes in the load resistance. The op-amp circuit effectively cancels out the load resistance. Since the current is independent of the load but depends only upon the input voltage, we call this a *current generator* (or voltage-to-current converter).

Among the many applications of this circuit is a *dc* regulated voltage source. If we let $v_{in} = E$ (a constant), the current through R_{load} is constant independent of variations of R_{load}.

2.7.3 Current-to-Voltage Converter

The circuit of Figure 2.19 produces an output voltage that is proportional to the input current (this can also be viewed as a *unity-gain inverting amplifier*). We analyze this circuit in using the properties of ideal op-amps. The reason for the presence of the *R/2* resistor between the non-inverting input and ground will become clear when we discuss bias balance in Chapter 9. We solve for the voltages at the input terminals to find

$$\begin{aligned} v_+ &= 0 \\ v_- &= v_{out} + i_{in}R = v_+ = 0 \end{aligned} \tag{2.50}$$

Hence, the output voltage, $v_{out} = -i_{in}R$, is proportional to the input current, i_{in}.

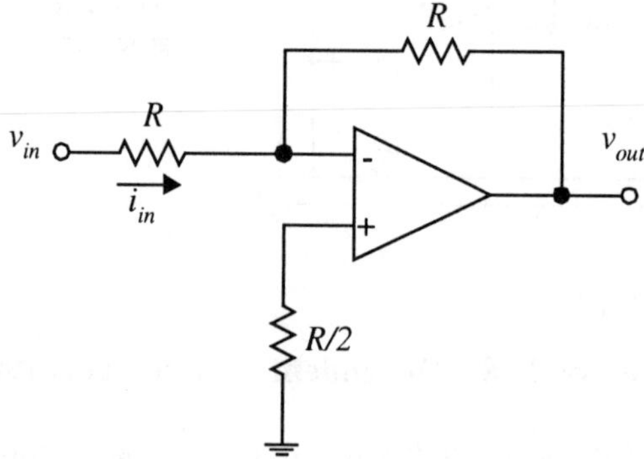

Figure 2.19 - Current -to-Voltage converter

2.7.4 Voltage-to-Current Converter

The circuit of Figure 2. 20, is a voltage-to-current converter. We analyze this circuit as follows:

$$\begin{aligned} v_+ &= v_{in} = v_- \\ v_- &= i_{load} R_1 = v_+ \end{aligned} \tag{2.51}$$

From Equation (2.51) we find,

$$i_{load} = \frac{v_{in}}{R_1} \tag{2.52}$$

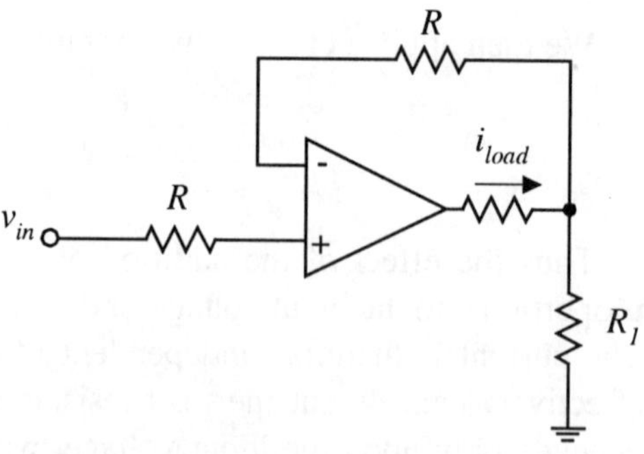

Figure 2.20 – Voltage to current converter

Therefore, the load current is independent of the load resistor, R_{load}, and is proportional to the applied voltage, v_{in}. This circuit develops a voltage-controlled current source. However, a practical shortcoming of this circuit is that neither end of the load resistor can be grounded.

As an alternative, the circuit shown in Figure 2.21 provides a voltage-to-current converter with one end of the load resistance grounded.

We analyze this circuit by writing node equations as follows:

$$\frac{v_+ - v_{in}}{R_1} + \frac{v_+ - v_{out}}{R_2} + i_{load} = 0$$
$$\frac{v_- - v}{R_1} + \frac{v_- - v_{out}}{R_2} = 0 = \frac{v_+ - v}{R_1} + \frac{v_+ - v_{out}}{R_2} \tag{2.53}$$

The last equality uses the fact that $v_+ = v_-$. There are five unknowns in these equations (v_+, v_{in}, v_{out}, v, and i_{load}). We eliminate v_+ and v_{out} to obtain,

$$i_{load} = \frac{1}{R_1}(v_{in} - v) \tag{2.54}$$

The load current, i_{load}, is independent of the load, R_{load}, and is only a function of the voltage difference, (v_{in} - v).

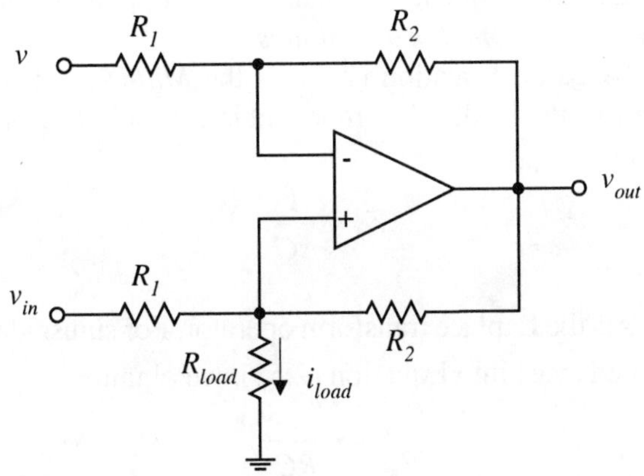

Figure 2.21 – Voltage-to-current converter

2.7.5 Inverting Amplifier with Generalized Impedances

The relationship of Equation (2.17) is easily extended to include non-resistive components if R_j is replaced by an impedance, Z_j, and R_F is replaced by Z_F. For a single input, as shown in Figure 2.22(a), the output reduces to

$$V_{out} = -\frac{Z_F}{Z_a} V_{in} \tag{2.55}$$

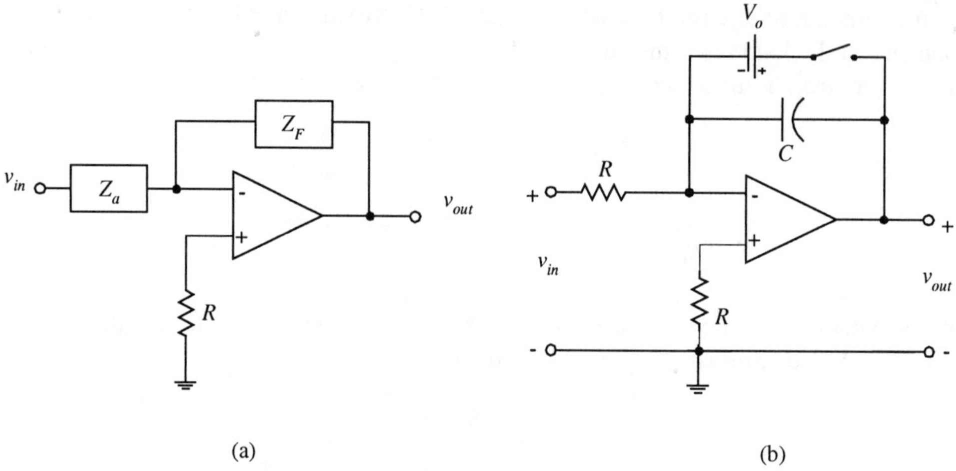

Figure 2.22 – Use of generalized impedance in place of resistance

Since we are dealing in the frequency domain, we use uppercase letters for the voltages and currents, thus representing the *complex amplitudes*.

One useful circuit based on Equation (2.55) is the *Miller integrator*, as shown in Figure 2.22(b). In this application, the feedback component is a capacitor, C, and the input component is a resistor, R, so

$$Z_F = \frac{1}{sC} \tag{2.56}$$

In Equation (2.56), s is the Laplace transform operator. For sinusoidal signals, $s = j\omega$. When we substitute these impedances into Equation (2.55), we obtain

$$\frac{V_{out}}{V_{in}} = -\frac{1}{RC} \cdot \frac{1}{s} \tag{2.57}$$

In the complex frequency domain, *1/s* corresponds to integration in the time domain. This is an *inverting integrator* because the expression contains a negative sign. Hence the output voltage is

$$v_{out}(t) = -\frac{1}{RC} \int_0^t v_{in}(\tau)\,d\tau + v_{out}(0) \tag{2.58}$$

where $v_{out}(0)$ is the initial condition. The value of v_{out} is developed as the voltage across the capacitor, C, at time $t = 0$. The switch is closed to charge the capacitor to the voltage $v_{out}(0)$ and then at $t = 0$ the switch is open. We use electronic switches, which we discuss more fully in Chapter 16. In the event that the initial condition is zero, the switch is still used to reset the integrator to zero output voltage at time $t = 0$.

If the feedback element is a resistor, and the input element is a capacitor, as shown in Figure 2.23, the input-output relationship becomes

$$\frac{V_{out}}{V_{in}} = -RC \cdot s \qquad (2.59)$$

In the time domain, this becomes

$$v_{out}(t) = -RC\frac{dv_{in}}{dt} \qquad (2.60)$$

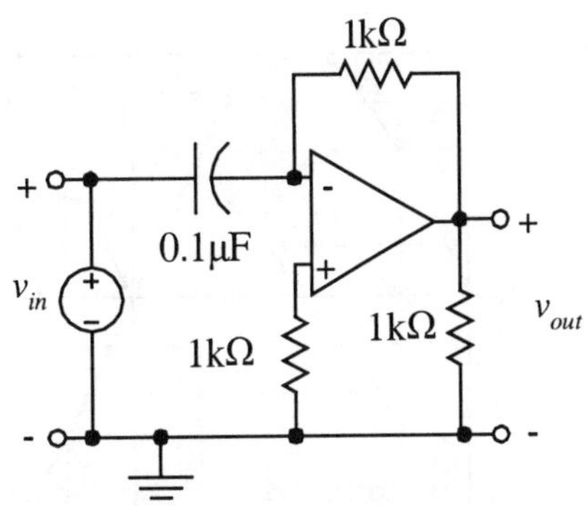

Figure 2.23 - Example of an inverting differentiator

The circuit is operating as an *inverting differentiator*. Note that the input capacitor, $Z_a = 1/sC$, does not provide a path for *dc*. This does not affect the result since the derivative of a constant is zero. For simplicity, let's use a sinusoidal input signal. Rearranging Equation (2.59) and substituting the numeric values for this circuit, we obtain

$$\begin{aligned} V_{out} &= -RCs \cdot V_{in} \\ &= -(1000) \cdot (0.1 \times 10^{-6}) \cdot j(2\pi \cdot 1000) \cdot V_{in} \\ &= -j0.628 \cdot V_{in} \\ &= 0.314\angle -90^{\circ} \quad \text{V} \end{aligned} \qquad (2.61)$$

The input voltage is inverted (180° shift) by this circuit and then scaled and shifted again (90° by the *j*-operator) by the value of *RCs* where $s = j\omega = j\,2\pi\,1000$ rad/sec.

Results of the simulation are shown in Figure 2.24. The input waveform peaks at 0.5 volts. The output voltage has a net shift (delay) of 90 degrees and the output voltage peaks at approximately 0.314 volts. This is in good agreement with the result of Equation (2.61).

We may also use the waveforms to show that this circuit performs the task of an inverting differentiator. We will confirm that the output waveform represents the slope of the input signal times a constant. The constant is the voltage gain of the circuit. The greatest rate of change of the input voltage waveform occurs at its zero-crossing. This corresponds with the time that the output waveform reaches its maximum (or minimum). Picking a representative point, say at time0.5 ms, and using graphical techniques, we compute the slope of the input voltage waveform as

$$slope = \frac{rise}{run} = \frac{\Delta voltage}{\Delta time} = \frac{0.5\text{V-(-0.5V)}}{0.335\text{ms-}0.650\text{ms}} = 3175 \quad \text{V/s} \qquad (2.62)$$

Scaling this rate of change (i.e., $\frac{d\,v_{in}}{dt}$) by the circuit voltage gain according to Equation (2.60) we expect the peak output voltage to be

$$\begin{aligned} v_{out} &= -RC \cdot \frac{dv_{in}}{dt} = -(1000)(0.1 \times 10^{-6}) \cdot \frac{dv_{in}}{dt} \\ &= (100 \times 10^{-6})(3175) \\ &= 0.3175 \quad \text{V} \end{aligned} \qquad (2.63)$$

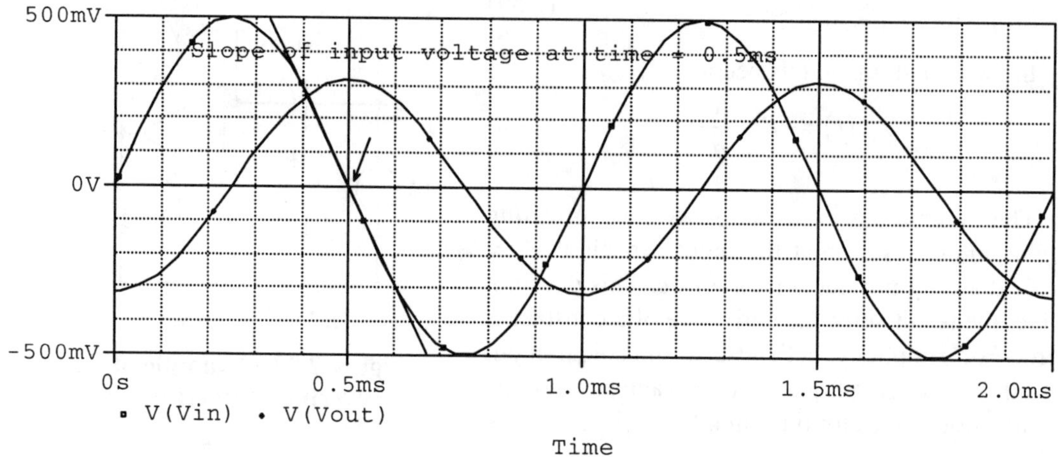

Figure 2.24 – Simulation results for inverting differentiator

2.7.6 Analog Computer Applications

In this section we present the use of interconnected op-amp circuits, such as summers and integrators, to form an analog computer which is used to solve differential equations. Many physical systems are described by linear differential equations, and the system can therefore be analyzed with the aid of an analog computer.

Let us solve for the current, *i(t)*, in the circuit of Figure 2.25. The input voltage is the driving function and the initial conditions are zero. We write the differential equation for the circuit as follows:

$$v(t) = L\frac{di}{dt} + Ri + \frac{1}{C}\int_0^t i(\tau)d\tau \qquad (2.64)$$

Now solving for *di/dt*, we obtain

$$\frac{di}{dt} = \frac{v(t)}{L} - \frac{Ri}{L} - \frac{1}{LC}\int_0^t i(\tau)d\tau \qquad (2.65)$$

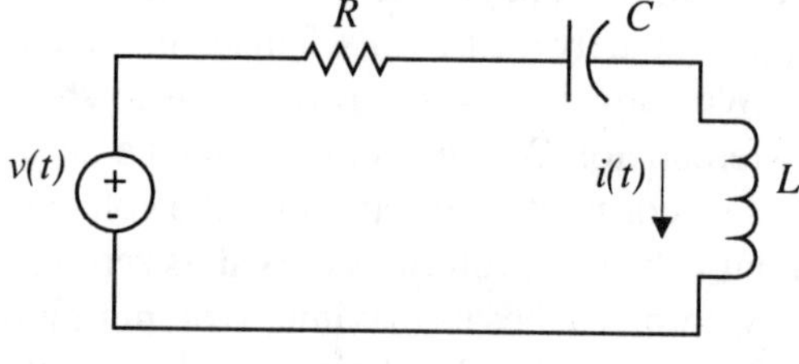

Figure 2.25 - Analog computer application

We know that for $t > 0$,

$$i(t) = -\int_0^t \left(-\frac{di}{d\tau}\right)d\tau + i(0) \qquad (2.66)$$

From Equation (2.65) we see that *-di/dt* is formed by summing three terms, which are found on Figure 2.26 at the input to the first integrating amplifier.

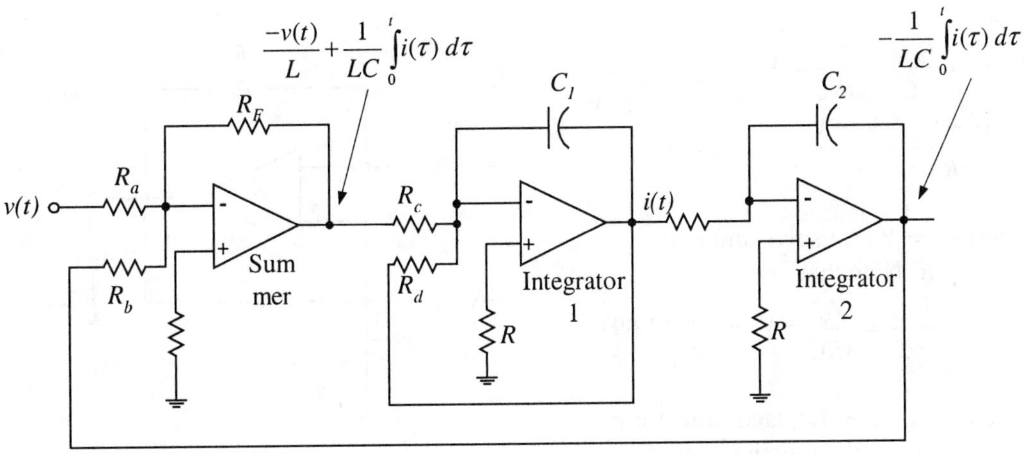

Figure 2.26 - Analog computer solution for Figure 2.25

The three terms are found as follows:

1. The driving function, *-v(t)/L*, is formed by passing *v(t)* through an inverting summer (Summer) with gain, *1/L*.
2. R_f/L is formed by taking the output of the first integrating amplifier (Integrator 1) and adding it at the amplifier input to the output of the summing amplifier (Summer).
3. The term

$$-\frac{1}{LC}\int_0^t i(\tau)d\tau \tag{2.67}$$

is the output of the second integrator (Integrator 2). Since the sign must be changed, we sum it with the unity gain inverting summer (Summer).

The output of the first integrator is *+i*, as seen from Equation (2.66). The constants in the differential equation are established by proper selection of the resistors and capacitors of the analog computer. Zero initial conditions are accomplished by switches across the capacitors, as shown in Figure 2.22(b).

2.7.7 Non-Inverting Miller Integrator

We use a modification of the dependent current generator of the previous section to develop a non-inverting integrator. The circuit is configured as shown in Figure 2.27.

This is similar to the circuit of Figure 2.21, but the load resistance has been replaced by a capacitance. We now find the current, I_{load}. The inverting voltage, V_-, is found from the voltage division between V_o and V_- as follows:

$$V_+ = \frac{I_{load}}{sC} = \frac{V_{in}}{sRC} = V_- = \frac{V_{out}}{2}$$
$$\frac{V_+ - V_{in}}{R} + \frac{V_+ - V_{out}}{R} + I_{load} = 0 \quad (2.68)$$

Since $V_+ = V_-$, we solve and find $I_L = V_{in}/R$. Note that

$$V_+ = \frac{I_{load}}{sC} = \frac{V_{in}}{sRC} = V_- = \frac{V_{out}}{2} \quad (2.69)$$

where s is the Laplace transform operator. The V_{out}/V_{in} function is then

$$\frac{V_{out}}{V_{in}} = \frac{2}{RC} \cdot \frac{1}{s} \quad (2.70)$$

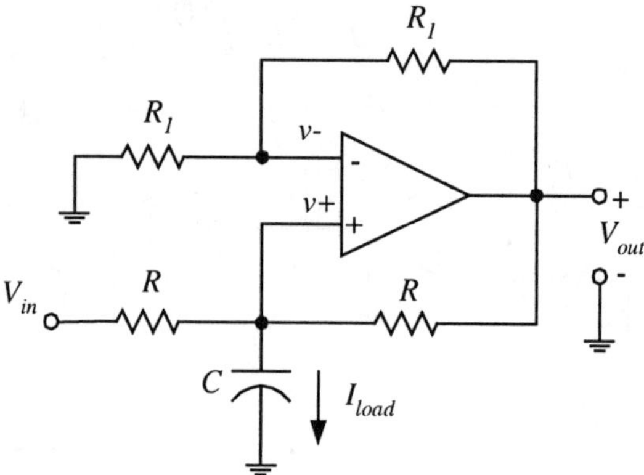

Figure 2.27 – Non-inverting integrator

Thus, in the time domain we have

$$v_{out}(t) = \frac{2}{RC} \int_0^t v_{in}(\tau)\, d\tau \quad (2.71)$$

The circuit is therefore a non-inverting integrator.

SUMMARY

The operational amplifier is a very useful building block for electronic systems. The real amplifier operates almost as an ideal amplifier with very high gain and almost infinite input impedance. For this reason, we can treat it in the same way we treat circuit components. That is, we are able to incorporate the amplifier into useful configurations prior to studying the internal operation and the electronic characteristics. By recognizing the terminal characteristics, we are able to configure amplifiers and other useful circuits.

This chapter began with an analysis of the ideal operational amplifier, and with development of equivalent circuit models using dependent sources. The dependent sources we studied early in this chapter form the building blocks of equivalent circuits for many of the electronic devices we study in this text.

We then explored the external connections needed to make the op-amp into an inverting amplifier, a non-inverting amplifier, and a multiple input amplifier. We developed a convenient design technique eliminating the need for solving large systems of simultaneous equations.

Finally, we saw how the op-amp could be used to build a variety of more complex circuits, including circuits which are equivalent to negative impedances (which can be used to cancel the effects of positive impedances), integrators and differentiators.

When we revisit operational amplifiers in Chapter 9, we will see that the practical devices perform very closely to the ideal devices.

PROBLEMS

Section 2.5

Problems 2.1 through 2.10: Find the output voltage, v_{out}, in terms of the input voltage, v_{in}, for each of the circuit shown in Figures P2.1 through P2.10.

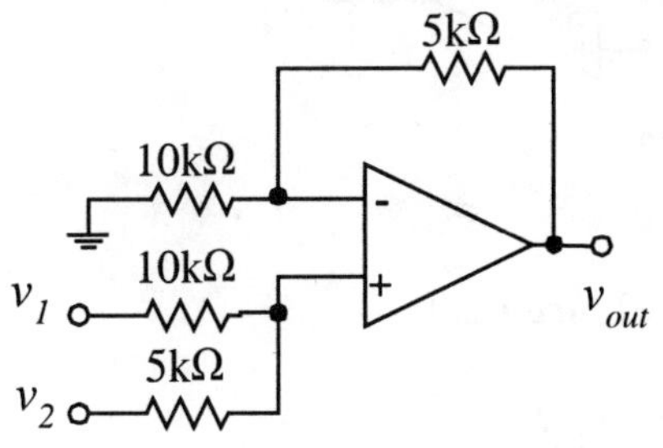

Figure P2.1

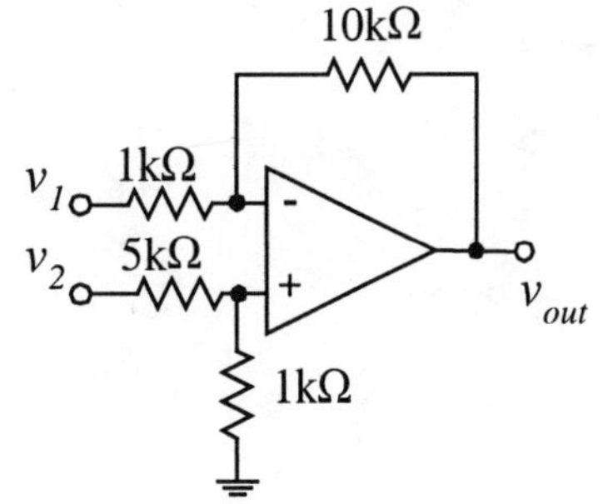

Figure P2.2

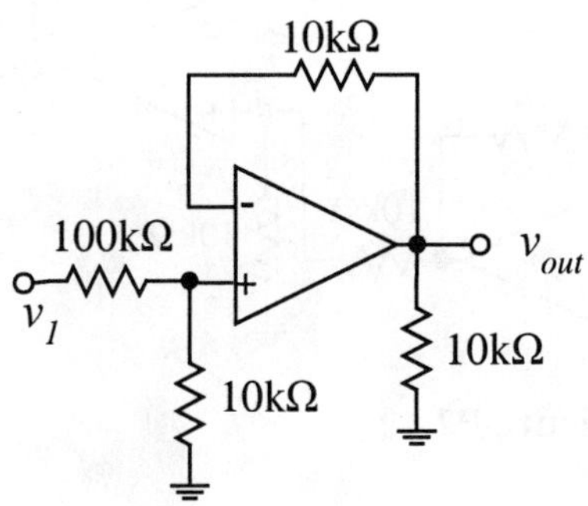

Figure P2.3

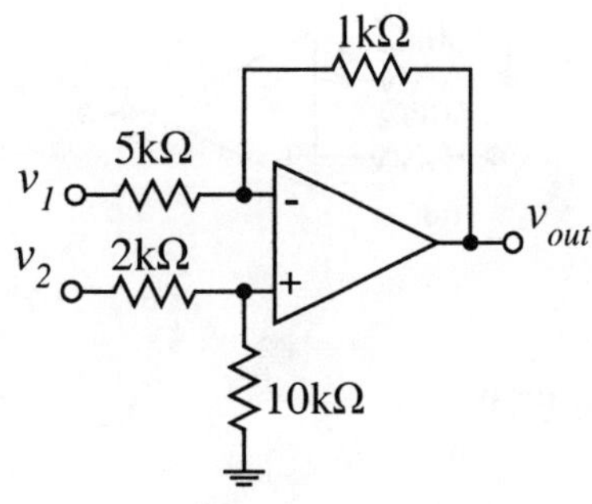

Figure P2.4

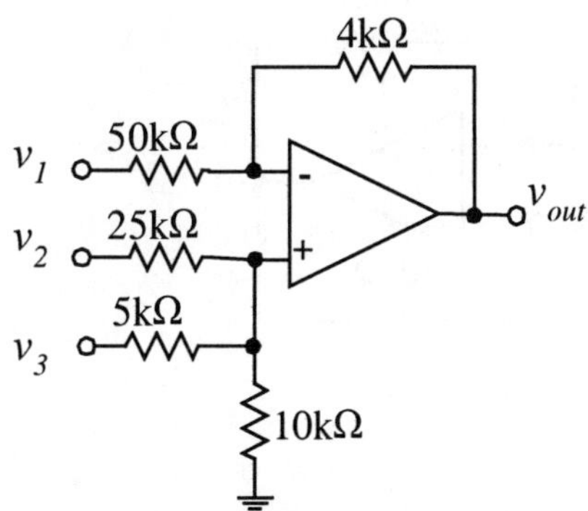

Figure P2.5

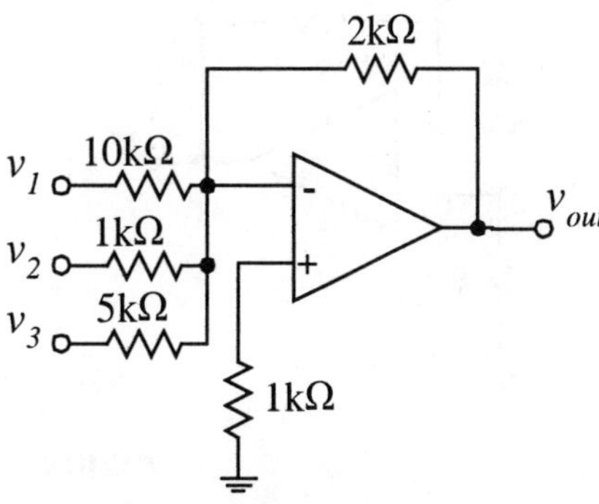

Figure P2.6

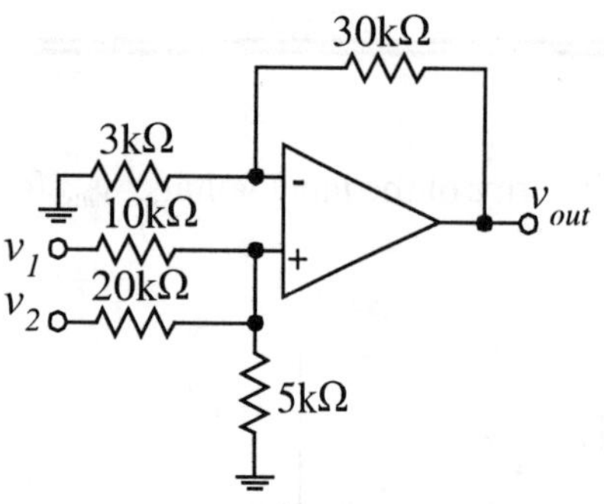

Figure P2.7

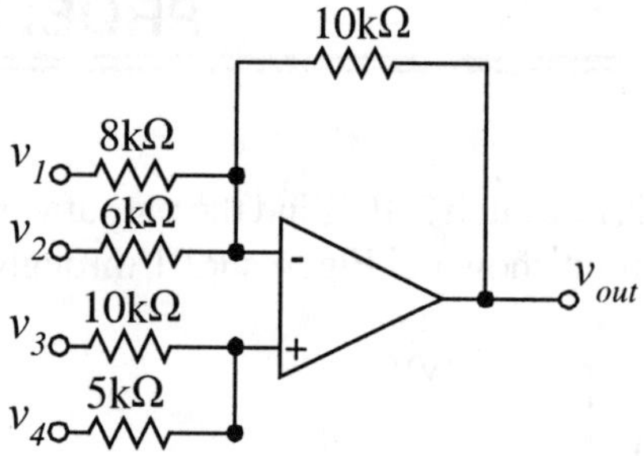

Figure P2.8

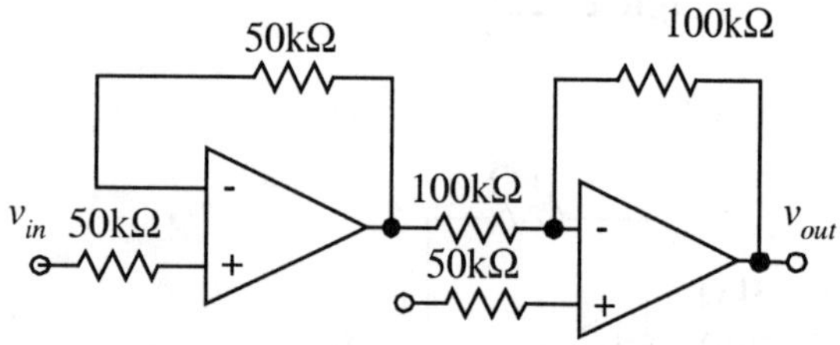

Figure P2.9

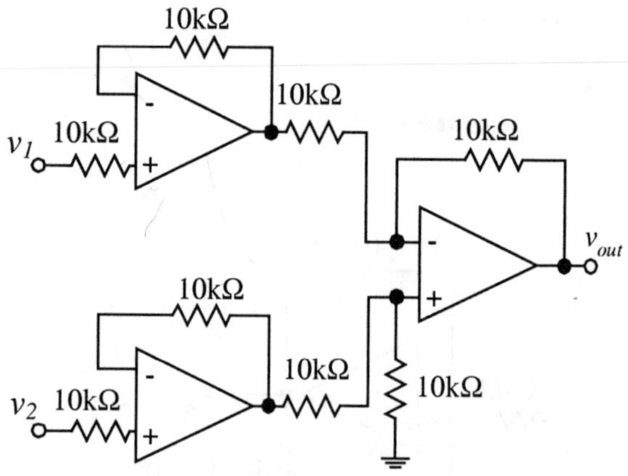

Figure P2.10

2.11 Construct an ideal op-amp mathematical model and solve for the gain ratio, v_{out}/v_{in} for each of the configurations of Figure P2.11.

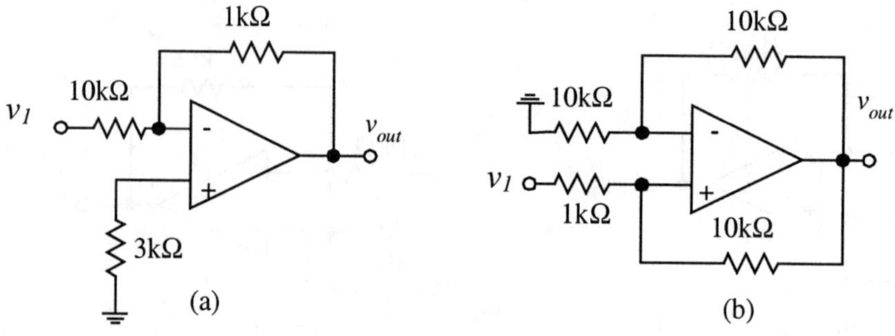

Figure P2.11

2.12 Find the output voltage, v_{out}, in terms of the input signals for the circuits of Figure P2.12. Use the ideal op-amp mathematical model.

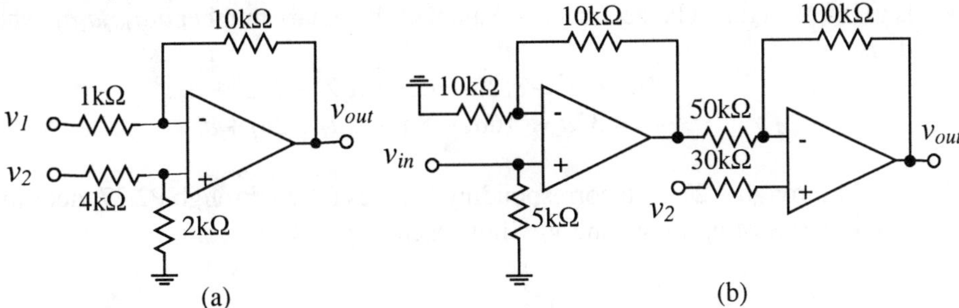

Figure P2.12

Section 2.6

In Problems 2.13 through 2.16, design an op-amp amplifier circuit to yield the relationships shown in each equation. In each case, use the procedure of Examples E2.4 and E2.5 and compare the results. Select R = 10 kΩ.

2.13 $v_{out} = v_1 + 10v_2 - 20v_a - 50v_b$

2.14 $v_{out} = 8v_1 + 8v_2 - 4v_a - 9v_b$

2.15 $v_{out} = 6v_1 + 8v_2 - 3v_a - 12v_b$

2.16 $v_{out} = 3v_1 + v_2 + 6v_3 - 4v_a - 5v_b$

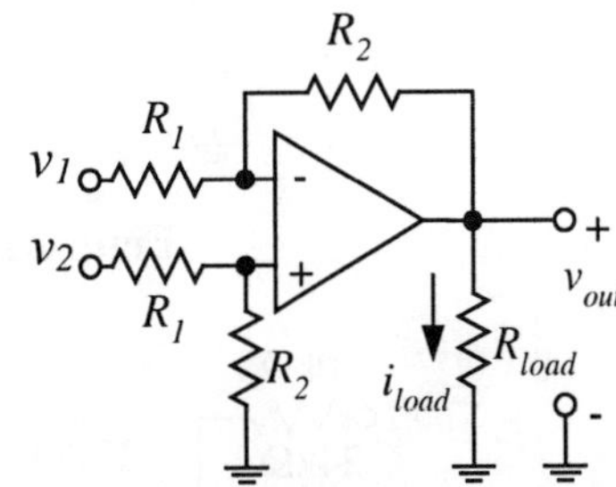

Figure P2.22

In Problems 2.17 and 2.18, design operational amplifiers to have the outputs shown. The amplifier should have a resistance of 20 kΩ at the + and - terminals. Draw the schematic and shown the resistor values on the schematic.

2.17 $v_{out} = 4v_1 - 3v_2 + 6v_3 - 5v_4 - v_5$

2.18 $v_{out} = 3v_1 - 5v_2 + 7v_3 - 2v_4$

In Problems 2.19 through 2.21, design operational amplifiers to have the outputs shown. The amplifier should have a minimum resistance of not less than 10 kΩ at any of the voltage inputs. Draw the schematic and indicate the resistor values on the schematic.

2.19 $v_{out} = 4v_1 - 9v_2 - 5v_3 + 6v_4 + 5v_5$

2.20 $v_{out} = 9v_1 + 4v_2 - 5v_3 - 6v_4 + 3v_5$

2.21 $v_{out} = 2v_1 - 8v_2 + 3v_3 - 7v_4 + 4v_5$

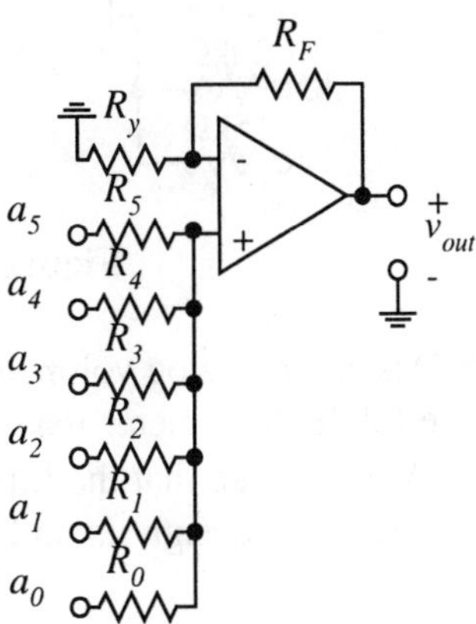

Figure P2.23

Section 2.7

2.22 For the circuit of Figure P2.22, what value of v_2 is required to produce v_{out} = 500 mV when v_1 = 40 mV, R_1 = 50 kΩ and R_2 = 150 kΩ? What is the value of the output current, i_{load}, for the above conditions and R_{load} = 4 kΩ?

2.23 A digital-to-analog (D/A) converter can be designed using an op-amp as shown in Figure P2.23. Design a 6-bit D/A converter with $R_{\min} = 10\ \text{k}\Omega$. What is a good choice for V_{CC} if logic 1 corresponds to 0.2 V? Hint: The decimal equivalent of the binary number $a_5a_4a_3a_2a_1$, where a_i is either 0 or 1, is

$$N = a_5 2^5 + a_4 2^4 + a_3 2^3 + a_2 2^2 + a_1 2^1 + a_o 2^o$$
$$= 32a_5 + 16a_4 + 8a_3 + 4a_2 + 2a_1 + a_o\ .$$

In Problems 2.24 through 2.27 with corresponding Figures P2.24 through P2.27, determine the output voltage in terms of v_1, v_2, v_3, and v_4. Show each step of your work.

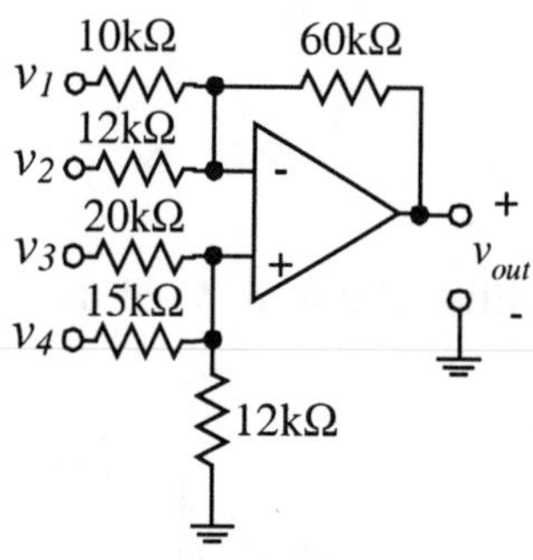

Figure P2.24

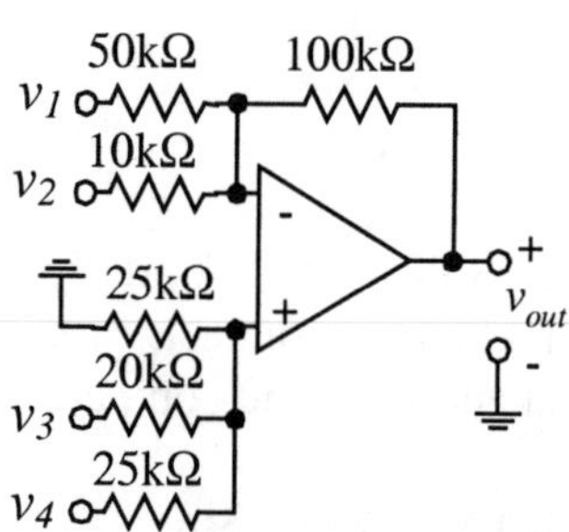

Figure P2.25

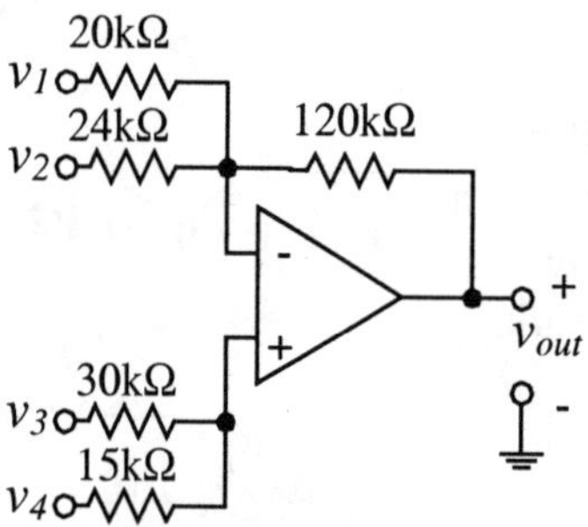

Figure P2.26

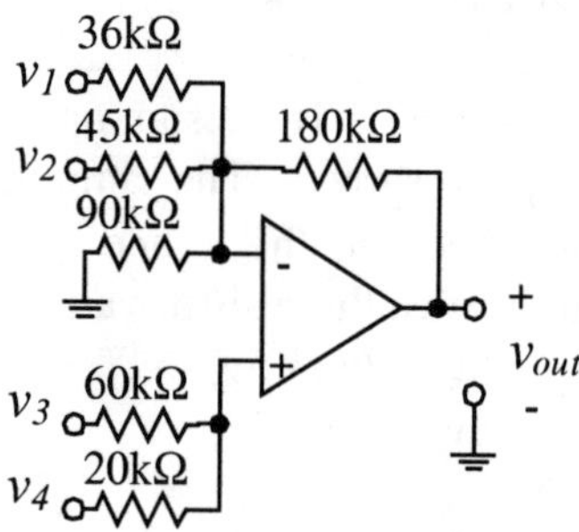

Figure P2.27

2.28 Design an analog voltmeter using the circuit shown in Figure P2.28. The meter reads full scale with a current of 100 μA. Find R so that the full scale reading is $v = +10$ V. Note that this design is independent of R_m, the meter resistance.

2.29 Design an op-amp circuit to produce a negative resistance of -10 $k\Omega$.

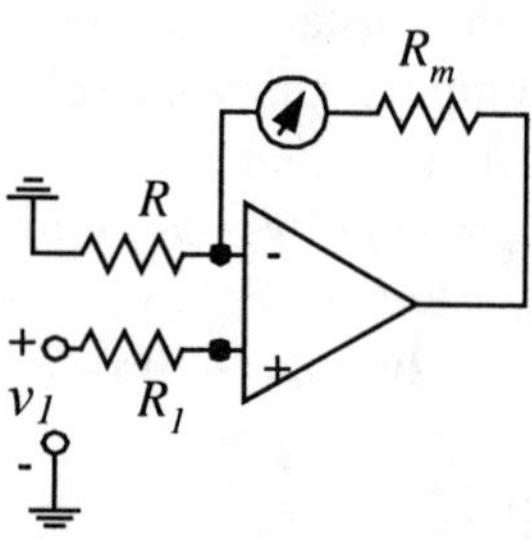

Figure P2.28

2.30 Design an analog computer op-amp circuit to solve the following equations:

$$\frac{dx}{dt} + 9x = 3$$

Use two summing amplifiers and one integrator in your design.

In Problems 2.31 through 2.33 and corresponding Figures P2.31 through P2.33, find i_{load} and v_{load} when $v_{in} = 0.2 \sin 1000t$ V. Are the op-amps *dc* bias balanced? Why?

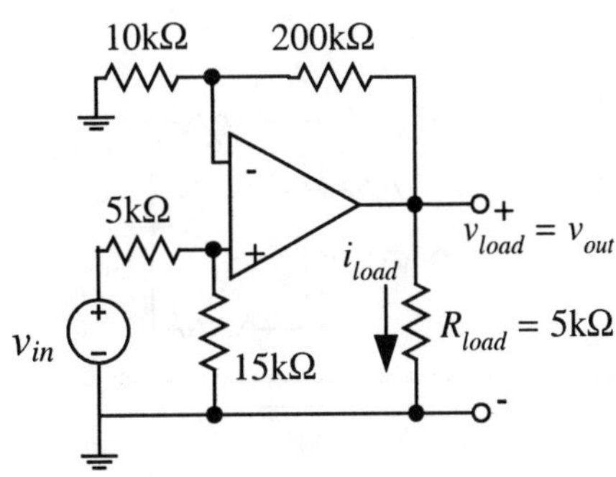

Figure P2.31

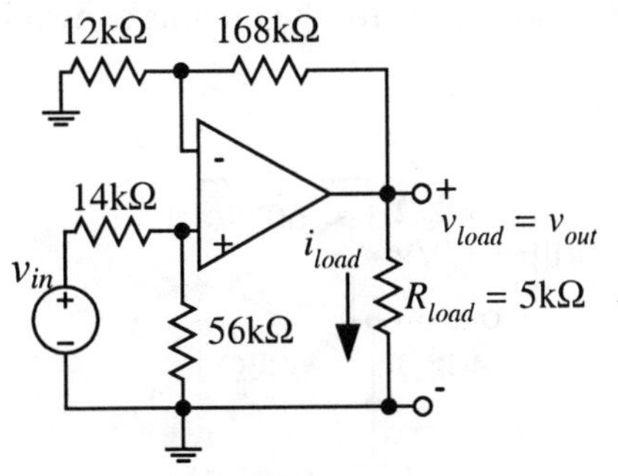

Figure P2.32

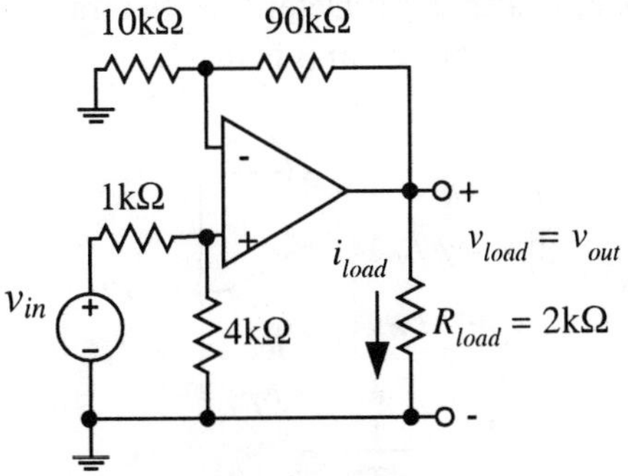

Figure P2.33

2.34 Design an analog computer op-amp circuit to solve the following two first-order simultaneous differential equations:

$$\frac{dx}{dt} + a_1x + b_1y = f_1(t)$$

$$\frac{dy}{dt} + b_2y + a_2x = f_2(t)$$

Use two integrating op-amps and two summing op-amps in your design.

2.35 Determine the gain, v_{out}/v_{in}, for the ideal op-amp circuit shown in Figure P2.35. Why does this circuit yield such a peculiar answer?

2.36 Determine v_{out} in terms of v_1 and v_2 for the circuit shown in Figure P2.36 when the op-amp is *dc* bias balanced.

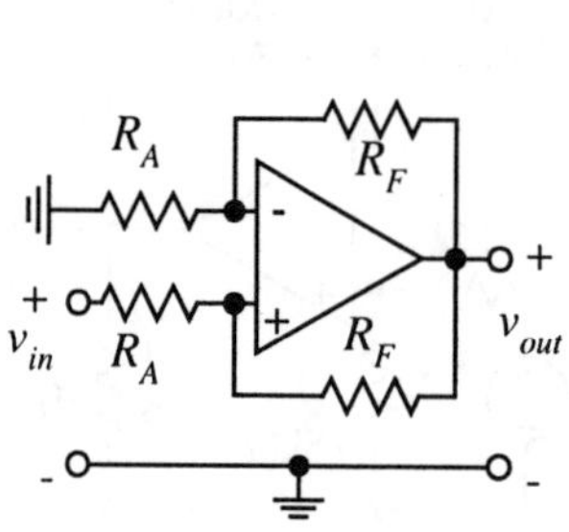

Figure P2.35

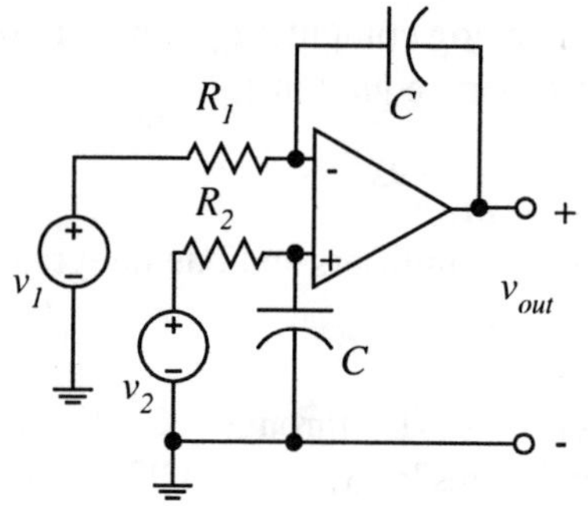

Figure P2.36

Problems 2.37 and 2.38: Determine the transfer ratio, v_{out}/v_{in} for the circuits shown in Figures P2.37 and P2.38. The op-amp is ideal.

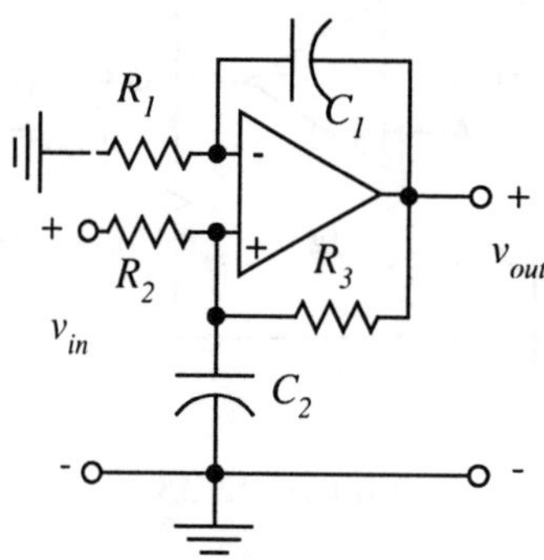

Figure P2.37

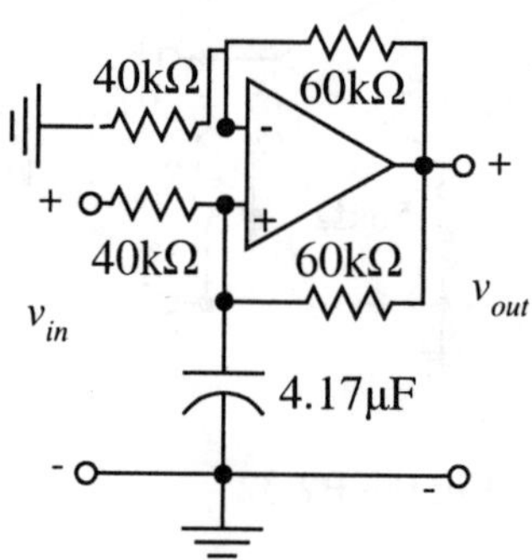

Figure P2.38

2.39 Determine v_{out} in terms of v_1 and v_2 for the circuit shown in Figure P2.39 when the op-amp is *dc* bias balanced.

2.40 Find the gain, v_{out}/v_{in}, for the ideal op-amp circuits shown in Figure P2.40.

2.41 Determine the voltage gain, v_{out}/v_{in}, for the ideal op-amp circuit of Figure P2.41 (please see next page). This will be a function of the variable resistor. The maximum value of the resistor is R when $x = 1$, and x ranges from 1 to 0. Plot the gain, v_{out}/v_{in}, as a function of x.

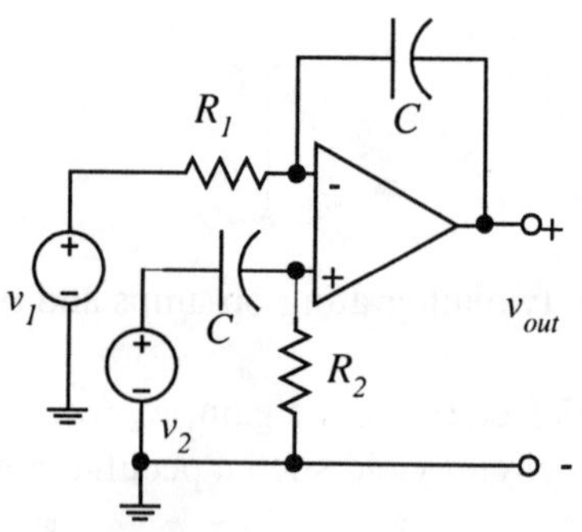

Figure P2.39

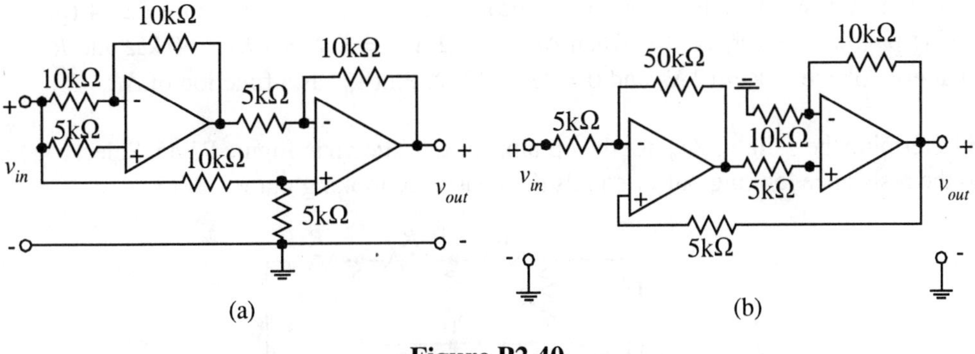

Figure P2.40

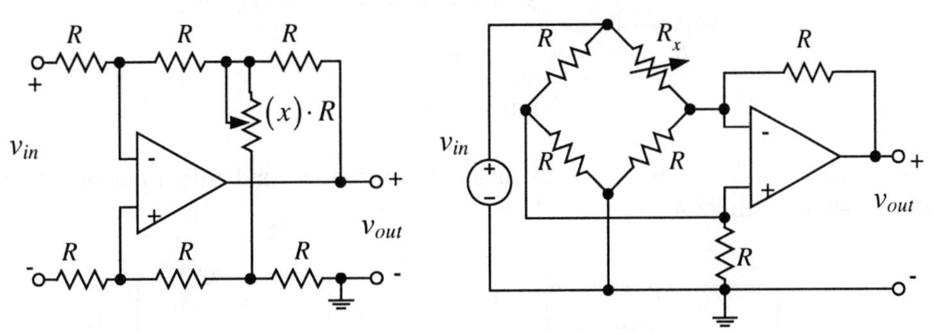

Figure P2.41 **Figure P2.42**

2.42 Plot the output voltage, v_{out}, as function of R/R_x for the ideal op-amp circuit of Figure P2.42. Assume that $V = 15$ V.

2.43 Given the op-amp circuit shown in Figure P2.43 determine v_{out} in terms of v_{in}.

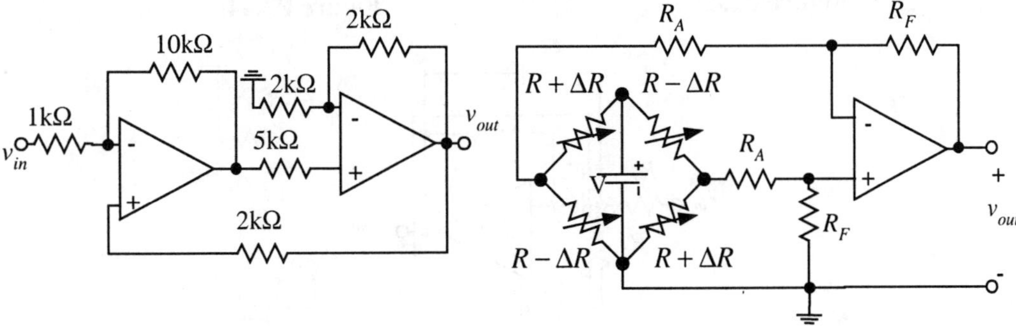

Figure P2.43 **Figure P2.44**

2.44 Design an instrumentation system to measure ΔR, as shown in Figure P2.44 (please see following page). Select R_F so that when $\Delta R = 30\ \Omega$, $v_{out} = 3$ V. Set $R_A = 30$ kΩ and $R = 1$ kΩ. The battery voltage is $V = 12$ V, and $0 < \Delta R < 30\ \Omega$. Plot v_{out} as a function of ΔR.

2.45 Determine the gain, v_{out}/v_{in}, for the op-amp system shown in Figure P2.45. Select a value for R_1 so the resistance looking out v_+ equals the resistance looking out v_-.

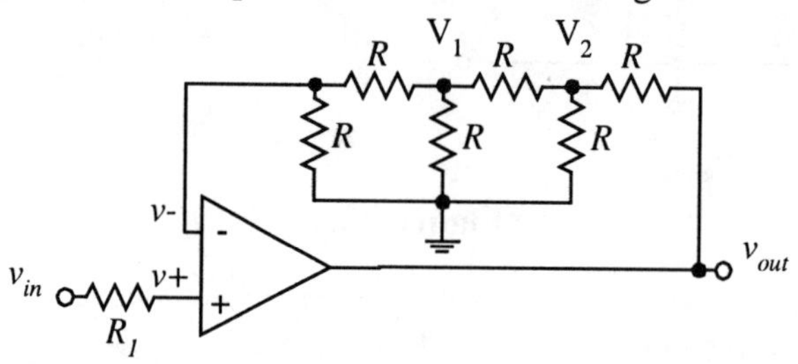

Figure P2.45

In Problems 2.46-2.48, derive the v_{out}/v_{in} characteristics for the second order filter circuits shown in Figures P2.46 through P2.48.

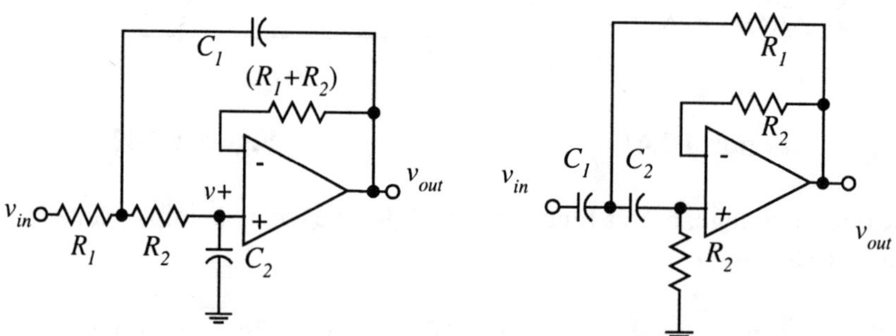

Figure P2.43 **Figure P2.44**

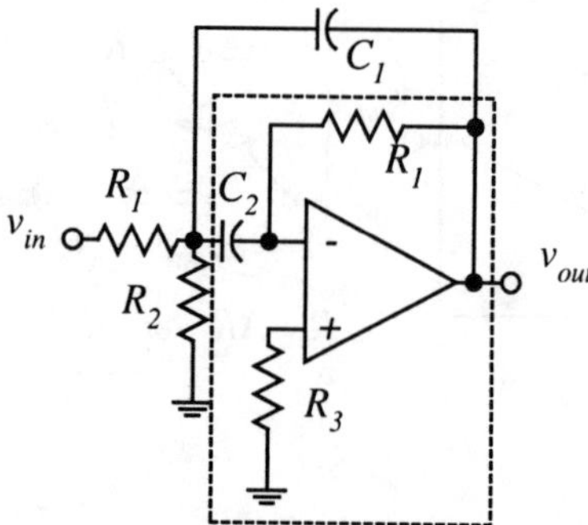

Figure P2.48

Chapter 3

Semiconductor Diode Circuit Analysis

This chapter introduces you to the simplest electronic device, the diode. In studying this device, you will learn many techniques that can be applied to analysis and design using more complex electronic components. Once you finish studying this material, you will understand:

- How semiconductors work and how current flows in them.
- The internal structure of the diode, and the applicable physical laws which govern its behavior.
- The use of diodes in circuits that perform nonlinear operations.
- Alternate types of diodes, such as Zener, Schottky, and photo.
- The design of elementary power supplies.
- General techniques for analyzing and designing circuits with diodes.

3.0 INTRODUCTION

The simplest nonlinear electronic device is the *diode*. A solid state diode is composed of two different materials placed together in a manner such that charge flows easily in one direction but is impeded in the other direction.

The diode was invented by Henry Dunwoody in 1906 when he placed a piece of electric furnace Carborundum between two brass holders. Later that year, Greenleaf Pickard developed a crystal radio detector in the form of a cat's whisker in contact with a crystal. Studies conducted from 1906 to 1940 indicated that silicon and germanium were excellent materials to use in the construction of these devices.

Many practical problems had to be overcome in the construction and fabrication of diodes. It took until the mid 1950s for engineers to solve the most critical of these problems. During the technological explosion of the late 1950s and early 1960s, solid state technology received a great deal of attention. This was driven by the need for light-weight, small and low-power consuming electronic components for use in the development of intercontinental missiles and space vehicles. Solid state devices had to achieve high reliability in applications where maintenance would be impossible. The result was the development of solid state components that are more economical and more reliable than their predecessor, the vacuum tube.

This chapter provides an introduction to the operation and applications of the solid state diode. This two-terminal device, is *nonlinear*. That is, applying the sum of two voltages produces a current which is *not* the sum of the two individual resulting currents. The diode behavior depends on the *polarity* of the applied voltage. The diode's nonlinear characteristic is the reason it finds so many useful applications in electronics.

You should be introduced to the physics of diodes to appreciate the origins of the equivalent circuits and to understand their limitations. We present a simplified approach to the topic, beginning with atomic structure and an examination of conduction in various materials. We then apply the developed theory to the semiconductor diode, examining the resulting nonlinear characteristics of this device.

The chapter concludes with an examination of several important diode applications. We pay particular attention to the design of voltage regulators. Special-purpose diodes such as *Schottky, varactor, light-emitting (LED)* and *photo* are then discussed.

3.1 THEORY OF SEMICONDUCTORS

There is a tendency among some engineers to think that the theory of semiconductors is not important – that circuits can be designed without knowing anything about the underlying physics and chemistry. In fact, as an engineer you must know something about the causes of the effects you observe. Real devices and systems rarely behave as the theory predicts. Unless you have some idea of the "inner working" of the device, you cannot explain any apparent contradictions. Without this knowledge, you will also be at a disadvantage when trying to interpret data sheets and computer simulation parameters.

The Bohr model of an *atom* contains a *nucleus* having a positive charge. *Electrons*, with negative charges, move around the nucleus in elliptical paths. These electrons distribute themselves in *shells*. Electrons in the outermost shell are known as *valence electrons.*

When extremely pure elements, such as silicon and germanium, are cooled from the liquid state, their atoms arrange themselves in orderly patterns called *crystals*, as illustrated in Figure 3.1 (please see next page). The valence electrons determine the exact shape or lattice structure of the resulting crystal. Silicon and germanium atoms each have four valence electrons. This is illustrated in Figure 3.2 (please see next page).

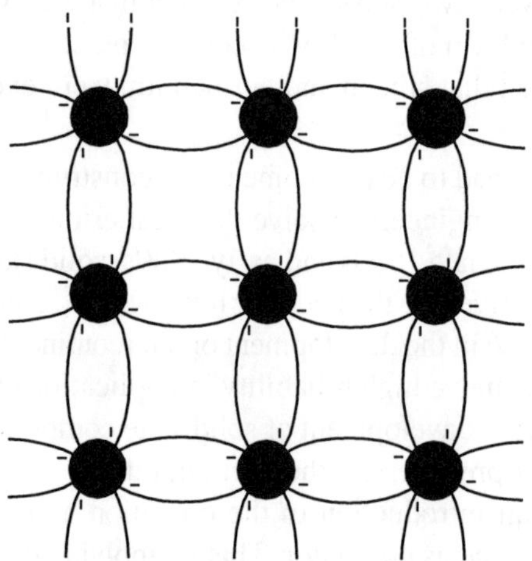

Figure 3.1 Crystal structure

The germanium atom has one more filled ring than does the silicon atom. The germanium outer ring is at a greater distance from the atom nucleus than is the silicon outer ring. The atoms are bound in a lattice structure so that each atom "shares" its four valence electrons with neighboring atoms in the form of *covalent bonds.* The covalent bonds hold the lattice together.

The valence electrons are bound tightly in the crystalline structure. However, it is possible for these electrons to break their bond and move about in a *conduction* mode. This happens if sufficient external energy is supplied (e.g., from light or heat).

Because of interaction among the atoms in a crystal, it is possible for the valence electrons to possess energy levels within a range of values. The further an electron is away from atomic nuclei, the higher is the energy level. Thus, as the crystal becomes "tighter", energy levels decrease.

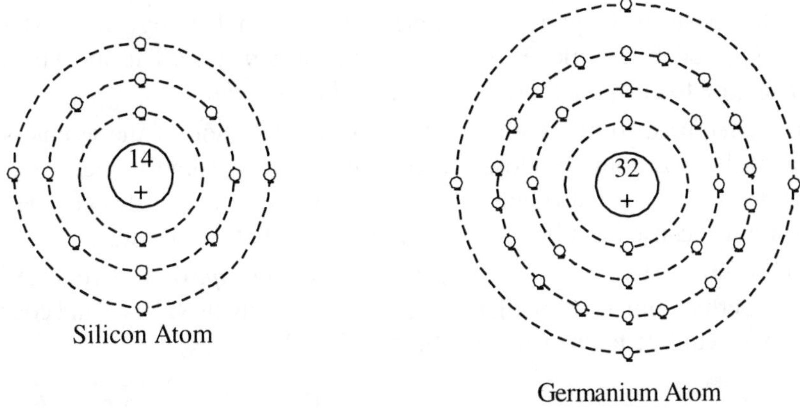

Figure 3.2 – Atomic structure of silicon and germanium

Just as there is a range, or band of energies for the valence electrons, there is another range of energy values for *free electrons* - those that have broken loose to participate in the conduction process. The two energy bands may, or may not overlap.

3.1.1 Conduction in Materials

Figure 3.3 presents three *energy level* diagrams.

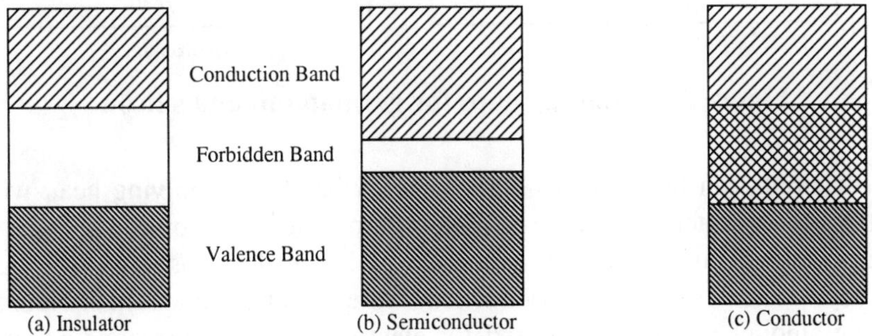

Figure 3.3 – Energy levels

In Figure 3.3(a), the energy bands are widely separated. The unshaded region represents a *forbidden gap* of energy levels in which no electrons are found. When this gap is relatively large, as shown in the figure, the result is an *insulator*.

Suppose that the band is relatively small, on the order of 1 electron volt (eV). (An electron volt is the amount of kinetic energy by which an electron increases when it falls through a potential of one volt. It is equal to 1.6×10^{-19} Joules.) This small band gap results in a *semiconductor*, as illustrated in Figure 3.3(b).

A *conductor*, or metal, results when the bands overlap as in Figure 3.3(c). There is no forbidden gap between the energy of a valence electron and that of a conduction electron in a conductor. This means that a particular valence electron is not strongly associated with its own nucleus. It is therefore free to move about throughout the structure. This movement of electrons, usually in response to an applied potential, is called *conduction*.

The energy required to break a covalent bond is a function of the atomic spacing in the crystal. The smaller the atom, the closer the spacing and the greater the energy required to break the covalent bonds. It is more difficult to break loose a conductive electron from silicon than one from germanium because the silicon crystals have closer lattice spacing.

This point is further illustrated by comparing the *energy gaps* of the two materials, as shown in Figure 3.4. Germanium has a smaller energy gap separating its valence and conduction bands, so less energy is required to cross the gap between bands.

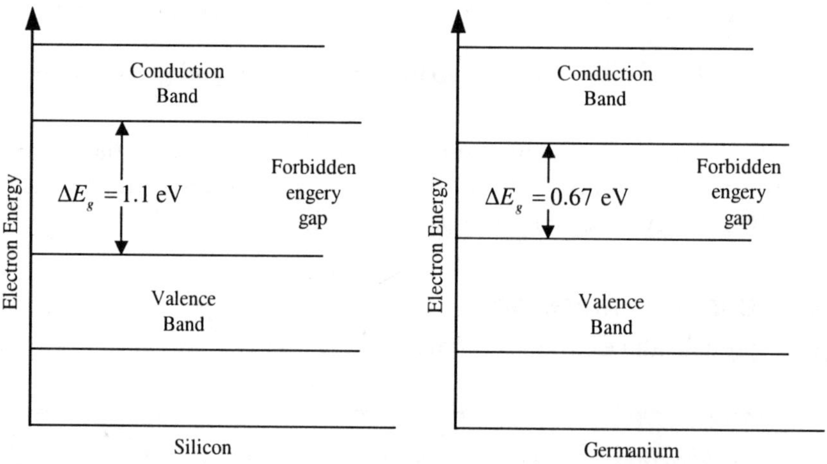

Figure 3.4 – Energy gaps for germanium and silicon

Electrons in materials can be raised to higher energy bands by applying heat, which causes vibration of the lattice. Materials that are insulators at room temperature can become conductors when the temperature is raised to a high enough level. Some electrons move to a higher energy band where they become available for conduction. The energy band diagram of Figure 3.5 is used to illustrate the amount of energy required for electrons to reach the conduction band. The abscissa of this graph is the atomic spacing of the crystal. As the spacing increases, the nuclei exert a smaller force on the valence electrons. The axis is marked with the atomic spacing for four materials. Carbon (C) is an insulator in crystalline form (diamond). Silicon (Si) and germanium (Ge) are semiconductors, and tin is a conductor. The energy gap shown in the figure represents the amount of external energy required to move the valence electrons into the conduction band.

3.1.2 Conduction in Semiconductor Materials

We saw the energy level diagram of a semiconductor in Figure 3.3(b). This represents a compromise between the easy motion of electrons experienced in a conductor, and the suppression of electron motion in an insulator. Semiconductors have fewer electrons in the conduction band than do conductors. We will see that by controlling the concentration of charges, we can control the current, thus making semiconductors useful in electronics.

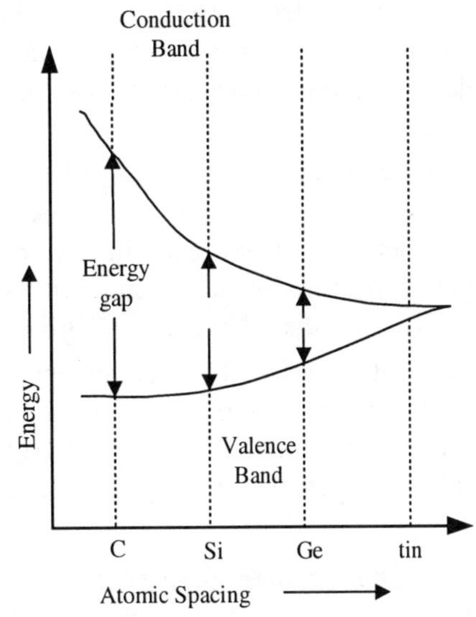

Figure 3.5 – Energy band diagram

Electrons are tightly held together in silicon and germanium atoms. The inner electrons are buried deep within the atom, whereas the valence electrons are part of the covalent bonding. They cannot break away without receiving a considerable amount of energy. One way to supply such energy is by heating the material.

At a temperature of absolute zero, there is no thermally-induced vibration in the crystal. No covalent bonds can be broken so there aren't any available electrons in the conduction band. At this temperature, current is zero and the semiconductor acts as an insulator.

Heat and other external sources of energy cause valence band electrons to break their covalent bonds and become free electrons in the conduction band. As an electron leaves the valence band, it leaves a *hole*. A nearby valence band electron can move in and fill the hole, thus creating a relocated hole with practically no exchange of energy. Figure 3.6 shows how the movement of electrons in covalent bonds contributes to conduction.

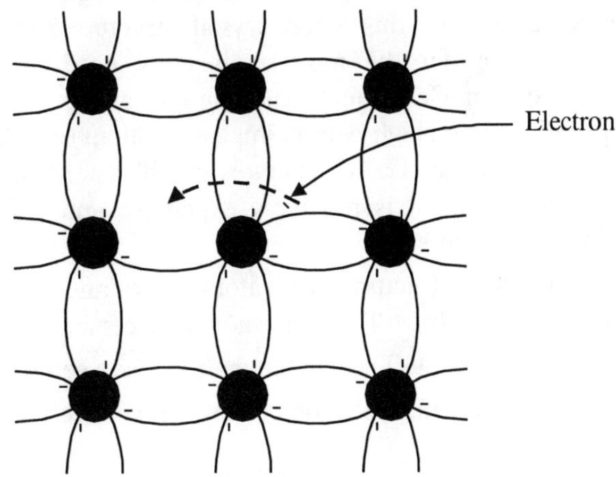

Figure 3.6 – Conduction from broken covalent bond

There are two independent groups of charge carriers: conduction electrons and holes. When a bond is broken, an electron is free to move through the crystal. As the negatively charged electron moves away, a positive charge remains (since the overall lattice is electrically neutral.) The broken bond remains behind and is positively charged. This bond attempts to restore itself to its normal completed state by capturing an electron. Even though the bound valence electrons are not free to move around through the crystal, it is possible for them to move from one bond to another provided that this destination bond is incomplete. The net result is that the broken bond still exists but has now moved in the opposite direction from that of the valence electron. A mobile positive charge, or *hole*, results. A hole has similar properties to those of a free electron (e.g., mass) but has exactly the opposite charge.

The two methods by which holes and electrons move through a silicon crystal are *diffusion* and *drift*. Thermal agitation causes random electron movement in a semiconductor. This phenomenon does not result in any net flow of charge. However if some mechanism causes a higher concentration at one end of the semiconductor thereby creating a gradient, the electrons can diffuse to the other end. This gives rise to a net charge flow, known as *diffusion current*.

The other method of movement, *drift*, results when an electric field is applied to the semiconductor and the free holes and electrons are accelerated in the electric field. The average velocity of this movement is called *drift velocity*, and the movement results in *drift current*. The relationship between the applied electric field and the drift current is analogous to Ohm's law.

3.1.3 Crystalline Structure

Semiconductors are materials where there exists a forbidden energy gap—gap in the energy levels where no electrons can exist. The valence electrons of the atoms of a semiconductor are not free to move throughout the volume of the material. Instead, they participate in the covalent bonds that hold the assembly of atoms together in a periodic crystalline structure.

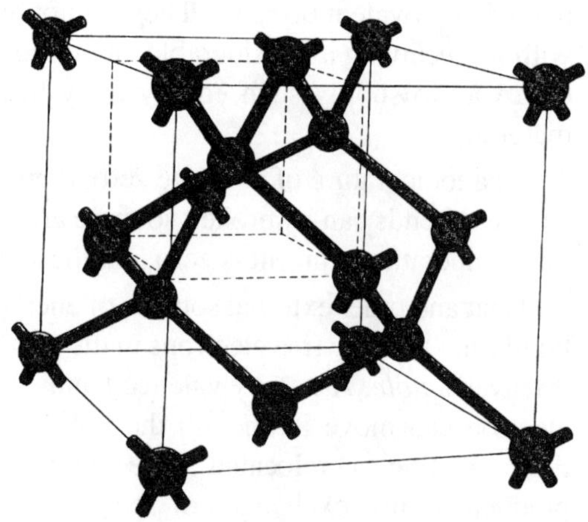

Figure 3.7 – Crystal structure of Si

Figure 3.7 shows the crystal structure of silicon (Si). Several other semiconductors (e.g., germanium) have this same crystal structure. Silicon is by far the most extensively used semiconductor. Germanium is used in specialized applications (e.g., high-current implementations). Gallium arsenide (GaAs) operates much faster than silicon, but it is relatively expensive and difficult to process.

In the lattice structure, every atom has four nearest neighbors and shares its valence electrons with those neighbors. The atoms are in the center of a tetrahedron. The lattice spacing of silicon is constant at 5.4 Å. The connecting rods between the atoms in Figure 3.7 can be thought of as indicating the spatial location of the valence electrons making up the covalent bonds.

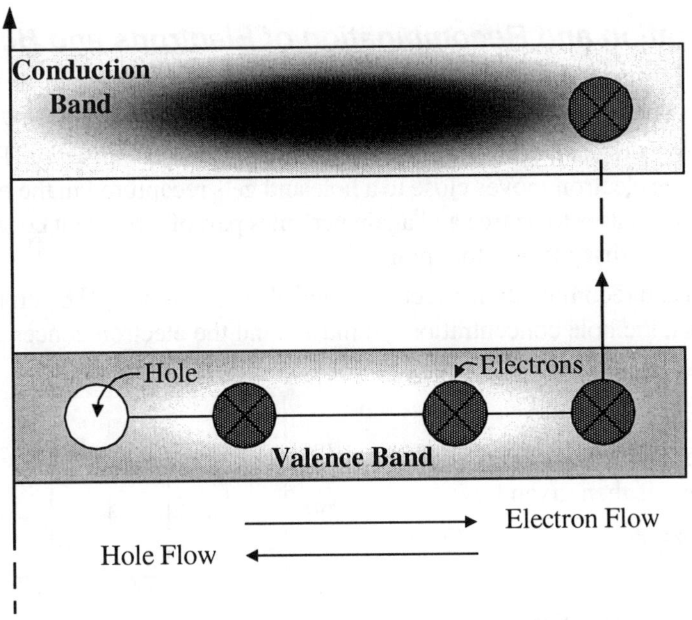

Figure 3.8 – Current flow

At 0°K all electrons are constrained to their covalent bonds. No free electrons are available and no conduction is possible. The material behaves as an insulator. At room temperature, some covalent bonds are broken. These broken bonds are a result of the random thermal vibration of the atoms and of the valence electrons. A few electrons acquire enough energy to "shake loose" from the bonds and become free. The energy required to break a covalent bond in silicon at room temperature is about 1.1 eV. The number of broken bonds is relatively low - about $10^{10}/cm^3$ at room temperature. Since there are about 10^{23} atoms per cm^3, only one out of every ten trillion atoms has a broken bond.

By comparison, diamond, which has the same crystalline structure, requires much higher energy to break a bond. Only about 10^8 atoms per cm^3 have broken bonds at room temperature. Diamond is thus an insulator.

Internal thermal energy increases the activity of electrons, thus moving valence electrons out of the influence of the covalent bond into the conduction band. In this way, there are a limited number of conduction band electrons under the influence of any applied external force (e.g., an electric field); these electrons move in one direction and establish a current.

Each time an electron is raised to a higher band, a hole is created in the valence band. The motion of holes is opposite in direction from that of electrons in the presence of an electric field, and is known as *hole current*. The holes act as if they are positive particles and contribute to the overall current flow.

As temperature is raised, a greater number of electrons is elevated to the conduction band, and current increases.

3.1.4 Generation and Recombination of Electrons and Holes

In a pure (intrinsic) semiconductor, the number of holes is equal to the number of free electrons. This is true since the generating processes create both a hole and an electron.

Hole-electron pairs can disappear. This process is called *recombination*. Recombination takes place when a free electron moves close to a hole and gets recaptured in the broken bond. At that point the electron ceases to be free and again becomes part of a covalent bond. Both a conduction electron and a hole disappear at that point.

Generation and recombination affect holes and electrons as pairs. Therefore, in intrinsic (pure) semiconductors, the hole concentration (p) must equal the electron concentration (n).

$$n = p = n_i \tag{3.1}$$

n_i is called the *intrinsic concentration*. The product, np, is then given by

$$np = n_i^2 \tag{3.2}$$

The intrinsic concentration, n_i, is a function of temperature. For example, in silicon there are no broken bonds at 0°K but there are 10^{10}/cm^3 broken bonds at room temperature. This temperature relationship is shown in Figure 3.9.

The formula for the temperature dependence is

$$n_i^2 = AT^3 e^{-E_G/kT} \tag{3.3}$$

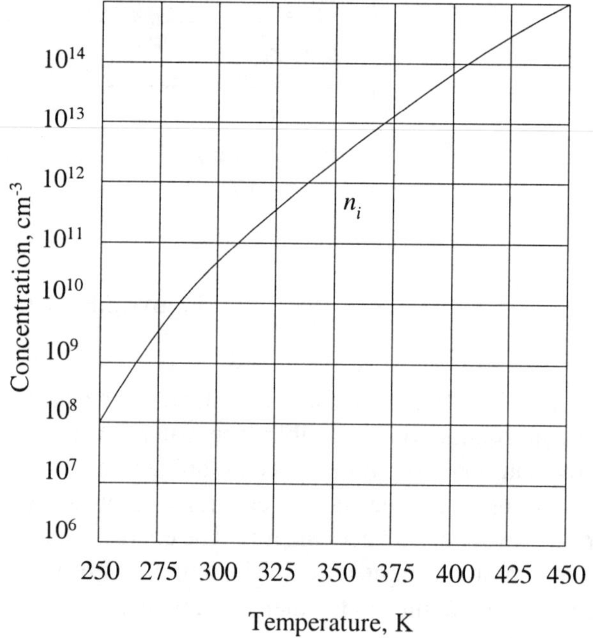

Figure 3.9 – Temperature dependence of n_i

where A is a proportionality constant, T is the absolute temperature in Kelvin, k is Boltzmann's constant (1.38066×10^{-23} J/°K), and E_G is the bandgap energy B the minimum energy required to break a covalent bond (1.12 eV for silicon at room temperature). For silicon, the constant A is 5.06×10^{43} (m^{-6})(°K^{-3}).

3.1.5 Doped Semiconductors

Currents induced in pure semiconductors are too small to permit many practical applications (typically less than 10^{-9}Å). The conductivity of a semiconductor can be greatly increased when small amounts of specific impurities are introduced into the crystal. This procedure is called *doping*. If the doping substance has extra outer shell electrons, it is known as a *donor*, and the doped semiconductor is called *n*-type. Since there are more electrons than holes, the *majority carriers* are electrons and the *minority carriers* are holes.

If the doping substance has a shortage of outer shell electrons, it is known as an *acceptor*, and the doped semiconductor is called *p*-type. The majority carriers then become the holes and the minority carriers, the electrons. Figure 3.10 illustrates the crystal structure of *n*-type and *p*-type semiconductors. The doped materials are known as *extrinsic semiconductors* while the pure substances are *intrinsic semiconductors*.

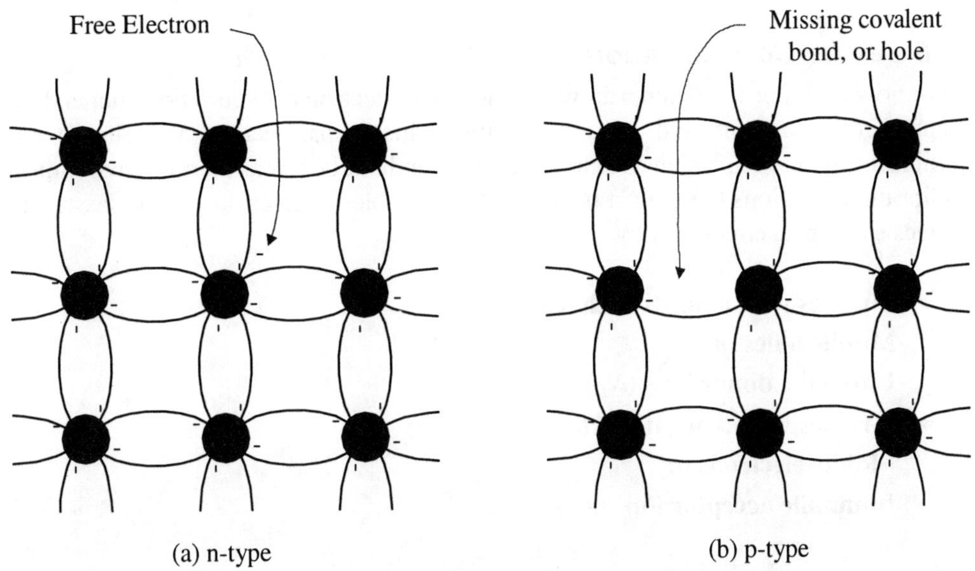

Figure 3.10 – Crystal structure of doped semiconductors

The resistance of a semiconductor is known as *bulk resistance*. A lightly doped semiconductor has a high bulk resistance.

3.1.6 n-type Semiconductor

Phosphorus, arsenic, and antimony are commonly used as donor impurities in silicon. They have five valence electrons instead of the four that silicon has. Their atoms fit readily into the silicon crystal structure without disturbing the lattice.

After covalent bonding of a pentavalent atom into the silicon lattice, the fifth valence electron is loosely bound and needs only 0.05 eV to be detached. In other words, at room temperature we create a free electron. The donor ion is bound in the lattice structure and thus donates free electrons without contributing free holes. Donor-doped silicon is referred to as *n-type silicon* or *n-silicon*.

3.1.7 p-type Semiconductor

Boron is the most commonly used acceptor in silicon – it has three valence electrons. Since one valence electron is missing, there is a vacancy in the bond structure – a hole. This vacancy can accept an electron, but when the electron moves in, a new vacancy is created. In other words, the hole is free to move around – an acceptor creates a mobile positive charge. The negatively charged boron atom is tied into the lattice and cannot move. An acceptor impurity thus contributes only a free hole to the conduction process. Acceptor-doped silicon is referred to as *p-type silicon* or *p-silicon*.

3.1.8 Carrier Concentrations

We now consider the manner in which hole and electron concentrations depend on donor-acceptor concentrations and on other semiconductor parameters. We first examine the equilibrium situation in which a semiconductor is undisturbed in its thermal environment. Under equilibrium conditions there must be no net flow of holes or electrons. Four classes of charged particles exist in a semiconductor:

- **Particles with a positive charge:**
  Mobile holes (p)
  Immobile donor ions (N_D).
- **Particles with a negative charge:**
  Mobile electrons (n)
  Immobile acceptor ions (N_A).

In each case the symbol in parentheses represents the volume concentration of the particular particle. Each of these particles carries a charge of magnitude q, the electron charge. The local charge density, ρ, can be written as

$$\rho = q(p + N_D - n - N_A) \tag{3.4}$$

Under equilibrium and with no electric field, ρ is equal to zero. Local charge neutrality must be preserved as a consequence of Gauss's law.

Equation (3.4) then becomes

$$n_0 - p_0 = N_D - N_A \tag{3.5}$$

where n_0 and p_0 represent equilibrium electron and hole concentrations. Impurity concentrations N_D and N_A are determined by processing parameters of the semiconductor so Equation (3.5) provides one constraint on the concentration of holes and electrons. Note that with no doping, $n_0 = p_0 = n_i$ as we discussed earlier.

A second constraint follows from the fact that the *product* of the equilibrium carrier concentrations is independent of the donor and acceptor impurity concentrations. It is dependent only on the absolute temperature.

$$n_0\ p_0 = n_i^2\,(T) \tag{3.6}$$

Since the product of the electron and hole concentrations is independent of doping, we write this product as n_i^2.

As long as the doping levels are not excessive, all impurity atoms are ionized. Every donor contributes one free electron and every acceptor contributes one free hole. This is not true at very low temperatures (temperatures below that of liquid nitrogen). At such temperatures, not all dopants are ionized.

We can now calculate the electron and hole concentrations as a function of the doping concentrations. The explicit solution can be simplified in most circumstances by noting that there are orders of magnitude difference between N_D, N_A, and n_i. In n-type materials, N_D is large compared with N_A and n_i, yielding

$$n_0 \approx N_D \tag{3.7}$$

$$p_0 \approx \frac{n_i^2}{N_D} \tag{3.8}$$

In p-type materials, on the other hand, N_A is large compared with N_D and n_i giving:

$$p_0 \approx N_A \tag{3.9}$$

In silicon, the hole concentration is $5 \times 10^{15}/\text{cm}^3$, and the electron concentration is $4.205 \times 10^4/\text{cm}^3$. The intrinsic concentration at room temperature is $n = p = n_i = 1.5 \times 10^{10}/\text{cm}^3$.

$$n_0 \approx \frac{n_i^2}{N_A} \tag{3.10}$$

It is important to note that this minute amount of doping does not affect the chemical or mechanical properties of the semiconductor. It does, however, have an enormous effect on the electrical properties.

3.1.9 Excess Carriers

We illustrated the relationship between donor/acceptor concentrations and hole/ electron concentrations in Section 3.1.8. An important difference between metals and semiconductors is that the local carrier concentration can be disturbed significantly without producing large deviations from electrical neutrality.

Because of the complementary charge of electrons and holes, equal changes in n and p do *not* produce a local charge density.

$$\begin{aligned} n &= n_0 + n' \\ p &= p_0 + p' \end{aligned} \tag{3.11}$$

n' and p' are the *excess* concentration above that predicted by thermal equilibrium. The charge density is then given by

$$\rho = q(p_0 + N_D - n_0 - N_A + p' - n') \tag{3.12}$$

If $n' \approx p'$ we have the quasi-neutral condition [see Equation (3.4)]. Note that ρ is still approximately zero, but the *np* product in this case is no longer equal to n_i^2. This is true since the system is no longer in equilibrium.

3.1.10 Recombination and Generation of Excess Carriers

A non-zero excess carrier concentration is a deviation from equilibrium. Physical mechanisms try to restore equilibrium.

If n' and p' are positive, meaning charge concentrations greater than equilibrium, *recombination* will take place. If n' and p' are negative, meaning concentrations lower than equilibrium, *generation* will take place.

The rate of recombination can be written as

$$R = an' + bp' \tag{3.13}$$

where a and b are proportionality constants. Under quasi-neutral conditions (i.e., $(n' = p')$) we can write

$$R = (a + b)n' = (a + b)p' \tag{3.14}$$

The rate of the recombination process is therefore proportional to the excess concentration.

$$R = \frac{n'}{\tau} = \frac{p'}{\tau} \tag{3.15}$$

The parameter τ, which has dimensions of time, is called the *carrier lifetime* of the excess carriers. The lifetime typically varies between nanoseconds and milliseconds. Carrier lifetime is not constant for a given semiconductor. It depends strongly on the preparation of the semiconductor and the processing history of the material as well as the doping levels.

3.1.11 Transport of Electric Current

We now focus on the two mechanisms through which current can flow in a material: (1) *drift* and (2) *diffusion.*

At all non-zero temperatures, atoms in the crystal lattice possess kinetic energy. This energy is in the form of vibrations about neutral positions in the lattice. There is a continuous interchange of energy between the vibrating ions and the free electrons in the form of elastic and inelastic collisions. The resulting electron motion is a random activity. There is a zero net motion of the charges so the net current is zero.

The thermal speed of carriers is given by

$$v_{thermal} = \sqrt{\frac{3kT}{m^*}} \quad \text{m/s} \tag{3.16}$$

In Equation (3.16), m^* is the *effective* mass of the carrier, k is Boltzmann's constant, and T is the absolute temperature. Because of the influence of neighboring atoms, a charge carrier does not behave as if it had the free electron mass (9.1×10^{-31} kg). A proportionality factor is used to compensate for this behavior.

At room temperature, the mean thermal speed of electrons and holes is 10^5 m/s, and they have collision frequencies of about 10^{11} s^{-1}. [Equation (3.16) yields a velocity of 1.17×10^5 m/s at room temperature if the free electron mass is substituted for m^*.]

3.1.12 Diffusion of Carriers

The process by which the charges cross the *pn* or *np* junction is known as *diffusion*. There will be no diffusion if the concentration of particles is uniform throughout the material. There is a concentration of free electrons in an n material but essentially none in a p material. When n and p material are joined, the electrons gradually diffuse from the n to the p material. The electrons continue to move until their concentration is uniform throughout the material.

The following observations are important:

- **Diffusion has nothing to do with the fact that the particles are charged.**
- **Diffusion occurs because of differing velocity components. There are a greater number of carriers with a velocity component directed from the region of high concentration toward the region of lower concentration than the number of carriers with oppositely-directed velocity components. This velocity is a result of thermal motion.**
- **Diffusion depends on the carrier-concentration *gradient*, not on the concentration itself.**

3.1.13 Drift in an Electric Field

Equilibrium can be disturbed by the application of an electric field. An electric field causes a net movement of carriers which is superimposed on the random thermal movement. This is shown in Figure 3.11. This net effect is called *drift*. The *drift velocity* is defined as follows.

$$\begin{aligned} v_h &= \mu_h \mathbb{E} \\ v_e &= -\mu_e \mathbb{E} \end{aligned} \tag{3.17}$$

where μ_h and μ_e are the hole and electron mobilities in m^2/Vs and $\mathbb{E}$ is the *electric field intensity* (the force exerted on a unit positive charge). The electron mobility for silicon is about 0.135 m^2/V·sec and the hole mobility is approximately 0.045 m^2/V·sec.

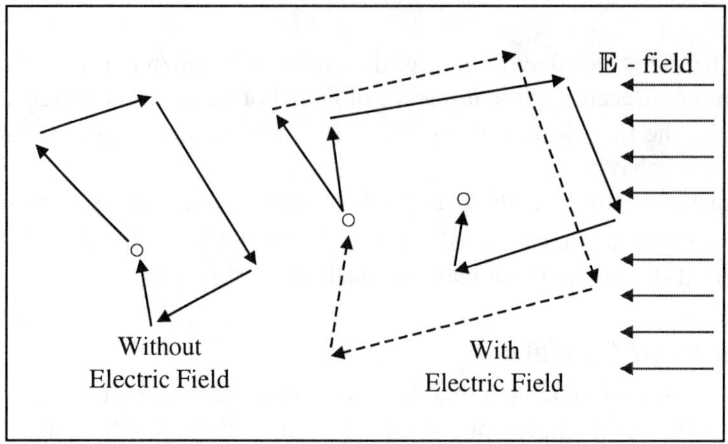

Figure 3.11 – Random thermal action

These mobilities are not constant. They have complex dependencies on both temperature and doping densities. The movement of the carriers is determined by scattering mechanisms. An electron that collides with either another electron (e.g., in a silicon atom or a doping atom) will get scattered and change direction. This scattering process depends on the temperature and on the amount of ions.

The electric current associated with drift is calculated in the following way. Assume there are N electrons contained in a length L of conductor, as shown in Figure 3.12. Further assume that it takes an electron t_o seconds to travel a distance of L meters in the conductor.

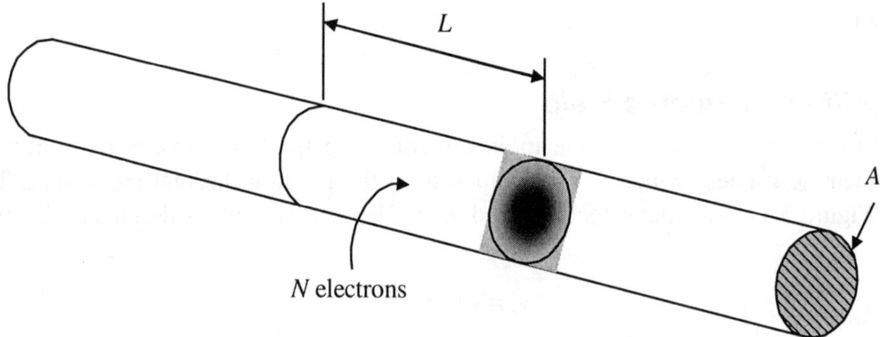

Figure 3.12 – Carrier flow in a conductor

The total number of electrons passing through any cross section of wire in a unit of time is N/t_o. The current, in amperes, is then

$$I = \frac{N}{t_o} q = \frac{Nq}{t_o} = \frac{Nq(L/T)}{L} = \frac{Nqv}{L} \quad (3.18)$$

where q is the electron charge.

Also by definition, the current density, J *[A/m²]*, is

$$J = \frac{I}{A} = \frac{Nqv}{LA} \tag{3.19}$$

since N/LA is the electron concentration and n has units of electrons/m³, we obtain

$$J = nqv \tag{3.20}$$

This derivation is independent of the form of the conducting medium.

From Equations (3.17) and (3.20) we find,

$$J = nqv = nq\mu\mathbb{E} = \sigma\mathbb{E} \tag{3.21}$$

where $\sigma = nq\mu$ is the conductivity in $(\Omega.\text{m})^{-1}$. Combining these equations yields,

$$I = JA = \frac{\sigma AL\mathbb{E}}{L} = \frac{\sigma AV}{L} = \frac{V}{R} \tag{3.22}$$

Certainly you recognize this as Ohm's law!

For holes and electrons in silicon we can now write,

$$\begin{aligned} J_h &= qp\mu_h\mathbb{E} \\ J_e &= qn\mu_e\mathbb{E} \end{aligned} \tag{3.23}$$

so the *total* drift current is

$$J = q(p\mu_h + n\mu_e)\mathbb{E} \tag{3.24}$$

Example 3.1

Find the average drift velocity in a silicon semiconductor doped with phosphorus. Assume a doping density of 1 per million, a cross-sectional area of 10^{-4} m², a current of 4 A, and the concentration of silicon atoms in a silicon crystal is

$$n_{Si} = 4.79\times10^{28} \quad \textit{atoms/m}^3$$

Solution: With 1 per million phosphorus atoms and $n = N_D$, we have $n = 4.97\times10^{22}$ electrons/m³ and a negligible density of holes,

$$v_e = \frac{J_e}{nq} = \frac{I/A}{nq} = \frac{4\times10^4}{\left(4.97\times10^{22}\right)\left(1.602\times10^{-19}\right)} = 5 \quad (\text{m/s})$$

The average drift velocity is thus orders of magnitude lower than the random thermal velocity.

Example 3.2

What is the resistivity of intrinsic silicon at room temperature? What is the resistivity of silicon doped with 1/million boron or phosphorus at room temperature?

Solution: For intrinsic material, we find

$$n = p = n_i = 1.5\times10^{16} \quad \left(\mathrm{m}^3\right)^{-1}$$

From Equation (3.24), we have

$$\sigma_i = q\left(\mu_e n + \mu_h p\right) = (0.135 + 0.045)\left(1.5\times10^{16}\right)\left(1.609\times10^{-19}\right)$$
$$= 4.34\times10^{-4} \quad (\Omega\mathrm{m})^{-1}$$

$$\rho_i = \frac{1}{\sigma_i} = 2.3\times10^3 \quad \Omega\mathrm{m}$$

For the phosphorus-doped *n*-Si,

$$\rho = 9.3\times10^{-4} \quad \Omega\mathrm{m}$$

and for the boron-doped *p*-Si,

$$\rho = 2.78\times10^{-3} \quad \Omega\mathrm{m}$$

These values show the tremendous effect of doping on the electrical properties of silicon. The resistivity values are only approximations since the mobilities are doping dependent.

3.2 SEMICONDUCTOR DIODES

You already are familiar with the simplest *linear* circuit element – the resistor. The voltage across this element is related to the current through it by Ohm's law. This relationship is shown graphically as a straight line (see Figure 3.13.) The slope of this line is the conductance of the resistor (the ratio of current to voltage.) The reciprocal of this slope is the *resistance*, in ohms. If the resistor is connected in any circuit, the operating point *must* fall somewhere on this curve. The actual operating point location is determined from constraints provided by the external circuitry.

In contrast to the resistor, the ideal diode is a *nonlinear* device. It exhibits a behavior which is dependent on the direction of applied voltage.

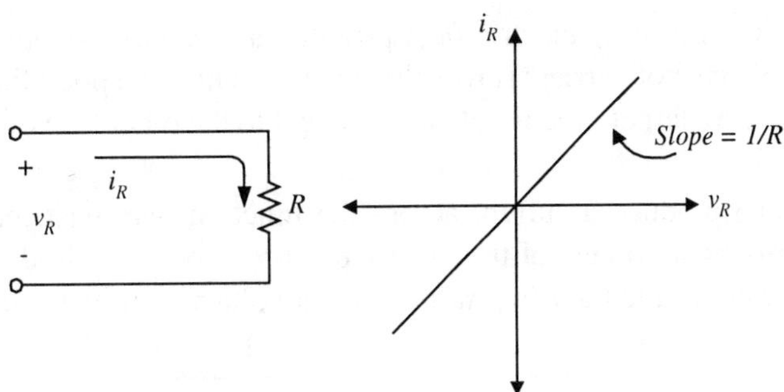

Figure 3.13 – Operating curve for a resistor

Figure 3.14 shows a *p*-type material and an *n*-type material placed together to form a junction. This represents a simplified model of diode construction. The model ignores gradual changes in concentration of the impurities in the material. Practical junction diodes are constructed from a single piece of semiconductor material with one side doped with *p*-type material and the other side with *n*-type material.

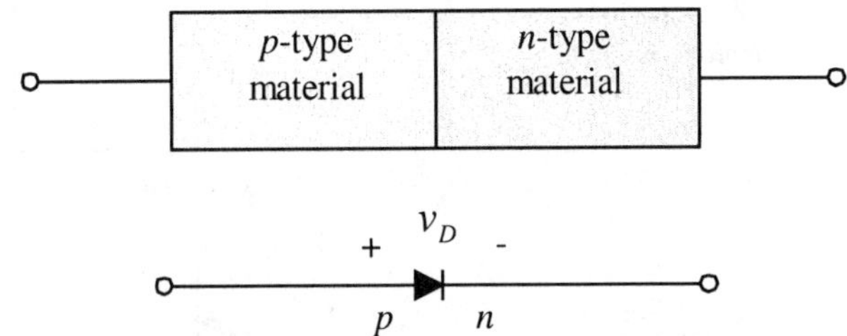

Figure 3.14 – Simplified diode model

Also shown in Figure 3.14 is the circuit symbol of the diode. Note that the "arrow" in this symbol points from the *p*- to the *n*-type material. This is the only direction that significant current can flow through the diode under normal operation.

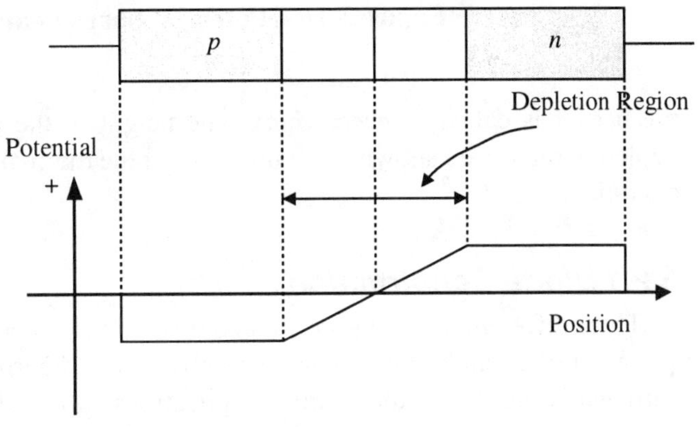

Figure 3.15 – Barrier potentials

When the *p*- and *n*-type materials exist together in a crystal, charge redistribution occurs. Some of the free electrons from the *n*-material diffuse across the junction and combine with the free holes in the *p*-material. You can also view this as free holes from the *p*-material diffusing across the junction and combining with free electrons in the *n*-material. As a result of this charge redistribution, the *p*-material near the junction acquires a net negative charge and the *n*-material near the junction acquires a net positive charge. These charges create an electric field and a potential difference between the two types of material that inhibits any further charge movement.

The result is a reduction in the number of current carriers near the junction. This happens in an area known as the *depletion region.*

The resulting electric field provides a *potential barrier* or *hill* in a direction that inhibits the movement of carriers across the junction. Once the potential barrier is formed, electrons or holes require a larger amount of energy to get to the other side of the junction. This is shown in Figure 3.15.

To produce a current across the junction, we must reduce the potential barrier or hill by applying a voltage of the proper polarity across the diode. A voltage that lowers the potential barrier is called a *forward bias*, and a voltage that increases

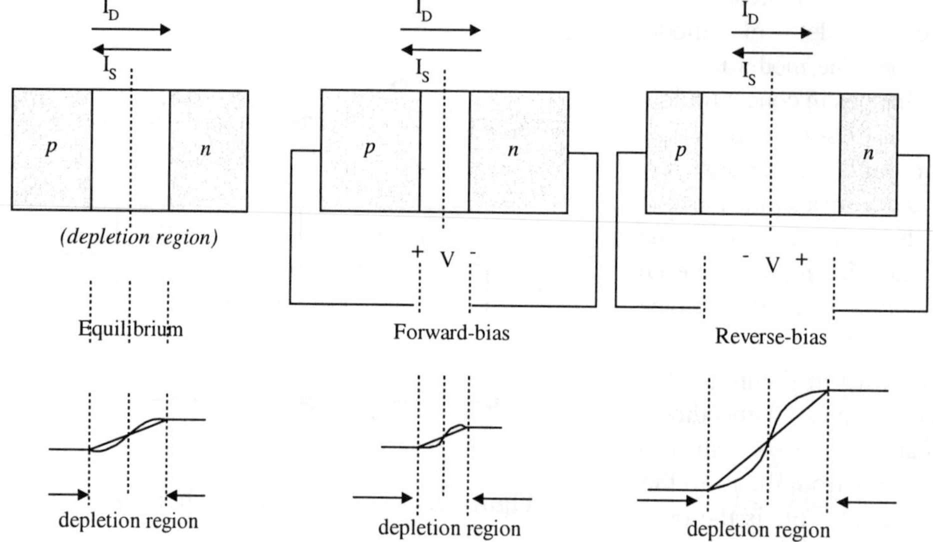

Figure 3.16 – Potential barriers and depletion regions

the barrier is called a *reverse bias.* The height of the potential barrier and the width of the depletion region are shown in Figure 3.16 for the thermal equilibrium, forward- and reverse-bias conditions.

3.2.1 Diode Construction

Three different materials are commonly used in the construction of diodes: germanium, silicon and gallium arsenide. Silicon has generally replaced germanium for diodes. Gallium arsenide is particularly useful in microwave applications, photo-detection and laser diodes. However, gallium arsenide is more expensive than silicon and the manufacture of gallium arsenide diodes is difficult. The precise distance over which the change from *p*- to *n*-type material occurs within the crystal varies with the fabrication technique. One feature of the *pn* junction is that the change in impurity concentration occurs in a relatively short distance. There are cases where the *pn* junction cannot be treated as an abrupt change in material type, notably when the diode is formed by diffusion. This causes the doping near the junction to be *graded* – that is, the donor and acceptor concentrations are a function of distance across the junction.

A *depletion region* exists in the vicinity of the junction, as shown in the left portion of Figure 3.16. This phenomenon is due to a combination of electrons and holes where the materials join. This depletion region has few carriers. The minority carriers on each side of the depletion region (electrons in the *p*- and holes in the *n*-region) migrate to the other side and combine with ions in that material. Likewise, the majority carriers (electrons in *n*-region and holes in *p*-region) migrate across the junction.

The two components of the current formed by the hole and electron movements across the junction add together to form the diffusion current, I_D. The direction of this current is from the *p*-side to the *n*-side. An additional current exists due to the minority carrier drift across the junction, and this is referred to as I_S. Thermally generated minority carriers (holes in the *n*-material and electrons in the *p*-material) diffuse to the edge of the depletion region. There they experience the electric field and are swept across the depletion region. The components of these actions combine to form the drift current. During open-circuit equilibrium conditions, the diffusion current is equal in magnitude (and opposite in direction) to the drift current.

If we now apply a positive potential to the *p*-material relative to the *n*-material, as shown in the center portion of Figure 3.16, the diode is said to be *forward biased*. The depletion region shrinks in size due to the attraction of majority carriers to the opposite side. That is, the negative potential at the right attracts holes in the *p*-region, and vice-versa. With a lower barrier, current can flow more readily. When forward-biased, $I_D - I_S = I$ after equilibrium is achieved, where I is the current through the junction.

Alternatively, if the applied voltage is as shown in the right portion of Figure 3.16, the diode is *reverse biased*. Free electrons are drawn from the *n*-material toward the right, and similarly, holes are drawn to the left. The depletion region gets wider and the diode acts as an insulator (i.e., like an open circuit).

3.2.2 Relationship Between Diode Current and Diode Voltage

An exponential relationship exists between the carrier density and applied potential of diode junction shown in Equation (3.25). This exponential relationship of the current i_D and the voltage v_D holds over a range of at least seven orders of magnitudes of current – that is a factor of 10^7. In Chapter 4, this remarkable exponential relationship is reviewed and then exploited for our understanding of the behavior of bipolar junctions of transistors.

$$i_D = I_o\left[\exp\left(\frac{qv_D}{nkT}\right) - 1\right] = I_o\left[e^{\left(\frac{qv_D}{nkT}\right)} - 1\right] \tag{3.25}$$

The terms in Equation (3.25) are defined as follows:

i_D = Current through the diode (dependent variable in this expression)

v_D = Potential difference across the diode terminals (independent variable in this expression)

I_o = Reverse saturation current (of the order of 10^{-15}A for small signal diodes, but I_o is a strong function of temperature)

q = Electron charge: $1.60\text{x}10^{-19}$ joules/volt
k = Boltzmann's constant: $1.38\text{x}10^{-23}$ joules/°K
T = Absolute temperature in degrees Kelvin (°K = 273 + temperature in °C)
n = Empirical scaling constant between 0.5 and 2, sometimes referred to as the *Exponential Ideality Factor*

The empirical constant, n, is a number that can vary according to the voltage and current levels. It depends on electron drift, diffusion, and carrier recombination in the depletion region. Among the quantities affecting the value of n are the diode manufacture, levels of doping and purity of materials. If $n=1$, the value of kT/q is 26 mV at 25°C. When $n=2$, kT/q becomes 52 mV. For germanium diodes, n is usually considered to be close to 1. For silicon diodes, n is in the range of 1.3 to 1.6. In this text, we follow standard practice of assuming $n=1$ for all junctions unless otherwise noted.

Equation (3.25) can be simplified by defining $V_T=kT/q$, yielding

$$i_D = I_o\left[\exp\left(\frac{v_D}{nV_T}\right)-1\right] = I_o\left(e^{\frac{v_D}{nV_T}}-1\right) \tag{3.26}$$

If we operate at room temperature (25°C) and apply only voltages with *forward-bias*, then the first term in the parentheses predominates and the current is approximately given by

$$i_D \approx I_o e^{\frac{v_D}{nV_T}} \tag{3.27}$$

This simplification is permitted since a forward bias is the result of a positive v_D which makes the exponential function much larger than 1.

The current-voltage $(I\text{-}V)$ characteristic of the diode is illustrated in Figure 3.17. The curve in the figure consists of two exponential curves. However, the exponent values are such that for voltages and currents experienced in practical circuits, the curve sections are close to being straight lines. For voltages less than V_{ON}, the curve is approximated by a straight line of slope close to zero. Since the slope is the conductance (i.e., i/v), the conductance is very small in this region, and the equivalent

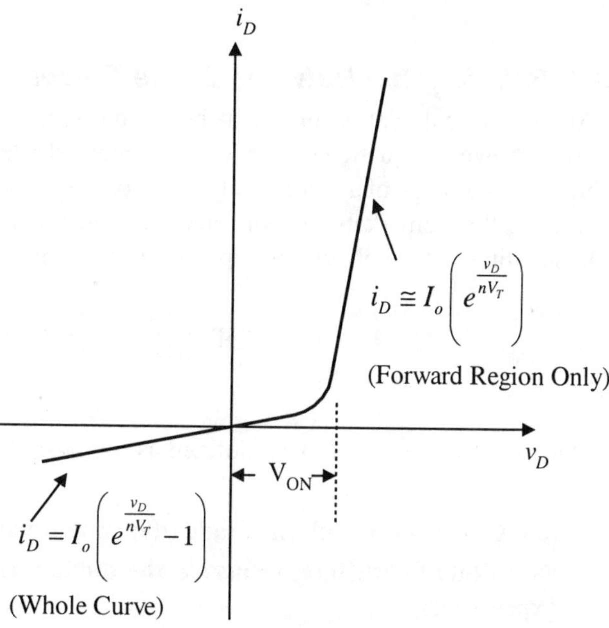

Figure 3.17 – Diode voltage–current relationship (not to scale)

resistance is very high. For voltages above V_{ON}, the curve is approximated by a straight line with a very large slope. The conductance is therefore very large, and the diode has a very small equivalent resistance.

We now have the necessary information to evaluate the relationship between current and voltage at an operating point. The slope of the curves of Figure 3.17 changes as the current and voltage change since the *I-V* characteristic follows the exponential relationship of relationship of Equation (3.26). We can differentiate the expression of Equation (3.26) to find the slope at any arbitrary value of v_D or i_D. This slope is the equivalent conductance of the diode at the specified values of v_D or i_D.

$$\frac{di_D}{dv_D} = \frac{I_o}{nV_T}\exp\left(\frac{v_D}{nV_T}\right) = \frac{I_o}{nV_T}e^{\frac{v_D}{nV_T}} \tag{3.28}$$

We can approximate the slope as a linear function of the diode current. To eliminate the exponential function, we substitute Equation (3.26) into the exponential of Equation (3.28) to obtain

$$\exp\left(\frac{v_D}{nV_T}\right) = \frac{i_D}{I_o} + 1 = \left(\frac{di_D}{dv_D}\right)\left(\frac{nV_T}{I_o}\right) \tag{3.29}$$

A realistic assumption is that $I_o << i_D$. Equation (3.29) then yields

$$\frac{di_D}{dv_D} = \frac{i_D + I_o}{nV_T} \approx \frac{i_D}{nV_T} \tag{3.30}$$

The approximation applies if the diode is forward biased. The *dynamic resistance* is the reciprocal of this expression, or

$$r_d = \frac{nV_T}{i_D + I_o} \approx \frac{nV_T}{i_D} \tag{3.31}$$

where again the approximation applies to forward-bias conditions. Although r_d is a function of i_D, we can approximate it as a constant if the variation of i_D is small. This corresponds to approximating the exponential function as a straight line within a specific operating range.

We use the term R_f to denote diode forward resistance. R_f is composed of r_d and the contact resistance. The contact resistance is the equivalent resistance that precedes r_d. It is a relatively small resistance composed of the resistance of the actual connection to the diode and the resistance of the semiconductor prior to the junction. The reverse-bias resistance is extremely large and is often approximated as infinity.

3.2.3 Diode Operation

Figure 3.18 illustrates the operating characteristics of a *practical* diode. The minimum voltage required to obtain noticeable current, V_{ON}, is approximately 0.7 V for silicon semiconductors (at room temperature), and 0.2 V for germanium semiconductors (at room temperature). The difference between the voltage for silicon and germanium stems from the atomic structure of the materials. V_{ON} is approximately 1.2 V for gallium arsenide diodes.

When the diode is reverse biased, there is some small *leakage current.* This occurs provided that the reverse voltage is less than the voltage required to break down the junction. The leakage current is much greater for germanium diodes than it is for silicon or gallium arsenide diodes. If the negative voltage becomes large enough to be in the breakdown region, a normal diode may be destroyed.

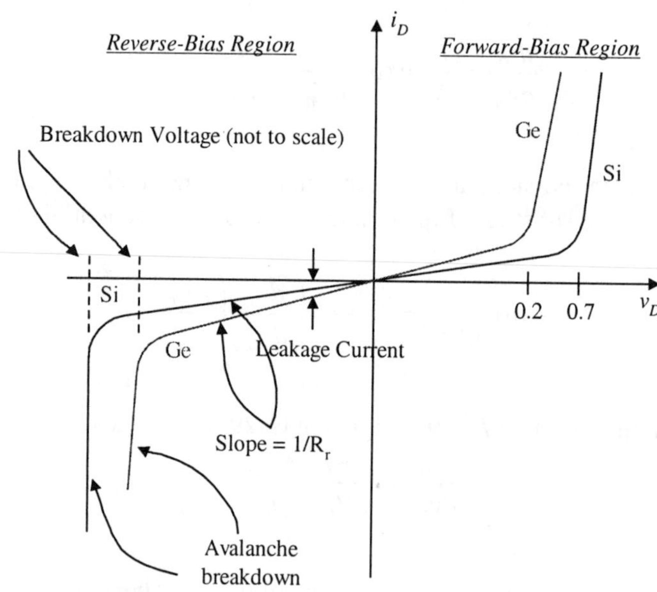

Figure 3.18 – Diode operating characteristics

This breakdown voltage is defined as the *peak inverse voltage (PIV)* in manufacturers' specifications (Representative specification sheets are shown in the Appendix. We refer to these often in this text, so you should take a minute to locate them at this time). The damage to the normal diode at breakdown is due to the avalanche of electrons which flow across the junction with the result that the diode overheats. The large current can destroy part of the diode (the portion that overheats). This breakdown point is sometimes referred to as the diode breakdown voltage (V_{BR}).

3.2.4 Temperature Effects

Temperature plays an important role in determining operational characteristics of diodes. Changes in the diode characteristics caused by changing temperature may require adjustments in the design and packaging of circuits.

As temperature increases, the turn-on voltage, V_{ON}, decreases. Alternatively, a decrease in temperature results in an increase in V_{ON}. This is illustrated in Figure 3.19, where V_{ON} varies *linearly* with temperature which is evidenced by the evenly spaced curves for increasing temperature in 25 °C increments.

The temperature relationship is described by Equation (3.32).

$$V_{ON}(T_{New}) - V_{ON}(T_{room}) = k_T(T_{New} - T_{room}) \tag{3.32}$$

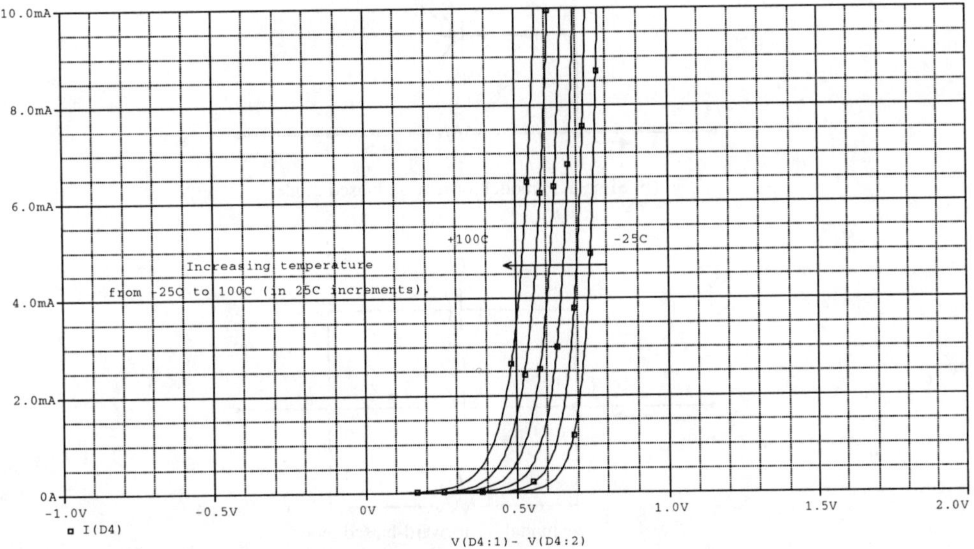

Figure 3.19 – Dependence of i_D on temperature versus v_D for real diode 1N4002 (k_T = -2.0 mV/°C)

The variables in Equation (3.32) are defined as

T_{room} = room temperature, or 25°C

T_{New} = new temperature of diode in °C.

$V_{ON}(T_{room})$ = diode voltage at room temperature.

$V_{ON}(T_{New})$ = diode voltage at new temperature

k_T = temperature coefficient in V/°C.

Although k_T varies with changing operating parameters, standard engineering practice permits approximation as a constant. Values of k_T for the various types of diodes at room temperature are given as follows:

k_T = -2.5 mV/°C for germanium diodes

k_T = -2.0 mV/°C for silicon diodes

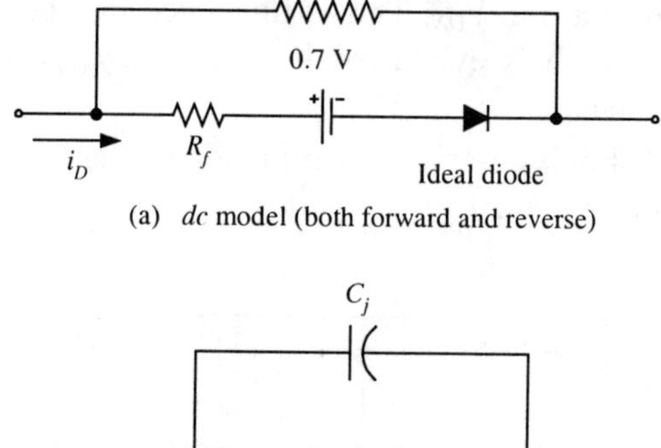

(a) *dc* model (both forward and reverse)

(b) Simple *ac* model for reverse-biased diode

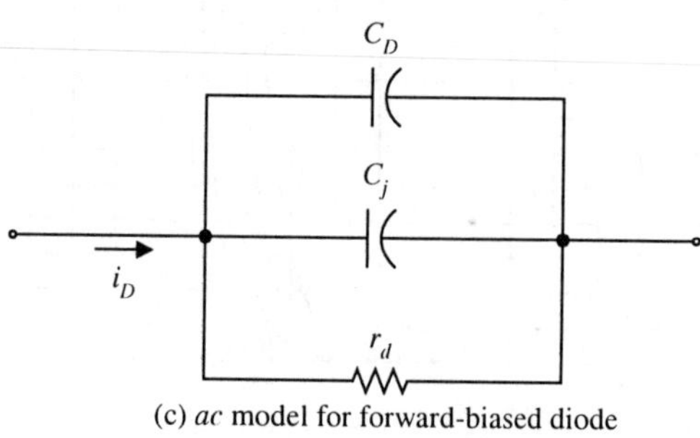

(c) *ac* model for forward-biased diode

Figure 3.20 – Diode models

The reverse saturation current[1], I_o, also depends on temperature. At room temperature, it increases approximately 16% per °C for silicon and 10% per °C for germanium diodes. In other words, I_o approximately doubles for every 5 °C increase in temperature for silicon, and for every 7 °C for germanium. The expression for the reverse saturation current as a function of temperature can be approximated as

$$I_o(at\ T_2) = I_o(at\ T_1)\exp(k_i(T_2 - T_1)) = I_o(at\ T_1)e^{k_i(T_2 - T_1)} \quad (3.33)$$

where $k_i = 0.15/°\mathrm{C}$ (for silicon) and T_1 and T_2 are two arbitrary temperatures.

EXERCISES

E3.1 When a silicon diode is conducting at a temperature of 25°C, a 0.7 V drop exists across its terminals. What is the voltage, V_{ON}, across the diode at 100°C?

[1] I_o is also known as the *scaling current* since its value is directly proportional to the cross sectional area of diode junction.

answer: $V_{ON} = 0.55\ V$

E3.2 The diode described in Exercise E3.1 is cooled to -100°C. What is the voltage required across the diode to establish a noticeable current at the new temperature?

answer: $V_{ON} = 0.95\ V$

3.2.5 Diode Equivalent Circuit Models

When we approximate the curve of Figure 3.18 as piecewise linear, we can develop a simple model for the diode (see Figure 3.20(a)). We assume that the diode does not operate in the breakdown region.

The resistor, R_r, represents the reverse-bias resistance of the diode, and is equal to the inverse of the slope of the (almost) horizontal portion of the operating curves. Typical values are several megohms.

The resistor, R_f, is the forward resistance, and is equal to the inverse of the slope of the (almost) vertical portion of the operating curves. It exists because of contact and bulk resistance of the diode, and typical values are less than 50 Ω.

The ideal diode in the model is a short circuit when forward biased. When this diode is forward biased in the model, the terminal resistance is the parallel combination of the two resistors, or

$$R_r \| R_f \approx R_f$$

The final approximation results from the large difference between the two resistor values. The ideal diode of the model is forward-biased when the terminal voltage exceeds 0.7 V.

When the diode of the model is reverse biased, the diode acts as an open circuit, and the terminal resistance of the model is simply R_r.

We examine frequency effects in detail in Chapter 10 of this text. However, at this time we point out that the *ac* circuit model of a diode is more complex because of frequency-dependent diode behavior. For example, when the diode is back biased, capacitance exists between the junctions. A simple model of the back-biased diode must include this capacitance, as shown in Figure 3.20(b). The capacitor, C_j, is the *junction capacitance*. It arises since the depletion region acts as a capacitor.

The simplified *ac* model of the forward-biased diode is shown in Figure 3.20(c). We have added a second capacitor, C_D, the *diffusion capacitance*, and replaced the forward resistance with a *dynamic resistance*, r_d. Diffusion involves movement of carriers and leads to a condition comparable to charge storage. Therefore, the consequences of diffusion include capacitive effects. The diffusion capacitance approaches zero for reverse-biased diodes.

3.2.6 Diode Circuit Analysis

Since the diode is a nonlinear device, we cannot use standard techniques to analyze circuits containing diodes. If you try to use Kirchhoff's law (or the techniques of loop and nodal analysis), you need a single equation to characterize the terminal characteristics of each device. Unfortunately, diode operation requires more than one equation depending on which region of operation is occurring.

Fortunately, there are simple approaches to dealing with this problem. We highlight three of the most popular approaches, these being graphical, piecewise linear approximation, and computer simulation. In simple terms, the diode will exhibit two states: (1) *open switch* or (2) *closed switch* as indicated by the model shown in Figure 3.21 for simple diode circuit analysis. (We will use the diode type and load resistor value later when we run a computer simulation.)

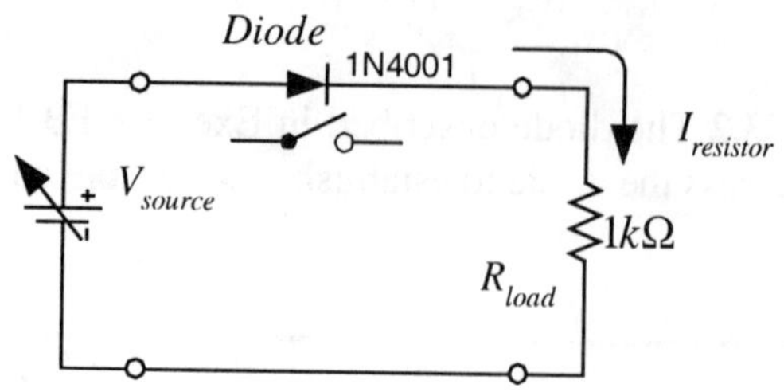

Figure 3.21 – Diode circuit analysis

Graphical Analysis

Suppose you wished to analyze the simple resistive circuit shown in Figure 3.22(a). You do not have to go through a lot of work to analyze the circuit. You could use loop analysis, but in all likelihood, you would use a simple voltage divider relationship to find that the output voltage is $\frac{1}{2}$ V.

You could have viewed this a different way by dividing the circuit at the dashed line. We can write one terminal relationship for the part to the left of the line, and another for the part to the right. The equation for the circuit on the left of the dashed line is

$$V_o = 1 - I_o \times 1\Omega \tag{3.34}$$

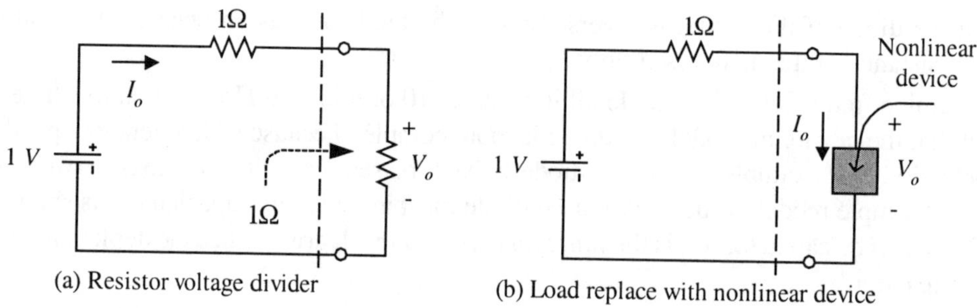

Figure 3.22 – Graphical circuit analysis

The equation for the portion to the right is simply Ohm's law for the resistor,

$$V_o = I_o \times 1\Omega \tag{3.35}$$

Equations (3.34) and (3.35) represent two simultaneous equations in two unknowns. We solve these for V_o to get a value of $\frac{1}{2}$.

Although it was easy to solve this system of equations, suppose you wished to find the simultaneous solution graphically. Figure 3.23(a) shows the graph of the two equations. The intersection of the two curves represents the simultaneous solution of the two equations.

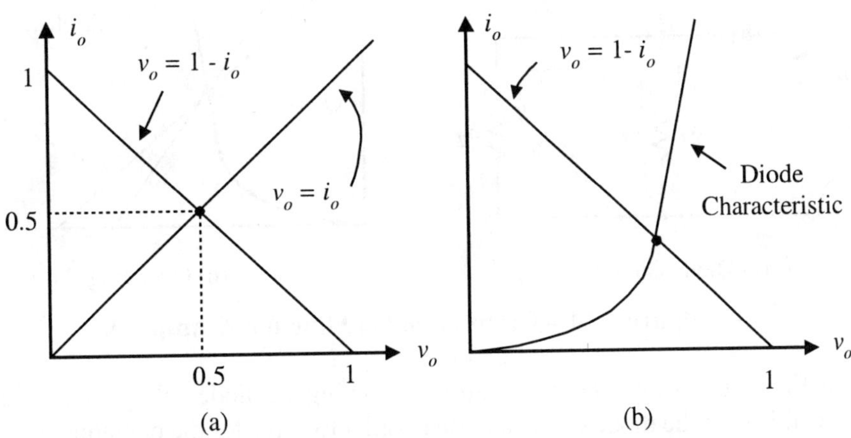

Figure 3.23 - Graph of simultaneous equations

This may seem like a lot of work to go through to solve a relatively simple circuit problem. However, now suppose that the output resistor is replaced by a nonlinear device (e.g., a diode) as in Figure 3.22(b). Then the *only* change we must make in the graphical analysis is to substitute the graph of the device terminal characteristics for the straight line (Ohm's law) in Figure 3.23(a). This is shown in Figure 3.23(b). We will use this graphical approach to solve relatively complex circuits in this and the following chapters

---

Example 3.3

Use graphical analysis to find the *ac* and *dc* voltages and currents in the diode for the circuit shown in Figure 3.24.

Solution: Let us designate the diode current and diode voltage as the two circuit unknowns. We therefore need two independent equations involving these unknowns to uniquely solve for the operating point. One of these equations is the constraint provided by the circuitry connected to the diode. The second is the actual diode voltage-current relationship. The simultaneous solution of these two equations can be done graphically.

Under *dc* conditions, the voltage source becomes simply V_S, and the capacitor is an open circuit. The loop equation can then be written as

$$V_S = V_D + V_{R_1} = V_D + I_D R_1 \tag{3.36}$$

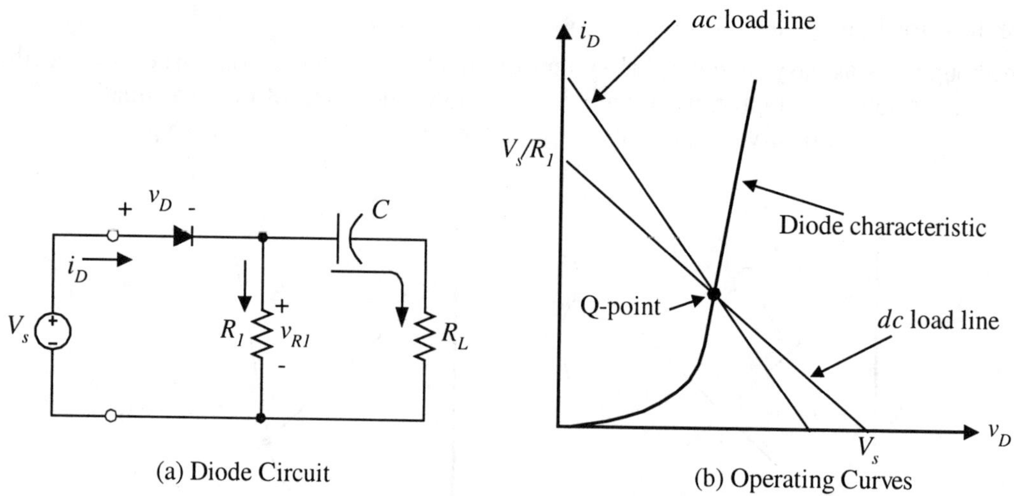

(a) Diode Circuit

(b) Operating Curves

Figure 3.24 – Circuit and load line for Example 3.3

This is the first of two simultaneous equations involving the diode voltage and current. We need to combine this with the diode characteristic in order to solve for the operating point. The graph of Equation (3.36) is shown in Figure 3.24(b). It is labeled *dc load line*. The diode characteristic is also shown on this same set of axes. The intersection of the two plots yields the simultaneous solution of the two equations, and is labeled, "Q-point" on the figure. This is the point at which the circuit operates when the time varying inputs are zero. The "Q" denotes the "quiescent" or rest condition.

If a time-varying signal is now added to the *dc* input, one of the two simultaneous equations changes. If we assume that the time varying input is of a high enough frequency to allow approximation of the capacitor as a short circuit, the new equation is given by

$$v_s = v_d + i_d \left(R_1 \| R_L\right) \tag{3.37}$$

We are considering only the time varying components of the various parameters[1]. Thus, the total parameter values are given by

$$\begin{aligned} v_D &= v_d + V_D \\ i_D &= i_d + I_D \end{aligned} \tag{3.38}$$

and the load line equation becomes

$$v_D - V_D = -\left(R_1 \| R_L\right)\left(i_D - I_D\right) + v_s \tag{3.39}$$

This equation is labeled the *ac load line* in Figure 3.24(b). Since Equation (3.39) only deals with time varying quantities, the axis intercept is not known. However, this *ac* load line must pass

---

[1] We use lower case letters for variables. This means we are referring to the time-varying components. Upper-case letters are used for dc values.

through the Q-point since at those times when the time varying part of the input goes to zero, the two operating conditions (*dc* and *ac*) must coincide. Thus, the *ac* load line is uniquely determined.

Piecewise-Linear Approximation

Piecewise-linear approximation techniques take advantage of the fact that the diode characteristic is made up of segments, each of which can be described by an equation. We observed that the curve within each region is approximately linear. Thus, the overall curve is made up of joining straight line segments.

As long as we avoid the breakdown region, the diode characteristic can be approximated by two straight lines. We use a horizontal line when $v_D < V_{ON}$ and a steep line for $v_D > V_{ON}$.

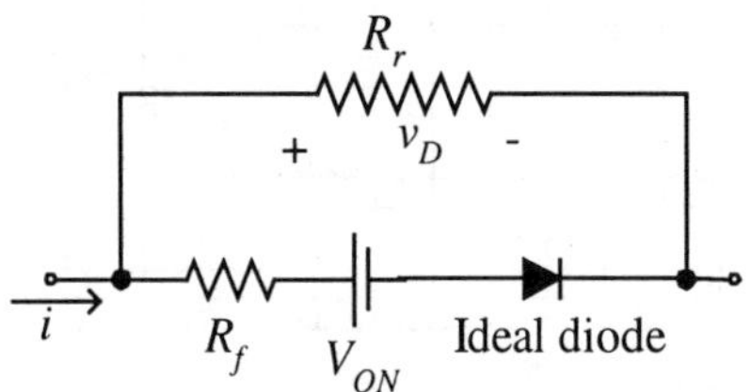

Figure 3.25 – Diode equivalent circuit model

An equivalent circuit model using straight line approximations is shown in Figure 3.25, where the *ideal diode* is a *voltage-controlled switch* that is closed for $v_D > V_{ON}$ and open for $v_D < V_{ON}$.

When v_D is less than V_{ON}, we follow the upper current path via the reverse resistance R_r (a relatively high value of resistance measured on the order of megaohms) of Figure 3.25. The diode then looks very much like an open circuit. In this region, we say that the diode is *OFF* or in the *reverse-bias state*, since almost no current flows in the diode in this range.

For the case when v_D is larger than V_{ON}, we follow the lower current path via the forward resistance R_f (a low resistance of a few ohms or less) in Figure 3.25. Now we say that the diode is *ON* or in the *forward-bias state* since the voltage across the diode is close to zero.

If the diode remains in only one of these two states throughout the operation of a circuit, we can replace the diode by its circuit equivalent. If the sources in the circuit cause the diode to move back and forth between the two states, the analysis is more complicated.

The two states are readily seen if we simulate the simple diode circuit shown in Figure 3.21. The simulation is presented in Figure 3.26(b). The series circuit current, $I_{resistor}$ is the independent variable and is plotted as a function (piecewise function) of the source voltage V_{source} (also identified as V_V1 in the simulation plot.

The simulation of the simple diode circuit of Figure 3.21 illustrates several points already made: (1) the resulting current plot is a horizontal line when $v_D < V_{ON}$ as a result of the *OFF* state of the diode, (2) the *ON* state (closed switch) is seen as a rising straight line for $v_D > V_{ON}$. and (3) the two segments make up the piecewise-linear approximation for the simple non-linear diode circuit behavior. An additional point can be made concerning the change in the circuit's behavior due to temperature change of the diode – the resulting current flow in the circuit is determined primarily by the 1kΩ series resistance and not by the diode temperature despite a large temperature variation of 125°C.

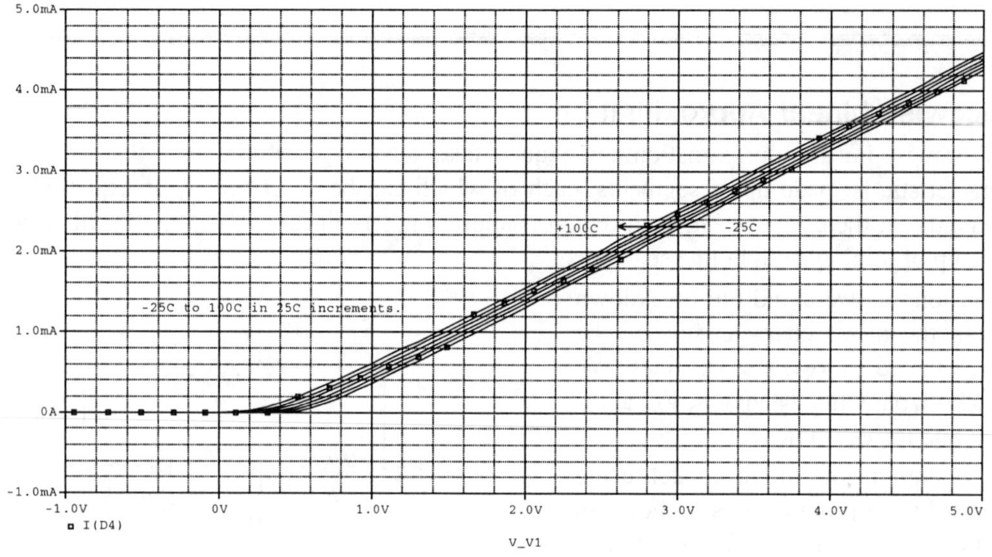

Figure 3.26 – Circuit simulation for Figure 3.21 - the simple diode circuit

We will see that analyzing simple circuits often involves a *guess and check* technique. That is, we begin by guessing which of the two states the diode is operating in. We then analyze the circuit using standard linear circuit analysis. If the analysis does not result in a contradiction (i.e., reverse current flow through or forward positive voltage across the diode), we assume our guess was correct. If the analysis results in a contradiction, we go back and assume the other state for the diode and resolve the problem.

Example 3.4

Find the output current for the circuit shown in Figure 3.27(a). Check your result using a computer simulation program.

Solution: Since the problem contains only a *dc* source, we use the diode equivalent circuit, as shown in Figure 3.27(b). Once we determine the state of the ideal diode in this model (i.e., either open circuit or short circuit), the problem becomes one of simple *dc* circuit analysis.

The state of this ideal diode can either be reasoned based upon the direction of sources, or if this is too complex, we can guess at the state. For example, if we guess that the diode is forward biased, we then solve the circuit substituting a short circuit for the diode. If the resulting current through the shorted diode is in the reverse direction, we know the guess was incorrect.

Alternatively, if we guess that the diode is reverse biased, an open circuit is substituted. If the solution shows a forward voltage across the open circuit, we know the guess was incorrect.

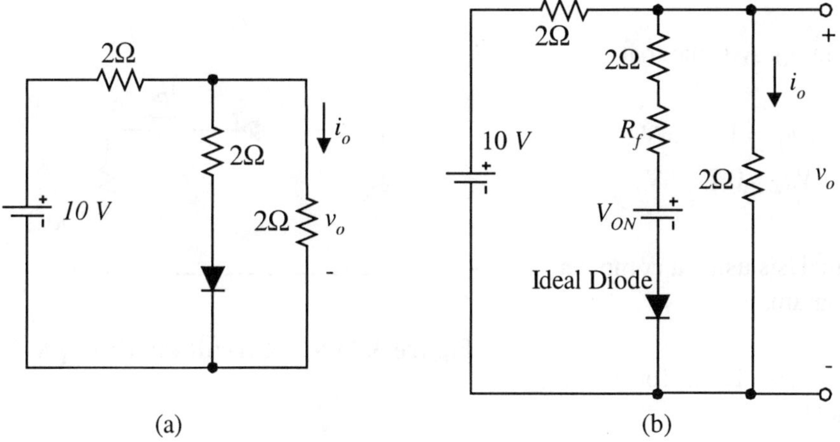

Figure 3.27 – Circuit for Example 3.4

For this particular problem, it is reasonable to assume that the diode is forward biased. This is true since the only external source is 10 V, which clearly exceeds the turn-on voltage of the diode, even taking the voltage division into account. The equivalent circuit then becomes that of Figure 3.27(b) with the diode replaced by a short circuit. We use simple circuit analysis (resistor combinations, superposition, loop or nodal analysis) to find that

$$v_{out} = \frac{10 + V_{ON} + 5R_f}{3 + R_f} \tag{3.40}$$

We now repeat the analysis using the Micro-Cap simulation program (other simulation programs, such as PSPICE may be used). We enter the circuit of Figure 3.27(a) using a battery for the *dc* source. Since the problem did not specify a particular diode, we ran the simulation using a 1N3491 diode (a common silicon diode). The parameters for this diode can be read from the library that forms a part of the program. The battery in the simulation contains a 0.001Ω source resistance. The Micro-Cap program provides for several types of analysis of this circuit. We can perform a *dc* analysis, which plots output vs. input voltage. We can then read the result from the graph for an input of 10 V. An alternative method is to run a transient analysis and to display the final values of the voltages. The result of this transient simulation is an output voltage of 3.64 V. The voltage across the diode is 0.91 V which represents V_{ON} plus the drop across the diode forward resistance. In order to compare this to the theoretical solution, we need to assume values for V_{ON} and R_f. As an example, suppose $V_{ON} = 0.7$ V and $R_f = 0.2$ Ω. Then the theoretical solution yields an output of 3.66 V.

Example 3.5:

The circuit of Figure 3.28(a), has a source voltage of

$$v_s = 1.1 + 0.1 \sin 1000t \, .$$

Find the current, i_D. Assume that

$$nV_T = 40 \quad \text{mV}$$
$$V_{ON} = 0.7 \quad \text{V}$$

Repeat your analysis using a computer simulation program.

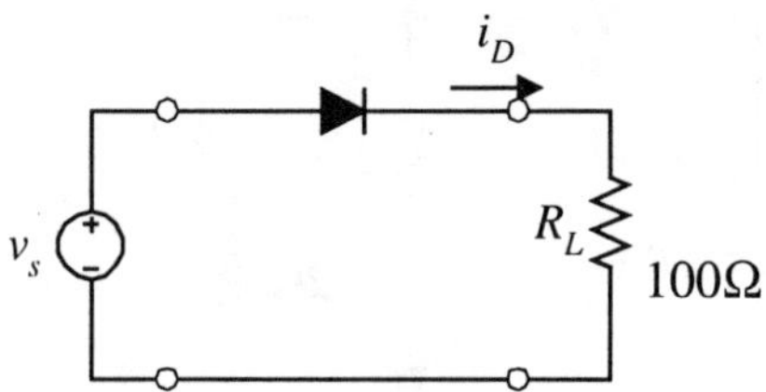

Figure 3.28(a) – Circuit for Example 3.5

Solution: We use KVL for the *dc* equation to yield

$$V_S = V_{ON} + I_D R_L$$

$$I_D = \frac{V_S - V_{ON}}{R_L} = 4 \quad \text{mA}$$

This sets the *dc* operating point of the diode. We need to determine the dynamic resistance so we can establish the resistance of the forward-biased junction for the *ac* signal. Assuming that the contact resistance is negligible, we have [see Equation (3.31)]

$$R_f = \frac{nV_T}{I_D} = 10 \quad \Omega$$

We use the symbol R_f instead of r_d since it includes the contact resistance. Now we can replace the forward-biased diode with a 10 Ω resistor. Again using KVL we have,

$$v_s = R_f \, i_d + R_L i_d$$

$$i_d = \frac{v_s}{R_f + R_L} = 0.91 \sin 1000\, t \quad \text{mA}$$

The diode current is then given by

$$i_D = 4 + 0.91 \sin 1000t \quad \text{mA}$$

Since i_D is always positive, the diode is always forward-biased, and the solution is complete.

If the *ac* current amplitude becomes greater than the *dc* current value, i_D is not always positive, and the assumption that the diode is forward biased is incorrect. Therefore the solution must be modified. In that case, when the *ac* current amplitude in the negative direction becomes larger than the *dc* value, the diode becomes reverse biased and the current is cut off.

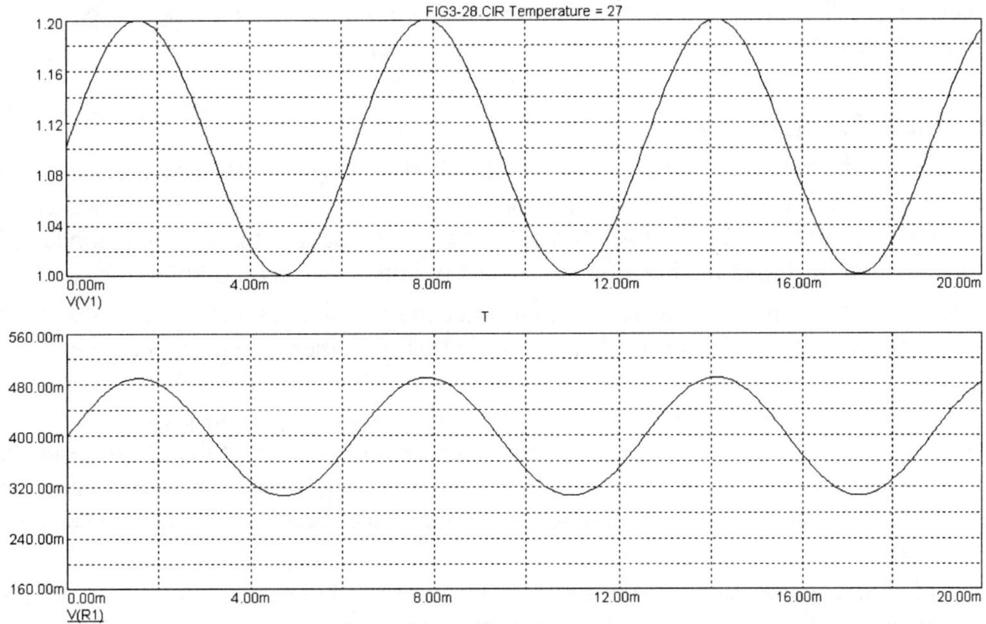

Figure 3.28(b) – Simulation result for Example 3.5

We now repeat the analysis using a computer simulation program (we ran this on Micro-Cap, Student Version). We can use the sinusoidal source component to model the offset source. We do this by modifying a library entry with the appropriate parameters. An alternative would be to place a sinusoidal source in series with a battery. The program does not permit zero source resistance, so we set this equal to a small value, 0.001Ω. Since the problem did not specify a specific diode, we choose the 1N3889 having parameters close to those given in the problem. Since the period of the input sinusoid is $2\pi/1000$, we set the simulation time at 0.02 seconds in order to view slightly more than three complete periods of the input and output. Figure 3.26(b) shows the results of the simulation. The top curve is the input voltage while the bottom curve is the output voltage (across the 100Ω resistor). We note that the output has a *dc* value of 0.4 V and amplitude of 0.095 V (actual values are printed out during the simulation, so it is not necessary to accurately read the graph). In order to find the diode current, we need simply use Ohm's law and divide this result by 100. We note that the simulation yielded a result of

$$i_D = 4 + 0.95\sin 1000t \quad \text{mA}.$$

3.2.7 Power Handling Capability

Diodes are rated according to their power handling capability. The ratings are determined by the physical construction of the diode (e.g., size of junction, type of packaging, and size of diode). The manufacturer's specifications are used to determine the power capability of a diode for certain temperature ranges. Some diodes, such as power diodes, are rated by their current carrying capacity.

Since diodes sometimes conduct relatively large currents, they must be mounted so that the heat generated in the diode can be dissipated away from the diode. In order to dissipate the internal heat generated, diodes can be mounted with heat sinks.

3.2.8 Diode Capacitance

The equivalent circuit of a diode, shown in Figure 3.29, includes a small capacitor. The size of this capacitor depends on the magnitude and polarity of the voltage applied to the diode as well as on the characteristics of the junction formed during manufacture. In the simple model of a diode junction, the region at the junction is depleted of both electrons and holes.

On the p-side of the junction, there is a high concentration of holes and on the n-side of the junction, there is a high concentration of electrons. Diffusion of these electrons and holes occurs close to the junction causing an initial *diffusion current.* When the holes diffuse across the junction into the n-region, they quickly combine with the majority electrons present in that area and disappear. Likewise, electrons also diffuse across the junction, recombine and disappear. This causes a *depletion region* (sometimes called the *space charge region*) near the junction. As a reverse voltage is applied across the junction, this region widens causing the depletion region to increase in size.

The depletion region resembles an insulator. Thus, a reverse-biased diode acts like a capacitor with a capacitance that varies inversely with the square root of the voltage drop across the semiconductor material.

The equivalent capacitance for high-speed diodes is less than 5 pF. The capacitance can be as large as 500 pF in high-current (low-speed) diodes.

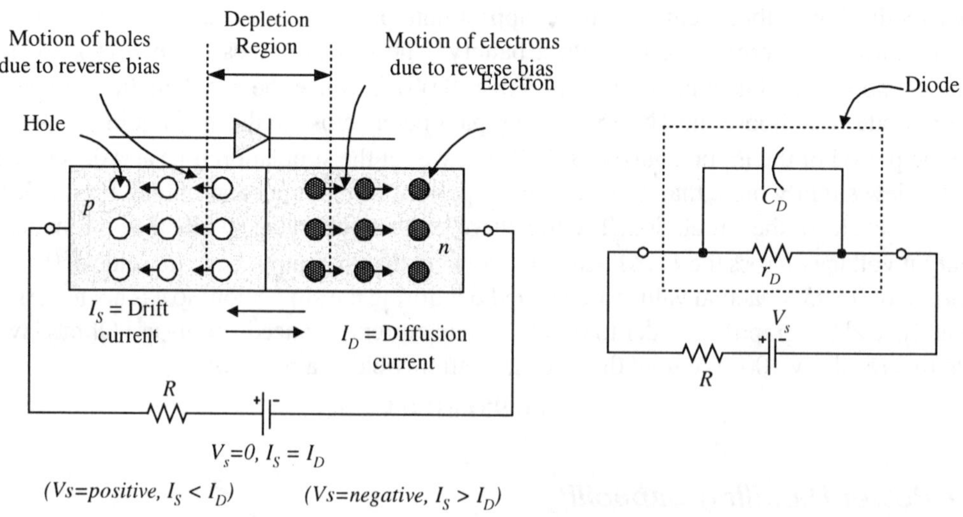

Figure 3.29 - Diode model and equivalent circuit

3.3 RECTIFICATION

We are now ready to see how the diode is configured to perform a useful function. The first major application we consider is that of *rectification.*

Rectification is the process of turning an alternating signal (*ac*) into one that is restricted to only one direction (*dc*). Rectification is classified as either *half-wave* or *full-wave.*

3.3.1 Half-Wave Rectification

Since an ideal diode can sustain current flow in only one direction, it can be used to change an *ac* signal into a *dc* signal.

Figure 3.30 illustrates a simple *half-wave rectifier* circuit. When the input voltage is positive, the diode is forward biased and can be replaced by a short circuit (assume the diode is ideal). The output voltage across the load resistor can then be found from the voltage divider relationship.

When the input voltage is negative, the diode is reverse biased, and can be replaced by an open circuit. The current is zero so the output voltage is also zero. Figure 3.30 shows an example of the output waveform assuming a 100 V amplitude sinusoidal input.

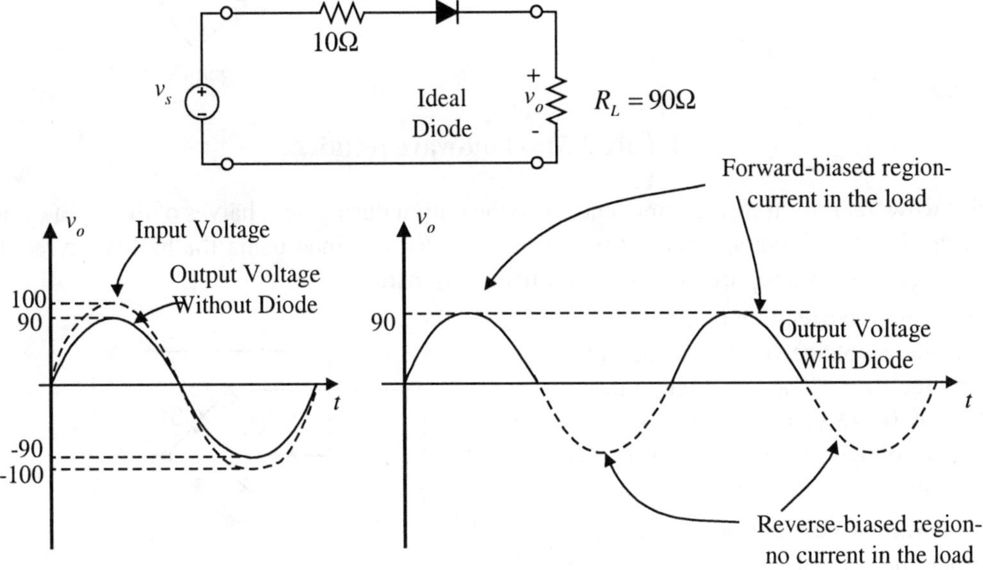

Figure 3.30 - Half-wave rectifier

The *average* of a periodic function is defined as the integral of the function over one period divided by the period. It is equal to the first term in a Fourier series expansion of the function. Note that while the input sinusoid has an average value of zero, the output waveform has an average of

$$v_{out_{avg}} = \frac{1}{T}\int_0^T v_{out}(t)\,dt = \frac{1}{T}\int_0^{T/2} 90\sin\frac{2\pi t}{T}\,dt = \frac{90}{\pi} = 0.318\times 90 \quad \text{V} \tag{3.41}$$

The average output voltage across the load resistor is 31.8% of the peak voltage produced at the half-wave rectifier *output* terminals. The half-wave rectifier can be used to create an almost constant *dc* output if the resulting waveform of Figure 3.30 is filtered. The filtering operation is discussed in Section 3.3.3. We note at this time that the half-wave rectifier is not very efficient. During one half of each cycle, the input is completely blocked from the output. If we could transfer input energy to the output during this half cycle, we would increase output power.

3.3.2 Full-Wave Rectification

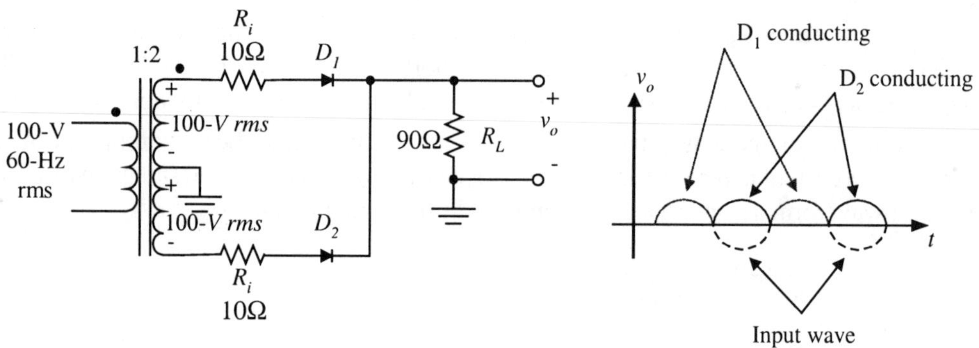

Figure 3.31 – Full-wave rectifier

A *full-wave rectifier* transfers input energy to the output during both halves of the input cycle. It provides increased average current per cycle over that obtained using the half-wave rectifier. Figure 3.31 shows a representative circuit using a transformer.

The full-wave rectifier produces *twice* the average voltage of that of the half-wave rectifier. The average output voltage is $0.318\times 2 = 0.636$ or 63.6% of the peak voltage. (You should verify this statement!)

Full-wave rectification is possible without the use of a transformer. For example, the *bridge rectifier* of Figure 3.32 accomplishes full-wave rectification.

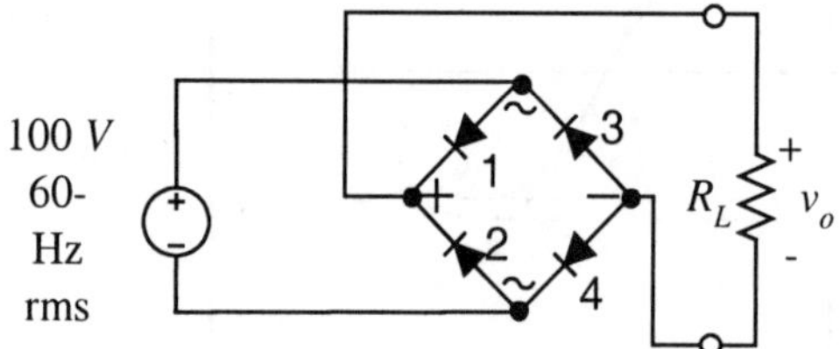

Figure 3.32 – Full-wave bridge rectifier

When the source voltage is positive, diodes 1 and 4 conduct and diodes 2 and 3 are open circuit. When the source voltage goes negative, the reverse situation occurs and diodes 2 and 3 conduct. This is indicated in Figure 3.33.

The bridge rectifier circuit has a practical shortcoming. If one terminal of the source is grounded, neither terminal of the load resistor can be grounded. To do so would cause a *ground loop* which would effectively short out one of the diodes. Therefore, it may be necessary to add a transformer to this circuit in order to isolate the two grounds from each other.

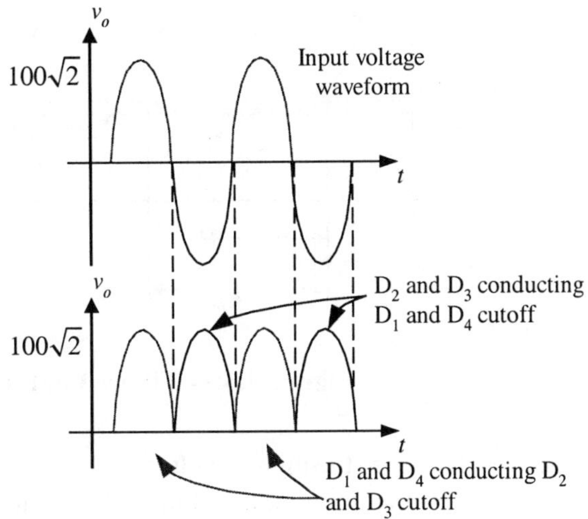

Figure 3.33 – Bridge rectifier diode conduction times

3.3.3 Filtering

The rectifier circuits of the previous section provide a *pulsating dc* voltage at the output. These pulsations, known as output *ripple*, can be reduced by filtering.

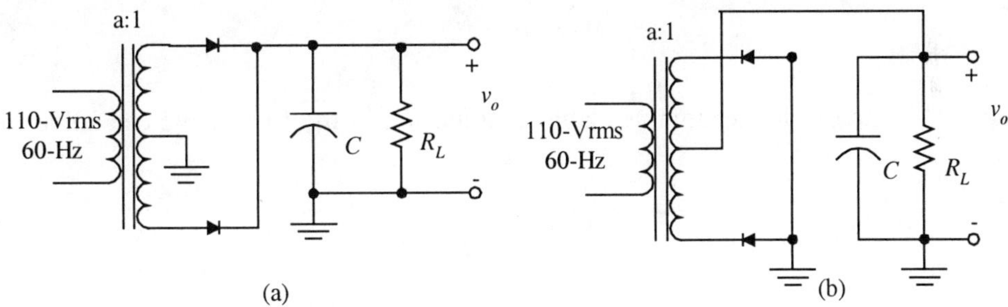

Figure 3.34 – Full-wave rectifier with filter

The most common type of filter employs a single capacitor. Figure 3.34(a) shows the full-wave rectifier where a capacitor has been added in parallel with the load resistor. The modified output voltage is shown in Figure 3.35 (please see next page). Note that the diodes have been reversed and placed close to ground potential [see Figure 3.34(b)]. This allows one side of the diode to be at ground potential. The diodes can then be attached to a ground plate thereby allowing dissipation of heat for high-power rectifier circuits.

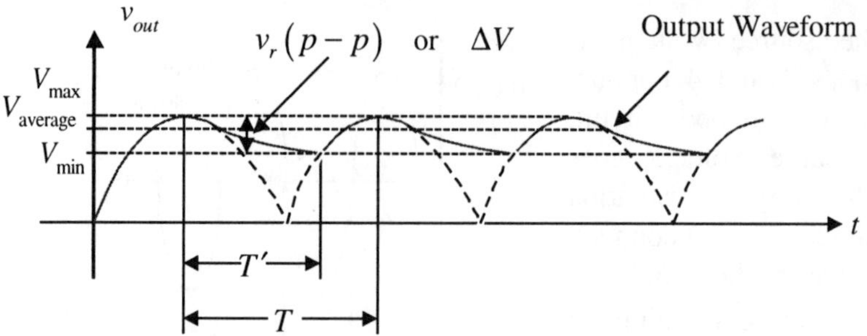

Figure 3.35 – Filtered output waveform

The capacitor charges to the highest voltage (V_{max}) when the input peaks at its most positive or negative value. When the input voltage falls below that value, the capacitor cannot discharge through either diode. Therefore, discharge takes place through R_L. This leads to an exponential decay given by the equation,

$$v(t) = V_{max}\, e^{-\left(\frac{t}{\tau}\right)} = V_{max}\, e^{-\left(\frac{t}{R_L C}\right)} \tag{3.42}$$

Design of this filter consists of choosing the capacitor value, C. For example, let us assume that the input is a sinusoid with amplitude, 100 V, and that the lowest output voltage we can accept in a given application is 95 V. Then,

$$95 = 100e^{-\frac{T'}{R_L C}} \tag{3.43}$$

where T' is the discharge time available as indicated in the figure. We can solve for C to obtain

$$C = 19.4\frac{T'}{R_L} \tag{3.44}$$

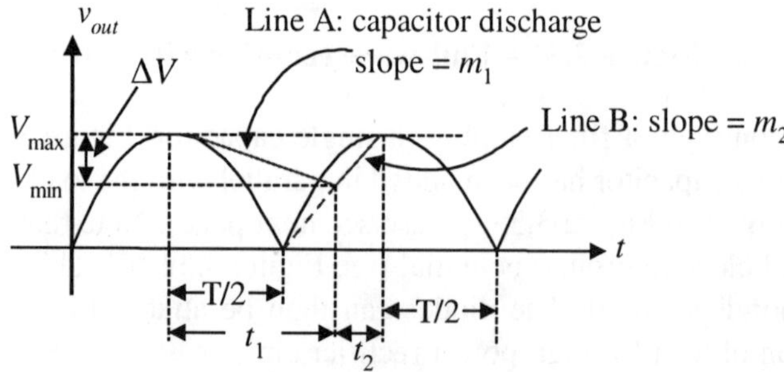

Figure 3.36 – Discharge time approximation

This formula is difficult to use in filter design since T' is dependent on the R_LC time constant and therefore, on the unknown, C. We shall make some approximations to arrive at a design equation. Certainly it is known that $T' < T$. For a 60 Hz input, the output fundamental frequency is 120 Hz. Therefore,

$$T = \frac{1}{f} = \frac{1}{120} = 8.333 \quad \text{ms} \tag{3.45}$$

We can estimate the value of the filter capacitor needed for a particular load using a straight line approximation, as shown in Figure 3.36. Although we will solve the equations for the indicated straight-line approximation, a further simplification is possible by assuming $t_2 = 0$. For many applications, this additional simplification yields acceptable results.

The initial slope of the exponential of Equation (3.42) is

$$m_1 = \frac{-V_{max}}{R_L C} \tag{3.46}$$

which is the slope of line **A** in the figure. The slope of line **B** of Figure 3.36 is

$$m_2 = \frac{V_{max}}{\left(T/2\right)} \tag{3.47}$$

Then

$$t_1 = \frac{-\Delta V}{m_1} = \frac{R_L C \Delta V}{V_{max}} \tag{3.48}$$

Using corresponding triangles, we find

$$t_1 = \frac{T}{2} + t_2 = \frac{T}{2} + \frac{TV_{min}}{2V_{max}}$$

$$t_1 = \frac{R_L C \Delta V}{V_{max}} = \frac{T\left(2 - \Delta V / V_{max}\right)}{2} \tag{3.49}$$

Substituting $T = 1/f_p$, where f_p is the number of pulses per second (twice the original frequency), we have

$$R_L C \frac{\Delta V}{V_{max}} = \frac{1}{2f_p}\left(2 - \frac{\Delta V}{V_{max}}\right) = \frac{1}{f_p}\left(1 - \frac{\Delta V}{2V_{max}}\right) \tag{3.50}$$

In most filter designs, we wish the ripple to be much less than the dc amplitude. Therefore,

$$\frac{\Delta V}{2V_{max}} \gg 1 \tag{3.51}$$

and Equation (3.50) becomes

$$C = \frac{V_{max}}{\Delta V f_p R_L} \tag{3.52}$$

This formula represents a conservative solution to the design problem. This is true since, if the straight line never goes below V_{min}, the exponential curve certainly will stay above this value.

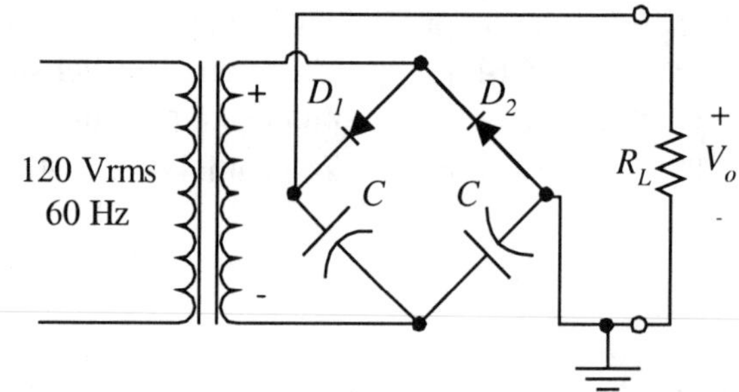

Figure 3.37 - Voltage doubler circuit

Let us now use equation (3.52) to solve for the capacitance in the example presented earlier. We assume that the input is a 60 Hz sinusoid of 100 V amplitude and that the lowest acceptable output voltage is 95 V. Thus, for this example, V_{max}=100 V, ΔV=5 V, and the frequency after rectification is 120 Hz for full-wave and 60 Hz for half-wave. Thus, from Equation (3.52),

$$C = \frac{100}{5 \times 120 R_L} = \frac{0.167}{R_L} \tag{3.53}$$

The above analysis shows that a filter can be designed to limit the output ripple from a rectifier. The amount of ripple is often a critical design parameter. Since this ripple does not follow any standard shape (e.g., sinusoidal or sawtooth) we need some way to characterize its size. The ripple voltage, $V_r(rms)$ is given by

$$V_r(rms) = \frac{V_{max} - V_{min}}{2\sqrt{3}} \tag{3.54}$$

Note that we use the square root of three rather than the square root of two in the denominator. The latter figure would be used to find the *rms* value of a sinusoid, which is the amplitude divided by the square root of two. For a sawtooth wave, the *rms* is the amplitude divided by the square root of three. These figures are verified by taking the square root of the average of the square of the waveform over one period. The shape of the ripple is closer to that of a sawtooth waveform than it is to a sinusoid. The average value of the ripple voltage is assumed to be the midpoint of the waveform (this is an approximation).

The *ripple factor* is defined as

$$\text{ripple factor} = \frac{V_r(rms)}{V_{dc}} \tag{3.55}$$

3.3.4 Voltage Doubling Circuit

Figure 3.37 shows a circuit which produces a voltage equal to approximately twice the maximum peak output of the transformer (at no load current).

This is known as a *voltage doubler circuit.* Notice that it is the same as the full-wave bridge rectifier of Figure 3.32 except that the two diodes have been replaced by capacitors. When the transformer output voltage has the polarity shown in the figure, there are two paths for the current leaving diode D_1; one path is through C_2, and this capacitor charges toward V_{max}. The other path is through the load resistor and C_1. If C_1 had already been charged to V_{max} during the previous cycle, it would effectively place another voltage source of V_{max} in series with the transformer output voltage. This results in doubling the maximum voltage to the load. The capacitors also act to reduce the amount of the voltage ripple at the output.

EXERCISES

E3.3 The circuit of Figure 3.34 is used to rectify a sinusoid of 100 V rms and 60 Hz. The minimum output voltage cannot drop below 70 V and the transformer has a turns ratio of 1:2. The load resistance is 2 kΩ. What size capacitor is needed across R_L?

Answer: 8.25 μF

E3.4 A half-wave rectifier output has 50 V amplitude at 60 Hz. Assuming no forward resistance in the diode, what minimum load could be added to the circuit when using a 50 μF capacitor to maintain the minimum voltage above 40 V?

Answer: 1.67 kΩ

E3.5 A full-wave rectifier similar to the one shown in Figure 3.34 has a transformer with a 5:1 turns ratio. What capacitance would be required to maintain a 10 V minimum voltage across a 100Ω load?

Answer: 233 μF

E3.6 What capacitance is needed if the voltage input in Exercise E3.5 varies between 110 V and 120 V rms at 60 Hz?

Answer: 233 μF

3.4 ZENER DIODES

A *Zener diode* is a device whose doping is performed in such a way as to make the *avalanche* or *breakdown* voltage characteristic very steep. If the reverse voltage exceeds the breakdown voltage, the *Zener* diode will normally not be destroyed. This is true as long as the current does not exceed a predetermined maximum value and the device does not overheat.

When a thermally-generated carrier (part of the reverse saturation current) falls down the junction barrier (refer to Figure 3.15), and acquires energy of the applied potential, the carrier collides with crystal ions and imparts sufficient energy to disrupt a covalent bond. In addition to the original carrier, a new electron-hole pair is generated. This pair may pick up sufficient energy from the applied field to collide with another crystal ion and create still another electron-hole pair. This action continues and thereby disrupts the covalent bonds. The process is referred to as *impact ionization*, *avalanche multiplication* or *avalanche breakdown*.

There is a second mechanism that disrupts the covalent bonds. The use of a sufficiently strong electric field at the junction can cause a direct rupture of the bond. If the electric field exerts a strong force on a bound electron, the electron can be torn from the covalent bond thus causing the number of electron-hole pair combinations to multiply. This mechanism is called *high field emission* or *Zener breakdown*. The value of reverse voltage at which this occurs is controlled by the amount of doping of the diode. A heavily-doped diode has a low *Zener* breakdown voltage, while a lightly-doped diode has a high *Zener* breakdown voltage.

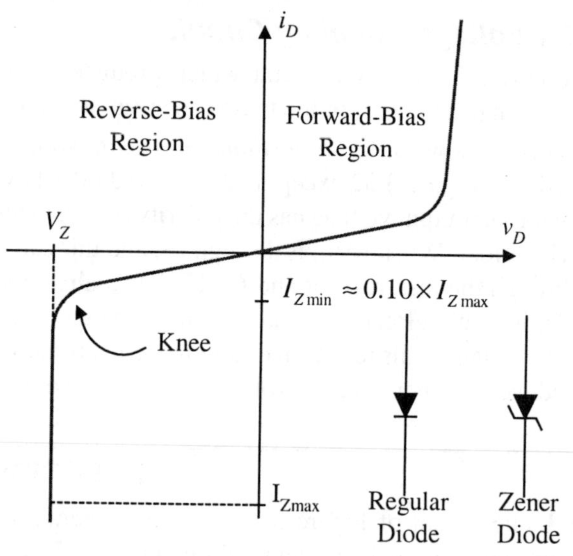

Figure 3.38 – Zener diode characteristic

Although we describe two distinctly different mechanisms to effect breakdown, they are commonly interchanged. At voltages above approximately 8 V, the predominant mechanism is the avalanche breakdown. Since the *Zener* effect (avalanche) occurs at a predictable point, the diode can be used as a voltage reference. The reverse voltage at which the avalanche occurs is called the *break-down* or *Zener voltage*.

A typical *Zener* diode characteristic is shown in Figure 3.38. The circuit symbol for the *Zener* diode is different from that of a regular diode, and is illustrated in the figure. The *maximum* reverse current, $I_{Z\,max}$, which the *Zener* diode can withstand is dependent on the design and construction of the diode. We will use a guideline that the *minimum Zener* current where the characteristic curve remains at V_Z (near the knee of the curve) is $0.1I_{Z\,max}$. The amount of power which the *Zener* diode can withstand ($V_Z I_{Z\,max}$) is a limiting factor in power supply design.

3.4.1 Zener Regulator

A *Zener* diode can be used as a voltage regulator in the configuration shown in Figure 3.39. The figure illustrates a varying load current represented by a variable load resistance. The circuit is designed so that the diode operates in the breakdown region, so it approximates an ideal voltage source. In the practical application the source voltage, v_s, varies and the load current also varies. The design challenge is to choose a value of R_i which permits the diode to maintain a relatively constant output voltage, even when the input source voltage varies and the load current also varies.

We now analyze the circuit to determine the proper choice of R_i. We use the node equation to solve for the *Zener* current, i_Z.

$$R_i = \frac{v_s - V_Z}{i_R} = \frac{v_s - V_Z}{i_Z + i_L} \tag{3.56}$$

$$i_Z = \frac{v_s - V_Z}{R_i} - i_L \tag{3.57}$$

The variable quantities in Equation (3.57) are v_S and i_L. In order to assure that the diode remains in the constant voltage (breakdown) region, we examine the two extremes of input/output conditions, as follows:

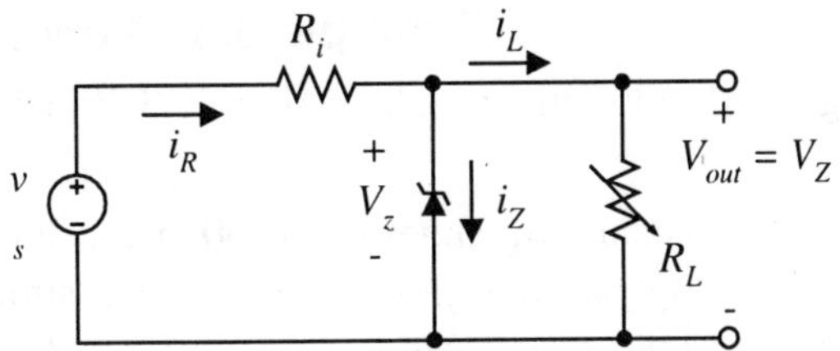

Figure 3.39 – Zener regulator

(1) The current through the diode, i_Z, is a minimum ($I_{Z\,min}$) when the load current, i_L is maximum ($I_{L\,max}$) and the source voltage, v_S is minimum ($V_{S\,min}$).
(2) The current through the diode, i_Z, is a maximum ($I_{Z\,max}$) when the load current, i_L, is minimum ($I_{L\,min}$) and the source voltage, v_S is maximum ($V_{S\,max}$)

When these characteristics of the two extremes are inserted into Equation (3.56), we find

$$R_i = \frac{V_{S_{min}} - V_Z}{I_{L_{max}} + I_{Z_{min}}} = \frac{V_{S_{max}} - V_Z}{I_{L_{min}} + I_{Z_{max}}} \tag{3.58}$$

$$\left(V_{S_{min}} - V_Z\right)\left(I_{L_{min}} + I_{Z_{max}}\right) = \left(V_{S_{max}} - V_Z\right)\left(I_{L_{max}} + I_{Z_{min}}\right) \tag{3.59}$$

In a practical problem, it is reasonable to assume that we know the range of input voltages, the range of output load currents, and the desired *Zener* voltage. Equation (3.59) thus represents one equation in two unknowns, the maximum and minimum *Zener* current. A second equation is found by examining Figure 3.38. To avoid the non-constant portion of the characteristic curve, we use an accepted rule of thumb that the minimum *Zener* current should be 0.1 times the maximum (i.e., 10%), that is,

$$I_{Z_{min}} = 0.1 \times I_{Z_{max}} \tag{3.60}$$

We now solve Equation (3.59) for $I_{Z\,max}$.

$$I_{Z_{max}} = \frac{I_{L_{min}}\left(V_Z - V_{S_{min}}\right) + I_{L_{max}}\left(V_{S_{max}} - V_Z\right)}{V_{S_{min}} - 0.9V_Z - 0.1V_{S_{max}}} \tag{3.61}$$

Now that we can solve for the maximum *Zener* current, the value of R_i is calculated from Equation (3.58).

Zener diodes are manufactured with breakdown voltages V_Z in the range of a few volts to a few hundred volts. The manufacturer specifies the maximum power the diode can dissipate. For example, a 1 W, 10V Zener can operate safely at currents up to 100mA.

Example 3.6 - Zener Regulator Design

Design a 10-volt Zener regulator [Figure 3.40(a)] for the following conditions:

(a) The load current ranges from 100 mA to 200 mA and the source voltage ranges from 14 V to 20 V. Verify your design using a computer simulation.

(b) Repeat the design problem for the following conditions: The load current ranges from 20 mA to 200 mA and the source voltage ranges from 10.2 V to 14 V.

Use a 10-volt Zener diode in both cases.

Solution: (a) The design consists of choosing the proper value of resistance, R_i, and power rating for the Zener. We use the equations from the previous section to first calculate the maximum current in the Zener diode and then to find the input resistor value. From equation (3.61), we have

$$I_{Z_{max}} = 0.533 \quad \text{A}$$

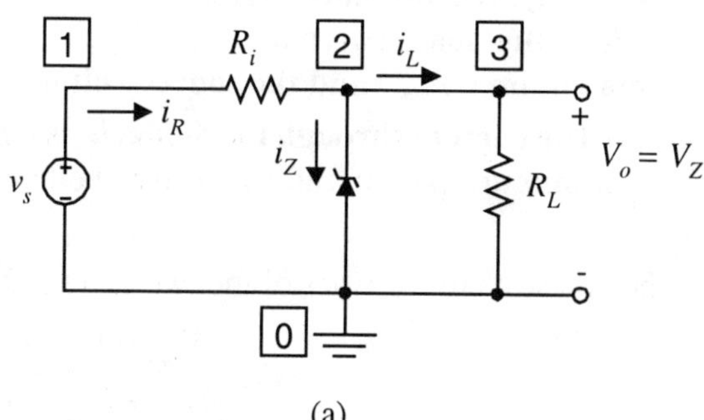

Figure 3.40(a) Zener diode regulator

Then, from Equation (3.58), we find R_i as follows:

$$R_i = \frac{V_{S_{max}} - V_Z}{I_{Z_{max}} + I_{L_{min}}} = \frac{20 - 10}{0.533 + 0.1} = 15.8\,\Omega$$

It is not sufficient to specify only the resistance of R_i. We must also select the proper resistor power rating. The maximum power in the resistor is given by the product of voltage with current, where we use the maximum for each value.

$$P_R = \left(I_{Z_{max}} + I_{L_{min}}\right)\left(V_{S_{max}} - V_Z\right) = 6.3 \quad \text{W}$$

Finally, we must determine the power rating of the Zener diode. The maximum power dissipated in the Zener diode is given by the product of voltage and current.

$$P_Z = V_Z I_{Z_{max}} = 0.53 \times 10 = 5.3 \quad \text{W}$$

We now check the design using PSPICE. The listing is given below, where we have numbered the nodes in Figure 3.40(a).

```
VIN,1,0,DC,0
VDUMMY,2,3,DC,0
RIN,1,2,15.8
IRL,3,0,100M
DZENER,0,2,ZENER
.MODEL,ZENER,D(BV=10)
.DC,VIN,8,20,0.1
.PROBE
.END
```

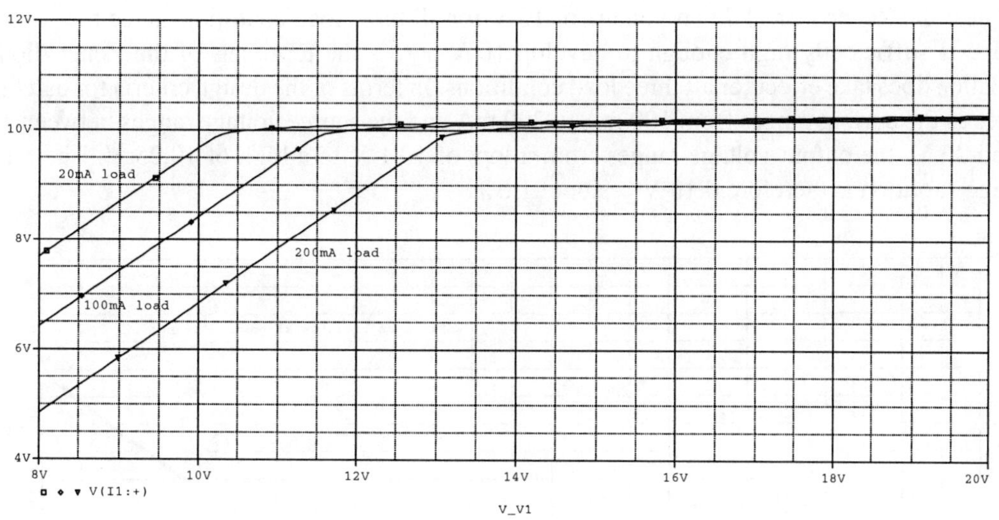

Figure 3.40(b) – Simulation result for Example 3.6

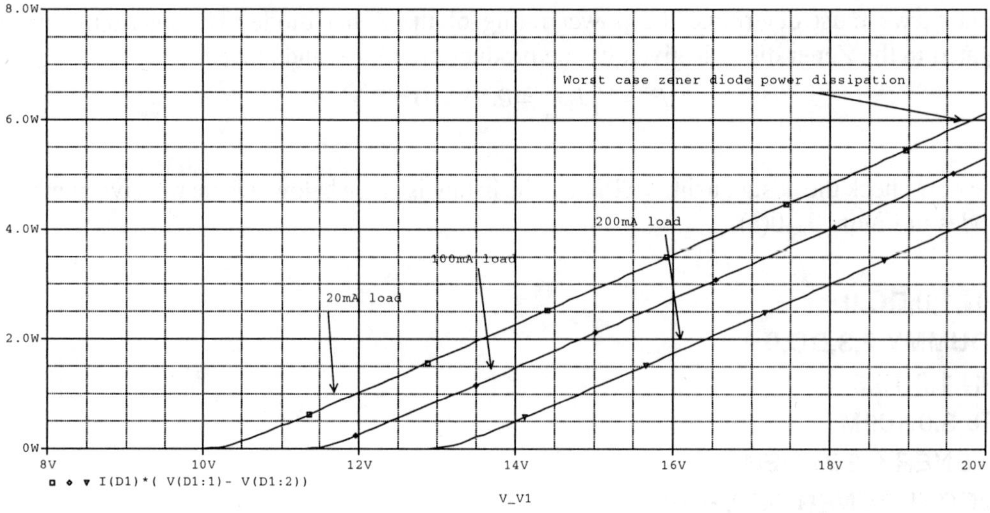

Figure 3.40(c)

To check the results against the design criteria, we have plotted in Figure 3.40(b) the output voltage as a function of input voltage for the three values of load current (extreme low (20 mA), extreme high (200mA), and a modest value (100mA)). Figure 3.40(b) shows the output voltage is held near the Zener's breakdown voltage of 10 V for all three load conditions once the source voltage is sufficiently high enough to develop 10 V across the terminals of the Zener diode regulation does take effect for all three load conditions. In terms of the design criteria for part (a), we see as the current ranges from 100 mA to 200 mA and the source voltage ranges between 14 V and 20 V, the output voltage ranges from a low of 10.1 V to a high of 10.25 V. The total voltage variation is therefore 0.15 V or about 1.5%.

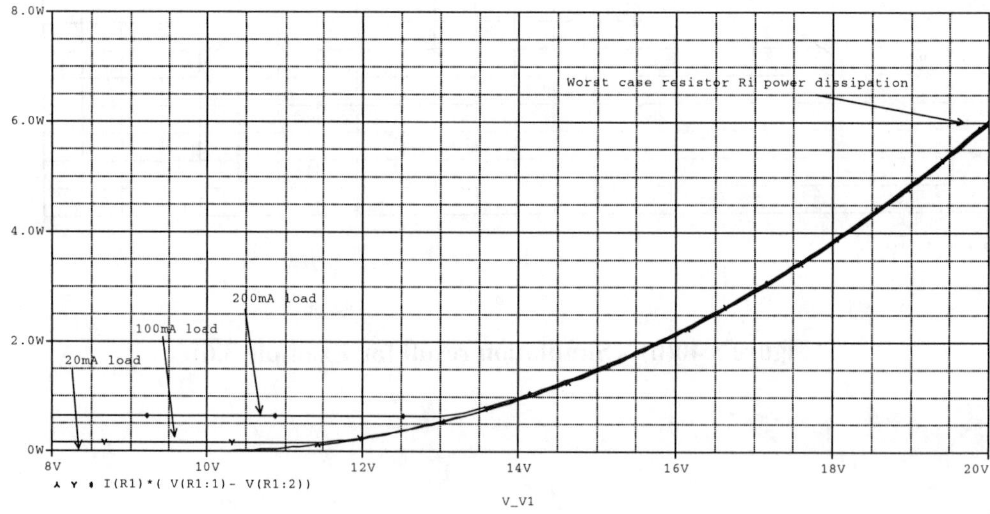

Figure 3.40(d)

The next two plots provide information concerning (1) the power rating of the Zener diode and (2) the power rating required for the series resistor R_i. First, we see from Figure 3.40(c), the worst case power dissipation for the Zener diode occurs for the combined condition of high supply voltage and low output load current. The simulation results of Figure 3.40(c) indicate the Zener dissipation is 5.3 watts. This is exactly the value computed earlier for the design criteria of 100 mA (part (a)). If the design criteria had set the load current to 20 mA then we see from Figure 3.40(c) that the expected Zener's power dissipation is a little higher, or about 6.10 watts (for a 20 mA load current). For the very extreme case of no load current (i.e., open circuit condition) the Zener diode would dissipate an even higher power of about

$$P_{Zener} = 10.25\text{V} \times \frac{(20\text{V} - 10.25\text{V})}{15.3\Omega} = 6.53 \quad \text{W}.$$

Next we turn our attention to the "voltage dropping" series resistor R_i. In Figure 3.40(d) we see power dissipated by this resistor converges in the simulation for all three cases to a worst case value very close to 6.3 watts. This agrees with the value computed in the solution above.

(b) Repeating these steps for the parameters of part (b) yields I_{Zmax} = -4 A. The negative value of $I_{z\ max}$ indicates that the margin between $V_{s\ min}$ and V_z is not large enough to allow for the variation in load current. That is, under the worst case condition of a 8 V input and 200 mA load current, the Zener cannot possibly sustain 10 V across its terminals. Therefore, the regulator will not operate correctly for any choice of resistance. We would have to either raise the source voltage or reduce the output current requirements.

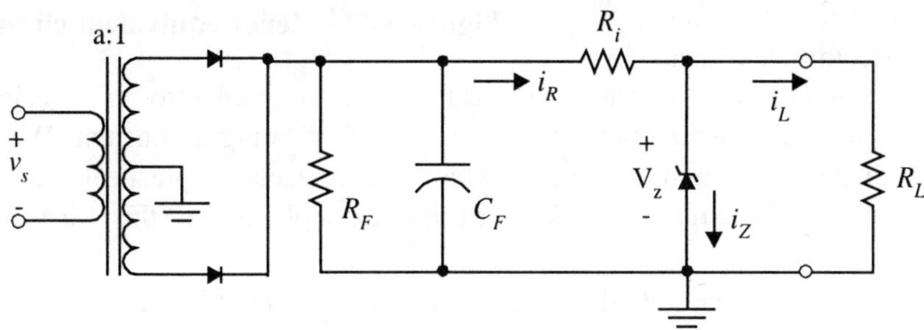

Figure 3.41 – Full-wave Zener regulator

The Zener regulator circuit of Figure 3.40(a) can be combined with the full-wave rectifier of Figure 3.31 to yield the full-wave Zener regulator of Figure 3.41.

R_F is a *bleeder resistor* used to provide a discharge path for the capacitor when the load is removed. Bleeder resistors normally have high resistances so as not to absorb significant power when the circuit is operating.

The value of C_F is found by adapting Equation (3.52)to this situation.

$$C_F = \frac{V_{S_{max}} - V_Z}{\Delta V f_p R_i} \tag{3.62}$$

The resistance in the equation is the equivalent resistance across C_F. The Zener diode is replaced by a voltage source, V_Z. The equivalent resistance is then the parallel combination of R_F with R_i. Since R_F is much larger than R_i, the parallel resistance is approximately equal to R_i. Since the voltage across R_i does not go to zero as is the case for the full-wave rectifier, the V_{max} in Equation (3.49) must be replaced by the total voltage swing. Thus, the capacitor is as specified in Equation (3.62), where we are assuming the transformer ratio is 1/2.

The largest voltage imposed on the regulator is $V_{S\,max}$. As before, ΔV is the peak-to-peak ripple and f_p is the fundamental frequency of the rectified waveform (i.e., twice the original frequency for full-wave rectification).

3.4.2 Practical Zener Diodes and Percent Regulation

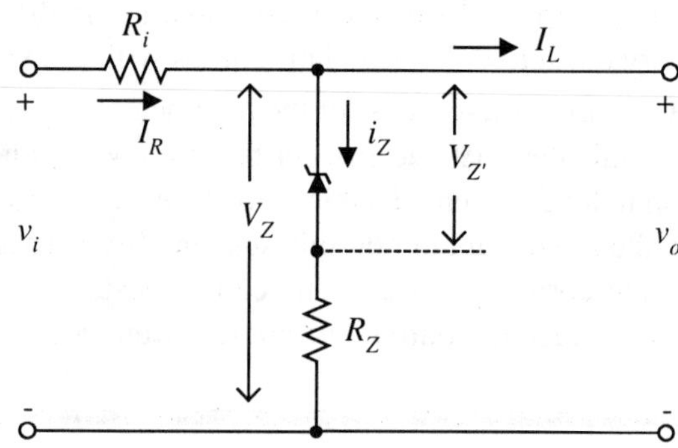

Figure 3.42 – Zener equivalent circuit

In the previous section we assumed that the Zener diode was ideal. That is, in the avalanche breakdown region, the diode behaves as a constant voltage source. This assumption means that the curve of Figure 3.38 is a vertical line in the breakdown region. In practice, this curve is not precisely vertical, and the non-infinite slope has the effect of a non-zero series resistance. The breakdown voltage is then a function of current instead of being a constant. We model the practical Zener diode as shown in Figure 3.42. This model replaces the practical Zener diode with an ideal diode in series with a resistance, R_Z. We use an example to show the effects of this series resistor.

Assume that a practical Zener diode is incorporated into the circuit of Example 3.6, with the diode resistance, $R_Z = 2\Omega$. We assume that $I_{Z\,min}$ is 10% of $I_{Z\,max}$, or 0.053 A. The output voltage (across the load) is no longer constant at 10 V because of R_Z. We find the minimum and maximum values of this voltage using the minimum and maximum current values. The voltage across the ideal diode of Figure 3.42 is 10 V, so we can write

$$\begin{aligned} V_{out_{min}} &= 10 + (0.053 \times 2) = 10.1 \quad \text{V} \\ V_{out_{max}} &= 10 + (0.53 \times 2) = 11.1 \quad \text{V} \end{aligned} \tag{3.63}$$

The *percent regulation* is defined as the total voltage swing divided by the *nominal* voltage. The smaller the percent regulation, the better the regulator. Therefore, for this example,

$$\% \text{ Reg} = \frac{V_{out_{max}} - V_{out_{min}}}{V_{out_{nominal}}} = \frac{11.1 - 10.1}{10} = 0.1 \quad \text{or} \quad 10\% \tag{3.64}$$

This value of regulation would be considered poor for most applications. The regulation could be improved by limiting the Zener current to a smaller value. This is accomplished by using an amplifier in series with the load. The effect of this amplifier is to limit the variations of current through the Zener diode.

EXERCISES

E3.7 A Zener diode regulator circuit (see Figure 3.39) has an input whose voltage varies between 10 V and 15 V, and a load whose current varies between 100 mA and 500 mA. Find the values of R_i and $I_{z\,max}$ assuming that a 6-volt Zener is used in this circuit.

Answer: 6.33 Ω; 1.32 A

E3.8 In Exercise E3.7, find the power ratings for the Zener diode and for the input resistor.

Answer: 7.92 W; 12.8

E3.9 In Exercise E3.7, find the value of capacitor required if the source is a half-wave rectifier output with a 60 Hz input.

Answer: 4740 μF

E3.10 Assume no resistor, R_F, were used in the circuit of Figure 3.41 and the transformer were a 4:1 centertapped transformer with a 120 V rms 60 Hz input. What value of R_i would be needed to maintain 10 V across a load whose current varies from 50 mA to 200 mA? Assume that the minimum voltage allowed at the regulator input is 14 V.

Answer: 14.8 Ω

E3.11 What value of capacitor is needed in the regulator of Exercise E3.10 in order to maintain a minimum voltage of 14 V?

Answer: 875 μF

E3.12 In the circuit of Exercise E3.10, assume that the input voltage varies from 110 V to 120 V RMS at 60 Hz. Select a value of capacitance which will accommodate both load current variation of 50 mA to 200 mA and the specified input voltage variation.

Answer: C = *1160 μF*

3.5 CLIPPERS AND CLAMPERS

Diodes can be used to clip an input signal or to limit parts of the signal. Diodes are also used in restoring a *dc* level to an input signal.

3.5.1 Clippers

Clippers are used to eliminate a part of a waveform which lies above or below some reference level. Clipping circuits are sometimes referred to as *limiters, amplitude selectors* or *slicers*. The halfwave rectification circuit of the previous section uses clipping action at the zero level. If a battery is added in series with the diode, a rectification circuit clips everything above or below the battery voltage, depending on the orientation of the diode. This is illustrated in Figure 3.43.

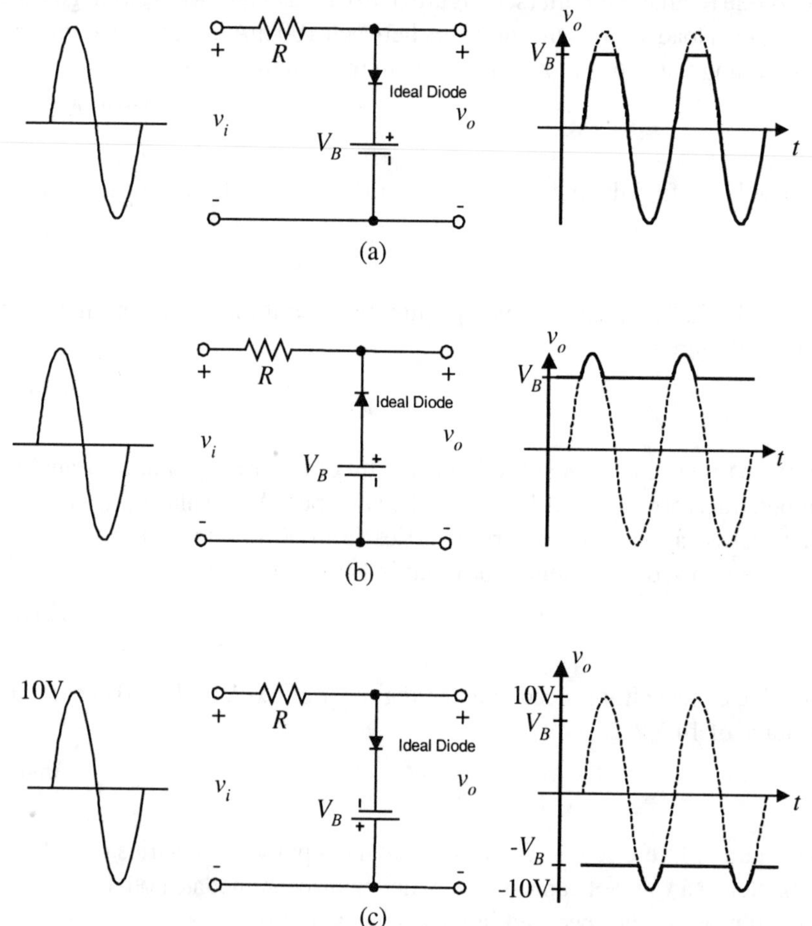

Figure 3.43 (parts a, b, and c) - Ideal clipping circuits

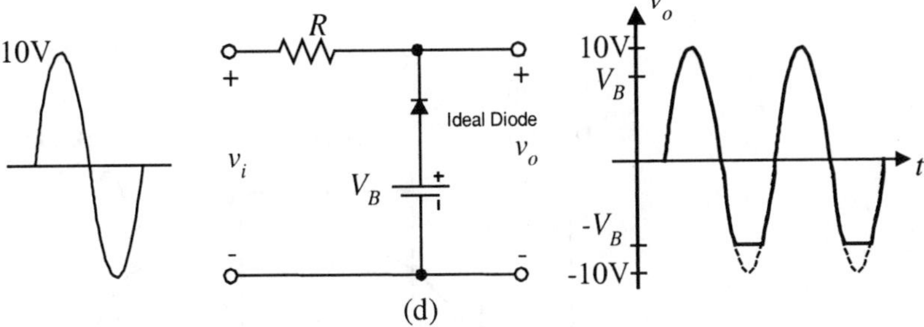

Figure 3.43(part d) - Ideal clipping circuits

The output waveforms indicated in Figure 3.43 assume that the diodes are ideal. We can relax this assumption by including two additional parameters in the diode model. First, we assume that a voltage of V_{ON} must be overcome before the diode will conduct. Second, when the diode is conducting, we include a forward resistance, R_f. Figure 3.44(a) shows the modified circuit. The effect of V_{ON} is to make the clipping level $V_{ON}+V_B$ instead of V_B. The effect of the resistance is to change the flat clipping action to one which proportionately follows the input voltage (i.e., a voltage divider effect). The resulting output is calculated as follows, and it is illustrated in Figure 3.44(b) on the following page. For $v_{in} < V_B+V_{ON}$, $v_{out} = v_i$. For $v_{in} > V_B+V_{ON}$,

$$v_{out} = v_{in}\frac{R_f}{R+R_f} + \left(V_B + V_{ON}\right)\frac{R}{R+R_f} \tag{3.65}$$

Positive and negative clipping is performed simultaneously. The result is a *parallel-biased clipper* which is designed by using two diodes and two voltage sources oriented in opposite directions. The circuit produces the output waveshape as shown in Figure 3.45 for practical diodes. The extension to practical diodes parallels the analysis leading to the results in Figure 3.44.

Another type of clipper is the *series-biased* clipper, which is shown in Figure 3.46 (please see next page). The 1 V battery in series with the input causes the input signal to be superimposed on a *dc* voltage of -1 V rather than being symmetrical about the zero axis. Assume that this system uses an ideal diode. Various configurations are shown in Figure 3.46 (please see next page). The diode of Figure 3.46(a) will conduct only during the negative-going shifted input signal. When the diode is conducting, the output is zero. We have a non-zero output when the diode is not conducting. In Figure 3.46(b), the reverse is true. When the conditioned signal is positive, the diode conducts and an output signal exists but when the diode is off, no output occurs. Although the operation of the two circuits is different, the two outputs are identical. In Figure 3.46(c) and (d) we reverse the polarity of the battery and obtain output waveforms as shown.

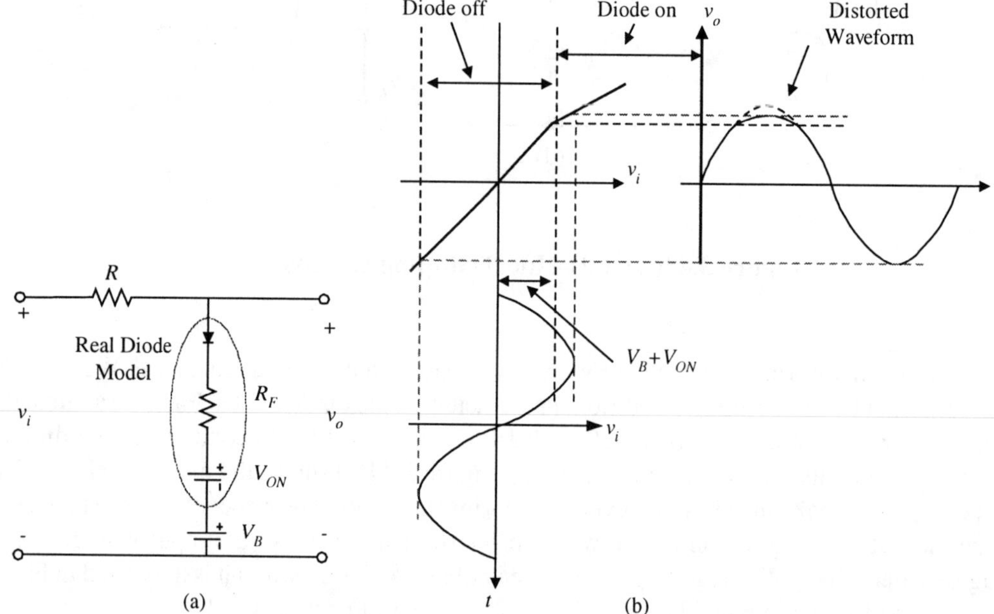

Figure 3.44 – Clipper using a practical diode

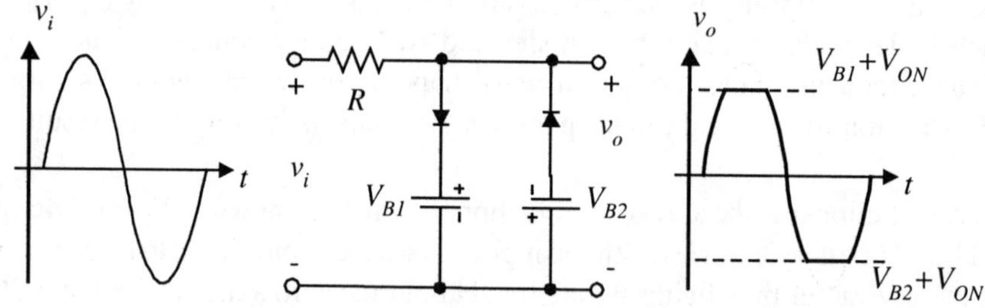

Figure 3.45 – Parallel-biased clipper

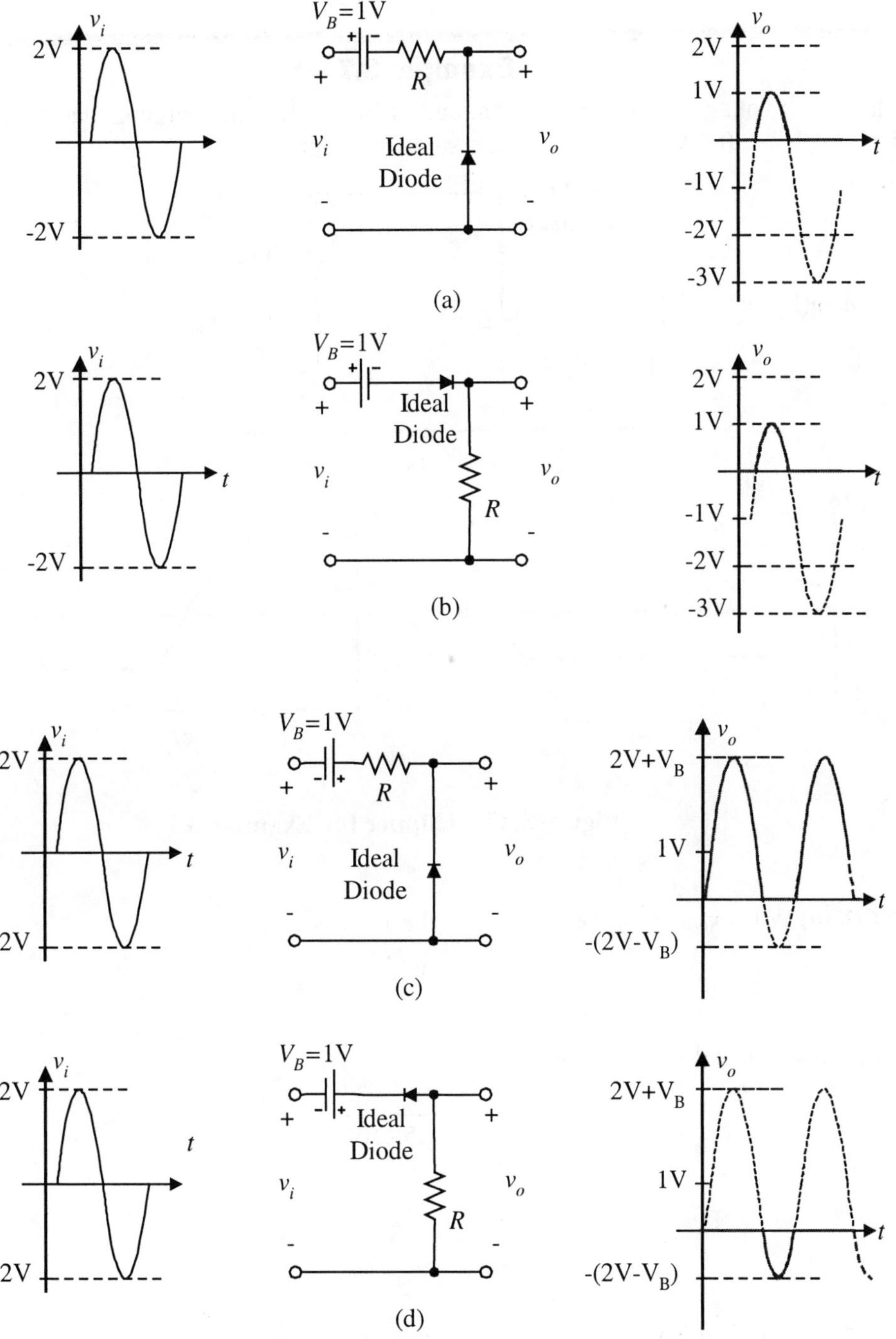

Figure 3.46 - Series-biased clippers

Example 3.7

Find the output voltage v_{out} of the clipper circuit of Figure 3.47(a) assuming that the diodes are (a) ideal; (b) $V_{ON} = 0.7$ V. For both cases, assume R_F is zero.

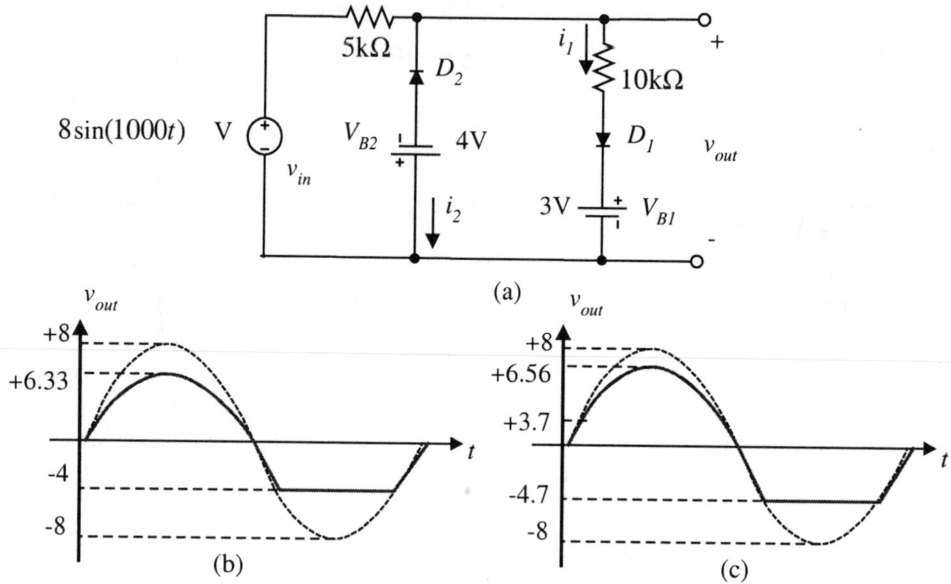

Figure 3.47 – Clipper for Example 3.7

Solution: (a) When v_{in} is positive and $v_{in} < 3$, then

$$v_{in} = v_{out}.$$

When v_{in} is positive and $v_{in} > 3$, then

$$i_1 = \frac{v_{in} - 3}{1.5\times10^4}$$

$$v_{out} = 10^4 i_1 + 3 = \frac{2}{3}v_{in} + 1$$

When v_{in} hits its peak at 8 V, v_{out} is 6.33 V. When v_{in} is negative and $v_{in} > -4$, then

$$v_{in} = v_{out}.$$

When v_{in} is negative and $v_{in} < -4$, then

$$v_{out} = -4 \quad \text{(V)}$$

The resulting output wave shape is shown in Fig. 3.47(b)

(b) When $V_{ON} = 0.7$ V, v_{in} is positive and $v_{in} < 3.7$ V, then

$$v_{in} = v_{out}.$$

When $v_{in} > 3.7$ V, then

$$i_1 = \frac{v_{in} - 3.7}{1.5 \times 10^4}$$

$$v_{out} = 10^4 i_1 + 3.7 = \frac{2}{3} v_{in} + 1.23$$

When v_{in} is 8 V, v_{out} is 6.56 V. When v_{in} is negative and $v_{in} > -4.7$ V, then

$$v_{in} = v_{out}$$

When $v_{in} < -4.7$ V, then

$$v_{out} = -4.7 \quad \text{V}$$

The resulting output wave shape is shown in Figure 3.47(c).

3.5.2 Clampers

A voltage waveform can be shifted by placing an independent voltage source, either constant or time varying, in series with the waveform. *Clamping* is a shifting operation, but the additive source is no longer independent of the waveform. The amount of shift depends on the actual waveform. Figure 3.48 shows an example of clamping.

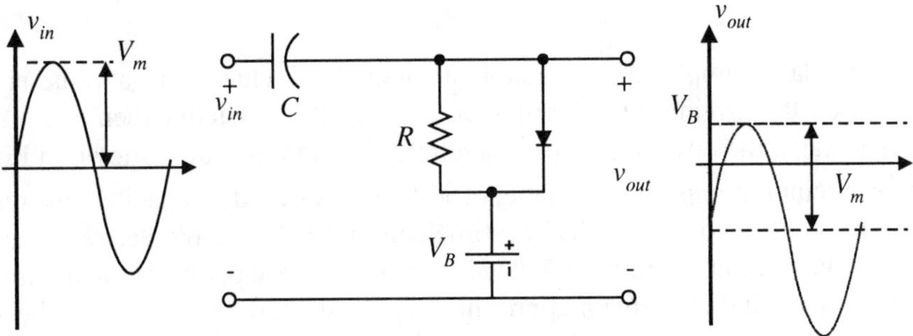

Figure 3.48 – Clamping

The input waveform is shifted by an amount which makes the shifted waveform peak at a value of V_B. Thus, the amount of shift is the exact amount necessary to change the original maximum to a new maximum, V_B. The waveform is "clamped" to a value of V_B. If we knew the exact value of the original maximum, V_m, we could accomplish this shift with an independent *dc* source in series with the waveform. The distinguishing feature of a clamper is that it adjusts the waveform without needing the initial knowledge of the exact shape. The amount of shift is determined by the actual waveshape. If the input waveform changes, the amount of shift will change such that the output is always clamped to V_B. The clamping circuit thus provides a *dc* component in an amount necessary to achieve the desired clamping level.

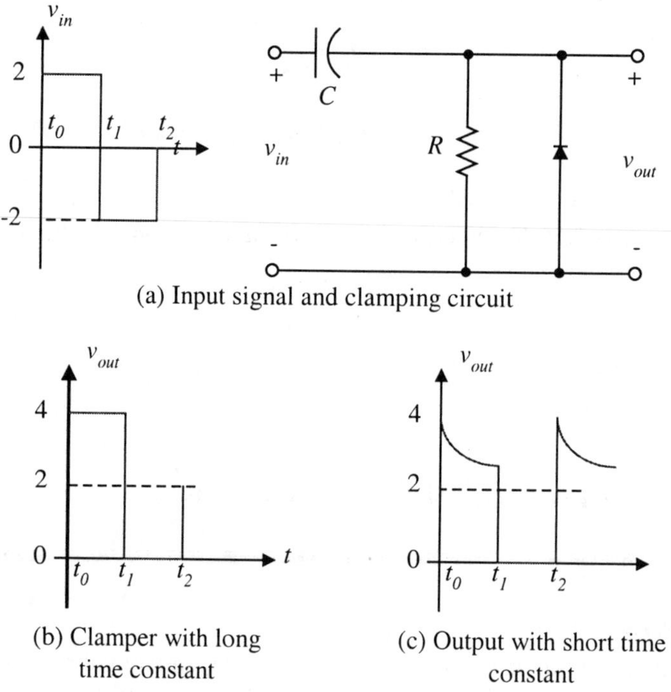

(a) Input signal and clamping circuit

(b) Clamper with long time constant

(c) Output with short time constant

Figure 3.49 – Clamping at zero volts

For this particular example, the capacitor of Figure 3.48 charges to a value equal to the difference between the original waveform peak and V_B. The capacitor then acts like a series battery of this voltage, thereby shifting the waveform down to the value shown in Figure 3.48.

A clamping circuit is composed of a battery (or *dc* supply), diode, capacitor, and resistor. The resistor and capacitor are chosen so that the time constant is large. We desire the capacitor to charge to a constant value and remain at that value throughout the period of the input waveform. If the capacitor voltage did not remain approximately constant, the output would be a distorted version of the waveform rather than a shifted version. Whenever the output tries to exceed V_B, the diode forward biases and the output is limited to V_B. During these times, the capacitor charges. When steady state is reached, the capacitor will be charged to a value of

$$V_C = V_m - V_B \tag{3.66}$$

Figure 3.49 illustrates a clamping circuit where the output is clamped to zero (i.e., there is no battery so $V_B = 0$). Because the diode is in the reverse direction from that of the previous circuit, the *minimum* rather than *maximum* of the output is clamped. That is, the capacitor can only charge in a direction that will add to the input voltage. The circuit is shown with a square wave as input. It is important that the voltage across the capacitor remain approximately constant during the half period of the input waveform. A design rule of thumb is to make the RC time constant at least five times the duration of the half period (i.e., five times either $t_1 - t_o$ or $t_2 - t_1$). If this design rule is followed, the RC circuit has less than 20% of a time constant to charge or discharge during the half period. This places the final value within 18% of the starting value [i.e., $e^{-0.2} = 0.82$]. If the time constant is too small, the waveform will be distorted as illustrated in the figure. To reduce the error to less than 18%, the time constant can be increased (e.g., to 10 times the half-period duration). The square wave input represents a *worst-case* situation since it places the greatest demands on the clamping circuit.

3.6 OP-AMP CIRCUITS CONTAINING DIODES

Numerous examples exist for using op-amps with diodes. We consider a wide range of these circuits in Chapter 13, and present several examples in this section.

Consider the ideal op-amp circuit shown in Figure 3.50 with

$$v_{in} = V \sin \omega t \tag{3.67}$$

The diode is conducting when v_+ attempts to go negative, and non-conducting when v_+ is positive.

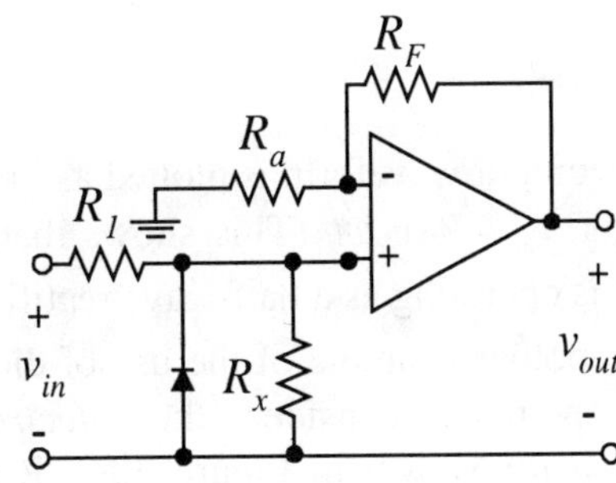

Figure 3.50 – Half-wave rectifier circuit

Starting with the diode ON, when v_+ attempts to go negative, the diode shorts and

$$v_+ = 0 \tag{3.68}$$

The inverting input voltage is found using the voltage-divider relationship,

$$v_- = \frac{R_a}{R_a + R_F} v_{out} \tag{3.69}$$

Now since $v_+ = v_- = 0$, we see that v_{out} must also equal zero.

Now starting with the diode OFF, when v_+ goes positive, the diode is open-circuited and a voltage divider relationship yields,

$$v_+ = \frac{R_X}{R_1 + R_X} v_{out} \tag{3.70}$$

As before, the inverting voltage input is given by

$$v_- = \frac{R_a}{R_a + R_F} v_{out} \tag{3.71}$$

Now since v_+ is equal to v_-, we equate these two expressions to obtain

$$v_{out} = v_{in} \frac{1 + R_F/R_a}{1 + R_1/R_X} = A v_{in} \tag{3.72}$$

where

$$A = \frac{1 + R_F/R_a}{1 + R_1/R_X} \tag{3.73}$$

The output waveform is plotted as Figure 3.51 for $v_{in} = V \sin \omega t$. This shows that the circuit is operating as a half-wave rectifier.

As another example of the use of diodes with op-amps, consider the *electronic thermometer* shown in Figure 3.52. Recall that the voltage across a diode varies with temperature according to the expression

$$\Delta V_{ON} = -2(T_2 - T_1) \quad \text{(mV)} \tag{3.74}$$

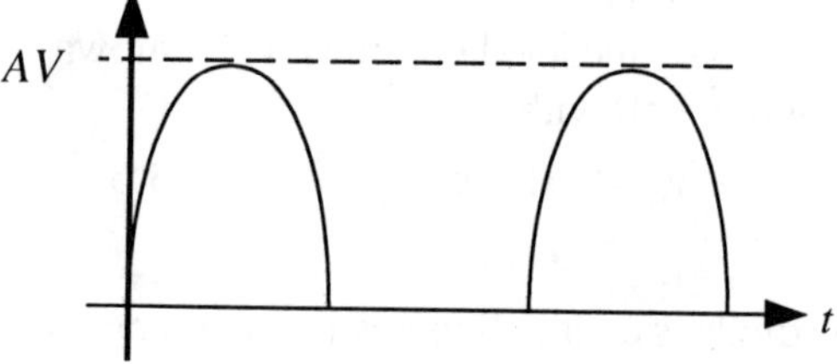

Figure 3.51 – Output of the half-wave rectifier

At room temperature (T_1=25°C) the voltage across the diode is 700 mV. The diode voltage decreases as the temperature increases. For example at T_2=125°C, the decrease in diode voltage is

$$\Delta V_{ON} = -2(125 - 25) = -200 \quad \text{mV} \tag{3.75}$$

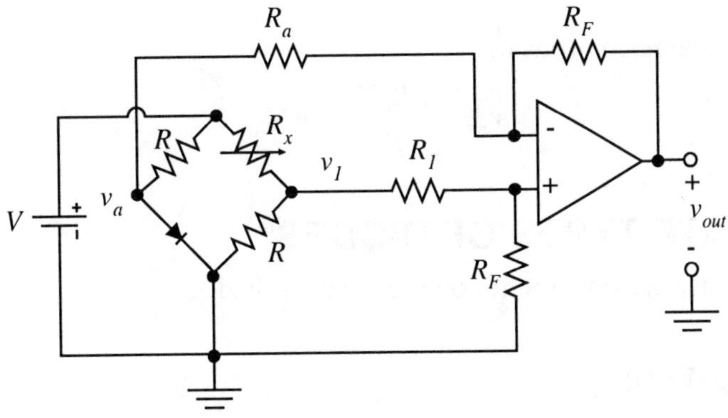

Figure 3.52 – Electronic thermometer

As a result, the diode voltage drops to 500 mV. This voltage variation can be used in the design of an inexpensive thermometer. We choose the resistance, R, so the diode is conducting and the diode voltage, which is the v_a input to the op-amp, is:

$$\begin{aligned} v_a = V_{ON} &= 700\,\text{mV} - 2\left(T_2 - 25^\circ C\right) \quad \text{mV} \\ &= \left(750 - 2T_2\right) \quad \text{mV} \end{aligned} \tag{3.76}$$

If we let $V = 10$ V and $R_I >> R$, $R_I >> R_x$, the bias voltage, which is the v_I input to the op-amp, is

$$v_1 = 10^4 \frac{R}{R + R_x} \quad \text{mV} \tag{3.77}$$

The op-amp equation is then

$$v_{out} = -\frac{R_F}{R_a} v_a + \left[\frac{R_F}{R_1 + R_F} \frac{R_F}{R_a \| R_F}\right] v_1 \tag{3.78}$$

If we let $R_a = R_1$ and substitute Equation (3.76) and Equation (3.77) into Equation (3.78), we obtain,

$$v_{out} = \frac{R_F}{R_1}\left[10^4 \frac{R}{R + R_x} - 750 + 2T_2\right] \quad \text{mV} \tag{3.79}$$

We wish to cancel the *dc* components in this expression, so we let

$$10^4 \frac{R}{R + R_x} = 750 \quad \text{mV} \tag{3.80}$$

Equation (3.79) then simplifies to

$$v_{out} = \frac{2R_F T_2}{R_1} \quad \text{mV} \tag{3.81}$$

3.7 ALTERNATE TYPES OF DIODES

This section briefly presents the following types of diodes:

- Schottky
- Light-emitting (LED)
- Photo

3.7.1 Schottky Diodes

A *Schottky diode* (or *Schottky Barrier diode*) is formed by bonding a metal, such as aluminum or platinum, to *n*- or *p*-type silicon. It is often used in integrated circuits for high-speed switching applications. Its symbol and construction are shown in Figure 3.53.

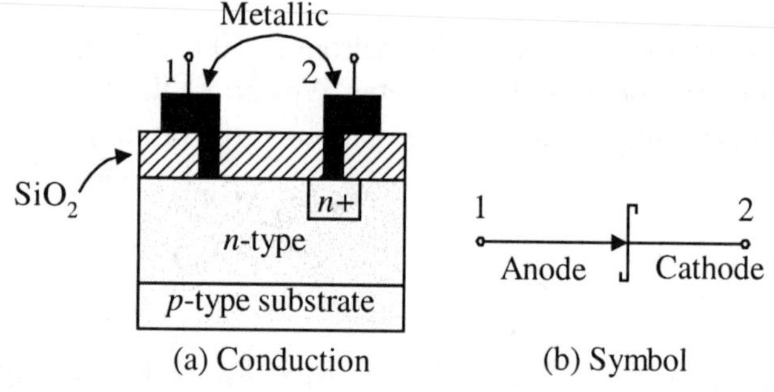

Figure 3.53 – Schotty diode

The Schottky diode has a voltage-current characteristic similar to that of the silicon *pn* junction diode, except that the forward break voltage, V_{ON}, is between 0.3 V and 0.7 V. The specific value of forward break voltage is determined by the manufacturing process. When the Schottky diode is operated in the forward mode, current is induced by the movement of electrons from the *n*-type silicon across the barrier and through the metal. Since electrons recombine relatively quickly through metals, the recombination time is small, on the order of 10 picoseconds. This is much faster than an ordinary *pn* junction diode. Therefore, the Schottky diode is of great value in high-speed switching applications. The capacitance associated with this diode is extremely small.

The metallic material in contact 1 and the lightly doped *n*-region form a rectifying junction while the heavily doped *n*-region and contact 2 form an ohmic contact. The forward direction electrons from the *n*-type silicon cross the barrier into the metal where there is a high concentration of electrons. This results in a *majority* carrier device.

Schottky diodes are useful in integrated circuit technology because they are easy to fabricate and can be manufactured at the same time as the other components on the chip. Fabrication of a *pn* junction diode requires one more *p*-type diffusion than does a Schottky diode. However, fabrication of a Schottky diode may require an extra metallization step. The low-noise characteristics of the Schottky diode make it ideal for application in power monitoring of low-level radio frequencies, detectors for high frequency, and Doppler radar mixers.

3.7.2 Light-Emitting Diodes (LED)

Certain types of diodes are capable of changing electric energy into light energy. The *light-emitting diode (LED)* transforms electric current into light. It is useful in various types of displays, and can sometimes be used as a light source for optical fiber communication applications.

An electron can fall from the conduction band into a hole and give up energy in the form of a photon of light. The momentum and energy relationships in silicon and germanium are such that the electron gives up its energy as heat when it returns from the conduction band to the valence band. However, the electron in a gallium arsenide crystal produces a photon when it returns from the conduction band to the valence band. There are not enough electrons in a crystal to produce visible light. However, when a forward bias is applied, large numbers of electrons are injected from the n-material into the p-material. These electrons combine with holes in the p-material at the valence band energy level, and photons are released. The light intensity is proportional to the rate of recombination of electrons, and therefore, proportional to the diode current. The gallium arsenide diode emits light waves at a wavelength near the infrared band. To produce light in the visible range, gallium phosphide must be mixed with the gallium arsenide.

When an LED is conducting, the forward voltage drop is approximately 1.7 V. The amount of light emitted by the LED depends on the current through the diode; the greater the current, the greater the light emitted. A current limiting resistor must be placed in series with the LED to avoid destroying the diode. The magnitude of this current limiting resistor is easily calculated by limiting the LED on-current to approximately 10 mA with a diode on-voltage of approximately 1.7 V. Example 3.8 illustrates the calculation.

Example 3.8

Select a current limiting resistor to properly light an LED when 5 V *dc* is applied to the LED as shown in Figure 3.54.

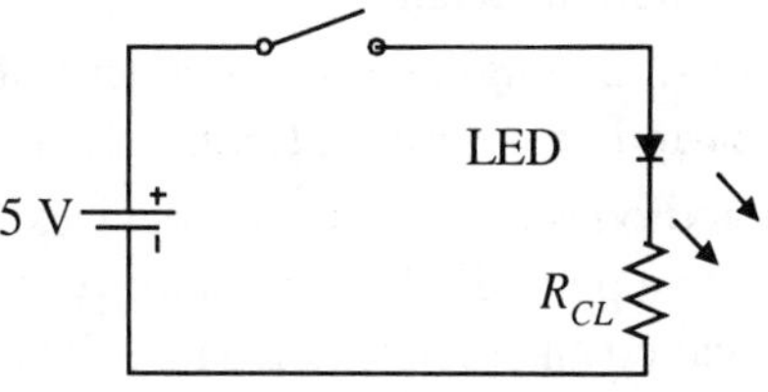

Figure 3.54 – Light emitting diode

Solution: We wish to limit the current through the LED to approximately 10 mA when the LED is conducting and when the on-voltage is 1.7 V. The voltage to be dropped across R_{CL} is 5 - 1.7 = 3.3 V. With 10 mA maximum current, the value of R_{CL} = 330Ω. This is a typical resistor value for use with 5 V LED displays.

3.7.3 Photo Diodes

A photo diode performs the inverse of an LED. That is, it transforms light energy into an electric current. *Reverse bias* is applied to the photo diode and the reverse saturation current is controlled by the light intensity that shines on the diode. The light generates electron-hole pairs, which induce current. The result is a photocurrent in the external circuit, which is proportional to the effective light intensity on the device. The diode behaves as a constant current generator as long as the voltage does not exceed the avalanche voltage. The response times are less than 1 μs. The sensitivity of the diode can be increased if the junction area is made larger since more photons are collected, but this will also increase the response time since the junction capacitance (and therefore the RC time constant) increases. We should note that without reverse bias, an illuminated photodiode will convert light energy into electrical energy. This arrangement, usually manufactured from low cost silicon, is known as a solar cell

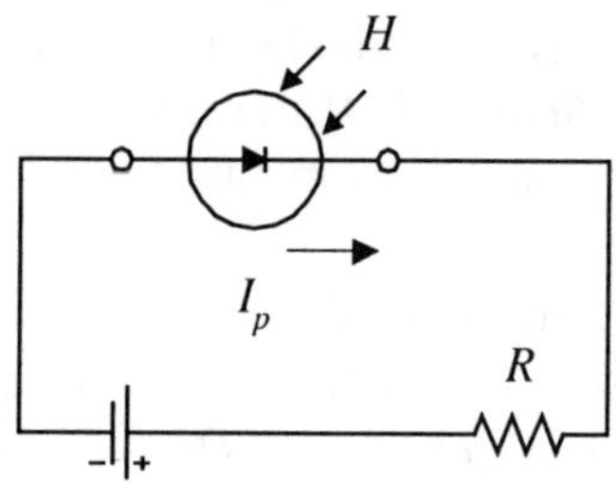

Figure 3.55 – Photo diode

Figure 3.55 shows a photo diode circuit. The characteristic curves of the photo diode for various light intensities, H, are shown in Figure 3.56. Photo diode current, I_p, can be estimated from the following equation:

$$I_p = gqH \tag{3.82}$$

where

g = quantum efficiency

q = charge on an electron: $1.6\times10^{-19}\,\text{C}$

$H = u \times A$ = light intensity in photons/s

u = photon flux density in photons/s-cm^2

A = junction area in cm^2

Most silicon light detectors consist of a photo diode junction and an amplifier, frequently on a single chip.

Photodiodes are very useful devices. Combining an LED with a photodiode in the same package results in a device called an optoisolator. The LED portion converts electrical energy into light energy which the photodiode detects and converts back to a change in its electrical properties. An optoisolator provides complete electrical isolation between its input terminals (the LED) and its output terminals (the photodiode).

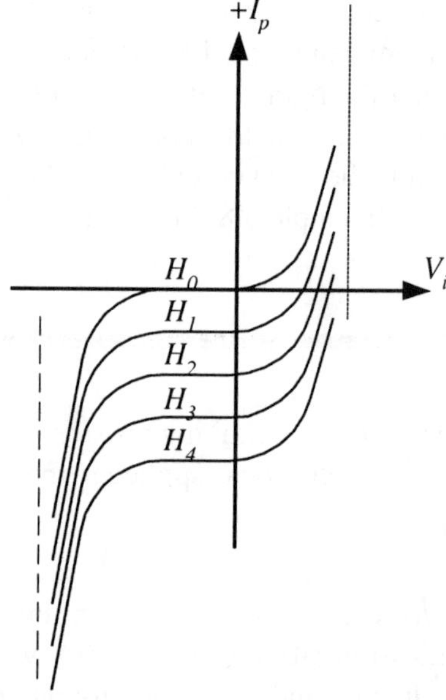

Figure 3.56 – Photo diode curves (not to scale)

3.8 MANUFACTURERS' SPECIFICATIONS

The construction of a diode determines the amount of current it is capable of handling, the amount of power it can dissipate, and the peak inverse voltage it will withstand without damage. Each manufacturer develops these criteria in specification sheets for the device. Examples of manufacturer specifications are given in the Appendix.

Listed next are the principal parameters than are found on a manufacturer's specification sheet for a rectifier diode:

1. **Type of device with generic number or manufacturer's numbers.**
2. **Peak inverse voltage (*PIV*).**
3. **Maximum reverse current at *PIV*.**
4. **Maximum *dc* forward voltage.**
5. **Average half-wave rectified forward current.**
6. **Maximum junction temperature.**
7. **Current derating curves.**
8. **Characteristic curves for changes in temperature so that the device can be *derated* for higher temperatures.**

In the case of Zener diodes, the following parameters usually appear on the specification sheets:

1. **Type of device with generic number of manufacturer's number.**
2. **Nominal Zener voltage (avalanche breakdown voltage).**
3. **Voltage tolerance.**
4. **Maximum power dissipation (at 25° C).**
5. **Test current, I_{ZT}.**
6. **Dynamic impedance at I_{ZT}.**
7. **Knee current.**
8. **Maximum junction temperature.**
9. **Temperature coefficient.**
10. **Derating curves for higher temperatures.**

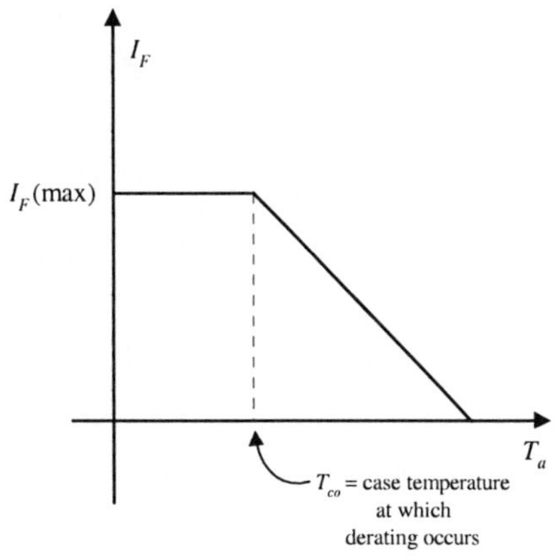

Figure 3.57 – Current derating curve

Figure 3.57 shows a typical *current derating curve.* This curve indicates the required adjustment in rated current as the temperature increases beyond ambient. A similar curve is often given for *power derating.* Although manufacturers usually do not provide the standard current derating curves, information provided is more than adequate to assure that the diode junction is not overheated when operated in the various circuit modes. In practice, designers should assure that the diode will be subjected to current values that are below the published maximum ratings. In some applications, such as military or space, greater derating may be required.

SUMMARY

This chapter introduced you to the simplest semiconductor device, the diode. We examined the underlying physics that governs the behavior of doped semiconductors and junctions. We then developed terminal characteristics of the diode. This permitted us to analyze operation of this device in a variety of configurations.

We studied many useful diode circuits, including rectifiers, voltage doublers, clippers and clampers. The Zener diode was presented as a building block in the design of voltage regulator circuits. We then combined diodes with ideal operational amplifiers to improve performance of the circuits studied at the beginning of the chapter.

We took a brief look at Schottky diodes, light-emitting diodes, and photo diodes. The chapter concluded with a presentation of practical specifications as supplied by manufacturers.

PROBLEMS

Section 3.2

3.1 A simplified *pn* junction is shown in Figure P3.1.

a. What is region "a" in Figure P3.1 known as? Why?

b. Briefly describe the reason this region exists.

c. When in equilibrium or open-circuit, what are the relative differences in the currents?

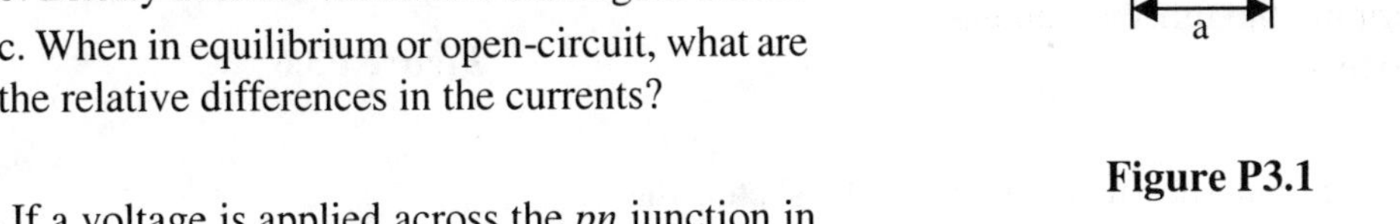

Figure P3.1

3.2 If a voltage is applied across the *pn* junction in Figure P3.1 with the positive voltage applied to the *p* side (i.e., forward biased):

a. What happens to the depletion region?

b. After equilibrium is established, what is the relationship of the drift and diffusion currents to the current in the circuit?

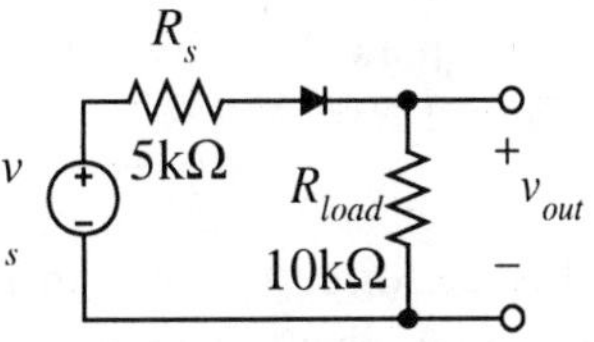

Figure P3.4

3.3 A silicon diode is placed in a circuit and is operating at 85°C. At 25°C the diode has a 0.68 V drop. What is the voltage drop of the diode when in the circuit?

Section 3.3

3.4 Sketch the output v_{out} of the circuit shown in Figure P3.4 when the input, v_s, is a 50 V peak-to-peak symmetrical square wave having a period of 2 s. Assume that the diode is ideal.

3.5 Sketch the output v_{out} of the circuit shown in Figure P3.5 (the diode is ideal) when v_s is a:

a. Symmetrical square wave of 50 V peak-to-peak with a period of 4 s.

b. Sine wave of 50 V peak-to-peak with a period of 4 seconds.

c. Symmetrical triangular wave of 20 V 0-to-peak with a period of 4 s.

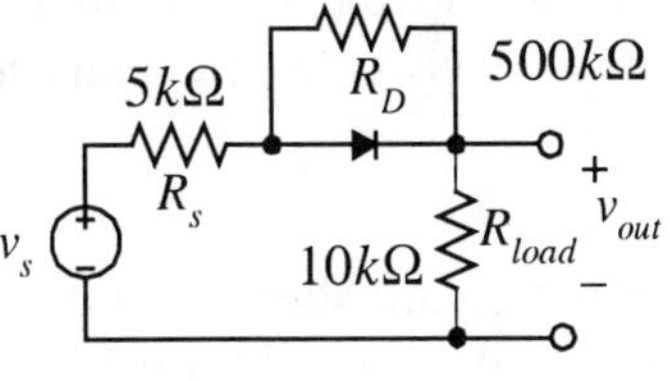

Figure P3.5

3.6 Sketch the output v_{out} of the circuit shown in Figure P3.6 when v_s is a 50 V peak-to-peak sine wave with a period of 4 s. Assume that the diode is ideal and $C = 0$.

3.7 Plot I_D versus V_D for a silicon diode if the reverse saturation current I_o = 0.01 μA, using n = 1.5 for silicon. Also determine the turn-on voltage for the diode.

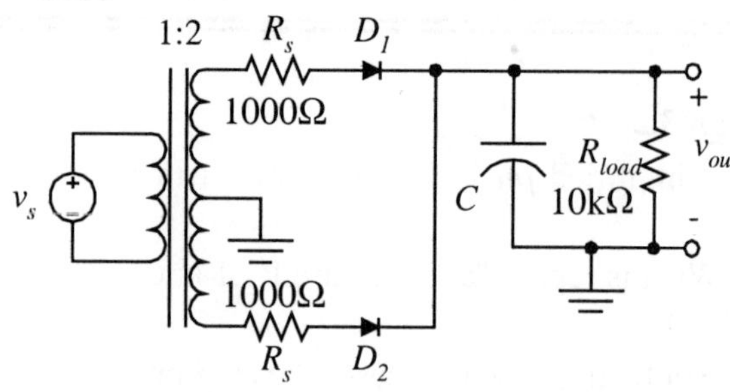

Figure P3.6

3.8 Plot I_D versus V_D for a germanium diode if the reverse saturation current I_o = 0.01 mA. Also determine the turn-on voltage for the diode.

3.9 For the circuit shown in Figure P3.9, sketch the output voltage, v_{out}, when the input voltage, v_s is an 18 V peak-to-peak sine wave. Assume the V_{ON} of the diode is 0.6 V and R_f = 0.

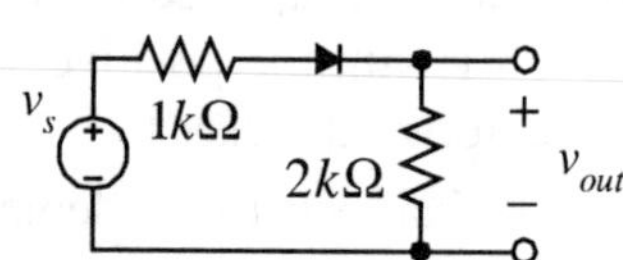

Figure P3.9

3.10 For the circuit shown in Figure P3.10, sketch the output voltage waveform v_{out} when the input voltage is a 100 V rms sine wave when V_{ON} = 0.7 V and R_f = 0.

3.11 A particular diode has a reverse saturation current of 0.2 μA, n = 1.6, and V_T = 26 mV. Determine the diode current when the voltage across the diode is 0.4 V. Also determine the forward resistance of the diode at this operating point.

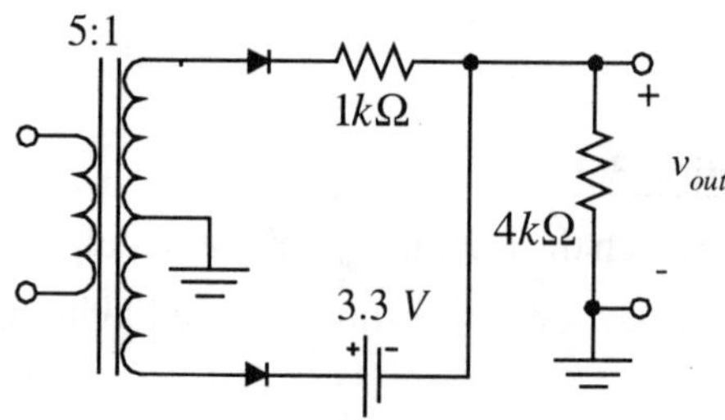

Figure P3.10

3.12 What are the states of the three diodes shown in the circuit in Figure P3.12 when the diodes are considered ideal?

3.13 For the circuit shown in Figure P3.13, determine the diode current when the *dc* voltage across the diode is 0.6 V for this range of current and nV_T = 40 mV.

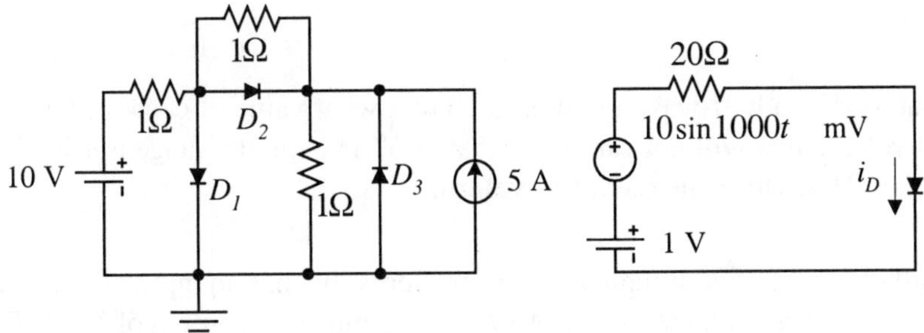

Figure P3.12 **Figure P3.13**

3.14 What is the output voltage v_{out} for the circuit shown in Figure P3.14? The *dc* voltage drop of the diode is 0.6 V, $nV_T = 40$ mV, and the input voltage is given by 0.5sin(2000*t*) V.

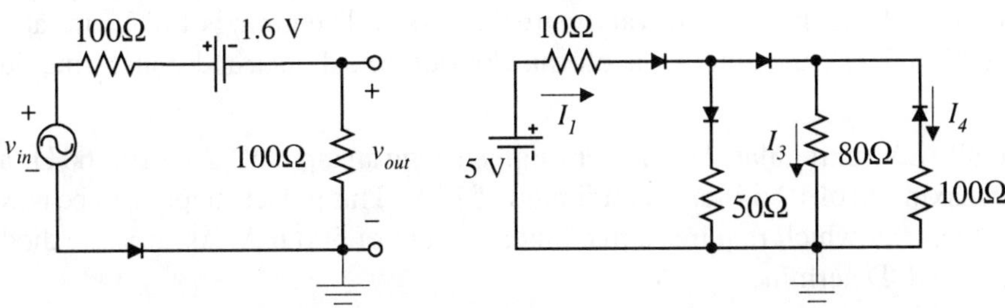

Figure P3.14 **Figure P3.15**

3.15 Determine I_3 for the circuit shown in Figure P3.15,

a. When the diodes are ideal.

b. When the diodes are considered non-ideal with $R_f = 10\ \Omega$; $V_{ON} = 0.7$ V; PIV = 100 V. Ignore reverse saturation current.

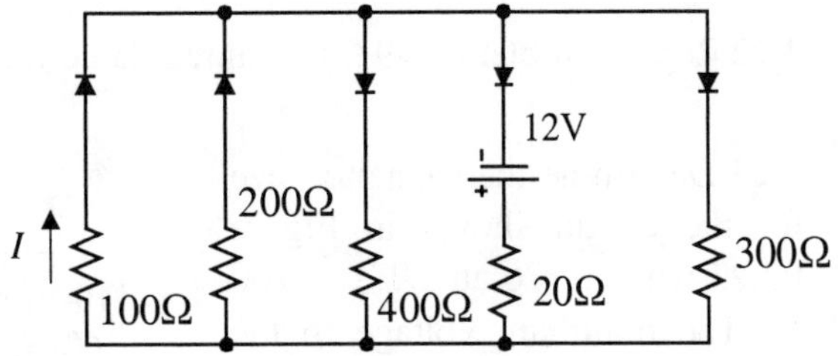

Figure P3.16

3.16 For the circuit shown in Figure P3.16, determine I:

a. When the diodes are ideal.

b. When the diodes are considered non-ideal with $R_f = 10\ \Omega$, $V_{ON} = 0.6$ V, and PIV = 80 V. Ignore reverse saturation current.

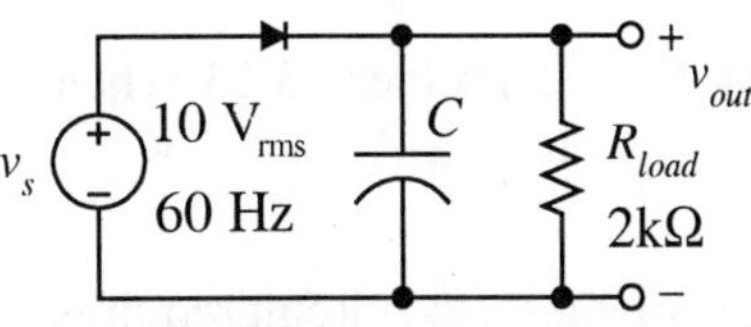

Figure P3.17

3.17 Determine the value of the capacitor needed to provide filtering for the circuit shown in Figure P3.17

so that the voltage does not drop below 12 V. Assume $R_f = 0$ and $V_{ON} = 0.7$ V. Sketch the output waveform.

3.18 If the output load of a half-wave rectifier is 10 kΩ, what value of capacitor is required to obtain an output voltage that will not vary more than 5%? The input voltage is 100 V rms at 60 Hz. Refer to Figure P3.4. Draw the output waveform.

3.19 Design a half-wave rectifier unregulated power supply that has an input of 120 V rms at 60 Hz and requires a maximum voltage output of 17 V and a minimum output of 12 V. The power supply will provide power to an electronic circuit that draws 1 A. Determine the circuit configuration, transformer winding ratio, and capacitor size. Assume the diodes and transformer are ideal.

3.20 If the output load of a full-wave rectifier is 10 kΩ, what value of capacitor is required to maintain an output voltage that will not vary more than 10%? The input is 120 V rms at 60 Hz. Refer to Figure P3.6. Draw the output waveform. Consider the diodes and transformer ideal.

3.21 Design a full-wave unregulated *dc* power supply having an input of 220 V rms 60 Hz and an output voltage maximum of 19.5 V and a minimum of 15 V. This power supply will be needed to provide power to a load which requires a maximum current of 500 mA. Assume the diode and transformer are ideal. Determine:

a. Circuit configuration (Draw the schematic)
b. Transformer winding ratio.
c. Capacitor size

3.22 Repeat Problem 3.19 for an unregulated full-wave negative voltage rectifier power supply.

3.23 Determine the capacitor size for the circuit shown in Figure P3.23 when $a = 6$ and $R_{load} = 100$ Ω. The minimum voltage to the load must not drop by more than 20%. Consider the diodes and transformer ideal.

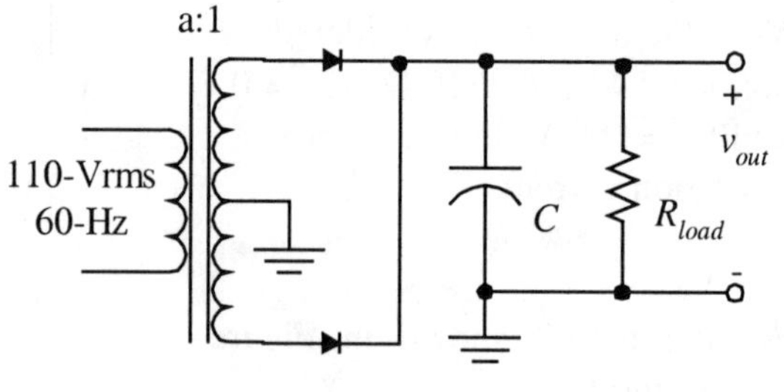

Figure P3.23

3.24 Repeat Problem 3.23 when the diodes have a $V_{ON} = 0.7$ V.

3.25 An integrated circuit requires plus and minus voltages for their operation. Using the circuit shown in Figure P3.25, determine the transformer winding ratio and the capacitor size needed to get a maximum of 14 V and a minimum of 12 V at the output when the input voltage is 120 V rms 60 Hz, $V_{ON} = 0.7$ V for each of the diodes and $R_f = 0$. Ignore transformer loss.

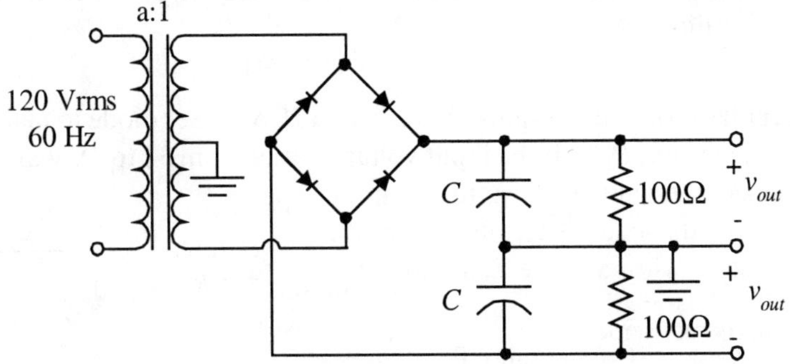

Figure P3.25

Section 3.4

3.26 (a) If the input voltage is as shown in Figure P3.26, what is the output voltage V_{out}? Sketch and label.

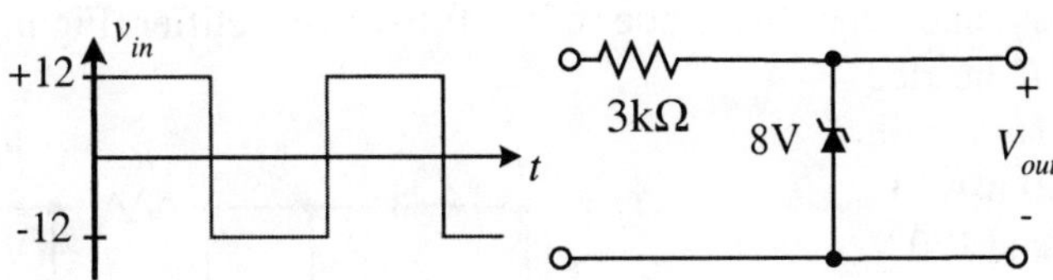

Figure P3.26

3.27 (a) If V_{in} is 12 V in Figure P3.27, what value of current can exist in R_{load} before the Zener diode voltage drops below 10 V?
(b) If V_{in} varies from 16 to 20 V in Figure P3.15, what is the variation in the output voltage V_{out} when $R_{load} = 2$ kΩ and $R_z = 10$ Ω.

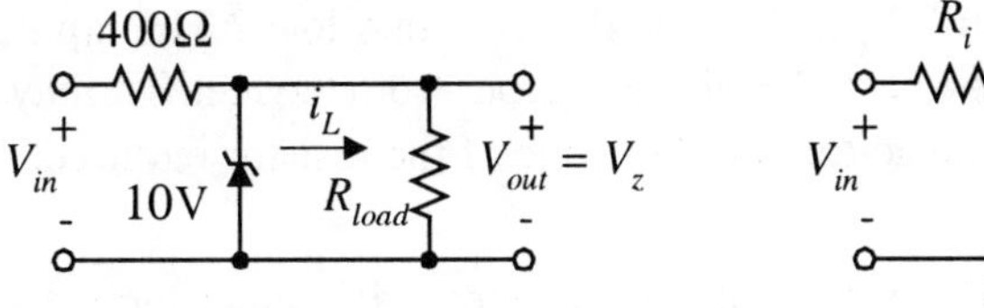

Figure P3.27

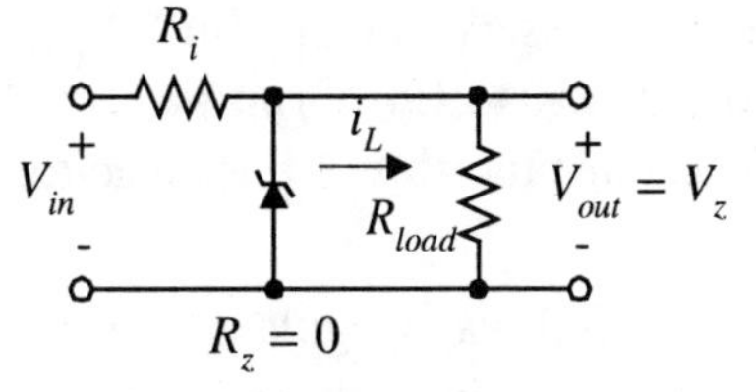

Figure P3.28

3.28 If a Zener diode is connected in the circuit shown in Figure P3.28, what is the value of resistor R_i that will maintain the load voltage at 10 V (V_z) when the load varies from 100 to 500 mA and the input voltage varies from 15 to 20 V? Determine the power rating required for the resistor and the Zener diode.

3.29 The Zener regulator shown in Figure P3.28 uses a 20 V Zener diode to maintain a constant 20 V across thc load resistor, R_{load}. If the input voltage varies from 32 to 42 V and the load varies 200 to 400 mA, select the value of R_i to maintain the constant voltage across the load. Determine the power rating required for the resistor and the Zener diode.

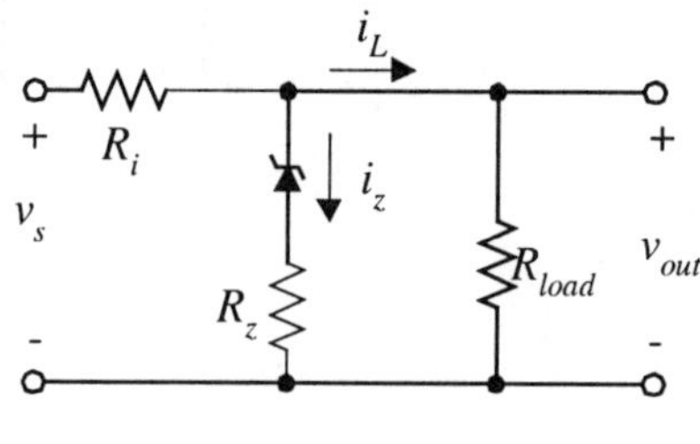

Figure P3.30

3.30 A Zener regulator as shown in Figure P3.30 uses a 9 V Zener diode to maintain a constant 9 V across the load with the input varying from 18 to 24 V and the output current varying from 400 to 800 mA. Assume R_z = 0.

(a) Select the value of R_i needed and determine its minimum power requirement.
(b) Determine the power rating of the Zener diode.
(c) Calculate the peak-to-peak output variation if R_z = 1 Ω.

3.31 Assuming no loss in the rectifier diodes of the full-wave rectifier (Figure P3.31) with $n = 2$, what is the value of R_i needed to maintain V_{load} at 16 V with a load current of 500 mA? V_s varies between 110 and 120 V rms 60 Hz. Assume V_Z = 16 V and R_z = 0. The voltage to the regulator will not drop to less than 10 V above V_Z.

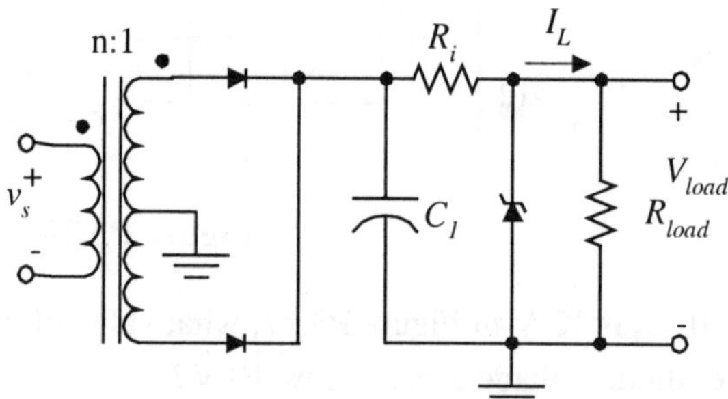

Figure P3.31

3.32 Assuming no voltage drop in the rectifier diodes of Figure P3.31 and n = 2, what is the value of R_i necessary to maintain V_{load} at 16 V with a 500 mA load? The input voltage to the transformer is 110 to 120 V rms 60 Hz. The filtered output from the rectifier may not vary more ±4 V. Determine the size of the capacitor and the value of the resistor required.

3.33 Design a full-wave regulated power supply when using a 4:1 center-tapped transformer and an 8 V, 1 W Zener diode that will provide a constant 8 V to a load varying from 200 to 500 Ω. The input voltage to the transformer is 120 V rms 60 Hz. Ignore losses in the transformer and diodes. Determine:

a. I_{Zmax} and I_{Zmin}
b. R_i and V_{smin}
c. Size of capacitor needed
d. Percent regulation when $R_z = 2\ \Omega$

3.34 Design a full-wave regulated power supply using a 5:1 center tapped transformer and an 8 V, 2 W Zener diode that will provide a constant 8 V to a load varying from 100 to 500 Ω. The input voltage to the transformer is 110 to 120 V rms 60 Hz. Ignore the losses in the transformer and diodes. Determine:

a. I_{Zmax} and I_{Zmin}
b. R_i and V_{smin}
c. Size of capacitor needed
d. Percent regulation when $R_z = 2\ \Omega$
e. Power rating of R_i

3.35 Using the values for the input voltage to R_i of Problem 3.32 but using a 12 V Zener, what would the value of R_i be to maintain 12 V at the output if the load varied from 20 to 600 mA? What capacitor is required?

3.36 Using the circuit of Figure P3.31 and assuming no loss in the rectifier diodes, what is the value of R_i to maintain 12 V across the load using a 12 V Zener when V_s is 105 to 125 V rms 60 Hz? The output of the rectifier drops 20% due to the size of the capacitor, C_1, and the load varies from 50 to 500 mA. Set $n = 2$. What is the size of the capacitor?

Section 3.5

3.37 For the circuit shown in Figure P3.37, determine the voltage waveforms of V_1 and V_2 assuming the diodes are ideal.

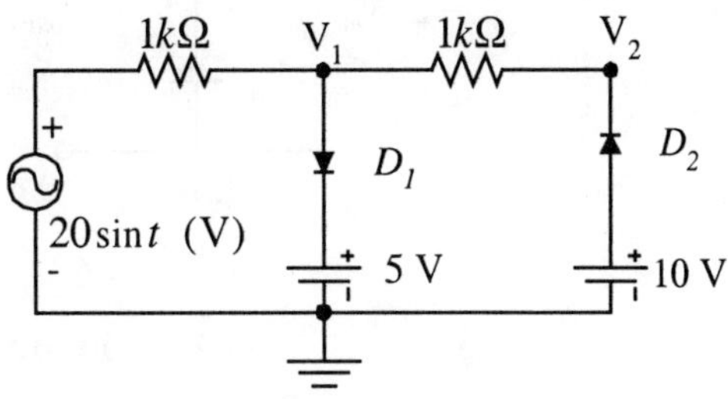

Figure P3.37

3.38 With an input waveform of 10sinωt, what is the output waveform for the clipping circuits shown in Figure P3.38? Assume that all diodes are ideal with $V_{ON} = 0$ and $R_f = 0$.

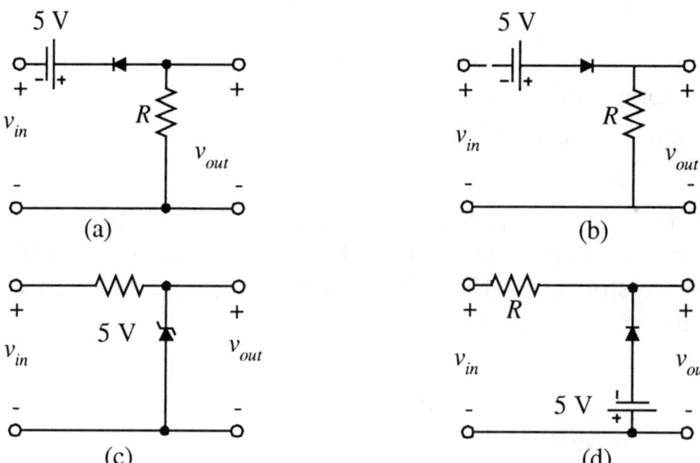

Figure P3.38

3.39 In the diode clipping circuits of Figure P3.39, $v_{in} = 20\sin\omega t$, $R = 2$ kΩ and $V_R = 10$ V. The reference voltage V_B is obtained from a tap on a 10 kΩ divider connected to a 100 V source. Neglect all capacitances. The diode forward resistance is 100Ω, $R_r \rightarrow \infty$, and $V_{ON} = 0$. Draw the input and output waveforms. Apply Thevenin's theorem to the reference voltage divider network.

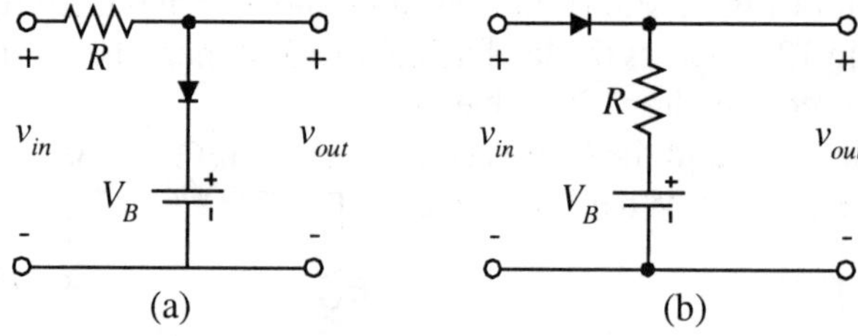

Figure P3.39

3.40 Sketch the output voltage v_{out} of the clipper circuit shown in Figure P3.40 when v_{in}=12sin1000t. Show the maximum and minimum values and where the sine wave changes on the sketch. Assume diodes are ideal.

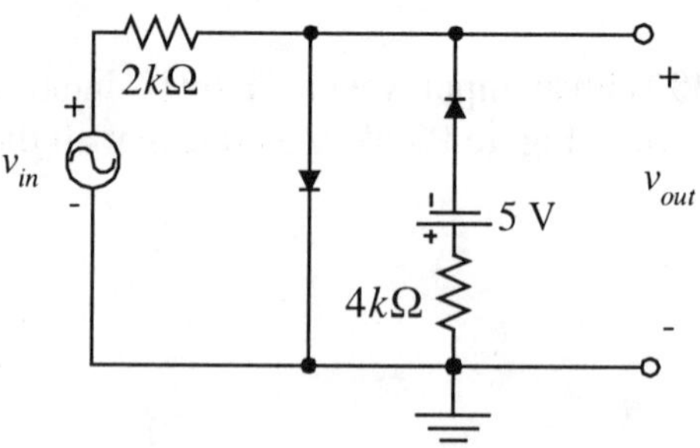

Figure P3.40

3.41 (a) The input voltage, v_{in}, to the clipper shown in Figure P3.41(a) varies linearly from 0 to 150 V. Sketch the output voltage v_{out}, on the same time plot as the input. Assume the diodes are ideal.

(b) Repeat part (a) for the circuit in Figure P3.41(b).

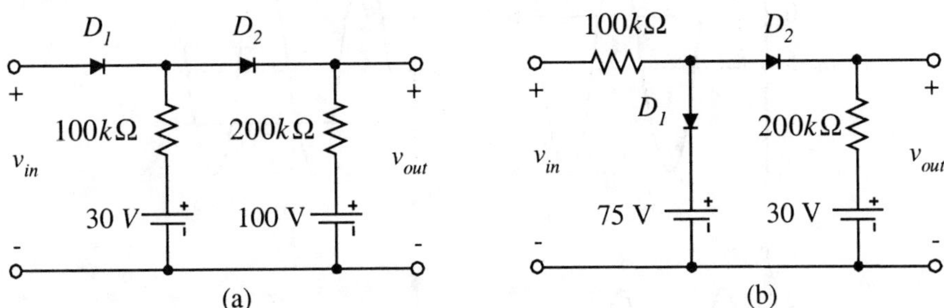

Figure P3.41

3.42 (a) Sketch the output waveform v_{out} *(t)* of the circuit shown in Figure P3.42(a) when v_{in} = 9sin1000*t* V. Show the maximum and minimum values on the sketch and the equation for the curves at different time intervals. Assume that the diodes are ideal.

(b) Repeat part (a) for the circuit of Figure P3.42(b).

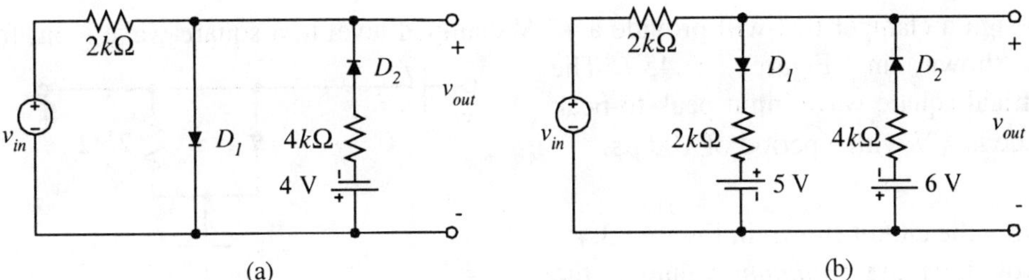

Figure P3.42

3.43 Design a clipper circuit to obtain the output voltage v_{out} shown in Figure P3.43 from an input symmetrical square wave of ± 10 V. Assume V_{ON} = 0.7 V.

3.44 What type of clipper is needed to obtain the waveforms illustrated in Figure P3.44? Assume the input is 10sin (*t*) V. Draw the circuits and label them.

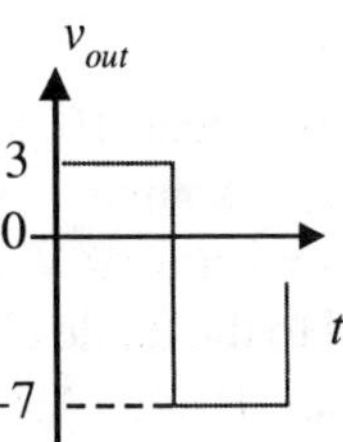

Figure P3.43

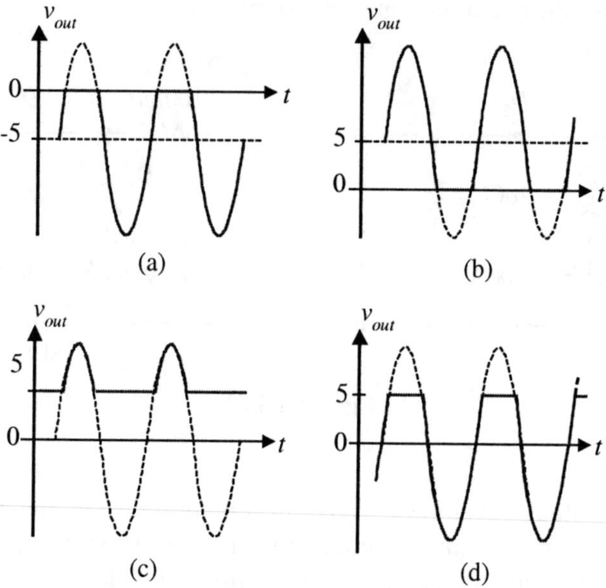

Figure P3.44

3.45 Design a clamper that will provide a +2 V clamped level to a square-wave input for the circuit shown in Figure P3.45. The symmetrical square wave input peak-to-peak amplitude is 4 V with a period of 100 μs.

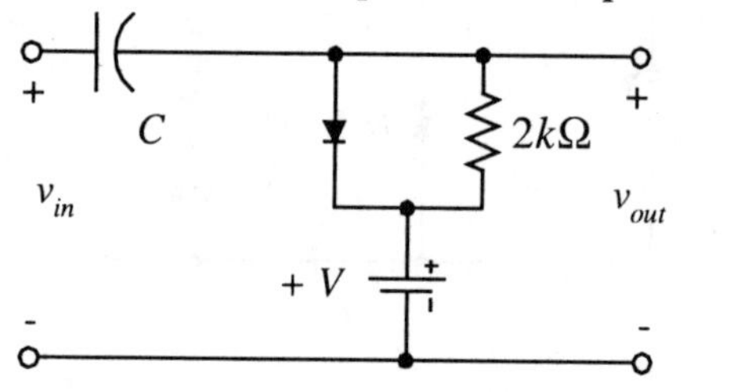

Figure P3.45

3.46 Using the circuit shown in Figure P3.45, what would be the *minimum* value of the resistor (shown as $2k\Omega$) which will not allow major distortion in the output when $C = 2\ \mu F$, v_{in} = 8sin1000t V, and $V = 2$ V. Sketch the output waveform.

3.47 An ideal 10 kHz sinusoidal voltage source whose peak excursions are 10 V with respect to ground to the diode clamping circuit of Figure P3.47. Assume $R \to \infty$, $R_s = 0$, $C = 1\ \mu F$, the diode has $R_r \to \infty$, $R_f = 0$, and $V_{ON} = 0$. Sketch the output waveform v_{out}.

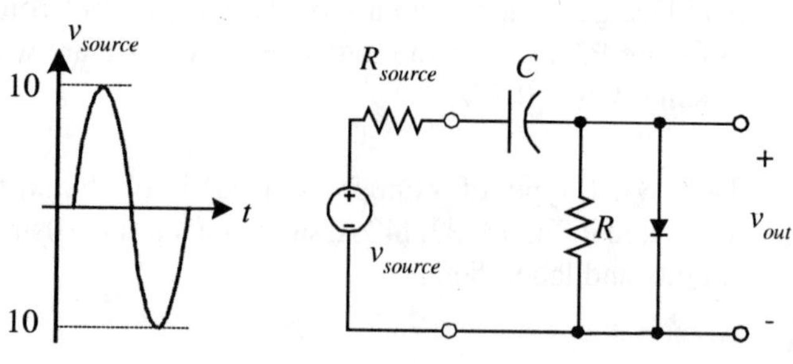

Figure P3.47

3.48 The signal shown in Figure P3.47 with a frequency of 5 kHz is applied to the circuit, with values $R_s = 0$, $R = 10\ \text{k}\Omega$, $C = 0.5\ \mu\text{F}$, $R_f = 0$, $R_r \to \infty$, and $V_{ON} = 0$.

a. Sketch the output waveform, v_{out}.
b. Repeat Part (a) if $R = 1\ \text{k}\Omega$ and $C = 0.001\ \mu\text{F}$.

3.49 Design a clamping circuit that will produce the output shown in Figure P3.49 (A 5-volt sinusoid shifted up by 7 volts). Assume the capacitor available is 0.1 μF and the input is $v_{in} = 5\sin 25{,}000t$ V. Assume $V_{ON} = 0.7$ V.

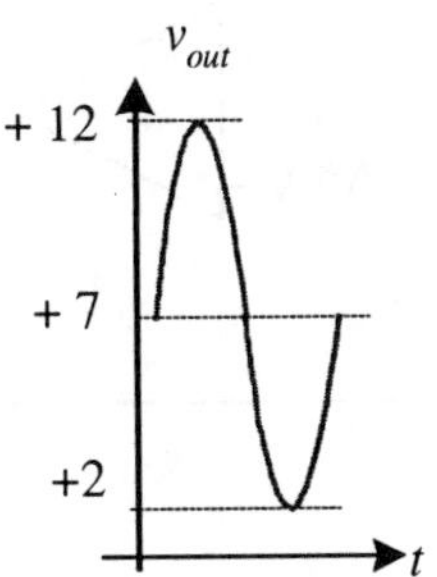

Figure P3.49

Section 3.6

3.50 Plot the output voltage v_{out} for the op-amp system shown in Figure P3.50 when the input voltage is given by $v_{in} = 10\sin 20t$. Assume that $V_{ON} = 0.7$ V and that $R_f = 0$.

3.51 Determine the output waveform v_{out} of the circuit shown in Figure P3.51. Assume $V_{ON} = 0 = R_f$.

3.52 Figure 3.47 is an electronic thermometer. Plot the output voltage, V_{out}, as the temperature varies from room temperature 25° to 125° C. The voltage across the diode varies according to the relationship

$$\Delta V_{ON} = -2(T_1 - T_2)\ \text{mV}$$

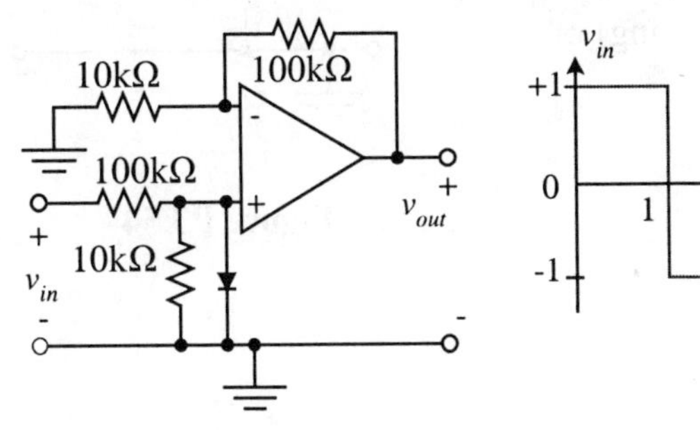

Figure P3.50

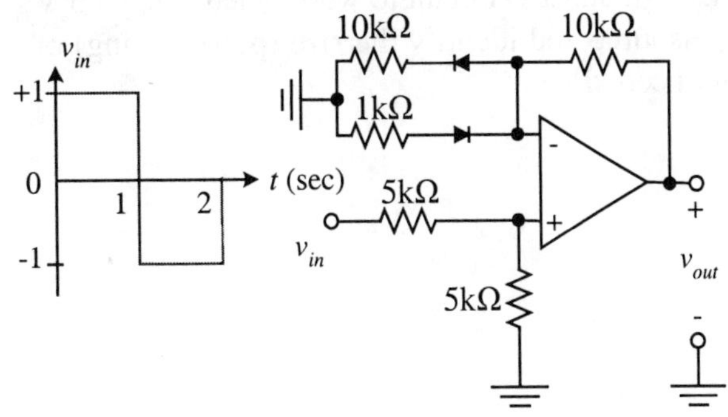

Figure P3.51

Select the resistor values so that the output, v_{out}, given by Equation (3.56) must be 5 V when the temperature is 125° C.

3.53 Plot the output voltage, v_{out}, as a function of the input voltage, v_{in}, for the circuit shown in Figure P3.53. The diode is ideal, so $V_{ON} = 0$ and $R_f = 0$.

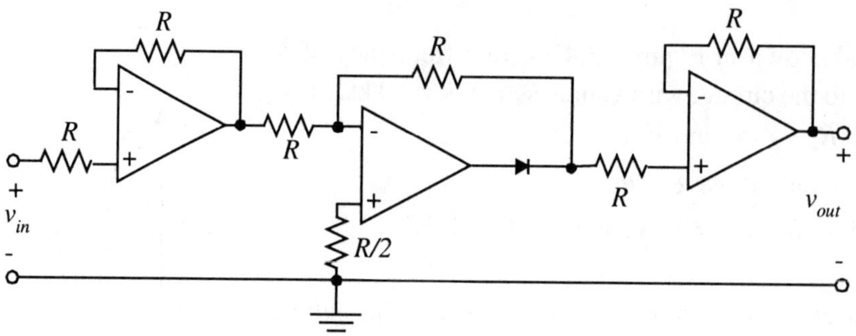

Figure P3.53

3.54 The input voltage v_{in} to the circuit of Figure P3.54 is

$$v_{in} = 10\sin\left(2\pi 60t\right)$$

Plot the output voltage, $v_{out}(t)$, when $R = 10$ kΩ, $V_{ON} = 0$ and $R_f = 0$. Specify the maximum value of the output voltage.

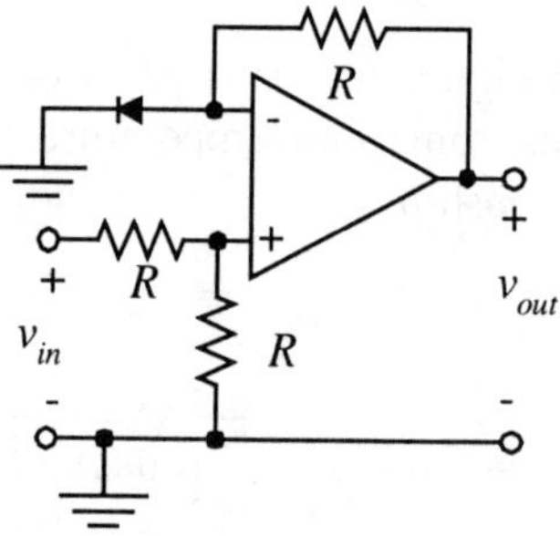

Figure P3.54

Section 3.7

3.55 Select a current limiting resistor to properly light an LED when 8 V is applied to the LED.

3.56 Design an LED circuit to work when using a 5 V voltage source and identify the size (power rating) of resistor needed.

Chapter 4
Bipolar Junction Transistor Circuits

Transistors are divided into two broad classes. These classes characterize the structure of the device and the physical principles that control the current-voltage characteristics. The two types are the bipolar junction transistor (BJT) and the field effect transistor (FET).

In this chapter, you will learn the basic operation of the BJT as well as the basic configurations for interconnecting this device in circuits. We concentrate on the low frequency and mid-band performance of the transistor. In Chapter 5, we will explore mid-band performance of single-stage linear amplifier circuits. High frequency performance is presented in Chapter 10. FETs and the circuits using them are presented in Chapters 6, 7, 10 and 15.

After reading this chapter, you will be familiar with:

- The internal structure and basic physics of the bipolar junction transistor.
- The most popular large-signal and small-signal models for this device.
- The behavior of the device under various input conditions.
- Analysis techniques using graphical solutions of equations.
- Typical manufacturer's data sheet specifications that relate to low and mid-band frequency operation of BJTs.
- Computer simulation model parameters used to simulate large signal and small signal BJT behavior in circuits.
- Single-stage amplifier configurations.
- Techniques for biasing amplifiers.
- The basics of integrated circuit fabrication and the types of devices that can be placed on an integrated circuit chip.

4.0 INTRODUCTION

Basic circuit analysis is the study of interconnections of passive devices and sources. Passive linear devices include resistors, capacitors and inductors. These devices perform the linear operations of scaler multiplication, integration and differentiation. *Independent sources* supply either a voltage or a current that is independent of the operation of the rest of the circuit. *Dependent sources* have an output voltage or current which is a function of a current or voltage somewhere in the circuit. In introductory circuits courses, dependent sources exist simply as elements in the circuits to be solved. In this chapter, we see that they arise from modeling of active devices such as bipolar junction transistors.

4.1 STRUCTURE OF BIPOLAR TRANSISTORS

The transistor is a three-terminal device. This contrasts with the diode, which is a two-terminal device. The diode consists of a p-type material and an n-type material; the transistor consists of three alternating types of material: two n-type materials separated by a p-type material (*npn* transistor) or two p-type materials separated by an n-type material (*pnp* transistor). Figure 4.1(a) is a schematic representation of a transistor.

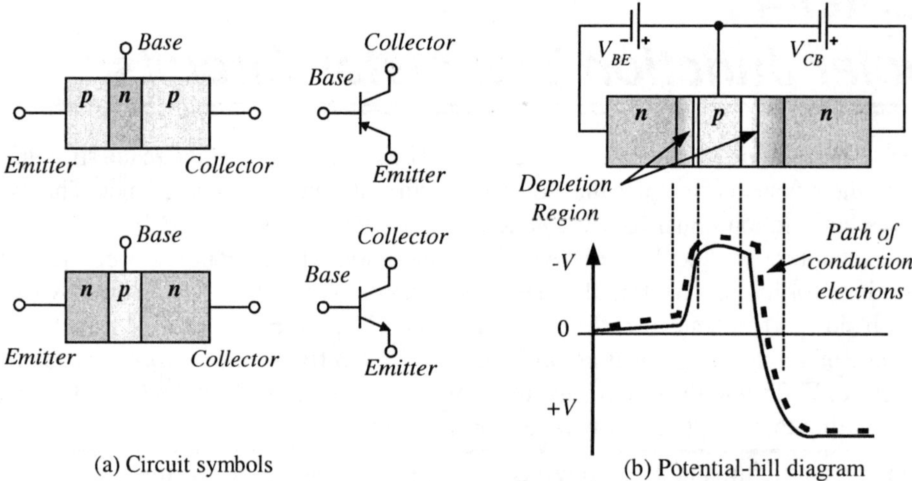

(a) Circuit symbols (b) Potential-hill diagram

Figure 4.1 – Schematic representation of a transistor

The three different layers or sections shown in Figure 4.1 are identified as emitter, base and collector. The *emitter* is doped heavily with the appropriate type of donor or accepter impurity. It is a medium-sized layer designed to emit or inject electrons (for *npn*) or holes (for *pnp*) through the base into the collector. The *base* is a medium doped, thin layer designed to pass electrons or holes from the emitter to the collector. Its primary purpose is to provide some electrical isolation between the emitter and collector and to provide a voltage contact point so that we can control the voltage across the emitter-base junction (and therefore *control* the current that flows into the collector). The *collector* is a lightly doped, thick layer designed to collect the electrons or holes injected by the emitter.

The transistor can be visualized as two *pn* junctions placed back-to-back. Since each of these junctions can be thought of as a diode, and because each diode can be either forward- or reversed-biased, there are four possible states for a transistor. We will see that the normal mode of operation (for analog applications) is to forward bias the emitter-base junction, and reverse bias the collector-base junction.

A simple but effective explanation of the *npn* transistor operation is developed using the potential hill diagram of Figure 4.1(b). The mode of operation depicted in this figure is called the *normal active mode.*

When the emitter-base junction is biased in the forward direction and the collector-base junction is biased in the reverse direction, there is only a small potential hill at the *np* junction – many electrons in the *n* material of the emitter near the junction have enough energy to progress to the top of the hill. Once on top of the potential hill, most of the *injected* electrons move easily through the *p*-material (base) to the *pn* (base-collector) junction. When they approach that junction, the electrons are under the influence of the positive supply voltage and move forward rapidly as they go down the potential hill. If the forward bias on the base-emitter junction is reduced, the height of the potential hill is raised. Electrons leaving the emitter have more difficulty in reaching the top of the hill. The electrons reaching the top are the ones with the highest amount of energy, and these electrons progress to the collector. The reduction of forward bias thus causes the current through the transistor to be reduced considerably. On the other hand, increasing the forward bias on the base-emitter junction reduces the potential hill and allows more emitter electrons to flow through the transistor.

The current in a junction transistor can also be understood by examining the charge carrier behavior and the depletion regions. The depletion regions have been indicated on Figure 4.1(b). Note that since the base-emitter junction is forward-biased, the depletion region is relatively narrow. The reverse is true for the base-collector junction. A large number of majority carriers (electrons) will diffuse across the base-emitter junction since it is forward-biased. These electrons then enter the base region and have two choices. They may exit the region through the connection to the voltage sources, or they may continue flowing to the collector region across the wide depletion region of the reverse-biased junction. We would normally expect the major portion of this current to return to the source, except for the following observations. Since the base region is very thin, these electrons need to travel less distance to be attracted to the positive potential of the collector connection. In reality, a small fraction of the electrons leave the base through the source connection. Thus, a major portion of the electrons flow is to the collector.

We now examine the current in greater detail. Refer to Figure 4.2(a) for the following discussion. The base-emitter junction acts as a forward-biased diode with a forward current of $i_B + i_C$. The collector-base junction is reverse biased and exhibits a small leakage current, I_{CBO}, in addition to a larger current caused by the interaction of currents in the base.

Looking at the currents in the three external connections, we see that

$$i_E = i_C + i_B \tag{4.1}$$

Note that we define the *positive* directions for i_C and for i_B to be *into* the transistor while the reverse is true for i_E.

We shall be developing equivalent circuits for the transistor, and these equivalent circuits will contain dependent sources. We therefore must establish the dependence of one parameter on another. To do so, we define several gain constants that characterize the manner in which one parameter affects another parameter.

The *common-base current gain,* α, is defined as the rate of change of collector current with a change in emitter current under the assumption that the voltage between collector and base is constant. That is,

$$\alpha = \left.\frac{\Delta i_C}{\Delta i_E}\right|_{v_{CB}=\text{constant}} \tag{4.2}$$

This quantity is illustrated in Figure 4.2(b), where I_{CBO} is the leakage current between base and collector.

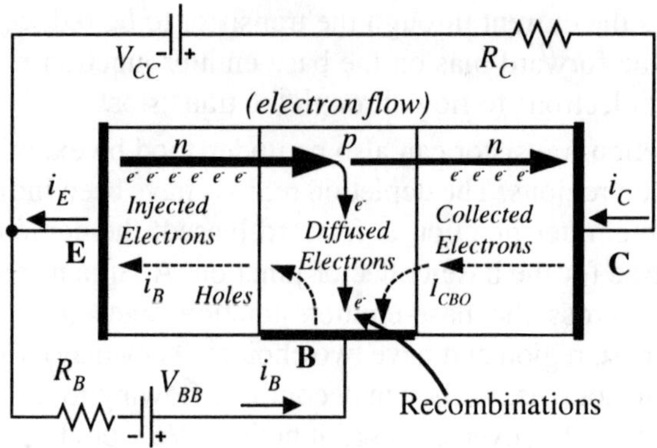

(a) Detailed inside view

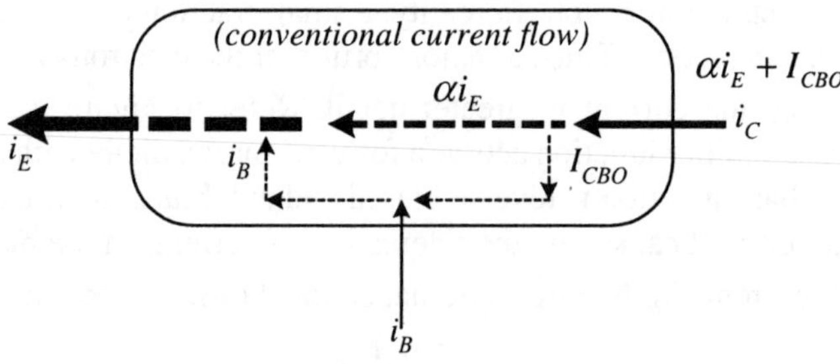

(b) Simplified view

Figure 4.2 – Internal Current in a transistor

We wish to find a relationship between the collector and base currents. The collector current is found by viewing Figure 4.2(b).

$$i_C = \alpha i_E + I_{CBO} \tag{4.3}$$

Combining Equation (4.3) with (4.1) and solving for i_B yields,

$$i_B = \frac{(1-\alpha)}{\alpha} i_C - \frac{I_{CBO}}{\alpha} \tag{4.4}$$

The common-base current gain, α, is usually in the range of 0.9 to 0.999. We can therefore often approximate its reciprocal as unity, yielding the approximation of base current,

$$i_B \approx \frac{(1-\alpha)}{\alpha} i_C - I_{CBO} \tag{4.5}$$

The ratio in the first term of Equation (4.5) is important. We can attach meaning to this ratio by defining a second gain factor, β, the *large-signal amplification factor* or the *direct-current amplification factor*. We define this as the rate of change in collector current as a function of base current. That is,

$$\beta = \frac{\Delta i_C}{\Delta i_B} = \frac{\alpha}{1-\alpha} \tag{4.6}$$

The last equality in Equation (4.6) is found by taking partial derivatives in Equation (4.5).

We can now rewrite Equation (4.5) using β instead of α. This yields the very important result,

$$i_B = \frac{i_C}{\beta} - I_{CBO} \tag{4.7}$$

In most cases, we can neglect I_{CBO} relative to i_C/β. We therefore have

$$\boxed{i_C \approx \beta i_B} \tag{4.8}$$

We now see why β is called the amplification factor.

Note that in practice, the exact value of β varies with base current. It also varies among transistors fabricated in the same production run. This variation presents us with design challenges. We will develop a design procedure that makes the value of collector current less sensitive to changes in β.

Before developing transistor models for use in solving circuits, we will make one additional useful approximation. Looking back at Equation (4.3), we see that if α is close to unity and I_{CBO} is small compared to the emitter current, we have

$$\boxed{i_C \approx i_E} \tag{4.9}$$

We will use the approximations of Equations (4.8) and (4.9) many times throughout this text. In most practical situations, these approximations will be sufficient to perform effective design.

4.2 LARGE-SIGNAL BJT MODEL

In the following sections, we will be developing transistor models by making linear approximations to the operating equations when the transistor operates over a relatively small range. We will also develop operating curves for the transistor. You will then have the tools to analyze circuits either

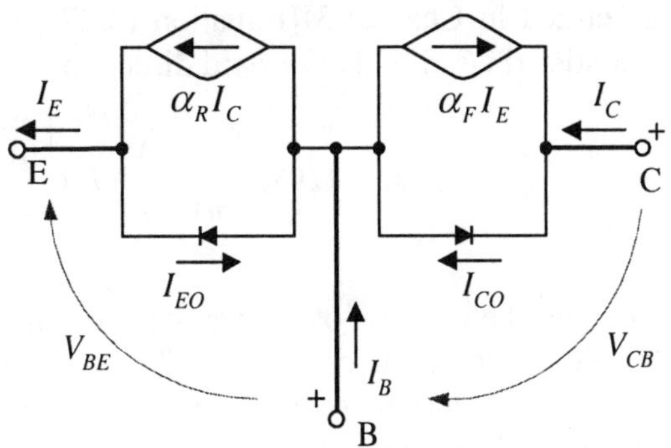

Figure 4.3 – Ebers-Moll *npn* transistor model

using graphical techniques or using simple models.

The current section presents models of the overall transistor operation without requiring that we restrict ourselves to a particular operating region. We present the *Ebers-Moll Model* which was developed from the observation that the transistor consists of two diodes. This model is used in SPICE computer simulation programs. Later in this text, we will find this model useful when the inputs swing over a wide range, as is the case with digital signals.

The Ebers-Moll model is presented in Figure 4.3. Note that the current between emitter and base consists of two components. The first is associated with the emitter-base diode, and the second is a fraction of the collector current that is coupled through the base to the emitter. Similarly, the current between collector and base consists of a diode component and a component of the emitter current coupled through the base.

The model in Figure 4.3 is known as the *transport* model version of the Ebers-Moll model. The controlled sources depend on *terminal currents* that physically exist in wires. There are other forms of the model. The *injection* model results directly from the *Ebers-Moll equations.* This model contains controlled sources that depend on *internal* diode currents. As such, it is more difficult to use in the analysis of circuits since these internal diode currents cannot be directly measured.

The model contains two current gain factors, α_R and α_F. The first of these is the *common-base reverse short-circuit current gain*, and is the rate of change of emitter current as a function of collector current. The second gain factor is the *common-base forward short-circuit current gain*, and is the rate of change of collector current as a function of emitter current. The value of α_F is close to unity, while α_R is usually less than 0.5. I_{EO} is the reverse emitter current that flows when I_C is zero. Similarly, I_{CO} is the reverse collector current that flows when I_E is zero. These two saturation currents are known as *open-circuit saturation currents.*

4.3 DERIVATION OF SMALL-SIGNAL AC MODELS

We now wish to develop models of the transistor that apply over specific operating ranges. Although the transistor is a nonlinear device, we can approximate its operation as linear provided we operate over a relatively small range. Our task in deriving the model becomes one of deriving several proportionality constants. We do this both from the physical equations and from the operating curves.

We learned in Chapter 3 [Equation (3.27)] that a *pn* junction has a current vs. voltage characteristics (biased in the forward direction) approximated by

$$i_C = I_o \exp\left(\frac{v_{BE}}{nV_T}\right) = I_o e^{\left(\frac{v_{BE}}{nV_T}\right)} = I_o e^{\left(\frac{V_{BE}+v_{be}}{nV_T}\right)} \tag{4.10}$$

We choose the notation of a lower case voltage or current with upper case subscript for the total (*ac* plus *dc*) currents or voltages. The upper case parameter with an upper case subscript represents the *dc* current or voltage. The lower case parameter with lower case subscript represents only the *ac* component of the current or voltage.

By expanding the exponential into a series[1] and retaining only the predominant terms (first and second terms), we get:

$$i_C = I_o\left[1+\left(\frac{V_{BE}+v_{be}}{nV_T}\right)\right] = I_o + \frac{I_oV_{BE}}{nV_T} + \frac{I_ov_{be}}{nV_T} \tag{4.11}$$

Because we used only the first two terms in the exponential expansion, this equation is valid only for small signals – it is sometimes referred to as the *small-signal approximation*. From this equation, we can see that the current in the collector is composed of a *dc* and an *ac* component. Then, the *ac* current is:

$$i_c = \frac{I_ov_{be}}{nV_T} = g_mv_{be} \tag{4.12}$$

We have substituted the symbol g_m for I_o/nV_T. This expression is referred to as the *transconductance* and represented by the symbol. It is the partial derivative of the *ac* collector current with respect to the *ac* base-emitter voltage. This partial derivative is evaluated at some specified location marked within the forward-biased region of the operating characteristic curve near the point marked Q ≈ (V_{BE}, I_{CQ}). The values of V_{BE} and I_{CQ} represent the steady-state, *dc* quiescent base-emitter voltage and emitter current, respectively. Viewing the transistor characteristic curve of Figure 4.4(a), we see that the transconductance, g_m, is the slope of the straight (almost vertical) portion of the emitter-base characteristic curve. [You should recognize this as a diode characteristic.]

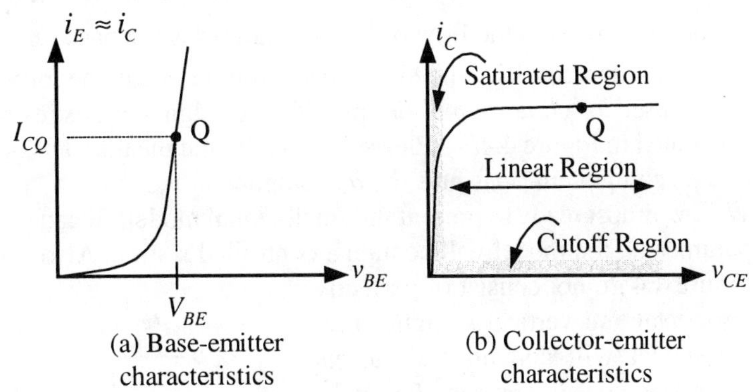

Figure 4.4 – Transistor characteristic curves

Since the characteristic is not perfectly vertical, the model contains a forward non-zero resistance. Note that this slope is not constant since the curve is not a perfect straight line. Therefore, the exact value of the transconductance, g_m, varies a little, depending on the *location* of the point Q. The reciprocal of the transconductance is resistance.

---

[1] For all real values of x, $e^x = 1 + x + \frac{x^2}{2!} + \frac{x^3}{3!} + \frac{x^4}{4!} + \ldots$

$$r_e = \frac{1}{g_m} = g_m^{-1} \tag{4.13}$$

This resistance represents the opposition to the *ac component* of the emitter current as it passes through the base-emitter junction. This *ac current* develops an *ac voltage* drop from base to emitter junction. That is $v_{be} = i_e r_e$.

From the *ac* perspective, we view the resistance r_e as the resistive opposition to the flow of emitter current developing the voltage v_{be} across the base-emitter junction. But from the base terminal perspective, the very small *ac* base current, i_b, flowing into the base-emitter junction will "see" the very same base-emitter voltage, v_{be}. That is, $v_{be} = i_e r_e = (\beta + 1) i_b \cdot r_e \approx \beta i_b \cdot r_e = i_b \cdot \beta r_e$. From the base current's perspective, the forward resistance across the base-emitter junction is given by

$$r_\pi = \frac{\partial v_{be}}{\partial i_b} = \beta r_e = \frac{\beta}{g_m} \tag{4.14}$$

We have used the fact that the collector current is approximately β times the base current. That is, the opposition to the flow of *ac* base current is the base junction resistance, $r_\pi = \beta r_e$.
Since the characteristic curve is almost a straight line in the forward-biased region, the transistor can be used as a *linear amplifier* provided the signal, v_{be}, is restricted to a relatively small range illustrated in Figure 4.4(a). Please note again that the total base-emitter voltage v_{BE} is composed of a *dc* component, V_{BE}, plus the *ac* component, v_{be}.
We are almost ready to present the small-signal model. Because of the inter-relationships among parameters, the model will contain a controlled source. Also, since the characteristic curves of Figure 4.4 do not consist of perfectly horizontal and vertical straight lines, the model will contain resistances. We now proceed to present the small-signal model, leaving the transistor output resistance, r_o, for a later discussion.

Since we know that the collector current is controlled by the base current, the output of the model contains a dependent current source of value $\beta \cdot i_b$. Equation (4.12) indicates that this can equivalently be written as $g_m v_{be}$. The resulting circuit model is shown in Figure 4.5.

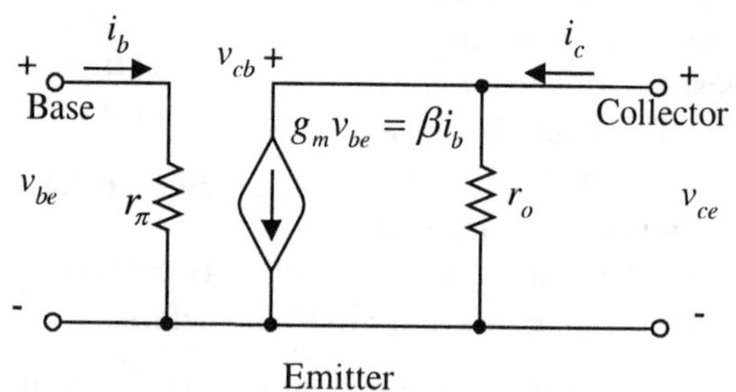

Figure 4.5 – Hybrid-π *ac* model for low- to mid-band frequencies

The figure includes the base junction resistance, r_π. We have not included a resistor between the base and collector. We omit this resistance since the base-to-collector junction is reverse-biased so that this resistance is very large – in most cases it can be ignored. The resistance from the base external terminal to the physical base material is small compared to the input resistance and can also be ignored in many cases. There is also a Norton resistance, r_o, associated with the current source. This resistance is usually a large value and may have little or no effect on the results of the model, depending on the size of the load resistance. We can determine the actual size of the output resistance, r_o, (Norton's resistance) – this will shown in Section 4.5 where we compare its value to the connected load resistance to determine if r_o should be considered. The model shown in Figure 4.5 is known as the hybrid-π *ac* model for the mid- (sometimes called the flat band) and low-frequency ranges.

4.4 TWO-PORT SMALL SIGNAL AC MODELS

In addition to the hybrid-π model of the previous section, we can model the BJT transistor using two-port network theory. These models are based on the external *V-I* characteristics so they can be fairly accurate for the frequency band where the model applies. The most common two-port network model for electronic circuits is the *h-parameter model*. The model accounts for the fact that each measurable parameter in the network consists of two components: one due to the driving forces at the first port and a second due to the driving forces at the second port.

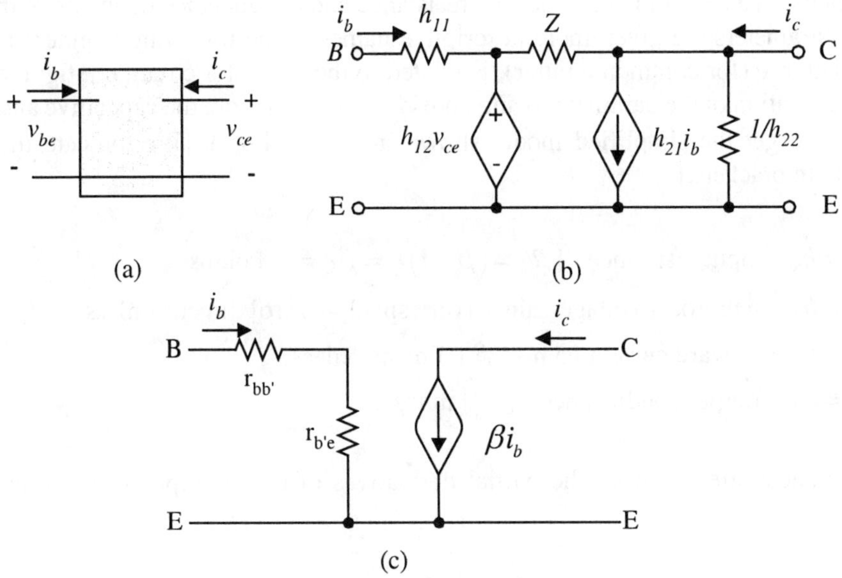

Figure 4.6 –Common-Emitter configuration

This is illustrated in Figure 4.6. We call this a *common-emitter* configuration since the emitter (E) is common to both input and output. More detail on various configurations is given in Section 4.8. We use lower case letters since the model is used for *small signal analysis.* That is, we will deal with the variations in input and output rather than total (*dc* plus *ac*) values. Assuming linearity, we can express the input voltage and output current by the following two equations:

$$v_{be} = h_{11} i_b + h_{12} v_{ce}$$
$$i_c = h_{21} i_b + h_{22} v_{ce} \tag{4.15}$$

or in matrix form

$$\begin{bmatrix} v_{be} \\ i_c \end{bmatrix} = \begin{bmatrix} h_{11} & h_{12} \\ h_{21} & h_{22} \end{bmatrix} \begin{bmatrix} i_b \\ v_{ce} \end{bmatrix}. \tag{4.16}$$

These equations express the observation made earlier that each parameter consists of two components. The four constants, h_{ij}, characterize the circuit inside the box of Figure 4.6(a). The equivalent circuit representative equations for the h-parameters are the basis for the model, as shown in Figure 4.6(b). The diagram shows the complex impedance, Z enclosed in a box. This impedance couples the output to the input, and it usually includes capacitive effects. We will be concerned with the capacitance when we deal with the high-frequency model since capacitances approach short circuits as the frequency approaches infinity. Since we are now considering only the mid-frequency band, the capacitive reactances (and inductive reactances) in the circuit will not be noticed. We need only consider the resistance and conductance elements of the model.

These parameters are given more descriptive names in the following manner. The second subscript letter, e (for common emitter), is related to the transistor circuit configuration which reflects the location of the parameter being considered. If we ignore the capacitive and inductive reactances we get the simplified model shown in Figure 4.6(c). [We indicate the hybrid-π equivalents in brackets.]

$h_{11} = h_{ie}$ = input resistance - [$R_{in} = (\beta + 1) r_e \simeq \beta r_e = r_\pi$] ohms

$h_{12} = h_{re}$ = reciprocal voltage gain – [very small $\approx$ zero] dimensionless

$h_{21} = h_{fe}$ = forward current gain - [β] dimensionless

$h_{22} = h_{oe}$ = output conductance - [r_o^{-1}] mhos

The h-parameters are given by the partial derivatives of the appropriate equations. That is,

$$h_{11} = h_{ie} = \frac{\partial v_{be}}{\partial i_b}$$
$$h_{12} = h_{re} = \frac{\partial v_{be}}{\partial v_{ce}}$$
$$h_{21} = h_{fe} = \frac{\partial i_c}{\partial i_b} \tag{4.17}$$
$$h_{22} = h_{oe} = \frac{\partial i_c}{\partial v_{ce}}$$

We see that h_{fe} is what we have called β. h_{re} is typically near zero. h_{ie} is the input resistance to the base of the transistor. It is usually split into two portions – $r_{bb'}$, the *base spreading resistance*, and $r_{b'e}$ (referred to as r_π in the hybrid-π model), a resistance related to the resistance of the *pn* junction. $r_{bb'}$ represents the resistance between the base contact and the base region and is typically less than 100Ω. $r_{b'e}$ can be as high as several thousand ohms. The output resistance, $1/h_{oe}$, is typically large. In fact, when a load resistor R_{load} is placed across the model's output terminals, the net ($r_o \| R_{load}$) output resistance can usually be approximated as the load resistance since the output resistance of the transistor is so large (i.e., $1/h_{oe} = r_o$ is in parallel with the load resistor). Therefore, we normally ignore h_{oe}. Putting all these observations together leads us to the simplified approximate model of Figure 4.6(c).

Now if we compare the hybrid-π model shown in Figure 4.5(b) and *h*-parameter model of Figure 4.6(c), we can make some quick approximations as follows:

$$r_\pi \approx h_{ie} = (\beta + 1) r_e \approx \beta r_e$$
$$\frac{\beta}{h_{ie}} \approx g_m$$
$$\beta i_b \approx g_m v_{be} \tag{4.18}$$
$$r_o \approx \frac{1}{h_{oe}}$$

These approximations give us some latitude in modeling the transistor circuits when values are given for certain parameters and not others.

4.5 CHARACTERISTIC CURVES

Since the transistor is a nonlinear device, one way to define its operation is with a set of characteristic curves. This is similar to the graphical approach used for diode circuit analysis in the previous chapter. There is a set of curves for each type of transistor. Since we are no longer dealing with two-terminal devices, equations involve at least three variables. Therefore, *parametric-curves* are usually used to describe transistor behavior. Figure 4.7 shows two typical plots (this is a repeat of Figure 4.4).

Figure 4.7(a) shows the emitter current as a function of the voltage between base and emitter when v_{CE} is held constant. Note that, as we might have expected, this curve resembles that of a diode since it is the characteristic of the current in a single junction.

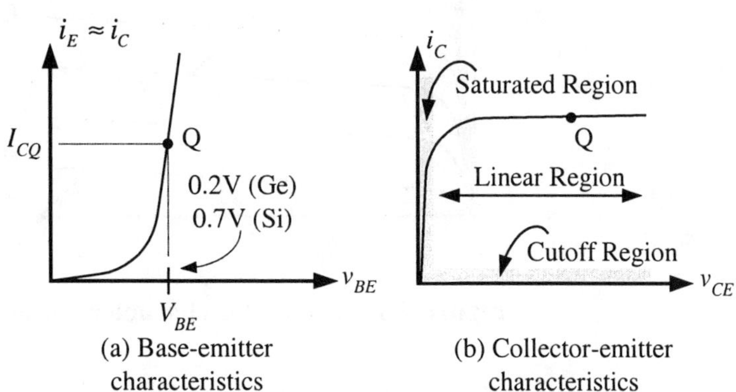

Figure 4.7 – Transistor characteristic curves

The slope of the characteristic curve is the

dynamic resistance of the transistor, r_d (in general, identified as r_e earlier). We can find an approximate value for the resistance by assuming a junction with $n = 1$. Referring to the equations in Chapter 3, we find

$$r_d = \frac{dv_D}{di_D} \approx \frac{nV_T}{I_o \exp(v_D/nv_T)} \approx \frac{26\text{ mV}}{I_C} \quad \text{(Also referred to as } r_e\text{.)} \qquad (4.19)$$

We have assumed that the collector current is approximately equal to the emitter current. A straight-line extension of the characteristic curve would intersect the v_{BE} axis at about 0.7V for silicon transistors and 0.2V for germanium.

If we now hold the base current constant, the collector-emitter junction is characterized by the curve of Figure 4.7(b). Note that the collector current is almost independent of the voltage between collector and emitter (i.e., the curve is approximately horizontal) throughout the *linear range* of operation. At base currents near zero, the collector current approaches zero in a nonlinear manner. This is known as the *cutoff* region of operation.

When the collector-to-emitter voltage is near zero, the collector current is maximum. This is known as the *saturation* region. It is not usable for amplification because of nonlinear operation.

Collector-emitter characteristic curves are parametric curves of collector current i_C versus collector-emitter voltage v_{CE} where the relatively small valued base current i_B is the parameter. Figure 4.8 shows an example of such curves. Each transistor type has its own unique set of characteristic curves.

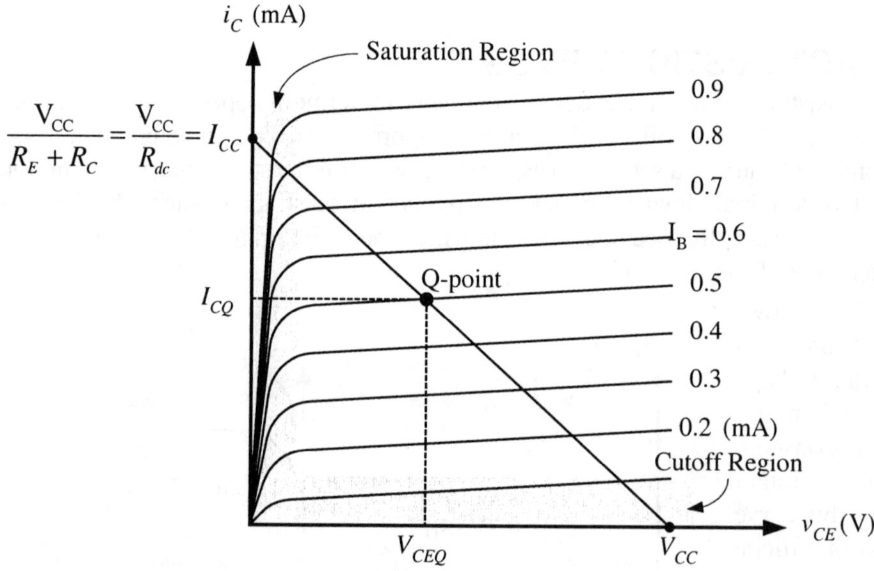

Figure 4.8 – Transistor characteristic curves

We will take a moment to illustrate the tremendous power of the curves in performing graphical circuit analysis. Suppose the transistor is configured as shown in Figure 4.9. This circuit contains resistors, *dc* sources, and the transistor. As we did in Chapter 3 for diodes, we can perform graphical analysis. We write circuit equations for the *linear* portion of the circuit, and use the transistor operating curves as the part of the simultaneous equations governing the transistor behavior.

We begin by applying Kirchhoff's voltage law around the collector-to-emitter loop to obtain

$$V_{CC} = i_C R_C + v_{CE} + i_E R_E \approx i_C(R_C + R_E) + v_{CE} \tag{4.20}$$

We have used the approximation that the collector current is almost equal to the emitter current. This equation defines a straight line having the form $y = mx + b$ and is plotted in Figure 4.8 where the variables are the collector current, i_C, and the collector-to-emitter voltage, v_{CE}. This straight line is known as the *dc load line* since it characterizes the constraint placed on the transistor by the load (collector) resistor, R_C, and the emitter resistor, R_E.

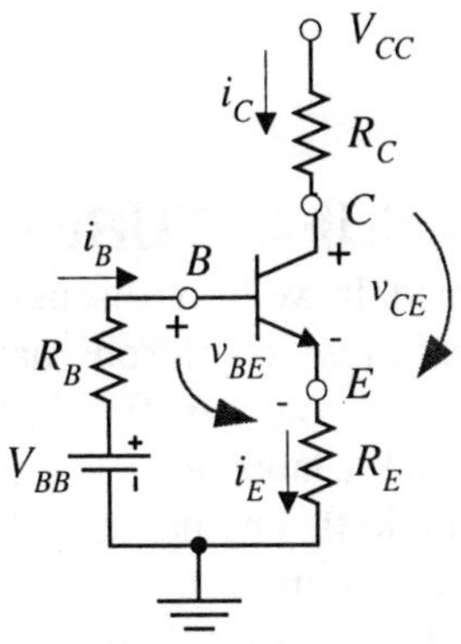

Figure 4.9 - Simple transistor circuit

The circuit operating point must be the simultaneous solution of the load line equation and the transistor characteristics. This is the intersection of the load line with the appropriate i_B parametric curve. Once V_{BB} is known, we can solve for the base current in this circuit, and then use the correct parametric curve. For purposes of illustration, we have assumed that this base current is 0.5 mA, and have indicated the simultaneous solution by the label *Q-point*. This terminology stands for *quiescent point*, and is called that because it represents the rest, or *dc* condition of the circuit. When we use transistors for various applications later in this chapter, we will see that the Q-point represents the starting position, and variations around this point carry the information in a circuit.

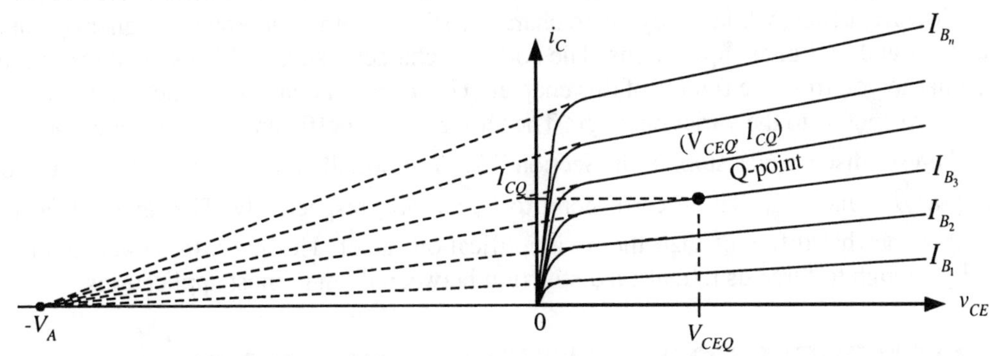

Figure 4.10 – I-V characteristics showing the Early effect for *npn* transistor

As you view Figure 4.8, note that the characteristic curves are not exactly horizontal - they have a slight positive slope. If these curves are extended to the left, they all cross the v_{CE} axis at a point as shown in Figure 4.10 (we have compressed the negative v_{CE} axis).

The value of v_{CE} at that point is defined as V_A, known as the *Early voltage.* The magnitude of this voltage can exceed 100V for a transistor. Using the value of V_A, we can determine the output impedance of the transistor when operating at a specific collector current. We define r_o as the *internal impedance* of a transistor at a specific operating point.

$$r_o = \frac{V_A + V_{CE}}{I_C} \approx \frac{V_A}{I_C} \tag{4.21}$$

4.6 MANUFACTURERS' DATA SHEETS FOR BJTS

The models we have discussed in the previous two sections attempt to give an ideal circuit configuration which closely matches the behavior of the practical transistor. In order to apply these models, you must first know the value of the various parameters. If you have the device available in the laboratory, you can conduct the necessary tests to establish the parameter values. You could do this by hooking the transistor into a circuit with sources and measuring devices. You could also use a measuring instrument called a *curve tracer* to develop the characteristic curves of the transistor and then read the parameters from these curves.

Another way to obtain the parameters is to reference the material supplied by the manufacturer. This material is in the form of *data sheets*, and we present several examples in the Appendix. You should refer to the 2N3903 data sheet during the following discussion.

The data sheet typically contains more information than needed to establish the transistor models. For example, you can usually find maximum ratings beyond which the transistor overheats, and can be destroyed. Note that all four h-parameter constants are given in the section labeled "SMALL-SIGNAL CHARACTERISTICS". Minimum and maximum values are given for each parameter except h_{oe}. The wide variation in the value of h_{fe} (i.e., β) is of concern and we address it when we design amplifiers.

The data sheets contain a variety of operating curves. The static characteristics are of concern to us at low frequency, while the dynamic characteristics become important at higher operating frequencies and in digital applications. The collector characteristics and "ON" voltages should be familiar to you from the figures of this chapter. The *dc* current gain as a function of collector current corresponds to the variation of β . The temperature coefficients will become important to us when we discuss bias stability in Section 7.2. We normally only mention β , but there is actually a β_{ac} and β_{dc}. These correspond to h_{fe} and h_{FE} respectively. The *dc* amplification factor is somewhat different than the *ac* amplification factor. However, these values do not differ by enough to force us to make a distinction between them in most applications.

4.7 BJT MODELS FOR COMPUTER SIMULATIONS

PSPICE, Micro-Cap, and most other circuit analysis programs contain sophisticated models for BJTs[1]. The some models include 40 parameters to describe the particular active device. The

[1]The model generally used is the *Gummel-Poon* model, which is more complicated than the Ebers-Moll model.

reason there are so many parameters is that the model attempts to closely imitate the nonlinear operating curves of the device. The computer is capable of tracking far more details than we can by hand, so the model can be more sophisticated than that presented in earlier sections of this chapter. In many analysis situations, you would set most of the parameters to their default values and would find that this complex model behaves almost the same as the simplified models we have discussed. We will now quickly review the syntax for including a BJT in a circuit. The SPICE statement is of the form,

Qname nc nb ne [ns] modelname [area][OFF][IC=vbe[,vce]]

Square brackets indicate that the quantity is optional. As an example, you might include a statement,

Q1 4 6 8 2N3904 IC=0.63,0.32

The Qname must start with the letter "Q" in SPICE. The integers nc, nb, ne, and ns are the node numbers associated with the collector, base, emitter and substrate (if included). The "area" is a parameter which either multiplies or divides parameters of the device. For example, an entry of 1.1 would increase the saturation current by 10% while decreasing the collector resistance by 10%. IC is an initial condition which allows you to specify initial voltages on the base-emitter and collector-emitter junctions. These initial conditions are only used for transient analysis.

In Micro-Cap, a ".MODEL" statement is included of the form,

.MODEL modelname NPN (model parameters)

This allows you to specify individual parameters for the device. If you use a standard device from the library (e.g., 2N3904), the program automatically copies all 40 parameter values for that device. As an example, you might include a model statement,

.MODEL Q1 NPN (IS=1E-15 BF=55 TR=.5N)

This statement would force Q1 to be an npn transistor with all but 3 of the 40 parameters set to their default values. The three that are different are the saturation current (being set to 10^{-15}), the forward beta (being set to 55) and the reverse transit time (set to 0.5 nanoseconds).

The following table lists all 40 parameters in the computer simulation (small-signal) model. It also shows the default value for each parameter.

SYMBOL	NAME	DEFAULT	UNITS
IS	Saturation Current	1E-16	A
BF	Maximum forward beta	100	*
NF	Forward current emission coefficient	1	*
VAF	Forward Early voltage	4	V
IKF	BF high current roll-off corner	4	A

ISE	BE leakage saturation current	0	A
NE	BE leakage emission coefficient	1.5	*
BR	Maximum reverse beta	1	*
NR	Reverse current emission coefficient	1	*
VAR	Reverse Early voltage	4	V
IKR	BR high-current roll-off corner	4	A
ISC	BC leakage saturation current	0	A
NC	BC leakage emission coefficient	2	*
RC	Collector resistance	0	Ω
RE	Emitter resistance	0	Ω
RB	Zero-bias base resistance	0	Ω
IRB	Current where RB falls by half	4	A
RBM	Minimum RB at high currents	RB	Ω
TF	Ideal forward transit time	0	S
TR	Ideal reverse transit time	0	S
XCJC	Fraction of BC dep. cap. to internal base	1	*
MJC	BC junction grading coefficient	0.33	*
VJC	BC junction built-in potential	0.75	V
CJC	BC zero-bias depletion capacitance	0	F
MJE	BE junction grading coefficient	0.33	*
VJE	BE junction built-in potential	0.75	V
CJE	BE junction zero-bias capacitance	0	F
MJS	CS junction grading coefficient	0	*
VJS	CS junction built-in potential	0.75	V
CJS	CS junction zero-bias capacitance	0	F
VTF	VBC dependence of TF	4	V
ITF	Transit time dependence on IC	0	A
XTF	Transit time bias coefficient	0	*
TF	Excess phase	0	*
XTB	Temperature coefficient for betas	0	*
EG	Energy gap	1.11	eV
XTI	Saturation current temperature exponent	3	*
KF	Flicker-noise coefficient	0	*
AF	Flicker-noise exponent	1	*
FC	Forward-bias depletion coefficient	0.5	*

* Dimensionless

Table 4.1

The model associated with these parameters is shown in Figure 4.11. The parameters shown on this figure (e.g., the junction capacitor, C_{BC}) are derived from the 40 parameters in the table. Each is specified by an equation that depends on the operating point of the transistor.

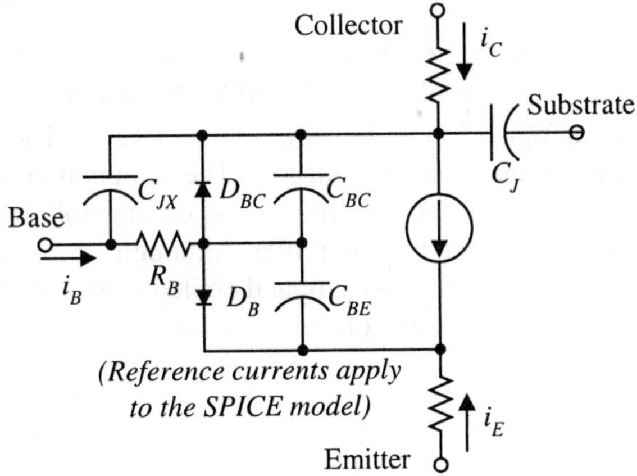

Figure 4.11 – Bipolar transistor model

Therefore, the computer simulation dynamically changes the parameters of Figure 4.11 as the simulation progresses.

4.8 SINGLE-STAGE AMPLIFIER CONFIGURATIONS

We have seen characteristic curves and models for the BJT. We must now consider the manner in which signals are coupled into and out of the transistor to perform a useful function. Because of the overall nonlinear behavior of the transistor, we usually operate the circuit in a portion of the characteristic curves where performance is close to linear. We use external *dc* sources to *bias* the transistor so that time-varying inputs vary parameters around some non-zero point. That is, if we simply apply a time varying input to a transistor, the operating point varies across a non-linearity since the junctions are changing state (e.g., from forward to reverse biased).

It often proves simpler to isolate *dc* conditions from *ac* conditions. Large capacitors are used for this purpose. The impedance of such capacitors is close to zero at operating frequencies of interest, but the capacitors look like open circuits (i.e., infinite impedance) at *dc* (0 Hertz).

Depending on the location of inputs, outputs, and ground, we define four basic configurations for the transistor. These are shown in Figure 4.12. The *common-emitter* amplifier is shown in Figure 4.12(a). The negative supply, $-V_{EE}$, is often set to zero (i.e., grounded). Under *ac* conditions, each of the three capacitors acts as a short circuit. The configuration gets its name from the observation that the emitter is common to both the input and output. The input is applied between base and emitter (under *ac* conditions), and the output is taken between collector and emitter.

The circuit of Figure 4.12(b) is similar to that of Figure 4.12(a), except the bypass capacitor is removed from the emitter resistor. The circuit is identical to the common emitter under *dc* conditions (when the capacitors act as open circuits), but the emitter is no longer grounded for *ac* inputs. Even though the emitter is not grounded, this is sometimes called a *common-emitter* configuration. However, to distinguish it from the previous circuit we will refer to it as an *emitter-resistor* configuration. There are very important operational differences between the two circuits.

The *common-collector* or *emitter-follower* configuration is shown in Figure 4.12(c). The output of this amplifier is taken from the emitter of the transistor.

The *common-base* configuration is shown in Figure 4.12(d). The input is connected to the emitter, and the output is taken at the collector. The common-emitter, emitter-resistor and common-base amplifiers are *voltage* amplifiers. The emitter follower is a *current* amplifier, *power* amplifier, or *impedance matching* amplifier. Although we illustrate these amplifiers with power supplies connected to both the collector and emitter sides, either of these power supplies could be set to zero (i.e., grounded) or isolated.

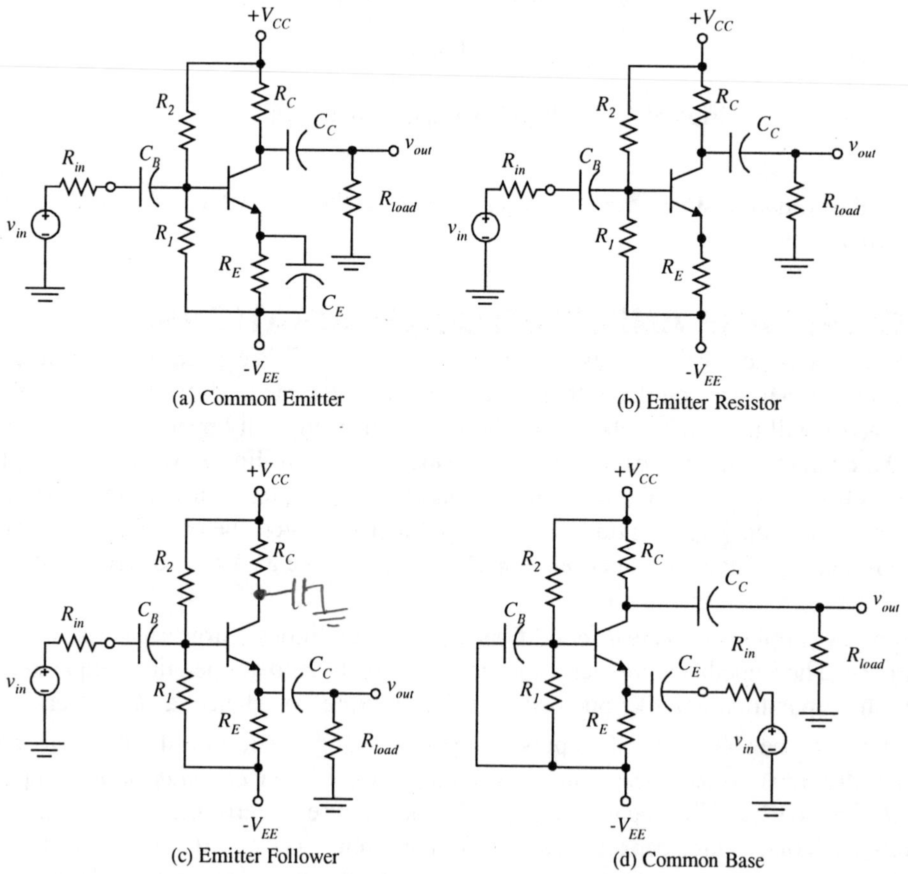

Figure 4.12 - Single-stage amplifier configurations

4.9 BIASING OF SINGLE-STAGE AMPLIFIERS

We have now established the methods for configuring the transistor in a circuit, and we also know the theory that affects transistor behavior. This theory is used to tell us how transistors behave in the linear region. We use *bias* circuitry to assure that the transistor operates in that desired region. This section uses basic circuit analysis to explore biasing techniques for the various amplifier configurations. We examine the effects of the bias circuitry in determining the operating point for the transistor. We do not analyze the *ac* operations of the transistor nor do we discuss design techniques - these are covered in Sections 4.11 and 4.12.

As can be seen from Figure 4.12, once the coupling capacitors are open-circuited, the various configurations look similar. In fact, the only difference is that the collector of the *emitter follower* circuit does not contain a resistor. This is the same as saying that R_C is zero (Remember this fact for later analysis.). Therefore, we need only examine the biasing analysis once, and the equations will be applicable to *all* configurations.

The capacitors are assumed to be open-circuit for *dc*, but short-circuit for all time-varying signals of interest (i.e., they have large capacitance). Therefore, when we later consider the response of these circuits to time-varying inputs, the equations will differ. Various additional resistors affect the circuit behavior.

Figure 4.13 shows the configuration of the transistor. We have open-circuited all capacitors in the circuits of Figure 4.12. This diagram contains several additional simplifications. We have reconfigured the base circuit to consist of a Thevenin equivalent resistor (R_B) and Thevenin *dc* voltage source (V_{BB}). A second simplification is to set the negative bi-polar supply voltage V_{EE} to zero. As long as capacitive coupling is used, this does not change the output. To see this, suppose we shift all voltages by V_{EE} in the circuit of Figure 4.12(a). The collector voltage becomes V_{CC}+V_{EE} and the -V_{EE} source becomes ground. These changes do not affect *ac* operation.

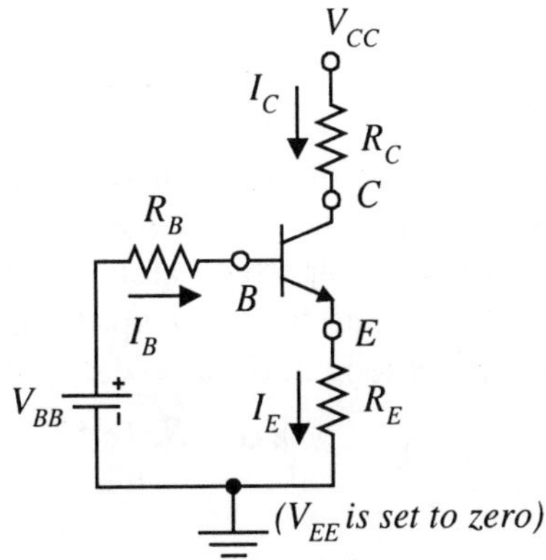

Figure 4.13 – Transistor amplifiers under *dc* conditions

The *Thevenin equivalent voltage* and *resistance* viewed *from* the transistor's base terminal to ground are found from the circuits of Figure 4.12 with C_B acting as an open circuit.

$$V_{TH} \doteq V_{BB} = \frac{R_1}{R_1 + R_2} \cdot V_{CC}$$

$$R_{TH} \doteq R_B = R_1 \| R_2 = \left[\frac{1}{R_1} + \frac{1}{R_2}\right]^{-1} = \frac{R_1 R_2}{R_1 + R_2} \tag{4.22}$$

Since we are analyzing the circuit under *dc* conditions, the variable input source voltage v_{in} of Figure 4.12 is set to zero. Kirchhoff's voltage law (KVL) around the base loop of Figure 4.13 yields

$$V_{BB} = I_B R_B + V_{BE} + I_E R_E$$

$$\text{or} \quad I_B = \frac{V_{BB} - V_{BE}}{R_B + \beta R_E} \tag{4.23}$$

$$\text{or} \quad I_B = \frac{I_E}{\beta + 1} \simeq \frac{I_E}{\beta} \simeq \frac{I_C}{\beta} \approx \frac{V_{BB} - V_{BE}}{R_B + \beta R_E}$$

Since the *dc* condition in the base loop sets the base current I_B to the value I_{BQ}, we have

$$\beta I_{BQ} = I_{CQ} \quad (\approx I_{EQ}).$$

We can arrange the relationships of Equation (4.23) to get the *bias equation*,

$$\boxed{I_{CQ} = \frac{V_{BB} - V_{BE}}{R_B/\beta + R_E}} \tag{4.24}$$

The *dc* operating point is known as the *quiescent point, Q-point, rest operating condition*, or *ac zero-signal point* of the circuit. I_{BQ} is the quiescent base current and I_{EQ} is the quiescent emitter current. I_C and I_E are approximately equal to each other.[1] Note that we use upper-case letters for both the variable and the subscript to indicate *dc* values. We now write the KVL around the collector-emitter loop in order to determine the *load line equation*.

$$V_{CC} = R_C I_C + V_{CE} + R_E I_E \approx (R_C + R_E) I_C + V_{CE}$$

$$\boxed{I_C = \frac{V_{CC} - V_{CE}}{R_C + R_E}} \tag{4.25}$$

where I_C and V_{CE} are the equation variables.

Equation (4.25) specifies the constraints placed by the external circuitry. It specifies a linear relationship between collector current and collector-emitter voltage. To find the various voltages and currents, we must perform the simultaneous solution of this linear equation with the equations describing the transistor behavior. Since the transistor is nonlinear, we often use graphical techniques. The plot of the relationship of Equation (4.25) is known as a *load line*.

The load line is drawn on the transistor's characteristic curves in Figure 4.14. The intersection of this load line with the appropriate transistor's operating curve defines the circuit parameters. With zero *ac* input signal, the operating point is the Q-point. Although we do not wish to assign specific values to V_{BB} and R_B at this time, we have selected I_{BQ} = 200 μA for purposes of illustration in the figure.

---

[1]The collector current is β times the base current. Since the emitter current is the sum of the base and collector current, it is (β+1) times the base current. For practical values of beta, β+1 and β are approximately equal, and we can assume that the emitter current is equal to the collector current, as we do throughout this text.

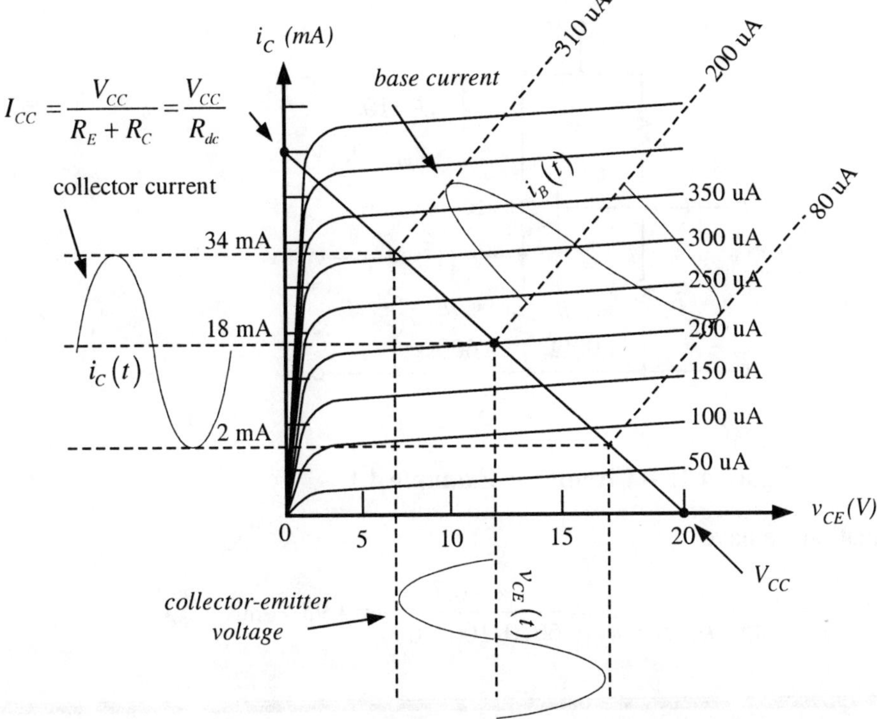

Figure 4.14 – Characteristic curves for CE amplifier

Since all amplifier circuit configurations have identical *dc* bias equivalent circuits, we will select the emitter follower configuration for illustration in the following example problem.

Example 4.1

Find the Q-point of the emitter follower circuit of Figure 4.15 with $R_1 = 10$ kΩ and $R_2 = 20$ kΩ. Assume the transistor has a β of 100 and $C \to \infty$.

Solution: We first find the Thevenin equivalent of the base bias circuitry.

$$R_B = R_1 \| R_2 = 6.67 \quad \text{k}\Omega$$

$$V_{BB} = \frac{R_1 V_{CC}}{R_1 + R_2} = \frac{12\left(10^4\right)}{30 \times 10^3} = 4 \quad \text{V}$$

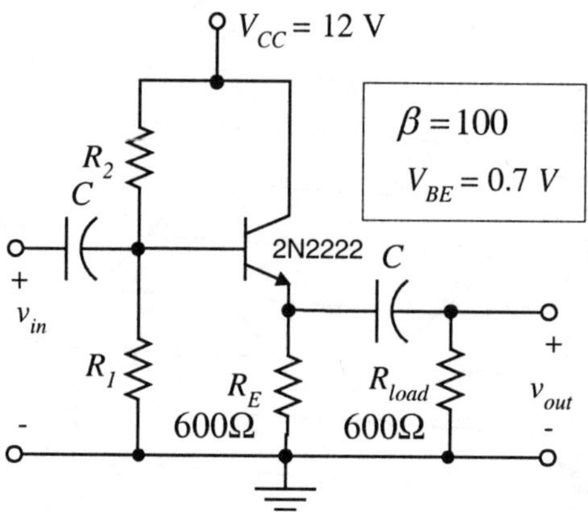

Figure 4.15 – Circuit for Example 4.1

From the bias equation we have

$$I_C = I_{CQ} = \frac{V_{BB} - V_{BE}}{R_B/\beta + R_E} = \frac{4 - 0.7}{6670/100 + 600} = 4.95 \quad \text{mA}$$

4.10 POWER CONSIDERATIONS

Power rating is an important consideration in selecting bias resistors since they must be capable of withstanding the maximum anticipated (worst case) power without overheating. Power considerations also affect transistor selection. Designers normally select components having the lowest power handling capability suitable for the design. Frequently, *de-rating* (i.e., providing a "safety margin" from derived values) is used to improve the reliability of a device. This is similar to using safety factors in the design of mechanical systems where the system is designed to withstand values that exceed the maximum.

4.10.1 Derivation of Power Equations

Average power is calculated as follows:

For *dc*:

$$P = VI = I^2R = \frac{V^2}{R} \quad \text{W} \tag{4.26}$$

For *ac*:

$$P = \frac{1}{T}\int_0^T v(t)\cdot i(t)\,dt \quad \text{W} \tag{4.27}$$

In the *ac* equation, we assume periodic waveforms where T is the period. If the signal is not periodic, we must let T approach infinity in Equation (4.26). Looking at the CE amplifier of Figure 4.12(a), the power supplied by the power source is dissipated either in R_1 and R_2 or in the transistor (and its associated collector and emitter circuitry). The power in R_1 and R_2 (the bias circuitry) is given by

$$P_{(bias)} = I_{R2}^2 R_2 + I_{R1}^2 R_1 \tag{4.28}$$

where I_{R1} and I_{R2} are the (downward) currents in the two resistors. Kirchhoff's current law (KCL) yields a relationship between these two currents and the base quiescent current.

$$I_{R1} = I_{R2} - I_B \tag{4.29}$$

KVL yields the base loop equation (assuming $V_{EE} = 0$),

$$I_{R2}R_2 + I_{R1}R_1 = V_{CC} \tag{4.30}$$

These two equations can be solved for the currents to yield,

$$\begin{aligned} I_{R1} &= \frac{V_{CC} - R_2 I_B}{R_2 + R_1} \\ I_{R2} &= \frac{V_{CC} + R_1 I_B}{R_2 + R_1} \end{aligned} \tag{4.31}$$

In most practical circuits, the power due to I_B is negligible relative to the power dissipated in the transistor and in R_1 and R_2. We will therefore assume that the power supplied by the source is approximately equal to the power dissipated in the transistor and in R_1 and R_2. This quantity is given by

$$P_{VCC} = \frac{1}{T}\int_0^T V_{CC}\left[I_{CQ} + i_c(t)\right]dt + P_{(bias\ circuit)} = V_{CC}I_{CQ} + \frac{V_{CC}^2}{R_1 + R_2} \tag{4.32}$$

where the source voltage V_{CC} is a *constant* value. The source current has a *dc* quiescent component designated by I_{CQ} and the *ac* component is designated by $i_c(t)$. The last equality of Equation (4.32) assumes that the average value of $i_c(t)$ is zero. This is a reasonable assumption. For example, it applies if the input *ac* signal is a sinusoidal waveform.

The average power dissipated by the transistor itself (not including any external circuitry) is

$$P_{(transistor)} = \frac{1}{T}\int_0^T v_{CE}(t)\, i_C(t)\,dt \tag{4.33}$$

For zero signal input, this becomes

$$P_{(transistor)} = V_{CEQ} I_{CQ} \tag{4.34}$$

Where V_{CEQ} and I_{CQ} are the quiescent (*dc*) values of the voltage and current, respectively.

For an input signal with maximum possible swing (i.e., Q-point in middle and operating to cutoff and saturation),

$$\begin{aligned} v_{CE}(t) &= V_{CEQ} - V_{CEQ}\sin\omega t = V_{CEQ}(1-\sin\omega t) \\ i_C(t) &= I_{CQ} + I_{CQ}\sin\omega t = I_{CQ}(1+\sin\omega t) \end{aligned} \tag{4.35}$$

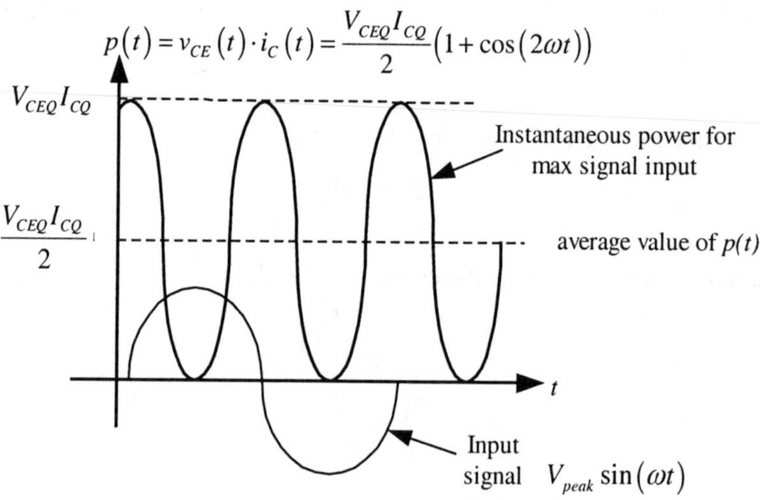

Figure 4.16 – Instantaneous transistor power dissipation

Putting these time functions in Equation (4.32) yields the power equation,

$$\begin{aligned} P_{(transistor)} &= \frac{1}{T}\int_0^T V_{CEQ} I_{CQ}\left(1-\sin^2\omega t\right)dt \\ &= \frac{1}{T}\int_0^T V_{CEQ} I_{CQ}\left(\frac{1}{2}+\frac{1}{2}\cos 2\omega t\right)dt = \frac{V_{CEQ} I_{CQ}}{2} \end{aligned} \tag{4.36}$$

From the above derivation, we see that the transistor dissipates its maximum power (worst case) when no *ac* signal input is applied. This is shown in Figure 4.16, where we note that the frequency of the instantaneous power sinusoid is 2ω.

Depending on the amplitude of the input signal, the transistor will dissipate an average power between $V_{CEQ}I_{CQ}$ and one half of this value. Therefore, the transistor is selected for zero input signal so it will handle the maximum (worst case) power dissipation of $V_{CEQ}I_{CQ}$.

We will need a measure of efficiency to determine how much of the power delivered by the source appears as signal power at the output. We define *conversion efficiency* as

$$\eta_{conversion} = \frac{P_{out}(ac)}{P_{in}(dc)} \times 100 . \qquad (4.37)$$

4.11 ANALYSIS AND DESIGN OF VOLTAGE AMPLIFIER BIAS CIRCUITS

In *analyzing* a transistor amplifier, the circuit components are all specified. We begin the analysis by examining the *dc* bias conditions. The Thevenin equivalent circuit for the base-emitter loop provides the values needed to solve the bias equation for I_C. (identified as I_{CQ}) The *dc* operating point is found. Then the circuit operation is examined under *ac* conditions. This requires shorting the coupling and bypass capacitors. Since this shorting causes the effective resistor values seen by the transistor to change, the operating curve (load line) also changes. The following analysis consists of finding these new operating conditions. The approach we will use is to find the *ac* load line. This line is comparable to the *dc* load line discussed in Section 4.9. However, the slope and intercepts are different since the resistor values have changed.

In *designing* an amplifier, the situation is reversed since the designer must select the circuit components and has the option of selecting I_C. For example, if a maximum output voltage swing is desired for the CE amplifier, I_C is placed in the center of the *ac* load line. On the other hand, if the input signal is small, I_C can be made just large enough so the *ac* signal output will not be clipped during the input signal maximum.

In design, the engineer starts calculations at the collector-emitter side of the amplifier rather than at the base-emitter side. After I_{CQ} has been determined, the bias equation is used to determine the values of R_1 and R_2 required for the transistor to operate at the selected quiescent collector current value of I_{CQ}.

4.11.1 Analysis Procedure

In *analysis* the values of R_1, R_2, V_{CC}, V_{BE}, R_E, R_C, R_{load}, and β are all known. This is true for any of the four configurations presented in Section 4.8. The analysis is conducted starting from the base side of the amplifier. The reason we begin with the base is to "decouple" the equations as much as possible. You could begin anywhere you wish, and develop enough independent equations to solve for the various unknowns. However, if you begin at the base, you will not have to solve a large system of simultaneous equations.

Begin the analysis by using R_1 and R_2 to determine the parameters V_{BB} and R_B for Thevenin's equivalent circuit, just as we did earlier (refer to Figure 4.13) From inside the transistor and looking out the base terminal, we see a rather complex circuit. There are the biasing resistors R_1 and R_2 and the signal source (i.e., signal generator, sensor, antenna, etc.). For now we do not include the signal source impedance. Therefore

$$\begin{aligned} V_{TH} &\doteq V_{BB} = V_{CC} \cdot \frac{R_1}{R_1 + R_2}, \text{[Voltage Divider Rule]} \\ R_{TH} &\doteq R_B = R_1 \| R_2 = \left[R_1^{-1} + R_2^{-1} \right]^{-1} = \frac{R_1 R_2}{R_1 + R_2}, \text{[Parallel Combination]} \end{aligned} \tag{4.38}$$

Then using Kirchoff's Voltage Law around the base loop, we have

$$V_{BB} = I_B R_B + V_{BE} + I_E R_E$$

and knowing that

$$I_B = \frac{I_C}{\beta} \text{ and } I_E \approx I_C,$$

we have a <u>*known*</u> value of quiescent collector current indicated by I_{CQ}. The value of I_{CQ} is *set* by the biasing circuit, R_1 and R_2 and in terms of the equivalent Thevenin circuit parameters, R_B and V_{BB}. This known value of collector current (set by the biasing circuit) is given by

$$I_{CQ} = \frac{V_{BB} - V_{BE}}{R_B/\beta + R_E} \quad \textit{(The Biasing Equation)} \tag{4.39}$$

The base circuit conditions set the collector current as Equation (4.39). We use the biasing equation to establish I_{CQ}. This equation specifies the *dc* load line equation used find the other ordinate, V_{CEQ} This specifies the *dc* load line equation, derived earlier from Kirchoff's Voltage Law (KVL) around the collector circuit (see Equation (4.25)). We now know the Q-point, (V_{CEQ}, I_{CQ}). In general, the *dc* load line equation identifies all the points on the *dc* load line (i.e., the ordered pairs (V_{CE}, I_C) which satisfies the KVL equation around the collector circuit). Rearranging Equation (4.25), we have

$$V_{CE} = V_{CC} - (R_E + R_C) I_C = V_{CC} - R_{dc} I_C \tag{4.40}$$

or in the slope intercept form of $y = mx + b$

$$I_C = \frac{-1}{(R_E + R_C)} \cdot V_{CE} + \frac{V_{CC}}{(R_E + R_C)}. \tag{4.41}$$

In the slope-intercept form, the *dc* load line equation evaluated *at* the Q-point becomes

$$I_{CQ} = \frac{-1}{R_E + R_C} \cdot V_{CEQ} + \frac{V_{CC}}{R_E + R_C} = \frac{-1}{R_{dc}} \cdot V_{CEQ} + \frac{V_{CC}}{R_{dc}} \tag{4.42}$$

The x-intercept is V_{CC}, which is found by setting $I_C = 0$ in Equation (4.42). The y-intercept is $\frac{V_{CC}}{R_E + R_C}$ (also represented by $\frac{V_{CC}}{R_{dc}}$) which is found by setting $V_{CE} = 0$ in Equation (4.42). These intercept points locate the end-points of the *dc* load line indicated in Figures 4.14 and 4.17. We use the notation R_{dc} to refer to the total resistance in the collector-emitter loop under *dc* conditions (i.e., capacitors open). Then we construct the *dc* load line of Equation (4.40) on the characteristic curves.

Under *ac* conditions, the load line changes. This is true since the capacitors become short circuits and signal variations (ac) are readily passed by the coupling and by-pass capacitors. Therefore the KVL loop equations must accommodate the very low impedances of the capacitors. For example, viewing the common emitter [Figure 4.12(a)], we see that the emitter resistor, R_E, is shorted out by the capacitor, C_E. Additionally, since C_C shorts, the load resistor is effectively in parallel with the collector resistor. This is true since, for *ac* analysis, we can assume that the *dc* source, V_{CC}, is grounded. The slope and x- and y-intercepts of the load line for *ac* signals therefore are different from those of the *dc* load line. When the *ac* inputs go to zero, the circuit operates at the Q-point. It is therefore sufficient to know the slope of the *ac* load line since we can then simply draw a line with that slope through the Q-point. Under *ac* conditions, the expression, $\frac{-1}{R_{ac}}$, establishes the slope of the *ac* load line. If the signal gets very small we expect the *ac* load line to converge to a point on the *dc* load line. So an important fact is established: *The ac load line must pass through the dc load line at the Q-point.* Thus, we have a geometry problem: We have a slope and a point, so let's find the equation for the *ac* load line. That is, given slope $\frac{-1}{R_{ac}}$ and point (V_{CEQ}, I_{CQ}), find the equation for this straight line. The *ac* load line is established from the equation

$$\frac{-1}{R_{ac}} = m = \frac{\Delta y}{\Delta x} = \frac{I_C - I_{CQ}}{V_{CE} - V_{CEQ}} \tag{4.43}$$

where R_{ac} is the *ac* equivalent resistance in the collector-emitter loop and the equation must hold for *all* ordered pairs (V_{CE}, I_C). Rearranging Equation (4.43) into the $y = mx + b$ form, we obtain

$$I_C = \frac{-1}{R_{ac}} V_{CE} + \left(\frac{V_{CEQ}}{R_{ac}} + I_{CQ} \right) \tag{4.44}$$

The x-intercept ($I_C = 0$) for the *ac* load line is $V'_{CE_{\text{ac intercept}}} = V_{CEQ} + I_{CQ} R_{ac}$ (labeled V'_{CC} in the figures to be consistent with the *dc* x-intercept label V_{CC}). The y-intercept ($V_{CE} = 0$) for the *ac* load line is $I'_{C_{\text{ac intercept}}} = \frac{V_{CEQ}}{R_{ac}} + I_{CQ}$ (labeled I'_{CC} or $I_{C_{\max}}$, or $\frac{V'_{CC}}{R_{ac}}$ in the figure. Actually, we now have three points and a slope to establish the *ac* load line! The *ac load line equation* is therefore

$$I_C = \frac{-1}{R_{ac}} V_{CE} + \frac{V'_{CC}}{R_{ac}} \quad \text{or} \quad V_{CE} = V'_{CC} - I_C R_{ac} \tag{4.45}$$

for *all* ordered pairs (V_{CE}, I_C) on the *ac* load line.

We take a moment now to review the evaluation of R_{dc} and R_{ac} for the configurations shown in Figure 4.12. We assume the capacitors are open circuits to obtain the value of R_{dc}. For the configuration of Figure 4.12(c), R_{dc} is simply equal to R_E. For configurations in Figure 4.12(a), (b), and (d), the *dc* resistance is $R_E + R_C$. Summarizing

$$\begin{aligned} R_{dc} &= R_E + R_C \qquad \text{[Figure 4.12(a), (b), (d)]} \\ R_{dc} &= R_E \qquad \text{[Figure 4.12(c)]} \end{aligned} \tag{4.46}$$

To determine R_{ac}, we assume the capacitors are short circuits. The *ac* resistance for the four configurations of Figure 4.12 is then given by

$$\begin{aligned} R_{ac}(a) &= R_C \| R_{load} \qquad \text{[common emitter]} \\ R_{ac}(b) &= R_C \| R_{load} + R_E \qquad \text{[emitter resistor]} \\ R_{ac}(c) &= R_E \| R_{load} \qquad \text{[emitter follower]} \\ R_{ac}(d) &= R_C \| R_{load} + R_E \| R_{in} \qquad \text{[common base]} \end{aligned} \tag{4.47}$$

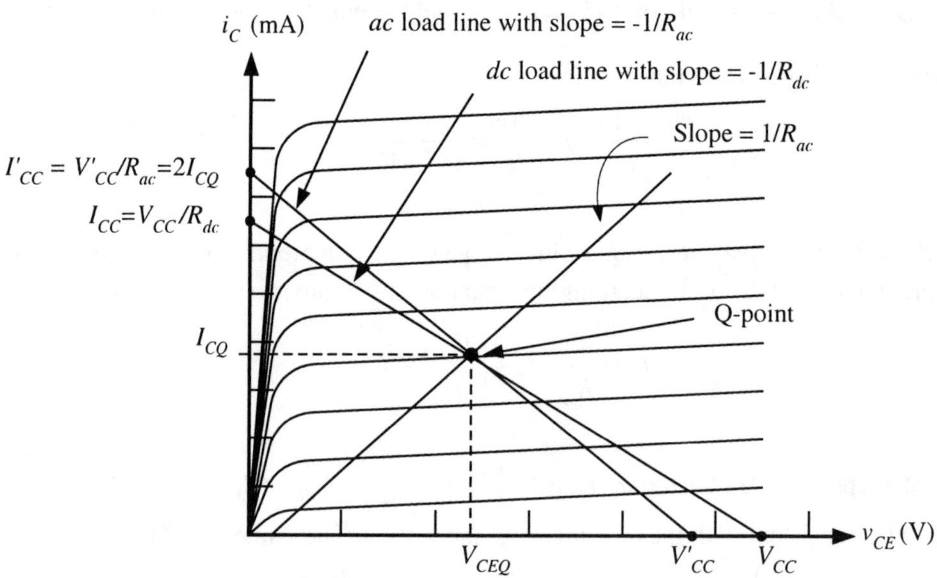

Figure 4.17 – Construction for maximum symmetrical swing

Once we have the *ac* load line, we can find the response due to a non-zero input signal. One parameter of interest is the *maximum* possible symmetrical output swing. If, for example, the *ac* input is a sinusoid voltage, we would hope that the *ac* output is also a sinusoid so that there is no distortion. If the output swing is too large, the transistor will leave the linear operating region. The maximum possible symmetrical output swing tells us the point at which distortion starts to occur.

We determine the maximum possible symmetrical output voltage swing using the load line construction on the characteristic curves. Refer to Figure 4.17 during the following discussion. We simply see how far i_C can vary from the Q-point before reaching the boundaries of the linear region. If the Q-point is not in the middle of the load line, the minimum of the two distances determines the maximum symmetrical swing. Suppose first that the Q-point is on the upper half of the *ac* load line. I_{CQ} is then subtracted from I'_{CC} (the point where the *ac* load line intersects the i_C-axis). Therefore (I'_{CC} - I_{CQ}) will provide the maximum peak *ac* amplitude of the output current of the transistor. Alternatively, if the Q-point is on the lower half of the *ac* load line, ($I_{CQ} - 0$) is the maximum peak *ac* amplitude of the output current of the transistor. Then, the maximum possible symmetrical output voltage swing is the current swing multiplied by the effective load resistance. For the common emitter, emitter resistor, and common base, the effective resistance is the parallel combination of R_C and R_{load}. The maximum possible output voltage swing (peak-to-peak) is given by

$$2\times I_C(maximum\ peak\ amplitude)\times(R_C \| R_{load}) \tag{4.48}$$

We conclude this section with a reminder that the process described in this text is best described as *analysis* techniques. The values of R_1, R_2, V_{CC}, V_{BE}, R_E, R_C, R_{load}, and β are all known. The analysis holds for any of the four amplifier configurations presented in Section 4.8.

Example 4.2 (Analysis)

Determine the Q-point for the CE amplifier given in Fig. 4.18(a) if $R_1 = 1.5$ kΩ and $R_2 = 7$ kΩ. A 2N3904 transistor is used with $\beta = 180$, $R_E = 100$ Ω and $R_C = R_{load} = 1$ kΩ. Also determine the P_{out}(ac) and the *dc* power delivered to the circuit by the source. Verify your result using a computer simulation.

Solution: We first obtain the Thevenin equivalent.

$$V_{BB} = \frac{R_1}{R_1 + R_2}\cdot V_{CC} = \frac{1500}{1500 + 7000}\cdot 5 = 0.882 \quad \text{V}$$

$$R_B = \frac{R_1 R_2}{R_1 + R_2} = 1.24 \quad \text{k}\Omega$$

We find the Q-point as follows:

$$I_{CQ} = \frac{V_{BB} - V_{BE}}{R_B/\beta + R_E} = \frac{0.882 - 0.7}{1240/180 + 100} = 1.70 \quad \text{mA}$$

Note that this is not a desirable Q-point location since V_{BB} is very close to V_{BE}. Variations in V_{BE} therefore significantly change I_C. We find $R_{ac} = R_C \| R_{load} = 500\Omega$ and $R_{dc} = R_C + R_E = 1.1$ kΩ. The value of V_{CE} representing the quiescent value associated with I_{CQ} is found as follows.

$$V_{CEQ} = V_{CC} - I_{CQ} R_{dc} = 5 - (1.70 \times 10^{-3})(1.1 \times 10^{-3}) = 3.13 \quad \text{V}$$

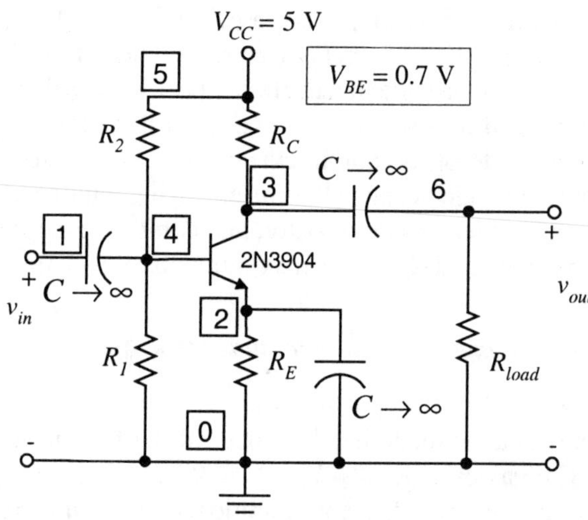

Figure 4.18(a) - Circuit for Example 4.2

Then

$$V'_{CC} = V_{CEQ} + I_{CQ} R_{ac} = 3.13 + (1.7 \times 10^{-3})(500) = 3.98 \quad \text{V}$$

Since the Q-point is on the lower half of the *ac* load line, the maximum possible symmetrical output voltage swing is

$$2(I_{CQ} - 0)(R_C \| R_{load}) = 2(1.70 \times 10^{-3})(500) = 1.70 \quad \text{V}_{\text{peak-to-peak}}$$

We now calculate the expected power.

$$P_{out}(ac) = \frac{1}{2} i_{load}^2 R_{load} = \frac{1}{2}\left(1.70\times10^{-3}\times\frac{1000}{2000}\right)^2 \times1000 = 0.361 \quad \text{mW}$$

$$P_{VCC}(dc) = I_{CQ} V_{CC} + \frac{V_{CC}^2}{R_1 + R_2} = 11.4 \quad \text{mW}$$

$$P_{transistor} = V_{CEQ} I_{CQ} = 3.13\text{V} \times 1.70\text{mA} = 5.32 \quad \text{mW}$$

The Q-point in this example is *not* in the middle of the load line so that output swing is not as great as possible. However, if the input signal is small and maximum output is not required, a small I_C can be used to reduce the power dissipated in the circuit.

The SPICE code for this example is shown below using the node assignments shown in Figure 4.18(a). Note that we have used values of 100 microfarad and 1000 microfarad for the bypass and coupling capacitors.

```
VIN,1,0,DC,0
C1,1,4,1000E-6
R1,4,0,1.5K
R2,4,5,7K
VCC,5,0,DC,5V
*GUMMEL POON BJT PARAMETERS
Q1,3,4,2,BJT
.MODEL,BJT,NPN(BF=180)
C2,3,6,100E-6
RE,2,0,100
CE,2,0,100E-6
RC,3,5,1K
RL,6,0,1K
.TRAN,.005M,1M
.PROBE
.END
```

In order to find the Q-point, we simply use the default "Bias Point Detail" settings for the initial analysis run. We note the computer simulation results shown in Figure 4.18(b) provides quiescent voltages (i.e., *dc* voltages) identified by light gray boxes for all nodes. The quiescent current flow values for each component are shown by dark boxes. The direction of current is readily determined by clicking on the selected dark box. A small red arrow appears on the screen indicating the direction of current flow. Note the emitter current values of Q1. As we mentioned earlier, SPICE references *positive* currents *into* the terminals of the transistor, thus we see a negative value of current flow *into* the emitter of Q1. This, in fact, means that the emitter current flows from the transistor through the emitter resistor R_E and then to ground as we expect. The collector-emitter quiescent voltage V_{CE}, identified in the SPICE listing above as nodes 3 and 2, is node voltage 3 minus node voltage 2 (i.e., (3.217V - 180.08mV) = 3.037V. The theoretical solution yielded a value of 3.13V. The complete *dc* computer simulation results are shown in Figure 4.18(b) [This printout was generated using Cadence PSpice, Student Edition.] The difference between this and the theoretical value of 3.13V can be traced to the transistor model. For example, we assumed a base-to-emitter voltage of 0.7V, while the actual value (calculated by the simulation) is approximately 0.68V. Since V_{BB} is only 0.882V, a small change in V_{BE} can result in a larger change in I_C.

The 2N3904 transistor's maximum forward beta was set to 180 for the simulation. This value is checked by computing the ratio of the collector current to the base current. The computer simulation yields a *dc* beta $\beta_{dc} = \dfrac{1.783\text{mA}}{17.78\mu\text{A}} = 101.3(dc)$. The *ac* beta will be discussed in greater detail in the following chapter.

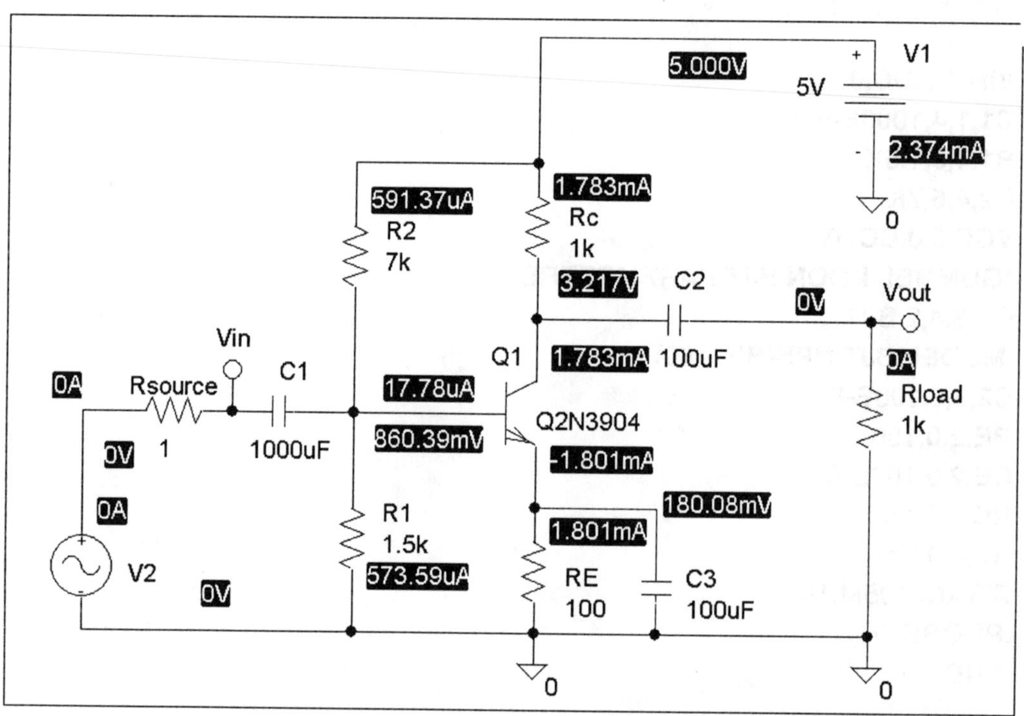

Figure 4.18(b) - Computer simulation result for Example 4.2

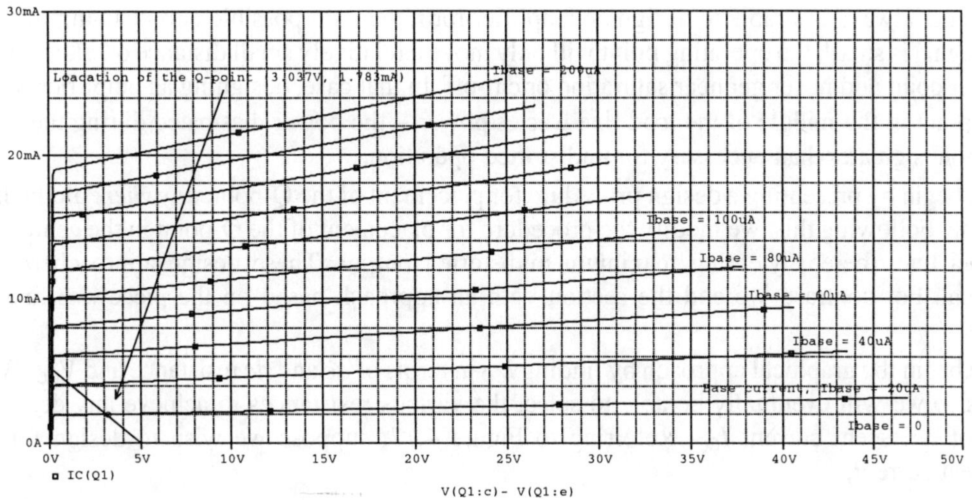

Figure 4.18(c) – Location of the Q-point. SPICE simulation of the characteristic curves for the transistor model 2N3904 for a maximum forward beta of 180 (The default maximum value of beta is 416.4).

We continue the comparison of the hand calculations (with the implied assumptions) and the computer simulation results for the steady-state (quiescent) power dissipations. The input power supplied to the circuit by the voltage source is easily computed as $V_{CC} \times I_{source} = 5\text{V}\times 2.374\text{mA}=11.87 \ \ (\text{mW})$ compared to 11.4 (mW) above. The transistor power dissipation that must be considered (worst case for this circuit) is $V_{CEQ} \times I_{CQ} = (3.217\text{V-}180.08\text{mV})\times 1.783\text{mA}=5.145 \ \ (\text{mW})$ compared to 5.32 (mW) computed above. The *ac* output power will be modeled in the next chapter.

The 2N3904 transistor characteristic I-V curves are shown in Figure 4.18(c) were generated from the SPICE model for a maximum forward beta of 180 [The parameter symbol BF represents the *maximum* forward beta transistor in the SPICE model.] For this example, the region of interest (lower left) of the characteristic curves was shown to have a *dc* beta $\beta_{dc} = 101.3(dc)$. Since the curves are not horizontal and evenly spaced, we expect beta to increase for regions toward the upper right. Indeed the reader may verify that $\beta_{dc} \approx 130$ in this region. However, the maximum 2N3904 collector current is 200 mA. Within this region (Not shown in Figure 4.18(c).), the maximum forward beta approaches 180. Low supply voltage for this example was chosen for illustration purposes.

4.11.2 Design Procedure

In *design* problems, we start with the collector-emitter side of the transistor rather than with the base side. We wish to place the Q-point at a specified location on the *ac* load line. We'll present several approaches. For the first approach, R_C and R_E are assumed to be given, and we need to determine the values of R_1 and R_2.

It is not always desirable to design an amplifier for maximum possible output swing. If the input signal is small, the operating point will only move a relatively small distance on either side of the Q-point and never get near saturation or cut-off. In that case, designing an amplifier with the Q-point in the middle of the load line wastes power – the power dissipated during the rest condition is greater than necessary for undistorted operation.

We begin by presenting a design procedure for placement of the Q-point *anywhere* along the load line. Following this, we modify the procedure for placement of the Q-point in the center of the load line, thereby yielding maximum undistorted output. These design approaches are graphical. For contrast, we end the section with an approach based on the piecewise linear model.

We begin the graphical approach by finding I_{CQ} in terms of *ac* and *dc* resistance and V_{CC}. We do this so we will eventually be able to select the various resistances to achieve any desired value of quiescent current I_{CQ}. Referring to Figure 4.17, suppose we wish to design for a quiescent current,

$$I_{CQ} = \delta I'_{CC} \tag{4.49}$$

I'_{CC} is the intersection of the *ac* load line with the current axis and δ is a number between 0 and 1. Note that when δ is equal to 0.5 then we will achieve the maximum possible undistorted symmetrical swing for the *ac* collector current. I'_{CC} is given by

$$I'_{CC} = \frac{V'_{CC}}{R_{ac}} = I_{CQ} + \frac{V_{CEQ}}{R_{ac}} \tag{4.50}$$

Combining Equations (4.49) and (4.50) we find V_{CEQ}.

$$V_{CEQ} = \frac{(1-\delta)}{\delta} \cdot I_{CQ} R_{ac} \tag{4.51}$$

Since the Q-point must also lie on the *dc* load line, we have

$$V_{CEQ} = V_{CC} - I_{CQ} R_{dc} \tag{4.52}$$

Equating (4.51) and (4.52) yields the Q-point equations.

$$\begin{gathered} V_{CEQ} = \frac{(1-\delta) I_{CQ} R_{ac}}{\delta} = V_{CC} - I_{CQ} R_{dc} \\ I_{CQ} = \frac{V_{CC}}{(1-\delta) R_{ac}/\delta + R_{dc}} \end{gathered} \tag{4.53}$$

Now that I_{CQ} has been determined, we use the *ac* load line equation [Equation (4.45)] to determine V_{CEQ}.

$$V_{CEQ} = V'_{CC}(1-\delta) \tag{4.54}$$

and for a Q-point in the middle of the *ac* load line,

$$V'_{CC} = 2\times\left(I_{CQ}R_{ac}\right) \tag{4.55}$$

If no other restrictions exist, we do not have enough equations to uniquely solve for the resistance. To specify the bias circuitry, we need an additional constraint. This is provided by what is known as *bias stability*. Stability relates to the sensitivity of certain operating results to changes in input parameters. We defer detailed discussion of bias stability to later [Chapter 7]. For now, we ask you to accept certain results.

For the emitter-resistor amplifier of Figure 4.12(b), bias stability can be achieved if a maximum of about 10% of the *dc* current flowing through R_2 goes into the base of the transistor (i.e., at least 90% of the current is shunted through R_1). Thus, a simple design rule for choosing the base resistors is that

$$I_{R1} \geq 9I_B = \frac{9I_E}{\beta+1} \approx \frac{9I_E}{\beta} \approx \frac{9I_C}{\beta} \tag{4.56}$$

where I_{R1} is the *dc* current through R_1. We now make the following substitution, where V_B is the voltage at the base.

$$\begin{aligned} I_E &= \frac{V_B - V_{BE}}{R_E} \\ I_{R1} &= \frac{V_B}{R_1} \end{aligned} \tag{4.57}$$

Equation (4.56) then becomes,

$$\frac{V_B}{R_1} \geq \frac{9(V_B - V_{BE})}{\beta R_E} \tag{4.58}$$

We first note that if we remove V_{BE} from the above condition, we make the condition stricter, so the bias stability condition still holds. Therefore,

$$\frac{V_B}{R_1} \geq \frac{9V_B}{\beta R_E} \geq \frac{9(V_B - V_{BE})}{\beta R_e} \tag{4.59}$$

We can now rearrange terms and cancel V_B from both sides of Equation (4.58) to get,

$$\begin{aligned} \frac{\beta R_E}{9} &\approx 0.11\beta R_E \geq R_1 \\ \frac{\beta R_E}{9} &\approx 0.11\beta R_E \geq R_B \end{aligned} \tag{4.60}$$

The second relationship in Equation (4.60) results from the observation that the Thevenin equivalent resistance, R_B, is the parallel combination of R_1 and R_2. It is therefore smaller than R_1 and we get a stricter inequality by making the substitution of R_B for R_1.

To provide for a safety margin, designers often set R_B equal to $0.1\beta R_E$ (which is also easier to remember). Thus,

$$R_B = 0.1\beta R_E \tag{4.61}$$

Using this rule, we can solve for the *dc* collector current using KVL and a Thevenin equivalent for the *dc* source and resistor at the base.

$$I_C = \frac{V_{BB} - V_{BE}}{0.1\beta R_E/\beta + R_E} = \frac{V_{BB} - V_{BE}}{1.1 R_E} \tag{4.62}$$

Equation (4.62) is used in the design process.

The bias equation can then be used to determine V_{BB}.

$$V_{BB} = V_{BE} + I_C(1.1 R_E) \tag{4.63}$$

Now that R_B and V_{BB} are known, we are ready to find R_1 and R_2. We solve Equation (4.38) to find R_1 and R_2.

$$R_1 = \frac{R_B}{1 - V_{BB}/V_{CC}} \qquad R_2 = \frac{V_{CC} R_B}{V_{BB}} \tag{4.64}$$

The design of the bias circuit is now complete. We can determine V_{out} (maximum undistorted symmetrical output) as we did in the analysis procedure. Assuming that the Q-point is on the lower half of the *ac* load line, (i.e., $\delta < 0.5$),

$$V_{out} = 2I_C(\text{maximum amplitude swing}) \times (R_C \| R_{load}) \tag{4.65}$$

If we wish to design for maximum output voltage swing (which we must do in many applications), we must place the Q-point in the middle of the *ac* load line. That is, the peak collector current must be twice the quiescent current. This specific case was included in the design procedures outlined above, but the expressions were written in terms of load line quantities. The result of the following derivation will express the location of the Q-point in terms of V_{CC}, R_{ac} and R_{dc}. From Equation (4.53), and setting $\delta = 0.5$, we see that the quiescent current is given by

$$I_{CQ}\big|_{\delta=0.5} = \frac{V_{CC}}{(1-\delta)R_{ac}/\delta + R_{dc}} = I_{CQ} = \frac{V_{CC}}{(1-0.5)R_{ac}/0.5 + R_{dc}} = \frac{V_{CC}}{R_{ac} + R_{dc}} \tag{4.66}$$

Since the peak collector current must be twice the quiescent current, we may write

$I_{C_{max}} \doteq I'_{CC} \approx 2 \cdot I_{CQ}$. We know this maximum current may also be expressed as $I'_{CC} = \frac{V_{CEQ}}{R_{ac}} + I_{CQ}$.

So we can write $2 \cdot \left[I_{CQ} \right] = \frac{V_{CE}}{R_{ac}} + I_{CQ}$. This implies that I_{CQ} must be set to $\frac{V_{CEQ}}{R_{ac}}$. But we already know that, in general, $I_C = \frac{-1}{R_{dc}} V_{CE} + \frac{V_{CC}}{R_{dc}}$ (*dc* load line equation) which holds for any point (V_{CE}, I_C) on the *dc* load line. Choosing now to used the needed value for I_C (set to $\frac{V_{CEQ}}{R_{ac}}$) in the *dc* load line equation, we have an important result:

$$V_{CEQ} = \frac{V_{CC}}{1 + \left(R_{dc} / R_{ac} \right)} \tag{4.67}$$

In other words, in order to have maximum voltage swing (or collector current swing), the Q-point must be located in the center of the *ac* load line at coordinates

$$\left(\frac{V_{CC}}{1 + \left(R_{dc} / R_{ac} \right)}, \frac{V_{CC}}{R_{ac} + R_{dc}} \right) \quad \text{[for } \delta = 0.5\text{]} \tag{4.68}$$

If you look back to Equations (4.53) and set δ = 0.5, you will see that those equations reduce to Equation (4.68).

Example 4.3 (Design)

Select R_1 and R_2 for maximum output voltage swing in the circuit shown in Figure 4.19.

Solution: We first determine I_{CQ} for the circuit.

$$R_{ac} = R_C \| R_{load} = 500 \quad \Omega$$

$$R_{dc} = R_E + R_C = 1100 \quad \Omega$$

$$I_{CQ} = \frac{V_{CC}}{R_{ac} + R_{dc}} = \frac{5}{500 + 1100} = 3.13 \quad \text{mA}$$

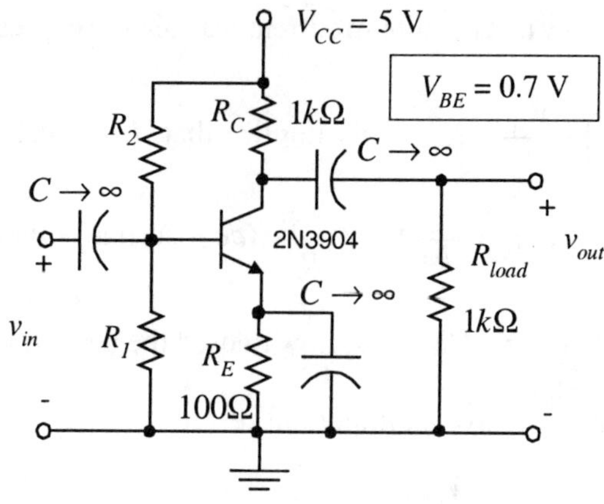

Figure 4.19 Circuit for Example 4.3

For maximum swing,

$$V'_{CC} = 2V_{CEQ}$$

The quiescent value for V_{CE} is then given by

$$V_{CEQ} = (3.13 \text{ mA})(500 \ \Omega) = 1.56 \quad \text{V}$$

The intersection of the *ac* load line on the v_{CE} axis is $V'_{CC} = 3.13$V. From the manufacturer's specification in the Appendix, β for the 2N3904 is 180. R_B is set equal to $0.1\beta R_{E,}$ so,

$$R_B = 0.1(180)(100) = 1.8 \quad \text{k}\Omega$$

$$V_{BB} = \left(3.13\times10^{-3}\right)(1.1\times100) + 0.7 = 1.044 \quad \text{V}$$

Since we know V_{BB} and R_B, we find R_1 and R_2,

$$R_1 = \frac{R_B}{1 - V_{BB}/V_{CC}} = \frac{1800}{1 - 1.044/5} = 2.28 \quad \text{k}\Omega$$

$$R_2 = \frac{R_B V_{CC}}{V_{BB}} = \frac{1800\times5}{1.044} = 8.62 \quad \text{k}\Omega$$

The maximum output voltage swing, ignoring the non-linearities at saturation and cutoff, would then be

$$\text{Max collector current swing} = 2I_{CQ}(R_C \| R_{load})$$
$$= 2(3.13mA)(500\Omega) = 3.13 \quad \text{V}$$

The load lines are shown on the characteristics of Figure 4.20.

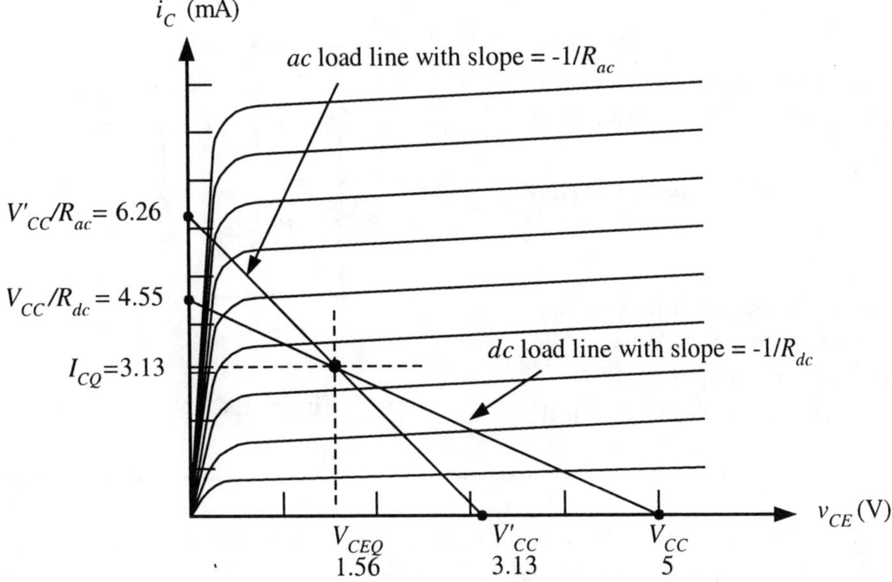

Figure 4.20 – Load lines for Example 4.3

We check the maximum power dissipated by the transistor to assure that it does not exceed the specifications. The maximum average power dissipated in the transistor is

$$P_{(transistor)} = V_{CEQ} I_{CQ} = (1.56\ (\mathrm{V}))(3.13\ \mathrm{mA}) = 4.87 \quad \mathrm{mW}$$

This is well within the 350 mW maximum given on the specification sheet. The maximum conversion efficiency is

$$\eta = \frac{P_{out}(ac)}{P_{VCC}(dc)} = \frac{\left(3.13\times10^{-3}/2\right)^2 \times 1000/2\times100}{5\times3.13\times10^{-3} + 5^2/10.9\times10^3} = 6.84\%$$

EXERCISES

E4.1 Find the maximum symmetrical peak-to-peak output voltage swing of the circuit of Figure E4.1 when R_1 =2 kΩ, R_2 = 15 kΩ, R_E = 200 Ω, R_C = 2 kΩ, R_{load} = 2 kΩ, β = 200, V_{BE} = 0.7V and V_{CC} = 15V.

Answer: 6.3V peak-to-peak

E4.2 In Exercise E4.1, design the amplifier for maximum possible symmetrical current swing. Find the values of R_1 and R_2.

(Answer: R_1 = 4.5 kΩ; R_2 = 36 kΩ)

E4.3 What is the maximum symmetrical voltage swing for the configuration of Exercise E4.2?

(Answer: 8.8V peak-to-peak)

E4.4 What is the output power of the amplifier of Exercise E4.2? What is the power supplied to the amplifier?

(Answer: 4.9 mW; 71.7 mW)

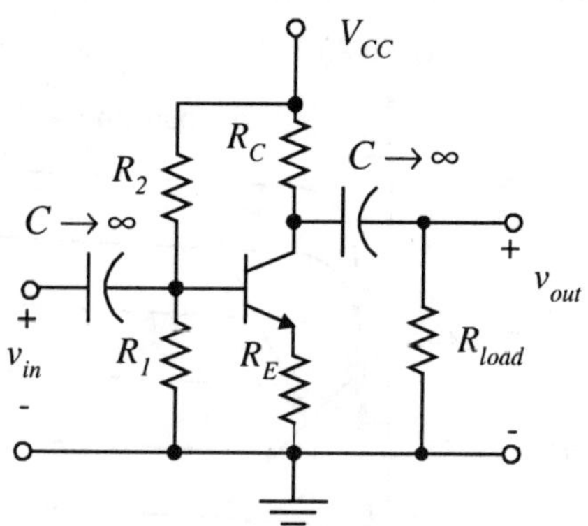

Figure E4.1

The design approach that we have been using is one which the values of R_C and R_E are provided which normally won't be the case. In the next chapter, we go one step further and you will have to solve for R_C and R_E when the amplifier gain is given or known. If you are designing an amplifier for maximum gain, then the value of R_E if not given will have to be selected such that it does not have too much effect on the *dc* transistor current and keeps the *dc* bias current within reason.

4.11.3 Amplifier dc Voltage Sources

The power supplied to an amplifier can be placed above the reference point (commonly referred to as positive with respect to ground) or below the reference point. The only criterion is that the polarity of the voltage must be proper for the operation of the transistor. In other words, the voltage must be positive to negative from the collector to the emitter for *npn* transistors or vice versa for *pnp* transistors. This allows us to use both positive and negative voltage sources as we did in the original presentation of amplifier configurations. By doing so, we can set the *dc* value of the output to any desired value, including zero.

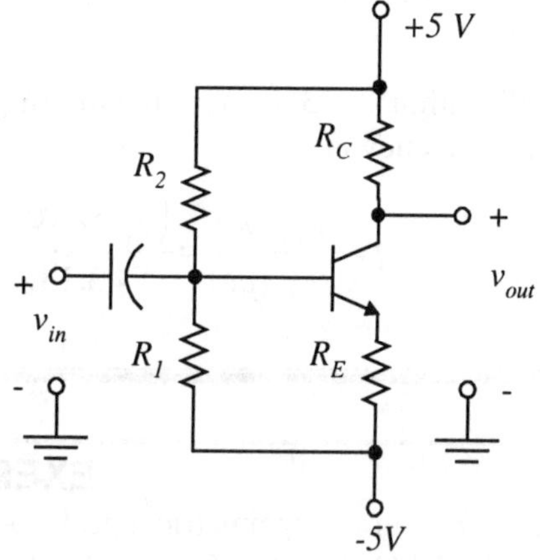

Figure 4.21 – Amplifier with two power supplies

We illustrate the amplifier in Figure 4.21. By setting $I_C R_C = 5\text{ V}$, the *dc* output taken from the collector is zero. The value of I_C is easily adjusted to whatever value needed by changing the values of R_1 and R_2. We will be using this concept when working with direct coupled amplifier in the next chapter.

EXERCISES

E4.5 Design a *dc* bias-stable common-emitter amplifier using the circuit shown in Figure 4.21 to obtain a quiescent output voltage of zero. Let $\beta = 150$, $V_{BE} = 0.7\text{V}$, $R_E = 100\ \Omega$ and $R_C = 1\ \text{k}\Omega$.

Answer: $R_1 = 1.71\ k\Omega;\ R_2 = 12\ k\Omega$

E4.6 Using the amplifier specified in Exercise E4.1, design the amplifier to provide an output for minimum current drain when $\delta = 0.2$.

Answer: $R_1 = 4.34\ k\Omega;\ R_2 = 51.2\ k\Omega$

4.11.4 Selection of Components

A design is not yet complete after the various component values are specified. It is still necessary to select the actual components to be used (e.g., choose the manufacturers' parts numbers from a catalog). For example, if the design requires a resistor of value 102.5 Ω, the designer will not be able to find that resistor in a standard parts catalog. Available nominal component values depend on tolerances. As an example, a 100-Ω resistor with a 5% tolerance can have any value between 95 Ω and 105 Ω. It would not make much sense for the manufacturer to offer another *off-the-shelf* resistor with a nominal rating of 101 Ω since that resistor could have a value between approximately 96 Ω and 106 Ω. The distance between adjacent nominal component values is therefore related to the tolerance, with such distance decreasing as the tolerance decreases (i.e., higher precision components). Standard values of resistors and capacitors are included in the Appendix.

Since component values are not readily available to high degrees of resolution, it would not make sense to carry out design calculations to an unreasonably large number of significant figures.

In our design examples, we specify values to at least three significant figures. This is important to assure that we still maintain accuracy to two significant figures following arithmetic operations. For example, suppose we must add (0.274 + 0.474). If these two numbers are rounded to two significant figures, we obtain (0.27 + 0.47 = 0.74). If we first do the calculation, we obtain (0.274 + 0.474 = 0.748) which rounds to 0.75. *Rounding the numbers prior to performing the addition results in an error in the second significant figure.* Thus, to reduce accumulated errors and to increase the confidence that our answers are accurate to two significant figures, we maintain at least three figures throughout the calculations.

4.12 ANALYSIS AND DESIGN OF CURRENT AMPLIFIER BIAS CIRCUITS

The emitter-follower (EF), or common-collector (CC), amplifier is a current amplifier. For this reason, it can be referred to as a power amplifier. It is illustrated in Figure 4.22.

The output of the EF amplifier is developed from the emitter to ground rather than from the collector to ground as is the case in the CE and emitter resistor amplifiers.

In the common emitter, there is a 180° phase shift between the base and collector voltages. As the input signal increases in value, the output signal decreases. In contrast to this, in the emitter follower, the output and input voltages are in phase with each other. The amplifier has a voltage gain of slightly less than unity. On the other hand, the current gain is significantly greater than one.

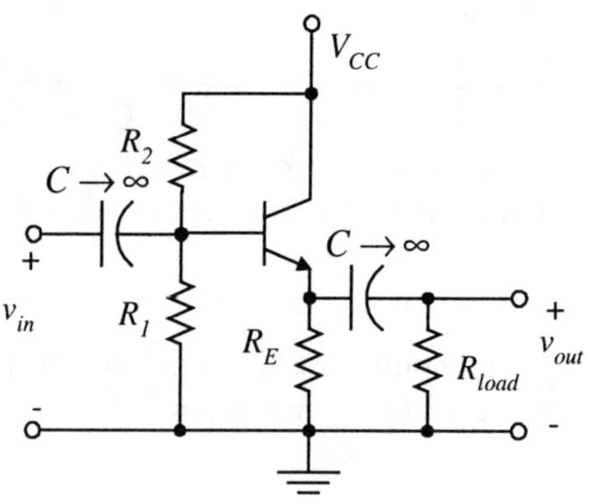

Figure 4.22 – Emitter-follower amplifier

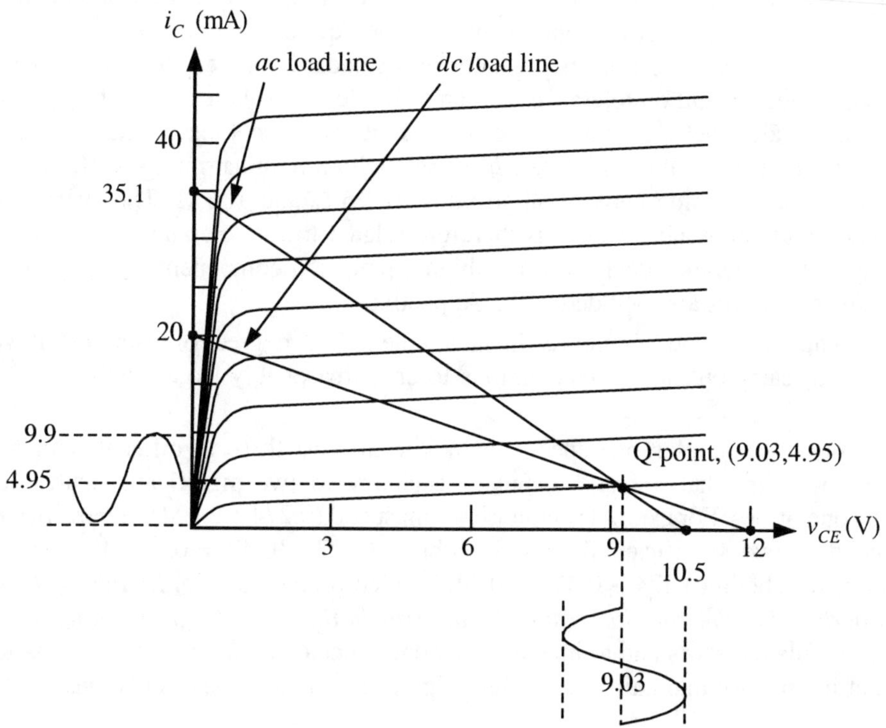

Figure 4.23 – Load line construction

We analyze this circuit in the same manner as we did the common emitter. The only differences are the values we use for R_{ac} and R_{dc}. For the emitter follower of Figure 4.22,

$$R_{ac} = R_E \| R_{load}$$
$$R_{dc} = R_E \tag{4.69}$$

Figure 4.23 illustrates a typical load line construction. The *dc* load line is specified by Equation (4.25).

$$i_C = \frac{V_{CC} - V_{CE}}{R_{dc}} \tag{4.70}$$

We showed earlier how to locate the Q-point for maximum swing, [see Equation (4.68)]. We therefore have

$$I_{CQ} = \frac{V_{CC}}{R_{ac} + R_{dc}} = \frac{V_{CC}}{R_E \| R_{load} + R_E}$$

$$V_{CEQ} = I_{CQ} R_{ac} = I_{CQ}(R_E \| R_{load}) \tag{4.71}$$

The effective load resistance for the emitter follower is different from that of the other amplifiers. It is now the parallel combination of R_E and R_{load}. The maximum output voltage swing is then

$$v_{out}(maximum\ output\ voltage\ swing) = 2 \times I_c(maximum\ amplitude) \times (R_E \| R_{load}) \tag{4.72}$$

Example 4.4 (Bias Circuit Design)

In the circuit of Figure 4.24 find the values of R_1 and R_2 that yield maximum symmetrical output swing as shown in Figure 4.23. Assume that a 2N2222 transistor is used with an average β of 100.

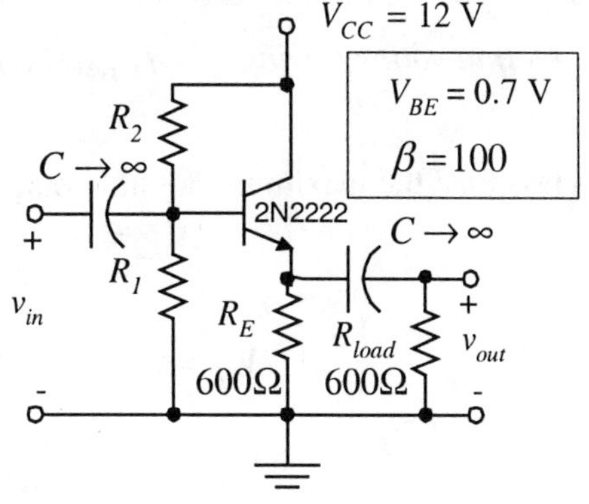

Figure 4.24 – EF amplifier for Example 4.4

Solution:

$$R_{dc} = R_E = 600 \quad \Omega$$
$$R_{ac} = R_E \| R_{load} = 300 \quad \Omega$$

$$I_{CQ} = \frac{V_{CC}}{R_{ac} + R_{dc}} = \frac{12}{600 + 300} = 13.3 \quad \text{mA}$$

Then

$$V_{CEQ} = I_{CQ} R_{ac} = (13.3 \times 10^{-3})(300) = 4.0 \quad \text{V}$$

In order to reduce the effects of variations in β, we choose

$$R_B = 0.1\beta R_E = 0.1(100\times600) = 6.0 \quad k\Omega$$

$$V_{BB} = V_{BE} + I_{CQ}\left(\frac{R_B}{\beta} + R_E\right) = 9.48 \quad V$$

From Equation (4.64) we obtain,

$$R_1 = \frac{R_B}{1 - V_{BB}/V_{CC}} = \frac{6000}{1 - 9.48/12} = 28.5 \quad k\Omega$$

$$R_2 = \frac{R_B V_{CC}}{V_{BB}} = \frac{6000\times12}{9.48} = 7.59 \quad k\Omega$$

The maximum output swing is then

$$Maximum\ output\ voltage\ swing = 2\times I_{CQ}\times\left(R_E \| R_{load}\right) = 2(0.0133)(300) = 8.0 \quad V$$

Example 4.5 (Bias Circuit Analysis)

Find the output voltage swing of the circuit of Figure 4.24 with $R_1 = 10$ kΩ and $R_2 = 20$ kΩ.

Solution: The Q-point location was calculated as part of Example 4.1 in Section 4.9. We found that the quiescent collector current is 4.95 mA. The output swing is then given by

$$Output\ voltage\ swing = 2\cdot I_{C\,peak}\cdot(R_E \| R_{Load}) = 2\left(4.95\times10^{-3}\right)(300) = 2.97 \quad V$$

This is less than the maximum possible output swing. Continuing the analysis,

$$V_{CEQ} = V_{CC} - I_{CQ}R_E = 9.03 \quad V$$

$$V_{CC}' = V_{CEQ} + I_{CQ}(R_E \| R_{load}) = 10.5 \quad V$$

$$I_{CC}' = \frac{10.5}{300} = 35.1 \quad mA$$

The load lines for this problem are shown in Figure 4.25.

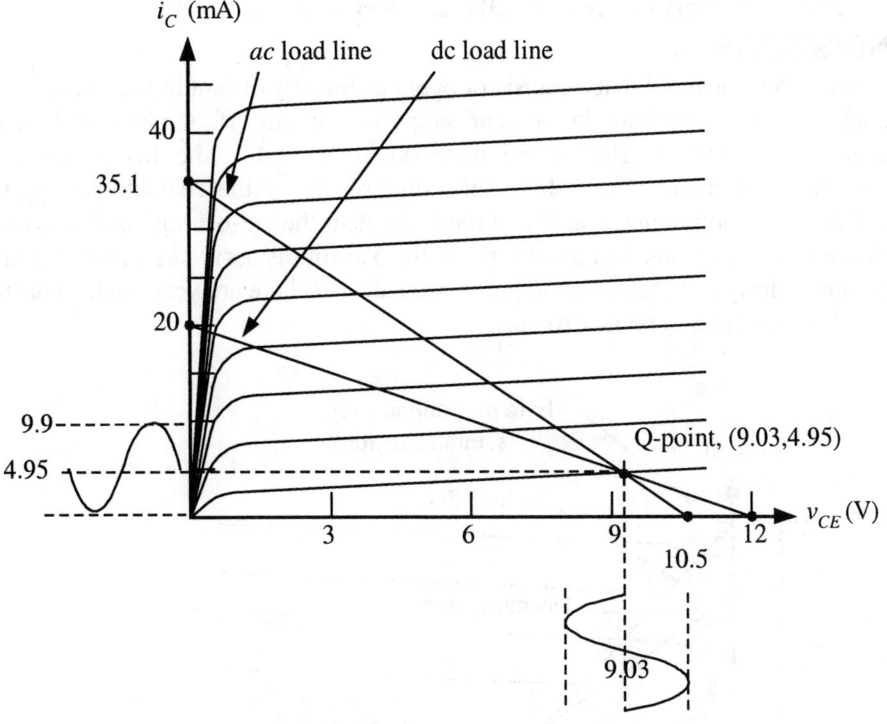

Figure 4.25 – Load lines for Example 4.5

EXERCISES

E4.7 What is the maximum symmetrical voltage swing for the amplifier of Figure 4.22(a) where $V_{CC} = 15\text{V}$, $R_1 = 8\ \text{k}\Omega$, $R_2 = 2\ \text{k}\Omega$, $R_E = 1\ \text{k}\Omega$, $R_{load} = 1\ \text{k}\Omega$, $V_{BE} = 0.7\text{V}$ and $\beta = 80$?

Answer: 7.8V peak-to-peak

E4.8 In Exercise E4.7, redesign the amplifier for the maximum symmetrical voltage swing. What are the new values of R_1, R_2 and V_{out}?

Answer: 36.4 kΩ, 10.3 kΩ, 10V peak-to-peak

E4.9 What is the conversion efficiency of the amplifier design in Exercise E4.8?

Answer: 8.4%

4.13 NONLINEARITIES OF BIPOLAR JUNCTION TRANSISTORS

In Section 4.5 we learned that a transistor operates linearly except in the saturation and cut-off regions. When we operate in or near saturation or cut-off, the output is a distorted reproduction of the input. The shaded regions shown in Figure 4.26 should therefore be avoided for linear amplification. Designers frequently discard 5% of the characteristic curve in the vicinity of the saturation region and 5% of the curve near the cut-off region. The actual size of the nonlinear region is a function of current, so the 5% simply serves as a rule of thumb and a starting point in design. If increased output is needed, or if there are very "tight" constraints on distortion, this may have to be modified.

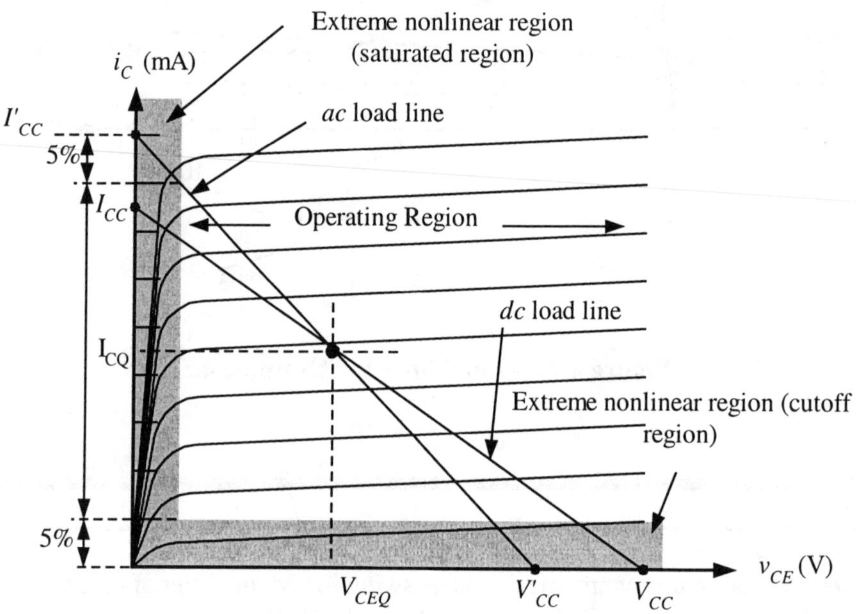

Figure 4.26 – Nonlinear portions of the characteristic curves

Using the 5% guideline and assuming the I_{CQ} has been placed in the *center* of the *ac* load line, the undistorted peak-to-peak output voltage is given by:

$$v_{out}(p-p) = 0.9 \times 2(|I_{CQ}|)(R_{load} \| R_C) = 1.8|I_{CQ}| \times (R_{load} \| R_C) \quad \text{[middle]} \qquad (4.73)$$

Suppose now that I_{CQ} is *not* in the middle of the load line. The circuit will then have a reduced symmetrical output swing. Figure 4.27 graphically illustrates this reduced swing. The maximum symmetrical output swing can be determined as follows. Let us assume that the collector current varies as a sinusoid with peak, I_{Cm}. This current in then given by

$$i_C(t) = I_{C_m} \sin \omega t \qquad (4.74)$$

Then the maximum undistorted output swing for a common emitter amplifier, emitter resistor amplifier, or common base amplifier must be established for the following two special cases:

For the case where I_{CQ} is below the center of the *ac* load line as in Figure 4.27(a), we have

$$I_{Cm} = I_{CQ} - 0.05 \times I'_{CC} \ [removing\ 5\%\ of\ I'_{CC}]$$

where I_{Cm} is the allowable undistorted peak swing of the collector current. I'_{CC} is the intercept of the *ac* load line with the i_C-axis found by

$$I'_{CC} = \frac{V'_{CC}}{R_{ac}}. \tag{4.75}$$

$$v_{out}(max\ undistorted\ swing) = 2I_{Cm}\left(R_{load} \| R_C\right) = 2\left(I_{CQ} - 0.05I'_{CC}\right)\cdot\left(R_{load} \| R_C\right) \tag{4.76}$$

For the case where I_{CQ} is above the center of the *ac* load line as in Figure 4.27(b),

$$I_{Cm} = 0.95 \times I'_{CC} - I_{CQ} \ \ [removing\ 5\%\ of\ I'_{CC}] \tag{4.77}$$

The maximum undistorted swing for a common-emitter amplifier, emitter-resistor amplifier, or common-base amplifier is then

$$v_{out}(max\ undistorted\ swing) = 2I_{Cm}\left(R_{load} \| R_C\right) = 2 \times \left(0.95 \times I'_{CC} - I_{CQ}\right)\cdot\left(R_{load} \| R_C\right) \tag{4.78}$$

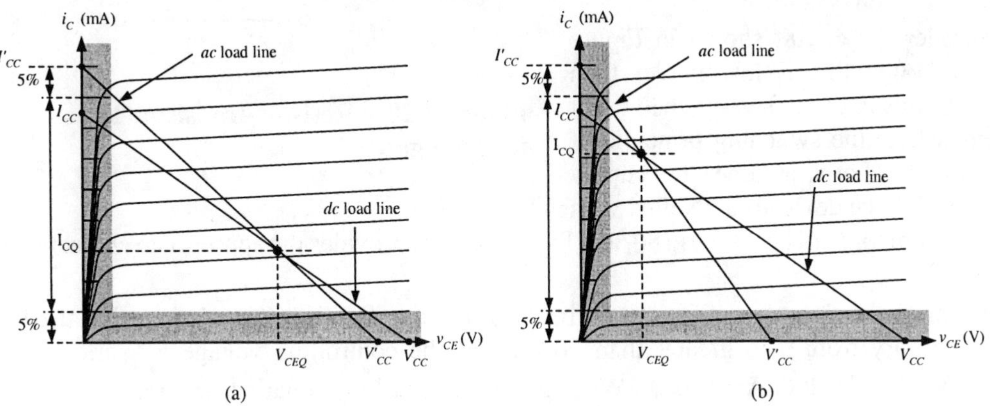

Figure 4.27 - Reduced swing on load line

For the emitter follower amplifier, the maximum undistorted output swing for biasing in the center of the *ac* load line is

$$v_{out}(max\ undistorted\ swing) = 2\left(\left|I_{Cm}\right|\right)\left(R_{load}\|R_E\right)$$
$$= 0.9I'_{CC}\left(R_{load}\|R_E\right) = 0.9\left(2\left|I_{CQ}\right|\right)\left(R_{load}\|R_E\right) \qquad \text{[middle]} \quad (4.79)$$
$$= 1.8\left|I_{CQ}\right|\left(R_{load}\|R_E\right)$$

When biasing is not in the middle of the *ac* load line for the emitter follower, the equations would be the same as those of Equations (4.75) and (4.78) except that the parallel combination of R_C with R_{load} is *replaced* by a parallel combination of R_E and R_{load}.

4.14 ON-OFF CHARACTERISTICS OF BJT CIRCUITS

So far we have been concentrating on how the transistor operates in the normal active mode. We have learned how to keep the transistor biased so that it only operates in that mode. This permits *ac* signals to be amplified linearly. Another major application of transistors is *switching* for digital logic operations. We want as wide a separation as possible in the voltages and currents representing a "1" state and a "0" state.

One way to create a wide separation is to define one of the logic states as the transistor being turned all the way *ON* (saturated), and the other state as the transistor being completely *OFF* (cut-off). We control these operations by controlling the emitter-base voltage since the transistor currents are exponentially dependent on this parameter.

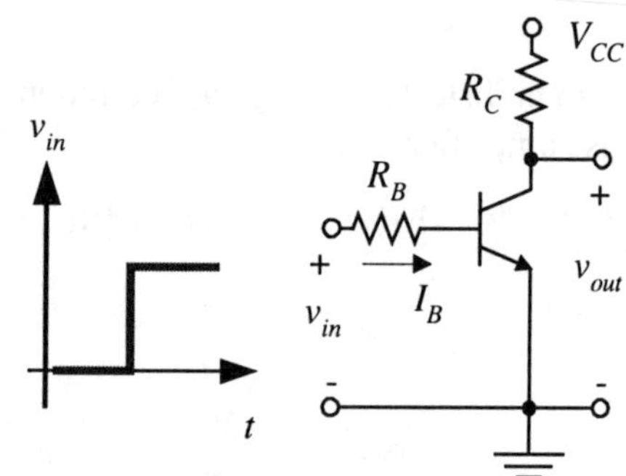

Figure 4.28 – Resistor-transistor logic inverter gate

Consider the circuit shown in Figure 4.28. Although this is far simpler than digital circuits in use today, we shall use it to demonstrate the switching principle of BJT circuits. Let's assume the supply voltage is 5V, the device is a 2N3904 with the maximum forward beta set to 180, and Figure 4.18(c) provides the appropriate characteristic curves.

We can cause this transistor to jump between the two limiting states by causing the bias current to vary from 0 to greater than 200 μA as the controlling voltage v_{in} varies $\pm 1\text{V}$. [$R_B \approx (1\text{V} - 0.7\text{V})/200\mu\text{A} = 1.5\text{k}\Omega$] Writing the collector loop equation, we find

$$V_{CC} = i_C(R_C + R_E) + v_{CE} \qquad (4.80)$$

If we now let the collector current approach zero, v_{CE} approaches the source voltage, $V_{CC} = 5\text{V}$. This is the cutoff condition or the *OFF* area of operation where no current flows in the transistor. Conversely, if v_{CE} approaches zero, we have

$$i_C = \frac{V_{CC}}{R_C + R_E} \tag{4.81}$$

This is the saturation region, or the *ON* area of operation. The transistor provides very little collector-emitter resistance to current flow. This condition cannot be exactly achieved due to the fact that this portion of the characteristic curves are not vertical straight lines. At the crossing of the 200 μA characteristic curve and the associated load line running from V_{CC} on the x-axis to I_{CC} on the y-axis, the collector-emitter voltage is not exactly zero. It is about 0.1 or 0.3V. As the characteristic curve approaches the $v_{CE} = 0$ line, it starts to very rapidly drops off. β is starting to decrease from the relatively stable value in the operating region to near zero. The value of i_B for saturation will be different for each circuit. To assure that the transistor is truly in saturation, the base current is usually made larger than 200 μA. Remember that the base-emitter junction must be forward-biased with a voltage greater than about 0.7V to get any significant current flow.

Even when the transistor is in saturation, the base-collector current relationship is $i_C = \beta i_B$. As the base current increases while in saturation, β starts decreasing (to offset the increase in base current). While in saturation, v_{CE} remains fairly constant. It might drop from 0.3 to 0.1V as the base current increases, but it does not vary beyond that range.

The base-emitter junction behaves as a diode, so the voltage must exceed V_{ON} of the junction for any significant current to flow.

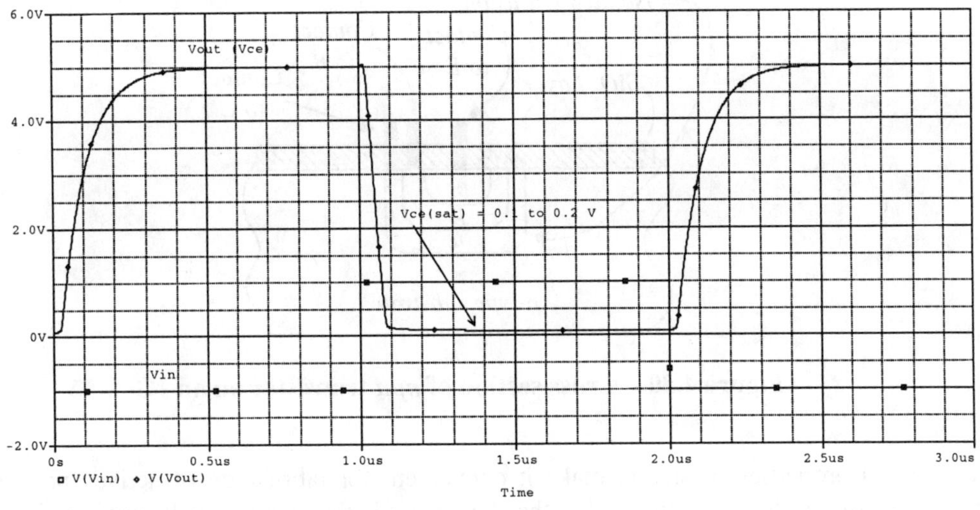

Figure 4.29 – Transistor circuit with square wave voltage input

Figure 4.29 shows the 2N3904 transistor circuit performance (SPICE simulation) with a ±1 V square wave input signal V_{in}. The output waveform is shown as V_{out} (V_{CE}) in the figure. The square wave could have been clamped at zero and still provide the same results. If we were to be precise, the output does have some non-zero rise time, fall time, delay and storage time during switching. However, in many cases these details are not important to the understanding of the theory of operation of digital circuits. The factors contributing to the delay are the time it takes to charge up the emitter-base capacitance and the time it takes for the minority carriers to cross the emitter junction to the base. Since the collector current is increasing or decreasing along an exponential curve, this also affects the time of transition from one state to the other.

Let's now examine the output voltage, v_{out} of Figure 4.29. The voltage varies from V_{CC} to v_{CE}(sat). The quantity, v_{CE}(sat) is between 0.1 and 0.3V for most transistors. Therefore, the *ON* voltage is the value of V_{CC} and the *OFF* voltage is between 0.1 and 0.3V. Notice the transistion times, turn-on and turn-off, are roughly 400 and 100 nano-seconds, respectively, for this transistor. The use of these types of circuits will be discussed further when we consider digital electronics.

4.15 INTEGRATED CIRCUIT FABRICATION

A complex circuit can often be fabricated on a single silicon chip. The circuit can be composed of transistors, resistors and capacitors, all of which are small enough to be located on the chip. We briefly discuss the fabrication of each of these elements in the following Sections.

4.15.1 Transistors and Diodes

Integrated circuit (IC) transistors and diodes are usually fabricated on a silicon substrate material although gallium arsenide is more commonly used for high-frequency applications.

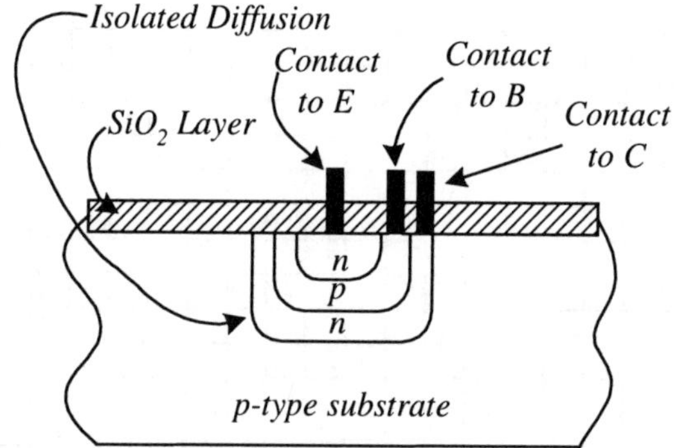

Figure 4.30 – Cross section of *npn* transistor on an IC

The physical properties of silicon make it convenient for fabrication of active and passive devices on a single chip. Silicon also has the characteristic that allows it to be easily oxidized to form insulating layers. The insulating property provides isolation between devices on the chip. This property also allows fabrication of different integrated circuit components at the same time on a single chip with the interconnections to provide the complete circuit. To fully understand how ICs are fabricated, you should become acquainted with the varying processes used for developing the different types of ICs. We will only mention some of these processes and leave the details to books on IC fabrication. Some of the processes used are oxidation, diffusion, ion implantation, chemical vapor deposition, metallization, epitaxial growth, and photolithography. A simple explanation of the development of an *npn* transistor follows.

A substrate of *p*-type material is subjected to an oxidizing atmosphere at an elevated temperature. This forms a thin layer of silicon oxide, or glass, on the surface of the substrate. The thin layer of silicon oxide is removed in selected areas using a photoengraving process, thus exposing the *p*-type material of the substrate. The silicon chip is then placed in an *n*-type atmosphere at an elevated temperature which causes the *n*-type atoms to diffuse into the exposed *p*-type material. The original process of obtaining the SiO_2 layer is then repeated. The photoengraving process is then repeated over a smaller area to form the base region. The chip is subjected to a *p*-type atmosphere at an elevated temperature which causes the *p*-type atoms to diffuse into the *n*-type silicon. The oxidation process is then repeated and a smaller area is photoengraved forming the emitter. This time, the chip is subjected to an *n*-type atmosphere to get the *n*-type diffusion as shown in Figure 4.30. Oxidizing and photoengraving is redone to expose each of the three layers of the transistor for the connections to the outside terminals. This is accomplished by depositing metal in those areas to form the terminals. If the junction between the substrate and the collector is maintained in a reverse-biased condition during the processing, the leakage current will be small and the substrate and the newly developed transistor is effectively insulated. As you can visualize from Figure 4.30, a number of devices can be made at the same time. Diodes can be fabricated on the chip if the exposure to the final *n*-type atmosphere is eliminated. To fabricate a *pnp* transistor, an *n*-type silicon substrate material is used and the types of impurities used during exposure processes are reversed.

4.15.2 Resistors

Resistors are produced on an IC at the same time as the transistors. For example, a thin channel of *p*-type material can be used to produce the resistor. This is isolated by use of a layer of *n*-type material. The *p*-type material is diffused during the same step in production as the base of the transistor. The amount of resistance is controlled by varying the thickness and the impurity level of the material. The channel width and its length affect the value of the resistance. In fact, the resistance is directly proportional to the length of the channel (assuming a constant width). If this fabrication technique does not provide a sufficiently high resistance, the channel can be overlaid upon itself several times thus increasing the effective length and resistance. Resistances above about 100 kΩ are usually avoided on ICs because of physical size limitations.

4.15.3 Capacitors

There are two types of capacitors used on an IC chip: a diffused capacitor and a MOS capacitor. The *diffused capacitor* takes advantage of the incremental junction capacitance of a reverse-biased *pn*-junction.

The *MOS capacitor* is made in a manner similar to that of a conventional capacitor. The lower conductor is a highly doped n-material; The insulator is a film of silicon dioxide; The other plate is a metallized layer which also forms one contact point. This type of capacitor provides about 400 to 600 pF per square millimeter. Because of the relatively large amount of space needed for capacitors, the number used in IC design is usually kept small.

4.15.4 Lateral Transistors

Lateral pnp transistors can be fabricated on ICs using simple planar technology. Small *p*-type material is used as the emitter and this is placed on a slab of *n*-material which is used as the base. A ring of *p*-channel material is used as the collector. The emitter *p*-type material is placed within this ring, with separating *n*-material used as the base. Holes are injected from the emitter and flow parallel to the surface across the *n*-type base region. The holes are collected by the *p*-type collector before reaching the base contact. The transistor action is lateral rather than vertical, as illustrated in Figure 4.31.

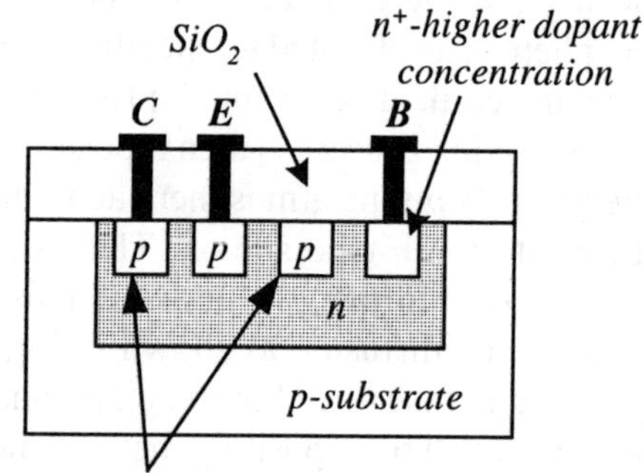

Figure 4.31 – Cross-section of a lateral transistor

Lateral *pnp* transistors have relatively low current gains (on the order of 10 to 50) because the base width is much larger than that of the standard *pnp*. Because they are easy to fabricate on ICs, these transistors are used for active loads, current sources, and level shifters (these are discussed in later chapters). An advantage of the lateral transistor is that the base-emitter breakdown voltage is much larger than that of a standard *npn* or *pnp* transistor [on the order of about 50V].

SUMMARY

Congratulations! You have finished what, in many ways, is the most difficult chapter of this text. This chapter not only introduced an electronic device that is far more complex than the diode of the previous chapter, but it also gave you an initial exposure to some very powerful analysis and design procedures. Once you understand the basic concepts we have presented, the remainder of your studies will follow a logical progression as you move into the exciting areas of practical applications.

We began this chapter with an analysis of the internal construction and operation of the bipolar junction transistor. After a brief introduction to the physics, we used the terminal behavior to derive small signal models. More than one model was presented, both because you will find a variety in the literature (and in computer simulation software), and because it is important to understand the limitations and advantages of the various models. We looked at manufacturers' specifications, and at the overall operating curves for the BJT. We also looked at models used by computer simulations.

Once we understood the operating modes of the transistor, we explored the ways in which the transistor is hooked to the outside world in order to perform useful functions. This brought us to the major configurations, and to the biasing techniques used to force us to operate the transistor in the desirable ranges of the operating curves. We also analyzed power utilization so you can check whether your designs are within manufacturer's specifications for maximum power.

We developed organized analysis and design techniques for the various circuit configurations. Since the number of unknowns in the design problem (i.e. the component values) is greater than the number of equations, we looked at various design guidelines which serve to address the trade-off considerations in a real-life design problem.

Although we do not deal extensively with digital circuitry until later in this text, we briefly examined the properties of transistor operation which allow the BJT to be used as a switch. The chapter concluded with an examination of the methods of incorporating BJTs into integrated circuit design.

PROBLEMS

Section 4.9

4.1 For the circuit shown in Figure P4.1, find I_C and I_B if:

a. $V_{BB} = 2V$, $R_B = 1\ k\Omega$, $R_E = 10\ \Omega$, and $R_C = 1\ k\Omega$.

b. $V_{BB} = 1V$, $R_B = 1\ k\Omega$, $R_E = 100\ \Omega$, and $R_C = 2.5\ k\Omega$.

c. $V_{BB} = .6V$, $R_B = 20\ k\Omega$, $R_E = 100\ \Omega$, and $R_C = 2\ k\Omega$.

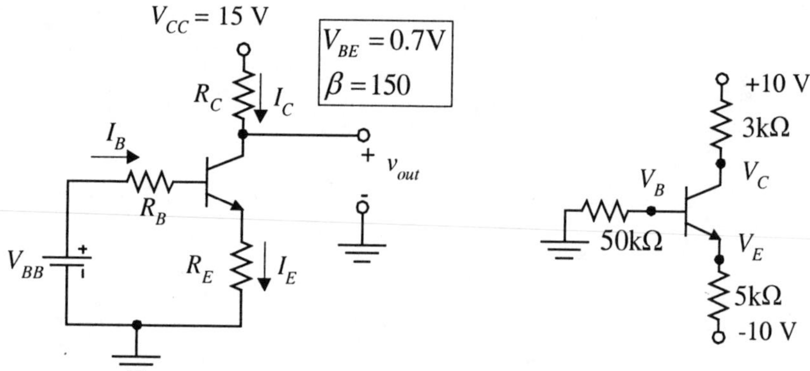

Figure P4.1 **Figure P4.2**

4.2 Determine the voltage at points V_C, V_E, and V_{CE} in the circuit shown in Figure P4.2 when $V_{BE} = 0.7V$ and $\beta = 100$.

4.3 Determine the voltage at points V_C, V_E, and V_{CE} in the circuit shown in Figure P4.3 when $V_{BE} = -0.7V$ and $\beta = 100$.

4.4 If the resistance, R_B, is made zero in Problem 4.3, what effect does this change have on the circuit operation?

4.5 Find the values of R_1 and R_2 necessary to place the Q-point of the circuit of Figure P4.5 in the center of the *dc* load line. Assume that $V_{CC} = -25V$, $R_C = 2\ k\Omega$, $R_E = 1\ k\Omega$ and β has the following values:

a. $\beta = 150$

b. $\beta = 100$

c. $\beta = 50$

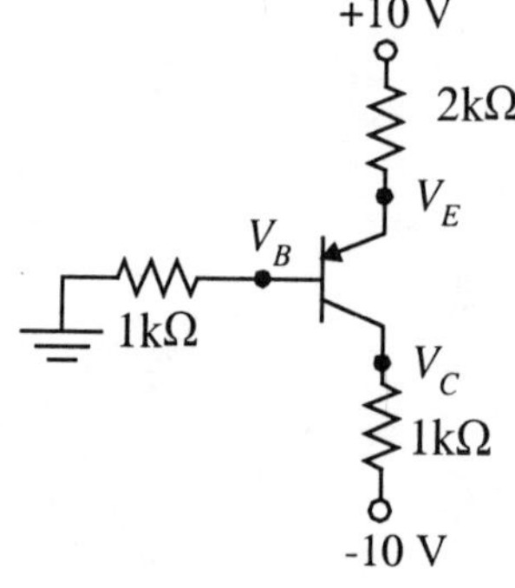

Figure P4.3

4.6 Find the maximum peak-to-peak amplitude swing of i_C in the circuit of Figure P4.6. Assume that $V_{CC} = 24V$, $R_C = 2\ k\Omega$, $R_E = 400\ \Omega$, and $\beta = 100$. Draw the *dc* load when:

a. $R_1 = 1\ k\Omega$; $R_2 = 7\ k\Omega$

b. $R_1 = 1\ k\Omega$; $R_2 = 35\ k\Omega$

c. $R_1 = 1\ k\Omega$; $R_2 = 3\ k\Omega$

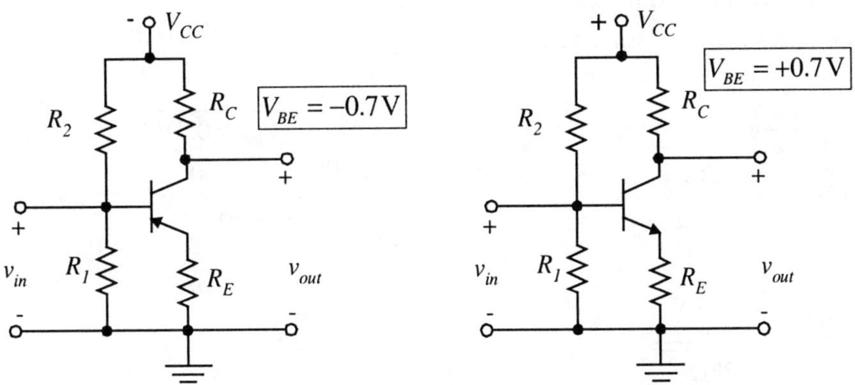

Figure P4.5 **Figure P4.6**

4.7 Find I_{CQ} and V_{CEQ} of circuit shown in Figure P4.7 when:

a. $R_1 = 10\ k\Omega$

b. $R_1 = \infty$

c. R_1 = value required for maximum output swing

4.8 For the circuit shown in Figure P4.8, determine the output voltage v_{out} when $V_{BE} = 0.7V$, $\beta = 200$, and $v_{in} = 0$.

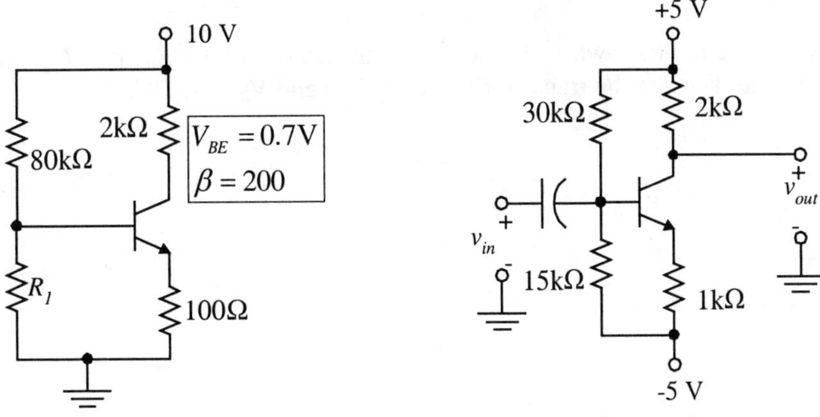

Figure P4.7 **Figure P4.8**

4.9 Determine R_1 and R_2 to obtain a zero quiescent output voltage for the circuit shown in Figure P4.9 when the transistor has a $\beta = 200$ and $V_{BE} = -0.6$V. (Assume $R_B = 10$ kΩ)

4.10 Find the following for the amplifier of Figure P4.10:

a. The values of R_1 and R_2 to achieve $I_{CQ} = 10$ mA.

b. The output symmetrical swing for the resistors in part (a).

c. Draw the *ac* and *dc* load lines.

d. Sketch the waveforms for i_C and v_{CE}.

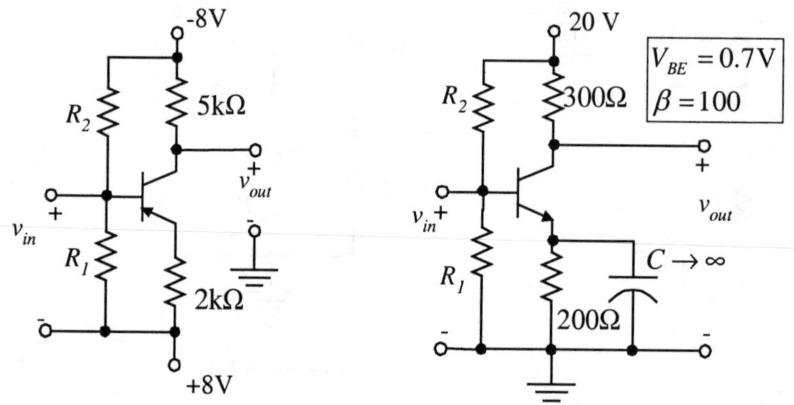

Figure P4.9 **Figure P4.10**

4.11 For the amplifier of Figure P4.10,

a. Find the values of R_1 and R_2 to achieve maximum symmetrical output swing.

b. Determine the value of that swing achieved in part (a).

c. draw the *ac* and *dc* load lines.

d. Sketch the waveforms of i_C and v_{CE}.

4.12 Analyze the circuit shown in Figure P4.12 to determine the R_B, V_{BB}, I_{CQ}, V_{CEQ}, and V_C (collector to neutral) when the transistor has a $\beta = 100$ and $V_{BE} = -0.7$V.

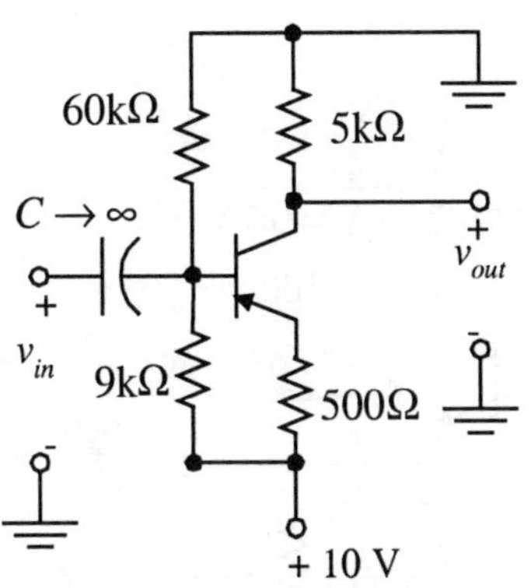

Figure P4.12

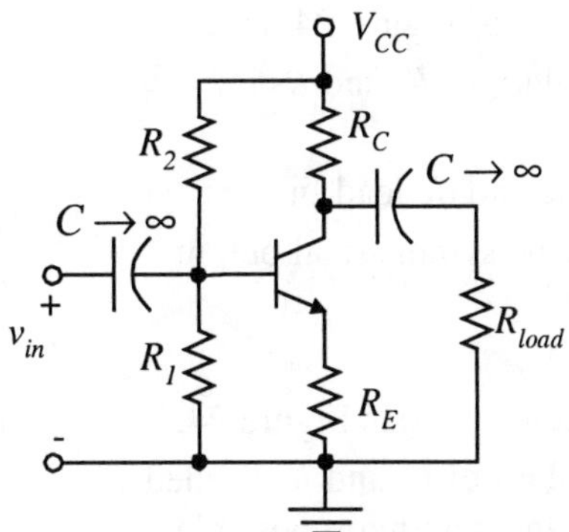

Figure P4.13

4.13 Find the output peak-to-peak symmetrical swing of i_C in the circuit of Figure P4.13 when $R_1 = 5\ \text{k}\Omega$, $R_2 = 50\ \text{k}\Omega$, $V_{CC} = 12\text{V}$, $V_{BE} = 0.7\text{V}$, $R_E = 300\ \Omega$, $\beta = 200$, and $R_C = R_{load} = 5\ \text{k}\Omega$.

4.14 With the circuit in Problem 4.13, find the values of R_1 and R_2 that yield the maximum possible symmetrical peak-to-peak swing of i_C. Draw the load lines.

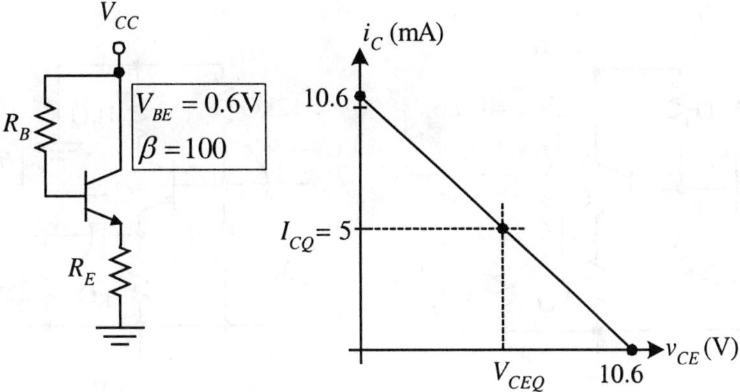

Figure P4.15

4.15 Find V_{CC}, R_B, and R_E in the circuit shown in Figure P4.15.

4.16 For the circuit of Figure P4.16:

a. Find the values of R_1 and R_2 if $I_{CQ} = 6$ mA

b. Draw the *ac* and *dc* load lines.

c. Determine the symmetrical output voltage swing.

4.17 For the circuit of Figure P4.16:

a. Find the values of R_1 and R_2 if I_{CQ} = 10 mA.

b. Draw the *ac* and *dc* load lines.

c. Determine the symmetrical output voltage swing.

4.18 For the circuit shown in Figure P4.16:

a. Find the values of R_1 and R_2 needed to achieve the maximum possible output voltage swing.

b. Draw the *ac* and *dc* load lines.

c. Determine the maximum symmetrical output swing.

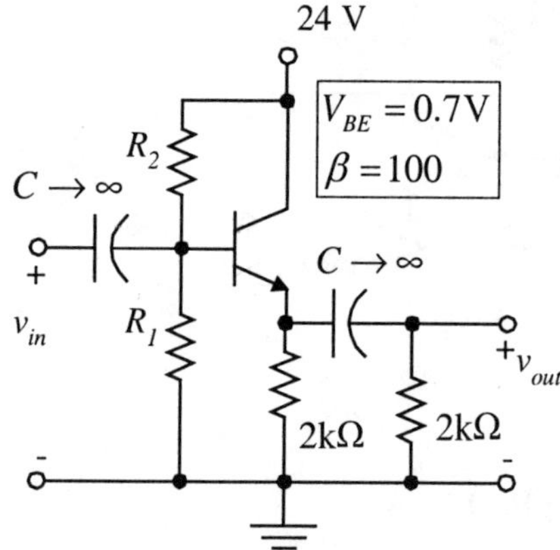

Figure P4.16

4.19 For the emitter-follower amplifier of Figure P4.19:

a. Determine the values of I_{CQ} and V_{CEQ}.

b. Determine the symmetrical output voltage swing.

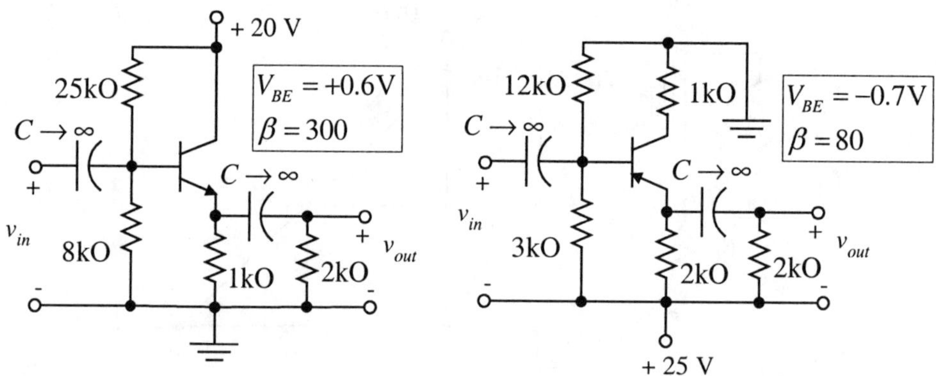

Figure P4.19 **Figure P4.20**

4.20 For the emitter-follower amplifier shown in Figure P4.20

a. Determine the values of I_{CQ} and V_{CEQ}.

b. Draw the *dc* and *ac* load lines.

c. Determine the symmetrical output voltage swing.

d. The 1 kΩ resistor is now bypassed with a capacitor. Describe the changes that occur in the circuit.

Section 4.10

4.21 For the amplifier of Problem 4.13, calculate the following:

a. Power supplied by the battery.

b. Power dissipated by R_1, R_2, R_E, and R_C.

c. Power dissipated by the transistor.

4.22 For the amplifier of Problem 4.14

a. Power supplied by the battery.

b. Power dissipated by R_1, R_2, R_E, and R_C.

c. Power dissipated by the transistor.

d. Compare the results with those obtained in Problem 4.21.

4.23 For the amplifier of Figure P4.13 where $R_1 = 3$ kΩ, $R_2 = 20$ kΩ, $R_C = R_{load} = 1$ kΩ, $R_E = 200$ Ω, $\beta = 100$, $V_{BE} = 0.7$V and $V_{CC} = 20$V, find the location of the Q-point. The transistor is replaced with another of different β. Find the minimum required value of β so that I_{CQ} does not change by more than 10%.

4.24 For the amplifier of Figure P4.24,

a. Find the values of R_1 and R_2 for $I_{CQ} = 8$ mA.

b. Determine the symmetrical output voltage swing for the values of part (a).

c. Draw the *ac* and *dc* load lines.

d. Determine the power dissipated by the transistor and the power dissipated by R_{load}.

Section 4.11

4.25 For the amplifier of Figure P4.24,

a. Find the values of R_1 and R_2 for $I_{CQ} = 4$ mA.

b. Determine the symmetrical output voltage swing for the values of part (a).

c. Draw the *ac* and *dc* load lines.

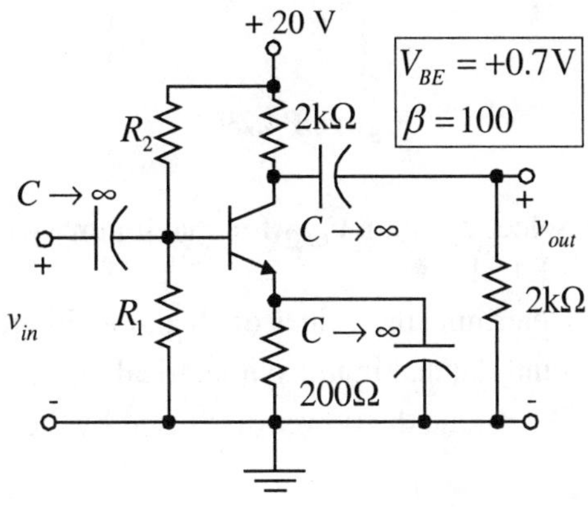

Figure P4.24

4.26 For the amplifier of Figure P4.24,

a. Find the values of R_1 and R_2 needed to achieve the maximum symmetrical swing.

b. Determine the symmetrical output voltage swing for the values of part (a).

c. Draw the *ac* and *dc* load lines.

4.27 For the amplifier in Problem 4.26, the transistor is replaced with another transistor with a β of 300 with no change in resistor values, what is the maximum output voltage swing with the new β? Compare the results with Problem 4.20 and discuss the differences.

4.28 For the amplifier in Problem 4.27, design the amplifier to obtain the maximum symmetrical output voltage swing by changing the values of R_1 and R_2. Also determine the output voltage swing and compare with the results of Problem 4.26 and 4.27.

4.29 Analyze the circuit shown in Figure P4.29 to determine the V_{BB}, R_B, I_{CQ}, V_{CEQ}, and V_{out}. [Assume $\beta = 100$ and $V_{BE} = -0.7\text{V}$]

4.30 Determine the value of R_C for a maximum symmetrical output voltage swing for the circuit of Figure P4.30. Draw the *dc* and *ac* load lines. Determine the peak-to-peak value of the maximum symmetrical output voltage.

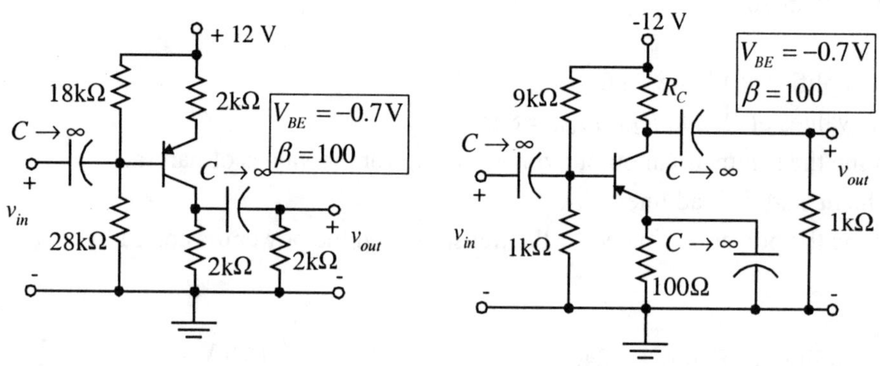

Figure P4.29 **Figure P4.30**

4.31 Select I_{CQ} and V_{CEQ} for maximum symmetrical output voltage swing for the circuit of Figure P4.31.

a. Determine the values of R_1 and R_2 in order to achieve this operating point.

b. Find the maximum symmetrical output voltage swing.

c. Determine the power dissipated by the transistor and the power delivered to the load.

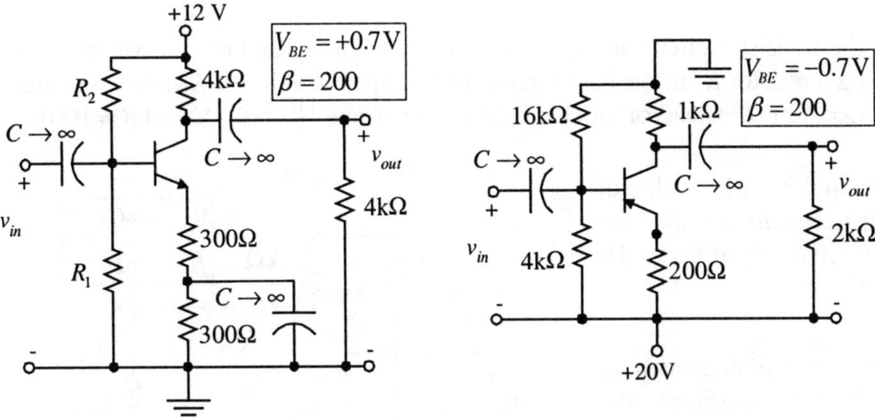

Figure P4.31 **Figure P4.32**

4.32 For the circuit of Figure P4.32,

a. Find I_{CQ} and V_{CEQ}.

b. Determine whether the amplifier is stable for large changes in β. You may assume β is in the range of $150 < \beta < 250$.

c. Draw the *dc* and *ac* load lines.

d. Determine the symmetrical output voltage swing.

4.33 An *ac* voltage source v_{TH} is applied directly to the base of an *npn* transistor as shown in Figure P4.33. The internal resistance of the *ac* voltage source is shown as R_{source}. Determine I_{CQ}, V_{CEQ}, and V_{out} when the *ac* input is zero. [Assume $\beta = 100$, $V_{BE} = 0.7V$, and R_B set to zero.]

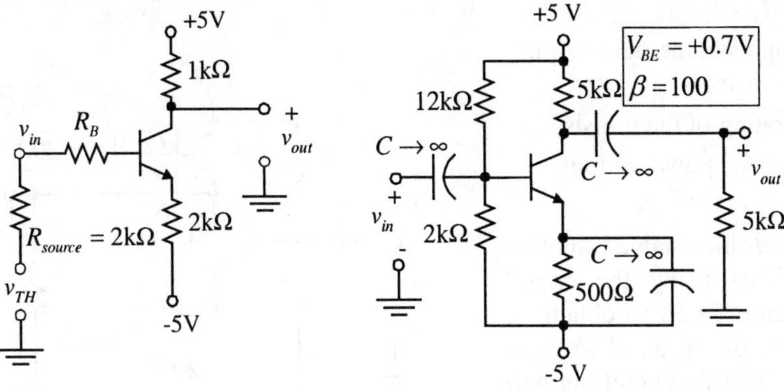

Figure P4.33 **Figure P4.36**

4.34 Design the transistor circuit in Figure P4.33 to have an output of zero when the input is zero by placing a resistor R_B in the base circuit. Determine the value of R_B needed to attain this value when $R_E = 500\ \Omega$ instead of the 2 kΩ shown. (Assume $V_{BE} = 0.7$V and $\beta = 100$)

4.35 In Problem 4.33, what value of resistor needs to be *added* in the base circuit to make the output go to 3V when $v_{in} = 0$?

4.36 Analyze the circuit shown in Figure P4.36 and determine the following: (Use $V_{BE} = 0.7$V and $\beta = 100$)

a. I_{CQ} and V_{CE}.

b. Symmetrical output voltage swing.

c. Power supplied from battery.

d. *ac* power output.

e. Load lines for the amplifier.

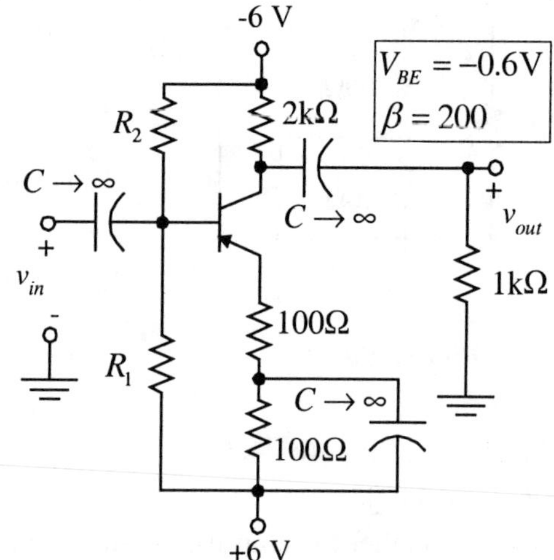

Figure P4.37

4.37 Design a common-emitter amplifier using the circuit shown in Figure P4.37 to obtain the maximum symmetrical output voltage swing. The design must be *dc* bias stable. (Use $V_{BE} = -0.6$V and $\beta = 200$) Determine:

a. I_{CQ} and V_{CEQ}.

b. R_1 and R_2.

c. Maximum symmetrical output voltage swing.

d. Power rating of the transistor.

e. Amplifier *ac* power output.

4.38 Design a *dc* bias-stable common-emitter amplifier using the circuit shown in Figure P4.38 to obtain an output of 1V zero-to-peak. (Use $V_{BE} = 0.7$V and $\beta = 200$) This amplifier will use minimum power from battery. Determine:

a. I_{CQ} and V_{CEQ}.

b. R_1 and R_2.

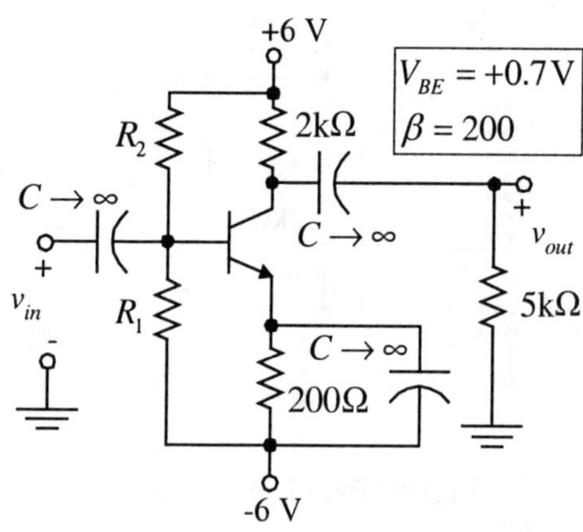

Figure P4.38

Section 4.12

4.39 Determine the maximum undistorted symmetrical output swing for the circuit shown in Figure P4.20 by selecting *new* values for R_1 (shown as 3 kΩ) and R_2 (shown as 12 kΩ). What are the values of these resistors? Draw new load line.

4.40 The collector resistor, R_C (shown as 1 kΩ), is bypassed by a capacitor in the circuit of Figure P4.20. Determine the maximum undistorted symmetrical output voltage swing by selecting *new* values of R_1 (shown as 3 kΩ) and R_2 (shown as 12 kΩ). What are the new values of these resistors? Find the power delivered to the load and the required power rating of the transistor.

4.41 By selecting new values of R_1 and R_2, determine the maximum undistorted symmetrical output voltage swing for the circuit of Figure P4.16 if the load resistor is reduced to 500 Ω. Find the power delivered to the load and the required power rating of the transistor.

4.42 Determine the values of R_1 and R_2 for the circuit shown in Figure P4.42 for a transistor having a $\beta = 100$ and a $V_{BE} = 0.7\text{V}$, when: (assume R_B =8 kΩ)

a. $V_{out} = 0$

b. $V_{out} = 2\text{V}$

c. $V_{out} = -2\text{V}$

4.43 Analyze the circuit shown in Figure P4.43 to determine V_{BB}, R_B, I_{CQ}, and V_{CEQ}. Assume $V_{BE} = -0.7\text{V}$ and $\beta = 200$.

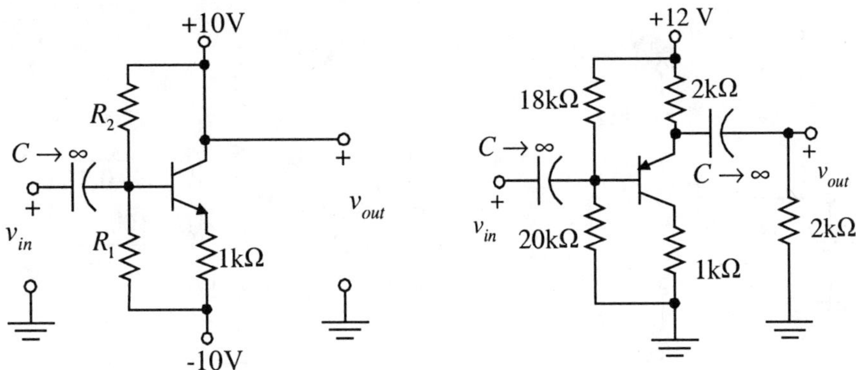

Figure P4.42 **Figure P4.43**

4.44 Design an emitter-follower amplifier using an *npn* transistor for maximum undistorted symmetrical output swing with the following specifications: R_B =250 Ω, $V_{CC} = 12\text{V}$, $R_E = R_{load} = 8$ Ω, $V_{BE} = 0.7\text{V}$, and $\beta = 200$. Also determine $P_{out}(\text{ac})$, the power supplied from the battery, and the transistor power rating.

4.45 Analyze the circuit shown in Figure P4.45 and determine the following when $\beta = 200$ and $V_{BE} = 0.7\text{V}$:

a. I_{CQ} and V_{CEQ}.
b. Undistorted Symmetrical voltage output swing.
c. Power supplied from the battery.
d. *ac* power output.
e. Power rating of the transistor needed.

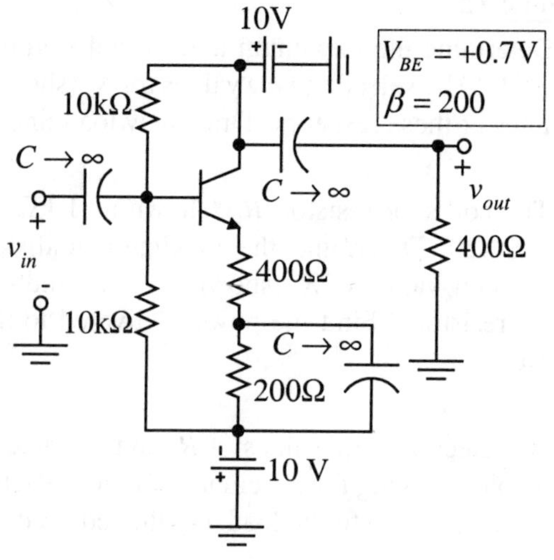

Figure P4.45

Section 4.13

4.46 With $v_{in} = 0$ in circuit of Figure P4.46 (please see next page), select a value of R_E which will force the transistor into cutoff. Assume $V_{BE} = 0.7\text{V}$, $\beta = 100$, and $V_{CE}(\text{sat}) = 0.2\text{V}$.

4.47 Using the circuit shown in Figure P4.47, determine V_B, V_C and V_E when: [Assume $V_{CE}(\text{sat}) = 0.2\text{V}$]

a. $R_B = 100\ \text{k}\Omega$.
b. $R_B = 10\ \text{k}\Omega$.

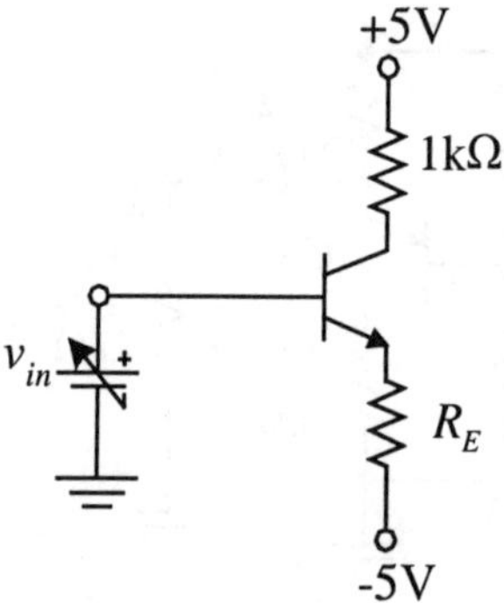

Figure P4.46

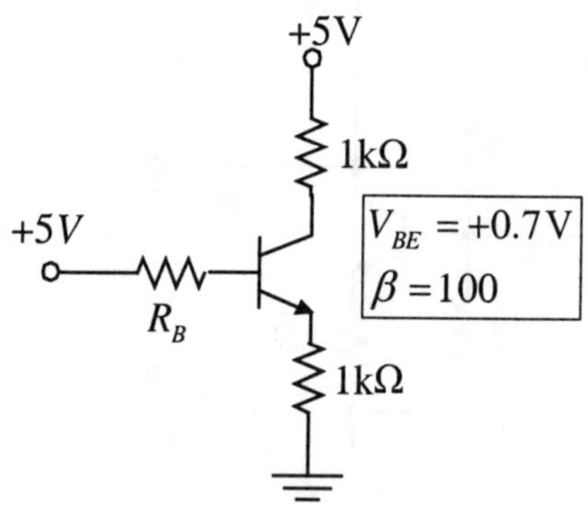

Figure P4.47

4.48 Determine the β_{sat} in the circuit shown in Figure P4.47 when:

a. $R_B = 50\ \text{k}\Omega$.
b. $R_B = 10\ \text{k}\Omega$.

4.49 Determine the β of the transistor at saturation in the circuit shown in Figure P4.49 when: Assume $V_{CE}(sat)$ = -0.2V.

a. R_B = 100 kΩ.
b. R_B = 10 kΩ.

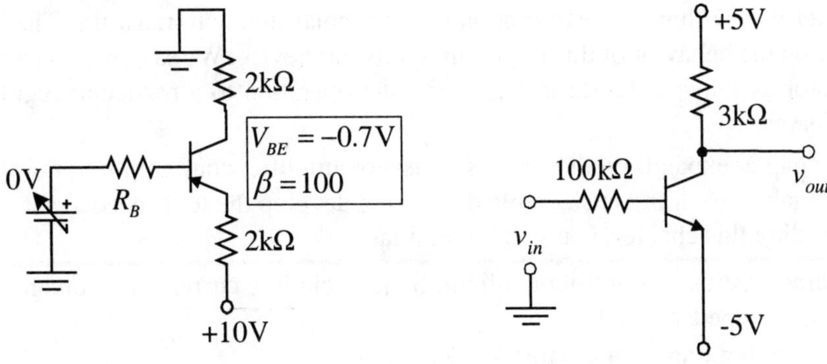

Figure P4.49 **Figure P4.50**

4.50 Determine V_{out} for the circuit shown in Figure P4.50 when V_{in} is: Assume β = 100, V_{BE} = 0.7V and $V_{CE}(sat)$ = 0.2V.

a. 0V
b. +5V
c. -5V

Chapter 5
Bipolar Junction Transistor Amplifiers

In this chapter we continue our exploration of the bipolar junction transistor. The previous chapter focused on thc behavior of this important nonlinear device. We saw that it is possible to treat the transistor as a linear device if we restrict the operation to a particular region of the characteristic curves.

The current chapter expands on the various transistor amplifier configurations introduced in Chapter 4. We analyze each in considerable detail, and develop the tools needed for amplifier design. After reading this chapter, you will be familiar with:

- Terminal characteristics of amplifier configurations, including current and voltage gain and input and output impedance.
- Methods for coupling transistor circuits to each other.
- Typical transistor configurations to produce *dc* current sources and approximate resistive loads for IC amplifiers.
- Simulation of single and multistage amplifier configurations.

5.0 INTRODUCTION

We concentrate on circuits that use the linear operation of the BJT resulting from the small-signal model. We look at the simplest set of circuits that amplify either the current, the voltage or both. These circuits are called *single stage* amplifiers – they are the simplest circuits that allow the transistors to provide gain (i.e., larger magnitude of the *ac* voltages or currents at the output than are applied at the input). Not all BJT circuits perform linear amplification. Some are used to perform digital logic operations. These are studied in Chapter 15. Often, the circuits that we present as linear amplifiers in this chapter can also be used to perform digital logic functions if we violate the conditions assumed for the small-signal model.

Since our analysis of single-stage BJT amplifiers is based on the small-signal model of the transistor, we must assure that the conditions necessary for use of this model apply. In particular, we will have to make sure the transistor stays in the *normal active* mode throughout the range of input signals. Since each *total* voltage is composed of an *average* (*dc*) value and a *time varying* (*ac*) value, we must carefully choose *dc* values so that the transistor remains in normal active mode for all expected *ac* voltages. The selection of *dc* voltages and currents (i.e., *dc biasing)* was introduced in Chapter 4. We now examine the circuit configurations to determine the operating characteristics of common, practical amplifiers.

5.1 COMMON-EMITTER AMPLIFIER

The common-emitter (CE) amplifier circuit is shown in Figure 5.1. Note that there is a bypass capacitor between the emitter and ground, and a coupling capacitor between the collector and load. These capacitors are large – they can be considered as short circuits for the range of frequencies of the input signals. They are open circuits for *dc* (i.e., we will remove them for bias calculations, as we did in Chapter 4).

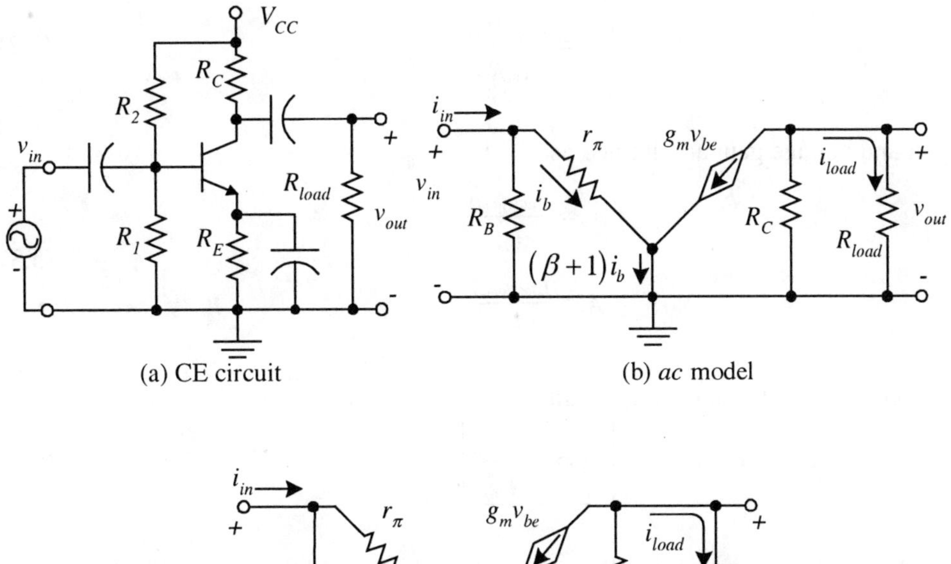

(a) CE circuit (b) *ac* model

(c) Input and output separated

Figure 5.1- The common-emitter amplifier

5.1.1 Gain Impedance Formula

We begin by deriving an important relationship between the *ac* quantities of voltage gain, A_v, and current gain, A_i. Figure 5.2 shows a block diagram of a four-terminal (two port) network with input resistance R_{in} and load resistance, R_{load}. Although we are assuming these to be resistors, they can also be complex impedances (Z_{in} and Z_{load} respectively).

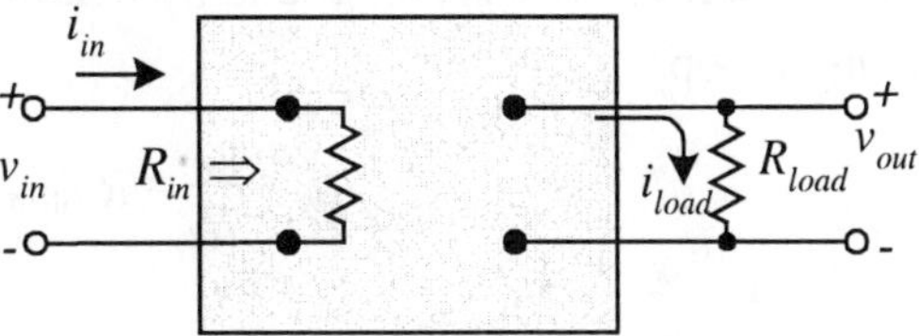

Figure 5.2 – Two-port network

The relationships between the input variables, v_{in} and i_{in}, and the output variables, v_{out} and i_{out}, are derived directly from Ohm's law. That is,

$$v_{out} = i_{load} R_{load}$$
$$v_{in} = i_{in} R_{in} \tag{5.1}$$

Forming the ratio of these two equations yields

$$\frac{v_{out}}{v_{in}} = \frac{i_{load} R_{load}}{i_{in} R_{in}} \tag{5.2}$$

Current gain and voltage gain are defined as

$$A_v = \frac{v_{out(load)}}{v_{in}}$$
$$A_i = \frac{i_{out(load)}}{i_{in}} \tag{5.3}$$

Then Equation (5.2) yields the desired result.

$$\boxed{A_v = \frac{A_i R_{load}}{R_{in}}} \tag{5.4}$$

Equation (5.4) is called the *gain impedance formula* and it is used throughout this text.

5.1.2 Input Resistance, R_{in}

We will use the hybrid-π model to derive the input resistance equation for each type of amplifier configuration. Two forms of the CE amplifier small-signal equivalent circuit are shown in Figures 5.1(b) and (c).

The equivalent circuit of Figure 5.1(b) can be used to derive the input resistance, R_{in}. Note that we have neglected the Early effect resistance, r_o, (see Figure 4.5) since it is usually large. If this is not the case, we must include the resistor, r_o, between the collector and emitter and modify the equations accordingly. The transistor β is usually large enough such that we can approximate $1+\beta$ as β. The current flow between emitter and ground is therefore approximately equal to βi_b. The input resistance is then found by writing Kirchhoff's voltage and current law equations for the input loop.

$$R_{in} = \frac{v_{in}}{i_{in}} = R_B \| r_\pi = \frac{R_B r_\pi}{R_B + r_\pi} \tag{5.5}$$

Substitute r_e (which is approximately $1/g_m$) for r_π / β to obtain the input resistance.

$$R_{in} = \frac{R_B r_e}{R_B/\beta + r_e} \tag{5.6}$$

In deriving Equation (5.6) we required that $\beta \gg 1$. We remind you that this inequality has also allowed us to substitute β for $\beta+1$. r_e is actually equal to $r_\pi/(1+\beta)$.

5.1.3 Current Gain, A_i

The current gain of the CE amplifier is defined as the ratio of load current to input current. Thus,

$$A_i = \frac{i_{load}}{i_{in}} \tag{5.7}$$

where the currents are shown in Figure 5.1(b). In order to obtain an expression for current gain in terms of the circuit parameters, we must derive expressions for these two currents. We can use current division in the base circuit to relate the input current to base current.

$$i_b = \frac{R_B i_{in}}{R_B + r_\pi} \tag{5.8}$$

Current division can be applied to the output circuit to obtain an expression for load current.

$$i_{load} = \frac{-R_C \beta i_b}{R_{load} + R_C} \tag{5.9}$$

The negative sign results from the direction of βi_b being opposite to that of i_{load}. We combine these equations to find the current gain.

$$A_i = \frac{i_{load}}{i_{in}} = \frac{-R_B R_C}{(R_B/\beta + r_\pi/\beta)(R_C + R_{load})} \tag{5.10}$$

5.1.4 Voltage Gain, A_v

The voltage gain is defined as the ratio of output voltage to input voltage. We can save time in deriving an expression for voltage gain if we borrow the results of the previous section. We relate current to voltage using Ohm's law:

$$\begin{aligned} v_{out} &= i_{load} R_{load} \\ v_{in} &= i_{in} R_{in} \end{aligned} \tag{5.11}$$

The voltage gain is then

$$A_v = \frac{v_{out}}{v_{in}} = \frac{i_{load}}{i_{in}} \frac{R_{load}}{R_{in}} = A_i \frac{R_{load}}{R_{in}} \tag{5.12}$$

We substitute Equations (5.6) and (5.10) into Equation (5.12) and also recognize that $r_\pi/\beta = r_e = 1/g_m$. This yields the desired result.

$$A_v = \frac{-\beta\left(R_{load}\|R_C\right)}{r_\pi} = \frac{-R_{load}\|R_C}{r_e} = -g_m\left(R_{load}\|R_C\right) \tag{5.13}$$

5.1.5 Output Resistance, R_o

The output resistance (Thevenin's equivalent resistance) of the amplifier's output circuit can be found using the h-parameter model for the transistor. With all coupling capacitors shorted the output resistance is the parallel combination of r_o and R_C, so

$$R_o = r_o\|R_C \approx R_C \tag{5.14}$$

The reason that the controlled source does not affect the output resistance is that the resistance is defined with the input voltage set to zero. Since r_o is typically much larger than R_C, the output resistance can be approximated by R_C.

Example 5.1

Design a common-emitter amplifier with a transistor having a $\beta = 200$ and $V_{BE} = 0.7$ V. Obtain an overall gain of $|A_v| \geq 100$ and maximum output voltage swing. Use the CE configuration shown in Figure 5.3 with two power supplies. R_{source} is the resistance associated with the source, v_{source}. Let R_{source} = 100 Ohms. The output load is 2 kΩ. Determine the resistor values of the bias circuitry, the maximum undistorted output voltage swing, and the stage voltage gain.

Solution: The maximum voltage across the amplifier is 10 V since the power supply can be visualized as a 10 V power supply with a ground in the center. In this case, the ground has no significance to the operation of the amplifier since the input and output are isolated from the power supplies by capacitors.

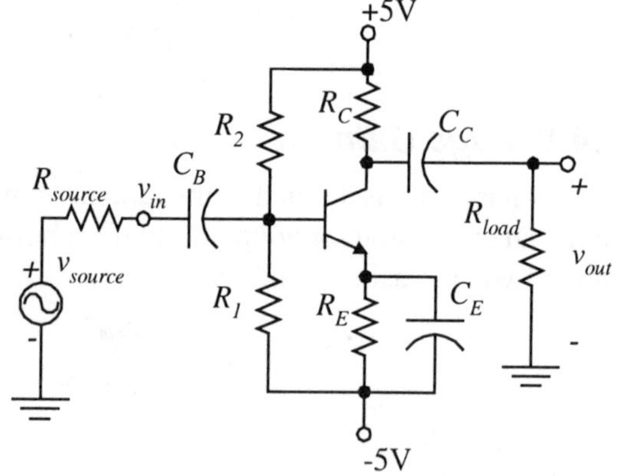

Figure 5.3 – CE amplifier for Example 5.1

We will have to select the value for R_C and we are really not given enough information to do so. However, this is not a big problem as we will see shortly. For now, let's choose $R_C = R_{load}$ (we will see in Example 5.2 the reason for this choice). We have another dilemma since neither R_{in} nor A_i are given. Therefore, we don't have enough information to solve for R_B – we can't use the bias stability criterion since we don't have the value of R_E either. We will have to (arbitrarily) select a value of R_B or R_E. If this leads to a contradiction, or "bad" component values (e.g., unobtainable resistor values), we can come back and modify our choice. Let us select a value for R_E that is large enough to obtain a reasonable value of V_{BB}. Selecting R_E as 400 Ω will not appreciably reduce the collector current yet it will help in maintaining a reasonable value of V_{BB}. Thus:

$$R_B = 0.1\beta R_E = 0.1(200)(400) = 8 \quad k\Omega$$

To insure that we have the maximum voltage swing at the output, we will use

$$I_{CQ} = \frac{V_{CC}}{R_{ac} + R_{dc}} = \frac{10}{1000 + 2400} = 2.94 \quad mA$$

$$V_{BB} = V_{BE} + I_{CQ}(R_B/\beta + R_E) = 0.7 + 2.9 \times 10^{-3}\left(\frac{8000}{200} + 400\right) = 1.99 \quad V$$

Note that we are carrying out our calculations to four places so that we can get accuracy to three places. The bias resistors are determined by

$$R_1 = \frac{R_B}{1 - V_{BB}/V_{CC}} = \frac{8000}{1 - 1.99/10} = 9.99 \quad k\Omega$$

$$R_2 = R_B\frac{V_{CC}}{V_{BB}} = 8000\left(\frac{10}{1.99}\right) = 40.2 \quad k\Omega$$

Since we designed the bias circuit to place the quiescent point in the middle of the *ac* load line, we can use

$$v_{out}(undistorted\ p - p) = 1.8(2.94 \times 10^{-3})(2\ k\Omega \,\|\, 2\ k\Omega\ ) = 5.29 \quad V$$

Now we can determine the gain of the amplifier itself.

$$|A_v| = g_m(R_C \| R_{load}) = \frac{2.94 \times 10^{-3} \times 1000}{26 \times 10^{-3}} = 113$$

Using voltage division, we can determine the gain of the *overall* circuit, but to do that we need the value of R_{in} when $r_\pi = 200{\times}0.026/0.00294 = 1.77\ k\Omega$

$$R_{in} = r_\pi \| R_B = 1.77\ k\Omega \| 8\ k\Omega = 1.45 \quad k\Omega$$

$$|A_v|_{overall} = \left|\frac{v_{out}}{v_{in}}\right| = 113 \times \frac{R_{in}}{R_{in} + R_{source}} = 106$$

This shows that the common-emitter amplifier provides high voltage gain. However, it is very noisy, it has a low input impedance, and it does not have the stability of the emitter resistor common emitter amplifier we will be studying next.

5.2 COMMON EMITTER WITH EMITTER RESISTOR (EMITTER-RESISTOR AMPLIFIER)

The emitter-resistor amplifier is shown in Figure 5.4(a). Note that the only difference between this circuit and the common-emitter circuit is that the emitter resistor is no longer bypassed with a large capacitor. The *dc* operation of the two circuits is identical since the capacitor is an open circuit for *dc*. However, we will find that elimination of the bypass capacitor greatly affects the *ac* operation.

The emitter-resistor amplifier is an example of a feedback circuit. The output current (collector-emitter current) flows through the emitter resistor, thereby *modifying* the base-to-emitter voltage. We will find that this form of feedback decreases the sensitivity of the design to changes in β. At the same time that the circuit reduces the sensitivity, it also reduces the overall gain.

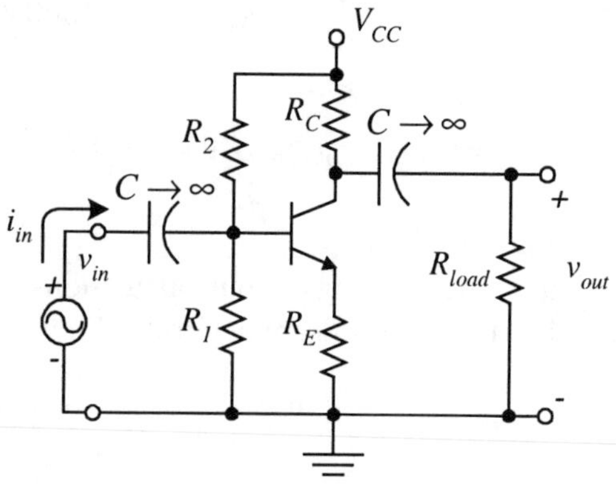

Figure 5.4(a) – Emitter-resistor amplifier

5.2.1 Input Resistance, R_{in}

The hybrid-π model is used to derive the input resistance equation for each type of amplifier configuration. The basic circuit was shown in Figure 5.4(a) and the equivalent circuit is shown in Figure 5.4(b).

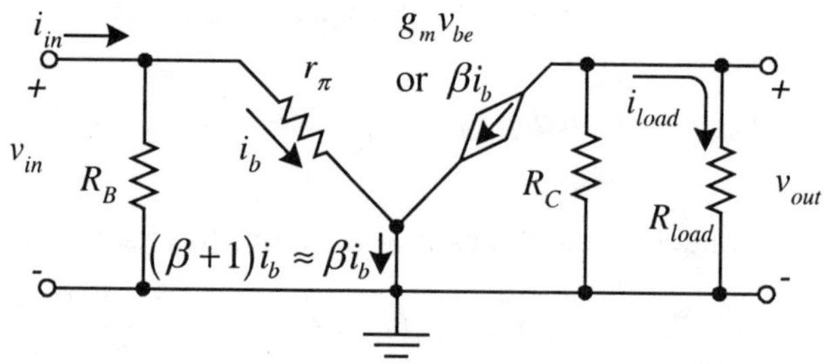

Figure 5.4(b) – Equivalent circuit

The equivalent circuit of Figure 5.4(b) is used to derive the input resistance, R_{in}. The current in R_E is approximately equal to βi_b (We again assumed that β is large enough such that we can approximate $\beta+1$ as β). If the circuit is now split as in Figure 5.4(c), the current through the resistor in series with r_π in the input loop is simply i_b. Thus, to keep the voltage at the same value existing in the original circuit, we must change the resistor value to βR_E. The input resistance is then found by writing Kirchhoff's voltage and current law equations for the input loop.

$$R_{in} = \frac{v_{in}}{i_{in}} = R_B \| \left(r_\pi + \beta R_E\right) = \frac{R_B(r_\pi + \beta R_E)}{R_B + r_\pi + \beta R_E} \tag{5.15}$$

We substitute r_e for r_π / β to obtain the input resistance equation,

$$R_{in} = \frac{R_B(r_e + R_E)}{R_B/\beta + r_e + R_E} \tag{5.16}$$

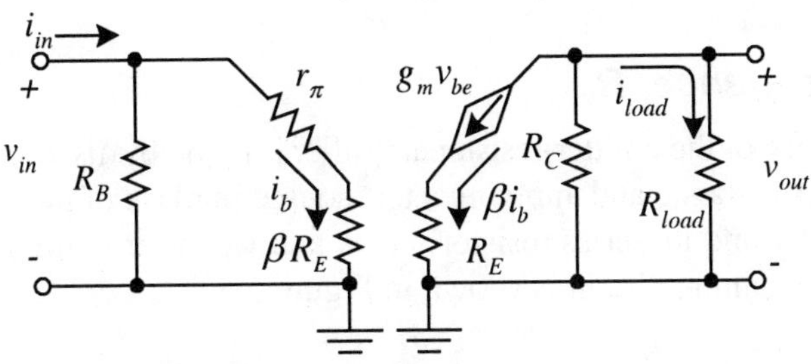

Figure 5.4(c) - Modified equivalent circuit

5.2.2 Current Gain, A_i

We approach finding the current gain much as we did for the CE amplifier. We can use current division in the base circuit to relate the input current to base current.

$$i_b = \frac{R_B i_{in}}{R_B + r_\pi + \beta R_E} \tag{5.17}$$

Current division can be applied to the output circuit to obtain an expression for load current.

$$i_{load} = \frac{-R_C \beta i_b}{R_{load} + R_C} \tag{5.18}$$

We combine these equations to find the current gain.

$$A_i = \frac{i_{load}}{i_{in}} = \frac{-R_B R_C}{(R_B/\beta + r_e + R_E)(R_C + R_{load})} \tag{5.19}$$

5.2.3 Voltage Gain, A_v

We find the input and output voltages as shown in Figure 5.4(b).

$$v_{out} = i_{load} R_{load}$$
$$v_{in} = i_{in} R_{in} \tag{5.20}$$

The voltage gain is then

$$A_v = \frac{v_{out}}{v_{in}} = \frac{i_{load}}{i_{in}} \frac{R_{load}}{R_{in}} = A_i \frac{R_{load}}{R_{in}} \tag{5.21}$$

We use the gain impedance formula and also recognize that $r_\pi / \beta = r_e = 1/g_m$. This yields

$$A_v = \frac{-\beta(R_{load} \| R_C)}{r_\pi + \beta R_E} = \frac{-R_{load} \| R_C}{r_e + R_E} = \frac{-g_m(R_{load} \| R_C)}{1 + g_m R_E} \tag{5.22}$$

5.2.4 Output Resistance, R_o

The output resistance of the emitter-resistor amplifier is found by disabling the *ac* independent source and its source resistance and applying a test source in place of the load. Short circuiting the input current source and its series resistor sets v_e and v_{be} to zero, turning off the dependent current source. The remaining circuit is shown in Figure 5.5.

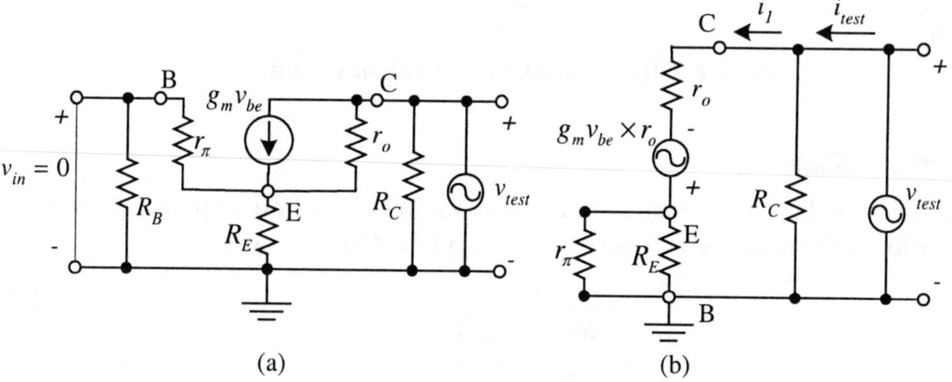

Figure 5.5 - Output resistance circuit for emitter-resistor amplifier

The output resistance R_o is the ratio of test voltage to resulting current.

$$R_o = \frac{v_{test}}{i_{test}}$$

$$i_{test} = \frac{v_{test}}{R_C} + i_1 \tag{5.23}$$

$$v_{be} = -i_1 \cdot (R_E \| r_\pi)$$

Solving for the current in the left branch of Figure 5.5(b) we find,

$$i_1 = \frac{v_{test} - g_m r_o i_1 (R_E \| r_\pi)}{r_o + R_E \| r_\pi}$$

$$i_1 = \frac{v_{test}}{r_o + (R_E \| r_\pi)(1 + g_m r_o)} \tag{5.24}$$

The output resistance is the parallel combination of R_C with R_{eq1} where R_{eq1} is the equivalent resistance of the left branch, given by

$$R_{eq1} = \frac{v_{test}}{i_1} = r_o + \left(R_E \| r_\pi\right)\left(1 + g_m r_o\right) \quad (5.25)$$

If r_o is much larger than R_C, the output resistance is approximately equal to R_C. That is,

$$R_o = R_C \| R_{eq1} \approx R_C \quad (5.26)$$

Example 5.2 Emitter-Resistor Amplifier Design

Design an emitter-resistor amplifier (see Figure 5.6(a)) to drive a 2 kΩ load using a *pnp* silicon transistor, $V_{CC} = -24$ V, $\beta = 200$, $A_v = -10$, and $V_{BE} = -0.7$ V. Determine all element values and calculate A_i, R_{in}, I_{CQ} and the maximum undistorted symmetrical output voltage swing for three values of R_C as given below:

(a) $R_C = R_{load}$
(b) $R_C = 0.1R_{load}$
(c) $R_C = 10R_{load}$

Verify your result for part (a) using a computer simulation.

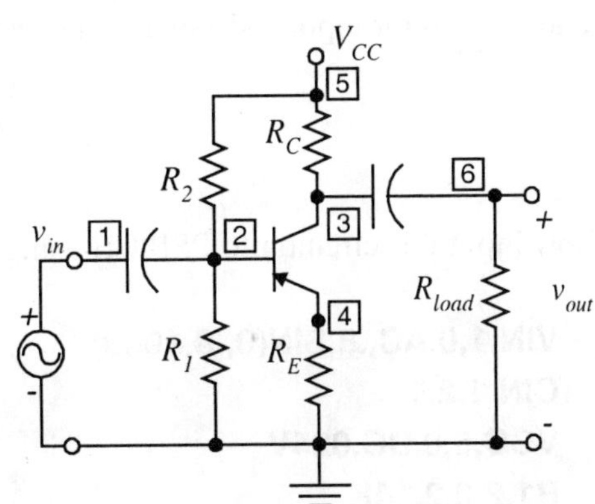

Figure 5.6(a) – Amplifier for Example 5.2

Solution: (a) [$R_C = R_{load}$] We use the various equations of Section 5.2 in order to derive the parameters of the circuit of Figure 5.6(a). Beginning with Equation (5.22) for the voltage gain, we can solve for R'_E.

$$A_v = -10 = -\frac{R_{load} \| R_C}{r_e + R_E} = -\frac{2k\Omega \| 2k\Omega}{r_e + R_E}$$

so

$$R'_E = r_e + R_E = 100 \quad \Omega$$

We can find the quiescent value of the collector current I_C from the collector-emitter loop using the equation for the condition of maximum output swing.

$$I_{CQ} = \frac{V_{CC}}{R_{dc} + R_{ac}} = -7.5 \quad \text{mA}$$

Now using results from Chapter 4, we find that r_e is 3.5 Ω. This is small enough that we shall ignore it to find that R_E = 100 Ω. Since we now know β and R_E, we can use the design guideline,

$$R_B = 0.1\beta R_E$$

to find that $R_B = 2$ kΩ.

The design discussion of the previous chapter can now be used to specify the biasing circuitry. You may wish to refer back to Chapter 4 for details. We find

$$V_{BB} = -1.52 \quad \text{V}$$

$$R_1 = 2.14 \quad \text{k}\Omega$$

$$R_2 = 31.6 \quad \text{k}\Omega$$

The maximum undistorted symmetrical peak-to-peak output swing is then

$$v_{out}(p - p) = 1.8 I_{CQ}\left(R_{load} \| R_C\right) = 13.5 \quad \text{V}$$

We now have all of the necessary parameters to use Equation (5.19) for current gain and Equation (5.16) for input resistance. This yields

$$A_i = -9.1$$

$$R_{in} = 1.82 \quad \text{k}\Omega$$

We now input this circuit into PSPICE using the node assignments shown in Figure 5.6(a).

```
VIN,1,0,AC,.8,SIN(0,.8,1000)
CIN,1,2,1
VCC,5,0,DC,024V
R1,2,0,2.14K
R2,2,5,31.6K
*GUMMEL POON BJT PARAMETERS
Q1,3,2,4,BJT
.MODEL,BJT,PNP(BF=200)
RE,4,0,100
RC,3,5,2K
C1,3,6,1
RL,6,0,2K
.TRAN,.005M,1M
.AC,LIN,15,100,100K
.PROBE
.END
```

Figure 5.6(b) shows a plot of the input and output voltages versus time [Node voltages V(6) and V(1) versus time]. From the plot, the gain is determined as $V_{peak}(out)/V_{peak}(in) = -7.5\text{V}/0.75\text{V} = -10$. To obtain this plot, we increased the amplitude of the input voltage V_{in} until distortion was observed in the output waveform $V(out)$. This distortion is illustrated for our purposes in Figure 5.6(b) when the output swing has a peak amplitude of approximately 7.5 V. The theoretical solution (allowing for the 5% margins in the saturation and cut-off regions) yields a peak-to-peak *undistorted* output swing of 13.5 V. The PSPICE solution also yields 13.5 V peak-to-peak *undistorted* output swing before noticeable distortion appears on the output waveform. (not shown).

(b) [$R_C = 0.1R_{load}$] We repeat the steps of part (a) to find

$$R_C = 200\ \Omega \qquad R_1 = 390\ \Omega$$

$$I_{CQ} = -57.4\text{ mA} \qquad R_2 = 4.7\text{ k}\Omega$$

$$\frac{r_\pi}{\beta} = r_e = 0.45\ \Omega \qquad v_{out}(p-p) = 18.7\text{ V}$$

$$R_B = 360\ \Omega \qquad A_i = -1.64$$

$$V_{BB} = -1.84\text{ V} \qquad R_{in} = 327\ \Omega$$

(c) [$R_C = 10R_{load}$] Once again, we follow the steps of part (a) to find

$$R_C = 20\text{ k}\Omega \qquad R_1 = 3.28\text{ k}\Omega$$

$$I_{CQ} = -1.07\text{ mA} \qquad R_2 = 85.6\text{ k}\Omega$$

$$\frac{r_\pi}{\beta} = r_e = 24.2\ \Omega \qquad v_{out}(p-p) = 3.9\text{ V}$$

$$R_B = 3.64\text{ k}\Omega \qquad A_i = -14.5$$

$$V_{BB} = -0.886\text{ V} \qquad R_{in} = 2.91\text{ k}\Omega$$

We compare the results of this example in Table 5.1 for the purpose of making the best choice for R_C.

	I_{CQ}	A_i	R_{in}	$v_{out}(p\text{-}p)$
$R_C = R_{load}$	- 7.5 mA	-9.1	1.82 kΩ	13.5 V
$R_C = 0.1R_{load}$	- 57.4 mA	-1.64	327 Ω	20.8 V
$R_C = 10R_{load}$	- 1.07 mA	-14.5	2.91 kΩ	3.9 V

Table 5.1 - Comparison for three selections of R_C

Example 5.2 indicates that of the three given ratios of R_C to R_{load}, $R_C = R_{load}$ has the most desirable performance[1] in the CE amplifier stage. We shall use this as a guide to develop a reasonable starting point in our designs. In most cases, this choice will provide performance that meets specifications. In some applications, it may be necessary to do additional analysis to find the "*optimum*" ratio of R_C to R_{load}.

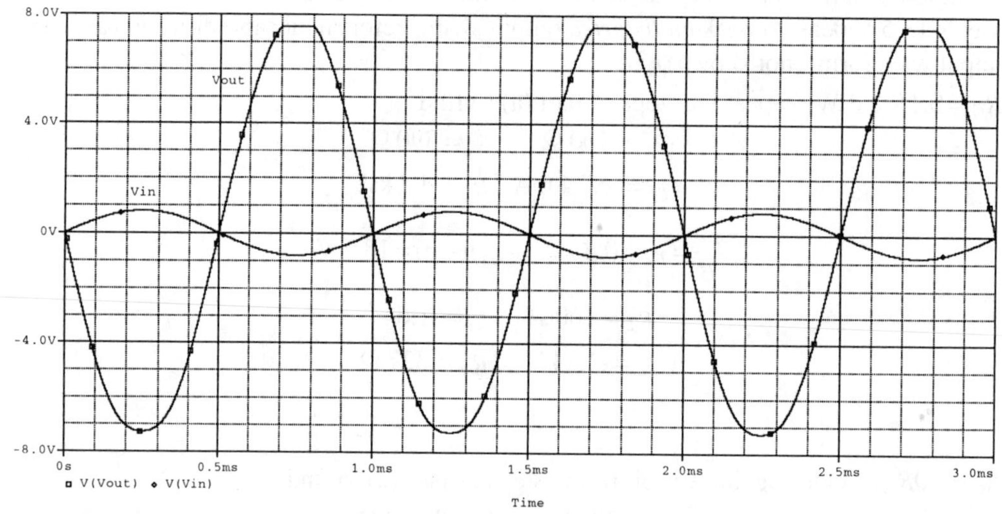

Figure 5.6(b) – Simulation results for most desired performance, $R_C = R_{load}$.

Example 5.3 - Capacitor-Coupled Emitter-Resistor Amplifier (Design)

Design an emitter-resistor amplifier (see Figure 5.7(a)) with $A_v = -10$, $\beta = 200$ and $R_{load} = 1\text{k}\Omega$. A *pnp* transistor is used and maximum symmetrical output swing is required. Check the values of A_v, A_i, R_{in}, and R_o, using a computer simulation.

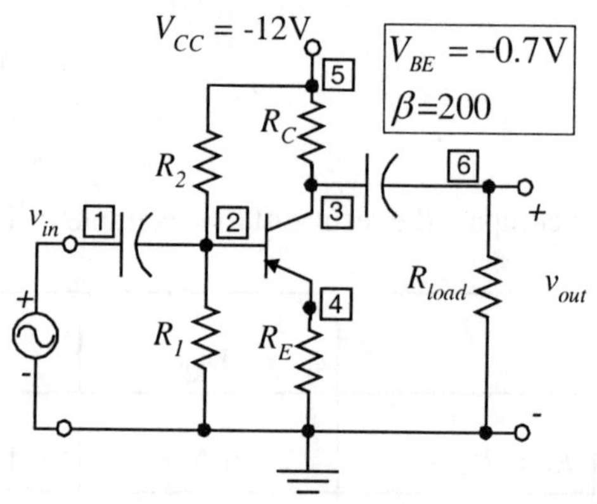

Figure 5.7(a) Emitter resistor amplifier

Solution: As a result of Example 5.2, we shall choose $R_C = R_{load} = 1\ \text{k}\Omega$. Using the equation for

[1] An important measure of the performance of an amplifier is its power gain G. The amplifier power gain is defined as $G \doteq \frac{P_{out}}{P_{in}} = \frac{v_{out} \cdot i_{load}}{v_{in} \cdot i_{in}} = A_v \cdot A_i$. Using $|A_v| = |-10|$ and Table 5.1 values for A_i, the power gains for $R_C = R_{load}, 0.1R_{load}, 10R_{load}$ are 91.0, 16.4, and 14.5 respectively.

A_v in order to solve for R_E.

$$A_v = -\frac{R_{load} \| R_C}{R'_E}$$

where $R'_E = R_E + r_e$. When known values are substituted into this equation, we find $R'_E = 50\ \Omega$. We need to know the value of r_e to find R_E. We first find R_{ac} and R_{dc}, and then calculate the Q-point as follows (we assume r_e is small, so $R_E \approx R'_E$):

$$R_{ac} = R_E + R_C \| R_{load} = 550\ \Omega$$

$$R_{dc} = R_E + R_C = 1050\ \Omega$$

With R_{ac} and R_{dc} determined, the design of this circuit now parallels the procedure for *ac* design given in Chapter 4. The first step is to calculate the quiescent collector current needed to place the Q-point in the center of the *ac* load line (i.e., maximum swing). The equation is

$$I_{CQ} = \frac{V_{CC}}{R_{ac} + R_{dc}} = -7.5 \quad \text{mA}$$

The quantity, r_π / β (or r_e), is found as follows.

$$r_e = \frac{26\,(\text{mV})}{|I_{CQ}|} = \frac{26\,(\text{mV})}{7.5\,(\text{mA})} = 3.47\ \Omega$$

Then

$$R_E = 50 - r_e = 46.5\ \Omega$$

If there were a current gain or input resistance specification for this design, we would use it to solve for the value of R_B. Since there is no such specification, we use the expression

$$R_B = 0.1\beta R_E = 0.1(200)(46.5) = 930\ \Omega.$$

Then continuing with the design steps,

$$A_i = \frac{-R_B}{R_B/\beta + r_\pi/\beta + R_B} \cdot \frac{R_C}{R_C + R_{load}} = -8.50$$

$$V_{CEQ} = V_{CC} - (R_C + R'_E) I_{CQ} = -4.125 \quad \text{V}$$

and

$$V_{BB} = I_{CQ} - \left(R_E + \frac{R_E}{\beta} \right) + V_{BE} = -1.08 \quad \text{V}$$

$$R_1 = \frac{R_B}{1 - V_{BB}/V_{CC}} = 1.02 \quad k\Omega$$

$$R_2 = \frac{R_B V_{CC}}{V_{BB}} = 10.3 \quad k\Omega$$

$$R_{in} = \frac{R_B(r_e + R_E)}{R_B/\beta + r_e + R_E} = 851 \quad \Omega$$

$$R_o = R_C = 1 \quad k\Omega$$

The last equality assumes that r_o is large compared to R_C.

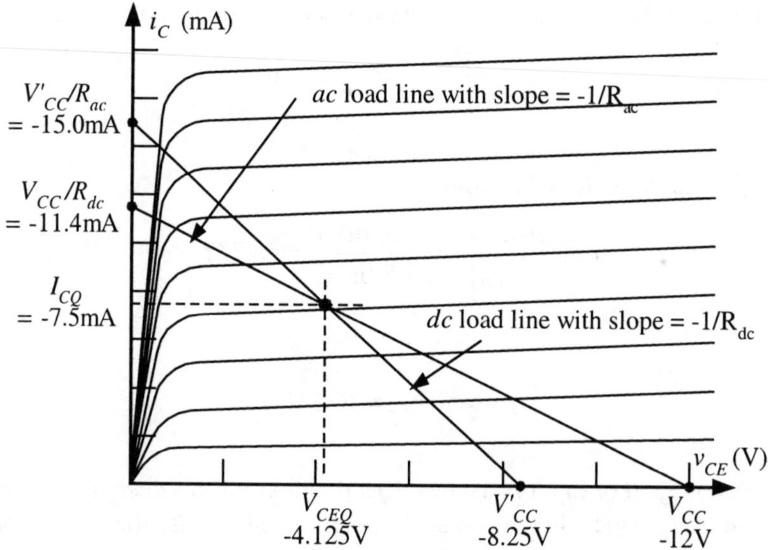

Figure 5.7(b) – Load lines for Example 5.3

The maximum undistorted peak-to-peak output swing is given by

$$1.8|I_{CQ}|(R_C \| R_{load}) = 1.8(0.0075)(500) = 6.75 \quad V$$

The power delivered into the load and the maximum power dissipated by the transistor are found using equations from Chapter 4.

$$P_{load} = \frac{1}{2}\left(I_{CQ}\frac{R_C}{R_C + R_{load}}\right)^2 R_{load} = \frac{I_{CQ}^2 R_{load}}{8} = 7 \quad mW$$

$$P_{transistor} = V_{CEQ} I_{CQ} = (-4.125V)(-7.5mA) = 31 \quad mW$$

The load lines for this circuit are shown in Figure 5.7(b).

We now use a computer simulation to check the results of this design. The first task is to input the circuit. For this problem we are using Micro-Cap to input the circuit. The only decisions concern the capacitors and the transistor. The capacitors must act as short circuits for the signals of interest and open circuits for the *dc* bias voltages. Since we are not concerned with frequency response at this time, we can set the capacitors at unrealistically large values, such as 1000 μF. The only transistor specifications are that β is 200 and the base-emitter voltage is -0.7 V. The transistor models used by the simulation program are considerably more sophisticated and include many parameters. We can either custom design a library entry with the given parameters, or choose a transistor that comes close to having these values. We chose to use the 2N3906 transistor which has a nominal β of 200 and V_{BE} of -0.75 V.

Most simulation programs offer at least three forms of analysis for electronic circuits in addition to other features The three common forms are *dc*, transient and *ac* analysis. The *dc* analysis provides a plot of output vs. input voltage under *dc* conditions. With proper designation of input and output, it can be used to check quiescent conditions. The *transient* analysis provides a time domain plot of any designated parameter(s). Following the execution of a transient analysis, the program can display the "final" values of all node voltages. This mode can be used to easily check the quiescent operating point. For the given circuit, the results yield a base voltage of -1.051 V, collector voltage of -5.24 V and an emitter voltage of -0.31 V. The quiescent voltages are therefore,

$$V_{BE} = -0.74 \text{ V}$$

$$V_{CEQ} = -4.94 \text{ V}$$

This contrasts to calculated values of -0.7 V and -4.125 V respectively. The variation is due to the transistor model (variation in β and V_{BE} with operating point) and to the tolerance of resistor values.

There are two ways in which we can find the gain. We can use an input source to insert a sinusoidal waveform and plot the output waveform. The gain is found by comparing amplitudes. The second, and easier method is to use the *ac* analysis feature of the simulation program. This module plots output gain as a function of frequency (it also plots other parameters, including phase, but we will deal with these in later chapters). We need only run the *ac* analysis over a reasonable frequency range (not so low as to make the coupling capacitors deviate from short circuits, and not high enough to force consideration of internal capacitance). The results of the simulation shown in Figure 5.7(c) for this example yields a voltage gain of $|-10.2|$ (or equivalently, 20.17dB) over the frequency range of interest. The required voltage gain of $|-10|$ is equivalent to 20 dB. The calculated current gain is $|-8.5|$ and the simulation results appear very close, at about -8.4 over the frequency range of interest, so the simulation has verified the design criteria.

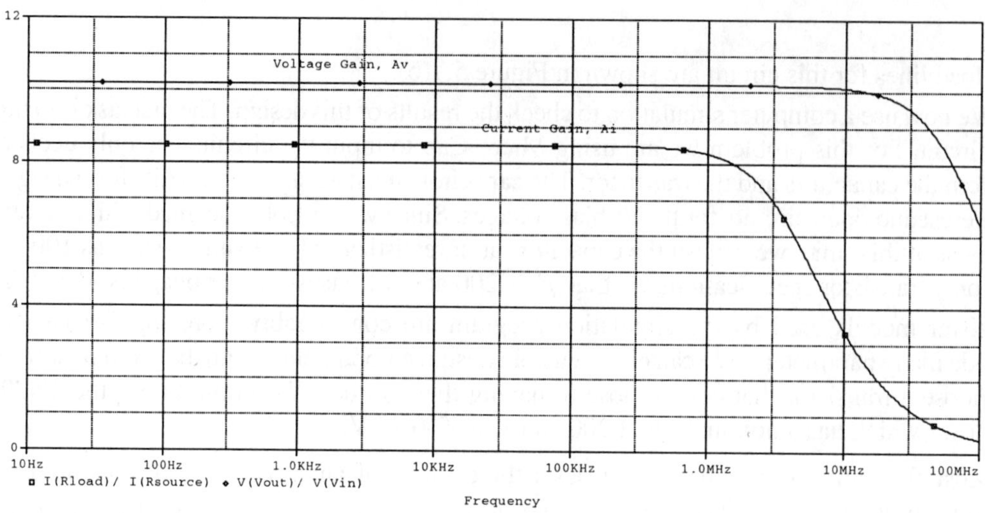

Figure 5.7(c) – Simulation voltage gain (approximately 10.2) and current gain (approximately 8.4)

Continuing the comparison, the computed input impedance and Thevenin's equivalent impedance for the output circuit were computed above to be $R_{in} = 851\Omega$ and $R_o = 1k\Omega$. The results of the simulation shown in Figure 5.7(d) and (e) verify these calculations. The input and output impedances obtained from the simulation are $R_{in} = 830\Omega$ (shown as $0.83k\Omega$ in the plot) and $R_o = 970\Omega$, shown in Figure 5.7(d) and (e), respectively.

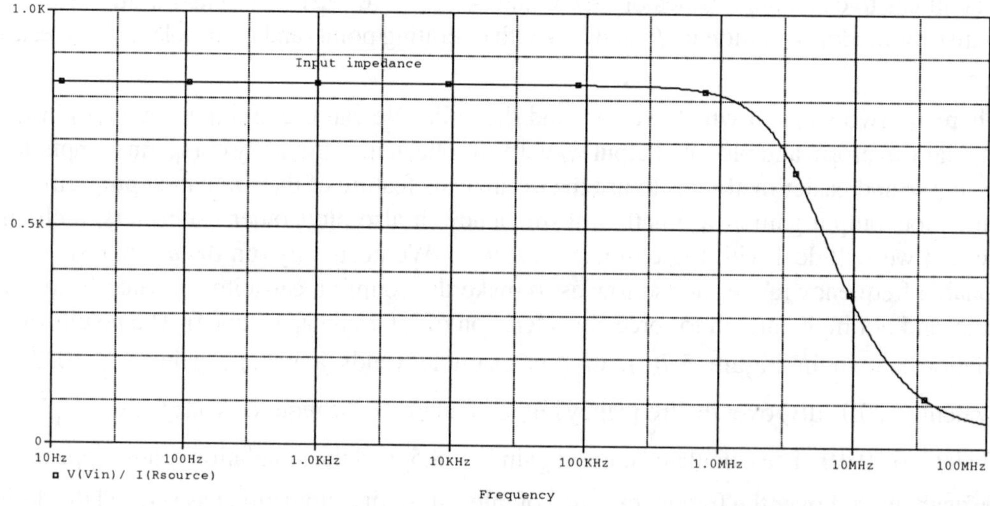

Figure 5.7(d) – The input impedance R_{in} versus frequency for the amplifier of Example 5.3

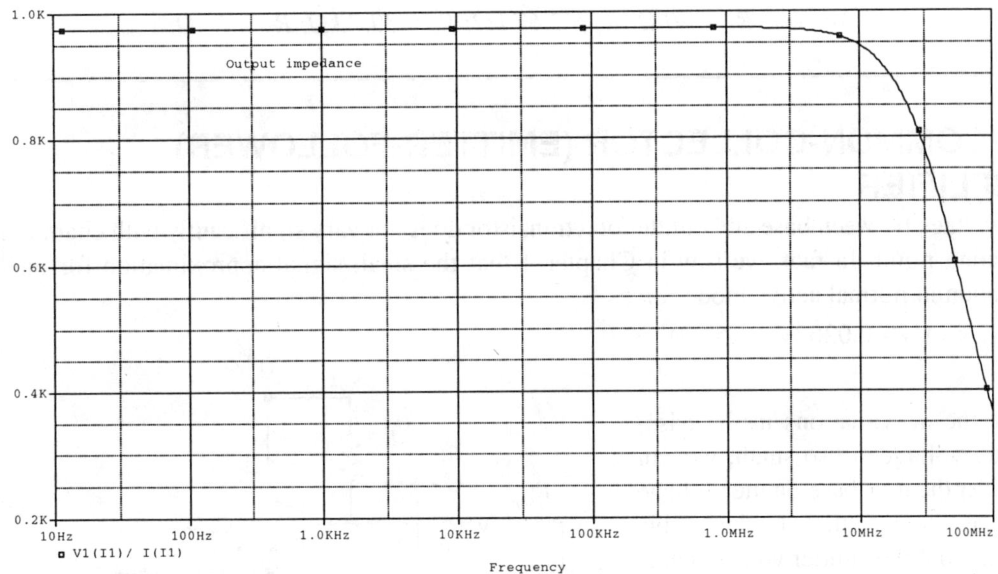

Figure 5.7(e) - The output impedance R_o versus frequency for the amplifier of Example 5.3

EXERCISES

E5.1 The amplifier of Figure 5.7(a) has V_{CC} = 15 V, $R_{load} \to \infty$, R_C = 5 kΩ, R_E = 500 Ω and $\beta = 200$. Determine R_1, R_2, A_v, A_i ,and the maximum undistorted symmetrical output voltage.

Answer: R_1 = 11.1 kΩ; R_2 = 103 kΩ; A_v = -9.63; A_i = -17.6; $v_{out(p\text{-}p)}$ = 12.3 V

E5.2 In Exercise E5.1, R_E is bypassed with a capacitor. What are the new values of R_1, R_2, A_v, A_i and R_o?

Answer: R_1 =11.1 kΩ; R_2 =101 kΩ; A_v=-275
A_i = -147; R_{in} = 2.67 kΩ; R_o =5 kΩ

E5.3 The *pnp* transistor amplifier shown in Figure 5.7 requires a voltage gain, $A_v = v_{out}/v_{in} = -5$ and an input resistance, R_{in} = 1 kΩ. R_{load} = 5 kΩ, V_{CC} = -12 V, V_{BE} = -0.7 V and β = 200. Determine the current gain, maximum undistorted output swing, and other resistor values.

Answer: A_i = -1; $v_{out\,max}$ = 6.35 V; R_1 = 1.1 kΩ; R_2 = 8.6 kΩ

E5.4 Design an amplifier (Figure 5.7(a)) with a voltage gain of A_v = -60, R_{load} = 5 kΩ and R_{in} = 5 kΩ. Design for a maximum undistorted voltage outut swing.

Answer: R_E = 25.0 Ω; R_1 = 13.4 kΩ; R_2 = 179 kΩ, A_i = -60; $v_{out(p\text{-}p)}$ = 7.12 V
(NOTE: This amplifier is not bias stable)

E5.5 Design an amplifier (Figure 5.7(a)) for maximum undistorted output swing with R_{load} = 6 kΩ, A_v = -60 and A_i = -20.

Answer: $R_E = 30\ \Omega$; $R_1 = 2.67\ k\Omega$; $R_2 = 39.7\ k\Omega$; $R_{in} = 2\ k\Omega$; $v_{out(p\text{-}p)} = 7.12\ V$

5.3 COMMON-COLLECTOR (EMITTER-FOLLOWER) AMPLIFIER

The voltage between base and emitter of a transistor does not vary significantly with changes in operating point. In fact, we saw in Chapter 4 that the small-signal approximation for linear operation in normal active mode forces

$$v_{be} \ll nV_T \approx 0.026\ \text{V} \qquad (5.27)$$

Since the *ac* variations in the base-emitter voltage are so small, we can consider the total base-emitter voltage to be constant. Under this assumption, the emitter voltage tends to "follow" the base voltage with a 0.7 V voltage drop. This observation allows us to configure the transistor in a way that proves useful in system design. The common-collector (CC) or emitter-follower (EF) circuit is shown in Figure 5.8(a).

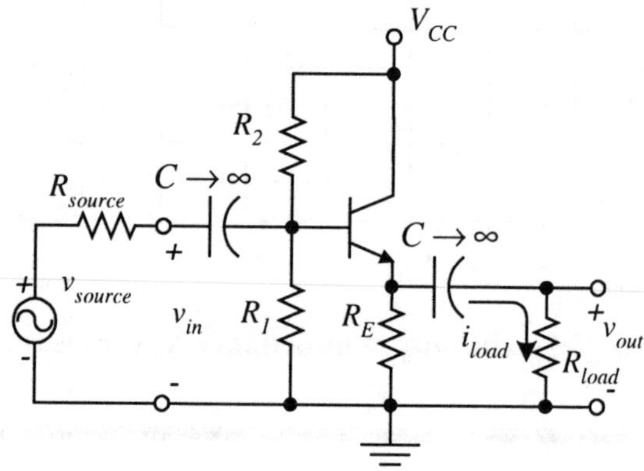

Figure 5.8(a) – The common-collector (CC) or emitter-follower (EF) circuit.

As with the common-emitter circuit, we calculate the four important parameters: input resistance, current gain, voltage gain, and output resistance.

5.3.1 Input Resistance, R_{in}

The capacitors, *C*, are once again considered to be short circuits for midrange frequencies. We first wish to solve for the input resistance. Let us begin by finding the resistance to the right of the dashed line in Figure 5.8(b), *R'*.

$$R' = \frac{v_{in}}{i_b} \qquad (5.28)$$

$$v_{in} = i_b r_\pi + (1+\beta) i_b \left(R_E \| R_{load}\right)$$

Now assuming that β is large (i.e., $(1+\beta) \approx \beta$), we have

$$R' = r_\pi + \beta\left(R_E \| R_{load}\right) \qquad (5.29)$$

Now solving for the input resistance,

$$R_{in} = R_B \| \left[r_\pi + \beta \left(R_E \| R_{load} \right) \right] = \frac{R_B \left[r_e + \left(R_E \| R_{load} \right) \right]}{R_B/\beta + r_e + \left(R_E \| R_{load} \right)} \tag{5.30}$$

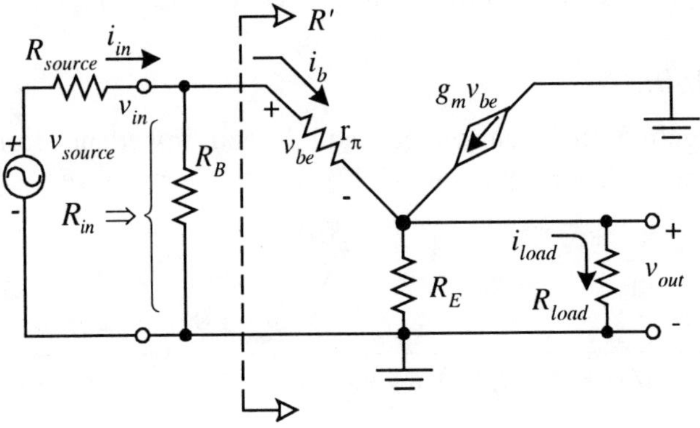

Figure 5.8(b) – Equivalent ac circuit for the CC (or EF) amplifier

In EF circuits where R_C is usually zero, the collector current is large. Then r_e (or r_π / β) is small compared with $R_E \| R_{load}$, so r_e can be ignored, and

$$R_{in} = R_B \| \left[\beta \left(R_E \| R_{load} \right) \right] \tag{5.31}$$

5.3.2 Current Gain, A_i

To obtain A_i, we find i_{in} and i_{out} and take the ratio. Current division applied to the output and input of Figure 5.8(b) yields,

$$i_{out} = i_{load} = \frac{i_b \beta R_E}{R_E + R_{load}}$$
$$i_b = i_{in} \frac{R_B}{R_B + r_\pi + \beta (R_E \| R_{load})} \tag{5.32}$$

The current gain is found from Equation (5.32) as the ratio,

$$A_i = \frac{i_{out}}{i_{in}} = \frac{R_B}{R_B/\beta + r_\pi/\beta + (R_E \| R_{load})} \cdot \frac{R_E}{R_E + R_{load}} \tag{5.33}$$

Equation (5.33) is the general expression for current gain. If r_π / β is much smaller than the parallel combination of R_E and R_{load}, then the following approximation results (assuming $R_B \ll \beta \left(R_E \| R_{load} \right)$:

$$A_i = \frac{R_B}{R_B/\beta + (R_E \| R_{load})} \cdot \frac{R_E}{R_E + R_{load}} \approx \frac{R_B}{R_{load}} \tag{5.34}$$

Note that current gain is positive for the EF amplifier since i_{in} is in phase with i_{out}.

5.3.3 Voltage Gain, A_v

We find the voltage gain from the current gain and the gain-impedance formula. Substituting the expressions for R_{in} and A_i from Equations (5.30) and (5.33), we have,

$$A_v = A_i \frac{R_{load}}{R_{in}}$$

$$= \frac{R_B}{R_B/\beta + r_\pi/\beta + (R_E \| R_{load})} \frac{R_E}{R_E + R_{load}} \frac{R_{load}[R_B + r_\pi + \beta(R_E \| R_{load})]}{R_B[r_\pi + \beta(R_E \| R_{load})]} \tag{5.35}$$

When like terms are cancelled from the numerator and denominator, and we note that $r_\pi = \beta r_e$, Equation (5.35) simplifies to

$$A_v = \frac{\beta(R_E \| R_{load})}{r_\pi + \beta(R_E \| R_{load})} = \frac{R_E \| R_{load}}{r_e + (R_E \| R_{load})} = \frac{g_m(R_E \| R_{load})}{1 + g_m(R_E \| R_{load})} \tag{5.36}$$

Since r_e (which is approximately $1/g_m$) is usually small compared to $R_E \| R_{load}$, we can approximate the gain as

$$A_v = 1 \tag{5.37}$$

Notice that the gain is positive since v_{in} is in phase with v_{out}.

5.3.4 Output Resistance, R_o

An alternative equivalent circuit for an EF amplifier is shown in Figure 5.9(a). Here we have used the CB model of the transistor instead of the CE model as employed in Figure 5.8(b). The resistance of the input voltage source is shown as R_{source}. We again use the test source technique for finding the output resistance. In Figure 5.9(b), we take this approach labeling the output current and voltage as i_{test} and v_{test} respectively. We write the equations for the circuit as follows:

$$i_b = \frac{-v_1}{R_{source} \| R_B}$$

$$v_1 - v_{test} = (1+\beta) i_b \frac{r_\pi}{\beta} \tag{5.38}$$

$$\frac{v_{test} - v_1}{r_\pi/\beta} + \frac{v_{test}}{R_E} = i_{test}$$

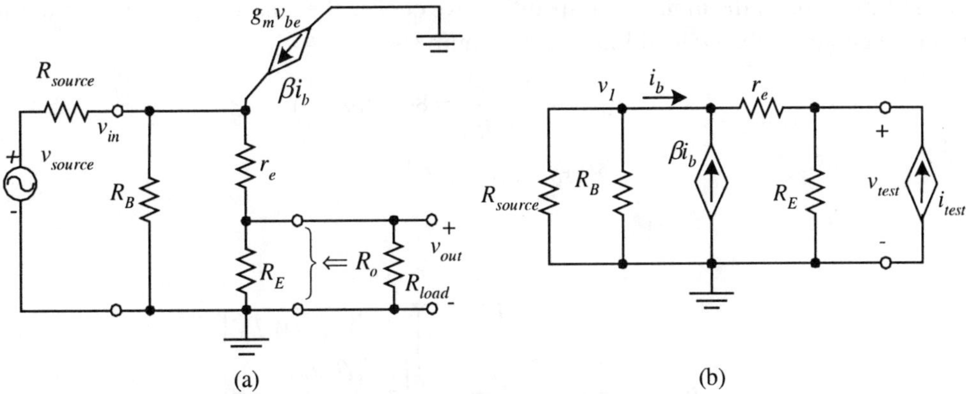

Figure 5.9 - Output resistance of EF configuration

We combine these equations to find the output resistance.

$$R_o = \frac{v_{test}}{i_{test}} = \left(\frac{r_\pi + R_{source}\|R_B}{\beta}\right)\|R_E \tag{5.39}$$

The output resistance is dependent upon the input parameters R_{source} and R_B. This is in contrast to the result for the CE amplifier where R_o depends only on R_C (See Section 5.1.5).

Example 5.4 - Capacitor-Coupled Common-Collector (Design)

Design a single stage *npn* EF amplifier (Figure 5.10(a)) with $\beta = 60$, $V_{BE} = 0.7$ V, $R_{source} = 1$ kΩ, and $V_{CC} = 12$ V. Determine the circuit element values for the stage to achieve $A_i = 10$ with a 100 Ω load.

Verify your design using a computer simulation. Compare calculated and simulated results over the frequency range of interest.

Solution: We must select R_1, R_2 and R_E, but again, we only have two equations. These two equations are specified by the current gain and the placement of the Q-point. Example 5.2 showed that the best choice for a CE amplifier is to make $R_C = R_{load}$. We could derive a similar result for R_E and R_{load} in the CC amplifier (Problem 5.26 develops this result). We shall therefore begin by constraining R_E to be equal to R_{load}. This yields a third equation,

$$R_E = R_{load} = 100\ \Omega$$

Now finding the load line slopes,

$$R_{ac} = R_E\|R_{load} = 50\ \Omega$$

$$R_{dc} = R_E = 100\ \Omega$$

Since the amplitude of the input is not specified, we choose the quiescent current to place the Q-point in the center of the *ac* load line for maximum swing.

$$I_{CQ} = \frac{V_{CC}}{R_{ac} + R_{dc}} = 80 \quad \text{mA}$$

$$V_{CEQ} = I_{CQ} R_{ac} = 4 \quad \text{V}$$

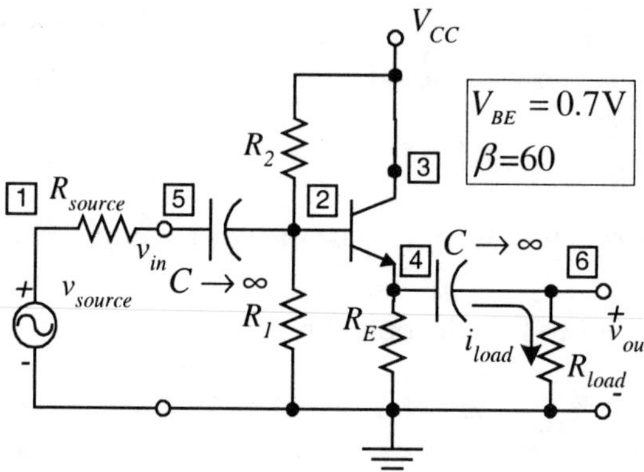

Figure 5.10(a) - Circuit and computer simulation for Example 5.4

We now find the value of r_π / β (or r_e):

$$r_e = \frac{26\,(\text{mV})}{|I_{CQ}|} = \frac{26\ (\text{mV})}{80\ (\text{mA})} = 0.33\ \Omega$$

Since r_e is insignificant compared to $R_E \| R_{load}$, it can be ignored. This is usually the case for EF circuits.

Using the equation for current gain we find

$$A_i = \frac{\beta R_E R_B}{(R_E + R_{load})[R_B + (R_E \| R_{load})\beta]}$$

Everything in this equation is known except R_B. We solve for R_B with the result

$$R_B = 1500\ \Omega$$

V_{BB} is found from the base loop.

$$V_{BB} = V_{BE} + I_{CQ}\left(\frac{R_B}{\beta} + R_E\right) = 10.7 \quad \text{V}$$

Continuing with the design as presented earlier, we find

$$R_1 = 13.8 \quad \text{k}\Omega$$
$$R_2 = 1.68 \quad \text{k}\Omega$$

The voltage gain of the CC amplifier is approximately unity. The input resistance is found from equations derived in Section 5.3.1.

$$R_{in} = R_B \| [\beta(R_E \| R_{load})] = 1 \quad \text{k}\Omega$$

The output resistance is found from equations derived in Section 5.3.4.

$$R_o = \left(\frac{R_\pi + R_{source} \| R_B}{\beta} \right) \| R_E = 9.36 \quad \Omega$$

The maximum peak-to-peak symmetrical output swing is given by equations derived in Chapter 4.

$$v_{out}(p - p) = 1.8 \, | I_{CQ} | \, (R_E \| R_{load}) = 7.2 \quad \text{V}$$

The power dissipated in the load, P_{load}, and the maximum power required of the transistor, $P_{Transistor}$, are

$$P_{load} = \frac{(0.9\, I_{CQ}/2)^2 R_{load}}{2} = 64.8 \quad \text{mW}$$
$$P_{Transistor} = I_{CQ} V_{CEQ} = 320 \quad \text{mW}$$

We now enter the circuit into PSPICE using the node numbers indicated in Figure 5.10(a). The PSPICE code is as follows:

```
VIN,1,0,AC,1,SIN(0,1,1000)
RS,1,11,1
CIN,11,2,1
VCC,5,0,DC,12V
R1,2,0,13.8K
R2,2,5,1.68K
*GUMMEL POON BJT PARAMETERS
```

```
Q1,5,2,4,BJT
.MODEL,BJT,NPN(BF=60)
RE,4,0,100
C1,4,6,1
VDUMMY,6,3,DC,0
RL,3,0,100
.AC,LIN,25,100,100K
.TRAN,.005M,1M
.PROBE
.END
```

Note that we have inserted a dummy voltage source in series with the output to monitor current as a convenience. Figure 5.10(b) shows the plot of the voltage gain [V(Vout)/V(Vin)] and the current gain [I(Rload)/I(Vin)] over the frequency range of interest. The results of the simulation for the voltage gain and the current gain are in excellent agreement with the calculated values. From Figure 5.10(b) $A_v = 1$ and $A_i = 9.95$ over the frequency range of interest. Actually, as we will see in Figure 5.10(f), the expected voltage gain A_v is slightly smaller than unity.

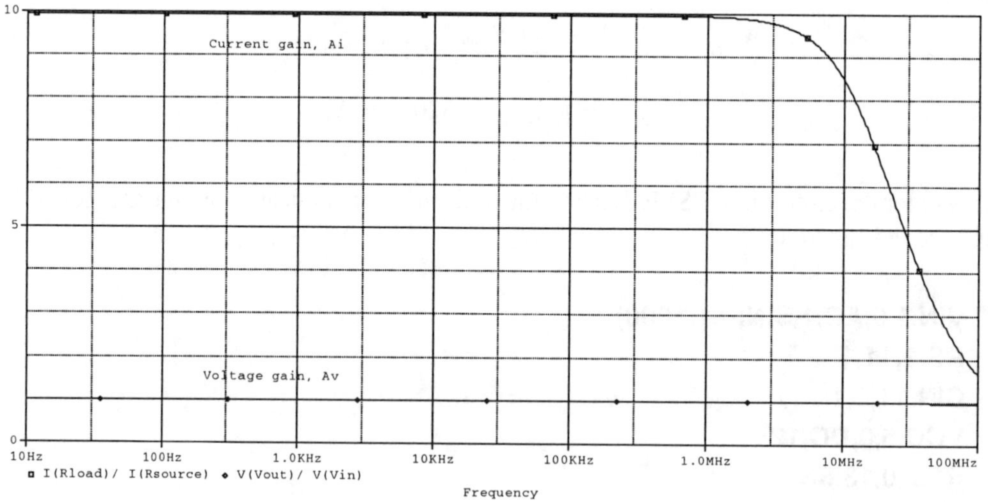

Figure 5.10(b) – Simulation results for the voltage gain and current gain for Example 5.4

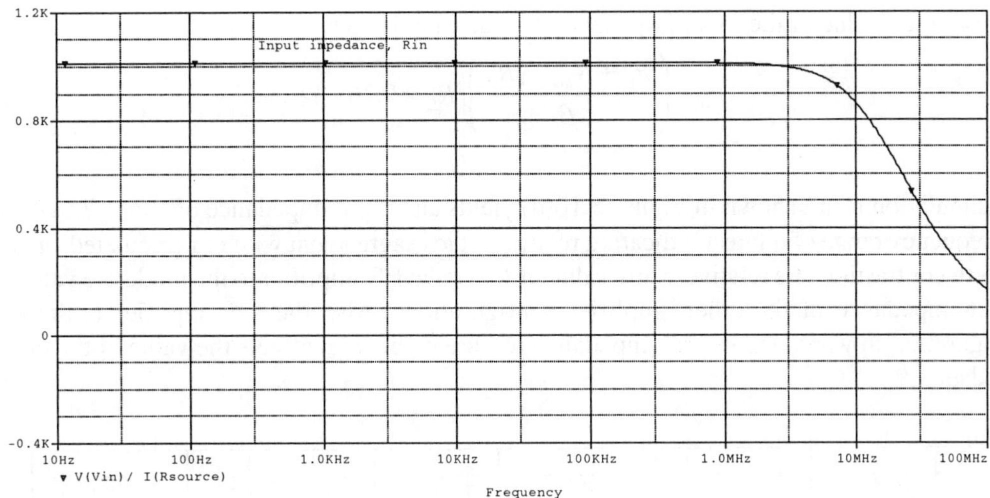

Figure 5.10(c) – The input impedance, R_{in}, as a function of frequency for Example 5.4

The expected value of the input impedance R_{in} was calculated above as

$$R_{in} = R_B \| [\beta(R_E \| R_{load})] = 1 \quad \text{k}\Omega \,.$$

The simulation results shown in Figure 5.10(c) yield an input impedance of about 1.1kΩ which indicates very close agreement between the calculated and simulation values.

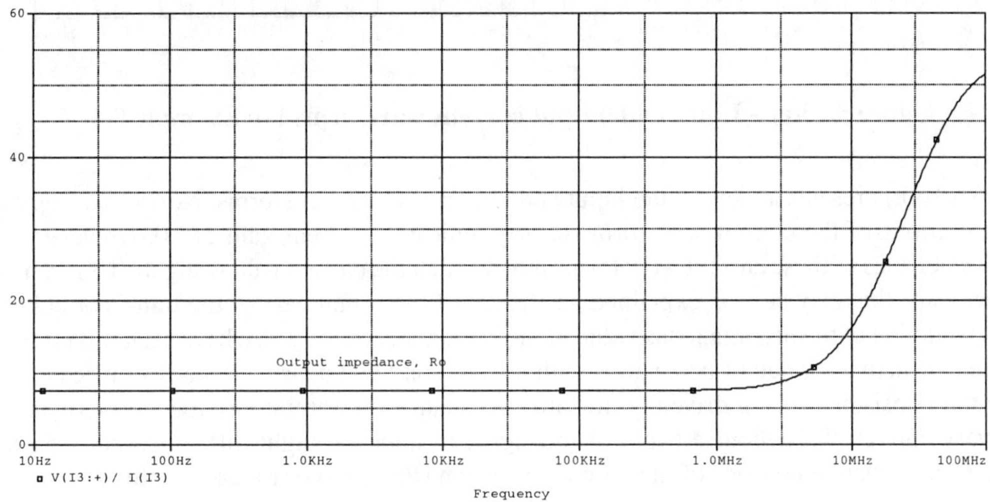

Figure 5.10(d) – The output impedance, R_o, as a function of frequency for Example 5.4

The expected value of the input impedance R_o was calculated as

$$R_o = \left(\frac{R_\pi + R_{source} \| R_B}{\beta} \right) \| R_E = 9.36 \quad \Omega .$$

The simulation result shown in Figure 5.10(d) yields an output impedance of about 7.6Ω over the frequency range of interest indicating relatively close agreement with our calculated value. It is worth contrasting this relatively low value of R_o for the EF amplifier to the moderate values of output impedance of the other amplifier configurations. Also the EF amplifier is the only configuration in which the source impedance (on the input side) affects the value of the output impedance R_o.

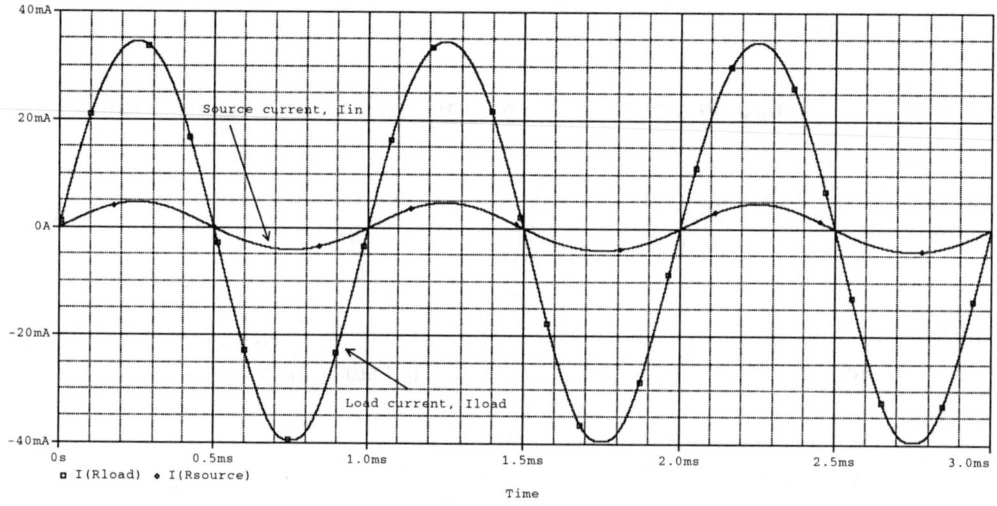

Figure 5.10(e) – Input and output current waveforms for Example 5.4

Figure 5.10(e) presents a view of the input and output *current* waveforms. Notice the *negative* going portions of the current waveforms clearly indicate a current gain of 10. However, the *positive* portions of these current waveforms indicate that the current gain is slightly less than 10. In large part, this may best be explained as a result of the actual beta of the transistor being a (weak) function of the instantaneous value of the collector current I_C. We have seen this effect in Chapter 4 where the value of beta varies with location on the transistor's characteristic curves. Since the transistor is being driven quite hard (from cut-off to saturation), the actual values of beta vary enough throughout a cycle of the signal to notice a slight difference between the positive and negative portions of the output waveform (I(Rload)) of Figure 5.10(e).

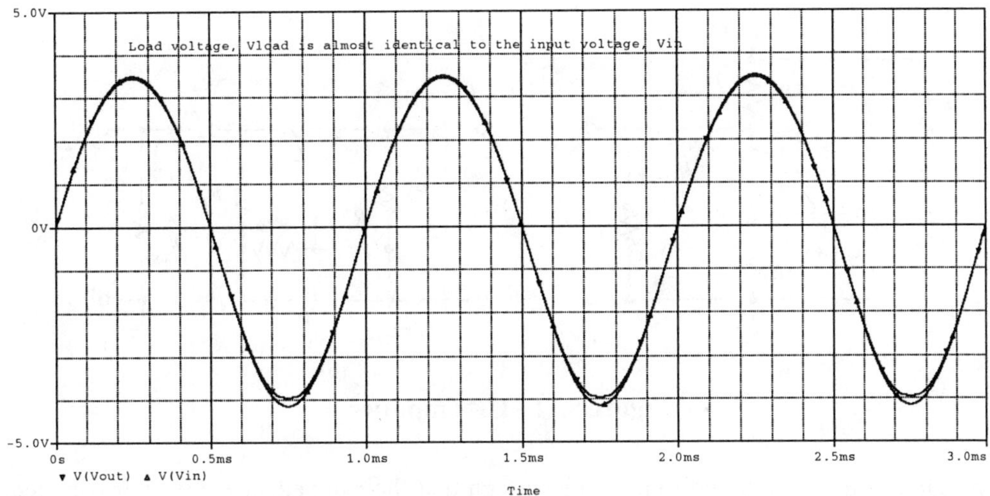

Figure 5.10(f) – Input and output voltage waveforms. Note V_{out} is slightly smaller than V_{in}.

Figure 5.10(f) presents a view of the input and output *voltage* waveforms. We know that the theoretical gain of an EF amplifier configuration is slightly less than unity. A careful examination of the input and output voltage waveforms verifies this fact (in fact, you may not even notice that Figure 5.10(f) contains two curves). However, it is convenient say that the expected voltage gain of the EF amplifier is unity.

In summary, we see that the simulation results verify our calculations. And the results confirm that the design requirements for this example have been achieved and verified by the close agreement between the expected behavior of this circuit configuration and the computer simulations provided by PSpice.

EXERCISES

E5.6 Design an EF amplifier (Figure 5.8) with $A_i = 15$, $V_{CC} = 18$ V, $\beta = 100$, $V_{BE} = 0.7$ V and $R_{load} = 200\ \Omega$. Find the peak-to-peak undistorted output voltage.

Answer: $R_1 = 28.3\ k\Omega$; $R_2 = 5.1\ k\Omega$; $R_E = 200\ \Omega$, $v_{out(p\text{-}p)} = 10.8\ V$

E5.7 Design an EF amplifier (with non-zero collector resistor) which has $R_{in} = 2$ kΩ, $R_C = 100\ \Omega$, $V_{CC} = 18$ V, $\beta = 100$, $V_{BE} = 0.7$ V and $R_{load} = 200\ \Omega$.

Answer: $R_E = 200\ \Omega$; $R_1 = 4.89\ k\Omega$; $R_2 = 5.1\ k\Omega, A_i = 10$; $v_{out(p\text{-}p)} = 6.48\ V$

5.4 COMMON-BASE AMPLIFIER

The common-base (CB) amplifier is shown in Figure 5.11(a). The circuit is reoriented and redrawn in Figure 5.11(b).

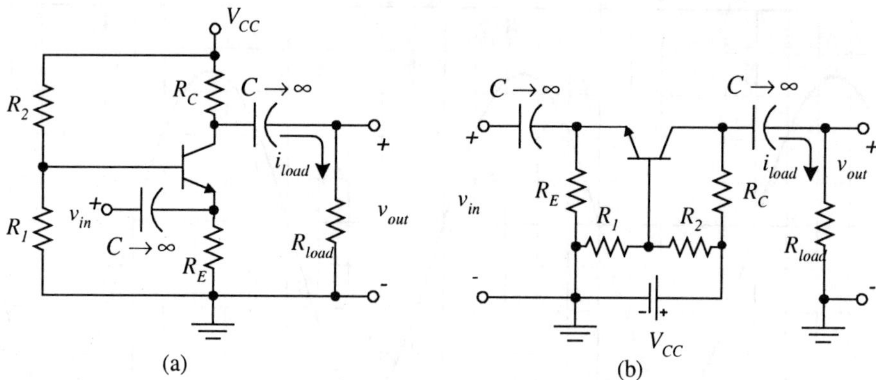

Figure 5.11 - CB amplifier

The capacitors are assumed to be large enough that their impedances are approximated as short circuits in the frequency range of the input signal. The input voltage source and its series resistor are attached to the emitter. The load is attached to the collector and the base is connected to *ac* ground.

5.4.1 Input Resistance, R_{in}

The equivalent hybrid circuit for the CB is shown in Figure 5.12 where the CE hybrid model is used. R_B is the parallel combination of R_1 and R_2. We derive R_{in} by taking the ratio of input

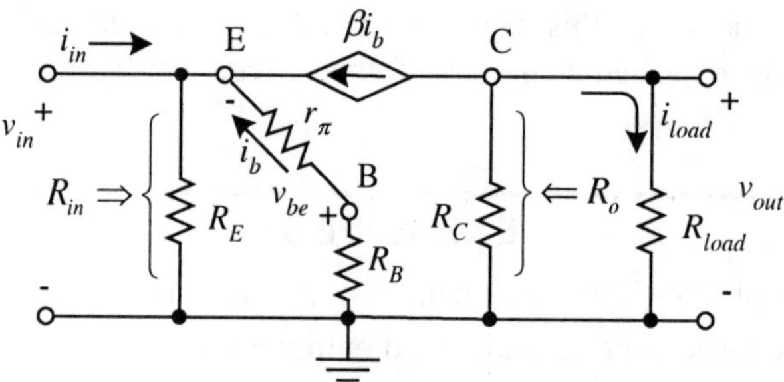

Figure 5.12 – CB amplifier equivalent circuit

voltage to current. The current in R_E is $i_{in} + (\beta + 1) \cdot i_b$. In the following analysis, we once again assume that β is large enough to permit substituting β for $\beta + 1$. Thus,

$$v_{in} = R_E(i_{in} + \beta i_b) \tag{5.40}$$

To find v_{in}/i_{in}, we must eliminate i_b from this equation. We see from Figure 5.12 that

$$i_b = -\frac{v_{in}}{r_\pi + R_B} \tag{5.41}$$

Substituting Equation (5.41) into Equation (5.40), we have

$$v_{in} = R_E\left(i_{in} - \frac{\beta v_{in}}{r_\pi + R_B}\right) \tag{5.42}$$

The input resistance is given by the ratio of input voltage to current.

$$R_{in} = \frac{v_{in}}{i_{in}} = \frac{R_E\left(r_e + {R_B}/{\beta}\right)}{R_B + r_e + {R_B}/{\beta}} = R_E \left\| \left(r_e + {R_B}/{\beta}\right) \right. \tag{5.43}$$

$r_e = r_\pi / \beta$ is usually only a few ohms, so R_{in} is quite small. This *low input resistance* represents a *serious* limitation of the CB configuration.

5.4.2 Current Gain, A_i

The current gain for the circuit of Figure 5.11 is found as follows:

$$A_i = \frac{i_{load}}{i_{in}} = -\frac{\beta i_b}{i_{in}} \cdot \frac{R_C}{R_C + R_{load}} \tag{5.44}$$

From the previous derivation for R_{in}, we have

$$\begin{aligned} i_b &= \frac{-v_{in}}{r_\pi + R_B} = \frac{-i_{in} R_{in}}{r_\pi + R_B} \\ &= \frac{-R_E i_{in}}{\beta R_E + r_\pi + R_B} \end{aligned} \tag{5.45}$$

We combine Equations (5.44) and (5.45) to find the current gain.

$$A_i = \frac{R_E}{R_E + r_e + R_B/\beta} \cdot \frac{R_C}{R_C + R_{load}} \tag{5.46}$$

5.4.3 Voltage Gain, A_v

The *gain impedance formula* is used to find A_v. We use A_i and R_{in} to obtain the expression for voltage gain.

$$A_v = A_i \frac{R_{load}}{R_{in}} = \frac{R_{load} \| R_C}{r_\pi/\beta + R_B/\beta} = \frac{R_{load} \| R_C}{r_e + R_B/\beta} = \frac{g_m (R_{load} \| R_C)}{1 + g_m R_B/\beta} \tag{5.47}$$

Note that if a bypass capacitor between base and ground is added, these equations change and the gain increases by a significant amount.

5.4.4 Output Resistance, R_o

As in the case of the CE amplifier, the dependent current generator $\beta \cdot i_b$ exhibits a high resistance. The output circuit of the CB amplifier is exactly the same as that of the CE amplifier.

$$R_o = R_C \tag{5.48}$$

Example 5.5 - Capacitor-Coupled CB (Design)

Design a CB amplifier using an *npn* transistor (Figure 5.11) with $\beta = 100$, $V_{CC} = 24$ V, $R_{load} = 2$ kΩ, $R_E = 400$ Ω and $V_{BE} = 0.7$ V. Design this amplifier for a voltage gain of 20.

Solution: Since there are fewer equations than there are unknowns, we need an additional constraint, so we set

$$R_C = R_{load} = 2 \quad \text{k}\Omega$$

This is in accordance with the results of Example 5.2. Then we have,

$$\frac{R_B + r_\pi}{\beta} = \frac{R_{load} \| R_C}{A_v} = 50 \quad \Omega$$

$$R_{ac} = 1.40 \quad \text{k}\Omega$$

$$R_{dc} = 2.40 \quad \text{k}\Omega$$

For maximum swing, we set I_C to

$$I_{CQ} = \frac{V_{CC}}{R_{ac} + R_{dc}} = 6.30 \quad \text{mA}$$

We now find that

$$r_e = \frac{0.026}{I_C} = 4.12 \quad \Omega$$

$$R_B = \beta(50 - 4.12) = 4.59 \quad \text{k}\Omega$$

Since we have already found $r_\pi / \beta = 50$, we can substitute this into the current gain equation to yield,

$$A_i = \frac{400}{400+50}\;\frac{2000}{2000+2000} = 0.44$$

$$R_{in} = R_E \left\| \left(r_e + \frac{R_B}{\beta} \right) \right. = 44 \quad \Omega$$

We use the bias equation to find the parameters of the input bias circuitry.

$$V_{BB} = V_{BE} + I_{CQ}\left(\frac{R_B}{\beta} + R_E \right) = 3.51 \quad \text{V}$$

The bias resistors are then given by

$$R_1 = \frac{R_B}{1 - V_{BB}/V_{CC}} = 5.38 \quad \text{k}\Omega$$

$$R_2 = \frac{R_B V_{CC}}{V_{BB}} = 31.4 \quad \text{k}\Omega$$

The maximum peak-to-peak undistorted output voltage is

$$v_{out}(peak - peak) = 1.8 \,|\, I_{CQ} \,|\, \left(R_{load} \| R_C \right) = 11.3 \quad \text{V}$$

Example 5.6 - Capacitor-Coupled CB (Analysis)

An *npn* transistor is connected in a CB configuration as shown in Figure 5.11. The voltage source is $V_{CC} = 20$ V, $\beta = 200$, $V_{BE} = 0.7$ V, $R_E = 200\ \Omega$, $R_1 = 5$ kΩ, $R_2 = 80$ kΩ, and $R_C = R_{load} = 5$ kΩ. A large capacitor is placed between the base of the transistor and ground. Determine the voltage gain, current gain, input impedance, and maximum undistorted symmetrical output voltage swing.

Solution: We find the Thevenin equivalent of the base circuitry.

$$R_B = R_1 \| R_2 = 4.71 \quad \text{k}\Omega$$

$$V_{BB} = 20 \times \frac{5 \times 10^3}{8.5 \times 10^4} = 1.18 \quad \text{V}$$

The Q-point location is found by writing a KVL equation around the base-emitter loop.

$$V_{BE} + I_C\left(R_E + \frac{R_B}{\beta} \right) = V_{BB}$$

where we assume that $I_C = I_E$. Substituting values and solving for I_C yields

$$I_C = 2.13 \quad \text{mA}$$

Then

$$r_e = \frac{r_\pi}{\beta} = \frac{26\text{mV}}{|I_{CQ}|} = 12.2 \quad \Omega$$

A_i and A_v are found from equations derived in Sections 5.3.2 and 5.3.3.

$$A_i = \frac{R_E}{R_E + r_e} \frac{R_C}{R_{load} + R_C} = 0.47$$

$$A_v = \frac{R_{load} \| R_C}{r_e} = \frac{\beta (R_{load} \| R_C)}{r_\pi} = 205$$

Note that we have not included R_B in the formula for A_i since it is bypassed by a large capacitor.

Solving for R_{in} using equations derived in Section 5.3.1, we obtain

$$R_{in} = R_E \| r_e = 11.5 \quad \Omega$$

To determine the maximum output voltage swing, we evaluate the *ac* and *dc* load line equations to determine whether I_{CQ} is above or below the center of the *ac* load line.

$$V_{CEQ} = V_{CC} - (R_C + R_E) I_{CQ} = 20 - 5.2\,(\text{k}\Omega)(2.13\,(\text{mA})) = 8.92 \quad \text{V}$$

The *ac* load line intersects the axis at $V'_{CC} = V_{CEQ} + I_{CQ} R_{ac}$ where $R_{ac} = R_{load} \| R_C + R_E = 2.7\,(\text{k}\Omega)$. Then

$$V'_{CC} = 8.9 + 2.13\,\text{mA} \times (2.7\,\text{k}\Omega) = 14.7 \quad \text{V}$$

$$I'_{CC} = \frac{V'_{CC}}{R_{ac}} = 5.44 \quad \text{mA}$$

Note that the Q-point is below the center of the load line [I_{CQ} = 2.13 (mA) and the center is at 5.44/2 = 2.72 (mA)]. Therefore, using the appropriate equation from Chapter 4, we obtain the peak-to-peak output voltage swing, as follows:

$$v_{out}(peak - peak) = 2\left(I_{CQ} - 0.05 I'_{C\max}\right)\left(R_{load} \| R_C\right) = 9.29 \quad \text{V}$$

A consolidation of the equations for each circuit configuration is shown in Table 5.2. The equivalent circuit for each of the four circuit configurations is shown in Table 5.3. These tables are given at the end of this chapter following the summary.

EXERCISES

E5.8 Determine the voltage gain of a CB amplifier (Figure 5.11) with $R_{load} = 3\ k\Omega$, $R_E = 500\ \Omega$, $V_{CC} = 15$ V, $V_{BE} = 0.7$ V, R_B=6 kΩ, and $\beta = 200$. The circuit is designed for maximum voltage output swing.

Answer: $A_v = 37.9$

E5.9 Repeat Exercise E5.8 assuming that a large capacitor is added from the base to ground.

Answer: $A_v = 157$

E5.10 Design a CB amplifier (Figure 5.11) having a voltage gain of 40. Determine the component values when $V_{CC} = 20$ V, $R_{load} = 4\ k\Omega$, $R_E = 500\ \Omega$, $V_{BE} = 0.7$ V and $\beta = 100$.

Answer: $R_1 = 4.6\ k\Omega$; $R_2 = 36.4\ k\Omega$; $R_C = 4\ k\Omega$; $R_{in} = 45\ \Omega$

5.5 TRANSISTOR AMPLIFIER APPLICATIONS

We now make some observations from the previous sections and suggest applications for the amplifier configurations based upon their properties.

The CE amplifier has significant current and voltage gain with moderate input and output impedance. The high input impedance is desirable, while the high output impedance poses some problems. The higher the output impedance, the less current can be drawn from an amplifier without a significant drop in output voltage. The CE is used most often for voltage amplification. It can provide a large output voltage swing. In multistage systems, this output becomes the input of the next stage of the system.

The emitter-resistor amplifier is similar to the CE amplifier but has a lower voltage gain and higher input impedance. Because of the feedback present in this amplifier, internal noise generated by the transistor is almost eliminated.

The EF (CC) amplifier provides a high current gain with a low output impedance. It has a high input impedance and a voltage gain near unity. Clearly, it is not suited for voltage amplification. The low output impedance makes this circuit useful for driving high current devices. It can be used as a *buffer* between a CE amplifier and a load. The CC amplifier is frequently used as a power amplifier. It is also used in impedance matching applications. This amplifier is normally found in the final output stage of a multistage amplifier as it not only drops the impedance to a low value, but also provides the necessary power to drive the load.

The CB amplifier has a low input impedance and a relatively high output impedance. These properties are less desirable for signal amplification. If the base is bypassed to ground with a capacitor, the amplifier has high voltage gain but the current gain is less than unity. Thus, if the source driving the amplifier has a low impedance, and the load is drawing little current, the CB can be used as a voltage amplifier. If the driving source has a higher impedance, we can offset this undesirable effect by using a CE amplifier to drive the CB amplifier. Thus, the overall input impedance is high.

5.6 PHASE SPLITTER

When two signals of opposite polarity are required, we use a *phase splitter*, as shown in Figure 5.13. This amplifier is simultaneously a common-emitter and a common-collector. We choose $R_C = R_E = R_{load}$ so that the output voltage at the collector is equal in magnitude to the output voltage at the emitter, but these voltages are 180° out of phase. The two signal outputs from this circuit are approximately equal in amplitude to the input signal: that is,

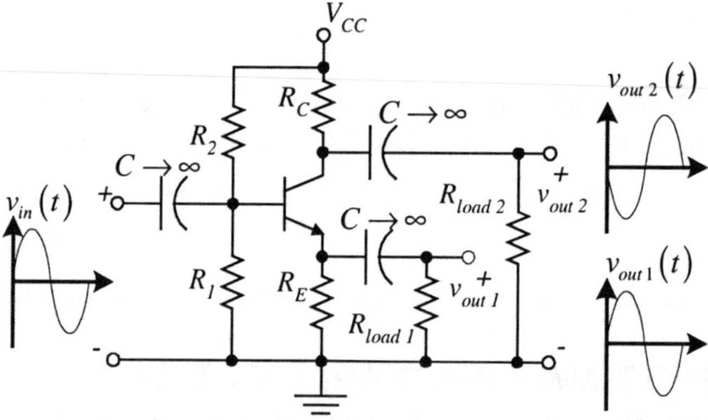

Figure 5.13 – Phase splitter

the voltage gain ratios, v_{out1}/v_{in} and v_{out2}/v_{in}, have a magnitude approximately equal to unity. The two outputs resulting from a sinusoidal input are sketched on the figure. The output at the emitter is in phase with the input signal while the output of the collector is 180° out of phase with the input signal.

EXERCISE

E5.11 The outputs of Figure 5.13 are each connected to a 2 kΩ load. What is the output voltage swing of the phase splitter when V_{CC} = 20 V? Also determine R_C, R_E, R_1 and R_2 for maximum output swing when β = 200 and V_{BE} = 0.7 V.

Answer: $R_C = R_E = 2\ k\Omega$; $R_1 = 66.9\ k\Omega$; $R_2 = 99.6\ k\Omega$
$v_{out(p\text{-}p)} = 6.7\ V$ *(each output)*

5.7 AMPLIFIER COUPLING

When a system is composed of more than one transistor stage, it is necessary to connect (couple) the transistor amplifiers to each other. There are several common ways of accomplishing this interconnection between amplifiers. In the following sections, we discuss capacitive, direct, transformer and optical coupling.

5.7.1 Capacitive Coupling

Capacitive coupling is the type that is illustrated in the designs of this chapter. It is the simplest and most effective way of decoupling the effects of the *dc* level of the first amplifier stage from those of the second stage. The capacitor removes the *dc* component from the *ac* signal. Thus, the biasing of an amplifier stage is not affected by the biasing of the previous stage. To insure that the signal is not significantly changed by the addition of a capacitor, it is necessary for the capacitor to look like a short circuit to all frequencies being amplified. Therefore we assume that the capacitor is large.

5.7.2 Direct Coupling

Two amplifiers are *direct coupled* if the output of the first amplifier is connected to the input of the second without the use of capacitors. An example is shown in Figure 5.14(a).

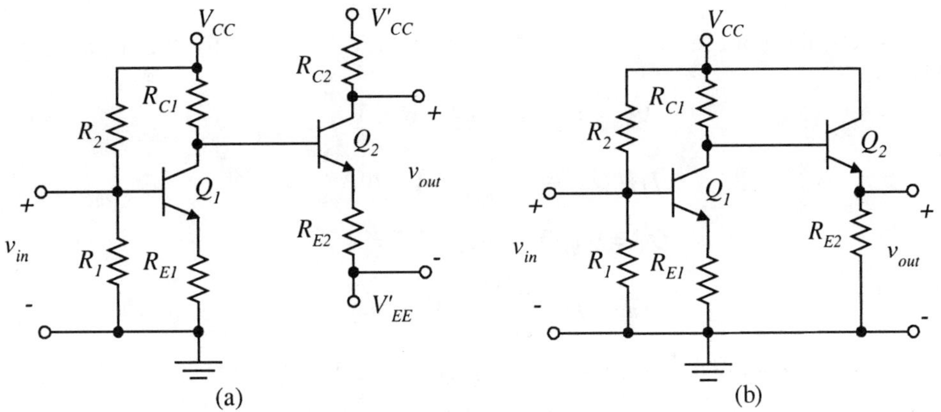

Figure 5.14 Direct-coupled amplifier

Note that there are three different *dc* power supply voltages, labeled V_{CC}, V'_{CC} and V'_{EE}. The *ac* output of the first stage is superimposed upon the *dc* quiescent level of the second stage. The *dc* voltage level of the previous stage's output interacts with the *dc* voltages of the second stage thereby affecting the bias conditions. To compensate for the changing of bias levels, the amplifier uses negative and positive *dc* voltage sources instead of a single V_{CC} source. A *level shifter*, can provide the bias voltage change (level shifters are presented in Chapter 9).

Direct coupling can be used effectively when coupling an EF amplifier to an emitter-resistor amplifier, as shown in Figure 5.14(b). Direct coupling eliminates the need for the coupling capacitor and the resistors R_1 and R_2 of the second stage. The direct-coupled amplifier has good frequency response since there are no series capacitors (i.e., frequency-sensitive elements) to affect the output signal at low frequency.

Direct coupling is commonly used in the design of integrated circuits. There are several reasons for its use. The resulting amplifier has excellent low-frequency response and can amplify *dc* signals. It is also simpler to fabricate on a chip since there is no need for capacitors. However, direct coupling has the disadvantages of requiring additional power supplies or level shifters and of being sensitive to drift (Drift is a slowly varying *dc* level change).

We note from Figure 5.14(b) that V_{CEQ} of the first amplifier is V_{BB} of the second amplifier. This causes problems if the emitter-resistor amplifier follows the EF amplifier since emitter-resistor amplifiers have a low V_{BB} - just above the 0.7 V needed to cause the transistor to conduct. We must therefore reduce the quiescent voltage, V_{CEQ}, to a low level thereby significantly reducing the output voltage swing. Later in this text we will explore techniques for maintaining large output swings. Alternatively, we can easily couple an emitter resistor amplifier to an EF amplifier (as shown in the figure) since V_{BB} for EF amplifiers can be reasonably large. This is illustrated in the following example.

Example 5.7:

Design a direct-coupled amplifier (Figure 5.14(b)) to have an 8 V peak-to-peak output voltage swing from Q_2. Assume $\beta = 200$ and $V_{BE} = 0.7$ V for both transistors, $R_{E2} = 2\ \text{k}\Omega$, $R_C = 4\ \text{k}\Omega$, $V_{CC} = 10$ V, $R_{in} = 5\ \text{k}\Omega$, and $A_v = -20$.

Solution: At Q_2, the voltage drop across R_{E2} must be 4 V 0-to-peak for the negative going signal. Therefore,

$$V_{CEQ}(Q_2) = 10 - 4 = 6 \quad \text{V}$$

$$I_{CQ}(Q_2) = \frac{4}{2000} = 2 \quad \text{mA}$$

$$V_{CEQ}(Q_1) = V_B(Q_2) = 4.0 + 0.7 = 4.7 \quad \text{V}$$

$$I_B(Q_2) = \frac{0.002}{200} = 10 \quad \mu\text{A}$$

$$V_{CEQ}(Q_1) = 4.7\ \text{V} = 10 - \left[I_{CQ}(Q_1) + I_B(Q_2)\right] \cdot (4\ \text{k}\Omega)$$

$$I_{CQ}(Q_1) + I_B(Q_2) = 1.33 \quad \text{mA}$$

Then

$$I_{CQ}(Q_1) = 1.32 \quad \text{mA}$$

$$R_{load}(Q_1) = r_\pi(Q_2) + \beta R_{E2} = \beta\left(\frac{26}{2} + 2000\right) = 403 \quad \text{k}\Omega$$

Since the EF amplifier gain is unity, we use the equation for A_v for the emitter-resistor amplifier to find,

$$-20 = -\frac{4\,k\Omega \| 403\,k\Omega}{R_E'}$$

$$R'_E = 198 \quad \Omega$$

Since $I_{CQ}(Q_1) = 1.32$ mA and $r_e = 19.7\ \Omega$,

$$R_E = 178 \quad \Omega$$

$$R_{in} = 5\,k\Omega = \frac{R_B \times 198}{R_B/200 + 198}$$

$$R_B = 5.72 \quad k\Omega$$

$$V_{BB} = 0.7 + 0.00132 \times \left(\frac{5720}{200} + 178 \right) = 0.973 \quad \text{V}$$

$$R_1 = \frac{5720}{1 - 0.973/10} = 6.34 \quad k\Omega$$

$$R_2 = 5720 \times \frac{10}{0.973} = 58.8 \quad k\Omega$$

This result illustrates that emitter resistor and EF amplifiers can be cascaded without creating problems, except that maximum output swing cannot be attained. In this particular example, only 8 V peak-to-peak signal output voltage was required. The *dc* coupling did not affect the output as long as that output does not exceed the limit of ±4 V. The coupling provides the ability to pass a *dc* signal.

5.7.3 Transformer Coupling

A transformer can be used to couple two amplifier stages. This type of coupling is often used when high frequencies are being amplified. Although transformers are more costly than capacitors, their advantages can justify the additional cost. Through appropriate choice of the turns ratio, a transformer can be used to increase either the voltage or current gain. For example, in the output stage of a power amplifier, the transformer is used to increase the current gain. There are other benefits associated with the use of a transformer. For example, the transformer can be tuned to resonance so that it becomes a band pass filter (a filter which passes desired frequencies while attenuating frequencies outside the desired band).

Coupling the output stage to the load in an emitter follower can be accomplished by using a transformer. Figure 5.15 illustrates this technique, where the amplifier is coupled into a speaker.

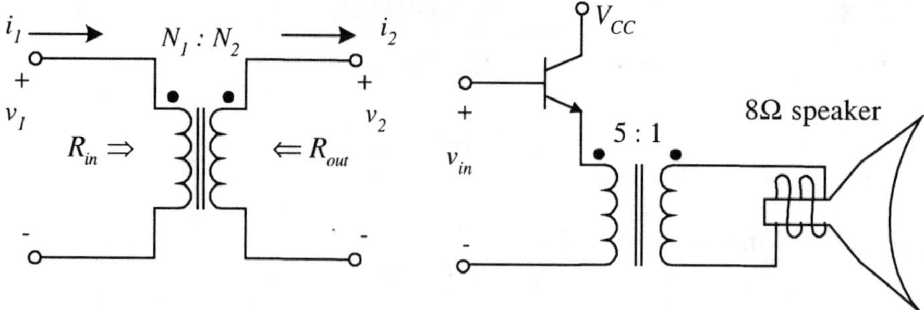

Figure 5.15 - Transformer coupling into a speaker

We refer to Figure 5.15 in reviewing the operation of a transformer. The input and output voltages are proportional to the transformer turns ratio as follows:

$$v_2 = v_1 \left(\frac{N_2}{N_1} \right) \tag{5.49}$$

where N_1 is the number of turns in the primary coil and N_2 is the number of turns in the secondary coil. The input and output currents are related inversely to the voltage since power must be conserved. Thus,

$$i_2 = i_1 \left(\frac{N_1}{N_2} \right) \tag{5.50}$$

Taking the ratio of voltage to current yields the impedance relationship,

$$Z_1 = \left(\frac{N_1}{N_2} \right)^2 \times Z_2 \tag{5.51}$$

Figure 5.15(b) illustrates an application of these results where the transformer is used to drive an 8-Ω speaker. If the transformer turns ratio is 5:1, the equivalent resistance seen by the transistor emitter is 200 Ω. If v_{in} is a sinusoid of amplitude 10 V, the emitter voltage is approximately the same value since the gain of the EF amplifier is unity. The voltage at the speaker is one-fifth of this, or a 2 V amplitude sinusoid. The current at the speaker is a 250 mA amplitude sinusoid (i.e. use Ohm's law at the speaker terminals), and the current in the transistor emitter is a 50 mA amplitude sinusoid. The biasing of these circuits will be deferred to Chapter 8 where we discuss the details of power amplifiers.

Example 5.8 – Transformer-Coupled Amplifier (Analysis)

Find the current gain, voltage gain and input resistance for the transformer-coupled amplifier of Figure 5.16.

Solution: Note that the total amplification for the stage is obtained by taking the products of the gains of each section (the sections are separated by dashed lines in the figure).

Since the *dc* operating parameters are not specified, we will make approximations of A_v, A_i and R_{in} as shown in Figure 5.16. We will be studying these types of amplifiers in more detail in Chapter 8.

The voltage gain of the transistor is found from the equation for the CE amplifier, where the collector resistance is found by reflecting the 500-Ω load resistance back through the transformer. The overall voltage gain, A_v, includes the voltage scaling effects of the two transformers. The results are shown directly on the figure.

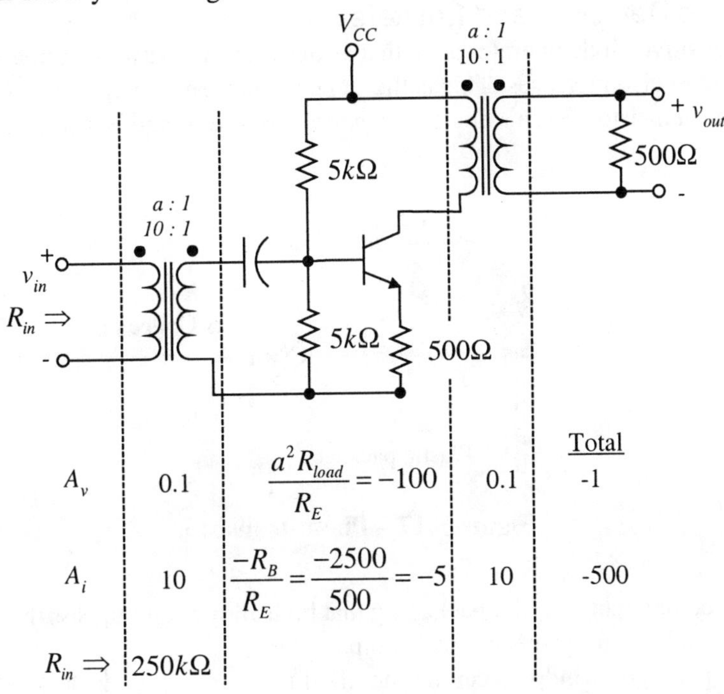

Figure 5.16 – Transformer-coupled amplifier of Example 5.8

The current gain, A_i, is similarly found. Note that there is only one resistor in the collector circuit, that being the load reflected through the transformer.

The input resistance to the transistor is R_B which is the parallel combination of R_1 and R_2, or 2500 Ω. This is reflected through the transformer to get R_{in}.

5.7.4 Optical Coupling

The applications that require optical coupling of electronic circuits can be categorized as follows:

- **Light sensitive and light emitting devices.**
- **Discrete detectors and emitters for fiber optic systems.**
- **Interrupter/reflector modules which detect objects by modifying the light path.**

- **Isolators/couplers which transmit electrical signals without wire connections.**

As an example of this last application, suppose we desire to use the 60-Hz power line as a driver for a clock. Because of the 15 to 25 (A) current available from the power line, we do not wish to make a wire connection for our timing needs, but choose instead an optical connection. In the event of a component failure (e.g., a capacitor or transformer shorting) an optical coupler would prevent a dangerous, perhaps fatal, wire connecting of the operator to the 110 V 60-Hz power line. We discuss some of the major optical devices in the following paragraphs.

Optoelectronic Detectors and Emitters

The light sensitive diode operates such that as the light intensity, H, increases, the current in the external circuit also increases. This is the same phenomenon that occurs as we increase the base current in a transistor. Such a device is a *photo-transistor*, and is illustrated in Figure 5.17.

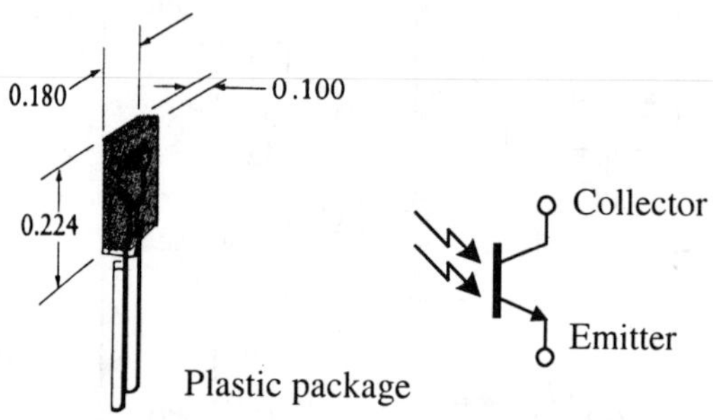

Figure 5.17 – Photo-transistor

Optoelectronic components require packaging that both allows light to pass through the package to the chip and also protects the chip. The semiconductor package "window" can be modified to provide lens action, which gives improved response along the optical axis of the lens and greater directional sensitivity. A typical package configuration is shown in Figure 5.18.

Communication systems (e.g., telephone lines) using optical fibers have replaced copper wire systems. The light is emitted into and out of the optical fiber with devices such as shown in Figure 5.18.

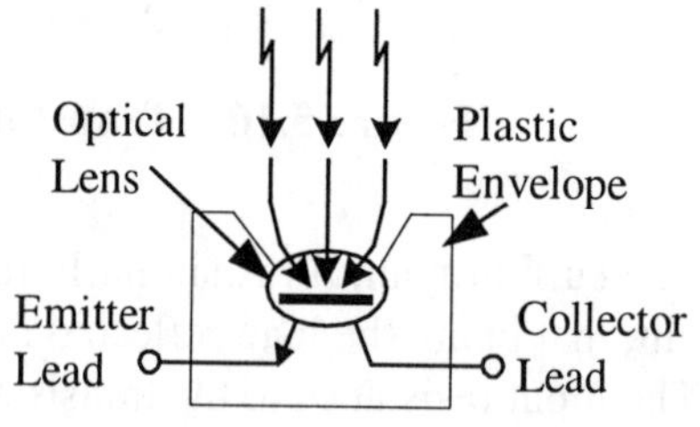

Figure 5.18 – Optoelectronic package configuration

Interrupter/Reflector Modules

In many applications, it is necessary to determine the mechanical position or velocity of a shaft. Use of a light emitter and detector in either an interrupter mode, as shown in Figure 5.19(a), or in a reflector mode, as shown in Figure 5.19(b), allows the engineer to measure mechanical shaft motion.

Optocouplers

When we wish to couple two electrical circuits without making any direct wiring connections, we can use *optocouplers* (also termed *optoisolators*) which have no wire connection between input and output. The light path, emitter to detector, is totally enclosed in the component and cannot be modified externally. The degree of electrical isolation between the two devices is controlled by the materials in the light path and by the physical distance between the emitter and detector. Greater physical distance provides better electrical isolation. A portion of a data sheet for an optoisolator is shown in Figure 5.20.

The H11A1 and H11A2 are gallium arsenide infrared emitting diodes coupled with a silicon phototransistor in a dual in-line package, with 6 terminals.

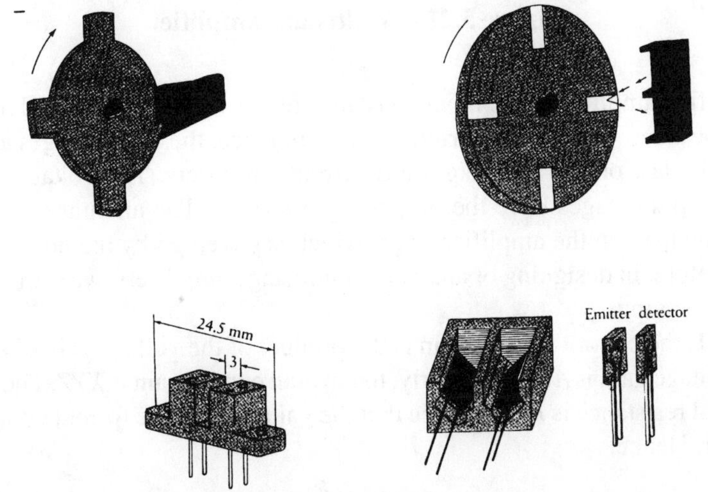

Figure 5.19 – Interupter/reflector modules

Infrared Emitting Diodes

Absolute maximum ratings: (25°C):

Power Dissipation	100*	milliwatts
Forward Current (Continuous)	60	milliamps
Forward Current (Peak) (Pulse width 1 μsec 300 P Ps)	3	ampere
Reverse Voltage	3	volts

*Derate 1.33 mW/°C above 25°C ambient

Phototransistors:

Power Dissipation	150	milliwatts
V_{CEO}	30	volts
V_{CBO}	70	volts
V_{ECO}	7	volts
Collector Current (Continuous)	100	millamps

Figure 5.20 – Optoisolator data sheet

5.8 MULTISTAGE AMPLIFIER ANALYSIS

Amplifiers are often connected in series (cascaded) as shown in Figure 5.21.

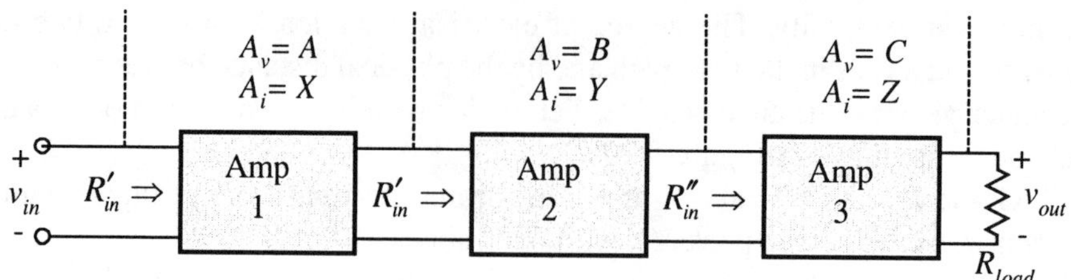

Figure 5.21 – Multistage amplifier

The load on the first amplifier is the input resistance of the second amplifier. The various stages need not have the same voltage and current gain. In practice, the earlier stages are often voltage amplifiers and the last one or two stages are current amplifiers. The voltage amplifier stages assure that the current stages have the proper input swings. The amount of gain in a stage is determined by the load on the amplifier stage, which is governed by the input resistance to the next stage. Therefore, in designing or analyzing multistage amplifiers, we start at the output and proceed toward the input.

In Figure 5.21, the overall voltage gain is the product of the voltage gain of each stage. That is, the overall voltage gain is *ABC*. Similarly, the overall current gain is *XYZ*. The input resistance is R_{in} and the load resistance is R_{load}. Notice that the gain impedance formula is applicable to the overall amplifier. Hence,

$$ABC = XYZ\,\frac{R_{load}}{R_{in}} \tag{5.52}$$

Example 5.9 - Multistage Amplifier (Analysis)

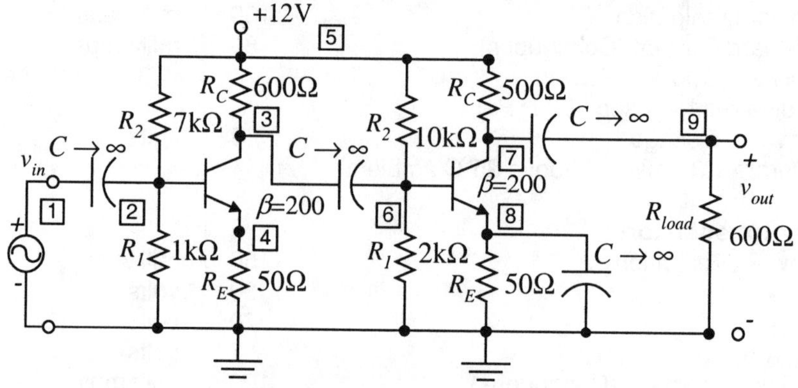

Figure 5.22 – Multistage amplifier of Example 5.10

Determine the current and voltage gains for the two-stage capacitor-coupled amplifier shown in Figure 5.22. Verify your solution using a computer simulation.

Solution: We develop the hybrid equivalent circuit for the multistage amplifier. This equivalent is shown in Figure 5.23.Primed variables denote output stage quantities and unprimed variables denote input stage quantities. Calculations for the output stages are as follows:

$$R'_B = 10\text{k}\Omega \| 2\text{k}\Omega = \frac{10^4 \times 2 \times 10^3}{10^4 + 2 \times 10^3} = 1.67 \quad \text{k}\Omega$$

$$V'_{BB} = 12\text{V} \times \frac{2\text{k}\Omega}{10\text{k}\Omega + 2\text{k}\Omega} = \frac{12 \times 2 \times 10^3}{10^4 + 2 \times 10^3} = 2 \quad \text{V}$$

$$I'_{CQ} = \frac{V'_{BB} - V_{BE}}{R'_B/\beta + R'_B} = 22 \quad \text{mA}$$

$$r'_e = \frac{26\ (\text{mV})}{I_{CQ}} = 1.17 \quad \Omega$$

For the input stage,

$$R_B = 7\text{k}\Omega \| 1\text{k}\Omega = \frac{7000 \times 1000}{7000 + 1000} = 875 \quad \Omega$$

$$V_{BB} = 12 \frac{1\text{k}\Omega}{1\text{k}\Omega + 7\text{k}\Omega} = \frac{12 \times 1000}{7000 + 1000} = 1.5 \quad \text{V}$$

$$I_{CQ} = \frac{1.5 - 0.7}{875/200 + 50} = 14.7 \quad \text{mA}$$

$$\text{r}_\text{e} = \frac{26\ (\text{mV})}{14.7\ (\text{mA})} = 1.77 \quad \Omega$$

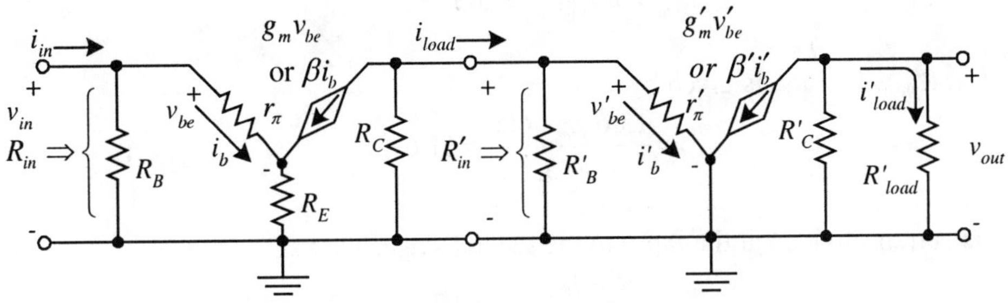

Figure 5.23 – Equivalent circuit for Example 5.9

We determine the input resistance using the equation from Table 5.3 as follows:

$$R_{in} = R_B \| (r_\pi + \beta R_E) = \frac{875 \times 200 \times (1.77 + 50)}{875 + 10{,}354} = 807 \quad \Omega$$

The current gain, A_i, is found by applying the equation from Table 5.3 twice, where the first stage requires using the correct value for R_{load} derived from the value of R_{in} to the next stage. Alternatively, we analyze Figure 5.23 by extracting four current dividers as shown in Figure 5.24.

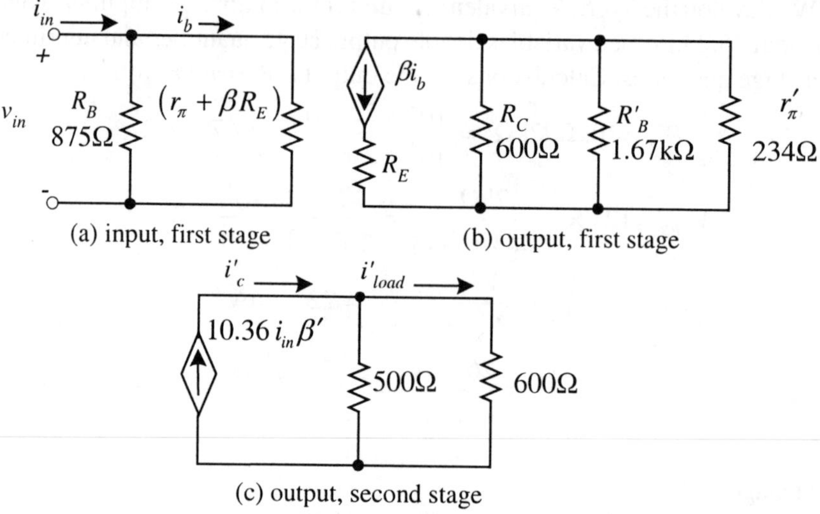

Figure 5.24 - Current dividers for circuit of Figure 5.23

The current division of the input stage is

$$i_b = \frac{R_B i_{in}}{R_B + r_\pi + \beta R_E} = 0.078\, i_{in}$$

The output of the first stage is coupled to the input of the second stage in Figure 5.24(b). The input resistance of the second stage is

$$R'_{in} = R'_B \| r'_\pi = 205 \quad \Omega$$

The current in R'_{in} is i_{load} and is given by

$$i_{load} = \frac{15.6\, i_{in} \times 600}{805} = 11.6\, i_{in}$$

Again, i_{load} is current-divided at the input to the second stage. Thus,

$$i'_b = \frac{-R'_B \cdot i_{load}}{R'_B + r'_\pi} = -10.2 \cdot i_{in}$$

The output current is found from Figure 5.24(c):

$$i'_{load} = \frac{10.2\, i_{in} \times 200 \times 500}{500 + 600} = 927 \cdot i_{in}$$

The current gain is then

$$A_i = 927$$

Now using the gain impedance formula, we find the voltage gain:

$$A_v = \frac{927 \times 600}{807} = 689$$

We now enter the circuit into PSPICE using the following code:

```
VIN,0,1,AC,.01,SIN(0,.01,1000)
VCC,5,0,DC,12
C1,1,2,1
R1,2,0,1K
R2,2,5,7K
Q1,3,2,4,TRANY
RC1,3,5,600
RE1,4,0,50
C2,3,6,1
R3,6,0,2K
R4,6,5,10K
Q2,7,6,8,TRANY
RC2,7,5,500
RE2,8,0,50
CE2,8,0,1
C3,7,9,1
VDUMMY,9,10,DC,0
RL,10,0,600
.MODEL,TRANY,NPN(BF=200)
.TRAN,.005M,1M
.AC,LIN,25,100,100K
.PROBE
.END
```

We plot the two gains in Figure 5.25. The voltage gain is approximately 445 and the current gain is 680. This does not compare favorably with theoretical values computed above for voltage and current gains of 689 and 927 respectively.

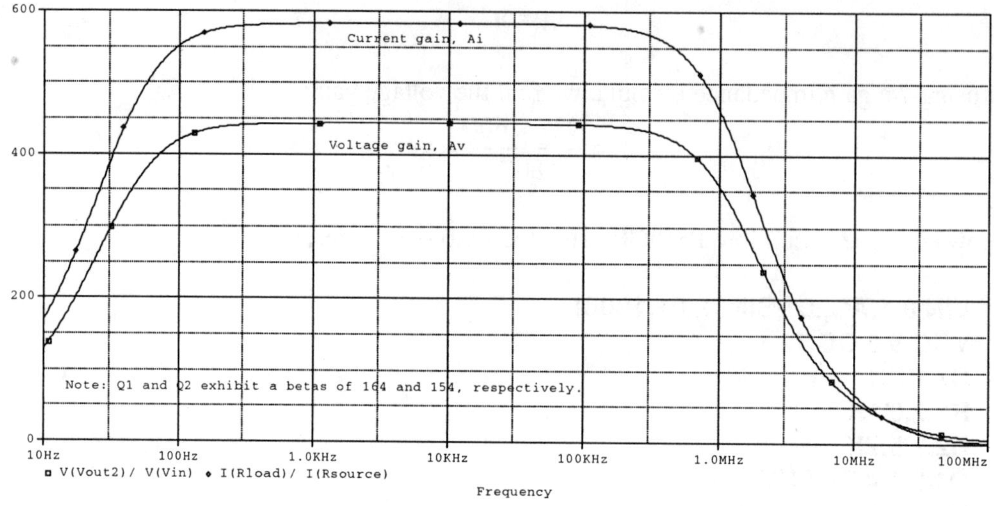

Figure 5.25 – Voltage and current gains over the frequency of interest for Example 5.9

However, we note that beta enters directly in each transistor gain expression,. For example, we assumed that for beta of 200

$$i'_{load} = \frac{10.2\, i_{in} \times 200 \times 500}{500 + 600} = 927 \cdot i_{in}$$

which yields the expected current gain for the last amplifier stage of $A_i = 927$. But in the region of operation on the characteristic curves the simulation yields a beta close to 154. That is, within the region of operation set by the biasing condition, we may compute the second stage current gain as

$$i'_{load} = \frac{10.2\, i_{in} \times 154 \times 500}{500 + 600} = 714 \cdot i_{in}$$

In a similar fashion, the computed current gain of the first amplifier stage may be adjusted for the actual operational beta (the simulation results indicate this value to be close to 164) rather than the assumed value of 200 given in the problem statement.

5.9 CASCODE CONFIGURATION

An interesting and useful multistage amplifier is the *cascode* configuration which is shown in Figure 5.26(a). This two-stage amplifier comprises a CE amplifier driving a CB amplifier. Transistor Q_1 forms the CE amplifier and the CB amplifier utilizes Q_2. This configuration has the advantages of increased output resistance and wider frequency response while maintaining high voltage gain.

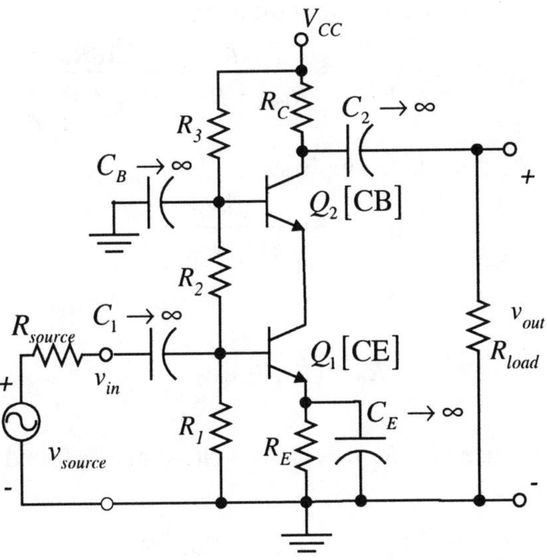

Figure 5.26(a) – Cascode configuration

The input resistance of the CE stage is relatively high. The low input impedance of the CB circuit forms the load resistance for the CE stage. The collector current of Q_2 is almost equal to the collector current of Q_1, which in turn drives the load ($R_{load} \| R_C$). This can be seen from the equivalent circuit of Figure 5.26(b). In this circuit, the capacitors are considered short circuits. The *dc* source, V_{CC}, is set to ground potential since we are interested in the *ac* component of the signals. Since R_E is bypassed by C_E, it is also eliminated from the equivalent circuit. Figure 5.26(b) can be verified by referring to the CE and CB equivalent circuits.

In the analysis of Figure 5.26(b), we let r_π be much smaller than $R_1 \| R_2$, so

$$i_b = i_i \frac{R_1 \| R_2}{r_\pi + R_1 \| R_2} \approx i_{in} \tag{5.53}$$

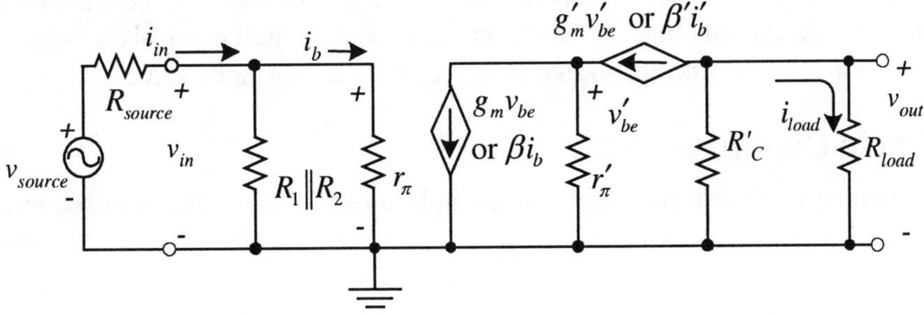

Figure 5.26(b) – Cascode configuration equivalent circuit

Since the collector current in each transistor is equal, $\beta i_b = \beta' i'_b$. The load current, i_{load}, is given by

Equation (5.54), where we have used current division.

$$i_{load} = \frac{-\beta' i_{b'} R_C}{R_{load} + R_C} = \frac{-\beta i_b R_C}{R_{load} + R_C} = \frac{-\beta i_{in} R_C}{R_{load} + R_C} \tag{5.54}$$

The current gain, A_i, for the two-stage amplifier is,

$$A_i = \frac{i_{load}}{i_{in}} = \frac{-\beta R_C}{R_{load} + R_C} \tag{5.55}$$

The input resistance is

$$R_{in} = \left(R_1 \| R_2\right) \| r_\pi \tag{5.56}$$

which is approximately r_π since ($R_1 \| R_2$)>>r_π. The voltage gain is found from the gain impedance formula.

$$A_v = A_i \frac{R_{load}}{R_{in}} = -\frac{\beta R_C}{R_{load} + R_C} \cdot \frac{R_{load}}{r_\pi} = \frac{-R_{load} \| R_C}{r_e} = -g_m(R_{load} \| R_C) \tag{5.57}$$

Equation (5.57) shows that the voltage gain of the cascode configuration is the same as that of a CE amplifier. The cascode configuration displays an output resistance that is larger than that of a single transistor amplifier. As a result, it is omitted in the circuit of Figure 5.26(b).

5.10 CURRENT SOURCES AND ACTIVE LOADS

In this section we explore alternate methods of simulating a *dc* current source for integrated circuit (IC) amplifier biasing. One type of current source often used to provide a fixed current is the *fixed bias transistor circuit*. The problem with this type of current source is that it requires too many resistors to be practically implemented on an IC. We will therefore investigate simpler types of current sources.

Many of the circuits used to generate bias currents are also useful for simulating large resistors. Since resistors larger than 100 kΩ use too much IC chip area, alternate methods for implementing resistors are useful. These methods include the use of current sources as a replacement for large resistors. The resistors in the following current sources are small and easy to fabricate on integrated circuit chips. When the current source is used to replace a large resistor, the Thevenin resistance of the current source is the equivalent resistance value.

5.10.1 A Simple Current Source

The simple two transistor current source shown in Figure 5.27 is commonly used in ICs.

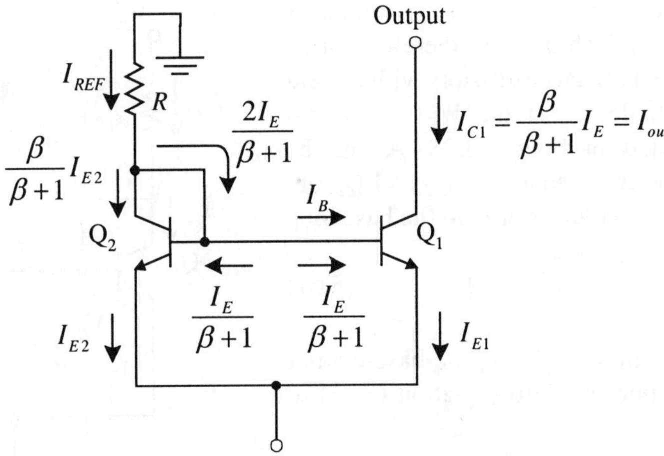

Figure 5.27 – Current source

A reference current is the input to a transistor connected as a diode. The voltage across this transistor drives the second transistor, where $R_E = 0$. Since the circuit has only one resistor, it can easily be fabricated on an IC chip. The disadvantage of this circuit is that the reference current is approximately equal to the current source. In this circuit, Q_2 is in the linear mode, since the collector voltage (output) is higher than the base voltage. The transistors, Q_1 and Q_2 are identical devices fabricated on the same IC chip. The emitter currents are equal since the transistors are matched and emitters and bases are in parallel. If we sum the currents of Q_2, we obtain

$$I_B + I_C = I_E \tag{5.58}$$

so

$$I_{out} = I_{C1} = I_{E1} \frac{\beta}{\beta+1} = I_{E2} \frac{\beta}{\beta+1} \tag{5.59}$$

Summing currents at the collector of Q_1 we obtain

$$I_{REF} = \left(\frac{\beta}{\beta+1} + \frac{2}{\beta+1} \right) I_E = \frac{\beta+2}{\beta+1} I_E \approx I_o \tag{5.60}$$

If β is large, the current gain is approximately unity and the current mirror has reproduced the input current. One disadvantage of this current source is that its R_{TH} is limited by the r_o of the transistor. That is,

$$R_{TH} = r_o = \frac{V_A}{I_C} \approx \frac{V_A}{I_{REF}}$$

5.10.2 Widlar Current Source

Because of the high gain of an op-amp, the bias currents must be small. Typical collector currents are in the range of 5 μA. Large resistors are often required to maintain small currents, and these large resistors occupy correspondingly large areas on the IC chip. It is therefore often desirable to replace these large resistors with current sources. One such device is the *Widlar current source*, as illustrated in Figure 5.28. As in the previous circuit, the two transistors, Q_1 and Q_2, are matched. We sum the voltages around the base loop of the two transistors to obtain

$$V_{BE1} - V_{BE2} - I_{E2} R_2 = 0 \tag{5.61}$$

We now solve Equation (4.10) for the base-emitter voltage, and substitute this into Equation (5.61) to obtain,

$$V_{BE} = V_T \ln\left(\frac{I_C}{\beta I_o}\right) \tag{5.62}$$

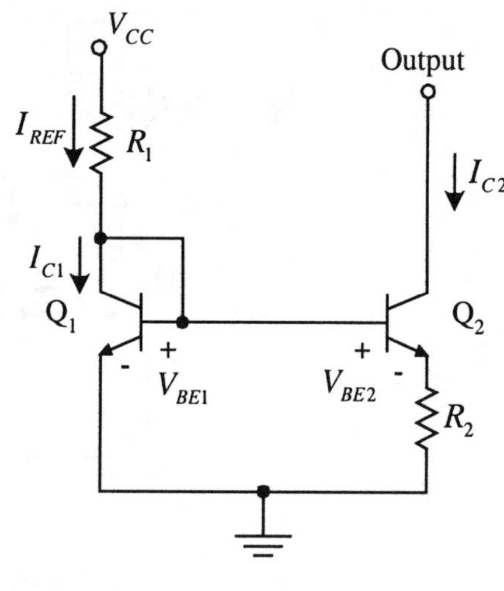

Figure 5.28 – Widlar current source

$$V_T \ln\left(\frac{I_{C1}}{\beta I_o}\right) - V_T \ln\left(\frac{I_{C2}}{\beta I_o}\right) - I_{E2} R_2 = 0$$

We assume that the transistors are matched so that I_o, β, and V_T are the same for both transistors. Thus

$$V_T \ln\left(\frac{I_{C2}}{I_{C1}}\right) = I_{E2} R_2 \approx I_{C2} R_2 \tag{5.63}$$

Hence

$$R_2 = \frac{V_T}{I_{C2}} \ln \frac{I_{C1}}{I_{C2}}$$

where

$$I_{C1} \frac{V_{CC} - V_{BE}}{R_1}.$$

For design purposes, I_{C1} is usually known since it is used as the reference for all current sources on the entire chip and I_{C2} is the desired output current. This allows us to solve Equation (5.63) for the required value of R_2.

The Widlar circuit can also be used to simulate a high resistance. The small-signal equivalent circuit is shown in Figure 5.29.

Since this circuit has no independent sources, it is equivalent to a single Thevenin resistance. However, with the controlled source, we cannot simply proceed to combine resistors in series or parallel. Instead, to find the value of this resistance, we assume a test current, i_{TH}, find the resulting voltage, v_{TH}, and take the ratio. Note that v_{TH} is the sum of v_1 and v_2. Therefore,

$$v_{TH} = v_I + (i_{TH} - \beta i_{B2})r_o$$
$$= -i_{B2} r'_\pi + (i_{TH} - \beta i_{B2})r_o \tag{5.64}$$

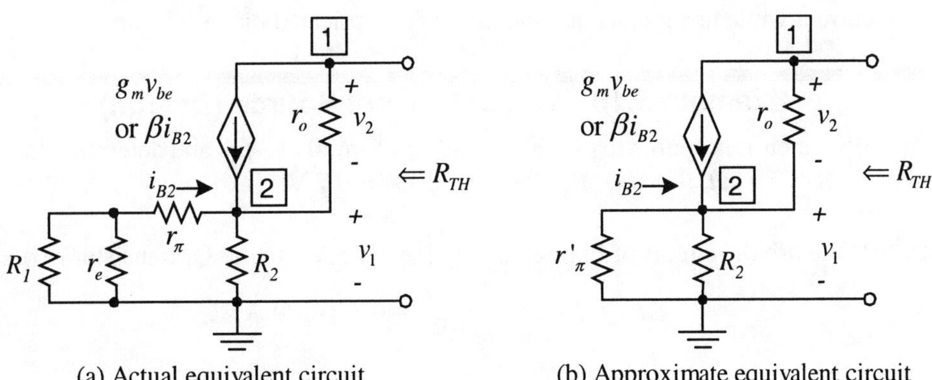

(a) Actual equivalent circuit (b) Approximate equivalent circuit

Figure 5.29 - Widlar Current Source Equivalent Circuit

In the last equality, we have defined r'_π as the ratio of output voltage to base current for the second transistor. The test current is equal to

$$i_{TH} = \beta i_{B2} + \frac{v_2}{r_o} \tag{5.65}$$

The equivalent output resistance is then given by

$$R_{TH} = \frac{v_{TH}}{i_{TH}} = \frac{r_o(1+\beta + r'_\pi / R_2) + r'_\pi}{1 + r'_\pi / R_2} \tag{5.66}$$

If we now make the realistic assumption that r'_π is much larger than R_2, this resistance can be approximated by

$$R_{TH} \approx r_o \left(1 + \frac{\beta}{r'_\pi / R_2}\right) \tag{5.67}$$

To give more intuitive meaning to this result, we note that

$$r'_\pi = \frac{\beta \cdot V_T}{I_{C2}} \tag{5.68}$$

The final result is then

$$R_{TH} = r_o \left(1 + \frac{I_{C2} R_2}{V_T}\right) \tag{5.69}$$

Equation (5.69) shows that the resistance depends on $I_{C2}R_2$, but this is simply the *dc* voltage drop across R_2. The larger the voltage drop, the higher the output resistance. Generally, the output

resistance of a simple current source is increased by the addition of resistances in the emitters of the current source transistors.
The following example illustrates how a current source can be designed to provide a small constant current while using resistors that are easily fabricated on an IC chip.

Example 5.10 - Widlar Current Source (Design)

Design a Widlar current source to provide a constant current of 3 μA and determine the R_{TH} with $V_{CC} = 12$ V, $R_1 = 50$ kΩ, $\beta = 100$, $V_A = 50$ V and $V_{BE} = 0.7$ V.

Solution: We use the circuit of Figure 5.28 and apply KVL to the Q_1 transistor to obtain

$$I_{C1} \approx I_{REF} = \frac{12 - 0.7}{5\times10^5} = 0.226 \quad \text{mA}$$

Using the characteristic equation

$$0.026 \ln\left(\frac{2.26\times10^{-4}}{3\times10^{-6}}\right) = 3\times10^{-6} R_2$$

we solve for $R_2 = 37.5$ kΩ. Noting that

$$R_{TH} = \frac{V_A}{I_C}\left(1 + \frac{I_{C2}R_2}{V_T}\right) = 88.8 \quad \text{M}\Omega$$

Since R_2 is less than 50 kΩ, it is practical to fabricate it on an IC.

5.10.3 Wilson Current Source

Another current source transistor configuration that provides a very large parallel resistance is the *Wilson current source* which uses three transistors and provides this capability and the output is almost independent of the internal transistor characteristics. The Wilson current source, as shown in Figure 5.30, uses the negative feedback provided by Q_3 to raise the output impedance.

The difference between the reference current and I_{C1} is the base current of Q_2.

$$I_{E2} = (\beta + 1) I_{B2} = I_{C3} \qquad (5.70)$$

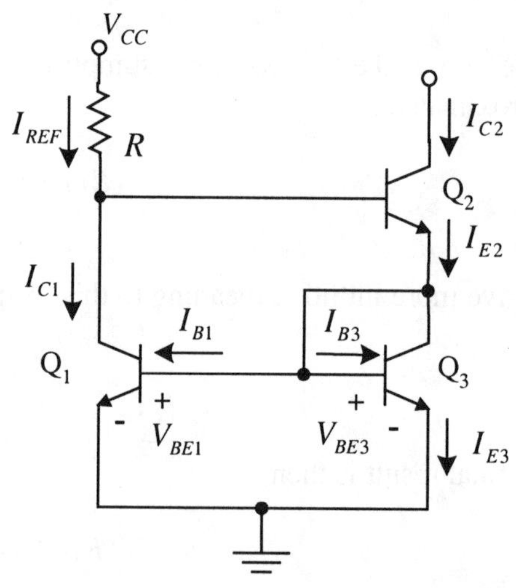

Figure 5.30 – Wilson current source

Since the base of Q_1 is connected to the base of Q_3, the currents in Q_1 are approximately independent of the voltage of the collector of

Q_2. As such, the collector current of Q_2 remains almost constant providing a high output impedance.

We now illustrate that I_{C2} is approximately equal to I_{Ref}. Applying Kirchhoff's current law at the emitter of Q_2 yields

$$I_{E2} = I_{C3} + I_{B3} + I_{B1} \tag{5.71}$$

Using the relationship between collector and base currents

$$I_{E2} = I_{C3}\left(1 + \frac{1}{\beta}\right) + \frac{I_{C1}}{\beta} \tag{5.72}$$

Since all three transistors are matched, $V_{BE1} = V_{BE2} = V_{BE3}$ and $\beta_1 = \beta_2 = \beta_3$

With identical transistors, current in the feedback path splits equally between the bases of Q_1 and Q_3 leading so that $I_{B1} = I_{B3}$ and therefore $I_{C1}=I_{C3}$. Thus, the emitter current of Q_2 becomes

$$I_{E2} = I_{C3}\left(1 + \frac{2}{\beta}\right) \tag{5.73}$$

The collector current of Q_2 is

$$I_{C2} = \frac{I_{E2}\beta}{\beta + 1} = \frac{I_{C3}(1 + 2/\beta)\beta}{\beta + 1} \tag{5.74}$$

Solving for I_{C3} yields

$$I_{C3} = \frac{I_{C2} \cdot (\beta + 1)}{\beta(1 + 2/\beta)} = I_{C2} \cdot \frac{\beta + 1}{\beta + 2} \tag{5.75}$$

Summing currents at the base of Q_2,

$$I_{C1} = I_{REF} - \frac{I_{C2}}{\beta}$$

$$I_{C2} = \beta\left(I_{REF} - I_{C1}\right) \tag{5.76}$$

Since $I_{C1} = I_{C3}$, we substitute I_{C3} to obtain

$$I_{C2} = \beta I_{REF} - \frac{\beta(\beta + 1)}{\beta + 2} I_{C2} \tag{5.77}$$

and solving for I_{C2},

$$I_{C2} = \frac{\beta^2 + 2\beta}{\beta^2 + 2\beta + 2} I_{REF} = \left[1 - \frac{2}{\beta^2 + 2\beta + 2}\right] I_{REF} \tag{5.78}$$

Equation (5.78) shows that β has little effect upon I_{C2} since, for reasonable values of β,

$$\frac{2}{\beta^2 + 2\beta + 2} \ll 1$$

(5.79)

$$I_{C2} \approx I_{REF}$$

To find the parallel *ac* resistance for the current source, we can perform an analysis similar to that used for Widlar current source. The resulting resistance is

$$R_{th} = \frac{\beta r_o}{2} = \frac{\beta V_A}{2I_{C2}} \tag{5.80}$$

5.10.4 Multiple Current Sources Using Current Mirrors

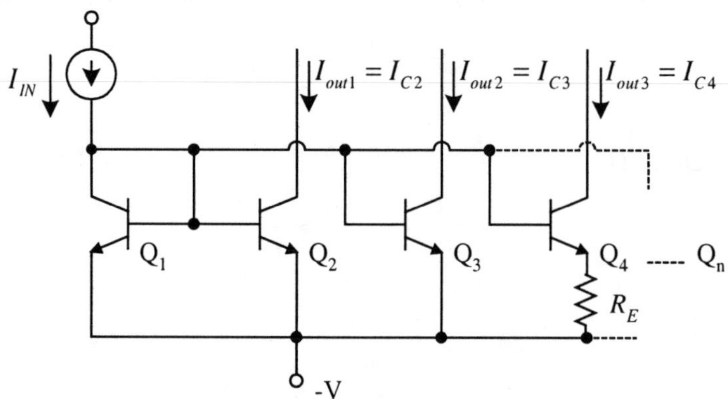

Figure 5.31 – Current mirror

A number of current sources can be obtained from a single reference voltage. If the current is approximately the same as the reference voltage, the simple current source can be used as shown in Figure 5.31 for Q_2 and Q_3. Notice that Q_4 has an emitter resistance which makes the current source a Widlar current source. Thus the amount of current delivered by this source can be determined by the size of the emitter resistor. This type of circuit is useful in integrated circuit chips as the one reference circuit can be used to develop current sources throughout the chip. When using the Widlar circuit, the currents can be different from the reference current.

The errors in base current, however, do accumulate when multiple outputs are used and the current gain tends to deviate from unity. In these types of circuits, lateral transistors can be used since it is not important that β be large. Lateral transistors usually have a β of approximately 20 which is more than adequate for current sources.

EXERCISES

E5.12 Design a Widlar current source to obtain a constant current of 50 μA. The battery voltage is 20 V, and a 4 mA reference current is used. Determine the resistor value required and R_{TH} of the current source when r_o(transistor) = 50 kΩ, $V_{BE} = 0.7$ V, $\beta = 200$ and $V_T = 26$ mV.

Answer: $R_1 = 4.83\ k\Omega$, $R_2 = 2.28\ k\Omega$, $R_{TH} = 265\ k\Omega$

E5.13 Design a Wilson current source to provide 100 μA when $V_{CC} = 15$ V. Use transistors with $\beta = 100$, $V_{BE} = 0.7$ V, and $V_T = 26$ mV. Determine R_{TH} when r_o of the transistor is 15 kΩ.

Answer: $R_1 = 136\ k\Omega$, $R_{TH} = 750\ k\Omega$

SUMMARY

Congratulations! You have now reached an important milestone in your study of electronics. You have learned the basics of BJT transistor amplifier analysis and design. We hope you have also gained an appreciation of techniques for applying concepts from physics to achieve practical goals. You have learned how to model complex devices using relatively simple circuitry. You have also been exposed to principles of design, where the number of unknowns is greater than the number of equations supplied by the specifications. Additionally, we saw the importance of computer simulations as a means of taking into account more complex parameters than can be done "by hand".

While we want you to stress understanding and the importance of the analysis process, we are supplying important summary tables on the next two pages. All of the results presented in these tables have been derived earlier in this chapter.

Table 5.2 summarizes the various BJT transistor amplifier configurations and the corresponding equivalent circuits. Table 5.3 presents the important parameters of the various transistor amplifier configurations. These include voltage gain, current gain, input resistance and output resistance.

We certainly hope these two tables will save you time when analyzing and designing systems. However, we caution you to make certain you understand the derivations, and particularly the assumptions, involved in each of the results. If you simply plug into equations without carefully analyzing the situation, you will probably make mistakes. The constraints of a real problem might not match the assumptions made in the derivations. *THINK! Don't just plug in! Thanks!!*

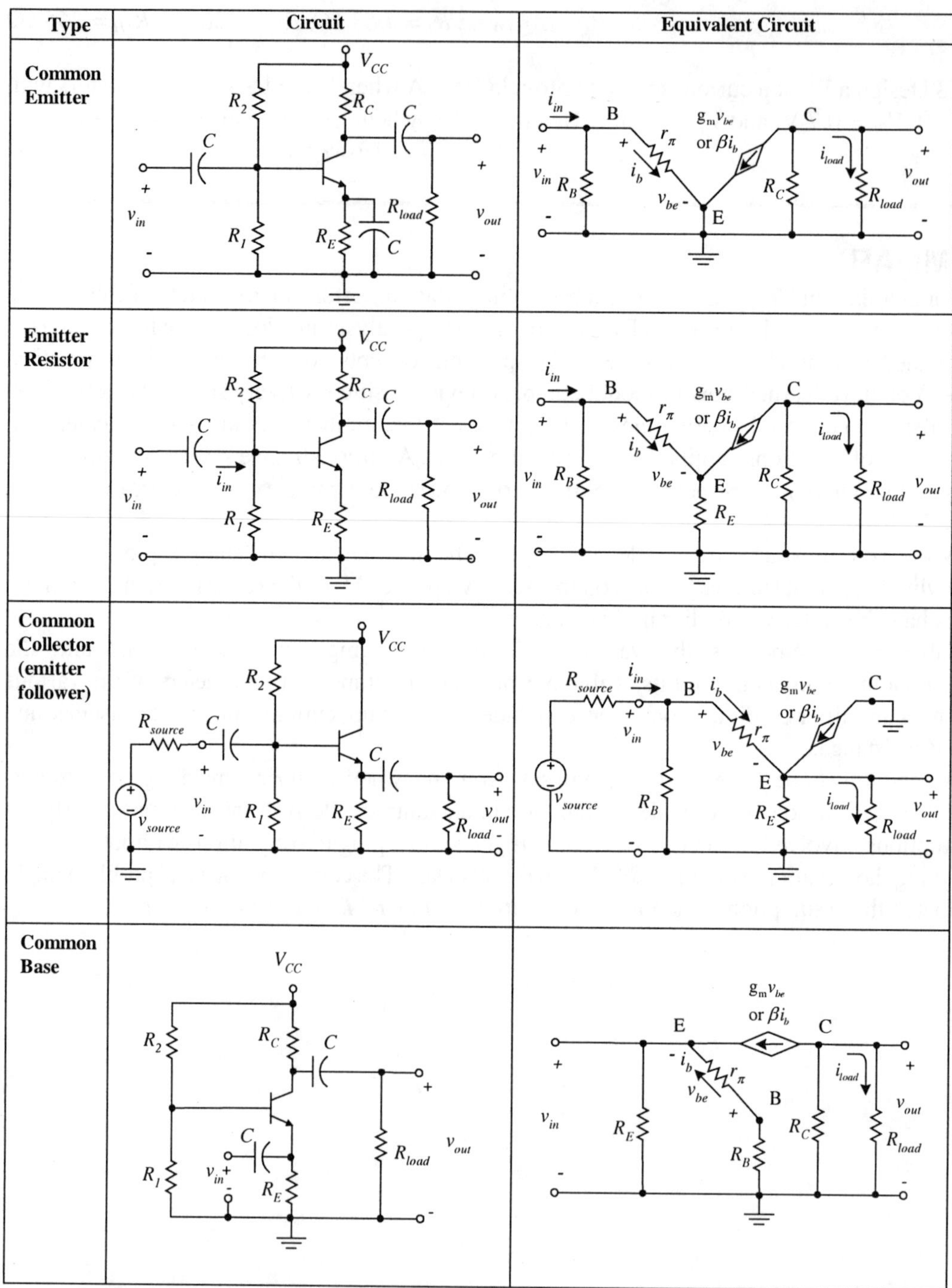

Type	Circuit	Equivalent Circuit
Common Emitter		
Emitter Resistor		
Common Collector (emitter follower)		
Common Base		

Table 5.2 - Equivalent circuits for amplifier configurations

Type	Voltage Gain (A_v)	Current Gain (A_i)	Input Resistance (R_{in})	Output Resistance (R_o)
Common Emitter	$-g_m\left(R_C \| R_{load}\right)$	$\dfrac{-R_B}{\dfrac{R_B}{\beta}+r_e}\cdot\dfrac{R_C}{R_C+R_{load}}$	$\dfrac{R_B r_e}{\dfrac{R_B}{\beta}+r_e}$ i.e., $R_B \| \beta r_e$	$\approx R_C$
Emitter Resistor	$\dfrac{-\left(R_C \| R_{load}\right)}{r_e+R_E}$	$\dfrac{-R_B}{\dfrac{R_B}{\beta}+r_e+R_E}\cdot\dfrac{R_C}{R_C+R_{load}}$	$\dfrac{R_B\left(r_e+R_E\right)}{\dfrac{R_B}{\beta}+r_e+R_E}$ i.e., $R_B \| \left[r_\pi+\beta R_E\right]$	$\approx R_C$
Common Collector (emitter follower)	$\dfrac{\left(R_E \| R_{load}\right)}{r_e+\left(R_E \| R_{load}\right)}$	$\dfrac{R_B}{\dfrac{R_B}{\beta}+r_e+\left(R_E \| R_{load}\right)}\cdot\dfrac{R_E}{R_E+R_{load}}$	$\dfrac{R_B\left[r_e+\left(R_E \| R_{load}\right)\right]}{\dfrac{R_B}{\beta}+r_e+\left(R_E \| R_{load}\right)}$ i.e., $R_B \| \left[r_\pi+\beta\left(R_E \| R_{load}\right)\right]$	$R_E \| \left(\dfrac{R_B \| R_{source}}{\beta}+r_e\right)$
Common Base	$\dfrac{\left(R_C \| R_{load}\right)}{r_e+\dfrac{R_B}{\beta}}$	$\dfrac{R_C}{R_C+R_{load}}\cdot\dfrac{R_E}{R_E+r_e+\dfrac{R_B}{\beta}}$	$\dfrac{R_E\left(r_e+\dfrac{R_B}{\beta}\right)}{R_E+r_e+\dfrac{R_B}{\beta}}$ i.e., $R_E \| \left(r_e+\dfrac{R_B}{\beta}\right)$	$\approx R_C$

Table 5.3 - Formulas for different amplifier configurations

PROBLEMS

Section 5.1

5.1 Find A_v for the amplifier shown in Figure P5.1 using the h-parameters where $h_{ie} = 2\ \text{k}\Omega$, $h_{re} = 0$, $h_{fe} = 200$, and $1/h_{oe} = 8\ \text{k}\Omega$. Can A_v for this amplifier be found using the hybrid-π model? If so, how?

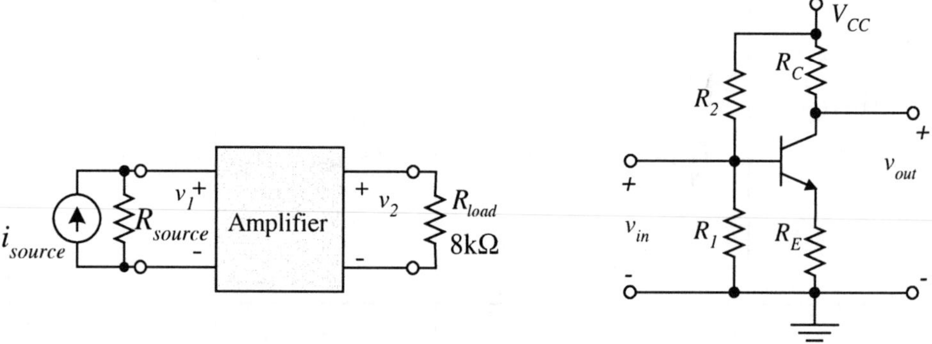

Figure P5.1 **Figure P5.2**

5.2 Derive equations for A_v, A_i, and R_{in} for the amplifier shown in Figure P5.2 using the hybrid-π model for the transistor.

5.3 Calculate R_{in}, A_v, and A_i when $R_B = R_{load} = 5\ \text{k}\Omega$, $R_E = 1\ \text{k}\Omega$ and $r_\pi = 0$ for the simplified amplifier shown in Figure P5.3. Let β be given by:

a. $\beta = 200$
b. $\beta = 100$
c. $\beta = 10$

5.4 Determine A_v, A_i and R_{in} for the simplified amplifier shown in Figure P5.3 when $R_{load} = R_B = 5\ \text{k}\Omega$, $r_\pi = 12\ \text{k}\Omega$, $\beta = 300$ and R_E is given by:

a. $R_E = 1000\ \Omega$
b. $R_E = 500\ \Omega$
c. $R_E = 100\ \Omega$
d. $R_E = 0$

Discuss the effects of changing R_E.

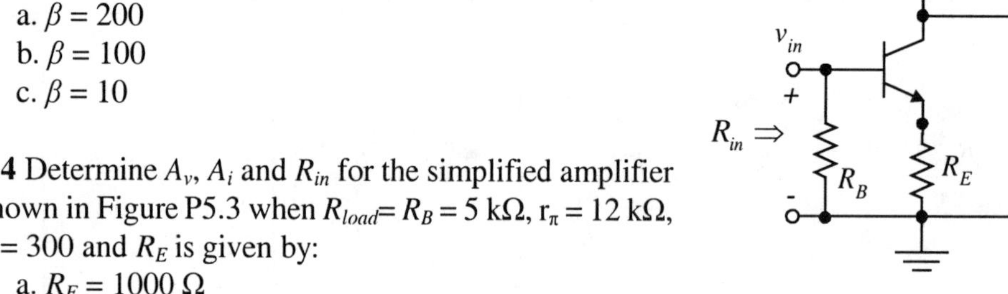

Figure P5.3

5.5 For the amplifier shown in Figure P5.2, $V_{BE} = 0.6$ V, $V_{CC} = 12$ V, $\beta = 300$, P_{load}(max average) = 100 mW and $A_v = -10$. Determine R_1, R_2, R_{in} and A_i. How much power is dissipated in the transistor?

5.6 For the amplifier shown in Figure P5.6, where $r_\pi = 10$ kΩ, $r_o = 100$ kΩ, $\beta = 100$, plot each of the following.

a. $A_i = i_{load}/i_{in}$ assuming $R_B << r_\pi$ as a function of the value of R_{load}. Let R_{load} vary from 0 to 500 kΩ.

b. A_i as a function of R_{load} but assume $r_o = 4$.

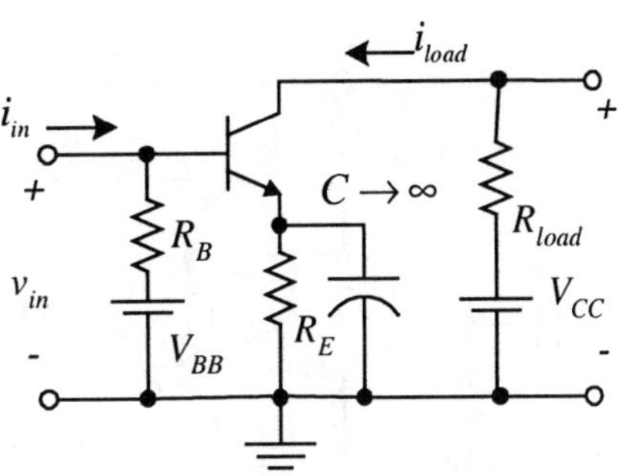

Figure P5.6

5.7 Compare input resistances and voltage gains for the *ac* equivalent amplifier circuits shown in Figure P5.7 (Figure continued on following page).

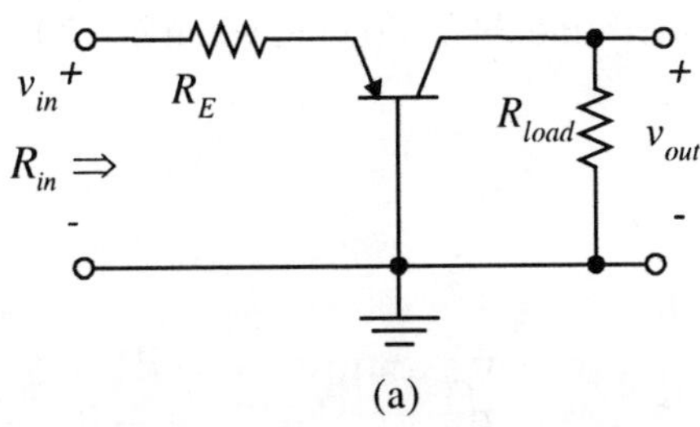

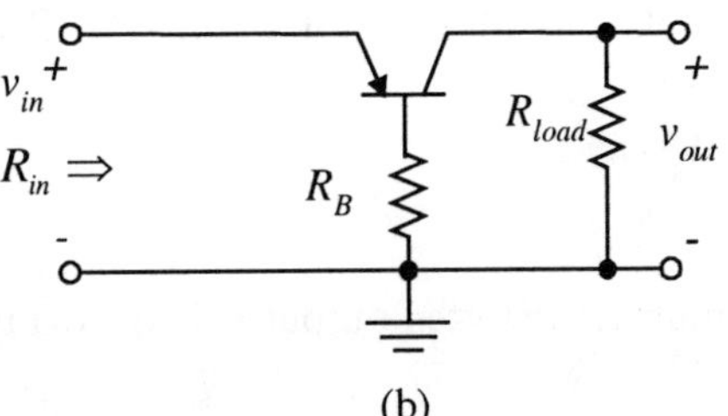

5.8 For the amplifier shown in Figure P5.8, determine the variation of A_i and R_{in} if β varies from 50 to 150 for the silicon transistor.

5.9 Determine r_π, A_i, R_{in}, v_{out}/v_{in} and R_o for the amplifier shown in Figure P5.9 if $\beta = 100$ and $r_O = \infty$.

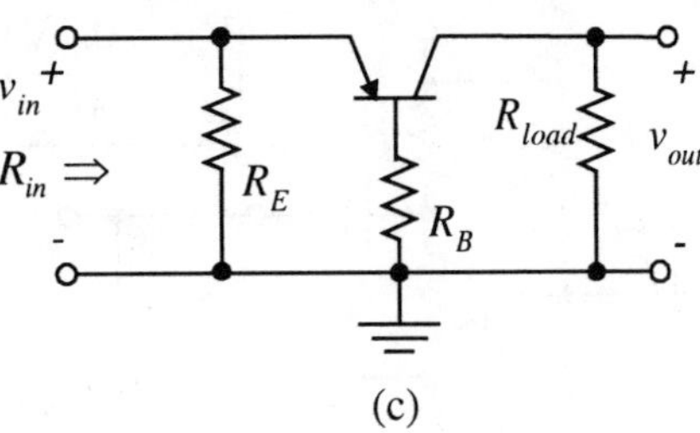

Figure P5.7

5.10 Design an amplifier as shown in Figure P5.10 using a *pnp* transistor when $R_{load} = 3$ kΩ, $A_v = -10$, $V_{BE} = -0.7$ V, $\beta = 200$, $A_i = -10$, and $V_{CC} = -12$ V. Determine all element values, R_{in} and the maximum voltage swing across R_{load}.

5.11 Design an amplifier as shown in Figure P5.10 using a *pnp* transistor when $R_{load} = 4$ kΩ, $A_v = -15$, $R_{in} = 20$ kΩ, $V_{CC} = -20$ V, $\beta = 300$, and $V_{BE} = -0.6$ V. Determine all element values, and the maximum peak-to-peak output voltage swing.

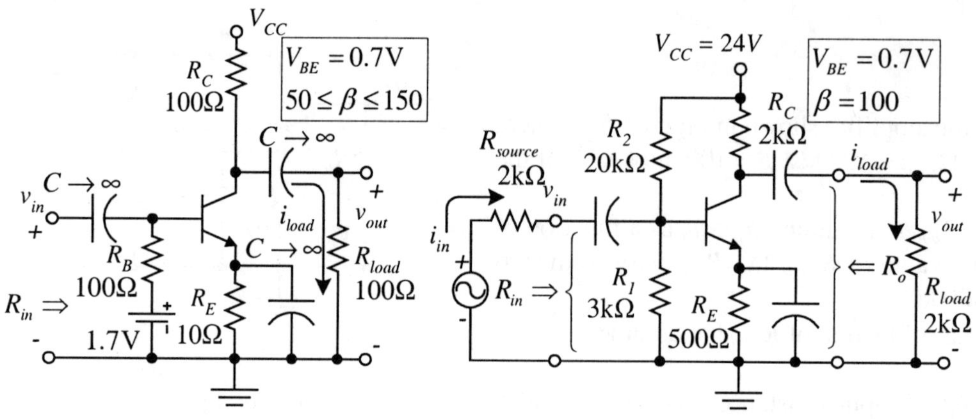

Figure P5.8

Figure P5.9

5.12 Analyze the circuit shown in Figure P5.12 and determine the following when $\beta = 200$ and $V_{BE} = 0.7$ V:

a. I_{CQ} and V_{CEQ}.
b. A_v and R_{in}.
c. A_i.
d. Maximum undistorted output voltage swing.

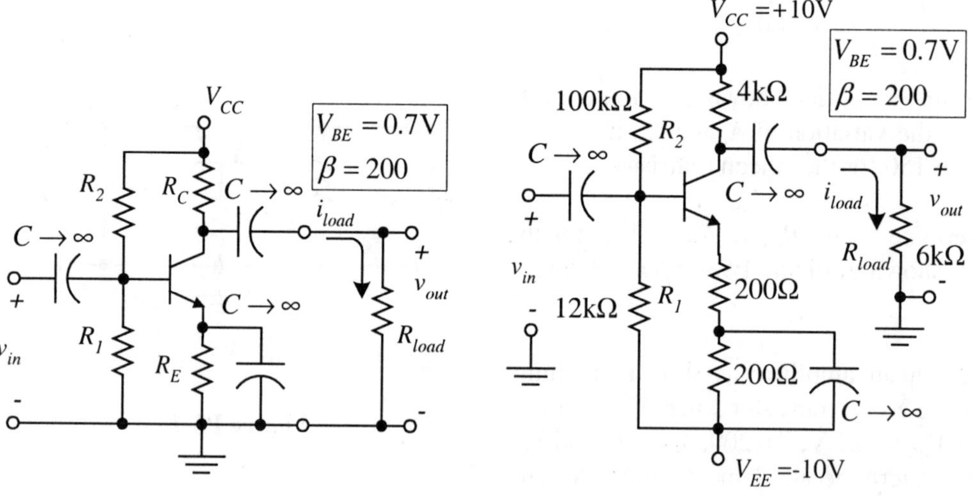

Figure P5.10

Figure P5.12

5.13 Design an amplifier as shown in Figure 5.4(a) when $R_{load} = 9$ kΩ, $A_v = -10$, $A_i = -10$, $V_{BE} = 0.7$ V, $\beta = 200$ and $V_{CC} = 15$ V. Determine all element values, R_{in}, and the maximum peak-to-peak output voltage swing.

5.14 Design an amplifier to obtain a voltage gain of -25 when $R_{in} = 5$ kΩ, $R_{load} = 5$ kΩ, $V_{CC} = 12$ V, $\beta = 200$ and $V_{BE} = 0.7$ V. Determine all resistor values, current gain and maximum output voltage swing. Use the circuit of Figure P5.10.

5.15 Analyze the circuit shown in Figure P5.15 and determine the following when $\beta = 300$ and $V_{BE} = 0.6$ V.

a. I_{CQ} and V_{CEQ}
b. Maximum undistorted output voltage swing
c. Power supplied from power supply
d. Voltage gain
e. Load Lines

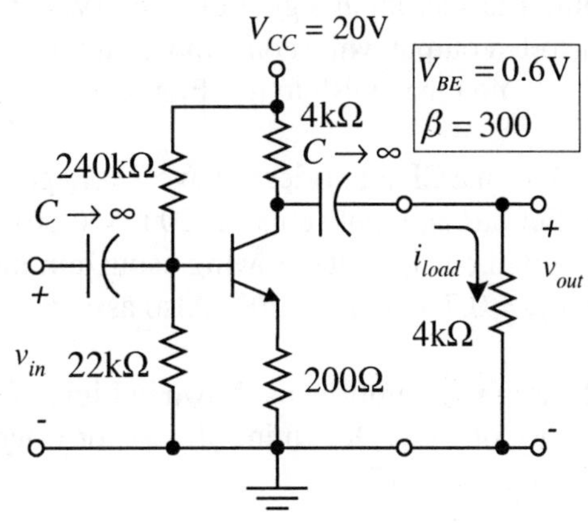

Figure P5.15

5.16 Design an amplifier to obtain a voltage gain of -10 when $R_{in} = 2$ kΩ, $R_{load} = 4$ kΩ, $V_{CC} = 15$ V, $V_{BE} = 0.6$ V and $\beta = 300$. This amplifier requires an output swing of 2 V undistorted peak-to-peak, so the design should be made for minimum current drain from the *dc* power source. Determine all resistor values and current gain.

5.17 Design an amplifier which has an overall gain of $A_v = -15$ when the input voltage has a source impedance (R_{source}) of 2 kΩ and the amplifier itself has an $R_{in} = 4$ kΩ, $V_{BE} = 0.7$ V, $\beta = 200$. (See Figure P5.17) The amplifier requires a maximum output voltage swing. Determine all resistor values, A_i and the maximum output voltage swing.

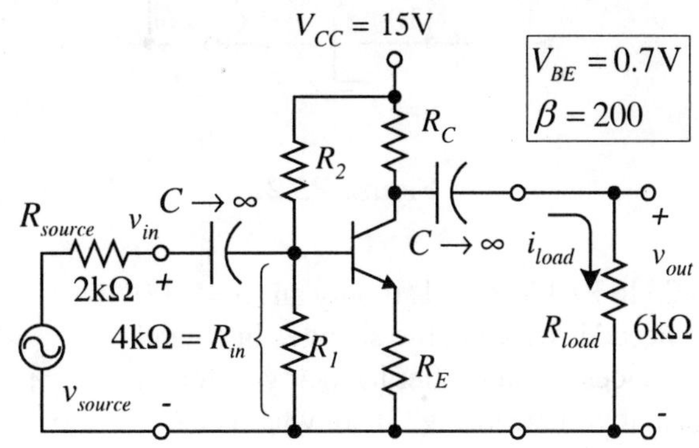

Figure P5.17

5.18 Design an emitter-resistor CE amplifier to provide $A_v = -12$ to a load of 20 kΩ when R_{in} is 15 kΩ. The amplifier will be designed to have $\delta = 0.4$ to keep I_{CQ} below the center of the load line to reduce the power consumed. Let $V_{CC} = 20$ V and the transistor have a β of 200 and V_{BE} of 0.7 V.

5.19 Design an emitter-resistor CE amplifier to provide $A_v = -20$ to a load of 10 kΩ when R_{in} is 8 kΩ. The amplifier will be designed to restrict the maximum output swing to 40% of maximum to reduce the *dc* power used. Let $V_{CC} = 15$ V and the transistor have a β of 200 and V_{BE} of 0.7 V.

5.20 Design an amplifier to have a voltage gain of -15 to a 6 kΩ load having an R_{in} of 5 kΩ. The amplifier has an input signal of 100 mV (0 to peak) and the amplifier will be designed for an undistorted output while consuming minimum *dc* power. Assume the transistor β is 200 and V_{BE} is 0.7 V. You may wish to use Figure P5.17 as a guide with R_{source} set to zero.

5.21 Design a CE amplifier to have a voltage gain of -100 to a 6 kΩ load having R_{in} of 2 kΩ. The amplifier has an input signal of 20 mV (zero to peak) and the amplifier will be designed for an undistorted output voltage swing using minimum *dc* power. Assume that the transistor is an *npn* with $V_{BE} = 0.7$ V and $\beta = 200$. Also assume that the *dc* supply voltage is $V_{CC} = 12$ V.

5.22 Design an amplifier as shown in Figure P5.22 to obtain a voltage gain of -200 with an input resistance of 1 kΩ. Determine all resistor values and the maximum output voltage swing when $\beta = 400$ and $V_{BE} = 0.7$ V.

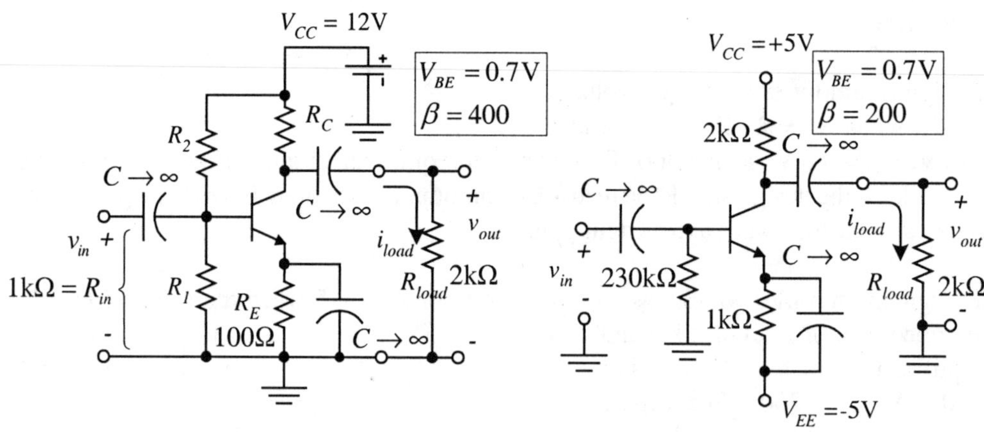

Figure P5.22 **Figure P5.24**

5.23 In Problem 5.21, if only an $A_v = -100$ is needed, what are the changes in R_1 and R_2? Does the amplifier have any different output voltage swing? If so, what is it?

5.24 Analyze the circuit shown in Figure P5.24 to determine the following:

a. I_{CQ}, A_v, and R_{in}

b. Undistorted symmetrical output voltage swing

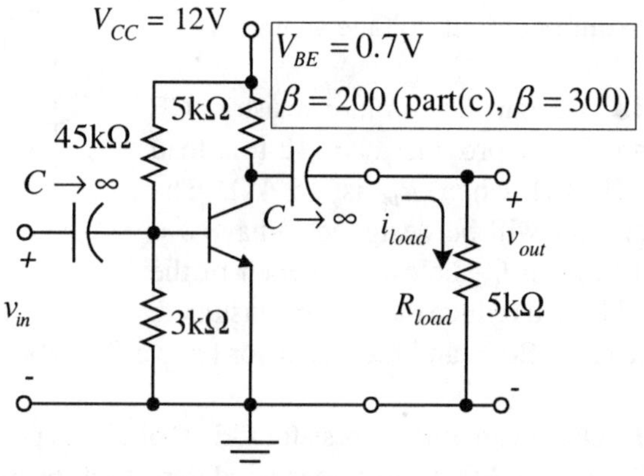

Figure P5.25

5.25 Analyze the circuit shown in Figure P5.25 to determine the following:

a. Will the amplifier be conducting in the normal operating region? If so, what are I_{CQ}, A_v, and R_{in}?

b. Will the amplifier be stable? Why?
c. The operating point if the transistor is installed which has a $\beta = 300$.

Section 5.2

5.26 Design the EF amplifier in Figure P5.26 to drive a 200-Ω load using a *pnp* silicon transistor. $V_{CC} = -24$ V, $\beta = 200$, $A_i = 10$, and $V_{BE} = -0.7$ V. Determine all element values and calculate R_{in}, I_{CQ}, and the undistorted symmetrical output voltage swing for each R_E given below:

a. $R_E = R_{load}$
b. $R_E = 0.2R_{load}$
c. $R_E = 5R_{load}$
d. Compare your results.

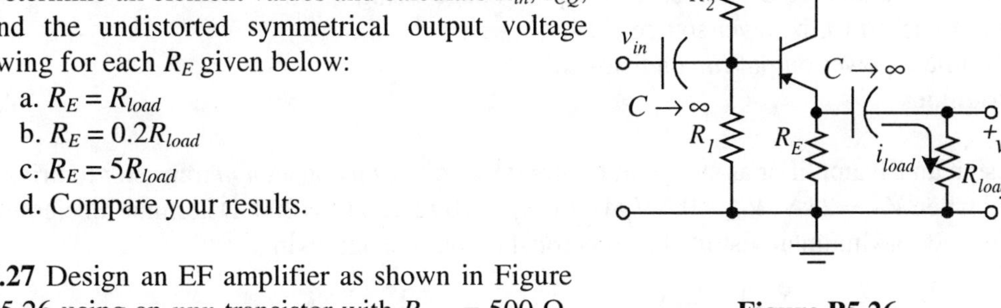

Figure P5.26

5.27 Design an EF amplifier as shown in Figure P5.26 using an *npn* transistor with $R_{load} = 500$ Ω, $V_{BE} = 0.7$ V, $A_i = 25$, $\beta = 200$ and $V_{CC} = 15$ V. Determine all element values, R_{in}, A_v and the maximum output voltage swing.

5.28 Design an EF amplifier to drive an 8Ω load when $\beta = 60$, $V_{CC} = -24$ V, $V_{BE} = -0.7$ V, $A_v = 1$ and $A_i = 10$. Use the circuit of Figure P5.26. Determine all element values, output voltage swing, and R_{in}.

5.29 Analyze the amplifier shown in Figure P5.29 to determine the following:

a. I_{CQ} and R_{in}
b. A_i
c. Maximum undistorted symmetrical output voltage swing

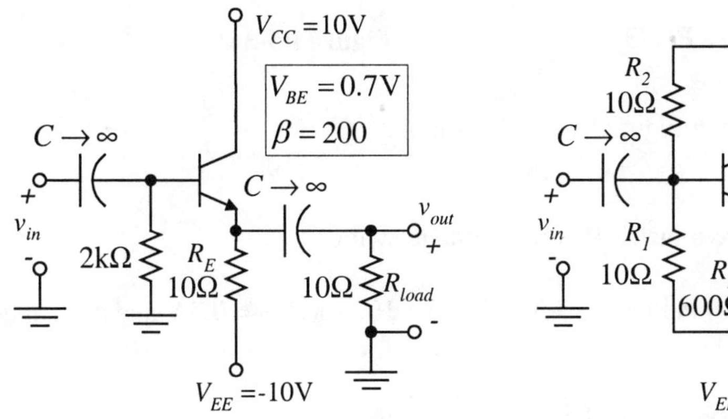

Figure P5.29 **Figure P5.31**

5.30 Design an EF amplifier as shown in Figure P5.26 using an *npn* transistor when $R_{load} = 1500\ \Omega$, $V_{BE} = 0.7$ V, $A_i = 10$, $\beta = 200$ and $V_{CC} = 16$ V. Determine all element values, R_{in}, A_v and the maximum output voltage swing.

5.31 Analyze the circuit shown in Figure P5.31 and determine the following when $\beta = 300$ and $V_{BE} = 0.6$ V.

a. I_{CQ} and V_{CEQ}
b. Maximum undistorted symmetrical output voltage swing
c. Power needed from power source
d. Maximum power output (*ac* undistorted)
e. Load lines

5.32 Design an EF amplifier as shown in Figure P5.26 except using an *npn* transistor to drive a 10Ω load when $V_{CC} = 24$ V, $V_{BE} = 0.6$ V, $A_v = 1$, $R_{in} = 100\ \Omega$, and $\beta = 200$. Determine all element values, A_i and maximum undistorted symmetrical output voltage swing.

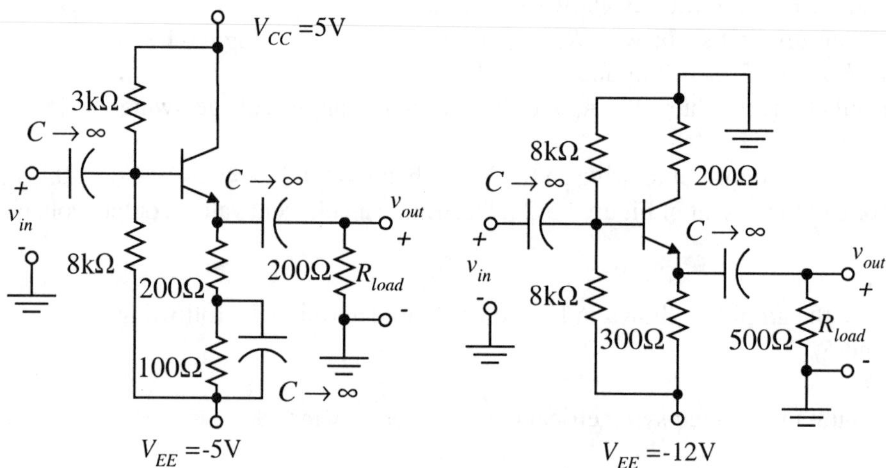

Figure P5.33 **Figure P5-34**

5.33 For the amplifier shown in Figure P5.33, determine:

a. I_{CQ} and V_{CEQ}
b. A_i and R_{in}
c. Maximum undistorted symmetrical output voltage swing

5.34 Analyze the circuit shown in Figure P5.34 when $\beta = 100$ and $V_{BE} = 0.7$ V and determine the following:

a. I_{CQ} and V_{CEQ}
b. Maximum undistorted symmetrical output voltage swing
c. Power supplied from the power source
d. Maximum power output (*ac* undistorted)
e. Current gain

Section 5.3

5.35 Design a CB amplifier (See Figure 5.11) which has a voltage gain of 10 and a 4 kΩ load. Use $\beta = 100$, $V_{BE} = 0.7$ V, $V_{CC} = 18$ V and $R_E = 500\ \Omega$. Determine values of I_{CQ}, R_1, R_2, R_B and the maximum undistorted symmetrical output voltage swing. What is the voltage gain when R_1 is bypassed with a large capacitor?

5.36 Design a CB amplifier using the values given in Problem 5.35 except that the voltage gain is 100. Determine value of R_1, R_2, I_{CQ}, R_B and the maximum output voltage swing.

5.37 For the amplifier shown in Figure P5.37, determine the following:

a. I_{CQ} and V_{CEQ}
b. A_v and R_{in}
c. Maximum undistorted symmetrical output voltage swing

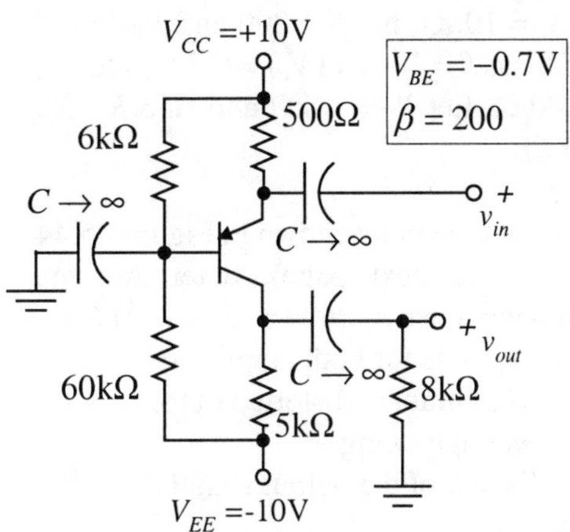

Figure P5.37

5.38 Design a CB amplifier for maximum voltage swing and at least 100 Ω input impedance, $R_{load} = 8$ kΩ, $V_{CC} = 12$ V and $R_E = 400\ \Omega$. Use an *npn* transistor with a $\beta = 200$ and $V_{BE} = 0.7$ V. Determine the voltage gain and all resistor values.

5.39 Analyze a CB amplifier for R_{in}, A_v and $V_{out(p\text{-}p)}$ that has the following values: $V_{CC} = 16$ V, $R_1 = 2$ kΩ, $R_2 = 25$ kΩ, $R_E = 200\ \Omega$, $R_C = R_{load} = 4$ kΩ, $\beta = 200$ and $V_{BE} = 0.7$ V. The base is *ac* grounded. (Use Figure 5.11 as guide)

5.40 For the amplifier shown in Figure P5.40, determine the following when $\beta = 200$ and $V_{BE} = 0.7$ V:

a. I_{CQ} and V_{CEQ}
b. A_v and R_{in}
c. Maximum undistorted symmetrical output voltage swing

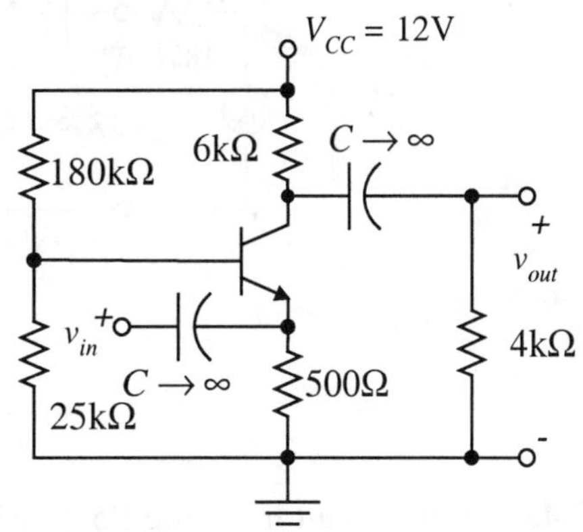

Figure P5.40

Section 5.6

5.41 Design a phase splitter to be connected to 3-kΩ loads. Use $V_{CC} = 12$ V, $V_{BE} = 0.7$ V, and $\beta = 200$. Determine the values of R_1 and R_2 for maximum output swing. Also, determine the maximum undistorted symmetrical output voltage swing for each output and sketch them. (Use Figure 5.13)

Section 5.7

5.42 Determine the values of V_1, V_2, V_3, V_4, I_{CQ1} and I_{CQ2} for the circuit shown in Figure P5.42. Assume that β is 300 or greater.

5.43 Directly couple a CE amplifier to an EF (See Figure 5.14(b)) for 4 V output swing with the following values: $V_{CC} = 12$ V, $A_v = 10$, Q_1 has $\beta = 200$ and $V_{BE} = 0.7$ V, Q_2 has $\beta = 100$ and $V_{BE} = 0.7$ V, and $R_{E1} = 100\ \Omega$. Let $R_C = 4$ kΩ and find R_1, R_2, and R_E.

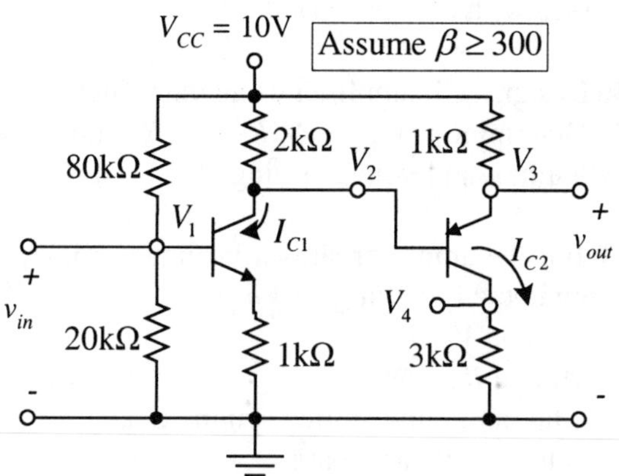

Figure P5.42

5.44 For the circuit shown in Figure P5.44 (please see next page), determine the following when $\beta = 400$ and $V_{BE} = 0.6$ V.

a. Q points for both amplifiers
b. Maximum undistorted output voltage swing
c. Sketch of the output signal
d. v_{out}/v_{in}.

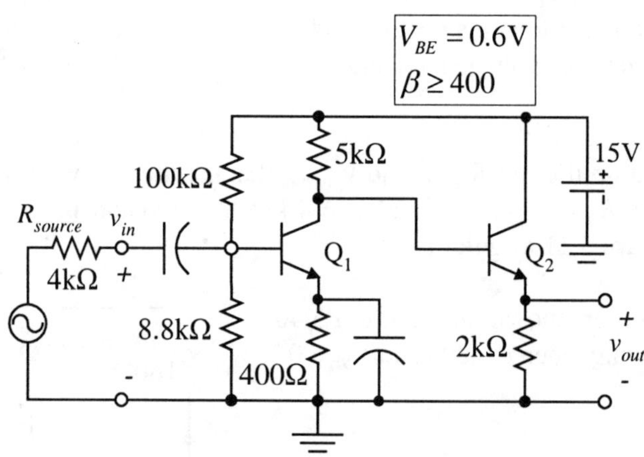

Figure P5.44

5.45 For the circuit in Figure P5.45 when $v_{in} = 0.1 \sin 1000t$ V, determine the voltage output [Assume $\beta = 200$ and $V_{BE} = 0.7$ V]:

a. From v_{out}(+) terminal to v_{out}(-) terminal.
b. From v_{out}(+) terminal to ground.

5.46 For the circuit in Figure P5.46, determine the following when both transistors have $\beta(s)$ = 200 and $V_{BE}(s) = \pm 0.7$ V:

a. Operating point for both amplifiers

b. A_v, R_o, and R_{in} for two stage amplifier

5.47 Determine the maximum input signal for Problem 5.46 to obtain a maximum undistorted symmetrical output swing.

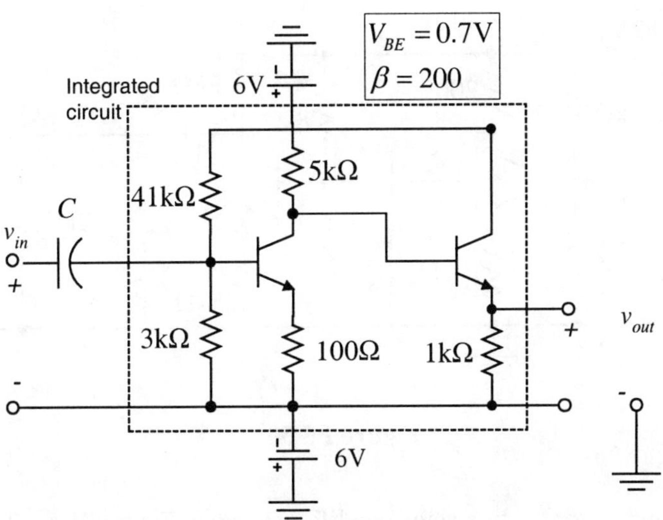

Figure P5.45

5.48 Determine A_v, A_i and R_{in} for the EF amplifier shown in Figure P5.48 when $\beta = 200$ and r_π = 0.

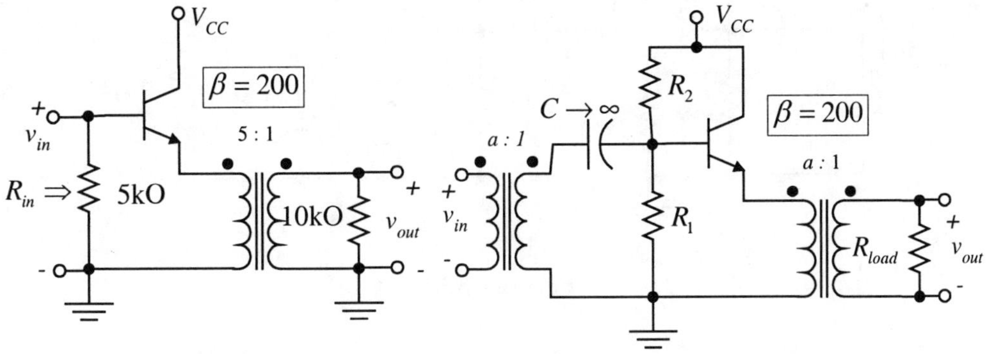

Figure P5.48 **Figure P5.49**

5.49 Determine the overall current and voltage gains and the input resistance for the transformer coupled amplifier as shown in Figure P5.49. Use an npn transistor with a = 4, $R_1 = 2$ kΩ, $R_2 = 4$ kΩ, $V_{CC} = 15$ V, $\beta = 200$ and $R_{load} = 500$ Ω. Neglect r_π.

Section 5.8

5.50 Determine A_i and A_v for the two-stage amplifier shown in Figure P5.50. The transistors are silicon.

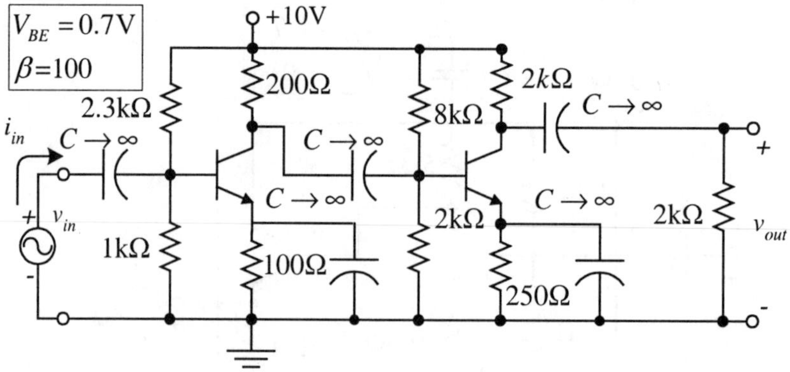

Figure P5.50

5.51 Determine A_i and A_v for the two-stage amplifier shown in Figure P5.51. The transistors are silicon.

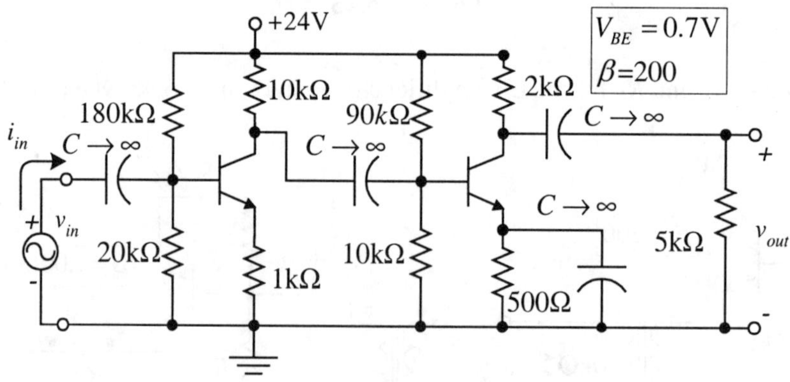

Figure P5.51

5.52 Determine A_v, A_i, and R_{in} for the two-stage amplifier shown in Figure P5.52. The transistors are silicon.

5.53 Design an amplifier using an npn transistor for maximum voltage output with the following requirements: $A_v = -25$, $R_{in} = 4$ kΩ, $R_{load} = 5$ kΩ, $V_{CC} = 12$ V, $\beta = 300$, $V_{BE} = 0.7$ V. Determine all resistor values, undistorted peak-to-peak output voltage swing, and current gain.

5.54 Find R such that at dc, $V_{out} = 0$ for the circuit of Figure P5.54. Also find I_{CQ1}, I_{CQ2}, R_{in}, R_o, and A_v. Assume that $V_{BE} = 0.7$ V and $\beta = 100$ for both transistors.

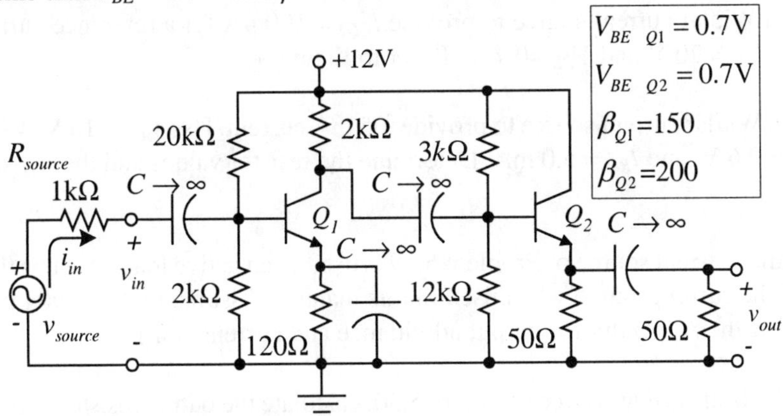

Figure P5.52

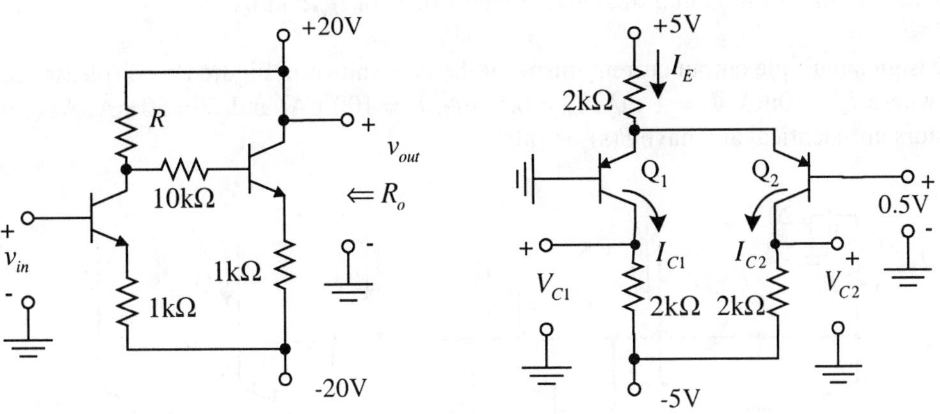

Figure P5.54 **Figure P5.56**

5.55 Analyze the amplifier in Figure 5.26(a) to determine A_v, A_i, R_{in}, and I_{CQ} when $R_1 = 2.5$ kΩ, $R_2 = R_3 = 10$ kΩ, $V_{CC} = 24$ V, $R_E = 1$ kΩ, $\beta = 100$, $V_{BE} = 0.7$ V and $R_C = R_{load} = 5$ kΩ.

5.56 Using simple analytical techniques for the circuit shown in Figure P5.56, determine the values of I_E, V_E, I_{CQ1}, I_{CQ2}, V_{C1}, and V_{C2}. Use $V_{BE} = -0.7$ V.

Section 5.10

5.57 Design a simple current source to provide 6 mA when using a V_{EE} = -12 V. Also, determine the R_{TH} of the current source. Assume V_{BE} = 0.7 V and V_A = 100 V.

5.58 Design a Widlar current source to provide I_{CQ2} = 10 μA. Assume V_{CC} = 30 V, R_I = 40 kΩ, and V_{BE} = 0.7 V. Refer to Figure 5.28.

5.59 Design a Widlar current source to provide I_{CQ2} = 100 μA for a reference current of 1 mA. Assume that V_{CC} = 20 V and V_{BE} =0.7 V. Refer to Figure 5.28.

5.60 Design a Widlar current source to provide .05 mA current. Use V_{CC}= 15 V, V_T = 26 mV, V_A = 50 V, V_{BE} = 0.6 V, and I_{Ref} = 5.0 mA. Determine the resistor values and the R_{TH} of the current source.

5.61 The Widlar current source of Problem 5.59 is used as an active load. What is the equivalent resistance of the current source when used in this manner. Assume that 2N3904 transistors are employed. (See the Appendix for output admittance and current gain).

5.62 For the Wilson current source of Figure 5.30, calculate the output resistance if V_{CC} =15 V, R = 12 kΩ, V_T = 26 mV, V_{BE} = 0.7 V, and β = 100. Assume that 2N3903 transistors are used in the 500 μA range (See Appendix).

5.63 In the circuit of Problem 5.62, what are the values of I_{Ref} and I_{CQ2}?

5.64 Design a multiple output current mirror of the type shown in Figure P5.64 (please see next page) where I_2 = 10mA, I_3 = 1 mA, I_4 = 0.1 mA, I_5 = 100 μA, and I_6 = 50 μA. Assume the transistors are identical and have $\beta(s)$ = 100.

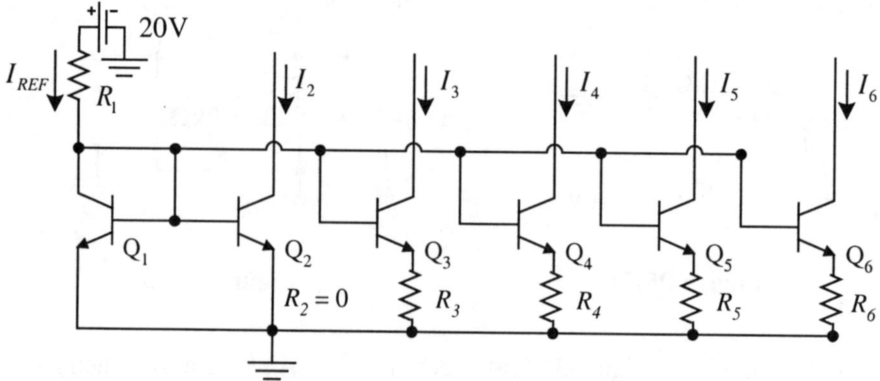

Figure P5.64

5.65 An integrated circuit requires several different values of current sources. Determine the values of the resistances in the circuit shown in Figure P5.65. Also, determine the R_{TH}(s) for each of the current sources shown when $I_2 = 20$ μA, $I_3 = 0.4$ mA, $I_4 = 5$ μA, and $I_5 = 2$ mA. Use $V_A = 80$ V, $V_{BE} = 0.7$ V, $V_T = 26$ mV, and $\beta = 200$.

5.66 For the multiple output current mirror shown in Figure P5.66, determine the values of all the resistances and the R_{TH}(s) for each of the current sources when $I_2 = 0.04$ mA, $I_3 = 2$ mA, $I_4 = 10$ μA, and $I_5 = 50$ μA. Use $V_T = 26$ mV, $V_A = 75$ V, $V_{BE} = 0.7$ V and $\beta = 200$.

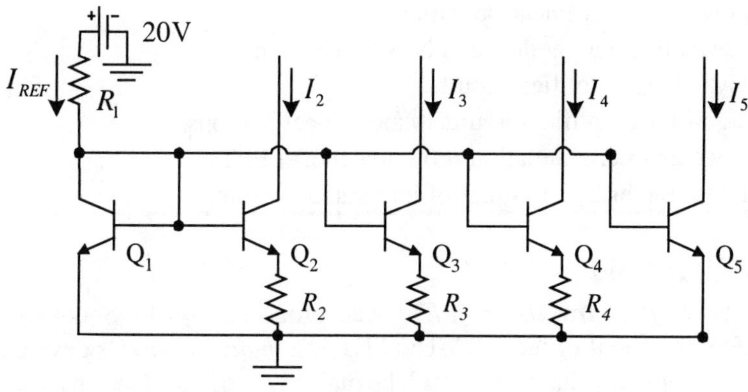

Figure P5.65

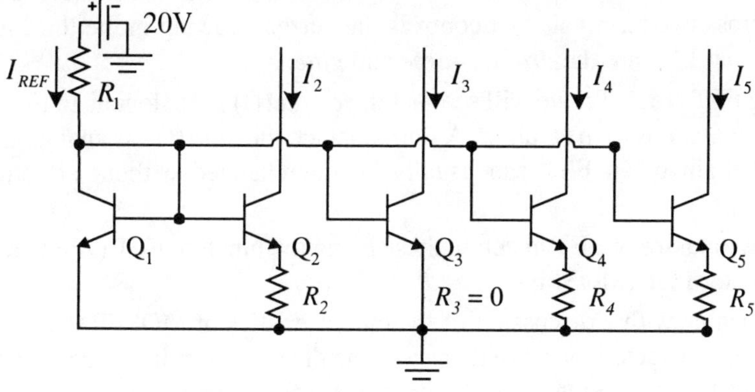

Figure P5.66

Chapter 6
Field-Effect Transistor Amplifiers

In this chapter, we parallel the approach we used for BJT transistors, this time concentrating on the field-effect transistor. After studying this material, you will

- Understand the difference between FETs and BJTs.
- Learn the differences between various forms of FETs.
- Know how to bias FETs for linear operation.
- Understand the small-signal models and how to use them.
- Be able to analyze FET amplifier circuits.
- Be able to design FET amplifier circuits to meet specifications.
- Understand how computer simulation programs model FETs.
- Know how FETs are fabricated as part of integrated circuits.

6.0 INTRODUCTION

The modern *field effect transistor (FET)* was proposed by W. Shockley in 1952. Its performance differs from that of the BJT. The FET is a *majority carrier* device. Its operation depends on using an applied voltage to control the majority carriers (electrons in n-type material and holes in p-type) in a channel. This voltage controls the current in the device by means of an electric field.

Field-effect transistors are three-terminal devices, but in contrast with the bipolar transistor, it is the voltage across two terminals that controls the current flowing in the third terminal. The three terminals in an FET are the *drain*, *source* and *gate*.

In comparing FETs to BJTs, we will see that the *drain* (D) is analogous to the collector and the *source* (S) is analogous to the emitter. A third contact, the *gate* (G), is analogous to the base. The source and drain of an FET can usually be interchanged without affecting transistor operation.

We discuss two classes of FET in detail, these being the junction FET (JFET) and the metal-oxide semiconductor FET (MOSFET).

The chapter begins with a discussion of the characteristics of MOSFETs and JFETs and a comparison of these characteristics. We then examine the ways of using these devices in circuits, and the techniques for biasing the various amplifier configurations.

As we examine analysis techniques in detail, we present computer simulation models. This is followed by detailed sections dealing with analysis techniques and with design methodology.

The chapter concludes with a brief discussion of other specialty devices.

6.1 ADVANTAGES AND DISADVANTAGES OF FETs

The advantages of FETs relative to BJTs are summarized as follows:

1. FETs are voltage-sensitive devices with high input impedance (on the order of 10^7 to 10^{12} Ω). Since this input impedance is considerably higher than that of BJTs, FETs are preferred over BJTs for use as the input stage to a multistage amplifier.
2. One class of FETs (JFETs) generates lower noise than BJTs.
3. FETs are more temperature stable than BJTs.
4. FETs are generally easier to fabricate than BJTs. Greater numbers of devices can be fabricated on a single chip (i.e., increased *packing density* is possible).
5. FETs react like voltage-controlled variable resistors for small values of drain-to-source voltage.
6. The high input impedance of FETs permit them to store charge long enough to allow them to be used as storage elements.
7. Power FETs can dissipate high power and can switch large currents.
8. FETs are not as sensitive to radiation as BJTs (an important consideration for space electronic applications).

There are several disadvantages that limit the use of FETs in some applications. These are:

1. FETs amplifiers usually exhibit poor frequency response because of high input capacitance.
2. Some types of FETs exhibit poor linearity.
3. FETs can be damaged in handling due to static electricity.

6.2 METAL-OXIDE SEMICONDUCTOR FET (MOSFET)

The metal-oxide semiconductor FET (MOSFET) is a four terminal device. The terminals are the *source (S), gate (G)* and *drain (D)*. The *substrate* or *body* forms the fourth terminal. The MOSFET is constructed with the gate terminal insulated from the channel with a silicon dioxide dielectric. MOSFETs can be either *depletion* or *enhancement mode*. We define these two terms shortly.

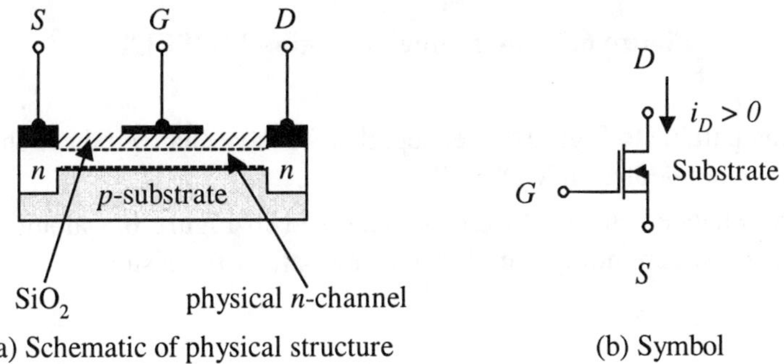

(a) Schematic of physical structure (b) Symbol

Figure 6.1 – *n*-channel depletion MOSFET

MOSFETs are sometimes referred to as IGFETs (Insulated Gate Field-Effect Transistors) due to the SiO_2 layer used as an insulator between the gate and the substrate. We begin our analysis with the depletion-mode MOSFET. Just as BJTs can be either *npn* or *pnp*, MOSFETs can be either *n*-channel (NMOS) or *p*-channel (PMOS). Figure 6.1 illustrates the physical structure and symbol for an *n*-channel depletion MOSFET. Notice that the substrate is connected to the source terminal. This will almost always be the case.

The depletion MOSFET is constructed with a *physical* channel inserted between the drain and the source. As a result, when a voltage, v_{DS}, is applied between drain and source, a current, i_D, exists between drain and source even though the gate terminal G remains unconnected ($v_{GS} = 0$ V).

The construction of the *n*-channel depletion MOSFET begins with *p*-doped silicon. The *n*-doped source and drain wells form low-resistance connections between the ends of the *n*-channel, as shown in the Figure 6.1. A thin layer of silicon dioxide is deposited covering the area between the source and the drain. The SiO_2 is an insulator. An aluminum layer is deposited on the silicon dioxide insulator to form the gate terminal. In operation, a negative v_{GS} pushes electrons out of the channel region, thereby depleting the channel. When v_{GS} reaches a certain voltage, V_T, the channel is *pinched off*. Positive values of v_{GS} increase the channel size, resulting in an increase of drain current. The depletion MOSFET can operate with either positive or negative values of v_{GS}. Since the gate is insulated from the channel, the gate current is negligibly small (on the order of 10^{-12} A).

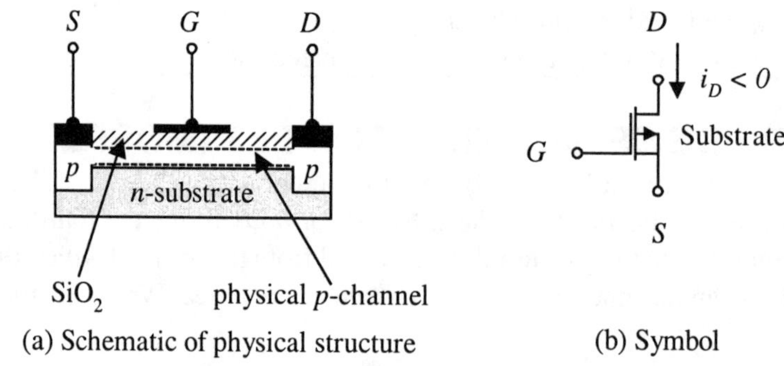

(a) Schematic of physical structure (b) Symbol

Figure 6.2 – *p*-channel depletion MOSFET

Figure 6.2 is comparable to Figure 6.1, except that we have changed the *n*-channel depletion MOSFET to a *p*-channel depletion MOSFET.

The *n*-channel enhancement MOSFET is illustrated in Figure 6.3 along with the circuit symbol. This is the most commonly used form of field-effect transistor.

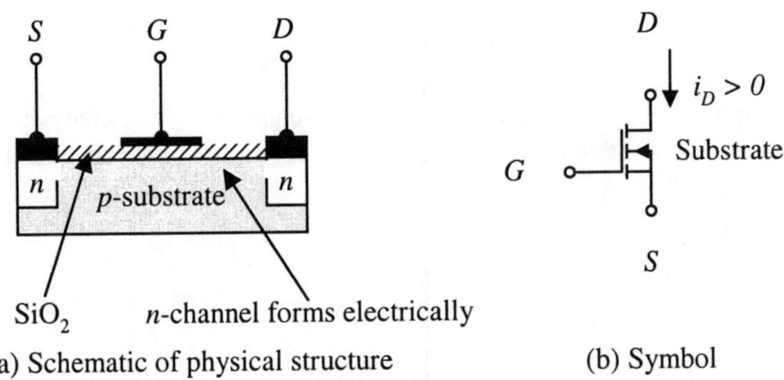

(a) Schematic of physical structure (b) Symbol

Figure 6.3 – *n*-channel enhancement MOSFET

The *n*-channel enhancement MOSFET differs from the depletion MOSFET by not having the thin *n*-layer. It requires a positive voltage between the gate and the source to establish a channel. This channel is formed by the action of a positive gate-to-source voltage, v_{GS}, which attracts electrons from the substrate region between the *n*-doped drain and the source. Positive v_{GS} causes electrons to accumulate at the surface beneath the oxide layer. When the voltage reaches a threshold, V_T, sufficient numbers of electrons are attracted to this region to make it act like a conducting *n*-channel. No appreciable drain current, i_D exists until v_{GS} exceeds V_T.

Figure 6.4 is comparable to Figure 6.3, except that we have changed the *n*-channel enhancement MOSFET to a *p*-channel enhancement MOSFET.

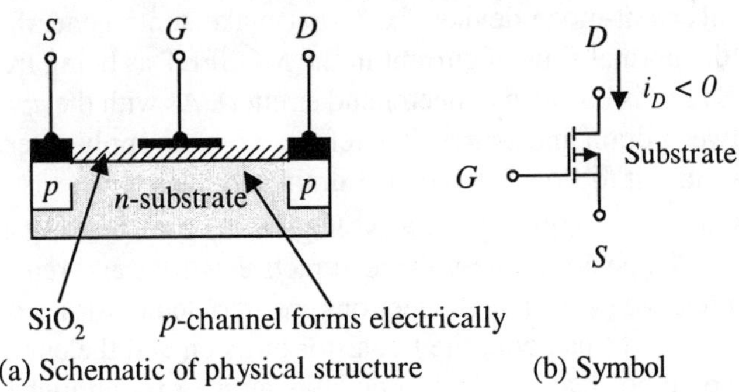

(a) Schematic of physical structure (b) Symbol

Figure 6-4 – *p*-channel enhancement MOSFET

As a summary, the MOSFET family exhibits the identifying i_D versus v_{GS} curves shown in Figure 6.5. Each characteristic curve is developed with sufficient drain-source voltage v_{DS} to maintain the device in the normal operating region of the i_D versus v_{DS} curves. The discussion in later sections will define the threshold voltage V_T for both enhancement MOSFETs and depletion MOSFETs.

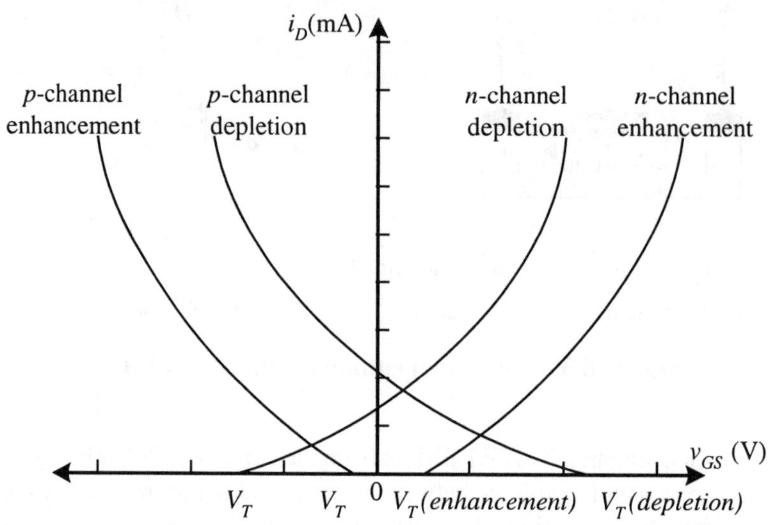

Figure 6.5 – i_D versus v_{GS} characteristics of the MOSFET family for sufficient drain source voltage V_{DS}

6.2.1 Enhancement-Mode MOSFET Terminal Characteristics

Now that we have presented the basic structure and basis for operation of the MOSFET, we use an approach similar to that of Chapter 4 for the BJT in order to examine the terminal behavior of the enhancement-mode device. Let's first make some general observations from Figure 6.1. Think of the normal flow of current in the MOSFET as being from the drain to the source (just as in the BJT, it is between collector and emitter). As with the *npn* BJT, two back-to-back diodes exist between drain and source. Therefore, we must apply external voltages to the gate in order to allow current to flow between the drain and the source.

If we ground the source, and apply a positive voltage to the gate, that voltage is effectively the gate-to-source voltage. The positive gate voltage attracts electrons and repels holes. When the voltage exceeds the threshold (V_T), enough electrons are attracted to form a conducting channel between drain and source. At this point, the transistor turns on and the current is a function of both v_{GS} and v_{DS}. It should be clear that V_T is a positive number for an *n*-channel device, and a negative number for a *p*-channel device.

Once a channel is created (i.e., $v_{GS}>V_T$), current flow can occur in that channel between drain and source. This current flow depends on v_{DS}, but it also depends on v_{GS}. When v_{GS} just barely exceeds the threshold voltage, very little current can flow. As v_{GS} increases beyond the threshold, the channel contains more carriers and higher currents are possible. Figure 6.6 shows the relationship between i_D and v_{DS} where v_{GS} is a parameter. Note that for v_{GS} less than the threshold, no current flows. For higher v_{GS}, the relationship between i_D and v_{DS} is approximately linear indicating that the MOSFET behaves like a resistor whose resistance depends on v_{GS}.

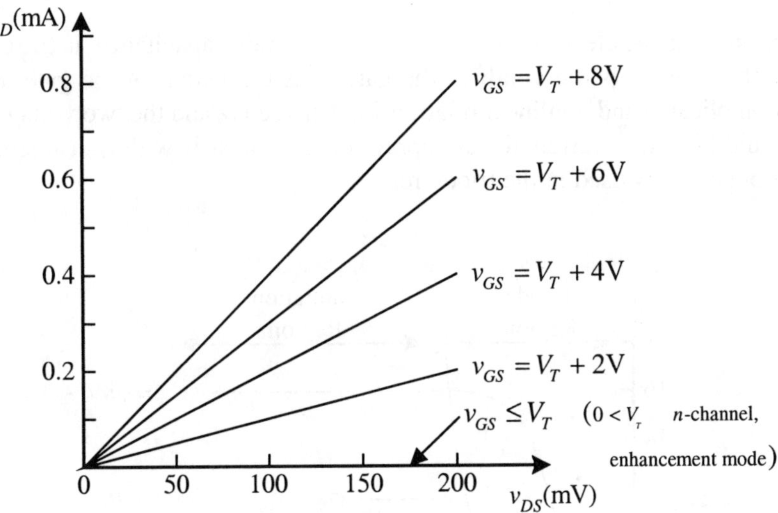

Figure 6.6 – i_D versus v_{DS} for an enhancement-mode *n*-channel MOSFET when v_{DS} is small

The curves of Figure 6.6 look like straight lines. However, they will not continue as straight lines when v_{DS} gets larger. Recall that a positive gate voltage is used to create the conduction channel. It does this by attracting electrons. The positive drain voltage is doing the same thing. As we approach the drain end of the channel, the voltage creating the channel approaches v_{GS}-v_{DS} since the two sources oppose each other. When this difference is less than V_T, the channel no longer exists for the entire space between source and drain. The channel is *constrained* at the drain end, and further increases in v_{DS} do not result in any increase in i_D. This is known as the normal operating region or *saturation* region shown in Figure 6.7 by the horizontal section of the characteristic curves. When the difference is greater than V_T, we call this the *triode* mode, because the potentials at all three terminals strongly affect the current.

The previous discussion leads to the operating curves of Figure 6.7.

The transition between the triode and the normal operating region (referred to as the saturation region and often identified as operation in the pinch-off mode) of operation is shown as the dashed line in Figure 6.7, where

$$v_{DS} = v_{GS} - V_T \tag{6.1}$$

At the triode region border, the knees of the curves approximately follow the relationship,

$$i_D = K\left[2\left(v_{GS} - V_T\right)v_{DS} - v_{DS}^2\right] \tag{6.2}$$

In Equation (6.2), K is a constant for a given device. Its value depends on the dimensions of the device and the materials used in its construction. The constant is given by,

$$K = \frac{1}{2}\mu_n C_{oxide}\frac{W}{L} \tag{6.3}$$

In this equation, μ_n is the electron mobility; C_{oxide}, the oxide capacitance, is the capacitance per unit area of the gate; W is the width of the gate; L is the length of the gate. Equation (6.2) indicates a complicated and nonlinear relationship between i_D and the two voltages, v_{DS} and v_{GS}. Since we would like drain current to vary approximately linearly with v_{GS} (independent of v_{DS}), the FET is not generally used in the triode region.

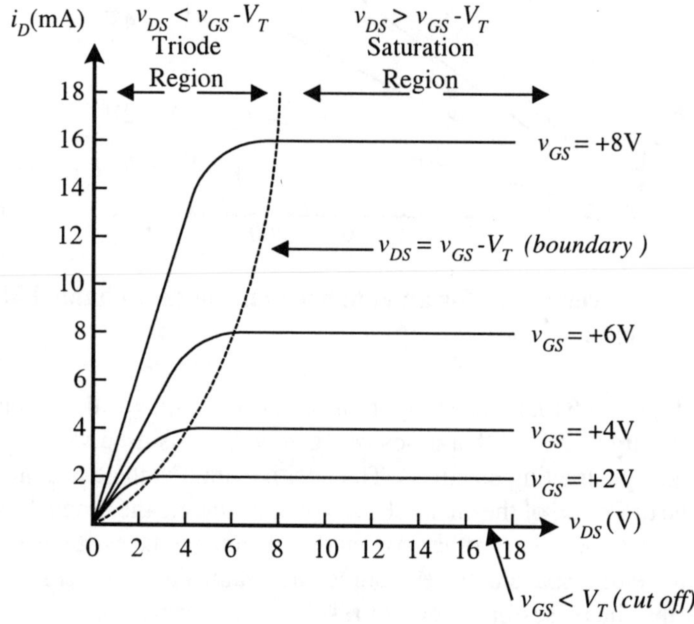

Figure 6.7 – i_D versus v_{GS} for an enhancement-mode MOSFET

We now wish to find an equation for the operating curves in the saturation region. We can establish the values at the transition between the triode and saturation region by evaluating Equation (6.2) at the transition (knee). That is,

$$\begin{aligned} i_D &= K\left[2\left(v_{GS} - V_T\right)v_{DS} - v_{DS}^2\right]\Big|_{v_{DS} = v_{GS} - V_T} \\ &= K\left[v_{GS} - V_T\right]^2 \end{aligned} \tag{6.4}$$

This equation establishes the magnitude of the drain current at the boundary (dashed line in Figure 6.8) as a function of the gate-to-source voltage v_{GS}. If necessary, we can account for the slight slope of the characteristic curves in the saturation region by adding a linear factor.

$$i_D = K\left(v_{GS} - V_T\right)^2\left(1 + \lambda v_{DS}\right) \tag{6.5}$$

In Equation (6.5), λ is a small constant (the slope of the near horizontal section of the characteristic curves shown in Figure 6.8). It is usually less than 0.001 (V^{-1}). Then

$$i_D \approx K(v_{GS} - V_T)^2 = KV_T^2\left(\frac{v_{GS}}{V_T} - 1\right)^2 \tag{6.6}$$

All of our previous discussion dealt with the NMOS transistor. We now briefly discuss the necessary modifications for PMOS. For PMOS, the values of v_{DS} will be negative. Additionally, to create a channel in PMOS, $v_{GS} \leq V_T$.

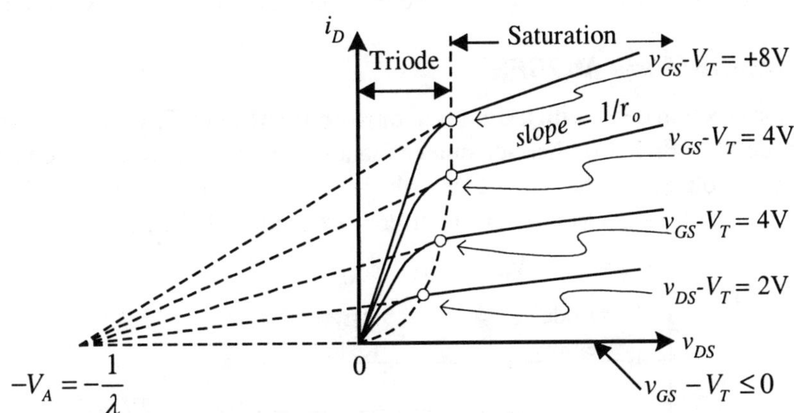

Figure 6.8 – Terminal characteristics of a MOSFET transistor

The only changes from the characteristics of NMOS transistors (Figure 6.7) is that the horizontal axis is now $-v_{DS}$ instead of $+v_{DS}$, and the parametric curves represent higher drain current as the gate voltage decreases (instead of increasing for the NMOS transistor). The curves for increasing current values correspond to more negative gate voltage. When $v_{GS} > V_T$, the transistor is cut-off. For enhancement PMOS, V_T is negative, and for depletion PMOS, V_T is positive.

The equation for the current at the triode region transition for the PMOS transistor is identical to that of the NMOS. That is,

$$i_D = K\left[2(v_{GS} - V_T)v_{DS} - v_{DS}^2\right] \tag{6.7}$$

Note that v_{GS} and v_{DS} are both negative quantities. The equation for the saturation region in the PMOS transistor is also identical to that of the NMOS. That is,

$$i_D = K(v_{GS} - V_T)^2(1 + \lambda v_{DS}) \approx KV_T^2\left(\frac{v_{GS}}{V_T} - 1\right)^2 \tag{6.8}$$

Note that λ is negative for PMOS transistors since the rate of change of the curve ($\partial i_D / \partial v_{DS}$) is negative.

Taking the partial derivative of both sides of Equation (6.6) with respect to v_{GS}, $\partial i_D / \partial v_{GS}$, we get

$$\frac{\partial i_D}{\partial v_{GS}} \doteq g_m \simeq -\frac{2KV_T^2}{V_T}\left(1-\frac{v_{GS}}{V_T}\right) = 2K\left(v_{GS}-V_T\right) \tag{6.9}$$

We prefer the value of g_m to be constant, especially for large signal swings. However, we only can approximate this condition if we use the FET for small signal applications. For large signal conditions, distortion of the waveform may be unacceptable in some applications.

6.2.2 Depletion-Mode MOSFET

The previous section dealt with the enhancement-mode MOSFET. We now contrast this to the depletion-mode MOSFET. For the *n*-channel enhancement mode, to acquire a channel we had to apply a positive voltage on the gate. This voltage had to be large enough to force sufficient numbers of mobile electrons to produce a current in an induced channel.

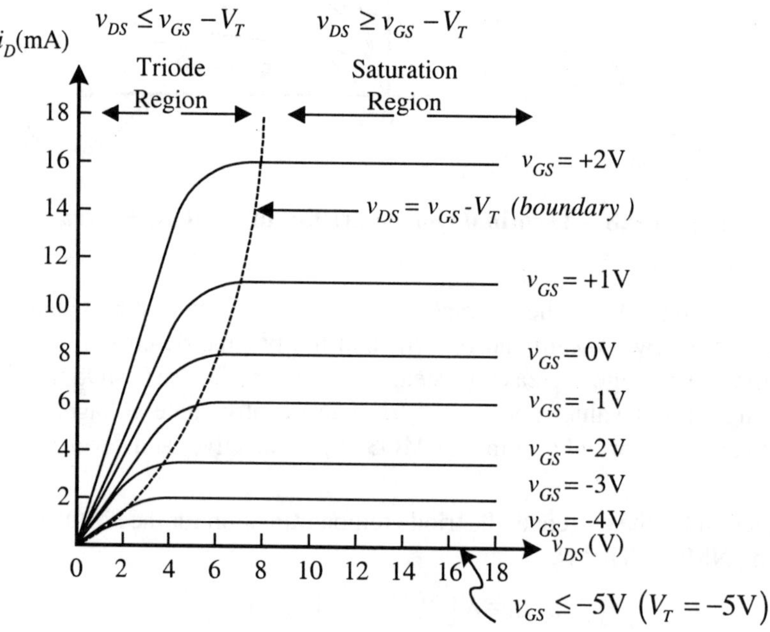

Figure 6.9 – Depletion mode *n*-channel MOSFET

In the *n*-channel depletion-mode MOSFET, we don't need this positive voltage since we have a physically implanted channel. This allows us to have current between the drain and source terminals even with negative voltages applied to the gate. Of course, there is a limit to the amount of negative voltage that can be applied to the gate while still having current flow between drain and source. This limit is again identified as the threshold voltage, V_T. The change from the enhancement mode is that the gate-to-source voltage can now be either negative or positive, as shown in Figure 6.9.

The equations that define the operation of the depletion- mode MOSFET are very similar to those of the enhancement mode. The value of the drain current when v_{GS} is zero is identified as I_{DSS}. This is often referred to as the *drain-source saturation current*, or the *zero - gate drain current*. Comparing the equations of the enhancement-mode MOSFET with those of the depletion mode, we find

$$I_{DSS} = KV_T^2 \tag{6.10}$$

We then find,

$$i_D = I_{DSS}\left(1 - \frac{v_{GS}}{V_T}\right)^2$$

$$g_m = -\frac{2I_{DSS}}{V_T}\left(1 - \frac{v_{GS}}{V_T}\right) \tag{6.11}$$

Depletion mode MOSFETs are available in discrete form, or they can be fabricated on integrated circuits chips right along with enhancement mode types. This includes both *p*-type and *n*-type. This allows more flexibility in circuit design techniques.

Example 6.1

Calculate the drain current, i_D, for the depletion MOSFET with transfer characteristics shown in Figure 6.10 for the following values of v_{GS}. Assume that V_T is -3.5 V and I_{DSS} is 7 mA.

(a) $v_{GS} = -1$ V
(b) $v_{GS} = -2$ V
(c) $v_{GS} = -3$ V
(d) $v_{GS} = +0.5$ V

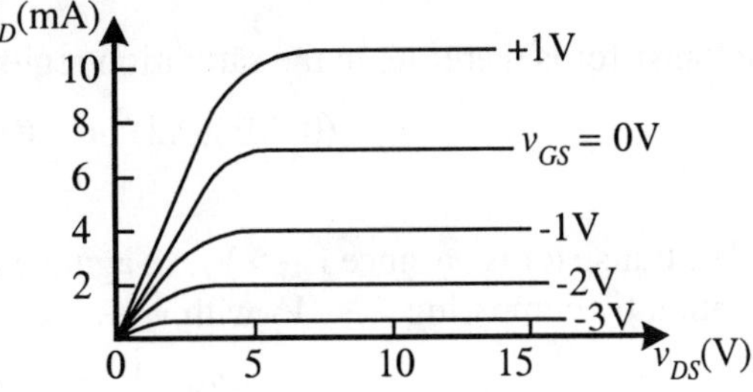

Figure 6.10 – Transfer characteristics for Example 6.1

Solution: We use Equation (6.8) for each case, where V_T is -3.5 V. The equation can be rewritten as

$$i_D = K(v_{GS} - V_T)^2(1 + \lambda v_{DS}) \approx KV_T^2\left(\frac{v_{GS}}{V_T} - 1\right)^2$$

Since the value of K is not given, we must use the curves to find it. We observe that the drain current is 7 mA when v_{GS} is zero. Therefore from Equation (6.10) we find I_{DSS} or $KV_T^2 = 7\text{mA}$.

$$i_D = 7\,(\text{mA})\left(1 - \frac{v_{GS}}{V_T}\right)^2 = 3.57 \quad \text{mA}$$

Similarly, for parts (b), (c), and (d), we find drain currents of 1.29 mA, 0.14 mA, and 9.14 mA respectively.

Example 6.2

Calculate i_D for an NMOS transistor with $V_T = 1$ V, $\lambda = 0.001$, and $K = 0.003$ A/V^2 when the terminal voltages are

a. $v_{GS} = 0.5$ V, $v_{DS} = 5$ V

b. $v_{GS} = 1.2$ V, $v_{DS} = 3$ V

c. $v_{GS} = 1.2$ V, $v_{DS} = 0.1$ V

Solution: (a) Since $v_{GS} < V_T$, the transistor is cutoff, so

$$i_D \approx 0$$

(b) The transistor is on since $v_{GS} > V_T$, so we need to test whether it is in triode or saturation operation by comparing v_{GS} - V_T with v_{DS}.

$$v_{GS} - V_T = 0.2 < 3 = V_{DS}$$

The transistor is therefore in the saturation region. The drain current is given by Equation (6.5).

$$i_D = (0.003)(0.2)^2[1 + (0.001)(3)] = 0.12 \quad \text{mA}$$

(c) The transistor is on since $v_{GS} > V_T$, so again we need to test whether it is in triode or saturation operation by comparing v_{GS} - V_T with v_{DS}.

$$v_{GS} - V_T = 0.2 > 0.1 = V_{DS}$$

The transistor is in triode mode. The drain current is given by Equation (6.2)

$$i_D = (0.003)[2(0.2)(0.1) - (0.1)^2] = 90 \quad \mu\text{A}$$

6.2.3 Large-Signal Equivalent Circuit

We now wish to develop an equivalent circuit which represents the large-signal characteristics of Figure 6.8 [Equation (6.5) or (6.8)] in the saturation region. Note that the drain current, i_D, depends on v_{GS} and v_{DS}. For a constant gate-to-source voltage, we operate along one of the parametric curves of the figure, and the relationship is an approximately straight line. A straight-line relationship between current and voltage is modeled by a resistor. The equivalent circuit therefore consists of a resistor in parallel with the current source where the value of the current source establishes the portion of the drain current due to v_{GS}. The slope of the curve depends on v_{GS}. The slope is the partial derivative,

$$r_O = \frac{\partial v_{DS}}{\partial i_D} \tag{6.12}$$

where r_O is the incremental output resistance. We see from Equation (6.5) [or (6.8)] that this resistance is given by

$$r_O = \frac{1}{\lambda K(V_{GS} - V_T)^2} \approx \frac{1}{\lambda I_D} \tag{6.13}$$

where we use upper-case V_{GS} to indicate that the resistance is defined for a particular constant value of gate-to-source voltage. The final approximation in Equation (6.13) results from Equation (6.5) with the assumption that λ is small. The resistance is therefore inversely proportion to the bias current, I_D. The large signal equivalent model is then given by Figure 6.11 where r_O is as developed in Equation (6.13).

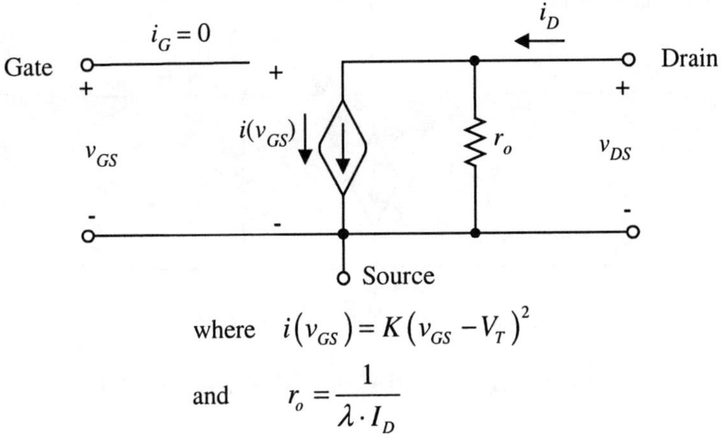

where $i(v_{GS}) = K(v_{GS} - V_T)^2$

and $r_o = \dfrac{1}{\lambda \cdot I_D}$

Figure 6.11 – Large-signal equivalent circuit

6.2.4 Small-Signal Model of MOSFET

We now wish to look at incremental effects related to Equation (6.5). The three circuit parameters in that equation, i_D, v_{GS} and v_{DS} are composed of both *dc* (bias) and *ac* components (that is why we have used upper case subscripts in the expressions). We are interested in the *ac* components for the small-signal model. We see that the drain current is dependent on two voltages, the gate-to-source and the drain-to-source. For incremental values, we can write this relationship as

$$i_d = g_m v_{gs} + \frac{v_{ds}}{r_O} = I_{DSS}\left(1 - \frac{v_{gs}}{V_T}\right)^2 (1 + \lambda v_{ds}) \tag{6.14}$$

In Equation (6.14), g_m is *the forward transconductance* and r_O is the output resistance. Their values are found by taking partial derivatives in Equation (6.5). Thus,

$$g_m = \frac{\partial i_d}{\partial v_{gs}} = 2K(V_{GS} - V_T)(1 + \lambda V_{DS}) \approx -\frac{2I_{DSS}}{V_T}\left(1 - \frac{V_{GS}}{V_T}\right)$$

$$r_O = \frac{\partial v_{ds}}{\partial i_d} = \frac{1}{K(V_{GS} - V_T)^2 \lambda} \tag{6.15}$$

The approximation in Equation (6.15) results from the observation that λ if small. Equation (6.14) leads to the small-signal model of Figure 6.12.

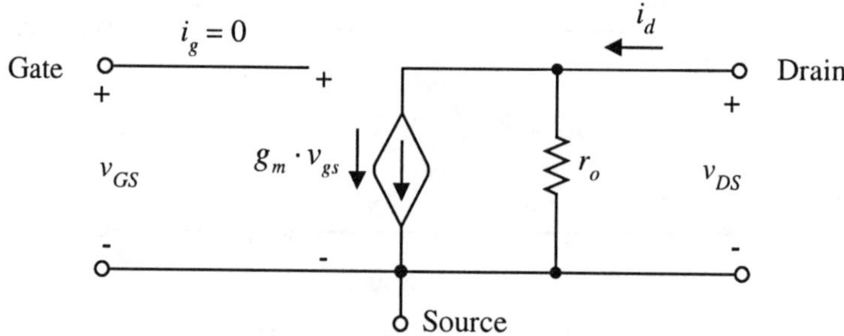

Figure 6.12 – Small-signal MOSFET model

Note the similarity of the model to that for the BJT derived in Chapter 4. The differences are that the FET has no gate current ($r_\pi \to \infty$), and the formulae for calculating g_m and r_o are different than those for the BJT.

Example 6.3

Calculate I_D, g_m and r_o for an NMOS transistor with $V_T = 1$ V and $K = 0.001$ A/V^2. Assume

(a) $v_{GS} = 1.5$ V, $v_{DS} = 3$ V, $\lambda = 0.01$ V^{-1}

(b) $v_{GS} = 1.2$ V, $v_{DS} = 3$ V, $\lambda = 0.01$ V^{-1}

(c) $v_{GS} = 1.5$ V, $v_{DS} = 4$ V, $\lambda = 0.01$ V^{-1}

(d) $v_{GS} = 1.5$ V, $v_{DS} = 3$ V, $\lambda = 0.001$ V^{-1}

Solution: For all cases, the transistor is in the saturation region, so the small signal model is valid as long as the *ac* conditions on v_{gs} are satisfied. To find the *dc* drain current, we use the equation

$$i_D = K(v_{GS} - V_T)^2(1+\lambda v_{DS})$$

(a) $I_D = (0.001)(0.5)^2(1.03) = 257.5 \quad \mu A$

(b) $I_D = (0.001)(0.2)^2(1.03) = 41.2 \quad \mu A$

(c) $I_D = (0.001)(0.5)^2(1.04) = 260.0 \quad \mu A$

(d) $I_D = (0.001)(0.5)^2(1.003) = 250.75 \quad \mu A$

Comparing the results, we see that the *dc* drain current in the saturation region is sensitive to V_{GS} but relatively insensitive to either V_{DS} or λ as long as $|\lambda| << 1$. This observation can be useful in setting *dc* biases for the FET amplifiers as we do in the following sections.

To find the transconductance parameter, g_m, we use the equation

$$g_m = 2K(V_{GS} - V_T)(1+\lambda V_{DS})$$

(a) $g_m = 2(0.001)(0.5)(1.03) = 1.03 \quad$ mA/V

(b) $g_m = 2(0.001)(0.2)(1.03) = 0.412 \quad$ mA/V

(c) $g_m = 2(0.001)(0.5)(1.04) = 1.04 \quad$ mA/V

(d) $g_m = 2(0.001)(0.5)(1.003) = 1.003 \quad$ mA/V

Again, we see that the transconductance parameter, g_m, is sensitive to V_{GS} but relatively insensitive to either V_{DS} or λ as long as $|\lambda| << 1$.

To find the resistance, r_o, we use the equation

$$r_o = \frac{1}{K(V_{GS} - V_T)^2\lambda}$$

(a) $r_o = \dfrac{1}{(0.001)(0.5)^2(0.01)} = 400 \quad k\Omega$

(b) $r_o = \dfrac{1}{(0.001)(0.2)^2(0.01)} = 2.5 \quad \text{M}\Omega$

(c) $r_o = \dfrac{1}{(0.001)(0.5)^2(0.01)} = 400 \quad \text{k}\Omega$

(d) $r_o = \dfrac{1}{(0.001)(0.5)^2(0.001)} = 4 \quad \text{M}\Omega$

6.3 JUNCTION FIELD-EFFECT TRANSISTOR (JFET)

The MOSFET has a number of advantages over the junction field-effect transistor (JFET). Notably, the input resistance of the MOSFET is higher than that of the JFET. For this reason, the MOSFET is selected in favor of the JFET for most applications. Nonetheless, the JFET is still used in limited situations especially for analog applications.

We have seen that enhancement MOSFETs require a non-zero gate voltage to form a channel for conduction. No majority-carrier current can flow between the source and the drain without this applied gate voltage. In contrast, the JFET controls the conductance of majority-carrier current in an existing channel between two ohmic contacts. It does this by varying the equivalent capacitance of the device.

Although we approach JFETs without using the results derived earlier for MOSFETs, we will see many similarities in the operation of the two types of devices. These similarities are summarized in Section 6.6.

A schematic for the physical structure of the JFET is shown in Figure 6.13. Like the BJT, the JFET is a three terminal device. It has basically only one *pn* junction between the gate and the channel rather than two as in the BJT (although there appear to be two *pn* junctions shown in Figure 6.13, these are connected in parallel by wiring the gate terminals together. They can thus be treated as a single junction).

The *n*-channel JFET, shown in Figure 6.14(a), is constructed using a strip of *n*-type material with two *p*-type materials diffused into the strip, one on each side. The *p*-channel JFET has a strip of *p*-type material with two *n*-type materials diffused into the strip, as shown in Figure 6.13(b). Figure 6.13 also shows the circuit symbols.

To gain insight into the operation of the JFET, let us connect the *n*-channel JFET to an external circuit as shown in Figure 6.14(a). A positive supply voltage, V_{DD}, is applied to the drain (this is analogous to the V_{CC} supply voltage for a BJT) and the source is attached to common (ground). A gate supply voltage, V_{GG}, is applied to the gate (this is analogous to V_{BB} for the BJT).

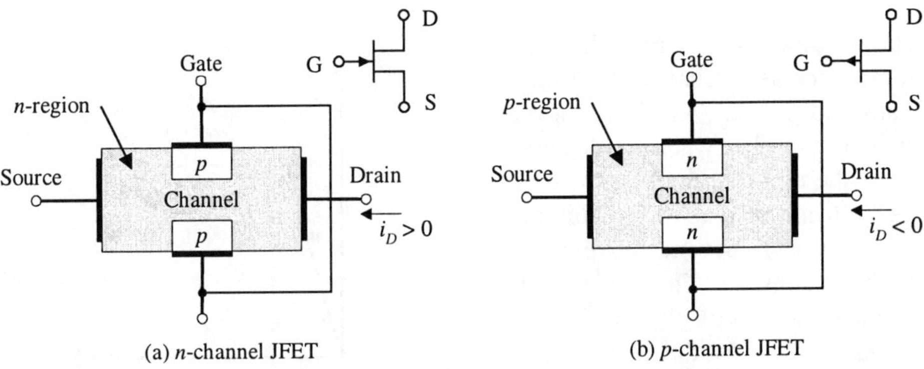

Figure 6.13 – Physical Structure of JFET

V_{DD} provides a drain-source voltage, v_{DS}, that causes a drain current, i_D, to flow from drain to source. Since the gate-source junction is reverse-biased, zero gate current results. The drain current, i_D, which is equal to the source current, exists in

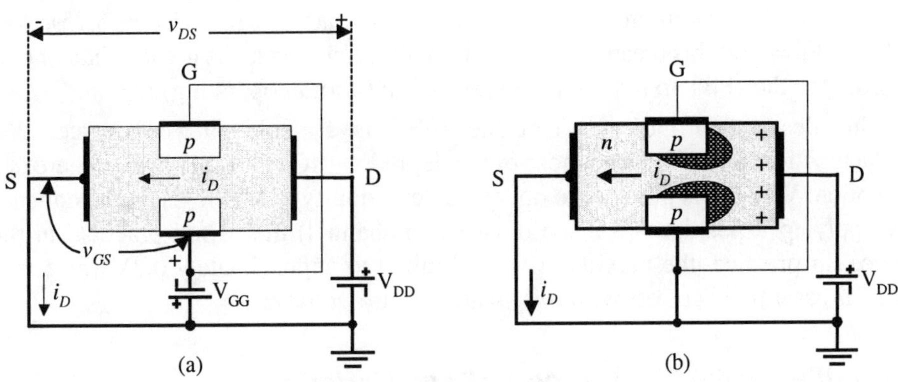

Figure 6.14 - *n*-channel JFET connected to external circuitry

the channel surrounded by the *p*-type gate. The gate-to-source voltage, v_{GS}, which is equal to $-V_{GG}$, creates a *depletion region* in the channel which reduces the channel width. This, in turn, increases the resistance between drain and source.

We consider JFET operation with $v_{GS} = 0$, as shown in Figure 6.14(b). The drain current, i_D, through the *n*-channel from drain to source causes a voltage drop along the channel, with the higher potential at the drain-gate junction. This positive voltage at the drain-gate junction reverse-biases the *pn* junction and produces a depletion region, as shown by the dark shaded area in Figure 6.14(b). When we increase v_{DS}, the drain current, i_D, also increases, as shown in Figure 6.15.

This action results in a larger depletion region and an increased channel resistance between drain and source. As v_{DS} is further increased, a point is reached where the depletion region cuts off the entire channel at the drain edge and the drain current reaches its saturation point. If we increase v_{DS} beyond this point, i_D remains relatively constant. The value of the saturated drain current with V_{GS} = 0 is an important parameter. It is the *drain-source saturation current*, I_{DSS}. We found it to be KV_T^2 for the depletion mode MOSFET. As can be seen from Figure 6.15, increasing v_{DS} beyond this so-called channel *pinch-off* point ($-V_P$, I_{DSS}) causes a very slight increase in i_D, and the i_D-v_{DS} characteristic curve becomes almost flat (i.e., i_D remains relatively constant as v_{DS} is further increased). Recall that V_T (now designated V_P) is negative for an n-channel device. Operation beyond the pinch-off point (in the saturation region) is obtained when the drain voltage, V_{DS}, is greater than $-V_P$ (see Figure 6.15). As an example, let's say V_P = -4V, this means that the drain voltage, v_{DS}, must be greater than or equal to –(-4V) in order for the JFET to remain in the saturation (normal operating) region.

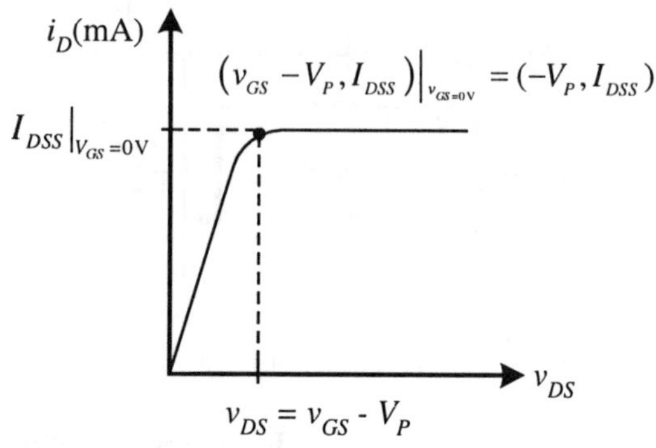

Figure 6.15 – i_D versus v_{DS} characteristic for n-channel JFET (V_{GS} = 0V)

This description indicates that the JFET is a depletion-type device. We expect its characteristics to be similar to those of the depletion MOSFETs. However there is an important exception: While it is possible to operate a depletion-type MOSFET in the enhancement mode (by applying a positive v_{GS} if the device is n-channel) this is not practical in the JFET-type device. In practice, the maximum v_{GS} is limited to approximately 0.3V since the pn-junction remains essentially cut-off with this small forward voltage.

6.3.1 JFET Gate-To-Source Voltage Variation

In the previous section, we developed the i_D-v_{DS} characteristic curve with V_{GS} = 0. In this section, we consider the complete i_D-v_{DS} characteristics for various values of v_{GS}. Note that in the case of the BJT, the characteristic curves (i_C-v_{CE}) have i_B as the parameter. The FET is a voltage-controlled device where v_{GS} does the controlling. Figure 6.16 shows the i_D-v_{DS} characteristic curves for both the n-channel and p-channel JFET.

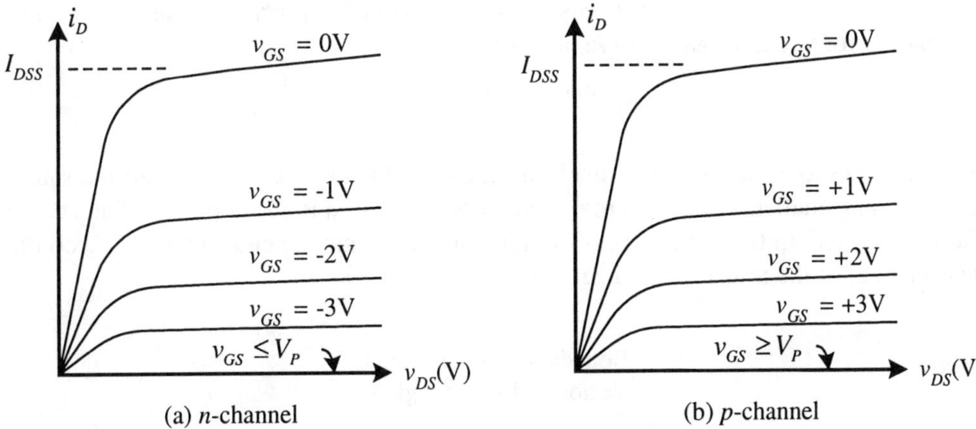

(a) *n*-channel (b) *p*-channel

Figure 6.16 - i_D-v_{DS} characteristic curves for JFET

As $|v_{GS}|$ increases (v_{GS} is more negative for an *n*-channel and more positive for a *p*-channel) the depletion region is formed and pinch-off is attained for lower values of i_D. Hence for the *n*-channel JFET of Figure 6.16(a), the maximum i_D reduces from I_{DSS} as v_{GS} is made more negative. If v_{GS} is further decreased (more negative), a value of v_{GS} is reached after which i_D will be zero regardless of the value of v_{DS}. This value of v_{GS} is called $V_{GS(OFF)}$, or *pinch-off voltage* (V_p). The value of V_p is negative for an *n*-channel JFET and positive for a *p*-channel JFET. V_p can be compared to V_T for the depletion mode MOSFET.

6.3.2 JFET Transfer Characteristics

The transfer characteristic is a plot of the drain current, i_D, as a function of drain-to-source voltage, v_{DS}, with v_{GS} equal to a set of constant voltages (v_{GS} = -3V, -2, -1V, 0V in Figure 6.16(a)). The transfer characteristic is nearly independent of the value of v_{DS} since after the JFET reaches pinch-off, i_D remains relatively constant for increasing values of v_{DS}. This can be seen from the i_D-v_{DS} curves of Figure 6.16, where each curve becomes approximately flat for values of $v_{DS}>V_p$.

In Figure 6.17, we show the transfer characteristics and the i_D-v_{DS} characteristics for an *n*-channel JFET. We plot these with a common i_D axis to show how to obtain one from the other. The transfer characteristics can be obtained from an extension of the i_D-v_{DS} curves as shown by the dashed lines in Figure 6.17. The most useful method of determining the transfer characteristic in the saturation region is with the following relationship (the Shockley equation):

$$\frac{i_D}{I_{DSS}} \approx \left(1 - \frac{v_{GS}}{V_P}\right)^2 \tag{6.16}$$

Hence, we need only know I_{DSS} and V_p to determine the entire characteristic. Manufacturers' data sheets often give these two parameters, so the transfer characteristic can be constructed. V_p in the manufacturer's specification sheet is shown as $V_{GS(OFF)}$. Note that i_D saturates, (i.e., becomes constant) as v_{DS} exceeds the voltage necessary for the channel to pinch off. This can be expressed as an equation for $v_{DS,sat}$ for *each* curve, as follows:

$$v_{DS,sat} = v_{GS} - V_p \tag{6.17}$$

As v_{GS} becomes more negative, the pinch-off occurs at lower values of v_{DS} and the saturation current becomes smaller. The useful region for linear operation is above pinch-off and below the breakdown voltage. In this region, i_D is saturated and its value depends upon v_{GS}, according to Equation (6.16) or the transfer characteristic.

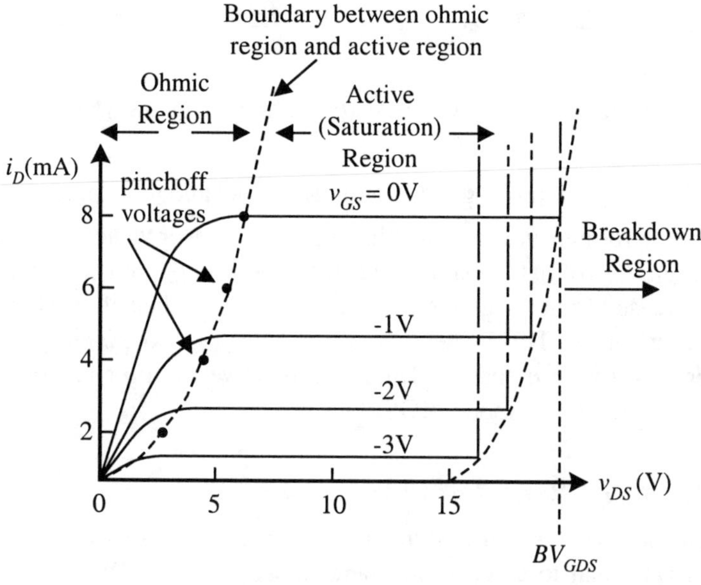

Figure 6.17 – JFET transfer characteristics curves

The transfer and i_D-v_{DS} characteristic curves for the JFET, which are shown in Figure 6.17, differ from the corresponding curves for a BJT. The BJT curves can be represented as evenly spaced for uniform steps in base current because of the linear relationship between i_C and i_B. The JFET and MOSFET have no current analogous to a base current because the gate currents are zero. Therefore, we are forced to show the family of curves i_D vs. v_{DS}, and the relationships are very nonlinear.

The second difference relates to the size and shape of the ohmic region of the characteristic curves. Recall that in using BJTs, we avoid nonlinear operation by avoiding the lower 5% of values of v_{CE} (i.e., the *saturation region).* We see that the width of the ohmic region for the JFET is a function of the gate-to-source voltage. The ohmic region is quite linear until the knee occurs close to pinch off. This region is called the *ohmic region* because when the transistor is used in this region, it behaves like an ohmic resistor whose value is determined by the value of v_{GS}. As the magnitude of the gate-to-source voltage decreases, the width of the ohmic region increases. We also note from Figure 6.17 that the breakdown voltage is a function of the gate-to-source voltage. In fact, to obtain reasonably linear signal amplification, we must utilize only a relatively small segment of these curves – the area of linear operation is in the active region.

As v_{DS} increases from zero, a break point occurs on each curve beyond which the drain current increases very little as v_{DS} continues to increase. At this value of drain-to-source voltage, pinch-off occurs. The pinch-off values are labeled in Figure 6.17 and are connected with a dashed curve that separates the ohmic region from the active region. As v_{DS} continues to increase beyond pinch-off, a point is reached where the voltage between drain and source becomes so large that *avalanche breakdown* occurs. (This phenomenon also occurs in diodes and in BJTs). At the breakdown point, i_D increases sharply with a negligible increase in v_{DS}. This breakdown occurs at the drain end of the gate-channel junction. Hence, when the drain-gate voltage, v_{DG}, exceeds the breakdown voltage (BV_{GDS} for the *pn* junction), avalanche occurs [for $v_{GS} = 0$ V]. At this point, the i_D-v_{DS} characteristic exhibits the peculiar shape shown on the right part of Figure 6.17.

The region between the pinch-off voltage and avalanche breakdown is called the *active region, amplifier operating region, saturation region*, or *pinch-off region.* The ohmic region (before pinch-off) is usually called the *triode region*, but it is sometimes called the *voltage-controlled region.* The JFET is operated in the ohmic region both when a variable resistor is desired and in switching applications.

The breakdown voltage is a function of v_{GS} as well as v_{DS}. As the magnitude of the voltage between gate and source is increased (more negative for *n*-channel and more positive for *p*-channel), the breakdown voltage decreases (see Figure 6.17). With $v_{GS} = V_p$, the drain current is zero (except for a small leakage current), and with $v_{GS} = 0$, the drain current saturates at a value,

$$i_D(v_{DS})\Big|_{v_{GS}=0\text{V}} = I_{DSS} \tag{6.18}$$

I_{DSS} is the *saturation drain-to-source current.*

Between pinch-off and breakdown, the drain current is saturated and does not change appreciably as a function of v_{DS}. After the JFET passes the pinch-off operating point, the value of i_D can be obtained from the characteristic curves or from the equation

$$i_D \approx I_{DSS}\left(1 - \frac{v_{GS}}{V_p}\right)^2 \tag{6.19}$$

A more accurate version of this equation (taking into account the slight slope of the characteristic curves) is as follows:

$$i_D = I_{DSS}\left(1 - \frac{v_{GS}}{V_p}\right)^2 (1 + \lambda v_{DS}) \tag{6.20}$$

λ is analogous to the λ for MOSFETs, and to $1/V_A$ for BJTs. Since λ is small, we assume that $|\lambda\, v_{DS}| \ll 1$. This justifies omitting the second factor in the equation and using the approximation for biasing and large signal analysis.

The saturation drain-to-source current, I_{DSS}, is a function of temperature. The effects of temperature upon V_p are not large. However, I_{DSS} decreases as temperature increases, the decrease being as much as 25% for a 100° increase in temperature. Even larger variations occur in V_p and I_{DSS} because of slight variations in the manufacturing process. This can be seen by viewing the Appendix for the 2N3822 where the maximum I_{DSS} is 10 mA and the minimum is 2 mA.

The currents and voltages in this section are presented for an *n*-channel JFET. The values for a *p*-channel JFET are the reverse of those given for the *n*-channel.

6.3.3 JFET Small-Signal ac Model

A JFET small-signal model can be derived following the same procedures used for the MOSFET. The model is based on the relationship of Equation (6.20). If we consider only the *ac* component of the voltages and currents, we have

$$i_d = g_m v_{gs} + \frac{v_{ds}}{ro} \tag{6.21}$$

The parameters in Equation (6.21) are given by the partial derivatives,

$$g_m = \frac{\partial i_d}{\partial v_{gs}} = -\frac{2I_{DSS}}{V_p}\left(1 - \frac{V_{GS}}{V_P}\right)(1 + \lambda V_{DS})$$

$$r_o = \frac{\partial v_{ds}}{\partial i_d} = \frac{1}{I_{DSS}\left(1 - \frac{V_{GS}}{V_P}\right)^2 \lambda} \tag{6.22}$$

The resulting model is shown in Figure 6.18. Note that the model is identical to the MOSFET model derived previously, except that the values of g_m and r_o are calculated using different formulae. Actually the formulas are identical if V_p is substituted for V_T.

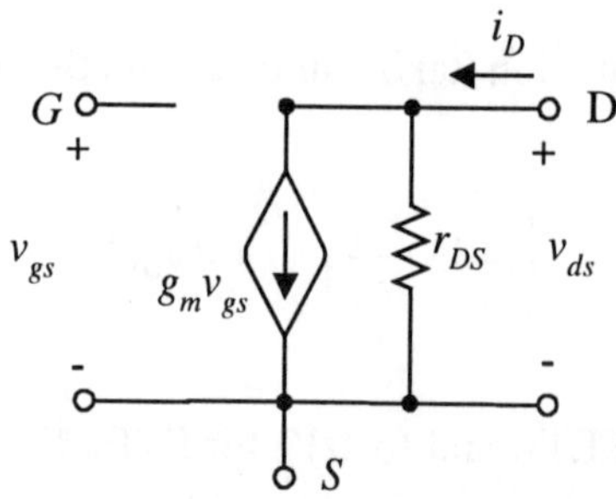

Figure 6.18 - JFET small signal *ac* model

Example 6.5:

Determine g_m for an n-channel JFET with characteristic curve shown in Figure 6.19.

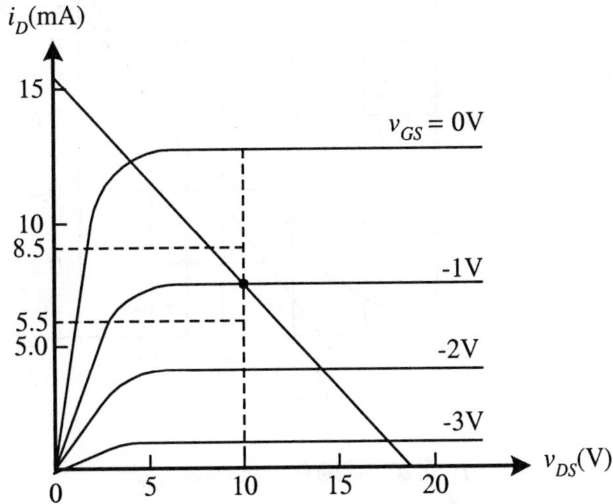

Figure 6.19 – i_D versus v_{DS} JFET characteristic curves

Solution: We select an operating region which is approximately in the middle of the curves; that is, between v_{GS} = -0.8 V and v_{GS} = -1.2 V; i_D = 8.5 mA and i_D = 5.5 mA. Now from Equation (6.22), we find

$$g_m = \left.\frac{\Delta i_D}{\Delta v_{GS}}\right|_{v_{GS}=constant} = 7.5 \quad m\Omega^{-1}$$

To design a JFET amplifier, the Q-point for the *dc* bias current can be determined either graphically, or by using circuit analysis assuming pinch-off mode for the transistor. The *dc* bias current at the Q-point should lie between 30% and 70% of I_{DSS}. This locates the Q-point in the most linear region of the characteristic curves.

The relationship between i_D and v_{GS} can be plotted on a dimensionless graph (i.e., a normalized curve) as shown in Figure 6.20.

The vertical axis of this graph is i_D/I_{DSS} and the horizontal axis is v_{GS}/V_p. The slope of the curve is g_m.

A reasonable procedure for locating the quiescent value near the center of the linear operating region is to select $I_{DQ} \approx I_{DSS}/2$ and $V_{GSQ} \approx 0.3V_p$. Note from Figure 6.20 that this is near the midpoint of the curve. Next, we select $V_{DS} \approx V_{DD}/2$. This gives a wide range of values for v_{ds} that keep the transistor in the pinch-off mode.

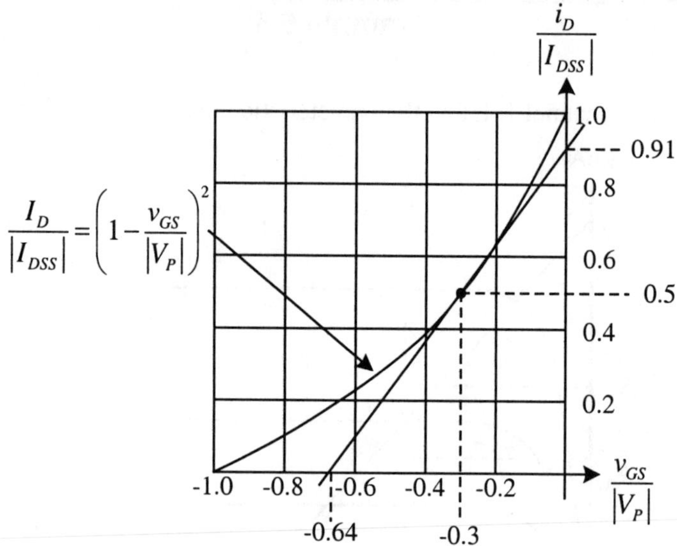

Figure 6.20 – i_D/I_{DSS} versus v_{GS}/V_p

We can find the transconductance at the Q-point either from the slope of the curve of Figure 6.20 or by using Equation (6.22). If we use this procedure, the transconductance parameter is given by,

$$g_m = 1.41\frac{I_{DSS}}{|V_p|} \tag{6.23}$$

Remember that this value of g_m depends on the assumption that I_D is set at one-half I_{DSS} and V_{GS} . $0.3V_p$. These values usually represent a good starting point for setting the quiescent values for the JFET.

Example 6.6

Determine g_m for a JFET where $I_{DSS} = 7$ mA, $V_p = -3.5$ V and $V_{DD} = 15$ V. Choose a reasonable location for the Q-point.

Solution: We start by referring to Figure 6.19 and selecting the Q-point, as follows:

$$I_{DQ} = \frac{I_{DSS}}{2} = 3.5 \quad \text{mA}$$

$$V_{DSQ} = \frac{V_{DD}}{2} = 7.5 \quad \text{V}$$

$$V_{GSQ} = 0.3V_p = -1.05 \quad \text{V}$$

The transconductance, g_m, is found from the slope of the curve at the point $i_D/I_{DSS} = 0.5$ and $v_{GS}/V_p = 0.3$. Hence,

$$g_m = \frac{1.41 I_{DSS}}{V_p} = 2840 \quad \mu\Omega^{-1}$$

Note that these results only apply for the case where I_{DQ} is set at $I_{DSS}/2$.

6.4 FET AMPLIFIER CONFIGURATIONS AND BIASING

The approaches that are used for biasing of BJTs can also be used for biasing MOSFETS. We can separate the approaches into those used for discrete component versus integrated circuit amplifiers. Discrete component designs use the large coupling and bypass capacitors to isolate the *dc* bias for each amplifier stage, much like the discrete component BJT amplifiers. IC MOSFET amplifiers are generally direct coupled because large capacitors are not practical. The IC MOSFET amplifiers are usually biased using *dc* current sources that are analogous to those used for the BJT IC amplifiers.

6.4.1 Discrete-Component MOSFET Biasing

Discrete-component biasing for MOSFET amplifiers is accomplished with the circuits shown in Figure 6.21. The gate-to-source voltage determines the type of circuit which may be required for that transistor configuration. For an enhancement mode transistor, there will always be a need for a positive voltage at the gate. In the voltage division biasing, there will be an R_1 and R_2 in order to obtain the positive voltage. For depletion MOSFETs or JFETs, R_2 can either be finite or infinite, as shown in Figure 6.21(b).

There are four useful amplifier configurations based on the manner in which connections are made to the capacitors shown in Figure 6.32. These configurations are analogous to the BJT amplifier configurations from Chapters 4 and 5.

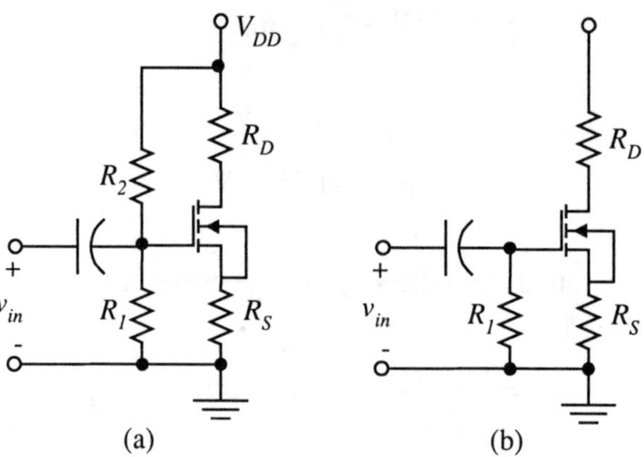

Figure 6.21 - Amplifier biasing configurations

•-**Common Source (CS)** - the *ac* input is applied at C_G, the *ac* output is taken at C_D, and C_S is connected to a *dc* voltage source or ground. This is analogous to the common-emitter configuration for the BJT.

•-**Source Resistor (SR)** - the *ac* input is applied at C_G, the *ac* output is taken at C_D and C_S is omitted. This is analogous to the emitter-resistor configuration for the BJT.

•-**Common Gate (CG)** - the *ac* input is applied at C_S, the *ac* output is taken at C_D and C_G is connected to a *dc* voltage source or ground. Sometimes in the CG configuration, C_G is omitted and the gate is connected directly to a *dc* voltage supply. The CG is analogous to the common base configuration for the BJT, although it is seldom seen in circuits.

•-**Source Follower (SF)** - the *ac* input is applied at C_G, the *ac* output is taken at C_S and the drain is either connected to a *dc* voltage supply directly or via C_D. This is sometimes called common drain (CD) and is analogous to the emitter follower configuration for the BJT.

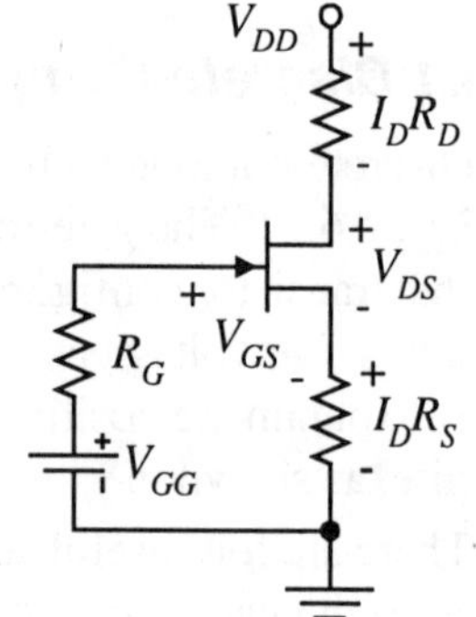

Figure 6.22 – Thevenin equivalent circuit

Each of these configurations is studied in more detail in Section 6.9.

Since the different configurations only vary in their connections via the capacitors, and the capacitors are open circuits to *dc* voltages and currents, we can study the *dc* bias for the general case. For amplifier design, we want the transistor to operate in the active operating region (also identified as the saturation region or pinch-off mode), so we assume the pinch-off I-V characteristic for the device. (We should always verify this assumption at the end of the design!)

To simplify the bias analysis, we use a Thevenin source to model the circuit at the gate of the transistor as shown in Figure 6.22.

$$R_G = R_1 \| R_2 = \frac{R_1 R_2}{R_1 + R_2}$$

$$V_{GG} = \frac{V_{DD} R_1}{R_1 + R_2} \tag{6.24}$$

Since there are three unknown variables to set for biasing (I_D, V_{GS}, and V_{DS}), we need three *dc* equations. First, the *dc* equation around the gate-source loop is written.

$$V_{GG} = V_{GS} + I_{DQ} R_S \tag{6.25}$$

Notice that since the gate current is zero, a zero voltage drop exists across R_G. A second *dc* equation is found from the Kirchhoff's law equation in the drain-source loop.

$$V_{DD} = V_{DS} + I_{DQ}(R_S + R_D) \tag{6.26}$$

The third *dc* equation necessary to establish the bias point is found from Equation (6.20) which is repeated here.

$$I_{DQ} = K\left(V_{GSQ} - V_T\right)^2\left(1 + \lambda V_{DSQ}\right) = I_{DSS}\left(1 - \frac{V_{GSQ}}{V_T}\right)^2\left(1 + \lambda V_{DSQ}\right)$$

$$\approx K(V_{GSQ} - V_T)^2 \approx KV_T^2\left(1 - \frac{V_{GSQ}}{V_T}\right)^2 = I_{DSS}\left(1 - \frac{V_{GSQ}}{V_T}\right)^2 \tag{6.27}$$

The first approximation applies if $|\lambda V_{DS}| << 1$ (which is nearly always true) and simplifies the solution of the coupled equations considerably.

We can put the equation for g_m [Equation (6.22)] into a similar format that will prove useful in design.

$$g_m\Big|_{\text{At the Q-point}} = 2K\left(V_{GSQ} - V_T\right)\left(1 + \lambda V_{DSQ}\right) \approx -\frac{2KV_T^2}{V_T}\left(1 - \frac{V_{GSQ}}{V_T}\right)$$

$$= -\frac{2I_{DSS}}{V_T}\left(1 - \frac{V_{GSQ}}{V_T}\right) \tag{6.28}$$

Equations (6.25)-(6.28) are sufficient to establish the bias. For discrete MOSFET amplifiers, we do not need to put the Q-point in the center of the *ac* load line as we often did for BJT biasing. This is because discrete FET amplifiers are normally used as the first stage in an amplifier chain to take advantage of the high input resistance. When used as a first stage or *preamplifier*, the voltage levels are so small that we do not drive the output of the preamplifier over large excursions.

6.5 MOSFET INTEGRATED CIRCUITS

When MOSFET transistors are fabricated as part of an integrated circuit, practical considerations require two major changes in circuit configurations. First, the large coupling and bypass capacitors used in discrete amplifiers cannot practically be fabricated in integrated circuits because of the small size. We get around this shortcoming by fabricating direct-coupled amplifiers.

The second major change is that we cannot easily fabricate the resistors used as part of the bias circuitry. Instead, we use active loads and current sources comprised of MOS transistors.

Integrated circuits use both NMOS and PMOS circuitry. CMOS is more common in digital circuitry, while NMOS is typically used for higher density ICs (i.e., more functions per chip).

Simulating active loads takes advantage of the slope of the MOS characteristic curves. Figure 6.23 shows two types of active loads. In Figure 6.23(a), we show an NMOS enhancement load, while 6.23(b) shows an NMOS depletion load. Also shown in the figure are the relevant characteristic curves.

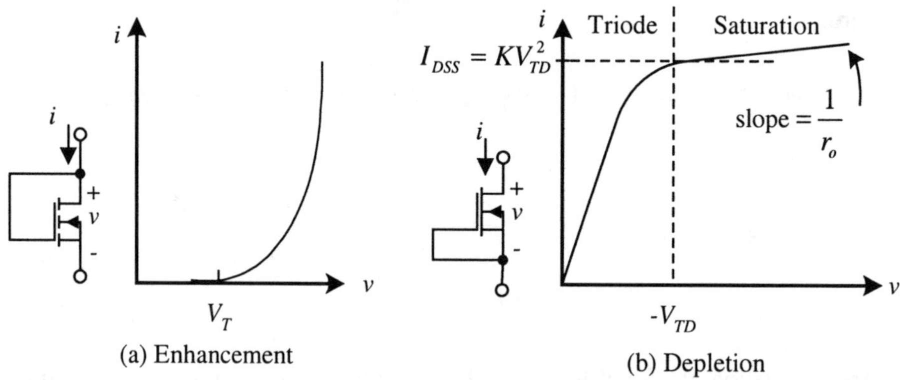

Figure 6.23 – Active loads

For the NMOS enhancement load, the relationship between voltage and current is given by

$$i = K(v - V_{TD})^2 \qquad (\text{for } v \geq V_{TD}) \tag{6.29}$$

The equivalent resistance of this configuration is $1/g_m$, where the value of the transconductance is that which applies at the bias point.

The NMOS depletion load has an equivalent resistance which is determined by the slope of the characteristic given by the following equation:

$$i_D = K\left(v_{GS} - V_T\right)^2\left(1 + \lambda v_{DS}\right) \quad \text{(saturated region)}$$

$$\approx K\left(v_{GS} - V_T\right)^2\Big|_{\text{with gate shorted to source}} \cong KV_{TD}^2\left(1 + \frac{v}{V_A}\right) = I_{DSS}\left(1 + \frac{v}{V_A}\right) \tag{6.30}$$

6.5.1 Biasing of MOSFET Integrated Circuits

Now that we have two techniques to simulate active loads, we can address the biasing issue. We use the active load in place of the load resistance in any of the circuit configurations. To show the technique for analyzing these, let us consider the NMOS amplifier using an enhancement load, as shown in Figure 6.24.

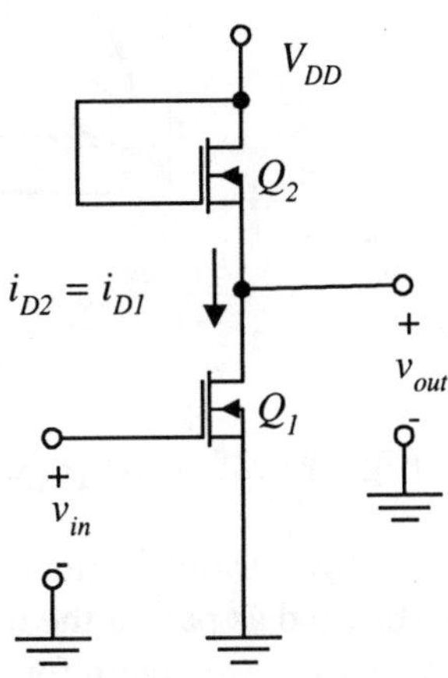

Figure 6.24 – NMOS amplifier with enhancement load

The transistor labeled Q_2 replaces R_D of our earlier circuitry. To determine the quiescent operating point, we use the same techniques as we did in Section 6.4, only substituting the enhancement load graphical characteristic for the resistor load line. That is, we need to find the simultaneous solution of the FET transistor characteristics with the equation for the load line. We can do this graphically as shown in Figure 6.25.

The parametric curves are the characteristic curves for the amplifying transistor, Q_1. The voltage vs. current characteristic of the active load, Q_2 are those of Figure 6.23. The output voltage, v_{out}, is the difference between V_{DD} and the voltage across the active load. The current in the active load is the same as the drain current in the amplifying transistor. We therefore construct the load line by taking the shifted mirror image of the characteristic of Figure 6.23. The operating point is the intersection of this curve with the appropriate transistor characteristic curve. We need to find the gate-to-source voltage to know which transistor curve to choose. As we will see next, the input bias voltage is often replaced by an active current source.

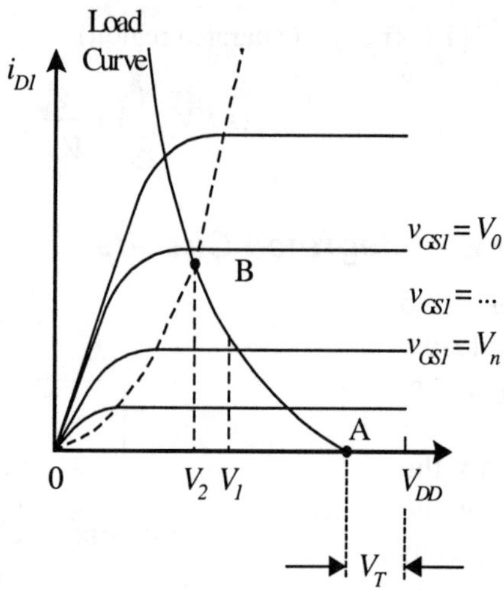

Figure 6.25 – Graphical solution for the Q-point

Now that we know how to simulate an active load, we turn our attention to the generation of a reference current to be used as part of the input bias circuitry. These current sources are used in much the same way that we used them for BJT amplifier biasing.

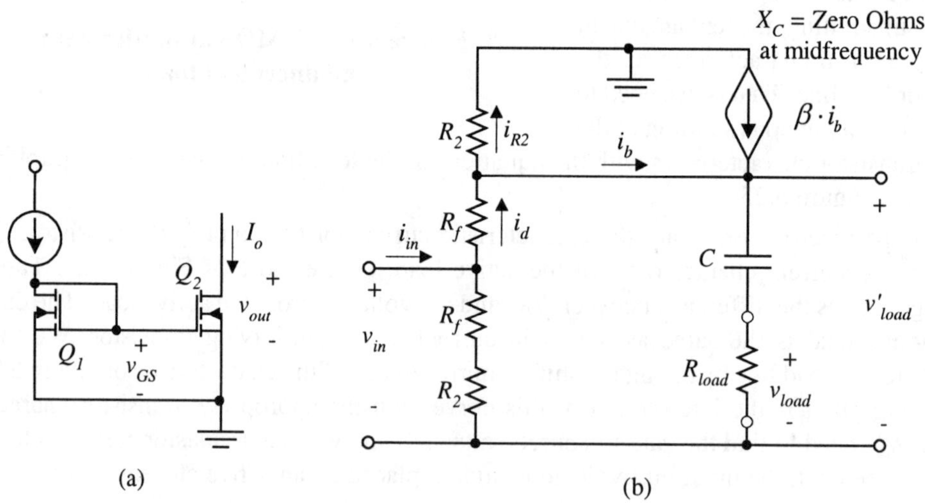

Figure 6.26 – Current mirror

We analyze the MOSFET *current mirror*. A current mirror is shown in Figure 6.26. This should be compared to the current mirror introduced in Section 5.10.4. The two transistors are assumed to be perfectly matched. The output current is the drain current of Q_2, and a reference current drives Q_1. If the transistors are perfectly matched, the output current will exactly equal the reference current. This is true since the transistors are connected in parallel. Just as was the case with the BJT current mirror, the reference current can be generated by applying a reference voltage across a reference resistance, as shown in Figure 6.26(b).

Putting the various subcircuits together (i.e., the active load and the reference current) results in the CMOS amplifier of Figure 6.27.

The gain of this amplifier is given by

$$A_v = \frac{v_{out}}{v_{in}} = g_{m1}\left(r_{O1} \| r_{O2}\right) \tag{6.31}$$

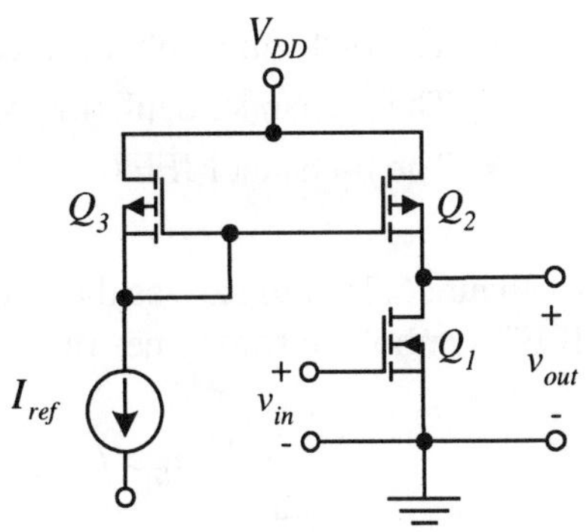

Figure 6.27 – CMOS amplifier

6.5.2 Body Effect

Our discussion of Section 6.2 referred to the substrate (or body) of the MOSFET. This substrate plays an important role in establishing the channel. In the operation of discrete MOSFETs, the body is often connected to the power source. In such cases, the substrate has no direct effect on the operation of the device, and the curves developed earlier in this chapter apply.

The situation changes when MOSFETs are fabricated as part of integrated circuits. In such cases, the substrate of each individual transistor is not isolated from other substrates. Indeed, a substrate is often shared among all of the MOSFETs on a chip. In a PMOS IC, the shared substrate would be connected to the most positive source terminal, while in NMOS it is connected to ground (or to a negative supply if present). This establishes a reverse bias between the source and the body of each transistor. The effect of this reverse bias is to change the operating characteristics. For example, in an *n*-channel device, it effectively raises the threshold (V_T). The amount by which the threshold changes depends on physical parameters and the device construction. For NMOS, this change can be approximated by

$$\Delta V_T = \gamma\left(\sqrt{2\phi_F + V_{SB}} - \sqrt{2\phi_F}\right) \tag{6.32}$$

In Equation (6.32), γ is a device parameter which varies between about 0.3 and 1 ($V^{-1/2}$). V_{SB} is the source-to-body voltage, and ϕ_F is the *Fermi potential*. This is a property of the material, and a typical value is 0.3 V for silicon.

6.6 COMPARISON OF MOSFET TO JFET

Before we see how to use the FET in an amplifier configuration, we pause to examine the essential similarity between the two broad classes of FET. We have considered the MOSFET in Section 6.2 and the JFET in Section 6.4. Within each class are the *n*-channel and *p*-channel devices. The MOSFET classification is further subdivided into enhancement and depletion transistors. These combinations lead to six possible types of devices:

- The *n*-channel enhancement MOSFET (enhancement NMOS)
- The *n*-channel depletion MOSFET (depletion NMOS)
- The *n*-channel JFET

- The p-channel enhancement MOSFET (enhancement PMOS)
- The p-channel depletion MOSFET (depletion PMOS)
- The p-channel JFET

Figure 6.28 summarizes the circuit symbols for these six types of devices. The arrows in the JFET symbol are sometimes moved to the Source terminal.

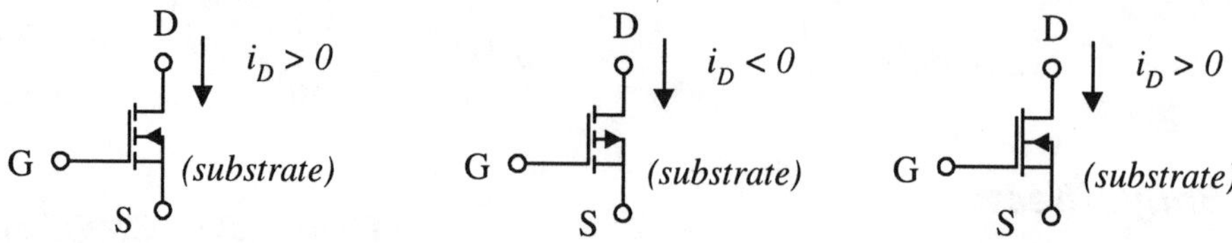

n-channel enhancement mode MOSFET   p-channel enhancement mode MOSFET   n-channel depletion mode MOSFET

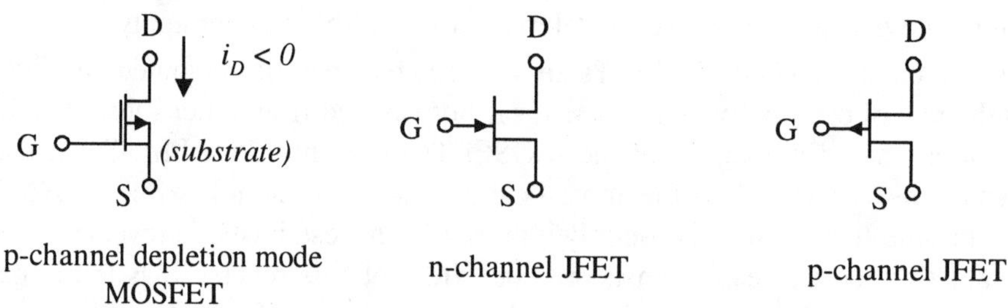

p-channel depletion mode MOSFET   n-channel JFET   p-channel JFET

Figure 6.28 - Circuit symbols for FETs

A channel is created and the transistor is ON when the gate-to-source voltage breaks the threshold voltage (V_T for MOSFETs and V_p for JFETs). For the three n-channel devices, the channel is created when

$$v_{GS} > threshold \tag{6.33}$$

Alternatively, for the p-channel devices, the channel is created when

$$v_{GS} < threshold \tag{6.34}$$

The threshold is positive for the enhancement NMOS, the depletion PMOS, and the p-channel JFET. It is negative for the depletion NMOS, the enhancement PMOS, and the n-channel JFET.

In order for the transistor to operate in the *triode region*, the drain-to-source voltage must obey the following inequalities:

For n-channel MOSFETs or JFETs,

$$v_{DS} \leq v_{GS} - threshold \tag{6.35}$$

For *p*-channel MOSFETs or JFETs, the opposite is true. That is, to operate in the triode region,

$$v_{DS} \geq v_{GS} - threshold \tag{6.36}$$

In either case, if the inequality is not obeyed, the transistor operates in the saturation region when it is on. These relationships are summarized in Table 6.1.

Type	Sign of V_T	Channel created when	Triode region exists if
Enhancement NMOS	+	$v_{GS} > V_T$	$v_{DS} \leq v_{GS} - V_T$
Depletion NMOS	-	$v_{GS} > V_T$	$v_{DS} \leq v_{GS} - V_T$
n-channel JFET	-	$v_{GS} > V_p$	$v_{DS} \leq v_{GS} - V_p$
Enhancement PMOS	-	$v_{GS} < V_T$	$v_{DS} \geq v_{GS} - V_T$
Depletion PMOS	+	$v_{GS} < V_T$	$v_{DS} \geq v_{GS} - V_T$
p-channel JFET	+	$v_{GS} < V_p$	$v_{DS} \geq v_{GS} - V_p$

Table 6.1 - FET Relationships

We now show the similarity in the equations for drain current for the MOSFET and JFET. In the saturation region, the drain current for the MOSFET is [Equation (6.8)],

$$i_D = K(v_{GS} - V_T)^2(1 + \lambda v_{DS}) \tag{6.37}$$

where K is given by,

$$K = \frac{1}{2}\mu_n C_{oxide}\frac{W}{L}$$

In the case of the JFET, the equivalent is Equation (6.20).

$$\begin{aligned} i_D &= I_{DSS}\left(1 - \frac{v_{GS}}{V_p}\right)^2(1 + \lambda v_{DS}) \\ &= \frac{I_{DSS}}{V_p^2}(v_{GS} - V_p)^2(1 + \lambda v_{DS}) \end{aligned} \tag{6.38}$$

This is identical to the equation for the MOSFET if we set V_T equal to V_p, and equate the constants,

$$K = \frac{I_{DSS}}{V_p^2} \tag{6.39}$$

The same equivalence is true for the triode region. We presented the drain current equation for the MOSFET [see Equation (6.4)]

$$i_D = K\left[2\left(v_{GS} - V_T\right)v_{DS} - v_{DS}^2\right] \tag{6.40}$$

This identical equation holds for the JFET with the substitution of V_p for V_T, and the value of K given in Equation (6.39).

In summary, the only difference in the equations for the MOSFET and JFET are the values of the constant K, and the fact that the threshold voltage in the MOSFET is equivalent to the pinch-off voltage in the JFET.

6.7 FET MODELS FOR COMPUTER SIMULATIONS

SPICE and MICRO-CAP contain sophisticated models for JFETs and MOSFETs. The JFET model (the SPICE 2G.6 model) contains 12 parameters. The MOSFET SPICE model contains 42 parameters in three levels. The lowest level model contains 25 parameters, while higher-order models add to this list. MICRO-CAP additional 10 parameters to the MOSFET model to bring the total to 52. The more parameters the model uses, the closer the simulation results are to the actual device operation. However, the more parameters in the model, the slower the simulation runs.

The reason there are so many parameters is that the model attempts to closely imitate the nonlinear operating curves of the device. The computer is capable of tracking far more details than we can by hand, so the model can be more sophisticated than that we use for a "paper" solution. In many analysis situations, you would set most of the model parameters to their default values and this complex model behaves almost the same as the simplified models we have discussed. While we discuss SPICE in an Appendix of this text, we will now quickly review the syntax for including a JFET or MOSFET in a circuit. The SPICE statement for a JFET is of the form,

Jname nd ng ns modelname [area] [OFF] [IC=vds[,vgs]]

Square brackets indicate that the quantity is optional. As an example, you might include statements,

J1 10 11 12 U308 1.5 OFF IC=25.0,8.0
.MODEL U308 NJF (VTO=-4, BETA= 0.000375)

The 10, 11 and 12 in the first statement are the node numbers for the drain, gate, and source. U308 is the model name. The area, which defaults to unity, multiplies or divides parameters for the model. The "OFF" instruction turns the JFET off for the first operating point. The "IC" sets initial conditions for the drain-to-source and gate-to-source voltages. The initial conditions are only used for transient analysis. The second statement is used to define the device having name U308 as an n-channel JFET with V_p (VTO) set to –4V and K(BETA) equal to $K = I_{DSS}/V_P^2$. For a *p*-channel JFET use the designator PJF instead of NJF and set the parameters VTO and BETA to match the *p*-channel parameters.

The following table lists the 12 parameters in the computer simulation model. It also shows the default value and units for each parameter.

SYMBOL	NAME	DEFAULT	UNITS
VTO	Threshold voltage	-2.0	V
BETA	Transconductance parameter	1E-4	A/V^2
LAMBDA	Channel-length modulation	0	V^{-1}
RD	Drain ohmic resistance	0	Ω
RS	Source ohmic resistance	0	Ω
CGS	Zero-bias gate-source junction capacitance	0	F
CGD	Zero-bias gate-drain junction capacitance	0	F
PB	Gate-junction potential	1	V
IS	Gate-junction saturation current	1E-14	A
FC	Forward-bias depletion coefficient	0.5	
KF	Flicker-noise coefficient	0	
AF	Flicker-noise exponent	1	

Table 6.2 - SPICE JFET Parameters

The model associated with these parameters is shown in Figure 6.29.

The SPICE MOSFET model is considerably more complex than that of the JFET. The lowest level (*level 1*) model contains 25 parameters which are detailed in Table 6.3. The SPICE statement is of the form:

Mname nd ng ns nb modelname
+[L=length][W=width][AD=drainarea][AS=sourcearea]
+[PD=drainperiphery][PD=sourceperiphery][NRD=drainsquares]
+[NRS=sourcesquares][NRG=gatesquares][NRB=bulksquares]
+[OFF][IC=vds][,vgs[,vbs]]]

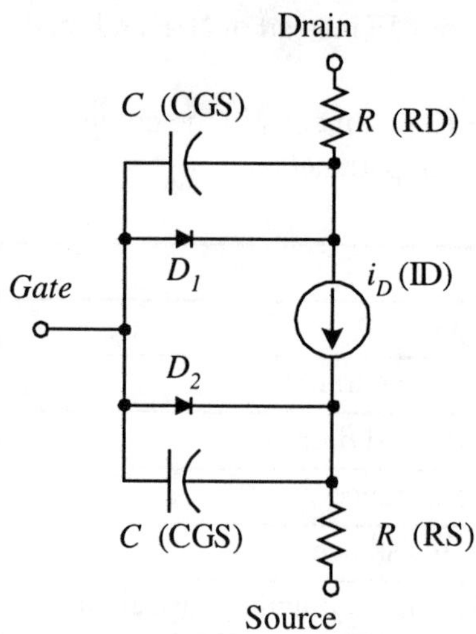

Figure 6.29 – JFET transistor model

Square brackets indicate that the quantity is optional. As an example, you might include a statement,

```
M1 1 2 3 0 MOSFET
.MODEL MOSFET NMOS(VTO = -4, KP = 0.00075)
```

D
node 2 node 1 $V_T = -4\text{V}$
G
node 3 $I_{DSS} = 6\text{mA}$
MOSFET
S

This example specifies node numbers 1,2,3 and 0 for the drain, gate, source, and body of the device. Note that KP = $2K$ (= $2I_{DSS}/V_P^2$). Use PMOS for *p*-channel instead of NMOS in the second statement.

SYMBOL	NAME	DEFAULT	UNITS
LD	Lateral diffusion (length)	0	m
KP	Process transconductance	2E-5	A/V^2
VTO	Zero-bias threshold voltage	0	V
GAMMA	Body-effect coefficient	0	$V^{1/2}$
PHI	Surface inversion potential	0.6	V
LAMBDA	Channel-length modulation	0	V^{-1}
RD	Drain ohmic resistance	0	Ω
RS	Source ohmic resistance	0	Ω
RSH	Source and drain sheet resistance	0	Ω/sq
CGDO	Gate-drain overlap capacitance	0	F/m
CGSO	Gate-source overlap capacitance	0	F/m

CGBO	Gate-bulk overlap capacitance	0	F/m
CBD	Bulk *p-n* zero-bias B-D capacitance	0	F
CBS	Bulk *p-n* zero-bias B-S capacitance	0	F
CJ	Bulk *p-n* zero-bias bottom capacitance	0	F/m^2
CJSW	Bulk *p-n* zero-bias sidewall capacitance	0	F/m
MJ	Bulk *p-n* zero-bias bottom grading coefficient	0.5	
MJSW	Bulk *p-n* zero-bias sidewall grading coefficient	0.33	
IS	Bulk *p-n* saturation current	1E-14	A
JS	Bulk *p-n* bottom current density	1E-8	A/m^2
PB	Bulk *p-n* bottom potential	0.8	V
TOX	Thin oxide thickness	1E-7	m
KF	Flicker-noise coefficient	0	
AF	Flicker-noise exponent	1	
FC	Forward-bias depletion coefficient	0.5	

Table 6.3 - MOSFET parameters

The parameters, their default values and units, are given in Table 6.3. The model associated with these parameters is shown in Figure 6.30.

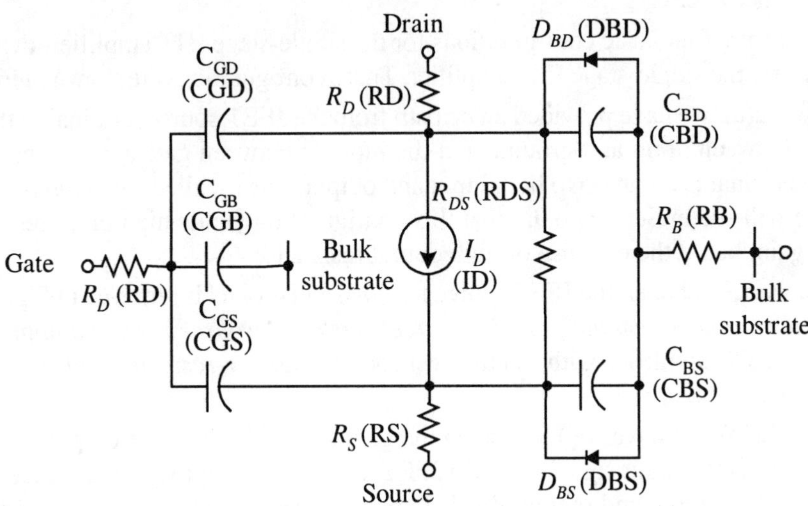

Figure 6.30 – MOSFET transistor model

6.8 FET AMPLIFIERS - CANONICAL CONFIGURATIONS

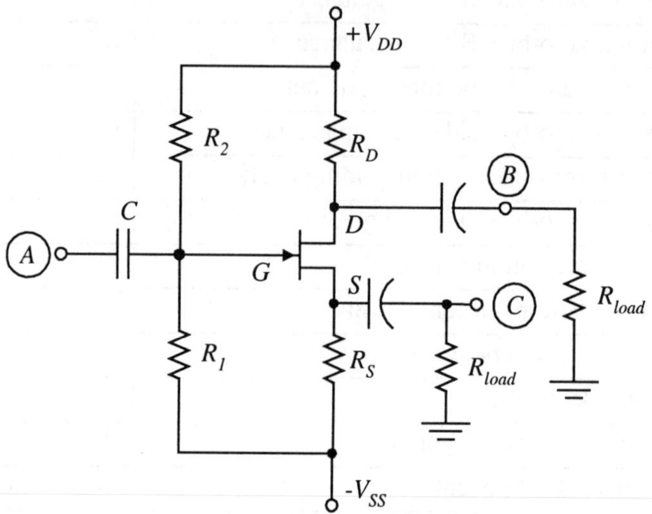

Figure 6.31 – FET amplifier – general configuration

Figure 6.31 shows a general configuration for an FET amplifier. In this figure, we show the symbol for an n-channel JFET, but the configuration applies to other FET devices depending on the sign of the sources. The output (load) is connected to either point B or C, and the input is connected to either A or C.

Just as there were four basic configurations for the single-stage BJT amplifier, there are four configurations for the single-stage FET amplifier. These configurations are shown in Figure 6.32.

In Figure 6.32(a), we have provided an *ac* path from the JFET source terminal to the ground. The output is between drain and ground, and the input is between gate and ground. Since the JFET source terminal is common to both input and output, this is called a *common-source (CS)* amplifier. We will see in Section 6.9.1 that this configuration yields high input resistance and high voltage gain, but at the expense of high output resistance.

If the capacitance between the JFET source terminal and ground is removed in Figure 6.32(a), we have the *common-source amplifier with source resistor* (or *source-resistor amplifier*). This is analogous to the CE amplifier with emitter resistor (the *emitter-resistor amplifier*) which we discussed in Section 5.2.

In Figure 6.32(b), we have (*ac*) grounded the gate terminal, taken the output from drain to ground, and applied the input signal between JFET source terminal to ground. Since the gate is (*ac*) common to both input and output, this is known as the *common-gate (CG)* amplifier. We will see in Section 6.9.2 that this configuration provides high voltage gain and low output resistance, but at the expense of low input resistance. Because of the low input resistance, this configuration is often used as a current amplifier with a current gain close to unity (e.g., to isolate signals).

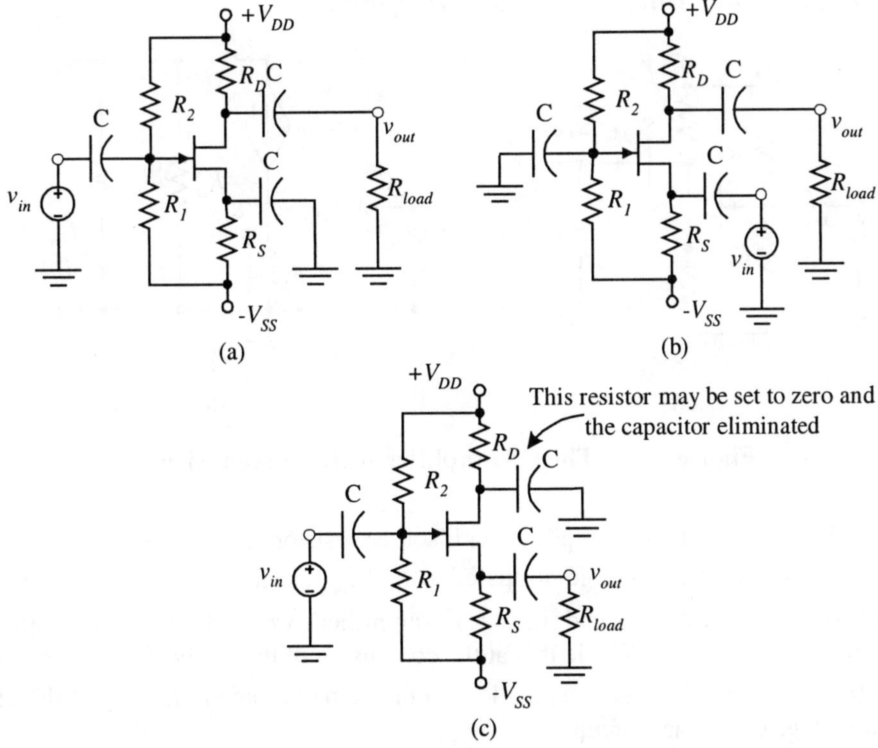

Figure 6.32 – FET single-stage amplifier configurations

Finally, Figure 6.32(c) shows a configuration with the drain grounded (*ac*), the signal input from gate to ground, and the output from the JFET source terminal to ground. Since the drain is common (*ac*) to both input and output, this is known as a *common-drain (CD)* configuration. Alternatively, it is called a *source follower (SF)* because of the way it operates. We shall see in Section 6.9.3 that the voltage gain is close to unity with low output resistance and high input resistance. The output (JFET source terminal) therefore "follows" the input, and this configuration is often used as a buffer.

6.9 FET AMPLIFIER ANALYSIS

In the previous section, we defined four basic configurations for FET amplifiers. This section examines each of these configurations, and we derive expressions for the gain (current and voltage), the input resistance and the output resistance.

6.9.1 The CS (and Source Resistor) Amplifier

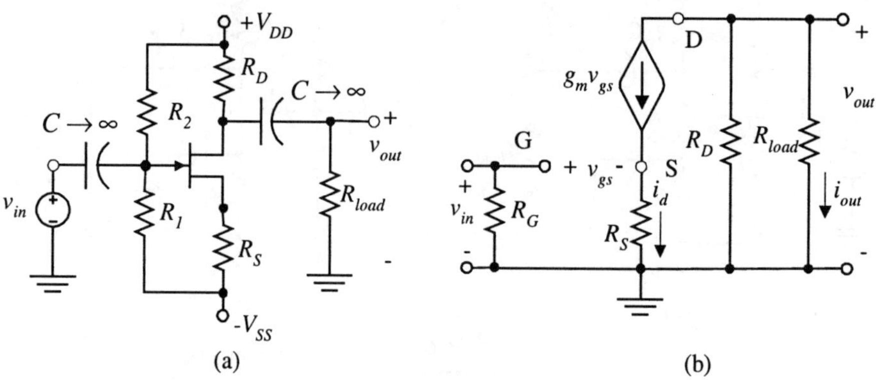

Figure 6.33 - The CS amplifier with source resistor

Figure 6.33(a) shows the CS amplifier with source resistor. The *ac* equivalent circuit is in Figure 6.33(b). We assume r_o is large compared to $R_D \| R_{load}$, so it can be neglected. If a capacitor is present between source and ground (i.e., the CS amplifier), we need simply set R_S equal to zero in the following *ac* equations. We do this at the conclusion of this derivation.

In part (b) of Figure 6.33, R_G is the parallel combination of R_1 and R_2 and V_{GG} is the Thevenin equivalent voltage of the bias circuit:

$$V_{GG} = \frac{V_{DD} R_1}{R_1 + R_2} \tag{6.41}$$

To analyze the *ac* equivalent circuit, we write a KVL equation around the gate circuit.

$$v_{gs} = v_{in} - R_S i_d = v_{in} - R_S g_m v_{gs} \tag{6.42}$$

$$v_{gs} = \frac{v_{in}}{1 + R_S g_m}$$

The output voltage, v_{out}, is given by

$$v_{out} = -i_d (R_D \| R_{load}) = \frac{-(R_D \| R_{load}) g_m v_{in}}{1 + R_S g_m}$$

The voltage gain, A_v, is now found.

$$A_v = \frac{v_{out}}{v_{in}} = \frac{-(R_D \| R_{load})}{R_S + 1/g_m} \tag{6.43}$$

If the source resistance, R_S, is bypassed by a capacitor, we let $R_S = 0$, and the voltage gain increases to

$$A_v = -g_m(R_D \| R_{load}) \tag{6.44}$$

This is typically a large negative number.

The input resistance and current gain are given by

$$R_{in} = R_G = R_1 \| R_2$$

$$A_i = \frac{i_{out}}{i_{in}} = \frac{A_v R_{in}}{R_{load}} = \frac{-R_G}{R_S + 1/g_m} \cdot \frac{R_D}{R_D + R_{load}} \tag{6.45}$$

Example 6.7

Find A_v for the JFET amplifier of Figure 6.34. This is the open-circuit voltage gain since no load resistor is shown. The Q-point is at $V_{DS} = 12$ V and $I_D = 7$ mA. The FET parameters are given by

$$g_m = 3.0 \text{ m}\Omega^{-1}$$
$$r_{DS} = 200 \text{ k}\Omega$$

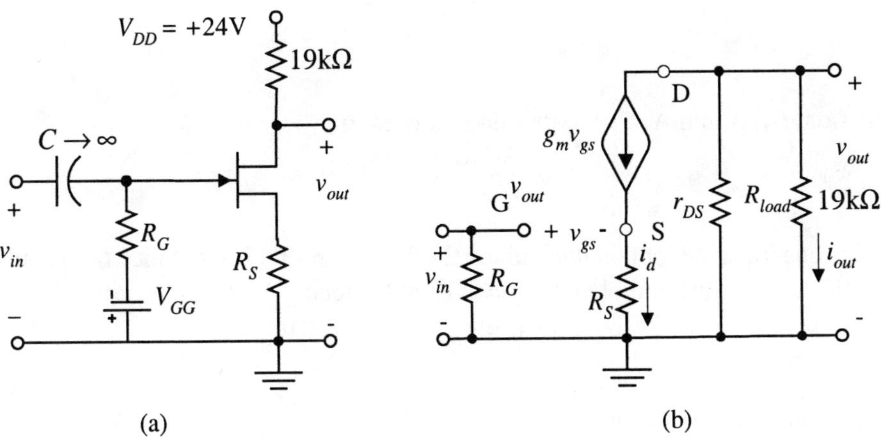

Figure 6.34 – JFET circuit for Example 6.7

Solution: From the equivalent circuit of Figure 6.34, we obtain

$$A_v = \frac{v_{out}}{v_{gs}} = \frac{-i_d(R_D \| r_{DS})}{v_{gs}} = -g_m(R_D \| r_{DS}) = -52$$

Example 6.8

Analyze the single-stage JFET CS amplifier shown in Figure 6.35 and determine A_v, A_i and R_{in}. Assume I_{DSS} = 2 mA and V_p = -2 V.

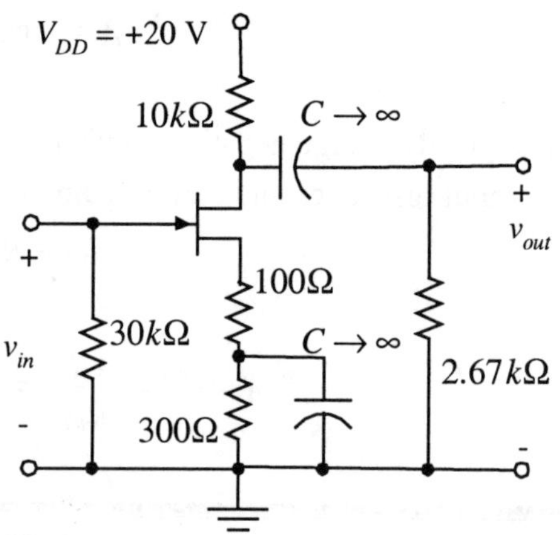

Figure 6.35 – CS amplifier for Example 6.8

Solution: We first determine g_m since both A_v and A_i depend on this parameter. Remember that the value of g_m depends on the Q-point location. We need two equations in order to find I_{DQ} and V_{GSQ}, as follows:

$$V_{GSQ} = -R_S I_{DQ} = -0.4\, I_{DQ}$$

and from equation (6.26),

$$\frac{I_{DQ}}{I_{DSS}} = \left(1 - \frac{V_{GSQ}}{V_p}\right)^2$$

When we combine these two equations, we obtain a quadratic in I_{DQ}.

$$\frac{I_{DQ}}{2} = \left(1 - \frac{-0.4\, I_{DQ}}{-2}\right)^2$$

In this equation, I_{DQ} is in mA. The expression reduces to

$$I_{DQ}^2 - 22.5 I_{DQ} + 25 = 0$$

We solve this quadratic and obtain two values; 21.33 mA and 1.17 mA. Since I_{DSS} is only 2 mA, we discard the larger value and obtain I_{DQ} = 1.17 mA. Hence

$$V_{GSQ} = (-0.4) I_{DQ} = -0.469 \quad \text{V}$$

We use Equation (6.27) to find g_m.

$$g_m = -\frac{2 I_{DSS}}{V_p}\left(1 - \frac{V_{GSQ}}{V_p}\right) = 1.53 \quad \text{m}\Omega^{-1}$$

Then $1/g_m$ = 653 Ω. We now find the voltage gain, input resistance and current gain from Equations (6.43) to (6.45).

$$A_v = -\frac{R_D \| R_{load}}{R_{Sac} + 1/g_m} = -2.8$$

$$R_{in} = 30 \quad k\Omega$$

$$A_i = A_v \frac{R_{in}}{R_{load}} = -31.5$$

Example 6.9

Determine the voltage gain, input resistance and current gain of the circuit shown in Figure 6.36. Assume a MOS transistor with $I_D = 6$ mA when $V_{GS} = 0$ and $V_T = -4$ V.

Solution: We first need to determine g_m and V_{GS} in order to find the Q-point of the transistor. Using KVL, we obtain

$$V_{GS} = -R_S I_D = -0.6 I_D$$

where I_D is in mA.

$$I_D = 6 \text{ mA} \quad \text{when } V_{GS} = 0$$

$$KV_T^2 = 6 \text{ mA} \quad \text{or } I_{DSS} = 6 \text{ mA}$$

From Equation (6.27),

$$I_{DQ} = KV_T^2 \left(1 - \frac{V_{GSQ}}{V_T}\right)^2 = 6\left(1 - \frac{-0.6 I_{DQ}}{-4}\right)^2$$

$$I_{DQ}^2 - 20.8 I_{DQ} + 44.4 = 0$$

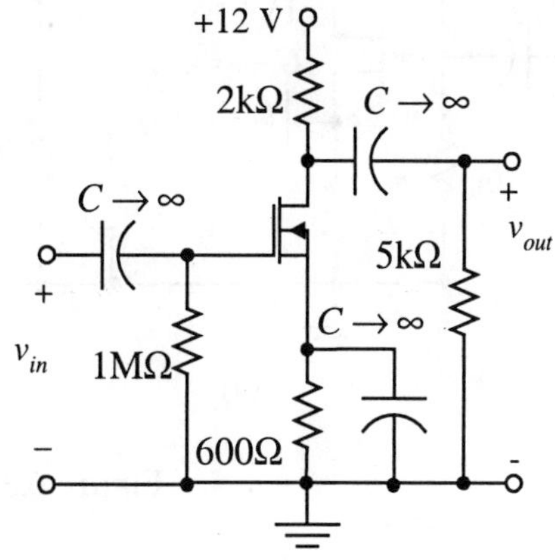

Figure 6.36 – Circuit for Example 6.9

Solving the quadratic, we find the roots to be 2.42 mA and 18.4 mA. We can discard the larger value since KV_T^2 is only 6 mA. Then

$$I_{DQ} = 2.42 \quad \text{mA}$$

$$V_{GSQ} = -0.6 I_{DQ} = -1.45 \quad \text{V}$$

We can now use Equation (6.28) to find,

$$g_m = \frac{2K \cdot V_T^2}{-V_T}(V_{GSQ} - V_T) = 1.91 \quad \text{m}\Omega^{-1}$$

$$A_v = -\ g_m\ R_D \| R_{load} = -2.74$$

$$R_{in} = R_G = 1 \quad \text{M}\Omega$$

$$A_i = -2.74 \frac{10^6}{5000} = -549$$

6.9.2 The CG Amplifier

Figure 6.37(a) shows the single-stage common-gate amplifier and Figure 6.37(b) shows its *ac* equivalent. We have once again neglected r_o under the assumption that it is large compared to the parallel combination of R_D with R_{load}.

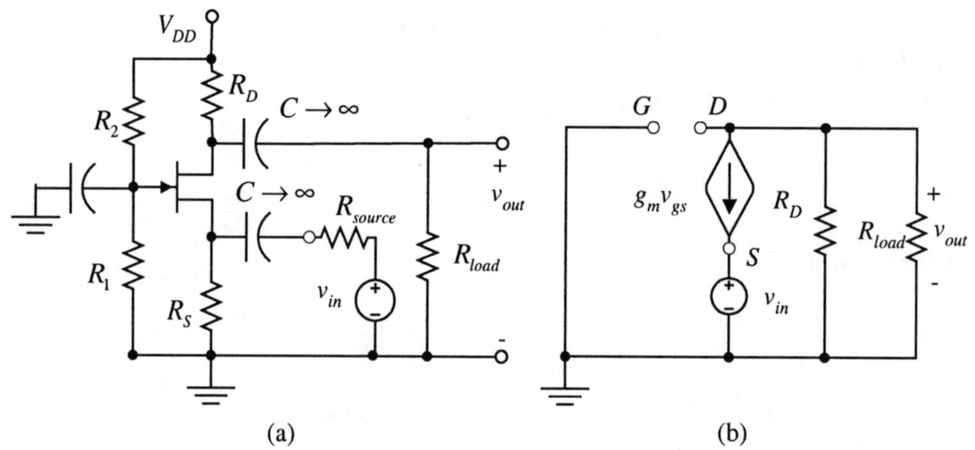

Figure 6.37 – CG amplifier

From Figure 6.37(b) leftmost loop, the gate-to-source voltage is given by

$$v_{gs} = -\ v_{in} \tag{6.46}$$

The current through R_S is

$$i_{in} = \frac{v_{in}}{R_S} = g_m v_{gs} + i_{in} \quad \text{or}$$

$$i_{in} = v_{in}\left(\frac{1}{R_S} + g_m\right) \tag{6.47}$$

so the (input) resistance seen by the source is

$$R_{in} = \frac{v_{in}}{i_{in}} = \frac{1}{1/R_S + g_m} = \frac{R_S \cdot g_m^{-1}}{R_S + g_m^{-1}} = R_S \left\| \frac{1}{g_m} \right. \tag{6.48}$$

This should be compared to Equation (6.45) for the CS amplifier. We see that if the gate resistance is high, the input resistance of the common-source amplifier can be much larger than that of the common-gate amplifier. In fact, the number of applications of the CG amplifier is limited due to the low input impedance.

The voltage gain is given by

$$A_v = \frac{v_{out}}{v_{in}} = \frac{-g_m v_{gs}\left(R_{load} \| R_D\right)}{-v_{gs}} = +g_m \cdot \left(R_D \| R_{load}\right) = +g_m \cdot \frac{R_D R_{load}}{R_D + R_{load}} \tag{6.49}$$

Comparing this with Equation (6.44), we see that the voltage gain for the CS amplifier with an unbypassed resistance in the source circuit is the same as that of the CG amplifier except the CG amplifier does not shift the phase.

The output resistance is simply given by R_D (put in a test current and measure the voltage while setting v_{in} to zero).

The current gain of the CG amplifier is

$$\begin{aligned} A_i = A_V \frac{R_{in}}{R_{load}} &= +g_m \cdot \frac{R_D R_{load}}{R_D + R_{load}} \cdot \frac{R_S \cdot g_m^{-1}}{R_S + g_m^{-1}} \cdot \frac{1}{R_{load}} \\ &= \frac{R_D}{R_D + R_{load}} \cdot \frac{R_S}{R_S + 1/g_m} \end{aligned} \tag{6.50}$$

Example 6.10

Determine V_{DS}, I_D, R_{in}, A_v and A_i for the single-stage JFET CG amplifier shown in Figure 6.37(a). Let $V_{DD} = 20$ V, $R_D = 4$ kΩ, $R_{load} = 6$ kΩ, $R_S = 500$ Ω, $I_{DSS} = 6$ mA, and $V_p = -4$ V.

Solution:

$$I_{DQ} = I_{DSS}\left(1 - \frac{V_{GSQ}}{V_p}\right)^2$$

$$\frac{1}{2} = \left(1 - \frac{V_{GSQ}}{-4}\right)^2$$

This yields the quadratic,

$$V_{GSQ}^2 + 8V_{GSQ} + 8 = 0$$

with solutions for V_{GSQ} of -1.17 V and -6.83 V. We reject the second value since it is higher than V_p.

Since we assumed that I_D is half of I_{DSS}, we have

$$I_{DQ} = 6 \times 10^{-3}\left(1 - \frac{-1.17}{-4}\right)^2 = 3 \quad \text{mA}$$

Solving for the other parameters yields,

$$V_{DSQ} = V_{DD} - I_{DQ}\left(R_D + R_S\right) = 20 - \left(3 \times 10^{-3}\right) \times \left(4.5 \times 10^{3}\right) = 6.5 \quad \text{V}$$

$$g_m = \frac{2I_{DSS}}{-V_p}\left(1 - \frac{V_{GSQ}}{V_p}\right) = \frac{2 \times \left(6 \times 10^{-3}\right)}{4}\left(1 - \frac{-1.17}{-4}\right) = 2.12 \quad \text{m}\Omega^{-1}$$

$$R_{in} = R_S \left\| \frac{1}{g_m} \right. = 500 \| 472 = 243 \quad \Omega$$

$$A_V = g_m\left(R_D \| R_{load}\right) = \left(2.12 \times 10^{-3}\right)\left(4\,k\Omega \| 6\,k\Omega\right) = 5.088$$

$$A_i = \frac{R_D}{R_D + R_{load}} \cdot \frac{R_S}{R_S + g_m^{-1}} = \frac{4\,k\Omega}{10\,k\Omega} \cdot \frac{500}{972} = 0.206$$

Example 6.11

Determine the A_v, A_i, R_{in}, g_m, V_{GS} and V_{DS} for the circuit of Figure 6.38 when the transistor has $I_D = 4$ mA when $V_{GS} = 0$ and $V_T = -3$ V.

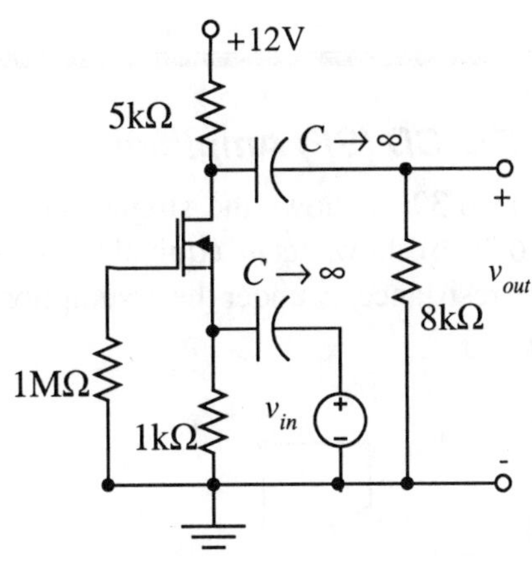

Figure 6.38 – Circuit for Example 6.11

Solution: We first need to determine V_{GS} and g_m in order to find the operating point of the transistor. Using KVL, we get

$$V_{GS} = -R_S I_D = -1000 I_D$$

Then if

$$I_D = 4\text{ mA} \quad \text{when } V_{GS} = 0,$$

$$KV_T^2 = 4\text{ mA} = I_{DSS}$$

From Equation (6.27), we find

$$I_{DQ} = KV_T^2\left(1 - \frac{V_{GSQ}}{V_T}\right)^2 = 4\left(1 - \frac{-I_{DQ}}{-3}\right)^2, \; I_{DQ} \text{ is in mA}$$

$$I_{DQ}^2 - 8.25 I_{DQ} + 9 = 0$$

The roots of this quadratic are at 1.29 mA and 6.96 mA. We can discard the larger value since KV_T^2 is only 4 mA. Then

$$V_{GSQ} = -1000 I_{DQ} = -1.29 \quad \text{V}$$

$$V_{DSQ} = 12 - \left(6 \times 10^3\right)(1.29 \times 10^{-3}) = 4.26 \quad \text{V}$$

Now from Equation (6.28) we get,

$$g_m = \frac{2KV_T^2}{V_T}\left(V_{GSQ} - V_T\right) = 4.56 \quad \text{m}\Omega^{-1}$$

From Equation (6.49),

$$A_v = g_m\left(R_D \| R_{load}\right) = \left(4.52 \times 10^{-3}\right)\left(5000 \| 8000\right) = 14.03$$

Equation (6.48) can be used to find the input resistance

$$R_{in} = R_S \left\| \frac{1}{g_m} \right. \simeq 180\,\Omega$$

6.9.3 The CD (SF) Amplifier

Figure 6.39(a) shows the single-stage common-drain source follower (SF) amplifier and Figure 6.39(b) shows its *ac* equivalent. As with each configuration we have analyzed, we omit the large resistance, r_o under the assumption it is much larger than the parallel combination of R_S with R_{load}.

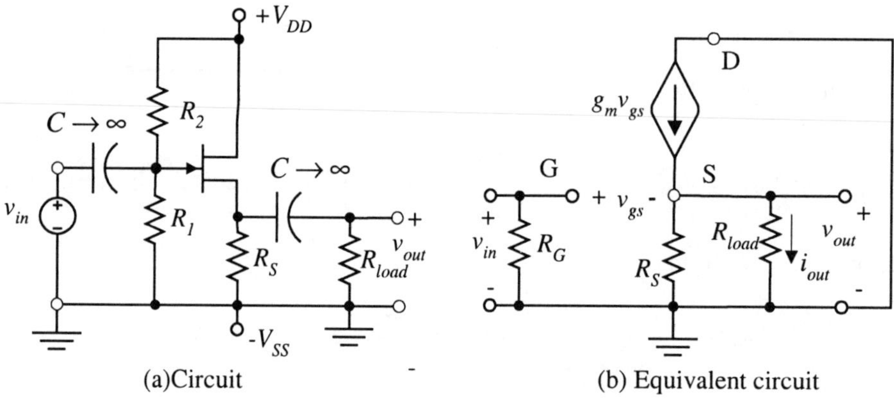

Figure 6.39 – The CD amplifier

The input resistance is simply $R_{in} = R_G$. Writing a KVL equation around the gate-to-source loop, we have

$$v_{gs} = v_{in} - g_m\left(R_S \| R_{load}\right)v_{gs} \tag{6.51}$$

from which we obtain

$$v_{in} = v_{gs}\left[1 + g_m\left(R_S \| R_{load}\right)\right] \tag{6.52}$$

The output voltage is

$$v_{out} = g_m\left(R_S \| R_{load}\right)v_{gs} \tag{6.53}$$

The voltage gain is the ratio of output to input voltage.

$$A_v = \frac{v_{out}}{v_{in}} = \frac{R_S \| R_{load}}{R_S \| R_{load} + 1/g_m} \tag{6.54}$$

Note that this voltage gain is less than unity, and it approaches one as the parallel combination of R_S with R_{load} increases.

We now find the current gain. The output current is the ratio of the output voltage to the load resistance. The input current is the input voltage divided by R_G. The gain is therefore given by

$$A_i = \frac{v_{out}}{R_{load}} \cdot \frac{R_G}{v_{in}} = A_v \frac{R_G}{R_{load}} = \frac{R_S \| R_{load}}{\left(R_S \| R_{load}\right) + 1/g_m} \cdot \frac{R_G}{R_{load}}$$

$$= \frac{R_S}{R_S + R_{load}} \cdot \frac{R_G}{(R_S \| R_{load}) + 1/g_m} \tag{6.55}$$

The output resistance can be found by replacing the load resistor with a test voltage, v_{test}, and then finding the resulting current, i_{test}. The current driven by this test source is found from a node equation at the source.

$$i_{test} = \frac{v_{test}}{R_S} - g_m v_{gs} \tag{6.56}$$

The gate-to-source voltage is simply $-v_{test}$ since we assume the input voltage is zero. Therefore, the output resistance is

$$R_{out} = \frac{1}{1/R_S + g_m} = R_S \Big\| \frac{1}{g_m} \tag{6.57}$$

This is normally relatively small.

Example 6.12

In Figure 6.39, use a MOSFET instead of a JFET which has an I_D of 5 mA when $V_{GS}=0$ and $V_T=$ -4 V. The transistor is operating at $I_{DQ}=2.5$ mA, $R_1=300$ kΩ, $R_2=450$ kΩ, $V_{DD}=12$ V, $R_S=2.4$ kΩ and $R_{load}=4$ kΩ. Determine A_v, A_i, R_{in} and R_{out}.

Solution:

$$R_G = 450\ \text{k}\Omega \| 300\ \text{k}\Omega = 180\quad \text{k}\Omega$$

$$V_{GG} = \frac{R_1}{R_1 + R_2} V_{DD} = 4.8\quad \text{V}$$

Using KVL around the gate circuit, we find

$$V_{GSQ} = V_{GG} - I_{DQ}R_S = -1.2 \quad \text{V}$$

Using Equation (6.22) we find

$$I_D = 5 \text{ mA} \qquad \text{when } V_{GS} = 0$$

$$KV_T^2 = 5 \text{ mA}$$

$$g_m = \frac{2KV_T^2}{V_T^2}(V_{GSQ} - V_T) = 1.75 \text{ m}\Omega^{-1} \qquad \text{or} \quad \frac{1}{g_m} = 571 \ \Omega$$

$$A_v = \frac{2.4 \text{ k}\Omega \| 4 \text{ k}\Omega}{2.4 \text{ k}\Omega \| 4 \text{ k}\Omega + 571} = 0.724$$

$$A_i = \frac{180 \text{ k}\Omega}{2.4 \text{ k}\Omega \| 4 \text{ k}\Omega + 571} \frac{2.4 \text{ k}\Omega}{2.4 \text{ k}\Omega + 4 \text{ k}\Omega} = 32$$

$$R_{in} = R_G = 180 \text{ k}\Omega$$

$$R_o = R_S \left\| \frac{1}{g_m} \right. = 2.4 \text{ k}\Omega \| 571 = 461 \ \Omega$$

6.10 FET AMPLIFIER DESIGN

We now explore the extension of the FET amplifier analysis presented earlier in this chapter to the design of FET amplifiers. We will attempt to define the unknowns in the design problem, and then develop equations for solving for these unknowns. As in most electronics design, the number of equations will be less than the number of unknowns. The additional constraints are established to meet certain overall objectives (e.g., minimum cost, less variation in performance due to parameter changes)

6.10.1 The CS Amplifier

The design procedure of a CS amplifier is presented in this section. We shall reduce JFET and the depletion MOSFET amplifier design to an organized procedure. While this may appear to reduce design to a very routine process, you must convince yourself that you understand the origin of each step since several variations may be subsequently required. If all you do to design a CS amplifier is to thoughtlessly "plug in" to the steps we present, you are missing the whole point of this discussion. As an engineer, you are seeking to do things that are *not* routine. Reducing theory to an organized approach is what you will be doing. You will not simply apply the approaches others have already done for you.

Amplifiers are designed to meet gain requirements assuming the desired specifications are within the range of the transistor. The supply voltage, load resistance, voltage gain and input resistance (or current gain) are usually specified. The designer's job is to select the resistance values R_1, R_2, R_D, and R_S. Refer to Figure 6.40 as you follow the steps in the procedure. This procedure assumes that a device has been selected and that its characteristics are known.

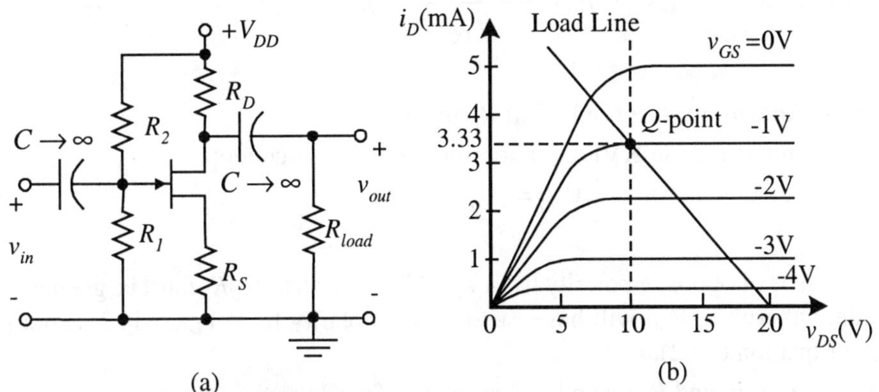

Figure 6.40 - JFET CS amplifier

First, select a Q-point in the saturation region of the FET characteristic curves. Refer to the curves of Figure 6.40(b) for an example. This identifies V_{DSQ}, V_{GSQ}, and I_{DQ}.

We now solve for the two resistors in the output loop, R_S and R_D. Since there are two unknowns, we require two independent equations. We begin by writing the *dc* KVL equation around the drain-source loop,

$$V_{DD} = V_{DSQ} + (R_S + R_D) I_{DQ} \tag{6.58}$$

Solving for the sum of the two resistors yields

$$R_S + R_D = \frac{V_{DD} - V_{DSQ}}{I_{DQ}} = K_1 \tag{6.59}$$

We have defined a constant, K_1, to avoid having to write this term in later equations. Equation (6.59) represents one equation in two unknowns, R_S and R_D.

We next use the voltage gain equations to yield a second equation in R_S and R_D. We can substitute Equation (6.59) into Equation (6.49) to obtain

$$A_v = \frac{-R_{load} \| R_D}{R_S + 1/g_m} = \frac{-R_{load} \| R_D}{(K_1 - R_D) + 1/g_m} \tag{6.60}$$

The resistance, R_D, *is the only unknown in this equation.* Solving for R_D results in a quadratic equation having two solutions, one negative and one positive. If the positive solution results in $R_D > K_1$, thus implying a negative R_S, a new Q-point must be selected (i.e., restart the design). If the positive solution yields $R_D < K_1$, we can proceed.

Now that R_D is known, we solve for R_S using Equation (6.59), the drain-to-source loop equation.

$$R_S = \frac{V_{DD} - V_{DSQ}}{I_{DQ}} - R_D \tag{6.61}$$

With R_D and R_S known, we need only find R_1 and R_2.

We begin by rewriting the KVL equation for the gate-source loop.

$$V_{GG} = V_{GSQ} + I_{DQ} R_S \tag{6.62}$$

The voltage, V_{GS}, is of opposite polarity from V_{DD}. Thus the term $I_{DQ}R_S$ must be greater than V_{GSQ} in magnitude. Otherwise, V_{GG} will have the opposite polarity from V_{DD}, which is not possible according to Equation (6.62).

We now solve for R_1 and R_2 assuming that the V_{GG} found has the *same polarity* as V_{DD}. These resistor values are selected by finding the value of R_G from the current-gain equation or from the input resistance. We solve for R_1 and R_2.

$$R_1 = \frac{R_G}{1 - V_{GG}/V_{DD}}$$

$$R_2 = \frac{R_G V_{DD}}{V_{GG}} \tag{6.63}$$

Suppose now that Equation (6.62) results in a V_{GG} that has the *opposite polarity* of V_{DD}. It is not possible to solve for R_1 and R_2. The practical way to proceed is to let $V_{GG} = 0$ V. Thus, $R_2 \to \infty$. Since V_{GG} is specified by Equation (6.62), the previously calculated value of R_S now needs to be modified. In Figure 6.41, where a capacitor is used to bypass a part of R_S, we develop the new value of R_S as follows:

$$V_{GG} = 0 = V_{GSQ} + I_{DQ} R_{Sdc}$$

$$R_{Sdc} = \frac{-V_{GSQ}}{I_{DQ}} \tag{6.64}$$

The value of R_{Sdc} is $R_{S1} + R_{S2}$ and the value of R_{Sac} is R_{S1}.

Now that we have a new R_{Sdc}, we must repeat several earlier steps in the design. We once again determine R_D using KVL for the drain-to-source loop.

$$R_D = K_1 - R_{Sdc} \tag{6.65}$$

The design problem now becomes one of calculating both R_{S1} and R_{S2} instead of finding only one source resistor.

With a new value for R_D of K_1 - R_{Sdc}, we go to the voltage gain expression of Equation (6.60) with R_{Sac} used for this *ac* equation rather than R_S.

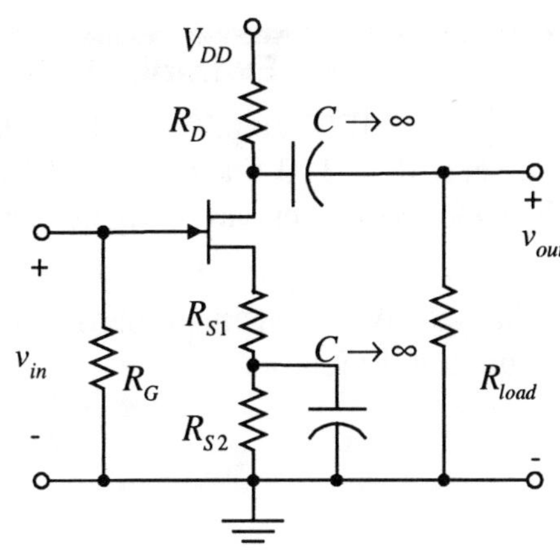

Figure 6.41 – CS amplifier

The following additional steps must be added to the design procedure:

We find R_{Sac} (which is simply R_{S1}) from the voltage gain equation.

$$A_v = \frac{-(R_D \| R_{load})}{R_{Sac} + 1/g_m} \tag{6.66}$$

R_{Sac} is the only unknown in this equation. Solving for this, we find

$$R_{Sac} = -\frac{R_D \| R_{load}}{A_v} - \frac{1}{g_m} \tag{6.67}$$

Suppose now that R_{Sac} is found to be positive, but less than R_{Sdc}. This is the desirable condition since

$$R_{Sdc} = R_{Sac} + R_{S2} \tag{6.68}$$

Then our design is complete and

$$R_I = R_{in} = R_G \tag{6.69}$$

Suppose that R_{Sac} is found to be positive but *greater* than R_{Sdc}. The amplifier cannot be designed with the voltage gain and Q-point as selected. A new Q-point must be selected. If the voltage gain is too high, it may not be possible to effect the design with any Q-point. A different transistor may be needed or the use of two separate stages may be required.

Example 6.13: JFET CS Amplifier (Design)

Design a CS JFET amplifier with a voltage gain of $A_v = -4$, $R_{in} = 100$ kΩ, $R_{load} = 20$ kΩ, $I_{DSS} = 6.67$ mA, $V_p = -3.33$ V and $V_{DD} = 20$ V. Use the circuit configuration shown in Figure 6.33 and the dimensionless curves of Figure 6.20.

Solution: We follow the procedure developed in this section. The Q-point is selected from Figure 6.20 as follows:

$$I_{DQ} = \frac{I_{DSS}}{2} = 3.33 \quad \text{mA}$$

$$V_{GSQ} = 0.3V_p = -1 \quad \text{V}$$

$$V_{DSQ} = \frac{V_{DD}}{2} = 10 \quad \text{V}$$

Then

$$g_m = 1.41\frac{I_{DSS}}{V_p} = 2.84 \times 10^{-3} \quad \Omega^{-1}$$

$$\frac{1}{g_m} = 350 \quad \Omega$$

Note that these results apply only when $I_{DQ} = I_{DSS}/2$. We now have from Equation (6.59),

$$R_D + R_S = \frac{20\text{ V} - 10\text{ V}}{3.33\text{ mA}} = 3\text{ k}\Omega = K_1$$

Using the *ac* gain equation [Equation (6.60)], we obtain

$$A_v = \frac{-(20\text{ k}\Omega \| R_D)}{3\text{ k}\Omega - R_D + 350\,\Omega} = -4$$

$$R_D^2 + (21.7\text{ k}\Omega)R_D - 67\text{ M}\Omega^2 = 0$$

Solving this quadratic for R_D we select the positive root, $R_D = 2.75$kΩ. Since this quantity is less than K_1, we proceed with the design. We find R_S using Equation (6.59).

$$R_S = 3\,k\Omega - R_D = 253\,\Omega$$

Equation (6.62) now yields,

$$V_{GG} = -1 + 253(3.33 \times 10^{-3}) = -0.158 \quad \text{V}$$

Since this negative voltage cannot be obtained by dividing the source voltage using resistors, we let $R_2 \to \infty$. Then

$$V_{GG} = 0 = V_{GSQ} + I_{DQ} R_{Sdc} = -1 + (3.33\times10^{-3}) R_{Sdc}$$

Solving for R_{Sdc} yields R_{Sdc} = 300 Ω.

Equation (6.65) then yields R_D = 3 kΩ - R_{Sdc} = 2.70 kΩ. R_{Sac} is then given by

$$R_{Sac} = \frac{R_D \| R_{load}}{A_v} - \frac{1}{g_m} = 245\Omega$$

The final circuit is shown in Figure 6.41 where the component values are

$$R_D = 2.70\ \text{k}\Omega$$

$$R_{S1} = R_{Sac} = 245\ \Omega$$

$$R_{S2} = R_{Sdc} - R_{Sac} = 300\ \Omega - 245\ \Omega = 55\ \Omega$$

$$R_G = R_{in} = R_I = 100\ \text{k}\Omega$$

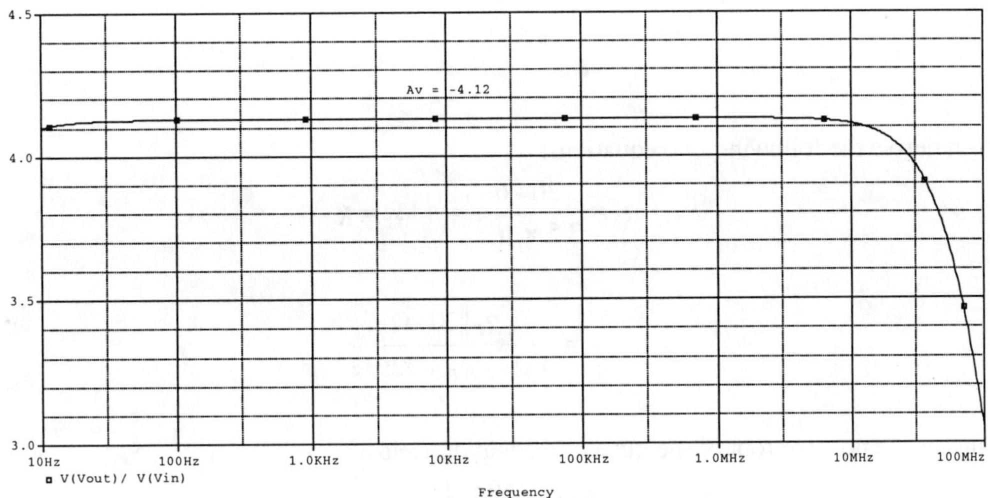

Figure 6.42 – SPICE simulation result for Example 6.13

A verification of our design is provided by a SPICE simulation of the circuit of Figure 6.41 using our calculated values for the circuit components. The simulation result for the JFET amplifier's voltage gain over the frequencies of interest is shown in Figure 6.42. The simulated voltage gain, A_v, is 4.12.

The following example extends our understanding of how the selection of Q-point location can affect the resulting voltage gain for JFET design (in contrast to the placement of the Q-point which had little to no effect on the circuit voltage gain for BJT designs).

Example 6.14 JFET CS Amplifier (Design)

Repeat Example 6.13, but select a Q-point that is within the saturation (normal operating region), but *not* in the center of the linear region. Use a transistor with $I_{DSS} = 6.67$ mA and $V_p = -3.33$ V. Verify your design using a computer simulation.

Solution: Let us arbitrarily select the new operating point as follows:

$$I_{DQ} = 3.5 \quad \text{mA}$$

$$V_{GSQ} = -0.92 \quad \text{V}$$

$$V_{DSQ} = 6 \quad \text{V}$$

We follow the design procedure of this section to obtain the following equations:

$$g_m = 2.83 \times 10^{-3} \quad \Omega^{-1}$$

$$\frac{1}{g_m} = 354 \quad \Omega$$

We then derive the following two equations:

$$R_D + R_S = \frac{20 - 6}{3.5 \times 10^{-3}} = 4\ \text{k}\Omega = K_1$$

$$A_v = -4 = \frac{-R_D \| 20\ \text{k}\Omega}{4\ k\Omega - R_D + 329\ \Omega}$$

Solving for the positive root of the quadratic equation yields,

$$R_D = 3.593\ \text{k}\Omega$$

Since this quantity is less than K_1, we can proceed. We derive the following equations:

$$R_S = 4\ \text{k}\Omega - 3.593\ \text{k}\Omega = 407 \quad \Omega$$

$$V_{GG} = -0.92 + 407(3.5\times10^{-3}) = 0.505 \quad \text{V}$$

We note that V_{GG} is the same polarity as V_{DD} (in contrast to the previous example), so we can immediately solve for R_1 and R_2.

$$R_1 = \frac{10^5}{1 - 0.702/20} = 103 \text{ k}\Omega$$

$$R_2 = 10^5 \left(\frac{20}{0.702} \right) = 3.96 \text{ M}\Omega$$

The final circuit is shown in Figure 6.43(a). In practice, if $R_2 >> R_1$ and if R_2 is greater than about 10 MΩ, we could remove R_2 from the circuit (i.e., set it equal to infinity). Doing so forces V_{GG} to 0 V rather than to a small positive voltage.

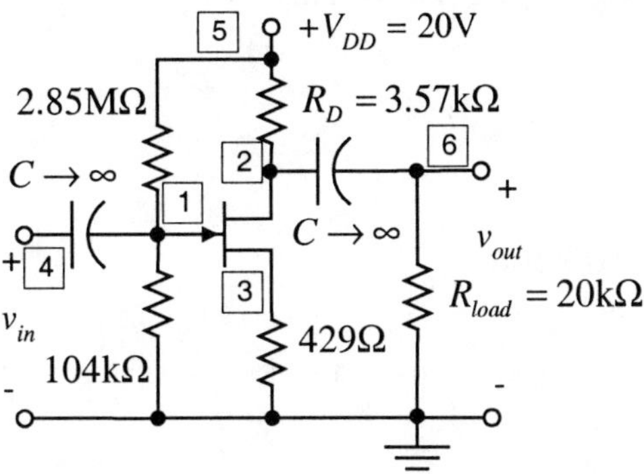

Figure 6.43(a) – Circuit component values for Example 6.14 design

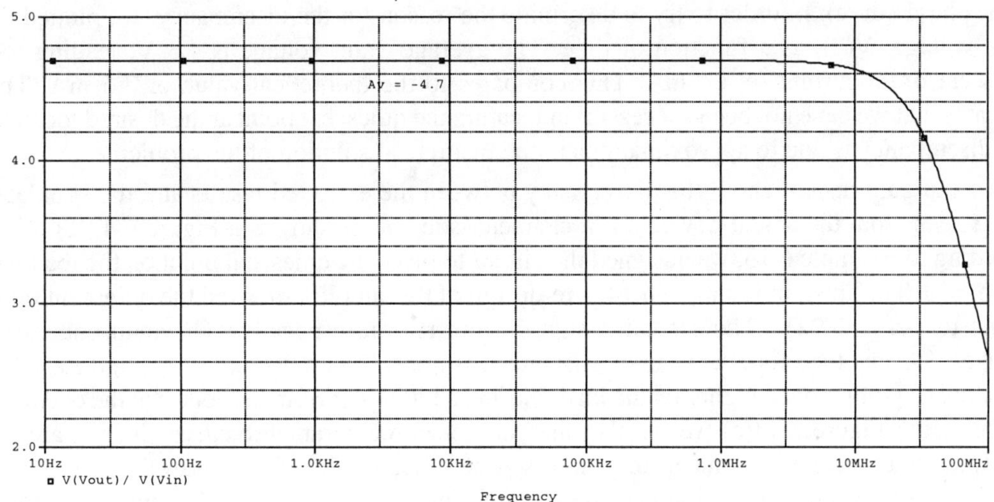

Figure 6.43(b) – SPICE simulation result for Example 6.14

We now use a computer simulation to check the result. The PSPICE listing follows, where we have assigned numbers to the nodes as shown in Figure 6.43(a).

```
VIN,4,0,AC,.5,SIN(0,.5,1000)
CIN,1,4,1
VCC,5,0,DC,20V
R1,1,0,104K
R2,1,5,2.85MEG
J1,3,2,1,EASY
.MODEL,EASY,NJF(BETA=.601M)
RD,2,5,3.57K
RS,3,0,429
C1,2,6,1
RL,6,0,20K
.AC,LIN,25,10,100Meg
.TRAN,.05M,1M
.PROBE
.END
```

In order to check the gain of the circuit, we have plotted V(6)/V(4) using an *ac* analysis. The result, shown in Figure 6.43(b), shows a gain of -4.7 instead of the -4 we designed for (note that an actual gain of –4.7 simply means in words that the minus sign would show up as an 180° shift of the phase curve). In order to try to determine the reason for the discrepancy, we plotted the drain voltage, V(2), as a function of time. The average drain voltage is 4.3 V, leading to a quiescent drain current of 4.4 mA. This compares to the theoretical value of 3.5 mA. This indicates that we have not been successful in locating the quiescent point at the desired location. The discrepancy is due to approximations in the theoretical solution of the problem.

We can gain insight about the discrepancy between the expected results and the simulated results seen from the actual device's I-V characteristic curves shown in Figure 6.43(c). First, according to Example 6.13, we designed the circuit to place the quiescent point on the load line for v_{GS} = -1.0V. Then, in Example 6.14, a re-design of this amplifier moved the quiescent point setting to v_{GS} = -0.92V. The second design did not require a negative Thevenin equivalent voltage, V_{GG}, and therefore the source resistance was not split into two parts, R_{Sac} and R_{Sdc}. The operating Q-point moved higher on the load line and a bit higher from the center of the operating region. From Figure 6.43(c) we see that the gate-to-source parametric curves for v_{GS} are not evenly spaced for equal increments of gate-to-source voltages. Therefore we saw the voltage gain increase in the second simulation because this non-linear relation is modeled appropriately in SPICE. The simulation uses the complete set of device parameters (12 total) given in Table 6.2. The previous theoretical design assumes evenly-spaced parametric curves.

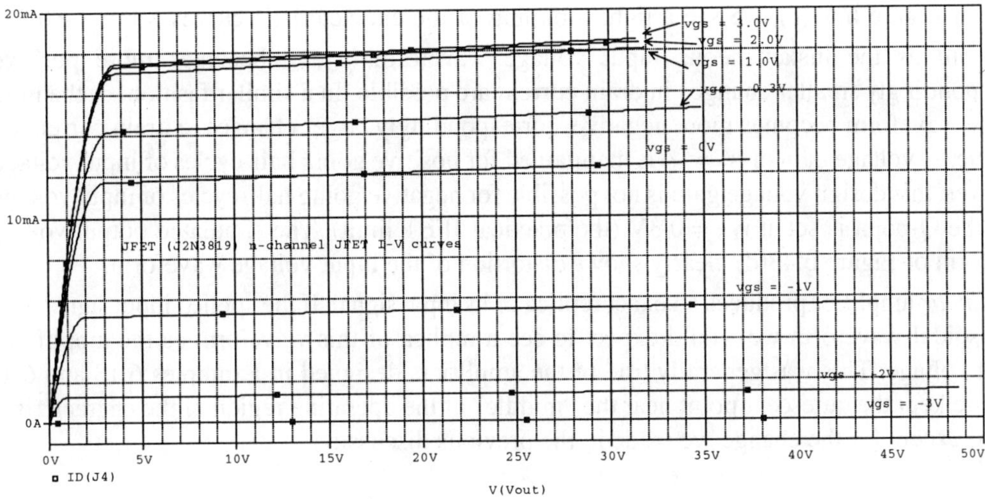

Figure 6.43(c) – I-V characteristic of a JFET

For small *forward* voltages, the JFET *pn*-junction remains essentially cut-off (approximately 0.3V).

A demonstration of this practical maximum voltage is provided by the simulation shown in Figure 6.43(d). For this simulation, the Q-point was moved along the load line from the negative portion (Examples 6.13 and 6.14), across zero ($v_{GS} = 0V$), to near the 0.3V location. The input source voltage, V(source) swings above and below zero by 0.5V. However, the output voltage, V(out) is not an inverted replica of the input signal as we might expect.

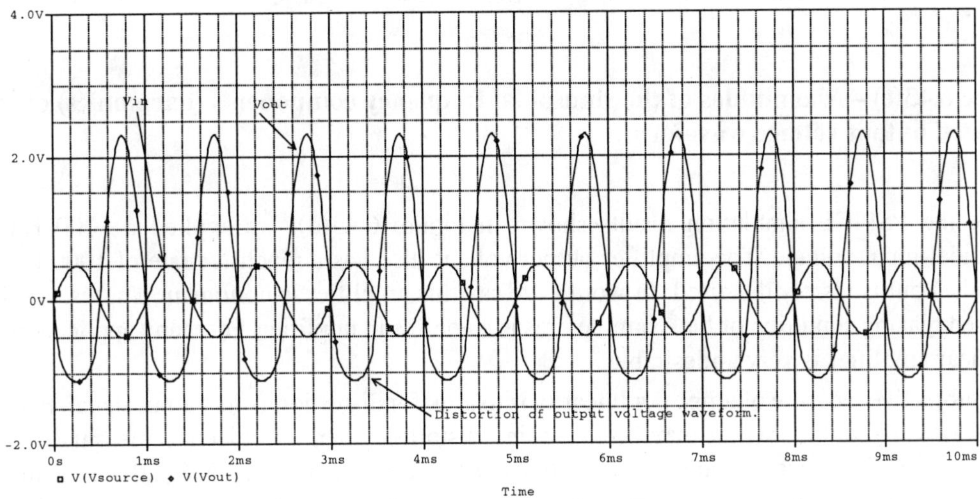

Figure 6.43(d) – Sinusoidal input waveform and the distorted output waveform

From Figure 6.43(c), we see a tight grouping of the characteristic curves for $v_{GS} \geq 0.3\text{V}$. Therefore as the instantaneous input voltage waveform, $v_{GS}(t)$, becomes more positive, correspondingly smaller changes in drain current are possible. In a similar fashion, as the input voltage waveform becomes more negative, correspondingly larger changes in drain current are possible. A voltage gain of $A_v = -4$ is maintained for positive going half-cycles of input voltage. However, this design voltage gain is not possible for negative going half-cycles of input voltage, since the Q-point is set at $v_{GS} = 0.3\text{V}$ (the practical JFET limit). The simulated output voltage waveform of Figure 6.43(d) clearly shows distortion of the input voltage waveform.

A *linear* amplifier produces an exact replica of its input signal. If the applied input signal were a sinusoidal waveform we would expect to see a replica of this waveform as the amplifier's output voltage. This was generally true of the amplifiers designed in Examples 6.13 and 6.14 since we kept the quiescent point near the "middle" of the operating region of the characteristic curves, except for the change we made in the previous discussion.

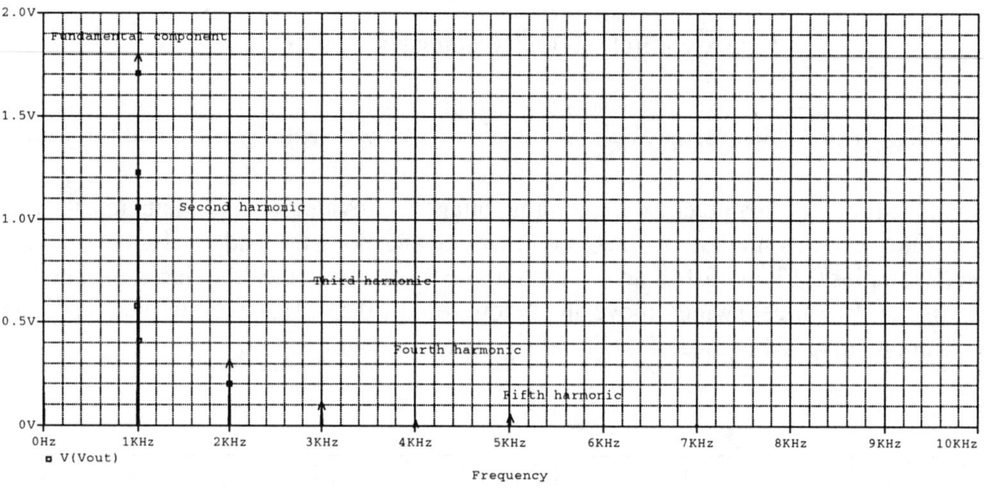

Figure 6.43(e) – Magnitudes of the sinusoidal frequency components (harmonics) of the distorted output voltage waveform.

For the PSPICE simulation results shown in Figure 6.43(d), we applied a 1000 Hertz sinusoidal input voltage. The amplifier output voltage also has a repetitive rate of 1000 Hertz (periodic) but is visibly distorted. In words, we say this amplifier is *nonlinear*. That is, for the imposed biasing condition of the example, this is a nonlinear amplifier. For many applications a nonlinear amplifier is very undesirable.

A subjective measure of amplifier linearity is to look for distortion in its output signal. Even a "good looking" output signal may be surprising distorted when an objective measure of the amplifier's performance is made. The distortion of a "pure" sinusoidal (input signal) results in the distorted waveform signal having harmonic frequency components. The frequency and amplitude of the undesired components provide an objective measure of the distortion of the amplifier's output voltage. For the imposed biasing condition of our last discussion, the JFET amplifier is operating in a highly nonlinear region of the characteristic curves. Frequencies up to the fifth are seen in the output voltage waveform shown in Figure 6.42(e).

The design guidelines of Section 6.3.3 place the Q-point near the middle of the operating region of the JFET characteristic curves. We now see the importance of following these procedures to design a linear amplifier especially if we intend to design the JFET amplifier for large signal swings.

Example 6.15 MOSFET CS Amplifier (Design)

Design a MOSFET CS amplifier [Figure 6.33 with the JFET changed to a MOSFET]. The MOSFET has $I_D = 8$ mA when $V_{GS} = 0$ and $V_T = -6$ V. The specifications are $A_v = -2$, $R_{in} = 400$ kΩ, $R_{load} = 5$ kΩ, and $V_{DD} = 15$ V. Find the values of all the resistors in the amplifier circuit.

Solution: Let us assume that we will locate the Q point at

$$I_{DQ} = 0.6 \cdot \left(KV_T^2\right)$$

$$V_{DSQ} = \frac{V_{DD}}{2}$$

We could have very well assumed something different, but we do need to keep the quiescent point somewhere around the middle of the load line to assure that we are in the most linear part of the characteristic curves. This results in

$$I_{DQ} = 0.6 \times 8 \times 10^{-3} = 4.8 \quad \text{mA}$$

We now solve for the gate-to-source voltage.

$$0.6 = \left(1 - \frac{V_{GSQ}}{V_T}\right)^2 \quad \text{so} \quad \frac{V_{GSQ}}{V_T} = 0.225$$

$$V_{GSQ} = -1.35 \quad \text{V}$$

We now have enough information to find g_m and the drain-to-source voltage.

$$g_m = \frac{2\left(KV_T^2\right)}{V_T^2}\left(V_{GSQ} - V_T\right) = 2.07 \times 10^{-3} \quad \Omega^{-1}$$

$$\frac{1}{g_m} = 484 \quad \Omega$$

$$V_{DSQ} = \frac{V_{DD}}{2} = 7.5 \quad \text{V}$$

In summary, the Q-point is located at

$$I_{DQ} = 4.8 \quad \text{mA}$$
$$V_{GSQ} = -1.35 \quad \text{V}$$
$$V_{DSQ} = 7.5 \quad \text{V}$$
$$g_m = 2.07 \quad \text{m}\Omega^{-1}$$

We apply KVL to find,

$$R_D + R_S = \frac{15 - 7.5}{4.8 \times 10^{-3}} = 1.56 \text{ k}\Omega$$

$$A_v = -2 = \frac{-R_D \| 5 \text{ k}\Omega}{(1.56 \text{ k}\Omega - R_D) + 484}$$

$$R_D^2 + 5.45 \times 10^3 R_D - 10.2 \times 10^6 = 0$$

The solution of this quadratic equation yields a drain resistance of 1.47 kΩ. The source resistance is then

$$R_S = 1.56 \text{ k}\Omega - 1.47 \text{ k}\Omega = 90 \ \Omega$$

If we now solve for V_{GG}, we find it is negative. We will let V_{GG} be zero and R_2 go to infinity. Then,

$$V_G = 0 = V_{GSQ} + I_{DQ} R_{Sdc}$$
$$R_{Sdc} = 280 \ \Omega$$
$$R_D = 1.56 \text{ k}\Omega - 280 \ \Omega = 1.28 \text{ k}\Omega$$
$$R_{Sac} = \frac{R_D \| R_{load}}{A_v} - \frac{1}{g_m} = 509 - 484 = 25 \ \Omega$$

This resistor is so small that in practice we could essentially bypass all of R_S (this would give an *ac* gain larger than 2) unless the specifications are critical. Finally, we use the input resistance to find

$$R_{in} = R_G = R_1 = 400 \text{ k}\Omega$$

EXERCISES

E6.1 Design a CS JFET amplifier that has an R_{load} of 10 kΩ, $V_{DD} = 12$ V, $R_{in} = 500$ kΩ, and $A_v = -2$. Use the circuit of Figure 6.32(a). Select the Q-point as $V_{DSQ} = 6$ V, $V_{GSQ} = -1$ V, $I_{DQ} = 1$ mA and $g_m = 2500$ μS.

Answer: $R_S = 1.22$ kΩ; $R_D = 4.78$ kΩ, $R_1 = 509$ kΩ; $R_2 = 27$ MΩ, $A_i = -100$

E6.2 Redesign the amplifier of Exercise E6.1 for a transistor with V_p = -4 V and I_{DSS} = 6 mA.

Answer: $R_1 = 500\ k\Omega$; R_2 6 4 $R_D = 1.61\ k\Omega$; $R_{Sdc} = 390\ \Omega$
$R_{Sac} = 223\ \Omega$; $A_i = -100$

E6.3 Design a CS amplifier as in E6.1 using a MOSFET with I_D = 7 mA when V_{GS} = 0 and V_T = -5 V.

Answer: $R_1 = 500\ k\Omega$; R_2 6 4 $R_D = 1.29\ k\Omega$; $R_{Sdc} = 420\ \Omega$
$R_{Sac} = 55\ \Omega$; $A_i = -100$

6.10.2 The CD Amplifier

We now present the design procedure for the CD JFET amplifier. The following quantities are specified: current gain, load resistance, and V_{DD}. Input resistance may be specified instead of current gain. Refer to the circuit of Figure 6.39 as you study the following procedure. Once again, we remind you that the process of reducing the theory to a set of steps is the important part of this discussion – not the actual steps.

First select a Q-point in the center of the FET characteristic curves with the aid of Figure 6.20. This step determines V_{DSQ}, V_{GSQ}, I_{DQ} and g_m.

We can solve for the resistor connected to the source by writing the *dc* KVL equation around the drain-to-source loop.

$$V_{DD} = V_{DSQ} + R_S I_{DQ} \tag{6.70}$$

from which we find the *dc* value of R_S,

$$R_{Sdc} = \frac{R_{DD} - V_{DSQ}}{I_{DQ}} \tag{6.71}$$

We next find the *ac* value of resistance, R_{Sac}, from the rearranged current gain equation, Equation (6.55).

$$R_{Sac} = \frac{R_{load}}{(R_G/A_i - R_{load})\, g_m - 1} \tag{6.72}$$

where $R_G = R_{in.}$ If the input resistance is not specified, let $R_{Sac} = R_{Sdc}$ and calculate the input resistance from Equation (6.72). If the input resistance is not high enough, it may be necessary to change the Q-point location.

If R_{in} is specified, it is necessary to calculate R_{Sac} from Equation (6.72). In such cases, R_{Sac} is different from R_{Sdc}, so we bypass part of R_S with a capacitor.

We now turn our attention to the input bias circuitry. We determine V_{GG} using the equation,

$$V_{GG} = V_{GSQ} + I_{DQ}R_S \tag{6.73}$$

No phase inversion is produced in a source follower FET amplifier and V_{GG} is normally of the same polarity as the supply voltage.

Now that V_{GG} is known, we determine the values of R_1 and R_2 from the Thevenin equivalent of the bias circuitry.

$$R_1 = \frac{R_G}{1 - V_{GG}/V_{DD}}$$

$$R_2 = \frac{R_G V_{DD}}{V_{GG}} \tag{6.74}$$

There is usually enough drain current in an SF to develop the opposite polarity voltage needed to offset the negative voltages required by the JFET gate. Therefore, normal voltage division biasing can be used.

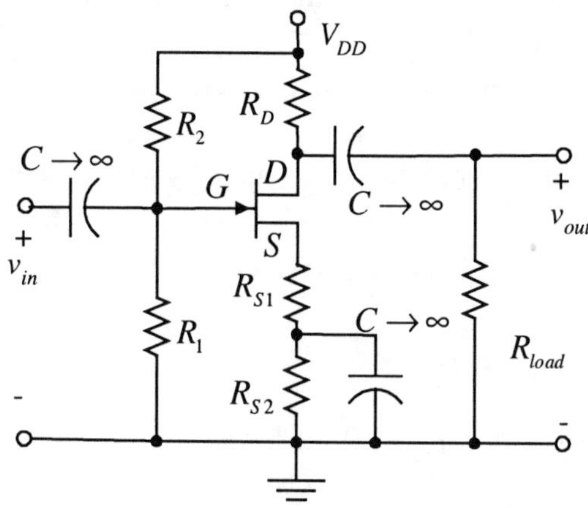

Figure 6.44 – CD amplifier with part of R_S bypassed

We now return to the problem of specifying the input resistance. We can assume that part of R_S is bypassed, as in Figure 6.44, which leads to different values of R_{Sac} and R_{Sdc}. We use Equation (6.71) to solve for R_{Sdc}. Next, we let R_G equal the specified value of R_{in}, and use Equation (6.72) to solve for R_{Sac}.

If the R_{Sac} calculated above is smaller than R_{Sdc}, the design is accomplished by bypassing R_{S2} with a capacitor. Remember that $R_{Sac} = R_{S1}$ and $R_{Sdc} = R_{S1} + R_{S2}$. If on the other hand, R_{Sac} is larger than R_{Sdc}, the Q-point must be moved to a different location. We select a smaller V_{DS} thus causing increased voltage to be dropped across $R_{S1} + R_{S2}$, which makes R_{Sdc} larger. If V_{DS} cannot be reduced sufficiently to make R_{Sdc} larger than R_{Sac}, then the amplifier cannot be designed with the given current gain, R_{in}, and FET type. One of these three specifications must be changed, or a second amplifier stage must be used to provide the required gain.

Example 6.16 - CD Amplifier (Design)

Design a CD JFET amplifier with the following specifications: $A_i = 12$, $R_{in} > 9\ \text{k}\Omega$, $R_{load} = 400\ \Omega$, $I_{DSS} = 20$ mA, $V_p = -6.67$ V, and $V_{DD} = 12$ V.

Solution: Following the procedure developed in this section, we begin by selecting the Q-point using Figure 6.20:

$$I_{DQ} = \frac{I_{DSS}}{2} = 10 \quad \text{mA}$$

$$V_{DSQ} = \frac{V_{DD}}{2} = 6 \quad \text{V}$$

Using the graphical technique, since $I_{DQ} = 0.5 I_{DSS}$ we obtain

$$V_{GSQ} = (0.3)(-6.67) = -2 \quad \text{V}$$

$$g_m = \frac{1.42 I_{DSS}}{V_p} = 4.26 \quad \text{m}\Omega^{-1}$$

$$\frac{1}{g_m} = 235 \quad \Omega$$

Since $R_{in} > 9\ \text{k}\Omega$, we let $R_S = R_{sac} = R_{Sdc}$ and

$$R_S = \frac{V_{DD} - V_{DS}}{I_{DQ}} = 600 \quad \Omega$$

R_G is found by rearranging Equation (6.55).

$$R_G = A_i\left(R_{load} + \frac{1 + R_{load}/R_S}{g_m}\right) = 9.5 \quad \text{k}\Omega$$

Since R_G is greater than 9 kΩ, we meet the design specification and we can continue to solve for the bias circuitry. This yields,

$$V_{GG} = -2 + (10 \times 10^{-3})(600) = 4 \quad \text{V}$$

$$R_1 = \frac{9500}{1 - 4/12} = 14.3 \quad \text{k}\Omega$$

$$R_2 = \frac{9500 \times 12}{4} = 28.5 \quad \text{k}\Omega$$

$$A_v = A_i \frac{R_{load}}{R_{in}} = 0.51$$

EXERCISE

E6.4 Design a CD JFET amplifier to provide a current gain of 15 to a load of 20 kΩ using V_{DD}= 12 V and an input resistance of R_{in} = 400 kΩ. Use an n-channel FET that has a V_p of -3 V and an I_{DSS} of 6 mA. Set the Q-point at $V_{DSQ} = V_{DD}/2$ and $I_{DQ} = 0.4I_{DSS}$. Determine the resistor values and the voltage gain of the amplifier.

Answer: Rsdc =2.5 kΩ; Rsac = 1.26 kΩ, R_1 *= 676 kΩ;* R_2 *= 980 kΩ,* A_v *= 0.75*

6.10.3 The SF Bootstrap Amplifier

We now examine a variation of the CD amplifier known as the *SF (or CD) bootstrap FET amplifier*. This circuit is a special case of the SF called the *bootstrap circuit* and is illustrated in Figure 6.45.

Here the bias is developed across only a part of the source resistor. This reduces the need for a capacitor bypass across part of the source resistor and thus attains a much larger input resistance than normally can be attained. This design allows us to take advantage of the high impedance characteristics of the FET without using a high value of gate resistor, R_G.

The equivalent circuit of Figure 6.46 is used to evaluate the circuit operation.

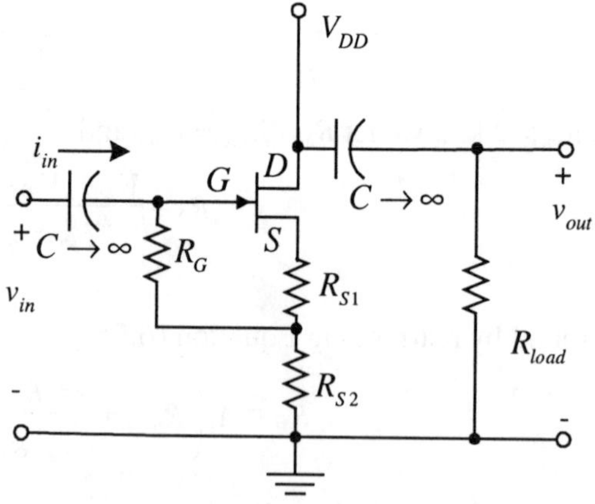

Figure 6.45 – Bootstrap source follower

We assume that i_{in} is sufficiently small to approximate the current in R_{S2} as i_1. The output voltage is then found to be

$$v_{out} \approx g_m v_{GS}\left(R_S \| R_{load}\right) \tag{6.75}$$

where

$$R_S = R_{S1} + R_{S2} \tag{6.76}$$

If the assumption about i_{in} is not valid, R_S is replaced by the expression

$$R_{S1} = \frac{(i_{in} + i_1)R_{S2}}{i_1} \tag{6.77}$$

A KVL equation at the input yields v_{in} as follows:

$$v_{in} = v_{GS} + i_1 R_{S1} + (i_1 + i_{in})R_{S2} \tag{6.78}$$

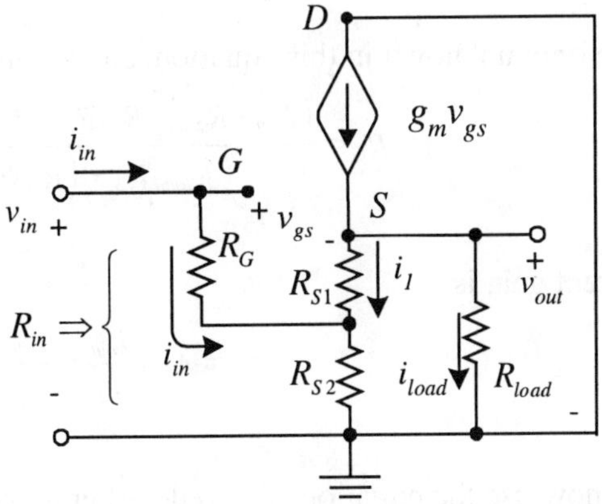

Figure 6.46 – ac equivalent circuit for bootstrap source follower

The current, i_1, is found from a current-divider relationship,

$$i_1 = \frac{g_m v_{GS} R_{load}}{R_S + R_{load}} \tag{6.79}$$

Combining Equations (6.79) and (6.78) yields,

$$v_{in} = v_{GS} + \frac{g_m v_{GS} R_{load} R_S}{R_{load} + R_S} + i_{in} R_{S2} \tag{6.80}$$

A second equation for v_{in} is developed around the loop through R_G and R_{S2} as follows.

$$v_{in} = i_{in} R_G + \left(\frac{g_m v_{GS} R_{load}}{R_S + R_{load}} + i_{in}\right) R_{S2}$$

$$= i_{in}(R_G + R_{S2}) + \frac{g_m v_{GS} R_{load} R_{S2}}{R_S + R_{load}} \tag{6.81}$$

We eliminate v_{in} by setting Equation (6.80) equal to Equation (6.81) and solve for i_{in} to obtain

$$i_{in} = \frac{g_m v_{GS}}{R_G}\left[\left(R_{load} \| R_S\right) + \frac{1}{g_m} - \frac{R_{load} R_{S2}}{R_S + R_{load}}\right] \tag{6.82}$$

The input resistance, $R_{in} = v_{in}/i_{in}$, is found by dividing Equation (6.81) by Equation (6.82) with the result,

$$R_{in} = \frac{R_G\left[1/g_m + \left(R_{load} \| R_S\right)\right]}{\left(R_{load} \| R_S\right) + 1/g_m - \left(R_{load} R_{S2}\right)/\left(R_S + R_{load}\right)} + R_{S2} \tag{6.83}$$

R_G is the only unknown in this equation, so we can solve to obtain,

$$R_G = \frac{\left(R_{in} - R_{S2}\right)\left[R_{S1} R_{load} + \left(R_S + R_{load}\right)/g_m\right]}{R_{load} R_S + \left(R_S + R_{load}\right)/g_m} \tag{6.84}$$

The current gain is

$$A_i = \frac{i_{out}}{i_{in}} = \frac{v_{out}}{R_{load} i_{in}} \tag{6.85}$$

We can now use the equations derived earlier along with the observation that $R_S - R_{S2} = R_{S1}$ in order to solve for the current gain.

$$A_i = \frac{R_G R_S}{R_{load} R_{S1} + (R_{load} + R_S)/g_m} \tag{6.86}$$

The voltage gain is

$$A_v = \frac{A_i R_{load}}{R_{in}} = \frac{R_G R_S R_{load}}{R_{in}\left[R_{S1} R_{load} + \left(R_S + R_{load}\right)/g_m\right]} \tag{6.87}$$

Note that the denominator in Equation (6.84) is larger than the numerator, thus showing that $R_G < (R_{in} - R_{S2})$. This proves that a large input resistance can be attained without having the same order of size as R_G.

Example 6.17 - Bootstrap SF (Design)

Design a SF bootstrap amplifier circuit for the following conditions: $R_{in} = 100\ \text{k}\Omega$, $R_{load} = 10\ \text{k}\Omega$, and $V_{DD} = 20$ V. The Q-point is selected at

$V_{DSQ} = 10$ V $\qquad I_{DQ} = 3.33$ mA

$V_{GSQ} = -1$ V $\qquad g_m = 2\ \text{m}\Omega^{-1}$

Solution: Designing this circuit consists of choosing values for R_{S1}, R_{S2} and R_G. The relationship, $V_{GSQ} = -1$ V, is used to find R_{S1}. We sum voltages around the gate-to-source loop assuming that i_{in} is approximately equal to zero, as follows:

$$0 = V_{GSQ} + R_{S1} I_{DQ}$$

$$R_{S1} = \frac{1}{3.3 \times 10^{-1}} = 300\ \Omega$$

In order to find R_{S2}, we write a KVL equation around the source-to-drain loop.

$$V_{DD} = V_{DSQ} + (R_{S1} + R_{S2}) I_{DQ}$$

Solving for R_{S2} yields

$$R_{S2} = 2.7\ \text{k}\Omega$$

We now find R_G using Equation (6.84) as follows:

$$R_G = \frac{R_{S1} R_{load} + \left(R_S + R_{load}\right)/g_m}{R_{load} R_S + \left(R_S + R_{load}\right)/g_m}\left(R_{in} - R_{S2}\right) = 25.3\ \text{k}\Omega$$

EXERCISE

E6.5 Determine the value of the resistors and current gain for a SF JFET Bootstrap amplifier which requires $R_{in} = 200$ kΩ, $R_{load} = 20$ kΩ, and $V_{DD} = 10$ V. The Q-point is selected as $V_{DSQ} = 5$ V, $V_{GSQ} = -1.5$ V, $I_{DQ} = 0.5$ mA and $g_m = 4\ \text{m}\Omega^{-1}$.

Answer: $R_G = 62.8$ kΩ; $R_{S1} = 3$ kΩ, $R_{S2} = 7$ kΩ; $A_i = 9.3$

6.11 OTHER DEVICES

Other devices that are an outgrowth of the normal two- and three-terminal devices are presented in this section.

6.11.1 Metal Semiconductor Barrier Junction Transistor

The *metal semiconductor barrier junction transistor* (MESFET) is similar to a FET, except that the junction is a metal semiconductor barrier, much as is the case with Schottky diodes. FETs made of silicon (Si) or gallium arsenide (GaAs) are constructed with diffused or ion implanted gates. However, there are advantages to using a Schottky barrier metal gate when the channel is *n*-type and short channel widths are needed. Gallium arsenide (GaAs) is difficult to work with, yet it makes good Schottky barriers that are useful in high frequency applications because electrons travel faster in GaAs than in Si. Using GaAs in MESFETs results in a transistor that exhibits good performance in microwave applications. In comparison with the silicon bipolar transistor, GaAs MESFETs have better performance at input frequencies above 4 GHz. These MESFETs exhibit high gain, low noise, high efficiency, high input impedance, and properties that prevent thermal runaway. They are used in microwave oscillators, amplifiers, mixers, and for high speed switching. GaAs MESFETs are used for high-frequency applications.

6.11.2 VMOSFET (VMOS)

Considerable research effort has been applied to increasing the power capability of solid state devices. An area that has shown much promise is the MOSFET where the conduction channel is modified to form a "V" rather than the conventional source-to-drain straight line. An additional semiconductor layer is added. The term *VMOS* is derived from the fact that the current between source and drain follows a vertical path due to the construction. The drain is now located on a piece of added semiconductor material, as illustrated in Figure 6.47. This allows the transistor drain area to be placed in contact with a heat sink to aid in dissipating the heat generated in the device. The V-shaped gate controls two vertical MOSFETs, one on each side of the notch. By parallelling the two S terminals, the current capacity can be doubled. VMOS is unsymmetrical so that the S and D terminals cannot be interchanged as is the case in low-power MOS FETs. Conventional FETs are limited to currents of the order of milliamperes, but VMOS FETs are available for operation in the 100A current range. This provides a great improvement in power over the conventional FET.

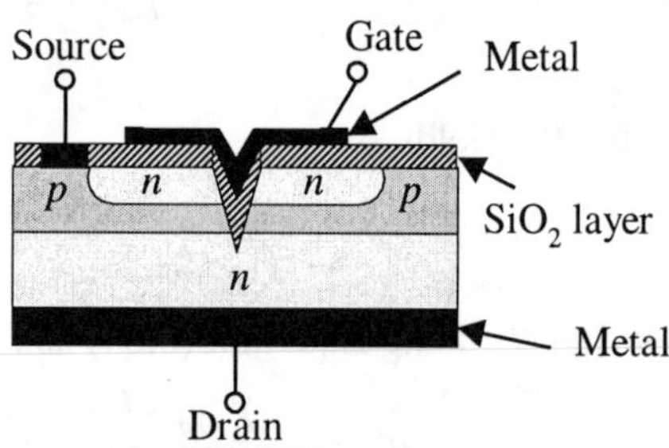

Figure 6.47 – VMOS construction

The VMOS device can provide a solution to high frequency, high power applications. Ten watt devices have been developed at frequencies in the lower ultra-high frequency (UHF) band. There are other important advantages of VMOS FETs. They have a negative temperature coefficient to prevent thermal runaway. They exhibit low leakage current. They are capable of achieving high switching speed. VMOS transistors can be made to have equal spacing of their characteristic curves for equal increments of gate voltage, so they can be used like bipolar junction transistors for high power linear amplifiers.

6.11.3 Other MOS Devices

Another type of MOS device is a *double-diffused process fabricated FET* sometimes called *DMOS*. This device has the advantage of decreasing the length of the channels, thus providing excellent low power dissipation and high speed capability.

Fabrication of a FET on small silicon islands on a substrate of sapphire is sometimes referred to as *SOS*. The islands of silicon are formed by etching a thin layer of silicon grown on the sapphire substrate. This type of fabrication provides insulation between the islands of silicon, thus greatly reducing parasitic capacitance between devices.

MOS technology has the advantage that both capacitors and resistors (using MOSFETs) are made at the same time as the FET, although large value capacitors are not feasible. Using an enhancement MOSFET, a two-terminal resistance is made and the MOSFET gate connected to the drain causes the FET to operate at pinch-off. The MOSFET gate is connected to the drain through a power source causing the FET to be biased where it will operate in the voltage-controlled resistance region of the characteristics. In this way, drain-load resistors are replaced by a MOSFET rather than a deposited resistor hence saving chip area.

SUMMARY

The purpose of this chapter was to introduce you to the analysis and design of amplifier circuits using field-effect transistors. The FET is quite different from the BJT. Its operation is controlled by a voltage as contrasted with the BJT which is a current-controlled device.

Our approach paralleled that of the BJT chapters. We began with an examination of the physical phenomena that govern FET behavior. In the process, we emphasized the contrast between FETs and BJTs. We began our study with MOSFETs and then turned our attention to JFETs. We developed small-signal models for these important devices. We used those models to analyze the various configurations of FET amplifiers. Once we knew how to analyze FET circuits, we turned our attention to design to meet specifications. We also examined the models used by computer simulation programs.

We briefly looked at the manner in which FETs are fabricated as part of integrated circuits. The chapter concluded with an introduction to other types of FET devices, including the MESFET and the VMOS.

PROBLEMS

Section 6.9

6.1 The characteristic curves for the operating region of a specific n-channel FET transistor can be approximated by the equation $i_D = 0.5(4 + v_{GS})^2$ mA when the following conditions hold: $R_S = 500\ \Omega$; $R_D = 2\ \text{k}\Omega$; $R_{in} = 100\ \text{k}\Omega$; $I_D = 5$ mA; $V_{DD} = 20$ V

Determine the following parameters:

(a) V_{GS}

(b) V_D

(c) V_{DS}

(d) R_1 and R_2

Refer to Figure P6.1.

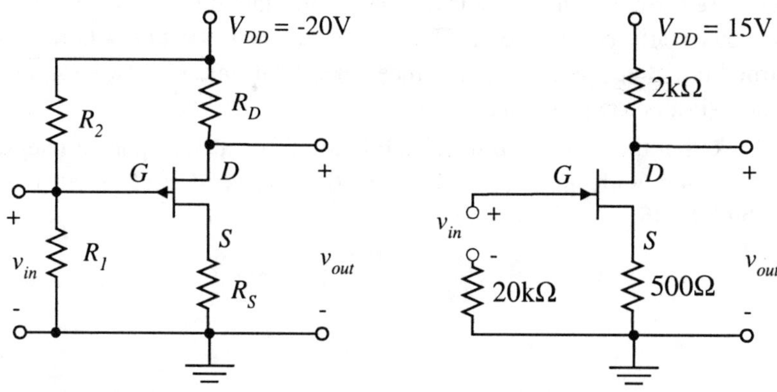

Figure P6.1

Figure P6.2

6.2 For the circuit shown in Figure P6.2, determine I_{DQ}, V_{DSQ}, and V_{GSQ} when the transistor used has $I_{DSS} = 10$ mA and $V_p = -5$ V.

6.3 Determine I_{DQ}, V_{DSQ}, and V_{GSQ} in the circuit shown in Figure P6.2, but substitute an n-channel MOSFET. The transistor used has an $I_D = 8$ mA when $V_{GS} = 0$ and $V_{GS} = -3$ V when $I_D = 0$.

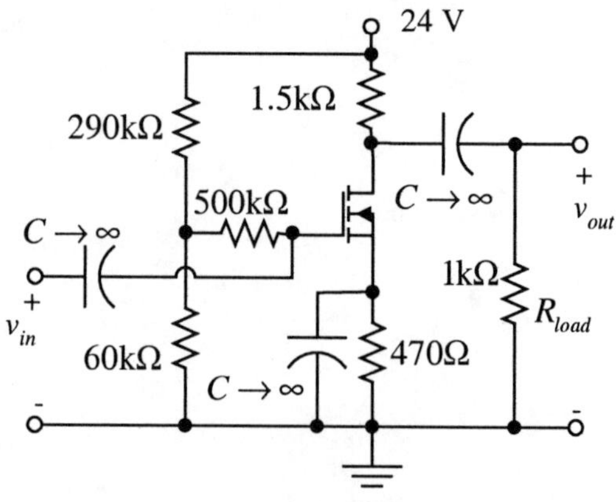

Figure P6.5

6.4 In the circuit in Figure 6.32(a), $R_1 = 21\ \text{k}\Omega$, $R_2 = 450\ \text{k}\Omega$, $R_S = 500\ \Omega$, $R_D = 1.5$

kΩ, $R_{load} = 4$ kΩ, and $V_{DD} = 12$ V. Find the following when $V_{DSQ} = 4$ V:

(a) I_{DQ}

(b) V_{GSQ}

(c) R_{in}

(d) A_v when $g_m = 3.16$ mΩ^{-1}

(e) A_i

6.5 The characteristic curve for a MOSFET transistor of i_d vs. v_{ds} for different magnitudes of v_{GS} in the operating region can be approximated by

$$i_D = 0.5(1 + v_{GS})^2 \text{ mA}$$

For the circuit shown in Figure P6.5 when $I_D = 4.5$ mA, determine:

(a) quiescent voltage from gate to source

(b) quiescent voltage from drain to ground

(c) quiescent voltage from drain to source

(d) input resistance to the stage

6.6 Analyze a common-gate JFET amplifier as shown in Figure 6.37(a) when $V_{DD} = 12$ V, $V_{SS} = 0$, $R_1 = 205$ kΩ, $R_2 = 8$ MΩ, $R_S = 500$ Ω, $R_D = 2$ kΩ, $R_{load} = 4$ kΩ, $I_{DQ} = 2.8$ mA, and the transistor has $I_{DSS} = 7$ mA and $V_P = -3$ V. Determine A_v, A_i, and R_{in} for the circuit.

6.7 The source-follower JFET amplifier as shown in Figure 6.39(a) has $V_{DD} = 12$ V, $V_{SS} = 0$, $R_D = 0$, $R_S = 1.5$ kΩ, $R_{load} = 3$ kΩ, $R_1 = 161$ kΩ, $R_2 = 264$ kΩ, and a transistor with $I_{DSS} = 8$ mA and a $V_P = -5$ V. Determine A_v, A_i, and R_{in} for the circuit.

6.8 The transistor in the source-follower amplifier in Figure 6.39(a) is changed to an *n*-channel MOSFET. Determine A_v, A_i, and R_{in} when $V_{DD} = 15$ V, $V_{SS} = 0$, $R_D = 0$, $R_S = 3$ kΩ, $R_{load} = 5$ kΩ, $R_1 = 218$ kΩ, $R_2 = 185$ kΩ, and the transistor has $I_D = 6$ mA when $V_{GS} = 0$ and $V_{GS} = -3$ V when $I_D = 0$.

Section 6.10.1

6.9 In the circuit of Figure 6.33(a), $R_D = 2$ kΩ, $R_{load} = 5$ kΩ, $R_{in} = 100$ kΩ, $R_S = 300$ Ω, and $V_{DD} = 15$ V. Find the values of R_1 and R_2 needed for the transistor to operate at 4 mA when $V_p = -4$ V and $I_{DSS} = 8$ mA. Also determine the voltage and current gain of the amplifier.

6.10 (a) Design a CS amplifier (Figure P6.1) using a *p*-channel JFET when the specification calls for $A_v = -10$ and $R_{in} = 20$ kΩ. Assume the Q-point is chosen at $I_{DQ} = -1$ mA, $V_{DSQ} = -10$ V, $V_{GSQ} = 0.5$ V.

(b) Calculate A_i, R_1, R_2, R_S and R_D. (Refer to the characteristic curve in Figure P6.10. Note that you may have to split R_S and bypass part of it).

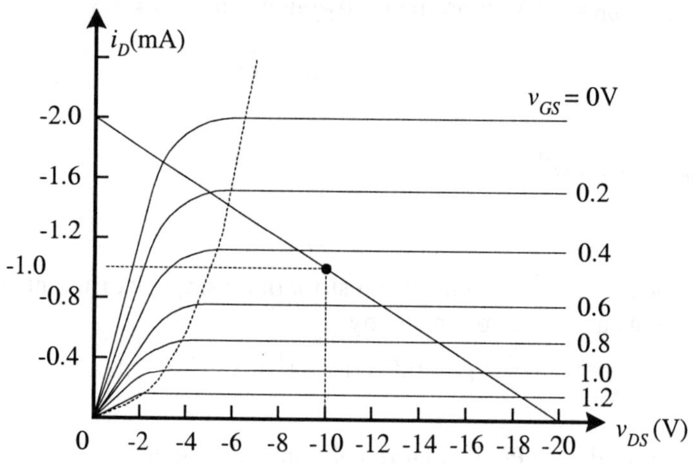

Figure P6.10

6.11 Repeat Problem 6.10 when an R_{load} of 20 kΩ is coupled to the drain with a capacitor. Note that you may need to choose a different Q-point.

6.12 Using the circuit of the type shown in Figure 6.33(a) with R_{load} =5 kΩ, A_v = -1.45, and V_{DD} = 12 V, find the values of all resistors for a Q-point selected at V_{GSQ} = -1.5 V, V_{DSQ} = 6 V, I_{DQ} = 2.4 mA, g_m = 3.17 mΩ^{-1}, and R_{in} = 200 kΩ.

6.13 Determine the I_{DSS} and V_p of the transistor used in Problem 6.12.

6.14 Design a CS amplifier using a MOSFET, as shown in Figure P6.14. Let R_{load} = 1 kΩ, A_v = -1, R_{in} = 15 kΩ. The Q-point is chosen at V_{GSQ} = 3 V, I_{DQ} = 7 mA, V_{DSQ} = 10 V, where g_m = 2300 μΩ^{-1}. Find values for all other elements.

6.15 Design a CS amplifier using an *n*-channel JFET for a circuit of the type shown in Figure 6.40(a). Let A_v = -1, V_{DD} = 12 V, R_{load} = 1 kΩ, R_{in} = 15 kΩ, I_{DSS} = 10 mA and V_p = -4 V. Use I_{DQ} = I_{DSS}/2.

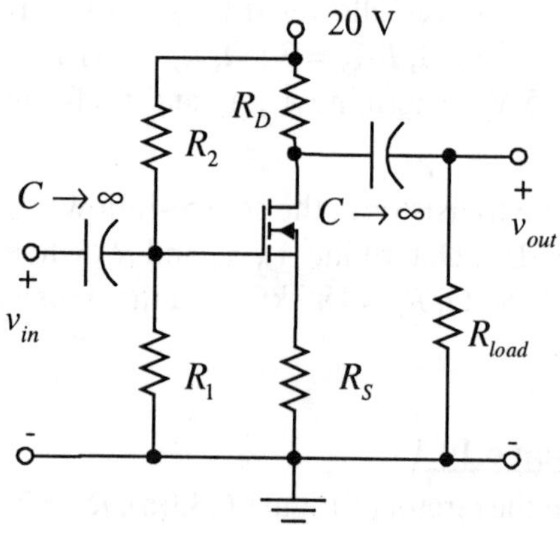

Figure P6.14

6.16 Design a CS amplifier using an *n*-channel JFET when R_{load} = 4 kΩ, A_v = -3, and R_{in} = 50 kΩ. Assume that a transistor is used which has a V_p = -4.2 V and I_{DSS} = 6 mA. Use the circuit of Figure 6.40(a) with V_{DD} = 20 V. Determine A_i.

6.17 Design an n-channel MOSFET CS amplifier that has $A_v = -2$, $A_i = -20$, $V_{DD} = 12$ V, and $R_{load} = 5$ kΩ. Determine all component values and the power rating of the transistor. (The circuit may require changes to meet the design). The selected transistor has a $V_{GS} = -5$ V when $I_D = 0$ and $I_D = 8$ mA when $V_{GS} = 0$. Use $I_{DQ} = 0.4I_D$ (when $V_{GS} = 0$) and $V_{DSQ} = V_{DD}/2$. Use Figure 6.40(a) as guide.

6.18 Design a CS p-channel MOSFET amplifier with $A_v = -4$, $A_i = -40$, $R_{load} = 8$ kΩ, and $V_{DD} = -16$ V. The selected transistor has a $V_{GS} = 3$ V when $I_D = 0$ and $I_D = -7$ mA when $V_{GS} = 0$. Use $I_{DQ} = 0.3I_D$ (value of I_D when $V_{GS} = 0$) and $V_{DSQ} = V_{DD}/2$. Use the circuit of Figure P6.18. Also determine the power rating of the transistor.

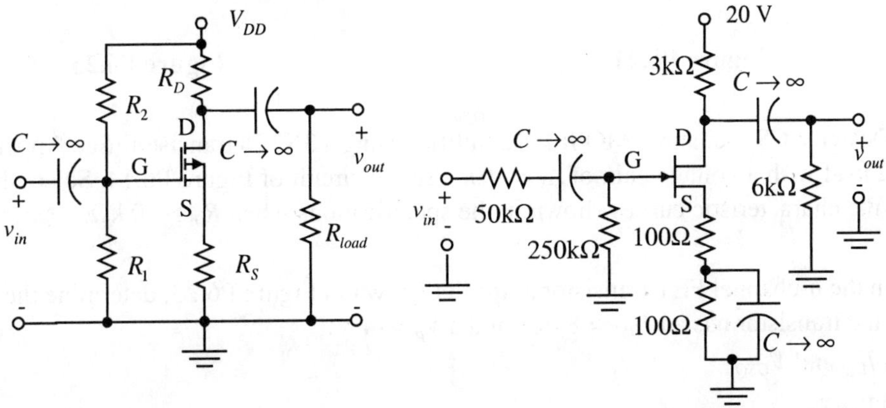

Figure P6.18 **Figure P6.19**

6.19 Analyze the circuit shown in Figure P6.19 and determine the following when the transistor has a $V_p = -3$ V and $I_{DSS} = 8$ mA:

(a) I_{DQ} and V_{GSQ}

(b) V_{DSQ} and g_m

(c) v_{out}/v_{in} and A_i

6.20 Design a CS p-channel MOSFET amplifier with a 5 kΩ load using the circuit shown in Figure P6.18. Let $V_{DD} = -20$ V, $A_v = -4$, $A_i = -20$, $V_{GS} = 6$ V when $I_D = 0$, and $I_D = -5$ mA when $V_{GS} = 0$. Determine the power rating of the transistor.

6.21 In the circuit shown in Figure P6.21, the n-channel JFET transistor amplifier has a $V_{GS} = -1.8$ V and the transistor used has an $I_{DSS} = 5$ mA. Determine:

(a) I_{DQ} and V_{DSQ}

(b) g_m and A_v

(c) A_i and R_{in}

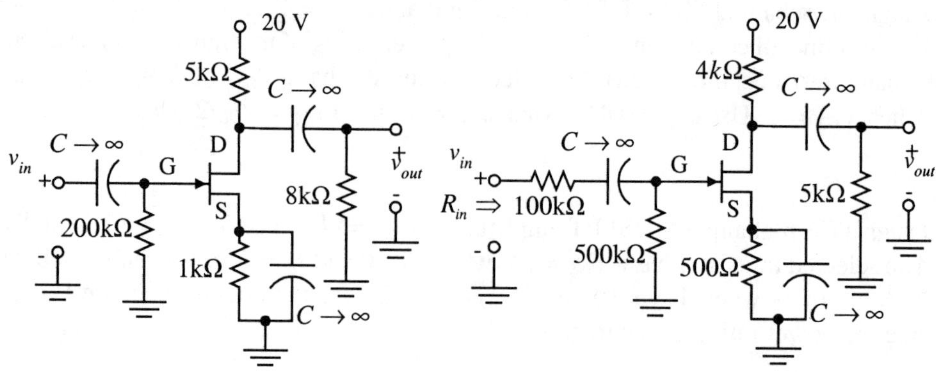

Figure P6.21 **Figure P6.23**

6.22 Design a CS n-channel MOSFET amplifier using a 3N128 transistor (See Appendix) for a 10 kΩ load with a voltage gain of $A_v = -10$. Use the circuit of Figure P6.14. Select the Q-point using the characteristic curves shown in the specifications when $R_{in} > 10$ kΩ.

6.23 In the n-channel FET transistor amplifier shown in Figure P6.23, determine the following when the transistor has an $I_{DSS} = 8$ mA and a $V_p = -4$ V:

(a) I_{DQ} and V_{GSQ}

(b) v_{out}/v_{in}

(c) A_i and R_{in} as shown in Figure P6.23

6.24 Design a CS n-channel MOSFET amplifier using a 3N128 transistor (See Appendix) for a 2 kΩ load with $A_v = -4$ and $R_{in} > 100$ kΩ. Assume that the Q-point is chosen as $V_{GSQ} = -0.6$ V, $V_{DSQ} = 10$ V, $I_{DQ} = 10$ mA, $V_{DD} = 20$ V.

6.25 Analyze a CS n-channel JFET amplifier as shown in Figure P6.25 when the load is 20 kΩ, $R_D = 8$ kΩ, $V_{DD} = 24$ V and $R_{in} = 50$ kΩ. Select the Q-point as $V_{GSQ} = -1.5$ V, $V_{DSQ} = 12$ V, $I_{DQ} = 1$ mA, and $g_m = 2.83$ mΩ^{-1}. Find all component values, A_i, and A_v.

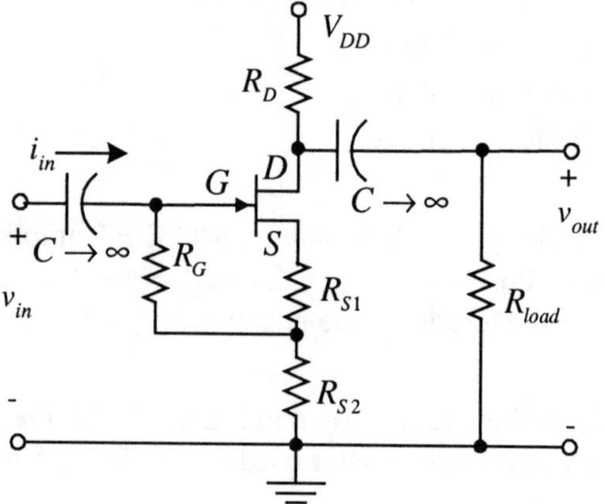

Figure P6.25

6.26 If the resistor, R_S, in Figure P6.18 is bypassed with a capacitor, what is the voltage gain? Assume that the Q-point is selected so that $g_m = 1.5$ mΩ^{-1}, $R_D = 3.2$ kΩ and $R_{load} = 5$

kΩ. Determine the current gain when $R_S = 500\ \Omega$, $R_1 = 200\ k\Omega$, and $R_2 = 800\ k\Omega$.

6.27 What is the voltage gain, A_v, and voltage gain of the stage of the circuit shown in Figure P6.18 if a signal is fed into the amplifier which has a source voltage resistance, R_{in} of 10 kΩ? Assume $R_D = 4\ k\Omega$, $R_{load} = 10\ k\Omega$, $R_S = 500\ \Omega$, $g_m = 2\ m\Omega^{-1}$, $R_1 = 25\ k\Omega$ and $R_2 = 120\ k\Omega$.

6.28 In the circuit shown in Figure P6.28, assume that R_S is bypassed entirely with a capacitor. $V_{DD} = 15$ V, $R_D = 2\ k\Omega$, $R_{load} = 3\ k\Omega$, $R_S = 200\ \Omega$, $R_1 = 500\ k\Omega$, $I_{DSS} = 8$ mA, and $V_P = -4$ V. Determine A_v, A_i, R_{in}, and the Q-point for the amplifier.

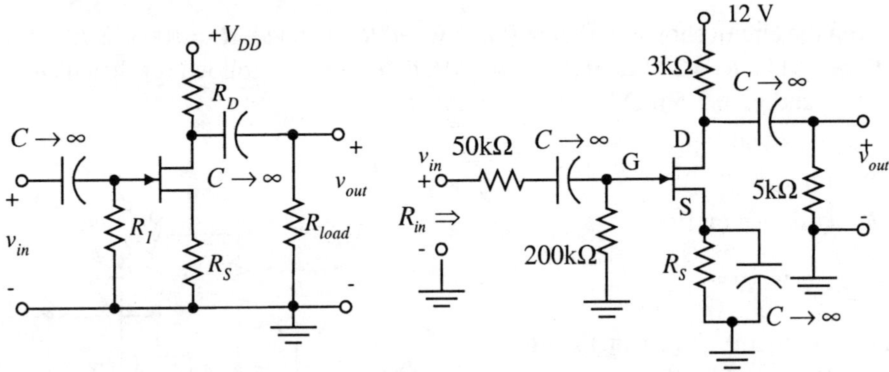

Figure P6.28 **Figure P6.29**

6.29 In the *n*-channel transistor amplifier shown in Figure P6.29, the voltage between the drain and ground is 6 V. Determine the size of R_S, A_v, A_i, and R_{in} for the amplifier if the transistor has an $I_{DSS} = 8$ mA and a $V_p = -3$ V. Also find the value of v_{out}/v_{in} and R_{in} of the whole stage.

6.30 In the circuit shown in Figure P6.28, $V_{DD} = 20$ V, $R_D = 2\ k\Omega$, $R_{load} = 10\ k\Omega$, $R_S = 200\ \Omega$, $R_1 = 1\ M\Omega$, $I_{DSS} = 10$ mA, and $V_p = -5$ V. Determine the Q-point, A_v, A_i, and R_{in} for the amplifier.

6.31 For the amplifier shown in Figure P6.28, $V_{DD} = 20$ V, $R_D = 2\ k\Omega$, $R_{load} = 6\ k\Omega$, $R_S = 100\ \Omega$, $R_1 = 1\ M\Omega$, $I_{DSS} = 10$ mA, and $V_p = -5$ V. Determine the Q-point, A_v, A_i, and R_{in} for the amplifier.

6.32 A CS amplifier circuit as shown in Figure P6.1 with $V_{DD} = +20$V using an *n*-channel JFET for which $I_{DSS} = 2$ mA and $g_{mo} = 2000\ \mu\Omega^{-1}$. If the value of $R_D = 10\ k\Omega$ and $R_S = 200\ \Omega$, what is the voltage gain, A_v, when V_{GS} is:

(a) -1 V

(b) -0.5 V

(c) 0 V

6.33 A CS amplifier circuit as shown in Figure P6.28 has a transistor with a $V_p = -4$ V, $I_{DSS} = 4$ mA and $R_{ds} = 500\ \Omega$. If $R_D = 2\ k\Omega$, $R_{load} = 4\ k\Omega$, and $R_S = 200\ \Omega$, what is the voltage gain, A_v, of the circuit if $V_{GSQ} = -1$ V? What happens to A_v as R_{ds} approaches infinity? What is A_v when $R_{ds} = 100\ k\Omega$?

6.34 Design a CS n-channel MOSFET amplifier as shown in Figure P6.14 when $R_{load} = 4\ k\Omega$, $A_v = -5$ and $A_i = -10$. Assume that the Q-point is selected as $V_{DSQ} = 10$ V, $V_{GSQ} = 4$ V, $I_{DQ} = 2$ mA and $g_m = 4000\ \mu\Omega^{-1}$.

6.35 Given the circuit shown in Figure P6.35 when $R_{in} = 50\ k\Omega$, $R_1 = 100\ k\Omega$, $R_2 = 800\ k\Omega$, $R_D = 4\ k\Omega$, $R_{load} = 6\ k\Omega$, $R_S = 200\ \Omega$, and $V_{DD} = 20$ V, determine the following when using a FET with a $V_{DS} = 6$ V and $g_m = 2.5\ m\Omega^{-1}$:

(a) I_{DQ}, V_{GG}, and V_{GSQ}

(b) A_v and v_{out}/v_{source}

(c) R_{in} as shown on figure

(d) A_i

6.36 For the circuit shown in Figure P6.35, if R_2 is removed (i.e., set to infinity), the FET transistor is operating at 2 mA. The component values are $R_{in} = 100\ k\Omega$, $R_D = 3\ k\Omega$, $R_{load} = 5\ k\Omega$, and $V_{DD} = 12$ V. Determine the following when the transistor has an $I_{DSS} = 8$ mA and $V_p = -4$ V:

(a) R_S

(b) A_v and v_{out}/v_{source}

(c) R_{in} as shown in figure

(d) A_i

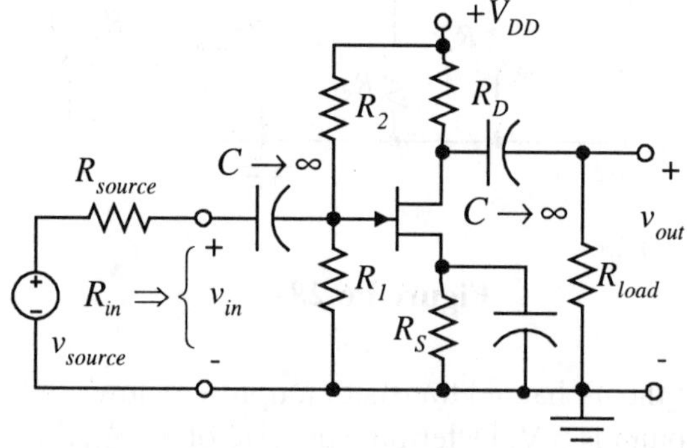

Figure P6.35

6.37 Design an amplifier using an n-channel MOSFET for a voltage gain of -4 with $R_{in} = 100\ k\Omega$ to a 5 kΩ load when $V_{DD} = 12$ V. The Q-point was selected to be $V_{DSQ} = 6$ V, $I_{DQ} = 2$ mA, $V_{GSQ} = -1$ V and $g_m = 4.0\ m\Omega^{-1}$. Determine:

(a) All resistor values ($R_1 = 400k\Omega$)

(b) Current Gain

(c) Draw the final circuit with resistor values

6.38 Determine the A_v, A_i, I_{DQ}, and R_{in} of the CG amplifier configuration as shown in Figure 6.37(a) with the JFET replaced by an n-channel MOSFET. The component values are $V_{DD} = 20$ V, $R_D = 5$ kΩ, $R_{load} = 8$ kΩ, $R_S = 800$ Ω, $R_1 = 103$ kΩ, $R_2 = 4$ mΩ, and the transistor has an $I_D = 5$ mA when $V_{GS} = 0$ and $V_{GS} = -3$ V when $I_D = 0$.

6.39 Design a CG amplifier using an n-channel MOSFET to match 250 Ω to a 5 kΩ load. Use a transistor which has an $I_D = 6$ mA when $V_{GS} = 0$ and $V_{GS} = -3$ V when $I_D = 0$. Assume that $R_G = 100$ kΩ, $V_{DD} = 20$ V, $I_{DQ} = 0.5\, I_D$ when $V_{GS} = 0$ and $V_{DSQ} = V_{DD}/2$. Determine all resistor values, A_v and A_i. Use Figure 6.37(a) as a guide.

Section 6.10.2

6.40 Design a SF amplifier using a p-channel JFET as shown in Figure P6.40 with $R_{in} = 20$ kΩ. Try to obtain a voltage gain, A_v, as close to unity as possible. Calculate A_i, R_1, R_2, and R_S. Use the characteristic curves as shown in Figure P6.10.

6.41 Repeat Problem 6.40 when a 20 kΩ load is capacitively coupled to the amplifier.

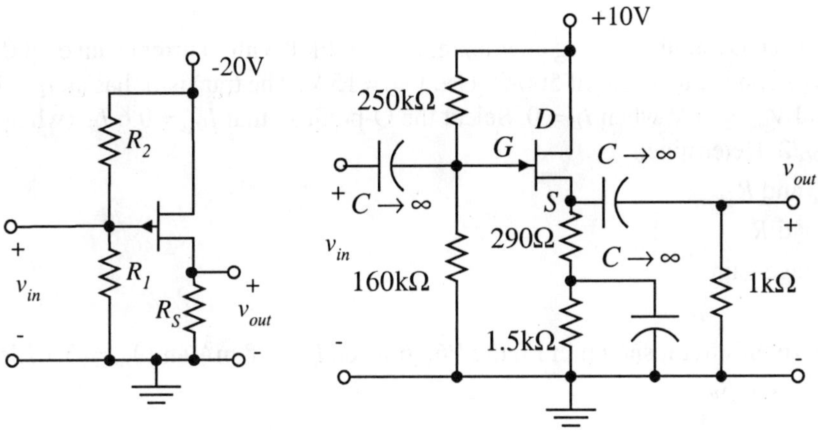

Figure P6.40 **Figure P6.42**

6.42 Analyze the circuit shown in Figure P6.42 when $I_{DSS} = 7$ mA and $V_p = -3$ V to determine I_{DQ}, V_{GSQ}, A_v, A_i, and R_{in}.

6.43 Design a CD MOSFET amplifier when $R_{load} = 100$ Ω, $A_i = 200$, and $R_{in} = 100$ kΩ. Use a transistor with $V_T = -6$ V and $I_{DSS} = 20$ mA. Determine A_v and all resistor values. Use the circuit of Figure P6.43.

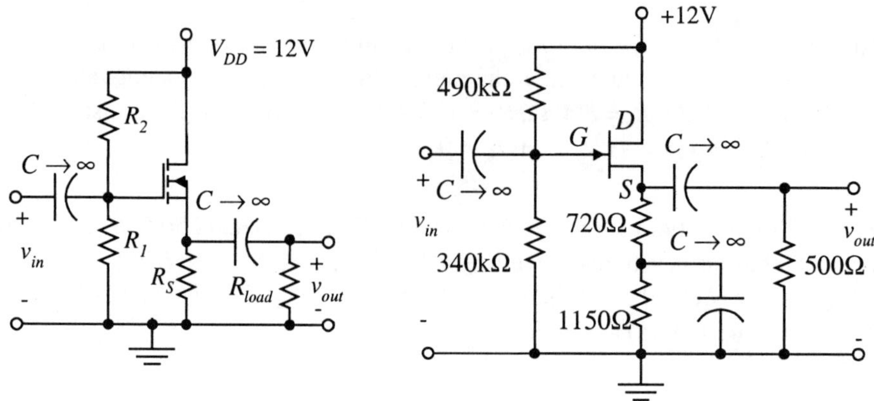

Figure P6.43 **Figure P6.46**

6.44 The circuit in Figure P6.43 has the following component values: $V_{DD} = 10$ V, $R_1 = 120$ kΩ, $R_2 = 610$ kΩ, $R_S = 1$ kΩ, $R_{load} = 4$ kΩ, and the transistor has an $I_D = 7$ mA when $V_{GS} = 0$ and $V_{GS} = -3$ V when $I_D = 0$. Determine the I_{DQ}, A_v, A_i, and R_{in} for the circuit.

6.45 Design a CD amplifier using an *n*-channel MOSFET with a current gain of 200 and an input resistance of 200 kΩ to a load of 500 Ω. Use $V_{DD} = 15$ V. The transistor has an $I_D = 10$ mA when $V_{GS} = 0$ and $V_{GS} = -4$ V when $I_D = 0$. Select the Q-point so that $I_{DQ} = 0.6\, I_D$ (when $V_{GS} = 0$) and $V_{DSQ} = V_{DD}/2$. Determine:

(a) R_{Sac} and R_{Sdc}

(b) R_1 and R_2

(c) Voltage gain

6.46 Analyze the circuit shown in Figure P6.46 when $I_{DSS} = 8$ mA and $V_p = -3$ V, determine I_{DQ}, V_{GSQ}, A_v, A_i, and R_{in}.

6.47 Design a CD amplifier using an *n*-channel JFET with a current gain of 300 and an input resistance of 400 kΩ to a 600-Ω load with $V_{DD} = 15$ V. The transistor has an $I_{DSS} = 8$ mA and a $V_p = -4$ V. Select the Q-point for $I_{DQ} = 0.4 I_{DSS}$ and $V_{DSQ} = V_{DD}/2$. Determine:

(a) R_{Sac} and R_{Sdc}

(b) R_1 and R_2

(c) Voltage gain

6.48 Design a CD amplifier using an *n*-channel MOSFET where $R_{in} = 120$ kΩ, $A_i = 100$, $R_{load} = 500$ Ω, $V_{DD} = 20$ V, and the transistor selected has $V_{GS} = -5$ V when $I_D = 0$ and $I_D = 15$ mA when $V_{GS} = 0$. Use the circuit of Figure P6.43 as a guide with $I_{DQ} = 0.6 I_D$ (when $V_{GS} = 0$) and $V_{DSQ} = V_{DD}/2$.

6.49 For the circuit shown in Figure P6.49, determine I_{DQ}, A_v, A_i, and R_{in} when the transistor has a V_p = -3 V and I_{DSS} = 10 mA.

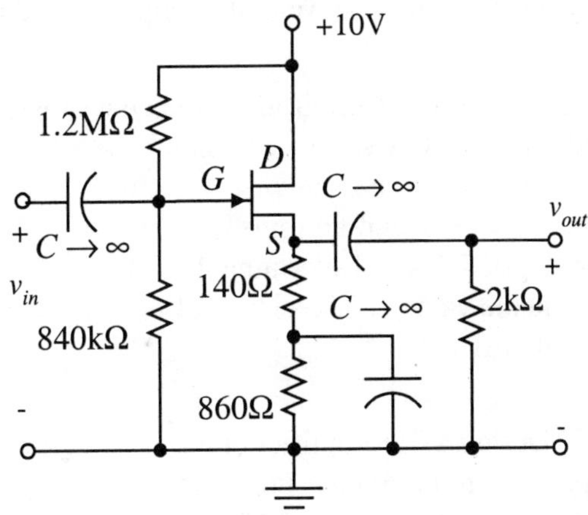

Figure P6.49

6.50 Design an SF amplifier using an *n*-channel JFET for a current gain of 100 and an input resistance of 500 kΩ. The load is 2 kΩ. Select the Q-point for the following parameters:

V_{DSQ} = 8 V, I_{DQ} = 5 mA, V_{GSQ} = -1 V, and g_m = 4 mΩ^{-1}

Determine the resistances and the voltage gain and draw the circuit when V_{DD} = 10 V.

6.51 Repeat Problem 6.50 except with a different transistor having the following parameters:

V_p = -3 V, I_{DSS} = 10 mA

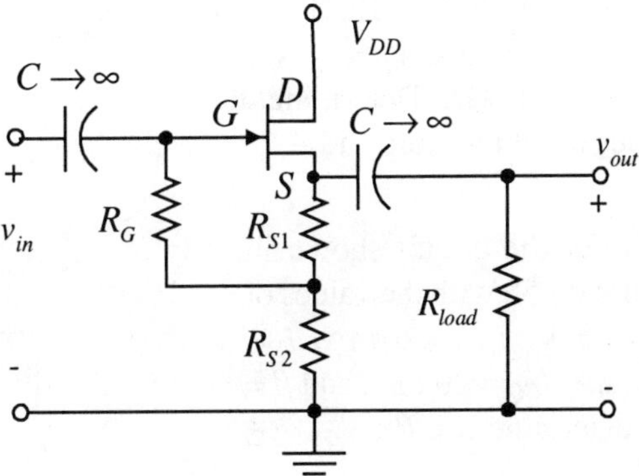

Figure P6.52

<u>**Section 6.10.3**</u>

6.52 Analyze the circuit shown in Figure P6.52 when V_{DD} = 16 V, and R_{load} = 8 kΩ. Use a transistor which has a V_p = -3.33 V and I_{DSS} = 10 mA. Determine all component values, A_i, and A_v when R_{in} = 12 kΩ.

6.53 For the circuit shown in Figure P6.52, design a SF bootstrap circuit when V_{DD} = 12 V, R_{load} = 1 kΩ, and R_{in} = 1 MΩ. The Q-point is chosen as follows: V_{DSQ} = 6 V, I_{DQ} = 6.1 mA, V_{GSQ} = -0.8 V. Also calculate the voltage and current gain.

6.54 In Figure P6.52, change the transistor from a JFET to a MOSFET and redo Problem 6.52. The MOSFET transistor has an I_D = 8 mA when V_{GS} = 0 and a V_{GS} = -3 V when I_D = 0. Determine all component values, A_v and A_i when R_{in} = 12 kΩ. Use I_{DQ} = 0.5 KV_T^2 and V_{DSQ} = 0.5 V_{DD}.

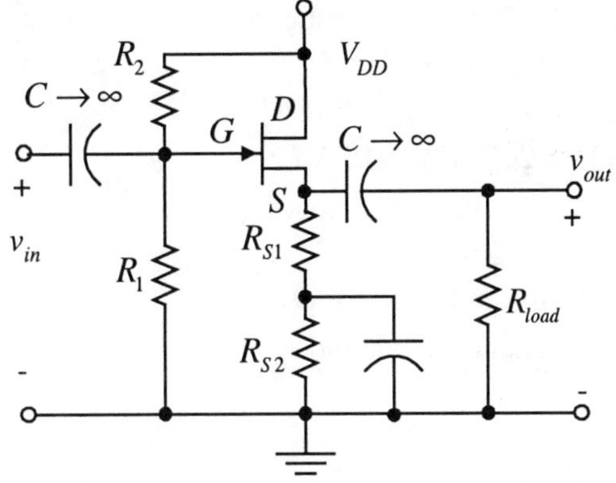

Figure P6.56

6.55 In Problem 6.52, find all component values, A_i, and A_v when $R_{in} = 200$ kΩ.

6.56 Design a CD amplifier of the type shown in Figure P6.56 with $R_{load} = 4$ kΩ, $R_{in} = 200$ kΩ, and $V_{DD} = 12$ V. Use an n-channel transistor which has an $I_{DSS} = 8$ mA, $V_p = -3$ V and an unusually low R_{ds} of 2.5 kΩ. Determine A_v, A_i, and the value of all resistors of the amplifier.

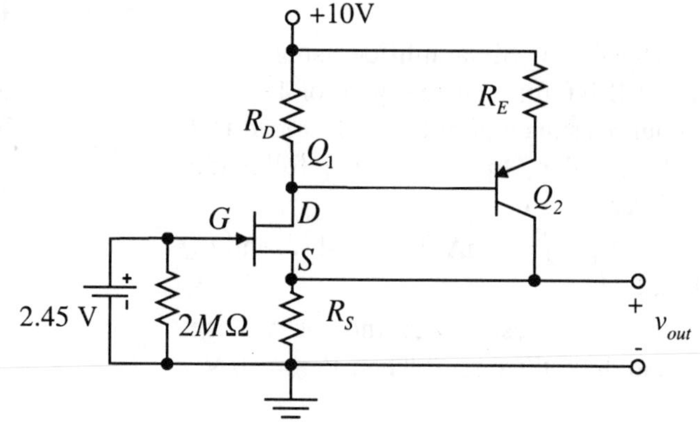

Figure P6.58

6.57 Design a CD amplifier of the type shown in Figure P6.56 to provide a current gain of 15 to a load of 20 kΩ. $V_{DD} = 12$ V and $R_{in} = 400$ kΩ. The transistor to be used is an n-channel JFET which has $I_{DSS} = 10$ mA, $V_p = -4$ V and an $R_{ds} = 4$ kΩ. Determine the values of all resistors and A_v.

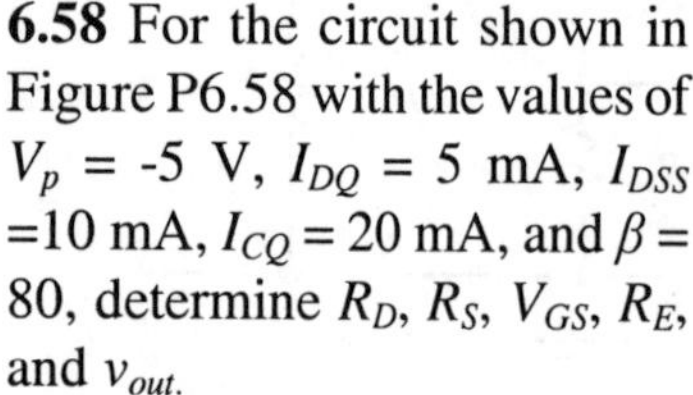

6.58 For the circuit shown in Figure P6.58 with the values of $V_p = -5$ V, $I_{DQ} = 5$ mA, $I_{DSS} = 10$ mA, $I_{CQ} = 20$ mA, and $\beta = 80$, determine R_D, R_S, V_{GS}, R_E, and v_{out}.

6.59 For the circuit shown in Figure P6.59, determine the following when:

Q_1 [$V_p = -3$ V, $I_{DSS} = 9$ mA]

Q_2 [$\beta = 200$, $V_{BE} = 0.7$ V]

(a) I_{DQ}, V_{GSQ}, V_{DSQ}, and g_m for Q_1

(b) I_{CQ} and V_{CEQ} for Q_2

(c) v_{out}/v_{in}, i_{out}/i_{in}, and R_{in}

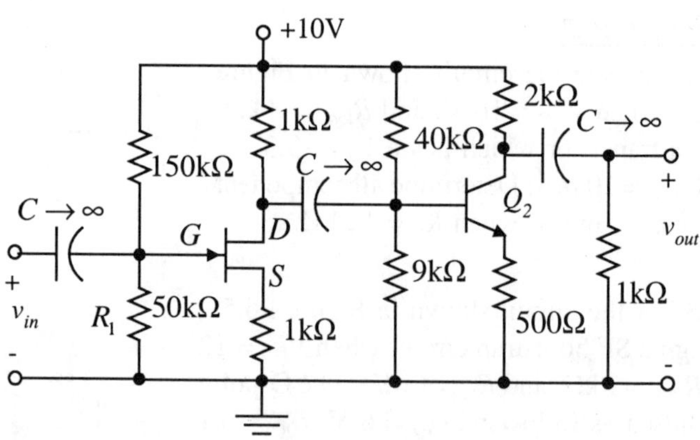

Figure P6.59

Chapter 7
Bias Stability of Transistor Amplifiers

7.0 INTRODUCTION

Parameter variations, such as those due to temperature changes, aging, and device substitutions, cause the operating point of a transistor circuit to vary from the nominal value. Designers often expend considerable effort to reduce the effects of these parameter variations since such changes can adversely affect performance. For example, a change in the location of the Q-point can reduce the maximum symmetrical undistorted output swing. Such changes could saturate or cut off the transistor.

Parameters vary because of changes in supply voltage, changes in temperature, and also as a result of tolerances in the transistor manufacturing process. This chapter studies the effects of these changes. Once the effects are understood, we examine several discrete amplifier configurations. Design examples are presented. We then introduce diode compensation as one method of reducing the effects of parameter variations. The chapter concludes with a summary of the design approach needed to insure bias stability.

When you complete this chapter, you will

- Understand the various biasing techniques.
- Understand the mechanisms for variations in amplifier operation.
- Be able to compensate for parameter variations using diode compensation.
- Be able to design BJT and FET amplifiers with stable bias characteristics.
- Be able to design amplifiers to reduce the effects of temperature variations.

7.1 TYPES OF BIASING

We now illustrate various biasing techniques using BJTs. The same biasing techniques can be applied to FETs, although the motivation is somewhat different. For example, temperature does not affect FET operation in the same manner as it does BJT operation.

Feedback (specifically, *negative* feedback) is defined as sending a part of the output back and subtracting it from the input. It reduces the effects of parameter variations. Many systems use feedback around high-gain IC amplifiers (op-amps), and we discuss the concept of feedback as used with the various biasing techniques. The intent is to illustrate useful techniques of *dc* biasing of transistor circuits. Feedback systems are examined in more detail in Chapter 12.

7.1.1 Current Feedback Biasing

Figure 7.1 illustrates a form of biasing which exhibits moderate stability. This is known as *current feedback*, where emitter (collector) current through R_E develops a negative feedback voltage.

The base resistor, R_B, is connected to the supply, V_{CC}. We begin by deriving the quiescent equations. The KVL equation for the bias current loop (assuming $I_E \approx I_C$) is given by,

$$V_{CC} = V_{BE} + I_B R_B + R_E I_C$$
$$= V_{BE} + I_C\left(\frac{R_B}{\beta} + R_E\right) \tag{7.1}$$

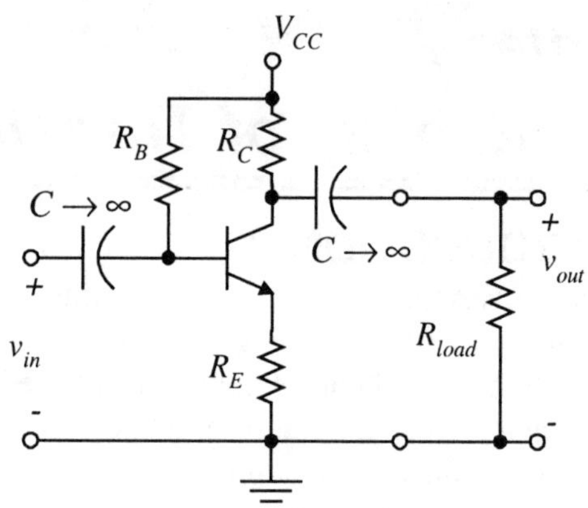

Figure 7.1 – Current feedback

We solve for I_C and I_B to obtain

$$I_C = \frac{V_{CC} - V_{BE}}{R_B/\beta + R_E} \tag{7.2}$$

$$I_B = \frac{I_C}{\beta} = \frac{V_{CC} - V_{BE}}{R_B + \beta R_E}$$

Note the value of I_B is affected by R_B, R_E, V_{CC}, V_{BE} and β. The specific values of these parameters then determine the quiescent operating point of the transistor.

Why is this configuration called "current feedback"? *Feedback* occurs when a circuit is configured in such a manner that the input is affected by the output. The emitter resistor in the circuit of Figure 7.1 provides a form of feedback. As the collector current increases, the voltage across the emitter resistor also increases. This increase in voltage across R_E reduces the base-emitter voltage and therefore also reduces the base current. This, in turn, decreases the collector current to reduce the effect of the original change. Because this effect is "fighting" against the increase in collector current, the situation is known as *negative current feedback.* The emitter resistor can be bypassed (for *ac* signals) with a capacitor. This eliminates the feedback for *ac* signals thus preventing reduction of gain. The *dc* stability is still affected by the feedback. In fact, for any reasonable value of voltage gain and β, the transistor will be driven into saturation. Therefore, we have difficulty achieving bias stability. If we limit the value of R_B to $0.1\beta R_E$ when using current feedback for *dc* bias stability (see Chapter 4), the relatively small base resistance restricts the *dc* bias current to a low level. This keeps the transistor from going into saturation.

7.1.2 Voltage and Current Biasing

A second type of feedback, shown in Figure 7.2, is *voltage feedback.*

Current feedback is still present due to R_E, so there are two forms of feedback present in this circuit. We feed back a portion of the output voltage through R_F and also feedback a portion of the output from the voltage developed across R_E. Increased gain can be achieved without affecting the *dc* biasing of the circuit by bypassing R_E with a capacitor.

The feedback resistor, R_F, is connected between the collector and base. The base-to-ground voltage is then composed of two components, one arising from the input voltage and one from the collector voltage.

We analyze this circuit by writing the *dc* equations between base and collector. In the following, we assume that the quiescent base current is much less than the quiescent collector current, and therefore can be ignored in the equations.

$$V_{CC} \approx I_C R_C + I_B R_F + V_{BE} + I_C R_E \tag{7.3}$$

$$= I_C R_C + \frac{I_C R_F}{\beta} + V_{BE} + I_C R_E$$

Now solving for the quiescent collector and quiescent base current, we have

$$I_C = \frac{V_{CC} - V_{BE}}{R_C + R_E + R_F/\beta} \tag{7.4}$$

$$I_B = \frac{I_C}{\beta} = \frac{V_{CC} - V_{BE}}{\beta(R_C + R_E) + R_F}$$

β appears in both equations. Variations in β therefore affect the Q-point location. It is desirable to make R_B equal to $0.1\beta(R_E+R_C)$ when using voltage and current biasing circuits as a rule of thumb. When using this criterion, it is impossible to obtain the maximum output voltage swing.

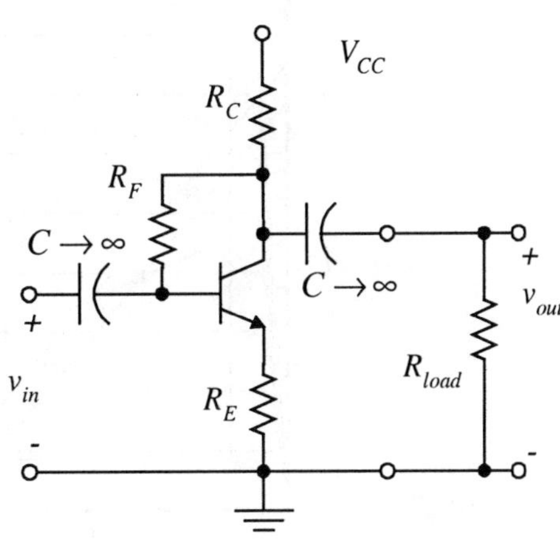

Figure 7.2 – Voltage feedback

EXERCISES

E7.1 Design a CE amplifier for maximum output voltage swing with a voltage gain of -10 and an output resistance of 10 kΩ. Use the circuit shown in Figure 7.1 with V_{CC}= 16V, V_{BE} = 0.7V and β = 100.

Answer: $R_C = 10\ k\Omega$; $R_E = 474\ \Omega, R_B = 1.48\ M\Omega$

E7.2 Design a CE amplifier with A_v = -10. Use the circuit of Figure 7.2 with R_{load} = 10 kΩ, V_{CC}= 16V, V_{BE} = 0.7V and β = 100.

Answer: $R_C = 10\ k\Omega$; $R_E = 474\ \Omega$, $R_F = 483\ k\Omega$; $v_{out(p\text{-}p)} = 9.0V$

E7.3 Select a value of R_F in the amplifier of Exercise E7.2 to provide bias stability against changes in β. What is the maximum undistorted symmetrical output voltage swing?

Answer: $R_F = 105\ k\Omega$; $v_{out(p\text{-}p)} = 2.85V$

7.2 EFFECTS OF PARAMETER CHANGES - BIAS STABILITY

Temperature variations cause some transistor parameters to change. In particular, the following parameters are temperature sensitive:

(1) Collector leakage current between base and collector (I_{CBO}).

(2) Base-emitter voltage (V_{BE})

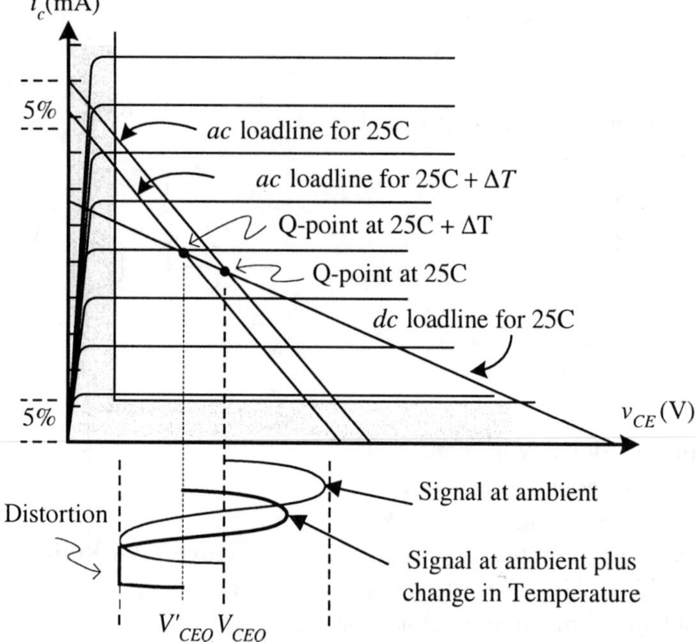

Figure 7.3 – V_{CEQ} and I_{CQ} with changes in temperature

The supply voltage, V_{CC}, and the β of the transistor also vary, but these are usually not dependent upon temperature. In many cases, the supply is sufficiently well-regulated that we can ignore changes in V_{CC}. However, for completeness in our derivation, such changes are included.

Variations in β can be significant, but the largest variations are caused by effects other than temperature. Variations in β are causes by random variations that occur during the manufacturing process.

As the temperature increases, the changes in the parameters cause the Q-point to move up (i.e., an increase in I_C). If the temperature is reduced, the Q-point moves down (i.e., a decrease in I_C). Either condition causes the maximum possible peak-to-peak output voltage swing to get smaller, as shown in Figure 7.3.

Collector current is a function of four variables, V_{BE}, I_{CBO} (the leakage current between collector and base), β, and V_{CC}. For small parameter changes, the variation in I_C is approximately given by

$$\Delta I_C = \frac{\partial I_C}{\partial V_{BE}} \Delta V_{BE} + \frac{\partial I_C}{\partial I_{CBO}} \Delta I_{CBO} + \frac{\partial I_C}{\partial \beta} \Delta \beta + \frac{\partial I_C}{\partial V_{CC}} \Delta V_{CC} \tag{7.5}$$

We define four *variation constants* as the partial derivatives of I_C with respect to the four variables. These constants are designated δ_V, δ_I, δ_β, and δ_{VCC}. In terms of these variation constants, Equation (7.5) becomes

$$\Delta I_C = \delta_V \Delta V_{BE} + \delta_I \Delta I_{CBO} + \delta_\beta \Delta\beta + \delta_{VCC} \Delta V_{CC} \tag{7.6}$$

The variation constants must have the appropriate units so that each term on the right side of Equation (7.6) has units of current. Let us now examine the four variables in Equation (7.6) in more detail.

The variation, ΔV_{BE}, is the change of the junction voltage between the base and emitter. This behaves in the same way as does the voltage across a diode, as discussed in Chapter 3. For a silicon transistor, the voltage varies linearly with temperature according to the following equation:

$$\Delta V_{BE} \approx -2(T_2 - T_1)\ \text{mV} \tag{7.7}$$

In Equation (7.7), T_2 and T_1 are in °K [Note when dealing with temperature differences, we can refer to either °K or °C].

The leakage current between the collector and base (the *reverse saturation current*) is also a function of temperature. The collector-to-base leakage current, I_{CBO}, approximately doubles for every 5°C temperature rise. This is given by Equation (7.8) where I_{CBO1} is the reverse leakage current at room temperature (25°C). We first saw in relationship in Equation (3.33).

$$I_{CBO2} = I_{CBO1} \times e^{k_i(T_2 - T_1)} \tag{7.8}$$

For silicon, k_i is 0.15/°C. The variation in collector-to-base leakage current is then

$$\Delta I_{CBO} = I_{CBO2} - I_{CBO1} = I_{CBO1} \cdot \left[e^{k_i(T_2 - T_1)} - 1 \right] \tag{7.9}$$

Since the primary variations of the other two parameters, V_{CC} and β, are due to factors other than temperature, information about the magnitude of these changes must be specified in the design statement.

7.2.1 CE Configuration

We find the variation constant for V_{BE}, δ_V, by first writing the KVL equation around the base-emitter loop. Refer to the circuit shown in Figure 7.4 and define V_{BB} and R_B as the Thevenin equivalent parameters for the base bias circuit. The quiescent collector current is then given by

$$I_C = \frac{V_{BB} - V_{BE}}{R_E + R_B/\beta} \tag{7.10}$$

where

$$V_{BB} = \frac{V_{CC} R_1}{R_1 + R_2}$$

$$R_B = R_1 \| R_2$$

The variation constant for base-emitter voltage is the partial derivative,

$$\delta_V = \frac{\partial I_C}{\partial V_{BE}} = -\frac{1}{R_E + R_B/\beta} \tag{7.11}$$

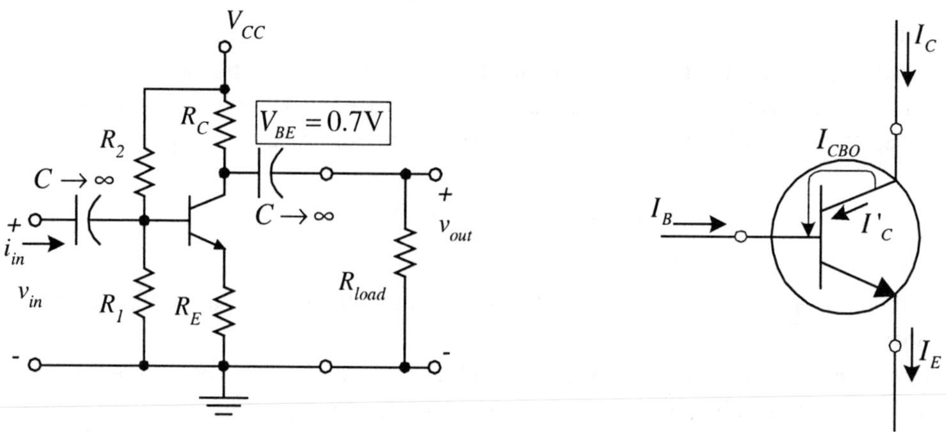

Figure 7.4 – Common-emitter amplifier **Figure 7.5 – Current in the transistor**

This variation constant decreases as the base and/or emitter resistance is increased. To design for minimum variation of collector quiescent current with changes in base-emitter voltage, we choose large resistances. Of course, we cannot use this observation in design until we examine the other parameters.

To find an expression for the variation constant for I_{CBO}, δ_I, we need a different expression for I_C. This is true since the expression of Equation (7.10) does not contain I_{CBO}. Figure 7.5 breaks the collector current into two parts. We see from the figure that

$$I_C = \beta(I_B + I_{CBO}) + I_{CBO} \approx \beta(I_B + I_{CBO}) \tag{7.12}$$

The last approximation in Equation (7.12) assumes that $\beta >> 1$. It might appear from Equation (7.12) that the partial derivative of the collector current with respect to I_{CBO} is $1+\beta$. However, this is not correct since I_B is also dependent on I_{CBO}. We therefore need an expanded expression for the base current. We find this by first writing the base-emitter loop (KVL) equation.

$$V_{BB} - V_{BE} = I_B(R_B + R_E) + R_E I_C \tag{7.13}$$

Combining Equations (7.12) and (7.13), we get

$$I_C = \frac{V_{BB} - V_{BE} + (R_B + R_E) I_{CBO}}{(R_B + R_E)/\beta + R_E} \tag{7.14}$$

The variation constant is found by taking the partial derivative, (since none of the other terms on the right side of Equation (7.14) have a direct dependence on I_{CBO}),

$$\delta_I = \frac{\partial I_C}{\partial I_{CBO}} = \frac{1}{1/\beta + R_E/(R_E + R_B)} \tag{7.15}$$

This variation constant decreases as the base resistance decreases. It might therefore seem appropriate in design to make the base resistance very small. However, doing so draws excessive current from the supply and also increases the variation constant associated with variations in base-emitter voltage. To properly choose the resistance values needed to increase stability, one must view the tradeoffs associated with specific parameter variations. In particular, you would have to see which of the four terms in Equation (7.6) predominates for a particular transistor and assumed power supply stability. Since this is a very complex analysis, we offer a "rule of thumb" that represents a compromise used in a wide variety of designs. The rule of thumb states that

$$R_B = 0.1\,\beta\, R_E \tag{7.16}$$

Using this rule of thumb, and assuming that β is large (on the order of 100 or more), we can assume $R_B >> R_E$. Under these conditions, δ_I is approximately given by

$$\delta_I = \frac{\beta}{1 + \beta R_E/R_B} \tag{7.17}$$

We now evaluate the variation constant for β. Although β does vary somewhat with temperature, the predominant variation is due to external factors. The range of values is usually given in the specification sheet for the transistor. The value of β used in the following equations is normally the mid value of the given range.

We start with the equation for collector current, Equation (7.14), and differentiate this with respect to β to obtain,

$$\frac{\partial I_C}{\partial \beta} = \frac{(R_B + R_E)\left[V_{BB} - V_{BE} + (R_B + R_E) I_{CBO}\right]}{(R_B + R_E + \beta R_E)^2} \tag{7.18}$$

If we can make the assumptions: $R_B >> R_E$, $\beta R_E >> R_B$ and $R_B I_{CBO} << (V_{BB} - V_{BE})$, the equation reduces to the following form:

$$\delta_\beta = \frac{R_B(V_{BB} - V_{BE})}{\beta^2 R_E^2} \tag{7.19}$$

The remaining variation constant is that associated with changes in the voltage supply V_{CC}. This is found from the collector-to-emitter loop equation.

$$I_C = \frac{V_{CC} - V_{CE}}{R_E + R_C}$$

$$\delta_{VCC} = \frac{\partial I_C}{\partial V_{CC}} = \frac{1}{R_E + R_C} \tag{7.20}$$

Putting all of these relationships together, the total change in I_C is found to be

$$\Delta I_C = -\frac{1}{R_E + R_B/\beta}\Delta V_{BE} + \frac{\beta}{1 + \beta R_E/R_B}\Delta I_{CBO} + \frac{R_B(V_{BB} - V_{BE})}{\beta^2 R_E^2}\Delta\beta + \frac{1}{R_E + R_C}\Delta V_{CC} \tag{7.21}$$

We will apply Equation (7.21) to several examples in order to find the variation in I_C that occurs when the temperature rises or drops. Using this equation, we can determine which terms cause the largest changes in I_C. If the total variation is too large for the amplifier application, we concentrate on the term(s) which cause the largest variation in I_C. Upon viewing this equation, we determine whether a parameter value should be raised or lowered. For example, if the second term is the largest, then it may be necessary to try to select a transistor which has a lower leakage current between collector and base (I_{CBO}). If this is not possible, the design must be changed to increase R_E/R_B.

Looking again at Equation (7.21), we observe that the transistor properties are such that the first two terms decrease when the temperature decreases, and they increase when the temperature rises. The last two terms are not explicitly temperature dependent. We would want to use the *worst case* values for these two terms. For example, when the temperature increases (and the signal of the first two terms is positive), we would use positive values for the last two terms for a worst case approach. Similarly, when the temperature is decreasing, we would use negative values for the last two terms.

Viewing the temperature dependence of Equations (7.11) and (7.15), we see that as temperature decreases, V_{BE} increases and I_{CBO} decreases. If we look at changes in quiescent collector current as temperatures decrease, we see that the first two terms in Equation (7.21) are negative. Since β and the supply voltage are not highly dependent on temperature, we conclude that as temperature decreases from ambient, I_C gets smaller.

EXAMPLE 7.1 - CE Amplifier

Design a CE amplifier with A_v = -10, R_{load} = 1 kΩ, and V_{CC} = 12V. The temperature varies between +25°C and +65°C. The selected transistor has an I_{CBO} = 0.05 μA at 25°C and a β that varies between 300 and 400. What is the maximum undistorted collector current swing?

Solution: Let us start the design by letting

$$R_C = R_{load} = 1\ \text{k}\Omega$$

Recall that setting R_C equal to R_{load} yields an optimum design. If our choice of 1 kΩ for these resistors results in unrealistic values for other components, we can come back and modify the choice. Now using the gain equation for CE amplifiers,

$$A_v = -\frac{R_{load} \| R_C}{R_E^{'}} = -10$$

so

$$R_E^{'} = 50\ \Omega$$

$$R_{ac} = R_E + R_C \| R_{load} = 550\ \Omega$$

$$R_{dc} = R_C + R_E = 1050\ \Omega$$

$$I_C = \frac{V_{CC}}{R_{ac} + R_{dc}} = 7.5\ \text{mA}$$

$$r_e = \frac{26\ \text{mV}}{|I_C|} = 3.47\ \Omega$$

$$R_E \approx 50 - 3 = 47\ \Omega$$

$$R_B = 0.1 \beta R_E = 1.65\ \text{k}\Omega$$

$$V_{BB} = I_C\left(\frac{R_B}{\beta} + R_E\right) + V_{BE} = 1.09\ \text{V}$$

For the temperature change from 25°C to 65°C, we first find the temperature-dependent variations in I_{CBO} and V_{BE}.

$$\Delta T = 40\quad {}^{\circ}C$$

$$\Delta I_{CBO} = I_{CBO1}(e^{0.15(40)} - 1) = 20.1\quad \mu\text{A}$$

$$\Delta V_{BE} = -2(40) = -80\quad \text{mV}$$

The variation in β is given as

$$\Delta\beta = 100$$

Since the problem says nothing about variations in V_{CC}, we assume that $\Delta V_{CC} = 0$. The change in I_C is now found from Equation (7.21).

$$\Delta I_C = 1.55\ \text{mA} + 0.64\ \text{mA} + 0.24\ \text{mA} = 2.43\ \text{mA}$$

We now find the new maximum symmetrical collector current swing. After movement in the positive direction, the new Q-point is at

$$I_{CQ} = (7.5 + 2.43)\text{ mA} = 9.93\text{ mA}$$

If we avoid the upper 5% of the load line because of nonlinearities, the maximum amplitude of the current swing is

$$(12.7 \times 0.95 - 9.93)\text{ mA} = 2.14\text{ mA}$$

The total swing of I_C has a peak-to-peak value of twice this amount, or 4.28 mA. This is the maximum peak-to-peak collector current for a distortion free output, and is illustrated in Figure 7.6. The maximum output voltage swing is reduced from 6.75V to 2.14V.

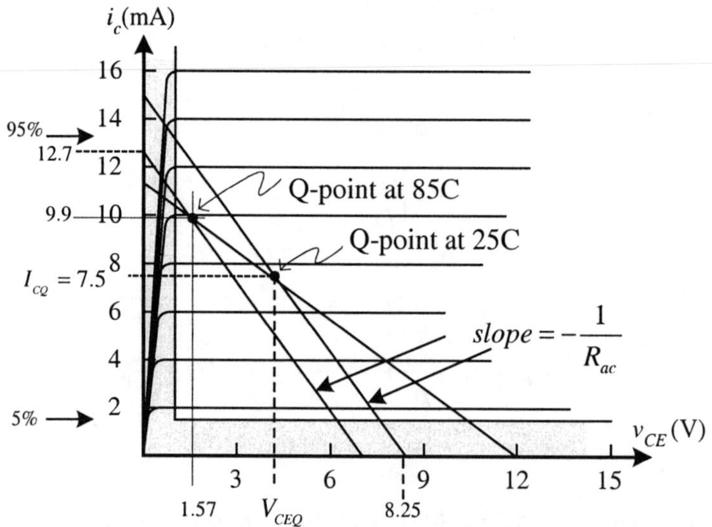

Figure 7.6 – Load lines for Example 7.1

In this design, the first term in the ΔI_C equation is the largest. Thus, the temperature effect on V_{BE} causes the largest change in I_C. If the amount of reduction in symmetrical output swing were not acceptable, we might try to reduce the temperature effect on V_{BE}. This could be accomplished by locating the amplifier in a cooler location or by providing for removal of heat from the transistor with a heat sink.

EXERCISES

E7.4 Determine the variation of I_C for a CE amplifier which is designed using the following criteria: $A_v = -10$, $R_{load} = 4\text{ k}\Omega$, $R_{in} = 5\text{ k}\Omega$, and $I_{CBO} = 0.001\ \mu\text{A}$ at 25°C. The value of β varies from 100 to 300 and the temperature ranges from 25°C to 85°C (see Figure 7.4).

Answer: I_C starts at 1.56 mA and increases to 2.63 mA at 85°C.

E7.5 What is the maximum undistorted symmetrical voltage output swing for the amplifier of Exercise E7.4?

Answer: 0V peak-to-peak

E7.6 If the amplifier in Example E7.4 is designed to operate from -25°C to +25°C, what is the variation in I_C?

Answer: I_C decreases by 0.754 mA

E7.7 What is the maximum undistorted symmetrical voltage output swing for the amplifier of Example E7.6?

Answer: 2.46V peak-to-peak

7.2.2 EF Configuration

The EF amplifier is shown in Figure 7.7. The biasing technique for this amplifier is similar to that of the CE with the one exception that the collector resistor, R_C, is equal to zero. Thus, the derivation is based upon the same bias equation,

$$I_C = \frac{V_{BB} - V_{BE}}{R_B/\beta + R_E} \tag{7.22}$$

The variation constants are then the same as those of the CE except that δ_{VCC} is $1/R_E$ rather than $1/(R_E+R_C)$. Equation (7.21) is once again used to find the variation in quiescent collector current.

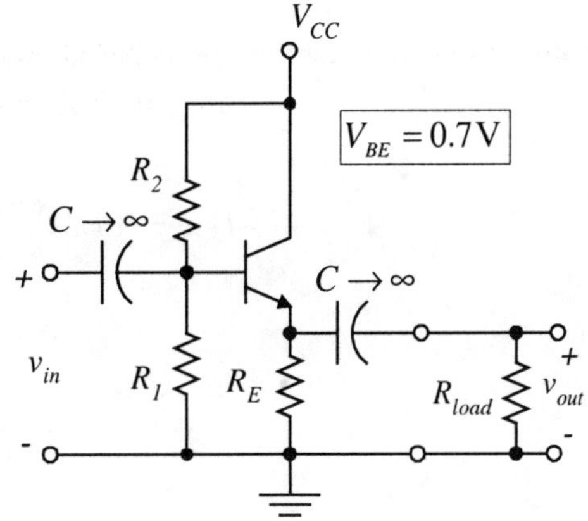

Figure 7.7 Emitter-follower amplifier

EXAMPLE 7.2 - EF Amplifier

Design an EF amplifier (See Figure 7.7) with $A_i = 10$, $I_{CBO1} = 0.05\ \mu\text{A}$ at 25°C and $R_{load} = 200\ \Omega$. The temperature varies between 25° and 85° while β varies between 80 and 120. The power supply voltage ranges between 17.5V and 18.5V.

Solution: Refer to Chapter 5 for the necessary design equations. We start by setting

$$R_E = R_{load} = 200\ \Omega$$

$$I_C = \frac{V_{CC}}{R_{ac} + R_{dc}} = \frac{18}{100 + 200} = 60\text{ mA}$$

Since this is an EF amplifier, we can ignore the effects of r_e in the current gain equation. The current gain is given by

$$A_i = 10 = \frac{R_B}{R_B/\beta + R_E \| R_{load}} \times \frac{R_E}{R_E + R_{load}}$$

so

$$R_B = 2.5\text{ k}\Omega$$

$$V_{BB} = V_{BE} + I_C\left(\frac{R_B}{\beta} + R_E\right) = 14.2\text{ V}$$

Calculating the parameter variations based on the given conditions, we have

$$\Delta V_{BE} = -\,2\Delta T = -2(60) = -120\text{ mV}$$

$$\Delta I_{CBO} = I_{CBO1}(e^{0.15\times 60} - 1) = 0.405\text{ mA}$$

$$\Delta\beta = 40$$

$$\Delta V_{CC} = 1$$

We find ΔI_C using equation (7.21) where we use the average β value of 100.

$$\Delta I_C = 0.53\text{ mA} + 4.50\text{ mA} + 3.38\text{ mA} + 5\text{ mA} = 13.4\text{ mA}$$

This change in I_C is shown in Figure 7.8. We find the maximum current swing from zero to the peak is

$$i_{Cp} = 104 \times 0.95 - (60 + 13.6)$$
$$= 25.2\text{ mA}$$

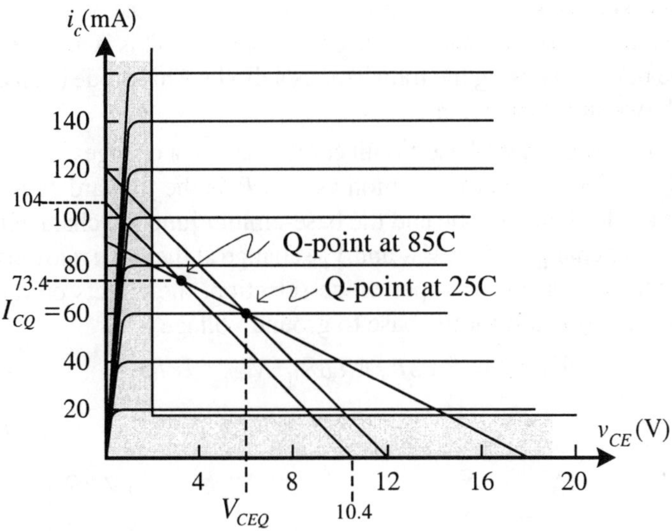

Figure 7.8 – Load lines for Example 7.2

and the maximum undistorted peak-to-peak voltage swing at the output load is

$$v_{out\ peak\text{-}to\text{-}peak} = 2(25.2 \times 10^{-3})(100)$$

$$= 5.04 \text{ V}$$

This represents a reduction in output voltage swing from 10.8V to 5.04V.

EXERCISES

E7.8 Design an EF amplifier for R_{load}=50 Ω, A_i = 15, V_{CC} = 15V, V_{BE} = 0.7V, and I_{CBO1}(25°C) = 0.005 μA. β ranges from 75 to 125 and the power supply voltage varies by ±1V. The amplifier is designed to operate at 100°C. What is I_C at 100°C and at 25°C?

Answer: $I_C(25^oC) = 200$ *mA,* $I_C(100^oC) = 275$ *mA*

E7.9 What is the maximum undistorted symmetrical voltage swing for the amplitude of Exercise E7.8 if the temperature is 100°C?

Answer: 1.69V peak-to-peak

7.3 DIODE COMPENSATION

The examples of the previous section show that changes in temperature can significantly affect the location of the Q-point. *Diode compensation* is a technique for reducing the effect of changes in temperature on I_C. A diode is selected that has similar temperature characteristics to those of the transistor. To insure that the diode and transistor characteristic curves are identical, an identical transistor can be used in place of the diode junction. This is accomplished by shorting the collector to the base, thus using the transistor as a diode. This diode (transistor) is connected in the circuit as shown in Figure 7.9(a).

The addition of the diode in the base circuit compensates for changes arising from temperature variation since V_{ON} varies in the same fashion as V_{BE}. R_f is the forward resistance of the diode. Assuming that the diode characteristic and the base-emitter junction characteristic are the same, then as the temperature changes, both V_{ON} and V_{BE} change at the same rate thus canceling out any variation in bias parameters. With proper diode selection, the effects of variations in V_{BE} are reduced. The new bias equation for the base to ground voltage is

$$V_B = V_{ON} + I_D R_f + I_D R_1 = V_{BE} + I_C R_E \tag{7.23}$$

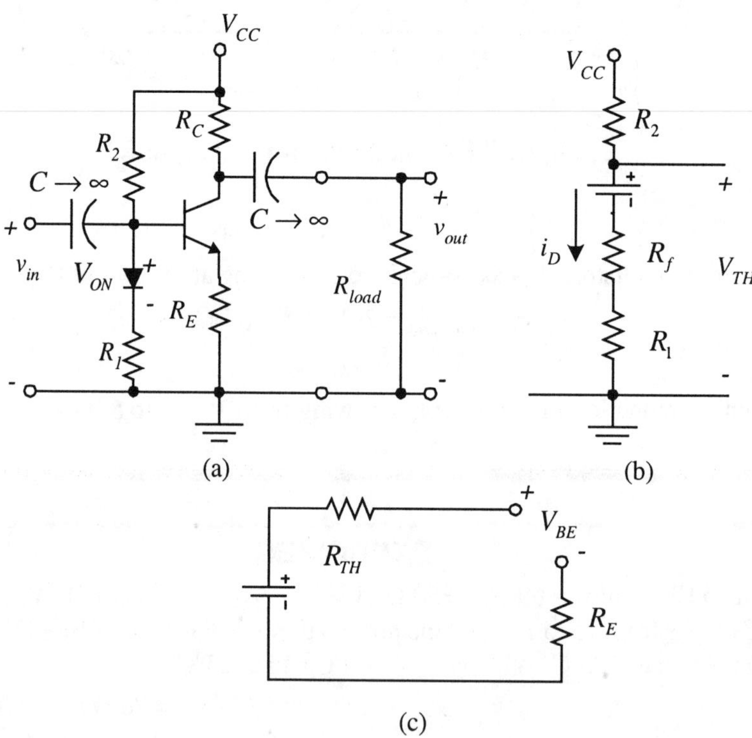

Figure 7.9 - Diode compensation

Let us perform an analysis for the example shown in Figure 7.9(a). We begin the analysis by finding the Thevenin equivalent for the bias circuit. Figure 7.9(b) illustrates the circuitry connected to the base of the transistor. In order to find the open-circuit voltage from the base to ground, we first find the diode current.

$$I_D = \frac{V_{CC} - V_{ON}}{R_1 + R_2 + R_f} \tag{7.24}$$

The Thevenin voltage and resistance, V_{TH} and R_{TH}, are then given by

$$V_{TH} = I_D R_1 + V_{ON} + I_D R_f$$

$$= \frac{V_{CC}(R_1 + R_f) + V_{ON} R_2}{R_1 + R_2 + R_f} \tag{7.25}$$

$$R_{TH} = R_2 \| (R_1 + R_f)$$

If $R_f << R_1$, then we can approximate these by

$$V_{TH} \approx \frac{V_{CC} R_1 + V_{ON} R_2}{R_1 + R_2}$$

$$R_{TH} \approx R_2 \| R_1 \tag{7.26}$$

The equivalent of the bias circuitry is shown in Figure 7.9(c). We find the quiescent base current as follows:

$$I_B = \frac{V_{TH} - V_{BE}}{R_{TH} + \beta R_E} \tag{7.27}$$

The quiescent collector current is found by multiplying the base current by β. Following substitution of the earlier expressions, we obtain

$$I_C = \frac{V_{TH} - V_{BE}}{R_{TH}/\beta + R_E}$$

$$= \frac{(V_{CC} R_1 + V_{ON} R_2)/(R_1 + R_2) - V_{BE}}{R_{TH}/\beta + R_E} \tag{7.28}$$

The sensitivity of this circuit to variations of temperature is found by forming the partial derivative as follows.

$$\frac{\partial I_C}{\partial T} = \frac{[R_2/(R_1 + R_2)]\, \partial V_{ON}/\partial T - \partial V_{BE}/\partial T}{R_{TH}/\beta + R_E} \tag{7.29}$$

Now if $R_2 >> R_1$, this can be simplified to yield

$$\frac{\partial I_C}{\partial T} \approx \left(\frac{\partial V_{ON}}{\partial T} - \frac{\partial V_{BE}}{\partial T} \right) \frac{1}{R_{TH}/\beta + R_E} \tag{7.30}$$

Equation (7.30) shows that if the diode temperature characteristic is matched to the base-emitter temperature characteristic, I_C can be made independent of changes in temperature. This applies if $R_1 << R_2$.

If R_1 is approximately equal to R_2, we can use two diodes in series to obtain better compensation. That is, a different approximation is appropriate if two diodes are placed in series with R_1. In this case,

$$I_C = \frac{(V_{CC}R_1 + 2V_{ON}R_2)/(R_1 + R_2) - V_{BE}}{R_{TH}/\beta + R_E}$$

$$\frac{\partial I_C}{\partial T} = \frac{2[R_2/(R_1 + R_2)]\partial V_{ON}/\partial T - \partial V_{BE}/\partial T}{R_{TH}/\beta + R_E} \tag{7.31}$$

When R_1 is approximately equal to R_2 then

$$\frac{\partial I_C}{\partial T} \approx \left(\frac{\partial V_{ON}}{\partial T} - \frac{\partial V_{BE}}{\partial T}\right)\frac{1}{R_{TH}/\beta + R_E} \tag{7.32}$$

7.4 DESIGNING FOR BJT AMPLIFIER BIAS STABILITY

To reduce the effects of parameter changes on the Q-point location, we concentrate on reducing each term in Equation (7.21). The design approach toward accomplishing this goal is outlined by the following four steps.

- Use diode compensation to subtract the changes that occur in V_{BE} from changes in temperature. The changes in V_{BE} are often significant and cause a large change in I_C. In using diode compensation, it is imperative that the characteristics of the diode(s) be the same as the characteristics of the transistor V_{BE}.
- Select a transistor with low I_{CBO} so that the temperature change will not significantly affect I_C, or reduce the temperature variations.
- Insure that the design uses some technique to reduce the effect of changes in β. For example, with voltage division biasing, R_B should be held to less than $0.1\beta R_E$. This reduces the effect of changes in β, as can be seen from the third term in Equation (7.21).
- Use a well-regulated power supply to reduce the change in V_{CC} to such a small value that the Q-point location will not be affected.

7.5 FET TEMPERATURE EFFECTS

Temperature changes cause large variations in the bias point of BJTs. Fortunately, temperature instability is not as big a problem with FET amplifiers. However, the drain current is affected somewhat by temperature variations. This should be considered in designing FET amplifiers that are required to operate in a varying-temperature environment. Temperature increases also cause the gate-to-source leakage current of a JFET to increase.

Increasing the temperature of a FET amplifier tends to decrease the mobility of charge carriers in the channel of the FET. The effect of the smaller number of charge carriers is to reduce the drain current. However, the increased temperature also narrows the depletion region, which tends to increase the drain current. These two effects are in opposition thus giving the FET its relatively low temperature coefficient. That is, the drain current changes are relatively small with large changes in temperature.

For some types of FET, the manufacturer specifies a quiescent drain current which, when used, will give nearly a zero temperature coefficient. This results from the decreased conductivity of the channel.

Since the temperature coefficient is not zero, it is good practice to consider bias stability in all circuit designs. One simple approach is to use a source resistor which results in negative feedback. This is shown in Figure 7.10(a).

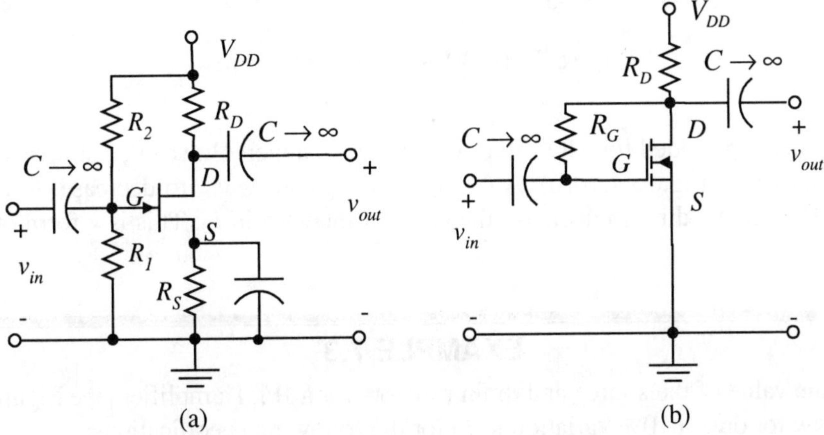

Figure 7.10 - FET amplifier

When the drain current increases, v_S becomes more positive causing v_{GS} to become more negative. Thus, as i_D increases, v_{GS} becomes more negative. This tends to decrease i_D. The result is that the amount of change in i_D is reduced. We illustrate this graphically in Figure 7.11.

The manufacturer typically provides a range of V_p and I_{DSS}. The v_{GS}-i_D curve as shown in Figure 7.11 is used to account for the two extremes of these values. Note that as the value of the source resistor increases, the variation in i_D decreases. This allows us to design the amplifier to reduce the effects of changes in drain current. A typical value of R_S which provides a reasonable I_D deviation is 10% of the value of R_D.

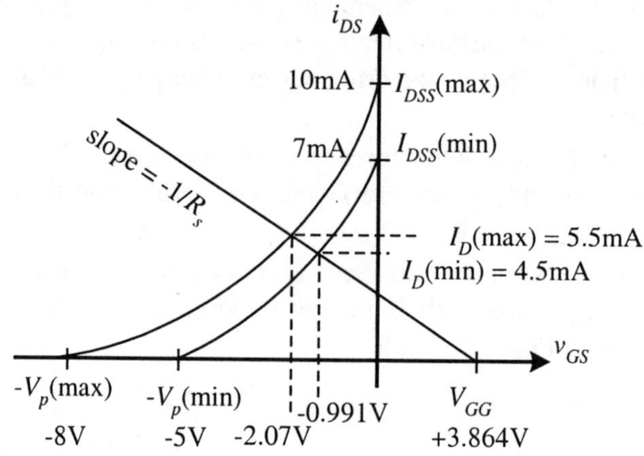

Figure 7.11 – FET operating curves

Bias stability is provided for MOSFETs in the same manner. However, a simpler circuit can be used as shown in Figure 7.10(b). An increase in i_D causes v_{DS} to decrease. Reducing v_{DS} reduces v_{GS} thereby tending to decrease the original increase in i_D. This is a form of negative feedback.

EXAMPLE 7.3

Determine the value of the source and drain resistors for a JFET amplifier [see Figure 7.10(a)] that will allow for only a 10% variation in I_D for the following specifications:

1. V_p ranges from –5 V to –8 V (maximum and minimum values from the transistor specifications)
2. I_{DSS} ranges from 7 mA to 10 mA (maximum and minimum values from the transistor specifications)
3. The nominal value of I_D is 5 mA varies by $\pm$ 10%.
4. V_{DD} = 12 V.
5. V_{DS} = 4 V.

Solution: A 10% variation in I_D is a variation from a minimum of 4.5 mA to a maximum of 5.5 mA. The intercepts in Figure 7.11 show that v_{GS} varies from -0.991 V to -2.07V. That is

$$V_{GS\,\min} = V_{P\min}\left(1-\sqrt{\frac{I_{D\min}}{I_{DSS\min}}}\right) = -5\left(1-\sqrt{\frac{4.5}{7}}\right) = -0.991 \quad \text{V}$$

$$V_{GS\,\max} = V_{P\max}\left(1-\sqrt{\frac{I_{D\max}}{I_{DSS\max}}}\right) = -8\left(1-\sqrt{\frac{5.5}{10}}\right) = -2.07 \quad \text{V}$$

Then the source resistance is given by

$$R_S = \left| \frac{V_{GS\,max} - V_{GS\,min}}{I_{D\,max} - I_{D\,min}} \right| = 1076\,\Omega$$

The line passing through these points intersects the v_{GS} axis, resulting in a value of V_{GG} of +3.864V.

$$V_{GS} = V_{GG} - 5\text{ mA} \times 1076\,\Omega = -1.529\text{ V}$$

$$V_{DD} = V_{DS} + (R_S + R_D)I_D \quad \text{or}$$

$$R_D + R_S = \frac{V_{DD} - V_{DS}}{I_D} = \frac{12\text{V}-4\text{V}}{5\text{mA}} = 1.6\text{ k}\Omega$$

Then

$$R_D = 1.6\text{ k}\Omega - R_S = 524\Omega$$

By selecting $R_S = 524\ \Omega$, we can ensure that I_D will not vary more than $\pm$ 10% for any variation of the transistor parameters, V_p and I_{DSS}, within the specified range.

7.6 REDUCING TEMPERATURE VARIATIONS

Changing the temperature of any electronic device changes its operating characteristics. An increase in temperature may even cause the device to fail. Therefore it is important for the designer to consider the operating temperature of devices used in a system.

For BJTs, an increase in the temperature of the junction results in an increase of I_C thus reducing the maximum output voltage swing.

Temperature increases can be caused either by external heat or by internal heat which is generated by operating the device at a high current level. Transistor capability is limited by the allowable transistor junction temperature which is specified by the manufacturer. This means that it is your responsibility as a designer to insure that your design does not allow the junction temperature to exceed the specified maximum value. It is also important that your design not allow the device to operate at or near the maximum allowable junction temperature or the reliability of the device could be reduced.

Some transistors are rated at a certain power capability or current level, but these rated levels cannot be achieved without keeping the junction temperature within the allowable limits. There are two ways to keep the junction temperature from rising too high: active and passive cooling. *Active cooling* involves the use of fans, air conditioners, or forced fluid flow near the devices. Such systems are expensive and bulky but they may be necessary when dissipation of large amounts of heat is required. The more inexpensive technique is to utilize *passive heat sinks* which employ metallic surfaces to conduct, and in some cases radiate, the heat to the surrounding media. To increase the dissipation of heat, cooling fins can be added to the metallic heat sink to increase the amount of surface area in contact with the surrounding media. A metal chassis supporting the electronic components is sometimes used as an effective and economical heat sink. If the problem is cold rather than heat, similar results can be achieved by using heaters.

Power transistors and other high-current devices require dissipation of large amounts of heat. These high-power devices are packaged in cases that permit contact between a metal surface and an external heat sink. In most cases, the metal surface of the device is electrically connected to one terminal. For example, power transistors have their cases connected to their collectors. For silicon transistors packaged in metal cases, the maximum operating junction temperature is usually 200°C. When transistors are packaged in plastic cases, the maximum temperature is usually 150° C.

To determine whether a particular heat sink is adequate for use with your design, some simple calculations are necessary. We use information from the specification sheets for the transistor and the heat sink selected. Examples of common heat sinks are shown in Figure 7.12.

Figure 7.12 - Common heat sinks

The *thermal resistance*, θ, which is defined as the temperature rise divided by the power transferred, is a constant independent of temperature. It only depends on the properties of the mechanical joint. When there are a number of joints in series, the total thermal resistance is the sum of the thermal resistances of the individual joints. The lower the thermal resistance of these mechanical junctions, the better the heat transfer. When a transistor is mounted on a heat sink, the total thermal resistance of the system is the sum of the thermal resistance from the junction to the case of the transistor, θ_{jc}, the thermal resistance from the case to the heat sink, θ_{cs}, and the thermal resistance from the heat sink to the ambient environment, θ_{sa}. Thus, the temperature of the transistor junction can be determined from the following formula:

$$T_j = T_a + \left(\theta_{jc} + \theta_{cs} + \theta_{sa}\right) P \tag{7.33}$$

where T_a is the temperature of the transistor environment in °C and P is the power to be dissipated by the transistor. Heat sink selection should prevent the transistor from operating at or near the maximum junction operating temperature since transistor life decreases rapidly when the operating temperatures are at or near the maximum.

EXAMPLE 7.4

Determine if a heat sink with a θ_{sa} of 3.3°C/watt (from the specification of the heat sink) will maintain a temperature below the transistor maximum junction operating temperature when the transistor is operating in an environment of 60°C temperature. The transistor junction-to-case thermal resistance, θ_{jc}, is 1.5°C/watt, maximum junction operating temperature is 200°C and the transistor is contained in a TO-3 package (see the transistor manufacturer's specifications). The TO-3 package has a θ_{cs} of 0.3°C/watt when the transistor is mounted with an insulated washer and a heat-conducting compound between the package and the heat sink (from the packaging specifications). The power of the transistor, $P_{(transistor)}$, operating in this circuit is 21 watts.

Solution: Using Equation (7.32) we have

$$T_j = 60 + (1.5 + 0.3 + 3.3)21 = 167^\circ\ \mathrm{C}$$

Hence, this heat sink is adequate to maintain the temperature of the junction well below the maximum junction temperature allowed by the specification.

SUMMARY

We began this chapter by exploring the problems caused by changes in transistor parameters. These changes arise due to manufacturing variability, and due to environmental factors. We saw how feedback could be used to reduce the undesired effects of parameter variations.

The chapter presented techniques for designing stable BJT and FET amplifier circuits. We explored various approaches toward reducing the effects of temperature variations. These approaches prove extremely important in real life electronic design. It would not be very productive to design a system which only meets specifications some of the time.

PROBLEMS

Section 7.1

7.1 Prove that $V_{CC} = V_{BB}$ for the circuit shown in Figure P7.1. Use the equations derived in Chapter 4.

7.2 In the circuit of Figure P7.1, let $R_{load} = 1$ kΩ, V_{CC} = 10V, and A_v = -8. Determine the values of R_B and R_E which would make the amplifier least susceptible to large changes in β. Assume V_{BE} = 0.7V and β = 150.

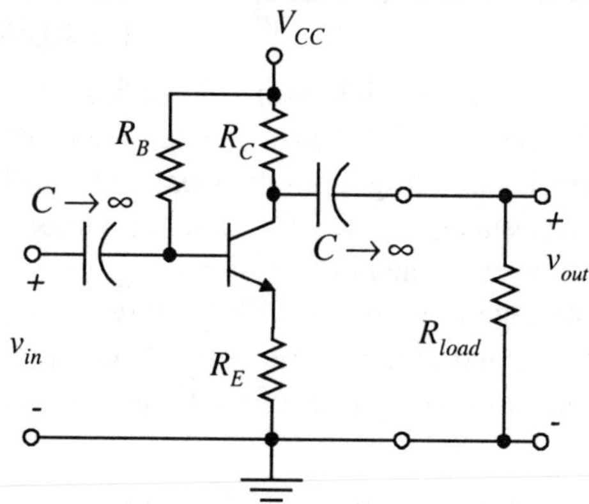

Figure P7.1

7.3 An amplifier with a resistor from the base to the source (to supply the bias voltage) is to be designed for A_v = -12, V_{CC} = 12V, $R_C = R_{load}$ = 2 kΩ, β = 200 and V_{BE} = 0.7V. Determine the resistor values. Can the amplifier be designed to have *dc* bias stability?

7.4 For an amplifier of the type shown in Figure P7.4, determine the values of R_F and R_E that will make the amplifier operate consistently for large changes in β. Let V_{CC} = 10V, R_{load} = 1 kΩ, A_v = -10, V_{BE} = 0.7V and β = 100. Determine the expected undistorted peak-to-peak output voltage.

7.5 Given V_{CC} = 12V, design an amplifier using voltage and current feedback with a voltage gain of -10 to a load of 10 kΩ. The *npn* transistor has a very stable β of 100 and V_{BE} = 0.7V. This circuit will be designed to obtain maximum output voltage swing. Determine:

(a) R_E, R_C, and R_F

(b) The maximum undistorted output voltage swing

(c) If the transistor had to be replaced with one which had an unstable β, what changes would be needed in the circuit to obtain *dc* bias stability? What would be the new undistorted output voltage swing?

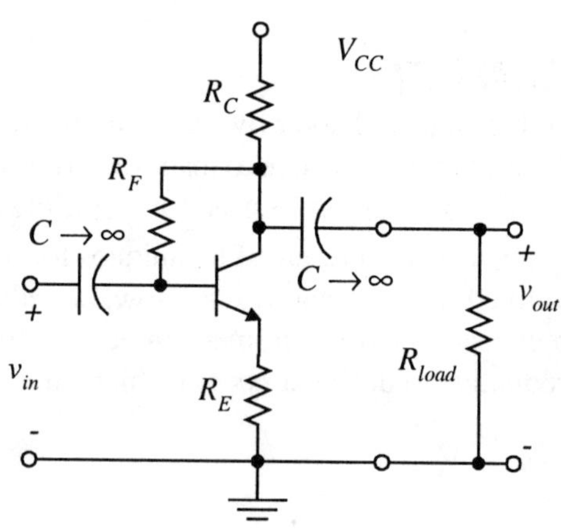

Figure P7.4

Section 7.2.1

7.6 Design an amplifier as shown in Figure P7.6 to obtain a voltage gain of -8. Do not exceed the power limit of the transistor, $P_{max} = 50$ mW. If the temperature changes from 25°C to 85°C and $I_{CBO}(25°C) = 0.003$ μA, what is the peak-to-peak undistorted voltage output at 85°C when $V_{CC} = 12$V?

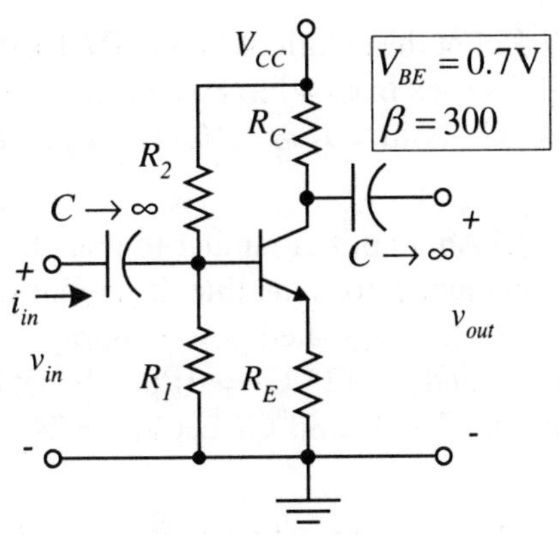

Figure P7.6

7.7 For the design of Problem 7.6, determine the maximum peak-to-peak output voltage if β varies from 250 to 350 and the power supply varies from 11.5 to 12.5V.

7.8 Design an amplifier to have a voltage gain of 8 and drive a 750Ω load. Use the configuration of Figure P7.8 with a transistor which has β = 300 and $I_{CBO}(25°C)$ = .08 μA. Determine the maximum peak-to-peak undistorted output voltage swing when the temperature rises to 85°C, β varies from 250 to 350, and $V_{CC} = 24$V.

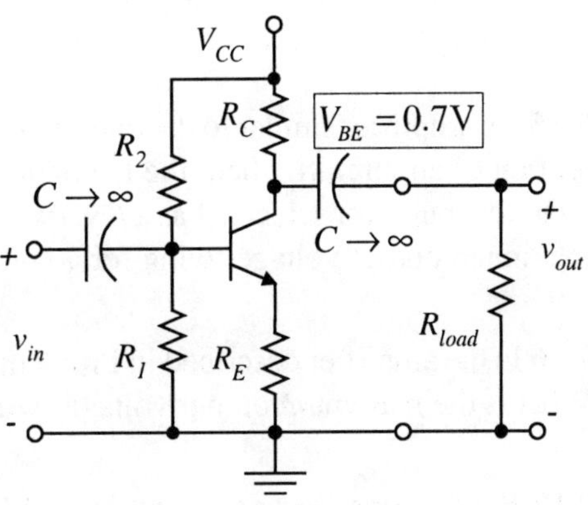

Figure P7.8

7.9 The amplifier shown in Figure P7.8 is designed for operation where the temperature is -25°C. Find the maximum peak-to-peak undistorted output voltage swing at -25°C if all parameters are the same as in Problem 7.8 except that β varies from 200 to 350.

Section 7.2.2

7.10 Design an EF amplifier to drive a 15-Ω load when $\beta = 60$, $V_{BE} = 0.7$V, $I_{CBO}(25°C) = 0.008$ μA, V_{CC} = 20V, and A_i = 8. If the temperature now changes from 25°C to 85°C, determine the peak-to-peak undistorted output voltage swing at 85°C. Use the circuit of Figure P7.10.

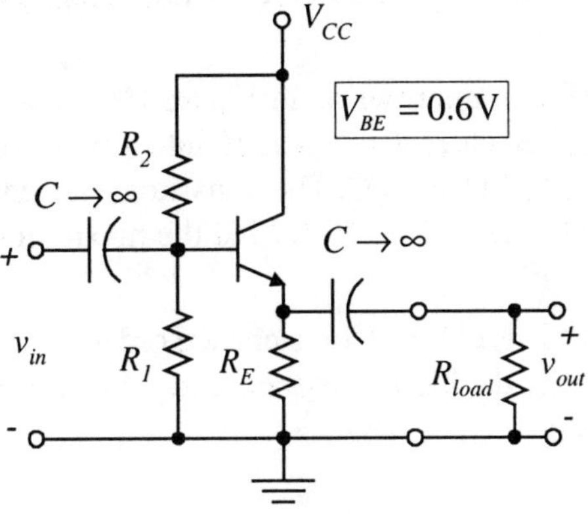

Figure P7.10

7.11 Design an EF amplifier to drive an 8-Ω load, as shown in Figure P7.10. Set the current gain, A_i = 10. Determine the peak-to-peak output voltage swing if the temperature rises to 75°C. Assume $I_{CBO}(25°C) = .008$ μA, $V_{BE} = 0.6$V, $V_{CC} = 24$V and

β varies over the range from 60 to 100.

7.12 For the circuit of Figure P7.10, determine the maximum peak-to-peak output voltage swing if β varies from 40 to 80 and the voltage supply varies from 19 to 21V with the temperature at 85°C. Assume $I_{CBO}(25°\text{C}) = .02\ \mu\text{A}$, $R_{load} = 200\ \Omega$, $V_{BE} = 0.6\text{V}$, and $A_i = 8.8$.

7.13 An amplifier similar to that shown in Figure P7.10 is being designed for application in a communications satellite. It is required to have a current gain of 10 and to drive a 20Ω load using a 24V 2% regulated power supply. The transistor selected has a β variation of 60 to 100, $V_{BE} = 0.7\text{V}$ and $I_{CBO}(25°\text{C}) = .01\ \mu\text{A}$. What is the maximum output voltage swing that can be obtained at -30°C and at 80°C? Let $V_{CC} = 24\text{V}$.

7.14 Using the stability factor, δ_B, find the value of R_E for an amplifier of the type shown in Figure P7.6. Use a silicon transistor designed such that the voltage across R_C will not vary more than ±0.5V. Assume the supply voltage is 20V, $V_{BE} = 0.7\text{V}$, $I_C = 10$ mA and β varies from 50 to 100.

7.15 An amplifier similar to the one shown in Figure P7.8 is being designed for the unheated tail section of an aircraft where the temperature ranges from 80°C to -50°C. The battery source is 24V, the transistor selected has a β variation of 200 to 300, and $I_{CBO}(25°\text{C}) = .02\ \mu\text{A}$. What is the maximum output voltage swing for a voltage gain of 10 if the load is 1 kΩ?

7.16 In the amplifier described in Problem 7.15, reduce the high temperature from 80°C to 50°C. What is the maximum output voltage swing for the amplifier after this modification?

7.17 For the amplifier described in Problem 7.15, the transistor originally planned to be used went out of production and the only other transistor available which would meet the requirements had an $I_{CBO}(25°\text{C})$ of .6 μA and a variation in β of 300 to 500. What is the maximum output voltage swing with the temperature changing from -50°C to +50°C?

7.18 An amplifier as in Figure P7.5 was designed to be used in a chemical plant where the required current gain was 10 into a 50Ω load. The specification requires that the amplifier operate from -75°C to 50°C. The transistor selected has an $I_{CBO}(25°\text{C}) = 0.01\ \mu\text{A}$ and a β variation of 200 to 300. Let $V_{CC} = 25\text{V}$. Find the maximum output swing of the amplifier.

7.19 In Problem 7.18, a change order was issued due to the addition of a new chemical process to change the high temperature to 100°C. With this change, what is the maximum output voltage swing?

Section 7.6

7.20 Determine whether a heat sink with θ_{sa} of 3.3°C/watt will maintain a temperature below the maximum transistor junction operating temperature when the transistor is operating in an environment of 80°C at a power rating of 15 watts. Assume $\theta_{jc} = 2$°C/watt and $\theta_{cs} = 0.5$°C/watt. The maximum transistor junction temperature is 180°C.

7.21 For Example 7.4, determine whether the transistor junction operating temperature would be exceeded if a heat sink with $\theta_{sa} = 4.5$°C/watt were used. How much would the output power have to be reduced in order to keep the transistor junction temperature at 10% below the maximum operating junction temperature?

Chapter 8
Power Amplifiers and Power Supplies

8.0 INTRODUCTION

We consider the design of power amplifiers in this chapter. The purpose of the power amplifier is to deliver a maximum undistorted symmetrical output voltage swing into a low-resistance load. A system may consist of several stages of amplification, the last of which is a power amplifier. The load fed by this power amplifier may be a loud speaker, an actuator, a transmitter, a motor, or some other analog device. The input to the system is a low-level voltage which is amplified through the voltage gain stages. The output of the voltage gain stages is of sufficient amplitude to drive the output power amplifier.

After studying the material in this chapter, you will be able to:

- Design biasing circuitry for Class A, B, AB, and C operation.
- Know the essential differences between various coupling techniques.
- Design a complementary symmetry diode compensated power amplifier circuit
- Design a Darlington circuit.
- Design regulated power supplies using both discrete components and integrated circuits.
- Analyze and design Zener-regulated power supplies.

8.1 CLASSES OF AMPLIFIERS

Power amplifiers are classified according to the percent of time that the collector current is non-zero. There are four principal classifications: Class A, Class B, Class AB and Class C. We discuss each of these in the following subsections.

8.1.1 Class A Operation

Class A operation is what we considered in the amplifiers of Chapters 4 and 5. The amplifier reproduces the input signal in its entirety. The collector current is non-zero 100% of the time. This type of operation is inefficient since I_C is non-zero even when the input signal is zero. The transistor therefore dissipates power in the rest, or quiescent, condition.

Figure 8.1 illustrates typical characteristic curves for Class A operation. The quiescent current, I_{CQ}, is often set to be in the center of the *ac* load line. The figure shows an example of a sinusoidal input and the resulting collector current at the output. Letter designators (a) through (e) identify corresponding points of time from the base current to the resulting collector current. The condition for maximum undistorted collector current swing is illustrated. We covered this in detail in Chapter 5.

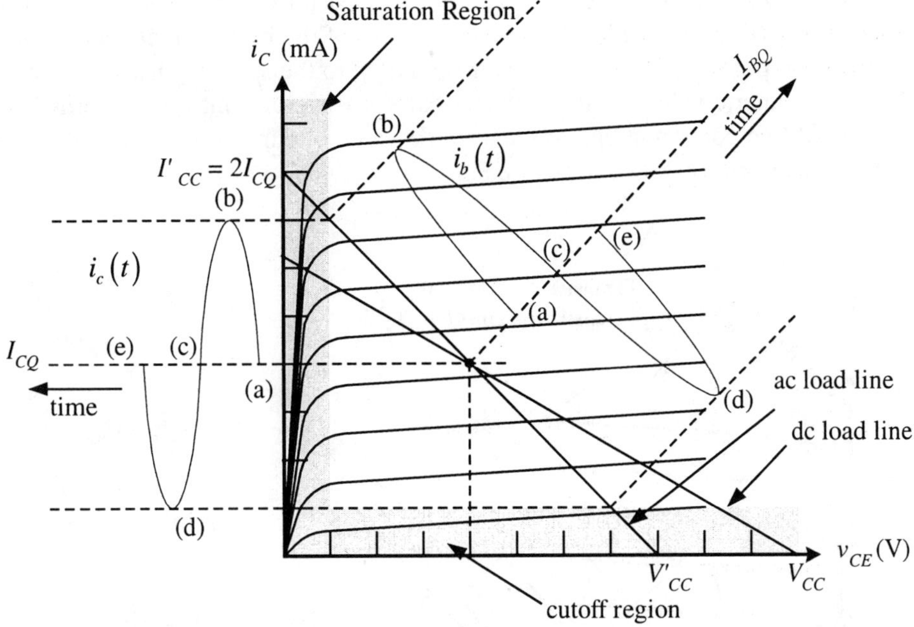

Figure 8.1 – Class A operation (full, undistorted swing)

8.1.2 Class B Operation

In *Class B* operation, one amplifier is used to amplify the positive half-cycle of the input signal while a second amplifier is used to amplify the negative half-cycle. This amplifier configuration is known as *push-pull* or *complementary symmetry.*

Since we restrict a single transistor to respond only to a half-cycle, two transistors are required to produce the complete waveform. Each of these transistors is biased at cutoff rather than in the middle of the operating range, as is the case for Class A operation. Each transistor operates one half of the time - the collector current of each is non-zero 50% of the time.

The advantage of Class B operation is that the collector current is zero when the signal input to the amplifier is zero. Therefore the transistor dissipates no power in the quiescent condition.

Among the disadvantages of a Class B amplifier is that the nonlinear cutoff region is included in the operating range. That is, unlike the Class A situation, the 5% of the operating region shaded at the bottom of Figure 8.1 is included in the operating region. Therefore some distortion results.

Figure 8.2 illustrates a typical characteristic curve for a pair of transistors in the push-pull configuration.

This figure is intended for conceptual purposes only since we discuss the amplifier in more detail later. Since two transistors are connected back-to-back, we have repeated the set of transistor curves for the second transistor, but the signs of the collector current and collector-to-emitter voltage have been reversed. That is, these two quantities increase in the downward and the left directions respectively for the second transistor characteristic. The upper-left portion of the figure represents the first transistor which only conducts during the positive half cycle of the input. The lower right portion represents the second transistor which is configured to conduct only during the negative half cycle. The numeric values of the base current waveform may be identified from the point on the load line corresponding to the specific characteristic curve in Figure 8.2. The numeric values of the collector current waveform may be identified from the point on the load line corresponding to the specific value of current on the vertical axis I_C. A typical output waveform is shown in Figure 8.3.

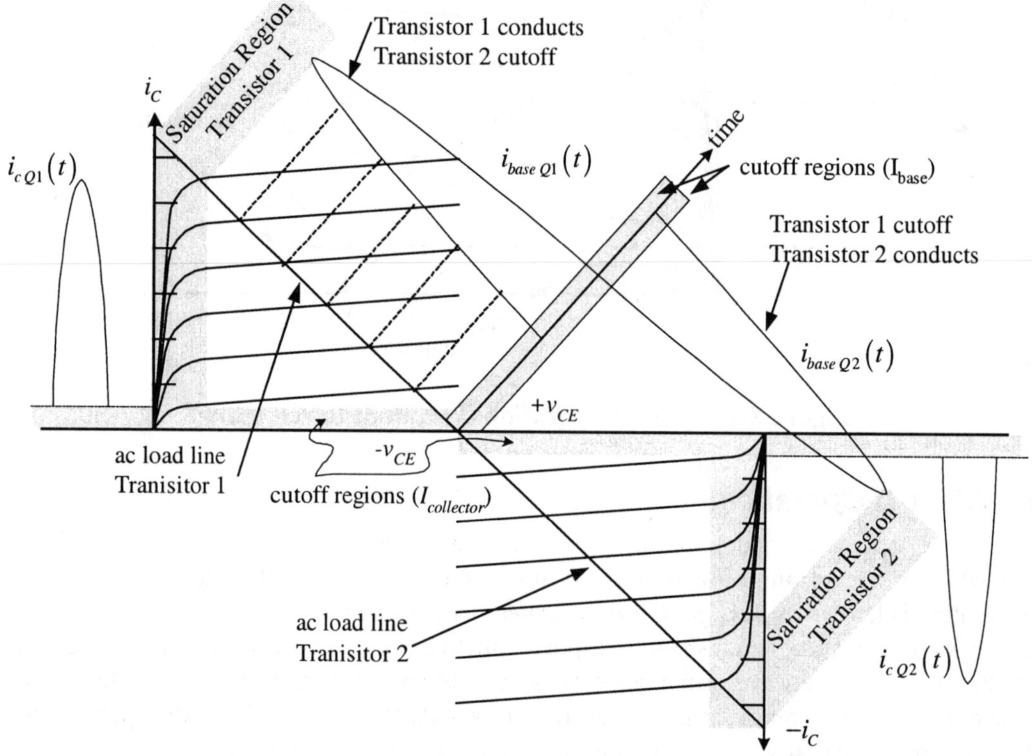

Figure 8.2 – Class B operation

The first transistor produces the positive part of the output and the second transistor produces the negative part. Also note that Figure 8.3(a) and (b) indicate some distortion near the point $i_C(t) = 0$. When these two curves are added together, the output shown in Figure 8.3(c) results. This resembles the sinusoidal input, but the waveform is distorted near collector current zero-crossings.

In a push-pull configuration, it is important that the two transistors must be carefully matched. In this way, the positive and negative portions of the input are amplified by the same amount.

8.1.3 Class AB Operation

Class A operation has the advantage of small distortion while Class B has the advantage of higher efficiency. Class AB operation is a compromise between these two extremes. The Q-point is set slightly above the cutoff value at the lower boundary of the linear (no distortion) portion of the operating curves. The transistor therefore supports a non-zero collector current for slightly more than 50% of the time.

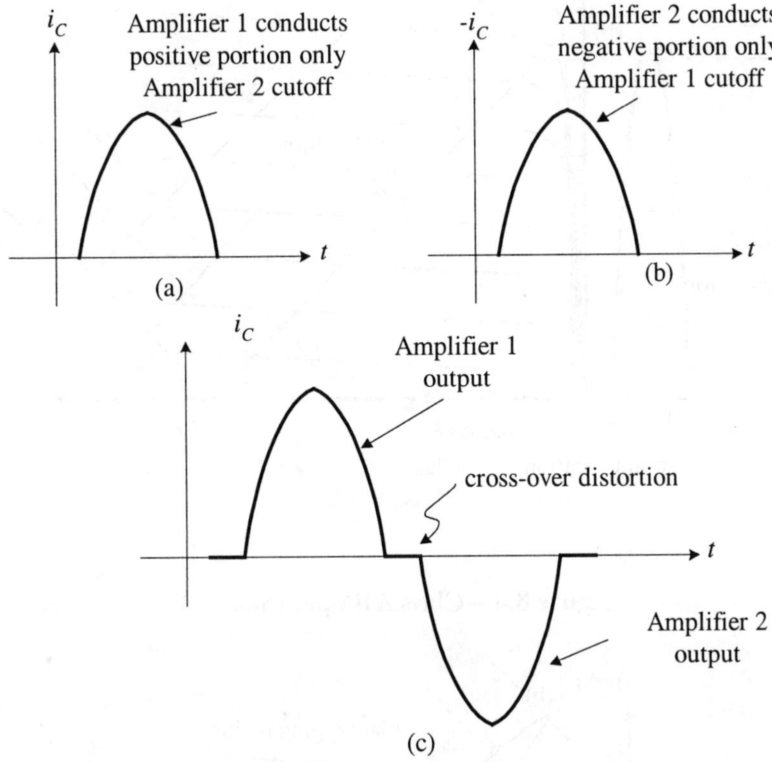

Figure 8.3 - Push-pull output waveform

Figure 8.4 illustrates the positive portion of the operating curve for a sinusoidal input and Class AB operation. Note that I_C is slightly above zero to reduce the cross-over distortion . The Class AB amplifier is used in a push-pull type configuration.

8.1.4 Class C Operation

A *Class C* amplifier load line is shown in Figure 8.5, where V_{BE} is set to a negative value.

The transistor (*npn*) is biased with a negative V_{BB}. Thus it will only conduct when the input signal is above a specified positive value. The collector current is non-zero less than 50% of the time.

If a sinusoid forms the input to a Class C amplifier, the output consists of sinusoidal "blips" at the frequency of the input. This is shown to the left of Figure 8.5. Since this signal is periodic, it contains a fundamental frequency component plus higher frequency harmonics. If this signal is passed through an inductor-capacitor (*LC*) circuit (i.e., a bandpass filter) tuned to the signal. This approach is often used if the signal to be amplified is either a pure sinusoid or a more general signal with a limited range of frequencies.

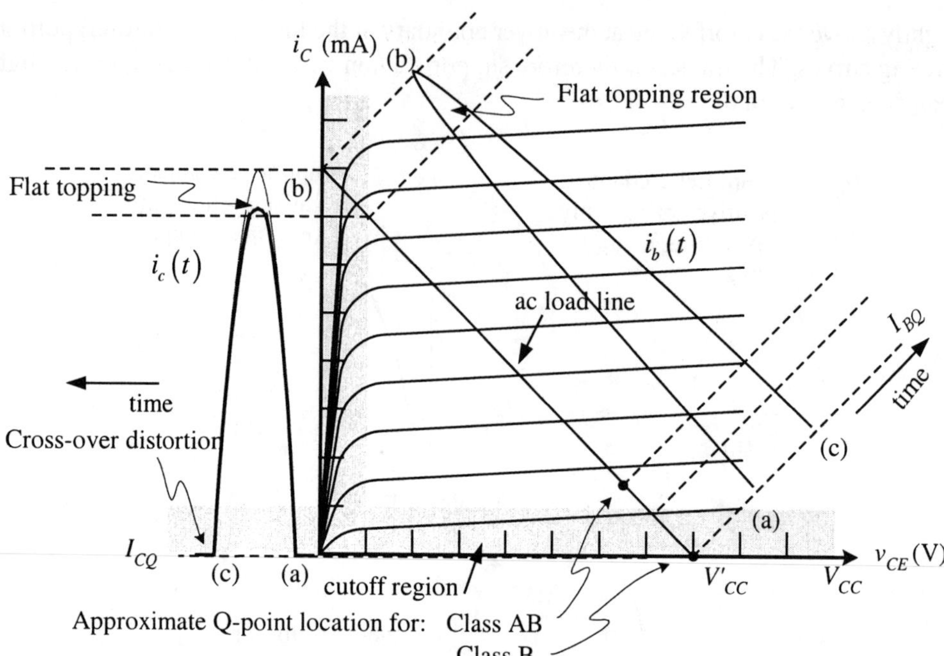

Figure 8.4 – Class AB operation

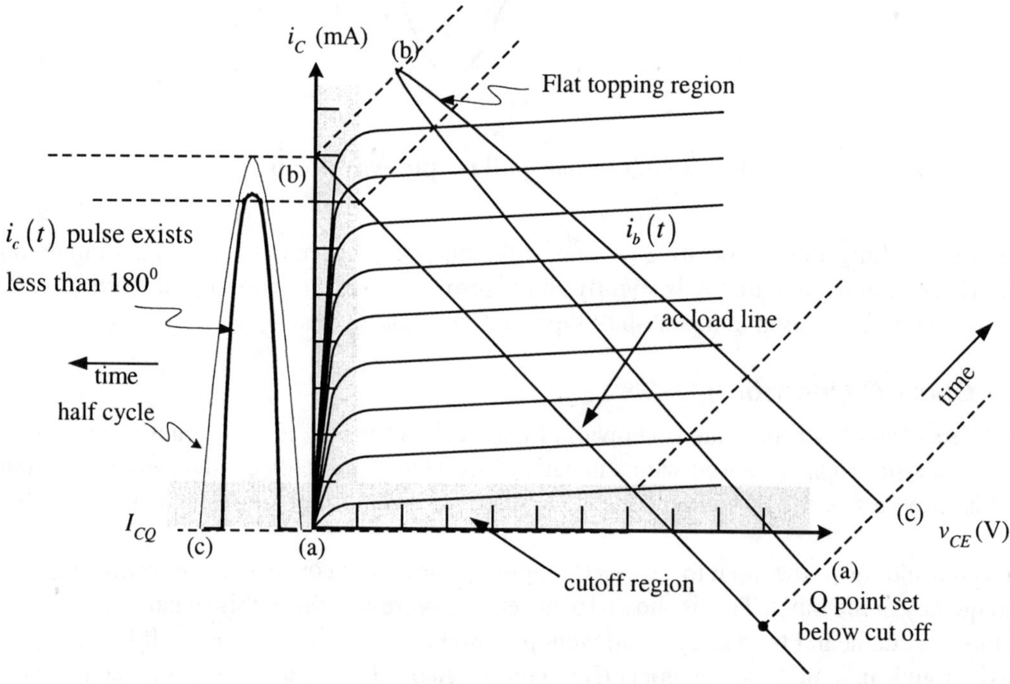

Figure 8.5 – Class C operation

Class C amplifiers are capable of providing large amounts of power. They are often used for radio frequency (RF) transmitter power stages, where a tuned circuit is included to eliminate the higher harmonics in the output signal.

8.2 POWER AMPLIFIER CIRCUITS - CLASS A OPERATION

Power amplifier circuits usually contain transistors capable of handling high power. These normally operate at higher voltages than do low-power transistors and therefore often require a separate power supply. Voltages of power transistors can exceed 450 V. Current ratings are also high, often in excess of 10 A of continuous current. Since these transistors need to dissipate high power, they are designed differently from low-power transistors. Protective circuits may be included to limit current. Additional effort is also expended to dissipate heat which builds up during operation.

We now discuss some useful circuit configurations for power amplifiers. These are categorized according to the type of coupling.

8.2.1 Inductively-Coupled Amplifier

High current gain is required to produce significant power in the output load. The output voltage swing can be increased by using an inductor instead of a resistor for the collector element. We will see that this also increases the efficiency of the circuit. The inductor is selected so that it approximates an open circuit for the input frequency but a short circuit for *dc*. In other words the inductive reactance must be relatively large at the lowest operating frequency. If ω_L is the lowest input signal frequency, then

$$\omega_L L \gg R_{load} \tag{8.1}$$

The internal resistance of the coil, R_{coil}, must be relatively small:

$$R_{coil} \ll R_{load} \text{ and } R_{coil} \ll R_E \tag{8.2}$$

Figure 8.6 illustrates the inductively-coupled amplifier circuit and its load lines. We choose the Q-point for maximum output swing. The current, I_{CQ}, is then given by

$$I_{CQ} = \frac{V_{CC}}{R_{ac} + R_{dc}} \tag{8.3}$$

The *ac* resistance is simply R_{load} since for *ac* the inductor is an approximate open circuit and the capacitors are short circuits. The *dc* resistance is R_E provided that we can neglect the resistance of the inductor. Therefore, [for maximum swing]

$$I_{CQ} = \frac{V_{CC}}{R_{load} + R_E} \tag{8.4}$$

Since both *dc* and *ac* load lines cross at the Q-point, the *ac* load line equation yields

$$I_{CQ} = -\frac{1}{R_{load}} \cdot V_{CE} \tag{8.5}$$

We have assumed $R_E \ll R_{load}$, which is usually true. Then from equations (8.4) and (8.5) we see that $V_{CE} \approx V_{CC}$ and the *ac* load line intersects the v_{CE} axis at approximately $2V_{CC}$. The use of the storage device (inductor) results in a voltage swing which is equivalent to effectively doubling the supply voltage. The inductor magnetic field stores energy during the conducting cycle thus acting like a second V_{CC} source in series with the *dc* supply.

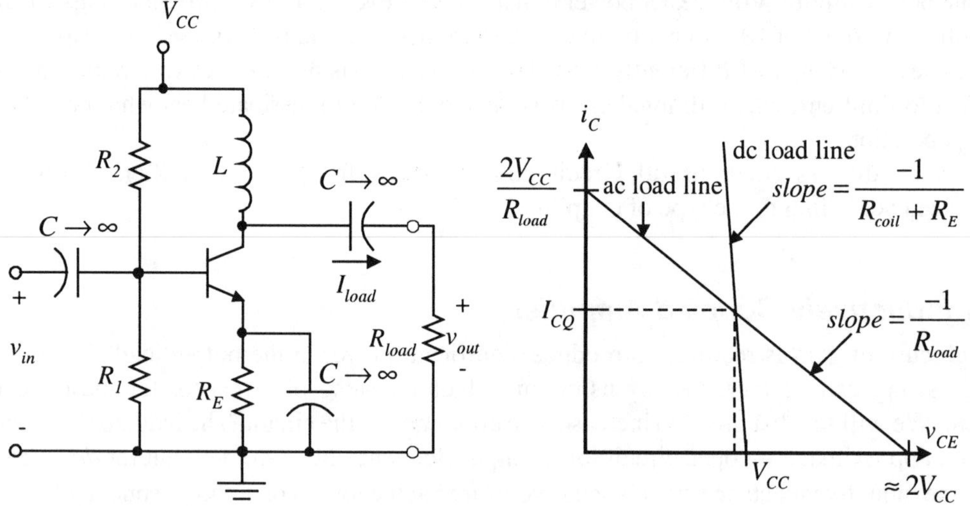

Figure 8.6 – Inductively-coupled amplifier

The inductively-coupled amplifier has a higher efficiency than does the amplifier that contains a collector resistance. To prove this, we now calculate the efficiency of this amplifier, assuming sinusoidal input signals.

The power supplied by the voltage source is

$$P_{supplied} \approx V_{CC} I_{CQ} = \frac{V_{CC}^2}{R_{load}} \tag{8.6}$$

We have neglected R_E in Equation (8.6) since we assume that $R_E \ll R_{load}$. The power delivered to the load, assuming the current is sinusoidal with amplitude, $I_{load\ max}$, is

$$P_{load} = \frac{I_{load\ max}^2 R_{load}}{2} = \frac{I_{CQ}^2 R_{load}}{2} \le \frac{V_{CC}^2}{2R_{load}} \tag{8.7}$$

We define *conversion efficiency* (η) as the ratio of *ac* load power to the power delivered by the source. This efficiency measure therefore depends on the power dissipated in the bias circuitry and in R_E. In order to derive a maximum value for efficiency, we assume that the power dissipated in the bias circuitry, in R_E, and in R_{coil} is negligible. The maximum conversion efficiency (with output swing at maximum) is then given by

$$\eta = \frac{V_{CC}^2/(2R_{load})}{V_{CC}^2/R_{load}} = 50\% \tag{8.8}$$

In a similar manner, we can show that the maximum efficiency of the amplifier with collector resistance in place of the inductor is 25%, or one-half of the efficiency found for the inductively-coupled amplifier. This result is reasonable since, in the circuit with a collector resistor, the load seen by the transistor is the parallel combination of the collector and load resistance. The maximum power delivered by the transistor is shared between these two resistors.

8.2.2 Transformer-Coupled Power Amplifier

Figure 8.7(a) illustrates the EF (CC) transformer-coupled power amplifier, and Figure 8.7(b) shows the load lines.

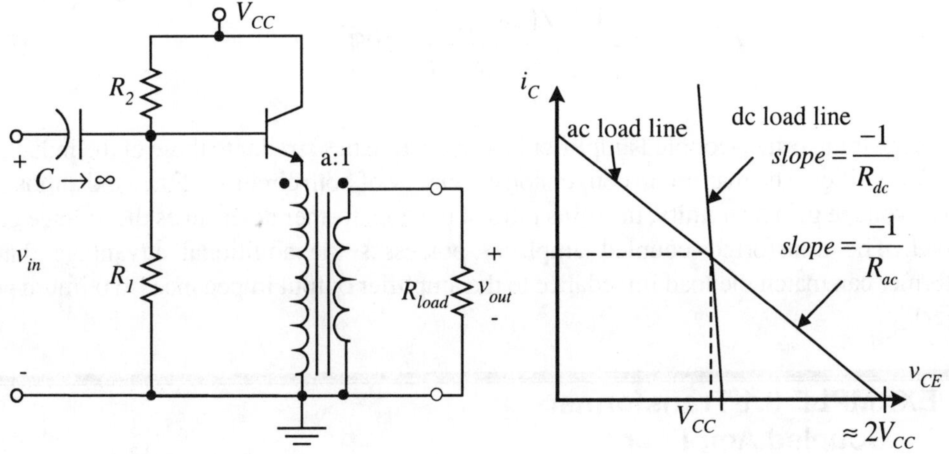

Figure 8.7 - Transformer-coupled power amplifier

Note that the slope of the *dc* load line depends on the resistance of the primary coil of the transformer. This resistance is usually small. The slope of the *ac* load line depends on the reflected load resistance.

If maximum output voltage swing is desired, we solve the design equation in order to place the Q-point in the center of the load line. Note that the load resistance reflected by the transformer is

$$R_{ac} = a^2 R_{load} \tag{8.9}$$

The Q-point is then given by

$$I_{CQ} = \frac{V_{CC}}{R_{ac}} \approx \frac{V_{CC}}{a^2 R_{load}} \tag{8.10}$$

In the last equality, we assume that the transformer primary resistance is negligible (i.e., $R_{dc}=0$).

In design of CE amplifiers, we showed earlier that the base resistance, R_B, is selected for bias stability using the design equation,

$$R_B = 0.1\beta R_E \tag{8.11}$$

In the design of EF amplifiers, a different criterion is used. The base resistance is constrained by the desired current gain, A_i, or by the specified input resistance, R_{in}. The voltage gain of this amplifier is near unity.

The maximum power transferred to the load, assuming a sinusoidal input at full drive and ignoring saturation effects, is

$$P_{load} = \frac{V_{load\,max}^2}{2R_{load}} = \frac{V_{CC}^2}{2a^2 R_{load}} \tag{8.12}$$

The maximum power conversion efficiency is then given by

$$\eta = \frac{V_{CC}^2/\left(2a^2 R_{load}\right)}{V_{CC}^2/\left(a^2 R_{load}\right)} = 50\% \tag{8.13}$$

Thus the transformer-coupled amplifier has characteristics similar to those of the inductively-coupled amplifier. The maximum conversion efficiency of both circuits is 50%, and although the EF has a voltage gain near unity, the turns ratio of the transformer determines the voltage gain to the load. The transformer-coupled amplifier possesses the additional advantage that the transformer can match the load impedance to the amplifier output impedance (maximum power transfer).

EXAMPLE 8.1 Transformer-Coupled Amplifier

Design a transformer-coupled amplifier (see Figure 8.8) for a current gain of $A_i = 80$. Find the power supplied to the load and the power required from the supply.

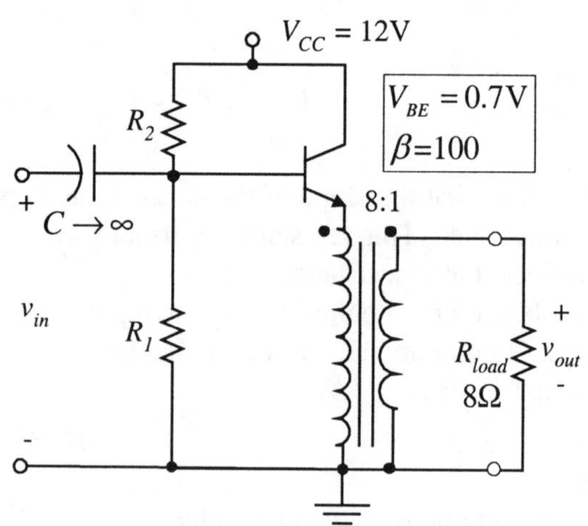

Figure 8.8 – Transformer coupled amplifier for Example 8.1

Solution: We first use the design equation to find the location of the Q-point for maximum output swing.

$$I_{CQ} = \frac{V_{CC}}{R_{ac} + R_{dc}} = \frac{12}{a^2 R_{load}} = 23.4 \text{ mA}$$

Since the problem statement requires a current gain of 80, the amplifier must have a current gain of 10 because the transformer provides an additional gain of 8. We use the equations from Chapter 5 to find the base resistance, R_B.

$$A_i = \frac{R_B}{R_B/\beta + r_e + R_E} = 10$$

where

$$R_E = a^2 R_{load} = 512\ \Omega$$

We note that r_e is sufficiently small to be neglected. Then, solving for R_B yields

$$R_B = 5.69\ \text{k}\Omega$$

$$V_{BB} = \frac{I_{CQ} R_B}{\beta} + V_{BE} = 2.03\ \text{V}$$

Now solving for the bias resistors,

$$R_1 = \frac{R_B}{1 - V_{BB}/V_{CC}} = 6.85\ \text{k}\Omega$$

$$R_2 = \frac{V_{CC} R_B}{V_{BB}} = 33.6\ \text{k}\Omega$$

The design is now complete. The power delivered by the source is given by

$$P_{VCC} = V_{CC} I_{CQ} + \frac{V_{CC}^2}{R_1 + R_2}$$

$$= 284\ \text{mW}$$

The power dissipated in the load is

$$P_{load} = \frac{(0.9 a I_{CQ})^2 R_{load}}{2} = 114\ \text{mW}$$

We have restricted operation to the linear region by eliminating 5% of the maximum swing near cutoff and saturation. The efficiency is the ratio of load power to source power.

$$\eta = \frac{114}{284} = 0.4 \text{ or } 40\%$$

EXERCISES

E8.1 Design an inductively-coupled CE amplifier for $A_v = -10$, $R_{in} = 4\text{k}\Omega$, $R_{load} = 2\text{k}\Omega$, $V_{CC} = 12\text{V}$, $\beta = 200$ and $V_{BE} = 0.7\text{V}$. Determine A_i, the power delivered to the load, and the maximum undistorted symmetrical voltage output swing.

Answer: $R_E = 200\Omega$; $R_1 = 5.2\text{k}\Omega$
$R_2 = 29.4\text{k}\Omega$; $A_i = -20$

$P_{out} = 20.3mW;\ v_{out(p\text{-}p)} = 18V$

E8.2 Design a transformer-coupled EF amplifier to drive an 8Ω load if V_{CC} = 20V; V_{BE} = 0.7V; β = 100; R_{in} = 2kΩ and the transformer has a turns ratio of 10:1. Determine the current gain, A_i, power output, and maximum undistorted voltage output swing.

Answer: $R_1 = 2.2k\Omega;\ R_2 = 33.8k\Omega$
$A_i = 250;\ P_{out} = 203mW$
$v_{out(p\text{-}p)} = 3.6V$

8.3 POWER AMPLIFIER CIRCUITS - CLASS B OPERATION

A Class B audio amplifier uses one transistor to amplify the positive portion of the input signal and another transistor to amplify the negative portion of the input signal. As indicated earlier, the Class B audio amplifier provides higher efficiency and lower output impedance to drive a typically low-impedance load. For example, a speaker load is normally 8 Ω.

The purpose of this introductory section is to provide an overview of the operation of this important power amplifier. Detailed analysis will be presented in following sections.

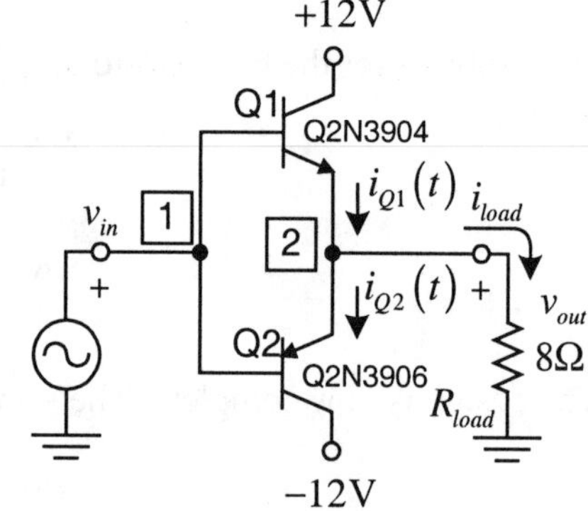

Figure 8.9 – Class B for PSPICE analysis

Figure 8.9 presents a simplified Class B amplifier circuit. The circuit is powered by a *symmetrical* ±12V *dc* voltage source. This arrangement simplifies the biasing circuit for transistors *Q1* and *Q2*. When the input signal $v_{in}(t)$ becomes positive and sufficiently large (>0.7V) transistor *Q1* conducts current from the +12V supply to ground through the 8Ω load resistance. During this half-cycle transistor *Q2* remains biased OFF by the positive going voltage of the signal source v_{in}. However, when the input signal $v_{in}(t)$ becomes negative and sufficiently less than -0.7V transistor *Q2* conducts current from ground to the -12V supply through the 8Ω load resistance. During this negative half-cycle transistor *Q1* remains biased OFF by the negative going voltage of the signal source.

The input signal for simulation of the circuit is the top waveform shown in Figure 8.10(a). $v_{in}(t)$ is a $\pm 10V_{peak}$ sinusoidal voltage signal turning transistor Q1 ON during the positive half-cycles and turning Q2 ON during the negative half-cycles. The sequence is shown in the middle and bottom waveforms of Figure 8.10(a). We illustrate the simulation's time domain calculations for the collector currents of transistors Q1 and Q2, $i_{Q1}(t)$ and $i_{Q2}(t)$, respectively.

The combined "push-pull" effect on the 8Ω load resistor is seen in the output voltage waveform and output load current waveforms shown in Figure 8.10(b). The top figure is the simulation result for the load voltage. The bottom waveform is the result for the load current. In this figure, we see *cross-over distortion* during the time that $-0.7V < v_{in}(t) < +0.7V$. During this relatively small period of time, neither transistor is conducting. The cross-over distortion contributes to the *total harmonic distortion* (THD) of the output signal.

As we will see in Section 8.3.1, the effect of the cross-over distortion problem can be reduced through careful selection of the biasing points for transistors *Q1* and *Q2*. We design for current conduction times that are slightly *longer* than one-half cycle (Class AB operation) rather than *exactly* one-half cycle (Class B).

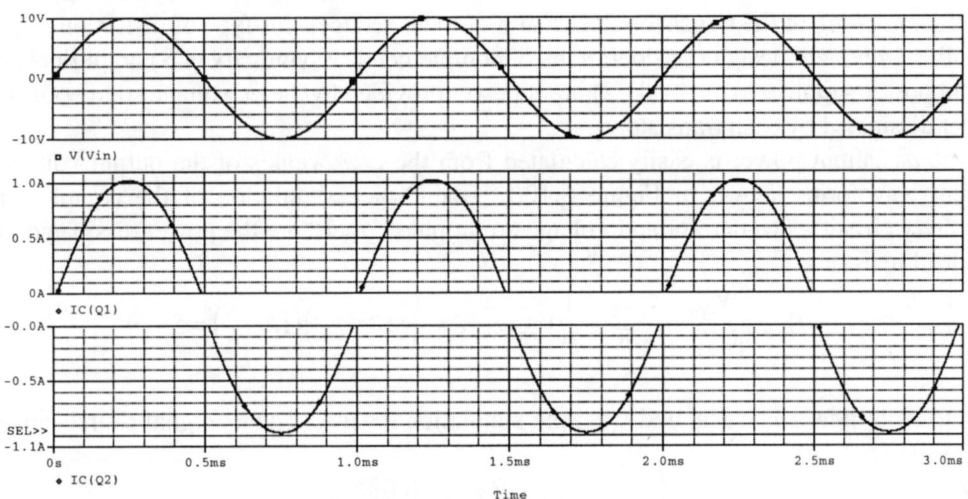

Figure 8.10(a) – Input voltage waveform (top), collector current waveform of transistor Q1 (middle), and collector current waveform Q2 (bottom)

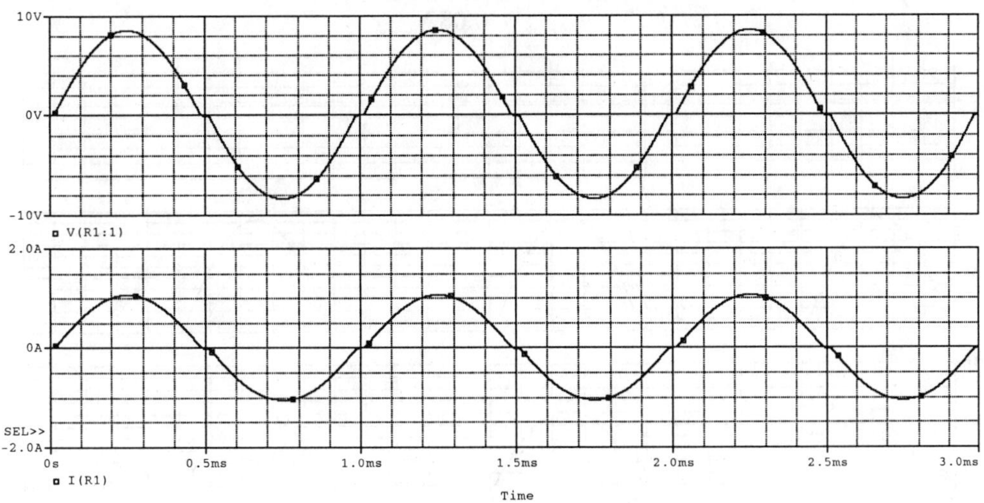

Figure 8.10(b) – Output voltage waveform (top) and Load current waveform (bottom) showing cross-over distortion.

A careful comparison of the conduction current waveforms in Figure 8.10(b) [or Figure 8.10(a)] shows that conduction of the *npn* transistor *Q1* is slightly larger than the conduction of the *pnp* transistor *Q2*. The peak current though transistor *Q1* during conduction is a little *over* 1 A, whereas, the peak current through transistor *Q2* is slightly *less* than 1A. This is an inherent problem of trying to mirror *npn* and *pnp* semiconductor construction in complementary devices (in this case, *npn* transistor 2N3904 and *pnp* transistor 2N3906). Asymmetry of the positive and negative output waveforms contribute to the total harmonic distortion (THD) of the output signal. Careful *matching* of the transistor electrical properties reduces this type of distortion.

Other important design considerations of complementary symmetry (CS) amplifiers are (1) output power supplied to the load, (2) input power provided by the *dc* voltage source(s), and (3) power dissipated by each transistor.

The *ac* output power is easily calculated from the peak values of the output voltage and current waveforms shown in Figure 8.10(b) (the Pspice simulation of the complementary symmetry circuit). The current and voltage are in phase, therefore the power dissipated by the 8Ω load resistor is

$$P_{load} = \frac{V_{peak}}{\sqrt{2}} \cdot \frac{I_{peak}}{\sqrt{2}} = \frac{1}{2} V_{peak} I_{peak} = \frac{1}{2}\left(10\mathrm{V_{peak}}\right)\left(1\mathrm{A_{peak}}\right) = 5 \quad \mathrm{W}$$

The *ac* input power is calculated from the simulation results. (The *ac* signal source current is $0.08\mathrm{A_{peak}}$)

$$P_{in} = \frac{V_{in\ peak}}{\sqrt{2}} \cdot \frac{I_{in\ peak}}{\sqrt{2}} = \frac{10\mathrm{V_{peak}}}{\sqrt{2}} \cdot \frac{0.08\mathrm{A_{peak}}}{\sqrt{2}} = 400 \quad \mathrm{mW}$$

We see the input impedance of this circuit is relatively low since

$$Z_{in\ CSDC} = \frac{V_{in\ peak}}{I_{in\ peak}} = \frac{10\mathrm{V_{peak}}}{0.08\mathrm{A_{peak}}} = 125 \quad \Omega$$

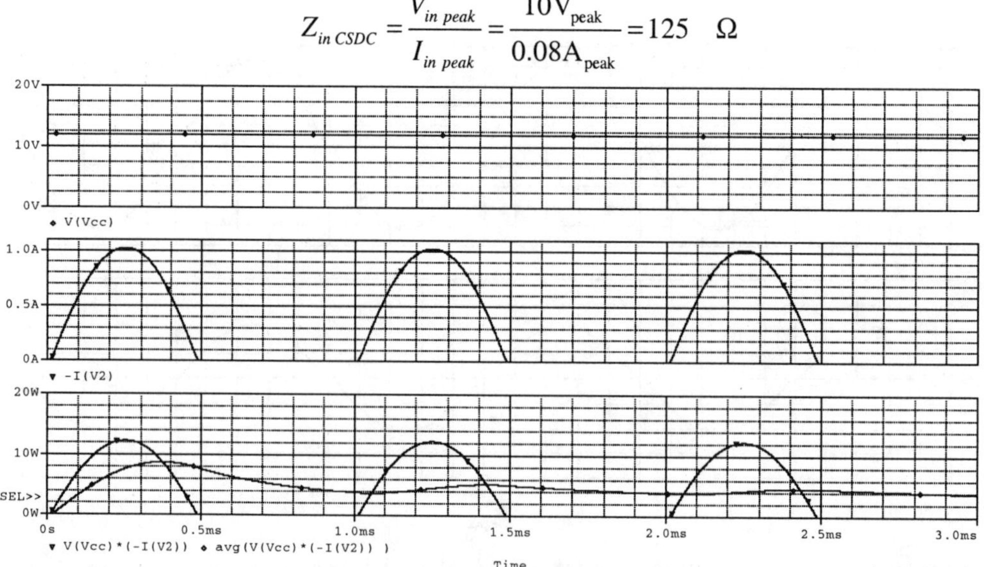

Figure 8.10(c) – Voltage (top) and current (middle) waveforms needed to compute the instantaneous power and average power delivered by the +12V voltage source

The power delivered by the *dc* voltage sources is determined by multiplying the *dc* source voltage (top waveform of Figure 8.10(c)) by the current from the *dc* source (middle waveform of Figure 8.10(c)). This product represents the *instantaneous* power. It must be averaged over time to obtain the *dc* input power. The instantaneous and average power waveforms are shown in the bottom set of waveforms of Figure 8.10(c). From this plot, after the initial transient period, the *average* power value tends to settle at about 4W. The *dc* input power for both dc voltage sources is about 8W.

The expected power dissipation of transistor $Q1$ is found from Figure 8.10(d) where the average power dissipated by this device appears to settle at the value 1.70W. Multiplying by 2, we have the total power dissipation of the transistors $Q1$ and $Q2$. The total power dissipated by the load (5W) plus the power dissipated by the transistors $(2\times 1.7\text{W})$ is the total power dissipated.

$$P_{total\ dissipated} = P_{load} + P_{transistors} = 5\text{W} + 2\times 1.70\text{W} = 8.40 \quad \text{W}$$

There appears to be an inconsistency here, since *dc input* power is only 8W, but the power *dissipated* by the load and both transistors totals 8.40W. However, this may be resolved if we include the third source of input power - the input signal source V_{in}. Since CS amplifiers offer low input impedances (125Ω in this example), signal sources driving CS amplifiers must provide considerable source signal power. Including the *ac* signal source input power, for this illustration, the net input power is

$$P_{net\ input} = P_{dc\ sources} + P_{ac\ signal\ source} = 8\text{W} + 0.40\text{W} = 8.40 \quad \text{W}$$

That is, the total power dissipated by the circuit equals the net power supplied to the circuit by the voltage sources.

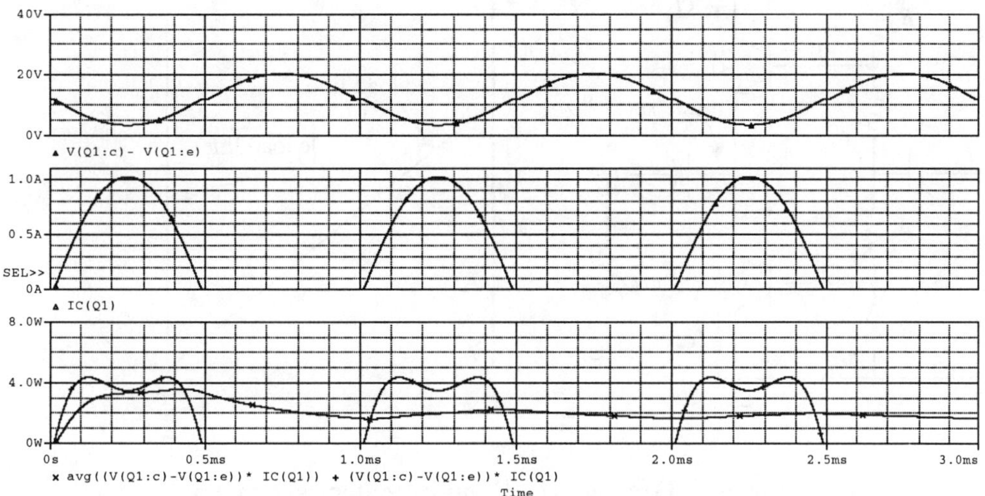

Figure 8.10(d) – Collector-to-emitter voltage waveform for Q1 (top), Collector current for Q1 (middle), and instantaneous power and average power dissipation for Q1 (bottom)

We remind the reader that all simulation results must be carefully consider in terms of the actual operation of the real-world circuit. Referring to the Appendix, we see the maximum device power dissipation P_D is 1.5W (at an ambient temperature of 25C) for the 2N3904/2N3906 transistors chosen for this simulation. The expected device dissipation is 1.70 W per device for our operational conditions. Active cooling of the transistors is required or perhaps selection of transistors with higher power dissipation is better option.

In summary, from the computer simulation of the simplified CS amplifier illustration, we observed that

(1) CS amplifiers have low input impedance,
(2) CS amplifiers have a voltage gain $A_v < 1$,
(3) CS amplifiers have significant current gain,
(4) CS amplifiers are composed of two EF amplifiers operating in a "push-pull" configuration,
(5) CS amplifiers may suffer from cross-over distortion and non-symmetrical current conduction, and
(6) simulation results must be carefully considered in view of real-world operational constraints of the maximum ratings of the selected devices.

In the following sections, we will analyze complimentary symmetry (CS) amplifiers operating in Class B or Class AB mode. Note that CS amplifiers may also be used in Class C mode, especially for high-efficiency, high-power radio frequency (RF) amplifier applications.

8.3.1 Complementary-Symmetry Class B and AB Power Amplifiers

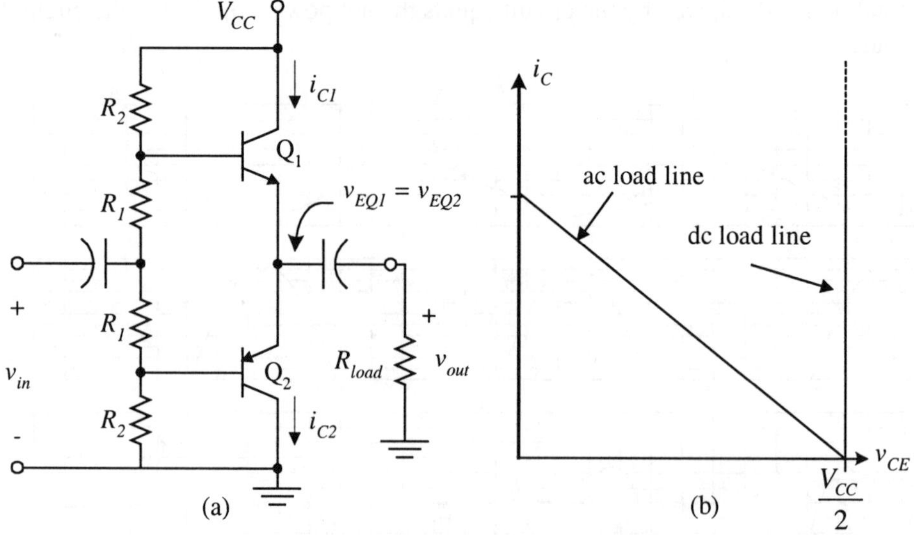

Figure 8.11(a and b) – Complementary symmetry

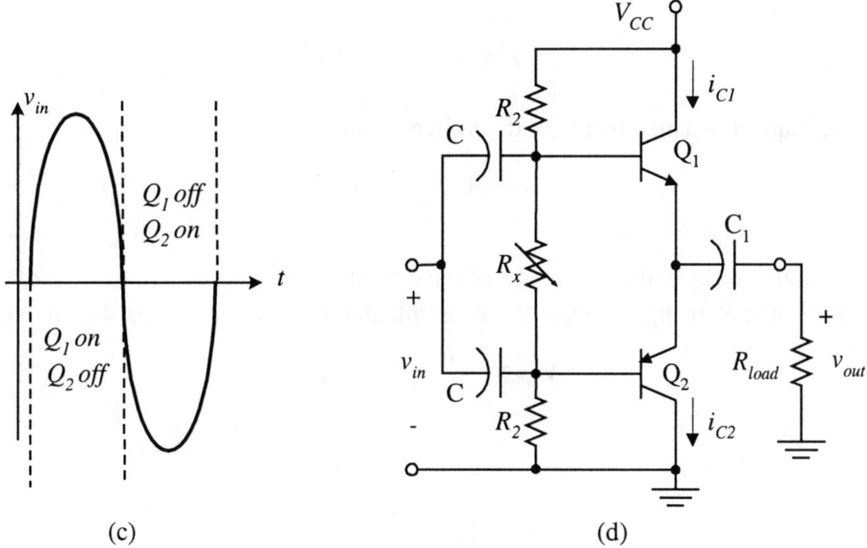

Figure 8.11 (c and d) – Complementary symmetry

A typical push-pull power amplifier can be designed with one *pnp* and one *npn* transistor having symmetrical characteristics as shown in Figure 8.11. We isolate the load with a capacitor (C_1) and a single power supply is used.

This upper transistor is *npn* and configured as an EF amplifier. The lower *pnp* transistor is also configured as an EF amplifier. The resistors are selected so that the base-to-emitter voltages of both transistors place the Q-points at the boundary between cutoff and active mode. As the input voltage increases during the positive half-cycle of the input, Q_1 conducts and Q_2 is cut off. When the input decreases in the negative voltage direction, the reverse situation occurs. This is shown in Figure 8.11(c).

The capacitor, C_1, serves two purposes. First, it blocks the *dc* from the load. Second, it provides the power supply voltage to Q_2 when Q_1 is not conducting. That is, the capacitor charges to a *dc* values of $V_{CC}/2$ at the connection of the two emitters.

The *dc* load line is vertical since the capacitor acts as an open circuit for *dc*.

$$R_{dc} \approx 0\Omega \tag{8.14}$$

Since I_{CQ} is zero, the amplifier is Class B.

As is the case of the transformer-coupled power amplifier, R_B is determined from the current gain or input resistance equations. The input resistance, R_{in}, is determined as follows ($r_e = 0$).

$$R_{in} = R_B \| \beta R_{load} = \frac{R_B R_{load}}{R_B/\beta + R_{load}} \tag{8.15}$$

Each half of the circuit operates as an EF amplifier and the equivalent base resistance in the circuit of Figure 8.11, R_B is approximately $R_2 \| R_2$ since $R_x \ll R_2$. The current gain is found from the current divider equation.

$$A_i = \frac{\beta R_B}{R_B + \beta R_{load}} = \frac{R_2}{R_2/\beta + 2R_{load}} \tag{8.16}$$

From the gain-impedance formula, the voltage gain is

$$A_v = A_i \cdot \frac{R_{load}}{R_{in}} = 1 \tag{8.17}$$

Notice that this reflects the EF nature of the circuit.

We can find R_1 and R_2 using one side of the circuit, and the solutions are as shown in Chapter 4.

$$V_{BB} = \frac{R_1}{R_1 + R_2} \cdot \frac{V_{CC}}{2} \tag{8.18}$$

We select $V_{BB} = V_{BE}$, and

$$R_1 = \frac{2R_2 V_{BE}}{V_{CC} - 2V_{BE}} \tag{8.19}$$

In order to avoid the nonlinear operating region near cutoff and thereby to obtain more symmetrical operation, the two R_1 resistors can be replaced by one adjustable resistor R_x, (which is larger than $2R_1$) in order to raise I_{CQ} above zero thereby compensating for the distortion [see Figure 8.11(d)]. This accomplishes Class AB operation. Another version of the amplifier has the input fed through one capacitor to the middle of the two R_1 resistors. This configuration operates much the same as that shown in Figure 8.11(a) except that the voltage gain is slightly reduced.

A capacitor is used to isolate the load in the circuit of Figure 8.11. The capacitor forms part of the current path for one transistor when the other is cut off. Thus, the capacitor charges during conduction of Q_1, and discharges during conduction of Q_2.

Some improvement in circuit operation is possible. The fluctuations of V_{BE} with temperature can be reduced by replacing the two R_1 resistors with diodes. These diodes should have characteristics similar to those of the transistor and they should be mounted on the same heat sink. This form of compensation is illustrated in the circuit of Figure 8.12.

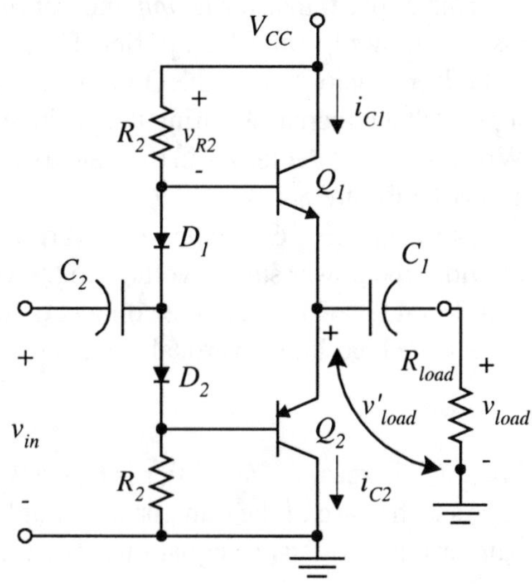

Figure 8.12 – Complementary symmetry with diode compensation

There are three areas of concern in the design of a complementary symmetry amplifier. The first is the *crossover distortion* discussed in Sections 8.1.2 and 8.3. This distortion can be reduced by placing a small resistor in series with each diode to cause I_{CQ} to be slightly above zero. This in turn causes both amplifiers to amplify the *ac* input signal simultaneously in the cutoff region, thus compensating for the lower individual amplification in that region.

The second area of concern is the possibility of *thermal runaway.* This is caused by the two complementary transistors having different characteristics or by the value of V_{BE} being reduced at high temperatures. It can lead to higher collector current, resulting in additional power dissipation and heating. This process continues until the transistor overheats and fails. Thermal runaway is prevented by placing a small resistor in series with each emitter to increase the bias level. With a 4 to 8Ω load, each resistor should be approximately 0.5 Ω.

The third area of concern is the distortion that results if the bias diodes, D_1 and D_2 stop conducting. One of the design requirements for the power amplifier of Figure 8.10 is to keep the diodes always turned on.

8.3.2 Complementary-Symmetry Diode-Compensated Class B Power Amplifiers (CSDC)

The design of the power amplifier shown in Figure 8.12 requires knowledge of the diode forward resistance, R_f. We refer to the manufacturer's data sheet for an estimate of this value. For example, if we use the 1N4001 through 1N4007, we can estimate the value of R_f from Figure 1 on the data sheet (See the Appendix). The value of R_f varies widely with the value of instantaneous forward current. The estimated value of $1/R_f$ is found from the slope of the curve of Figure 1 of the data sheet. The values of instantaneous voltage and current are read from the curve as follows:

Instantaneous Forward Voltage	Instantaneous Forward Current
0.8 V	90 mA
0.7 V	10 mA
0.6 V	1.5 mA

We calculate two values of R_f from these data by taking the inverse of the slopes.

$$R_{f1} = \frac{0.8 - 0.7}{90 - 10} \times 10^3 = 1.25\ \Omega$$
$$R_{f2} = \frac{0.7 - 0.6}{10 - 1.5} \times 10^3 = 11.8\ \Omega \tag{8.20}$$

The value of R_f is a variable that depends on the diode forward current. Fortunately, the design of the amplifier is not highly dependent upon the value of R_f and we use a fixed value for R_f in this design procedure. We will approximate R_f as 10 Ω for this example.

It is important that the diode bias current be large enough to keep the diodes in their forward-biased region for all input voltages. The maximum negative peak current through the diode must be less than the direct current bias. That is, the *dc* component of current must be larger than the *ac* component such that when it adds to the *ac* component, the resultant current does not go negative. If this were not true, the diode would be reverse-biased and distortion would result. This restriction is stated as

$$I_D > |i_{dp}| \tag{8.21}$$

where i_{dp} is the amplitude (peak) of the *ac* component of diode current.

We shall take two different approaches toward completing the design. The first approach derives equations from the *ac* equivalent circuit, while the second uses approximate limiting parameters to obtain an estimate for the value of R_2.

We begin by examining the *ac* equivalent circuit as shown in Figure 8.13. i_b is the transistor *ac* base current and v'_{load} is the *ac* voltage across the load $[R_{load} - jX_C]$ at the low frequency.

The quantity, r_e, is omitted from Figure 8.13 since it is assumed to be very small compared to the other circuit resistors. The direct current, I_D, through the diode is given by

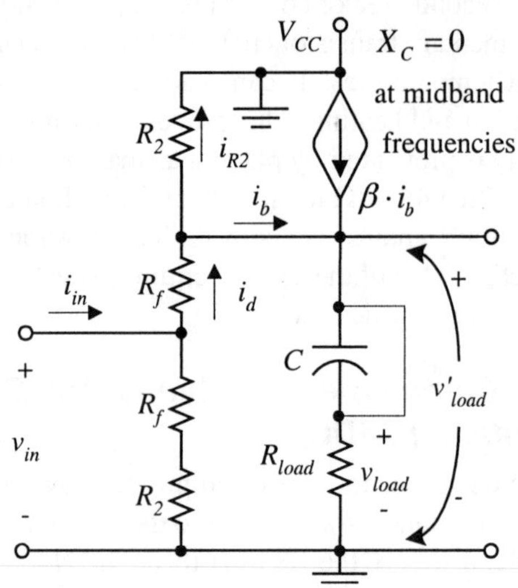

Figure 8.13 – Base equivalent circuit (for positive half-cycle)

$$I_D = \frac{(V_{CC}/2) - 0.7}{R_2} \tag{8.22}$$

where we estimate the value of base-to-emitter voltage as 0.7 V. The *peak* signal current through the diode in the reverse direction, i_{dp}, is given by Equation (8.23). We add an additional subscript, *p* to the parameters defined in the figure, to indicate that the peak value of the variable is being used.

$$i_{dp} = i_{bp} + i_{R2p} = i_{bp} + \frac{v'_{load\ p}}{R_2} \tag{8.23}$$

Equation (8.23) is derived by assuming that the voltage gain is unity for the EF amplifier. That is, the *ac* voltage across R_2 is the same as the voltage from the base to ground, or $v_{in} = v'_{load}$.

By equating I_D to i_{dp}, we find the *limiting condition* for operating in the forward-biased diode condition [see Equation (8.21)]. From this, R_2 can be found as follows:

$$\frac{V_{CC}/2 - 0.7}{R_2} = i_{bp} + \frac{v'_{load\ p}}{R_2} \tag{8.24}$$

so

$$R_2 = \frac{V_{CC}/2 - 0.7 - v'_{load\,p}}{i_{bp}}$$

$$i_{bp} = \frac{V_{CC}/2 - 0.7}{R_2\left(1 + \beta R_{load}/R_2\right)} \tag{8.25}$$

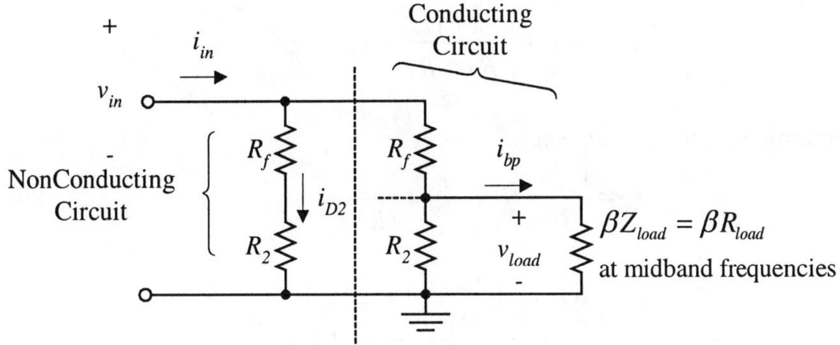

Figure 8.14 – Input equivalent circuit (for one-half cycle)

Since the amplifier is an emitter follower, $v_{in} = v'_{load}$. At midband frequencies, the voltage across C is zero, so the entire voltage, v_{load}, appears across R_{load}. Therefore, $v'_{load} = v_{load}$.

Hence the value of $v'_{load\,p}$ in Equation (8.25) can be written as

$$v'_{load\,p} = R_{load} \cdot \beta i_{bp} = R_{load} \cdot i_{Cp} \tag{8.26}$$

The input resistance is determined from the equivalent circuit shown in Figure 8.14. We have assumed that $Z_{load} = R_{load}$ at the midband frequencies of the amplifier.

The capacitor is assumed to be a short circuit for mid-frequency operation. Note that R_{load} reflects back as βR_{load} and the diodes have a forward resistance of R_f.

The input resistance is found from Figure 8.14 as follows:

$$R_{in} = \left(R_f + R_2\right) \big\| \left[R_f + \left(R_2 \| \beta R_{load}\right)\right] \tag{8.27}$$

The current gain is found using current division. The voltage across D_1 with Q_1 conducting is

$$v_{D1} = R_f\left(i_{bp} + \frac{v_{load}}{R_2}\right)$$

$$i_{D2} = -\frac{v_{D1} + v_{load}}{R_f + R_2} \tag{8.28}$$

$$i_{in} = \frac{v_{D1} + v_{load}}{R_f + R_2} + i_{bp} + \frac{v_{load}}{R_2}$$

Continuing with the expression for i_{in}:

$$\begin{aligned}
i_{in} &= \frac{v_{D1} + v_{load}}{R_f + R_2} + i_{bp} + \frac{v_{load}}{R_2} \\
&= \frac{R_f\left(i_{bp} + \frac{v_{load}}{R_2}\right) + v_{load}}{R_f + R_2} + i_{bp} + \frac{v_{load}}{R_2} \\
&= \frac{R_f i_{bp} + \frac{R_f}{R_2} R_{load}\beta i_{bp} + R_{load}\beta i_{bp}}{R_f + R_2} + i_{bp} + \frac{v_{load}}{R_2} \\
&= \left(\frac{R_f + \frac{R_f}{R_2} R_{load}\beta + R_{load}\beta}{R_f + R_2} + 1 + \frac{R_{load}\beta}{R_2}\right)\cdot i_{bp}
\end{aligned}$$

Since $\beta i_{bp} = i_{out}$, we have

$$\begin{aligned}
A_i &= \frac{\beta i_{bp}}{i_{in}} \\
&= \frac{\beta}{\left(\frac{R_f + \frac{R_f}{R_2} R_{load}\beta + R_{load}\beta}{R_f + R_2} + 1 + \frac{R_{load}}{R_2}\beta\right)} \\
&= \frac{\beta_2\left(R_f + R_2\right)R_2}{R_2 R_f + \beta R_f R_{load} + \beta R_2 R_{load} + \left(R_f + R_2\right)R_2 + \left(R_f + R_2\right)\beta R_{load}}
\end{aligned}$$

and noting that

$$\left(R_2 \| \beta R_{load}\right)\left(R_2 + \beta R_{load}\right) = \frac{\left(R_2 + \beta R_{load}\right)\left(R_2 \beta R_{load}\right)}{\left(R_2 + \beta R_{load}\right)}$$

we have an expression for the current gain.

$$A_i = \beta \frac{i_{bp}}{i_{in}} = \frac{\beta\left(R_f + R_2\right)R_2}{\left(2R_f + R_2 + R_2 \| \beta R_{load}\right)\left(R_2 + \beta R_{load}\right)} \tag{8.29}$$

Example 8.2

You are designing a CS*DC* circuit that requires a 4 V (zero-to-peak) output into an 8 Ω load. Suppose V_{CC} is 15 V and the transistor has $\beta = 100$. Design the circuit so that the diodes remain on during the entire cycle of the input signal.

Solution: The *dc* current through the diode would be $(V_{CC}/2\text{-}0.7)/R_2$. This results in $i_d = 6.8/R_2$. The *ac* zero-to-peak current through the diode could not exceed the *dc* current through the diodes - otherwise the diodes would not be turned on and the *ac* current would be distorted. The *ac* current in the diodes is

$$i_{dp} = \frac{4}{8 \times 100} + \frac{4}{R_2}$$

Setting $I_D = i_{dp}$, we find that $R_2 = 560\ \Omega$. This value of resistance ensures that the diodes remain ON.

8.3.3 Power Calculations for Class B Push-Pull Amplifier

The power delivered by the *ac* source is split between the transistor and the resistors in the bias circuitry. The *ac* signal source adds an insignificant additional amount of power since base currents are small relative to collector currents. Part of the power to the transistor goes to the load, and the other part is dissipated by the transistor itself. The following equations specify the various power relationships in the circuit.

The average power supplied by the *dc* source is

$$P_{VCC} = V_{CC} I_{DC} = V_{CC} \frac{1}{T} \int_0^T i_{CC}(t)dt \tag{8.30}$$

$i_{CC}(t)$ is the total current and is composed of two components: the *dc* current through the base bias resistor and diode combination, and the *ac* collector current through transistor, Q_1. Under quiescent conditions (i.e., zero input) Q_1 is in cutoff mode. Collector current flows during the positive half of the output signal waveform. Therefore we only need to integrate this component of the power supply signal over the first half cycle

$$I_{C1,avg} = \frac{1}{T} \int_0^{T/2} I_{C\max} \sin\left(\frac{2\pi t}{T}\right) dt = \frac{1}{\pi} I_{C1,\max} \tag{8.31}$$

The maximum values of collector current and power delivered to the transistor are

$$I_{C\,max} = \frac{V_{CC}}{2R_{load}}$$

$$P_{VCC}\Big|_{Q1,Q2} = \frac{V_{CC} I_{Cmax}}{\pi} = \frac{V_{CC}^2}{2\pi R_{load}} \tag{8.32}$$

The *ac* output power, assuming a sinusoidal input, is

$$P_{out}(ac) = \frac{I_{C\max}^2 R_{load}}{2} \tag{8.33}$$

The maximum *ac* output power is found by substituting $I_{C,max}$ for $I_{C1,max}$ to get

$$P_{out}(\text{ac max}) = \frac{1}{2}\left(\frac{V_{CC}}{2R_{load}}\right)^2 R_{load} = \frac{V_{CC}^2}{8R_{load}} \tag{8.34}$$

The total power supplied to the stage is the sum of the power to the transistor and the power to the bias and compensation circuitry.

$$P_{VCC} = \frac{V_{CC} I_{C\,max}}{\pi} + \frac{V_{CC}^2}{2R_f + 2R_2} \tag{8.35}$$

If we subtract the power to the load from the power supplied to the transistors, we find the power being dissipated in the transistors. Since this power is shared equally between the two transistors, the power dissipated by a single transistor is one half of this value. Thus,

$$P_{transistor} = \frac{1}{2}\left(\frac{V_{CC} I_{C\max}}{\pi} - \frac{I^2{}_{C\max} R_{load}}{2}\right) \tag{8.36}$$

We are assuming that the base current is negligible.

The efficiency of the Class B push-pull amplifier is the ratio of the output power to the power delivered to the transistor. Thus we neglect the power dissipated by the bias circuitry.

$$\eta = \frac{V_{CC}^2/8R_{load}}{V_{CC}^2/2\pi R_{load}} = \frac{\pi}{4} = 0.785 \quad \text{or} \quad 78.5\% \tag{8.37}$$

This amplifier is more efficient than a Class A amplifier. It is often used in output circuits where efficiency important design requirement.

The amplifier designer must specify is the power rating of the transistor. That is, it is important to know the maximum power dissipated by a single transistor. This parameter is found by differentiating Equation (8.36) with respect to $I_{C1,max}$ and setting the derivative to zero. Thus we will find the value of $I_{C1,max}$ that results in maximum dissipated power, as follows:

$$\frac{dP}{dI_{C\,max}} = 0 = \frac{1}{2}\left(\frac{V_{CC}}{\pi} - I_{C\,max} R_{load}\right)$$

$$I_{C1,\max} = \frac{V_{CC}}{\pi R_{load}} \tag{8.38}$$

We now substitute this value back into Equation (8.36) to find the maximum power:

$$P_{\max} = \frac{1}{2}\left(\frac{V_{CC}^2}{\pi^2 R_{load}} - \frac{V_{CC}^2}{2\pi^2 R_{load}}\right) = \frac{V_{CC}^2}{4\pi^2 R_{load}} \tag{8.39}$$

In choosing a transistor, it is important that the power rating is equal to or exceeds the maximum power of Equation (8.39).

EXAMPLE 8.3 – Class B Push-Pull Amplifier (Design)

Design a diode-compensated complementary-symmetry audio amplifier (Figure 8.12) with a power output of 1/2 W into an 8 Ω speaker. Use a 12 V power supply and silicon transistors with $\beta = 60$. The diodes have forward resistance of 8 Ω. Determine the current gain, power delivered to the amplifier, and power ratings of the transistors.

Solution: We first determine the value of I_{Cmax} needed to achieve the specified load power. From Equation (8.33) we obtain

$$P_{load} = \frac{I_{Cmax}^2 R_{load}}{2} = \frac{1}{2} \quad \text{W}$$

$$I_{Cmax} = \sqrt{\frac{1}{R_{load}}} = 0.354 \quad \text{A}_{\text{peak}}$$

The maximum load voltage, $v_{load\,p}$, is simply R_{load} times the maximum current, or 2.83 V. The ratio of collector current to base current is β. Therefore, the peak base current must be

$$i_{bp} = \frac{I_{C\,max}}{\beta} = 5.9 \quad \text{mA}_{\text{peak}}$$

We can find R_2 using Equation (8.25).

$$R_2 = \frac{V_{CC}/2 - 0.7 - v'_{load\,p}}{i_{bp}} = 419\ \Omega$$

R_{in} and the input current are determined at midband frequencies from Equation (8.28).

$$V_{D1} = R_f\left(i_{bp} + \frac{v_{load}}{R_2}\right) = 0.1 \quad \text{V}$$

The input current is also given by Equation (8.28).

$$i_{in} = \frac{v_{D1} + v_{load}}{R_f + R_2} + i_{bp} + \frac{v_{load}}{R_2} = 19.5 \quad \text{mA}$$

The input resistance is found from Equation (8.27).

$$R_{in} = \left(R_f + R_2\right) \Big\| \left[R_f + \left(R_2 \| \beta R_{load}\right)\right] = 150 \quad \Omega$$

Current gain is found from the ratio of output to input current, as in Equation (8.29).

$$A_i = \beta \frac{i_{bp}}{i_{in}} = 18.2$$

The power to the amplifier including the bias circuitry, is given by Equation (8.35):

$$P_{VCC} = \frac{V_{CC} I_{Cmax}}{\pi} + \frac{V_{CC}^2}{2R_f + 2R_2} = 1.52 \quad \text{W}$$

The power rating of each transistor is given by Equation (8.39):

$$P_{trans} = \frac{V_{CC}^2}{4\pi^2 R_{load}} = 0.456 \quad \text{W}$$

EXAMPLE 8.4 Class B Push-Pull Amplifier Design

Design a complementary symmetry push-pull diode-compensated Class B amplifier (see Figure 8.15) to drive a 4Ω load to ±3 V, zero-to-peak. Use *npn* and *pnp* transistors each having a β of 100 and $V_{BE} = \pm 0.7$ V. The diodes have forward resistance, $R_f = 10\ \Omega$. Determine all quiescent voltages and currents for $V_{CC} = 16$ V. Calculate the maximum power which is delivered from the power supply, the power delivered to the load, and the power rating of the transistors to be used.

Solution: The peak collector and peak base currents are related by β. Thus,

$$i_{bp} = \frac{i_{Cp}}{\beta}$$

Since $V_{load\ max}$ is given as 3 V, we find

$$i_{Cp} = \frac{3}{4} = 750 \quad \text{mA}_{peak}$$

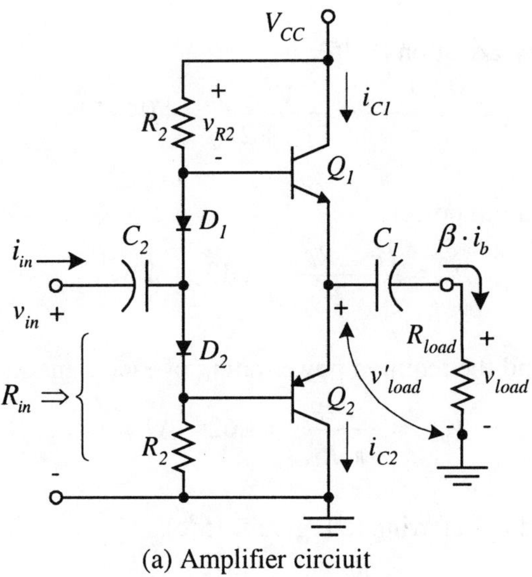

(a) Amplifier circiuit

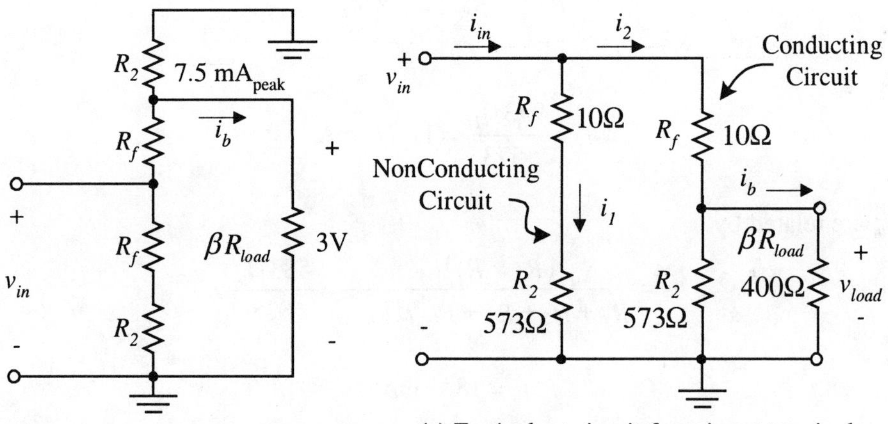

(b) Equivalent circuit midrange

(c) Equivalent circuit from input terminals

Figure 8.15 – Circuit for Example 8.4

Therefore,

$$i_{bp} = 7.5 \quad \text{mA}_{\text{peak}}$$

We solve for R_2 where $v_{load\,p} = 3\ \text{V}_{\text{peak}}$, using Equation (8.25).

$$R_2 = \frac{V_{CC}/2 - 0.7 - v_{load\,p}}{i_{bp}} = 573\ \Omega$$

At mid frequency, the input resistance is given by Equation (8.27).

$$R_{in} = (R_f + R_2) \| \left[R_f + (R_2 \| \beta R_{load}) \right] = 173\ \Omega$$

The supply power is given by Equation (8.35).

$$P_{VCC} = \frac{V_{CC} I_{Cmax}}{\pi} + \frac{V_{CC}^2}{2R_f + 2R_2} = 4.04 \quad \text{W}$$

Equation (8.33) yields the output power.

$$P_{out} = \frac{I_{C\,max}^2 R_{load}}{2} = 1.13 \quad \text{W}$$

Equation (8.39) is used to find the required power rating of each transistor.

$$P_{trans} = \frac{V_{CC}^2}{4\pi^2 R_{load}} = 1.62 \quad \text{W}$$

The current gain, A_i, is found by referring to Figure 8.15(c):

$$i_b = \frac{R_2 \cdot i_2}{R_2 + \beta R_{load}} = \frac{573 \cdot i_2}{973}$$

Therefore,

$$i_2 = \frac{973 \cdot i_{bp}}{573} = 12.7 \quad \text{mA}$$

i_2 and i_{in} are related by

$$i_2 = \frac{(R_f + R_2) i_{in}}{R_f + R_2 + R_f + R_2 \| \beta R_{load}} = \frac{583 \cdot i_{in}}{828}$$

Hence,

$$i_{in} = 18 \quad \text{mA}$$

Finally, the current gain is

$$A_i = \frac{\beta i_b}{i_{in}} = 41.6$$

EXERCISES

E8.3 Design a complementary-symmetry diode-compensated Class B amplifier to drive a 4 Ω load with 1 W of power. Use *npn* and *pnp* matched transistors each having $\beta = 100$ and $V_{BE} = \pm 0.7$ V with equivalent characteristic diodes having $R_f = 50\ \Omega$. Let $V_{CC} = 12$ V. Determine R_2, R_{in}, P_{trans} and $A_i = i_{out}/i_{in}$.

Answer: $R_2 = 350\ \Omega$; $P_{trans} = 0.91$ W
$A_i = 29$; $R_{in} = 149\ \Omega$

E8.4 Design a complementary-symmetry diode-compensated Class B power amplifier to deliver 2 W to a 10Ω load. Use a matched pair of *npn* and *pnp* transistors each having $\beta = 100$ and $V_{BE} = \pm 0.7$ V with equivalent characteristic diodes having $R_f = 5\ \Omega$. Determine R_2, R_{in} and A_i when $V_{CC} = 16$ V.

Answer: $R_2 = 154\ \Omega$; $R_{in} = 74\ \Omega$; $A_i = 7.1$

8.4 DARLINGTON CIRCUIT

Figure 8.16 illustrates a *Darlington Circuit.* This configuration is composed of two cascaded transistors. It possesses desirable characteristics that sometimes make it more useful than a single transistor. The circuit has high input impedance, low output impedance and high current gain. A disadvantage of the Darlington transistor pair is that the leakage current of the first transistor is amplified by the second transistor.

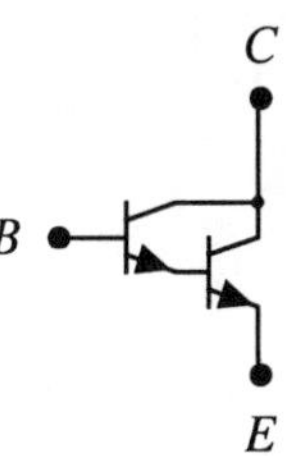

Figure 8.16 – Darlington transistor pair

The Darlington transistor pair can be used in either a EF or CE amplifier configuration. If the two transistors are connected as an EF amplifier as shown in Figure 8.17, the betas of the two transistors multiply together. The combination looks like a single high β transistor.

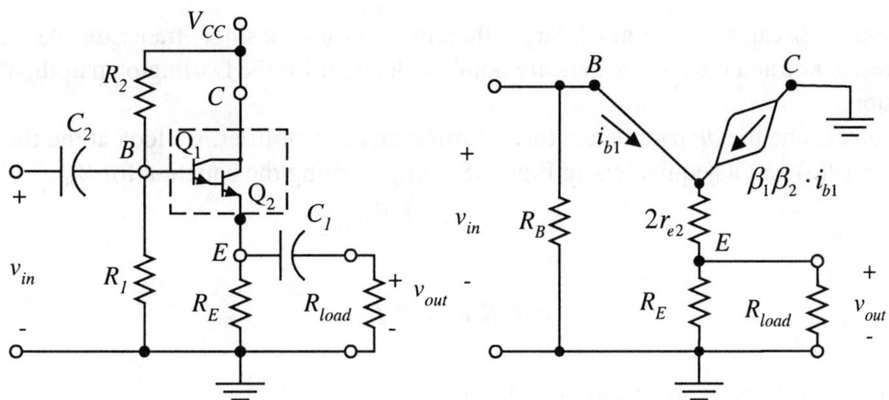

Figure 8.17 – EF amplifier using a Darlington pair

Figure 8.18 – *ac* equivalent circuit of a Darlington pair

Since the quiescent point for the first transistor is different from that of the second, r_π for the two transistors is different. As can be seen from the equivalent circuit of Figure 8.18, the equivalent load on the first transistor is $\beta_2\left(R_{load} \| R_E\right)$ while the load on the second transistor is only $R_{load} \| R_E$.

In practice, the first transistor can be of lower power rating than the second. The input resistance of the second transistor constitutes the emitter load for the first transistor.

The values of R_{in} and A_i are determined as follows:

$$R_{in} = R_B \| \left[\beta_1 \beta_2 \left(2r_{e2} + R_E \| R_{load}\right)\right]$$

(8.40)

$$A_i = \frac{\beta_1 \beta_2 \cdot i_{b1}}{i_{in}} \cdot \frac{R_E}{R_E + R_{load}}$$

where

$$i_{b1} = \frac{R_B}{R_B + \left(2r_{e2} + R_E \| R_{load}\right)\beta_1 \beta_2} \cdot i_{in}$$

$$i_{in} = \frac{R_B + \left(2r_{e2} + R_E \| R_{load}\right)\beta_1 \beta_2}{R_B} \cdot i_{b1}$$

We then obtain

$$A_i = \frac{R_B}{R_B / \beta_1 \beta_2 + 2r_{e2} + R_E \| R_{load}} \cdot \frac{R_E}{R_E + R_{load}} \tag{8.41}$$

We see that R_B can be made much larger than in the case of a single transistor. As a result, the input resistance and the current gain are both much larger for the Darlington pair than for single transistors.

To determine the *ac* parameters for a Darlington CE amplifier, we look at the the circuit of Figure 8.19(a) and its equivalent in Figure 8.19(b). Writing the equation for R_{in} yields

$$R_{in} = R_B \| \left(r_{el} + \beta_1 r_{e1}\right)$$

(8.42)

$$= R_B \| \left(\beta_1 r_{el} + \beta_1 \beta_2 r_{e2}\right)$$

The various resistances in Equation (8.42) are given by

$$r_{\pi 1} = \beta_1 r_{e1}$$

$$r_{\pi 2} = \beta_2 r_{e2}$$

$$r_{e2} = \frac{V_T}{I_{C2}} \tag{8.43}$$

$$r_{e1} \approx \frac{V_T}{I_{C1}} = \frac{V_T}{I_{B2}} = \frac{\beta_2 V_T}{I_{C2}} = \beta_2 r_{e2}$$

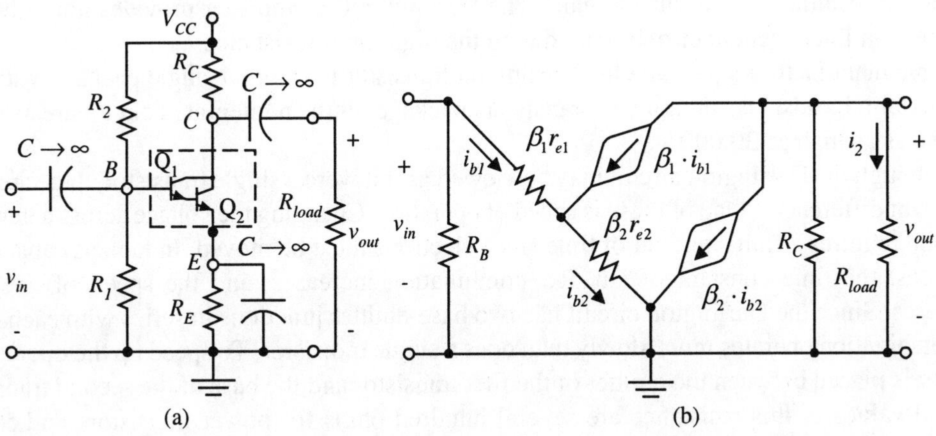

Figure 8.19 – Darlington CE amplifier

The input resistance is then

$$R_{in} = R_B \| \left[\beta_1 \beta_2 r_{e2} + \beta_1 \beta_2 r_{e2} \right] = R_B \| 2\beta_1 \beta_2 r_{e2} \tag{8.44}$$

We must find the current in order to determine the gain. Using current division, we obtain

$$i_{b1} = \frac{R_B}{R_B + r_{\pi 1} + \beta_1 r_{\pi 2}} \cdot i_{in} = \frac{R_B}{R_B + 2\beta_1 \beta_2 r_{e2}} \cdot i_{in}$$

$$i_{in} = \frac{R_B + 2\beta_1 \beta_2 r_{e2}}{R_B} \cdot i_{b1} \tag{8.45}$$

The current gain is then

$$A_i = \frac{i_2}{i_{in}} = \frac{-(\beta_1\beta_2 i_{b1})R_C/(R_C + R_{load})}{(R_B + 2\beta_1\beta_2 r_{e2})i_{b1}/R_B}$$

$$= \frac{-R_B}{R_B/\beta_1\beta_2 + 2r_{e2}} \cdot \frac{R_C}{R_C + R_{load}} \tag{8.46}$$

Using the gain-impedance formula, we find the voltage gain.

$$A_v = \frac{A_i \cdot R_{load}}{R_{in}} = \frac{-\beta_1\beta_2(R_C \| R_{load})}{2\beta_1\beta_2 r_{e2}} = \frac{-R_C \| R_{load}}{2r_{e2}} \tag{8.47}$$

Most amplifiers with a bypassed emitter resistance have excellent voltage gain but low input resistance, resulting in low current gain. The Darlington CE amplifier provides not only good voltage gain but excellent current gain due to the high input resistance.

Some manufacturers package the Darlington transistor pair into a single package with only three external leads. Darlington pair transistors packaged into an integrated circuit are available with betas as high as 30,000.

Although the Darlington circuit may be viewed as if it were a single transistor, there are some important differences. One of these is speed of operation. Changing the voltage across a transistor junction requires a finite amount of time since electrons must be moved. In fact, as capacitance increases, the time constant of any RC combination increases, and the speed of operation decreases. Since the Darlington circuit has two base-emitter junctions in series with each other, the combination operates more slowly than does a single transistor. To speed up the operation, a resistor is placed between the emitter of the first transistor and the base of the second transistor. Typical values of this resistance are several hundred ohms for power transistors and several thousand ohms for signal transistors. Since two base-emitter junctions exist, the overall V_{BE} is 1.2 to 1.4 V instead of approximately 0.7 V.

EXAMPLE 8.5 - Darlington Pair Class A Amplifier (Design)

Design an EF amplifier using a Darlington transistor pair (Figure 8.17) that has a combined β of 10,000 and $V_{BE} = 1.4$ V. The amplifier must drive a load of 20 Ω with $R_{in} = 3$ kΩ and $V_{CC} = 12$ V. Determine A_i and P_{out}.

Solution: Set $R_E = R_{load}$ since there is one less equation than unknowns. We calculate R_B from knowledge of R_{in} as follows.

$$R_{in} = R_B \| [\beta_1\beta_2(R_E \| R_{load})]$$

$$3\text{ k}\Omega = \frac{R_B(10^5)}{R_B + 10^5}$$

Solving for R_B yields

$$R_B = 3.09\text{k}\Omega$$

where we have neglected r_e. The Q-point is at

$$I_{CQ} = \frac{V_{CC}}{R_{ac} + R_{dc}} = 400 \text{ mA}$$

We use the bias equation to find V_{BB}.

$$V_{BB} = V_{BE} + I_{CQ}\left(\frac{R_B}{\beta_1\beta_2} + R_E\right) = 9.52 \text{ V}$$

The bias resistors are given by

$$R_1 = \frac{R_B}{1 - (V_{BB}/V_{CC})} = 15.0 \text{ k}\Omega$$

$$R_2 = \frac{R_B V_{CC}}{V_{BB}} = 3.89 \text{ k}\Omega$$

The current gain is

$$A_i = \frac{R_B}{R_B/(\beta_1\beta_2) + R_E \| R_{load}} \cdot \frac{R_E}{R_E + R_{load}} = 150$$

The output power is

$$P_{out} = \frac{1}{2}\left(\frac{I_{CQ}}{2}\right)^2 R_{load} = 0.4 \text{ W}$$

The Darlington pair provides a large increase in current and power gain over the single transistor amplifier. It also provides a higher input resistance than can be obtained using a single transistor amplifier.

EXERCISES

E8.5 Design an EF amplifier using a Darlington transistor pair (Figure 8.17) to drive an 8Ω load with a combined β of 20,000, V_{BE} = 1.4 V, V_{CC} = 20 V and A_i = 500. Find R_E, R_1, R_2, R_{in} and P_{out}.

Answer: $R_E = 8\ \Omega$; $R_1 = 17\ k\Omega$; $R_2 = 5.6\ k\Omega$

$R_{in} = 4\ k\Omega$; $P_{out} = 2.3\ W$

E8.6 Design a CE amplifier using a Darlington transistor pair (Figure 8.19) with combined β = 25000, V_{BE} = 1.2 V, V_{CC} = 20 V, A_v = -120, A_i = 200, R_E = 200 Ω, and R_{load} = 5 kΩ. Determine the following:

(a) R_1, R_2, and R_{in}
(b) Maximum undistorted output voltage swing
(c) Input *dc* power required

Answer: (a) $R_1 = 9.24\ k\Omega$, $R_2 = 99.6\ k\Omega$, $R_{in} = 8.33\ k\Omega$; (b) $V_{out} = 11.2\ V$; (c) $P_{in} = 53\ mW$.

8.5 POWER SUPPLY USING POWER TRANSISTORS

We now explore the design of power supplies. We begin with a supply that uses discrete transistors. We then examine approaches using integrated circuits. We analyze regulated power supplies using both the 8700 series of integrated circuit regulators and the LM317 adjustable regulator.

8.5.1 Power Supply Using Discrete Components

In Chapter 3 we analyzed the regulated power supply using a Zener diode as the voltage-controlling device. We also used Zener diodes to temperature stabilize IC bias circuits. A simple Zener diode power regulator circuit is shown in Figure 8.20 (This is a repeat of Fig. 3.39.).

The output voltage is determined by the reverse breakdown voltage of the diode. This is nearly a constant for a wide range of currents. To obtain better regulation, the Zener diode can be connected to the base circuit of a power transistor as is shown in Figure 8.21.

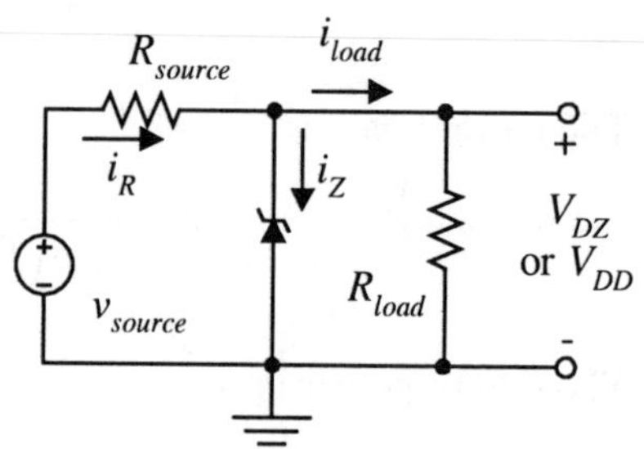

Figure 8.20 – Zener power supply

This configuration reduces the current flow in the diode. The power transistor used in this configuration is known as a *pass* transistor. The purpose of C_L is to insure that the variations in one of the regulated power supply loads will not be fed to other loads. That is, the capacitor effectively shorts out high-frequency variations.

Because of the current amplifying property of the transistor, the current in the Zener diode is small. Hence there is little voltage drop across the diode resistance, and the Zener approximates an ideal constant voltage source.

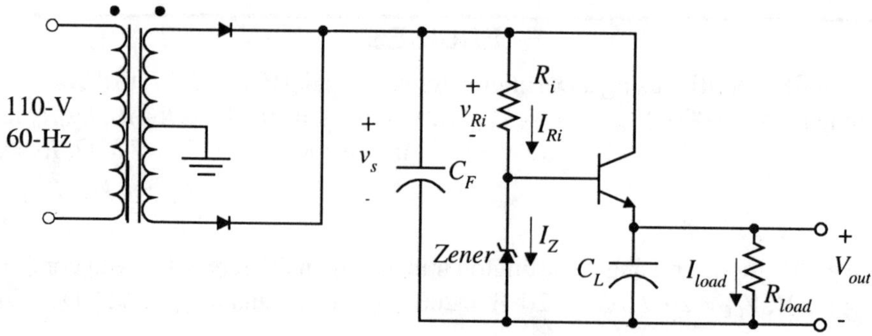

Figure 8.21 – Regulated power supply

The current in resistor R_i is the Zener diode current plus the base current in the transistor, I_{load} / β. We take the two conditions,

1. V_{Smax}, I_{Zmax}, $I_{load\ min}/\beta$
2. V_{Smin}, I_{Zmin}, $I_{load\ max}/\beta$

We calculate R_i for both conditions and since R_i is constant, we equate these two expressions as in Equation (8.48).

$$R_i = \frac{V_{S\max} - V_Z}{I_{Z\max} + I_{load\ \min}/\beta} = \frac{V_{S\min} - V_Z}{I_{Z\min} + I_{load\ \max}/\beta} \tag{8.48}$$

In Section 3.4.1, we derived a design guideline that set $I_{Z\min} = 0.1 I_{Z\max}$. Then we equate the expressions for Equation (8.48) to obtain,

$$\left(V_{S\max} - V_Z\right)\left(0.1 I_{Z\max} + \frac{I_{load\ \max}}{\beta}\right) = \left(V_{S\min} - V_Z\right)\left(I_{Z\max} + \frac{I_{load\ \min}}{\beta}\right) \tag{8.49}$$

Solving for I_{Zmax}, we obtain,

$$I_{Z\max} = \frac{I_{load\ \min}\left(V_Z - V_{S\min}\right) + I_{load\ \max}\left(V_{S\max} - V_Z\right)}{\beta\left(V_{S\min} - 0.1 V_{S\max} - 0.9 V_Z\right)} \tag{8.50}$$

Equation (8.50) is the same as Equation (3.61) except that $I_{Z\max}$ is reduced by the β of the transistor. The design is accomplished as in Chapter 3 with the exception that the value of $I_{Z\max}$ is reduced. We determine the equivalent load as seen by the capacitor, C_F, by looking at the circuit of Figure 8.21. We estimate the load resistance by taking the ratio of the minimum source voltage to the maximum load current. Since R_{load} is large and in parallel, it can be ignored. This is the worst case since it represents the smallest load and therefore the maximum load current.

$$R_{load}(equivalent) = R_{load}(worst\ case) = \frac{V_{S\min}}{I_{load\ \max}} \tag{8.51}$$

We substitute Equation (8.51) into Equation (3.62) to estimate the capacitor size.

$$C_F = \frac{V_{Smax} - V_Z}{\Delta V\ f_p\, R_{load}(equivalent)} \tag{8.52}$$

Since the voltage gain of an EF amplifier is unity, the output voltage of the regulated power supply is,

$$V_{load} = V_Z - V_{BE} \tag{8.53}$$

The percent regulation of the power supply is given by

$$\% \, reg = \frac{V_{Z\max} - V_{Z\min}}{V_Z} \times 100$$

$$= \frac{R_Z(I_{Z\max} - I_{Z\min})}{V_Z} \times 100 \tag{8.54}$$

The percent of regulation is reduced since I_{Zmax} is much smaller because of the division by β.

EXAMPLE 8.6 - Regulated Power Supply Using Discrete Components (Design)

Design an 11.3V regulated power supply (see Figure 8.21) for a load current that varies between 400 mA and 500 mA. Assume an input of 120 V rms at 60 Hz into a 3:1 center-tapped transformer. Use a 12V Zener with $R_Z = 2\ \Omega$. The transistor has $V_{BE} = 0.7$ V and $\beta = 100$. Set C so $\Delta v_S = 30\%$.

Solution: The design consists of choosing values for R_i and for C_F. We first find $V_{S\max}$ by multiplying the rms voltage by $\sqrt{2}$ to obtain 170 V. The transformer output on either side of the center tap is one-sixth of the input, so $V_{S\max}$ is 28.3 V. Since $\Delta v_S = 30\%$,

$$V_{Smin} = (0.7)(V_{Smax}) = 19.8 \text{ V}$$

$$I_{load\max} = 500 \text{ mA}$$

$$I_{load\min} = 400 \text{ mA}$$

and

$$V_Z = 12 \text{ V}$$

Now using Equation (8.50), we obtain,

$$I_{Z\max} = \frac{I_{load\min}(V_Z - V_{S\min}) + I_{load\max}(V_{S\max} - V_Z)}{\beta(V_{S\min} - 0.1V_{S\max} - 0.9V_Z)} = 8.15 \text{ mA}$$

Notice that the transistor keeps the value of I_{Zmax} quite small since β appears in the denominator of Equation (8.50). We calculate the value of R_i from Equation (8.48).

$$R_i = \frac{V_{S\max} - V_Z}{I_{Z\max} + I_{load\min}/\beta} = 1.34 \text{ k}\Omega$$

Note that

$$R_{load}(equivalent) = \frac{V_{S\min}}{I_{load\max}} = 39.6\ \Omega$$

The capacitor size is estimated from Equation (8.52):

$$C_F = \frac{V_{S\max} - V_Z}{(V_{S\max} - V_{S\min}) f_p R_{load}(equivalent)} = 701\ \mu F$$

Equation (8.54) can be used to evaluate the percent of regulation at the load.

$$\%\ regulation = \frac{R_Z(I_{Z\max} - I_{Z\min})}{V_Z} \times 100 = 0.122\ \%$$

8.5.2 Power Supply Using IC Regulator (Three-Terminal Regulator)

Monolithic integrated circuits have greatly simplified the design of a wide variety of power supplies. Using a single IC regulator and a few external components, we can obtain excellent regulation (on the order of 0.01%) with good stability and reliability and with overload protection.

IC regulators are produced by a number of manufacturers. The IC regulator improves upon the performance of the Zener diode regulator. It does this by incorporating an operational amplifier. In this section, we present basic design considerations for IC regulators. These techniques are useful in the design of power supplies for a variety of low power applications. We consider the internal theory of operation of these and other three-terminal voltage regulators in the current section. These products vary in the amount of output current. The most common range of output current is 0.75 A to 1.5 A (depending on whether a heat sink is used).

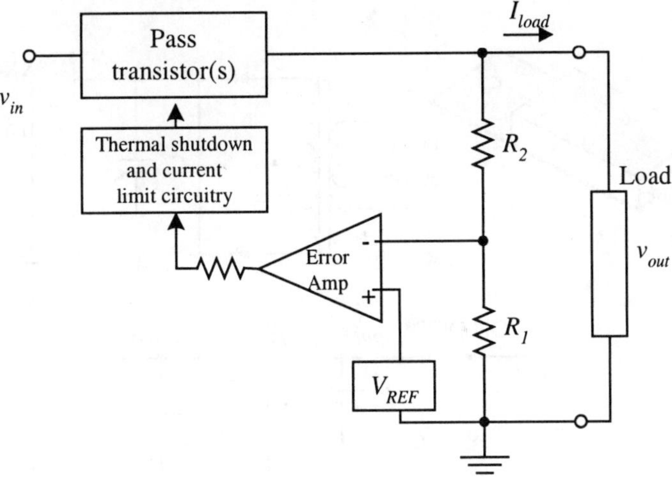

Figure 8.22 – Functional block diagram of IC regulator

The functional block diagram of Figure 8.22 illustrates the method of voltage regulation using this *series regulator*. The name series regulator is based on the use of a *pass transistor* (a power transistor) which develops a variable voltage which is in "series" with the output voltage. The voltage across the pass transistor is varied in such a manner as to keep the output voltage constant.

A reference voltage, V_{REF}, which is often developed by a Zener diode, is compared with the voltage divided output, v_{out}. The resulting error voltage is given by

$$v_{\varepsilon} = error\ voltage = V_{REF} - \frac{R_1}{R_1 + R_2} v_{out} \tag{8.55}$$

The error voltage v_{ε} is amplified through a discrete amplifier or an operational amplifier and used to change the voltage drop across the pass transistor. This is a feedback system which generates a variable voltage across the pass transistor in order to force the error voltage to zero. When the error voltage is zero, we obtain the desired equation by solving Equation (8.55) for v_{out}.

$$v_{out} = \left(1 + \frac{R_2}{R_1}\right) V_{REF} \tag{8.56}$$

Note that since R_1, R_2 and V_{REF} are constant, v_{out} is also a constant, independent of variations in the load current or in the input voltage.

Thermal shutdown and current-limit circuitry exists between the error amplifier and the pass transistor. This circuitry protects the regulator in case the temperature becomes too high or an inadvertent short circuit exists at the output of the regulator.

The maximum power dissipated in this type of series regulator is the power dissipated in the internal pass transistor, which is approximately $(V_{Smax} - V_{out})I_{L\ max}$. Hence, as the load current increases, the power dissipated in the internal pass transistor increases. If I_{load} exceeds 0.75 A, the IC package should be secured to a heat sink. When this is done, I_{load} can increase to about 1.5 A.

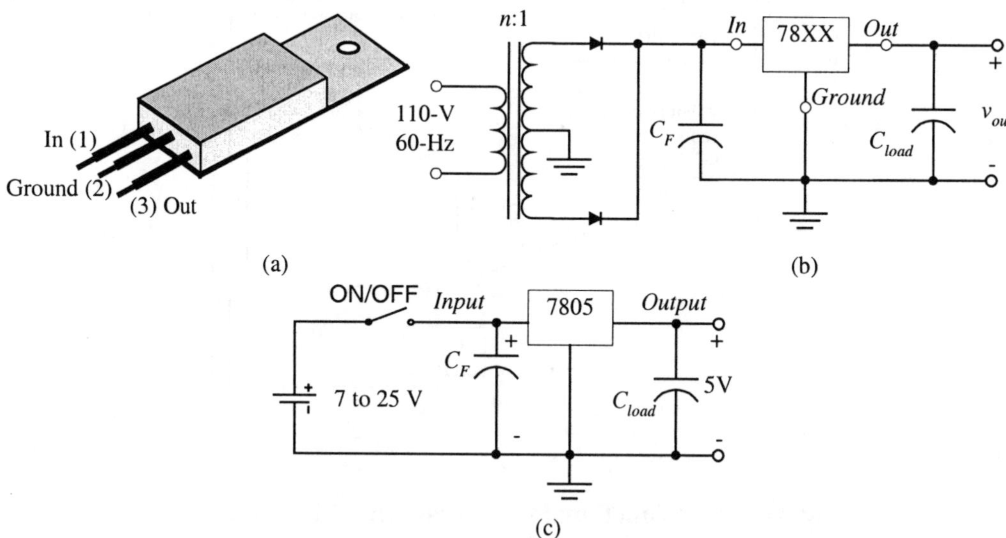

Figure 8.23 – 78XX Series Regulator

We now focus our attention on the 78XX series of regulators. The last two digits of the IC part number denote the output voltage of the device. Thus, for example, a 7808 IC package produces an 8V regulated output. These packages, although internally complex, are inexpensive and easy to use.

Specification sheets appear in the Appendix, and these should be referred to during the following discussion. There are a number of different voltages that can be obtained from the 78XX series IC; they are 5, 6, 8, 8.5, 10, 12, 15, 18, and 24 V. In order to design a regulator around one of these ICs, we need only select a transformer, diodes, and filter. The physical configuration is shown in Figure 8.23(a). The ground lead and the metal tab are connected together. This permits direct attachment to a heat sink for cooling purposes. A typical circuit application is shown in Figure 8.23(c).

The specification sheet for this IC indicates that there must be a common ground between the input and output, and the minimum voltage at the IC input must be above the regulated output. In order to assure this last condition, it is necessary to filter the output from the rectifier. The C_F in Figure 8.23(b) performs this filtering when combined with the input resistance to the IC. We use an n:1 step down transformer, with the secondary winding center-tapped, to drive a full-wave rectifier.

The minimum and maximum input voltages for the 78XX family of regulators are shown in Table 8.1.

TYPE	MIN	MAX
7805	7	25
7806	8	25
7808	10.5	25
7885	10.5	25
7810	12.5	28
7812	14.5	30
7815	17.5	30
7818	21	33
7824	27	38

Table 8.1 - Minimum and maximum input voltage for 78XX regulator

We use Table 8.1 to select the turns ratio, n, for a 78XX regulator. As a design guide, we will take the average of V_{max} and V_{min} of the particular IC regulator to calculate n. For example, using a 7805 regulator, we obtain

$$\frac{V_{\max} + V_{\min}}{2} = \frac{7 + 25}{2} = 16 \qquad (8.57)$$

The center tap provides division by 2 so the peak voltage out of the rectifier is $115\sqrt{2}/2n = 16$. Therefore, $n = 5$. This is a conservative method of selecting the transformer ratio.

The filter capacitor, C_F, is chosen to maintain the voltage input range to the regulator as specified in Table 8.1.

The output capacitor, C_{load}, aids in isolating the effect of the transients that may appear on the regulated supply line. C_{load} should be a high quality tantalum capacitor with a capacitance of 1.0 μF. It should be connected close to the 78XX regulator using short leads in order to improve the stability performance.

This family of regulators can also be used for battery powered systems. Figure 8.23(b) shows a battery powered application. The value of C_F is chosen in the same manner as for the standard filter.

The 79XX series regulator is identical to the 78XX series except that it provides negative regulated voltages instead of positive.

EXAMPLE 8.7:

Design an IC circuit regulator to generate a 12V output into a load whose current varies from 100 mA to 500 mA. The input is 115 Vrms at 60 Hz.

Solution: We use the circuit of Figure 8.23(b) with a 7812 regulator. The center-tapped transformer and full-wave rectifier must produce a minimum voltage of at least 14.5 V and a maximum voltage of no more than 30 V. This information is obtained from Table 8.1. The input peak voltage is $115\sqrt{2}$ or 163 V. The center-tapped secondary divides this by 2 to yield 81.5 V. Let us choose the mid-point between 14.5 and 30, or 22.25 V to select the transformer ratio. This yields a transformer ratio of 81.5/22.25 or 3.68.

Since $V_{Smin} = 14.5$ V (from Table 8.1) and $V_{Smax} = 22.3$ V, we have

$$C_F = \frac{V_{S\max}}{\Delta V\ f_p R_{load}} = 822\ \mu\text{F}$$

We have used the fact that

$$\Delta V = 22.3 - 14.5 = 7.8\ \text{V}$$

and

$$R_{load}(\textit{worst case}) = 29\ \Omega$$

The value of C_{load} is determined by the types of variations that occur in the load. A typical selection for this application is a 1.0 μF high-quality tantalum capacitor.

EXERCISES

E8.7 Design a 7.3V regulated power supply for an 800±100 mA load. The input is 110 V rms at 60 Hz and a 4:1 center-tapped transformer is used. $V_Z = 8$ V and $\Delta v_S = 20\%$ The transistor has $V_{BE} = 0.7$ V and $\beta = 100$. Assume a full-wave rectifier and $R_Z = 5\ \Omega$. Find R_i, C_F and the percentage of regulation.

Answer: $R_i = 777\ \Omega$; $C_F = 2380\ \mu F$;
% *Regulation* = 0.439%

E8.8 A 7815 IC is used as the regulator with a center-tapped transformer to full-wave rectify a 200V peak-to-peak input voltage. What is the required turns ratio and filter capacitor size to provide an output of 12 V at 400 mA?

Answer: $n = 2.11$; $C_F = 724\ \mu F$

8.5.3 Power Supply Using Three-Terminal Adjustable Regulator

The LM317 is an adjustable three-terminal positive voltage regulator capable of supplying more than 1.5 A over a 1.2 to 37 V output range. It is easy to use and requires only two external resistors to set the output voltage. Both line and load regulation are better than in standard fixed voltage regulators. The LM317 is packaged in a standard transistor package, and provides overload protection, including current limiting and thermal overload protection. Figure 8.24 shows a connection diagram for the LM317.

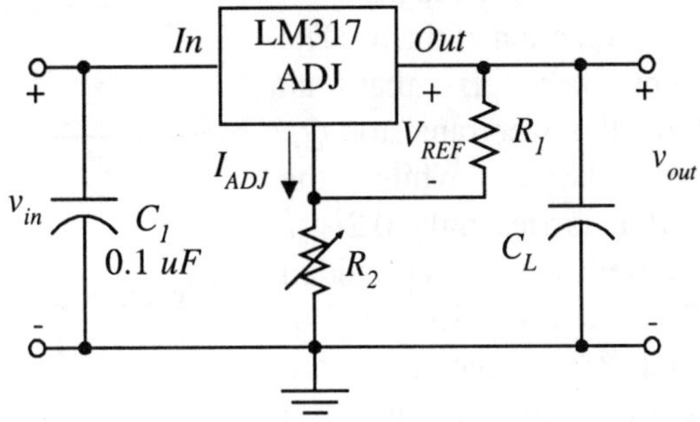

Figure 8. 24 – LM 317 regulator

The capacitor, C_L is optional and when it is included, the transient response improves. Output capacitors in the range of 1 to 10 μF (tantalum electrolytic) are used to provide improved output impedance and rejection of transients. The capacitor C_1 is needed if the device is physically located far from filter capacitors.

In operation, the LM317 has a precision internal voltage reference that develops a nominal 1.25V voltage, V_{REF}, between the output and the adjustment terminal. The reference voltage appears across the *program resistor*, R_1. Since V_{REF} is constant, there is a constant current, I_1, through the program resistor. The output voltage is then given by,

$$V_{out} = V_{REF} + (I_1 + I_{ADJ})R_2$$

$$= V_{REF} + \frac{V_{REF}R_2}{R_1} + I_{ADJ}R_2 \tag{8.58}$$

$$= V_{REF}\left(1 + \frac{R_2}{R_1}\right) + I_{ADJ}R_2$$

Note that if V_{REF}, R_1, R_2, and I_{ADJ} are all constants, then V_{out} is also a constant.

An input bypass capacitor is usually used. A typical selection for most applications is a 0.1μF disc or 1μF solid tantalum capacitor. This capacitor shorts out high frequency variations that occur in adjoining circuitry.

8.5.4 Higher Current Regulator

Most IC regulators are limited to an output current of about 1.5 A. This is due to the large amount of power dissipated in the internal pass transistor.

The configuration of Figure 8.25 allows us to increase the output current to about 5 A while still preserving the thermal shutdown and the short circuit protection of the IC. The concept here is that an additional power transistor, Q_1, passes $0.8i_{load}$ while the regulator carries only $0.2i_{load}$. The current sharing is provided by R_1, R_2, and D_1. Since V_{BE} of Q_1 and V_{ON} of the diode are equal by design, the voltages across R_1 and R_2 are equal. Hence the current through R_1 will be four times the current through R_2 (since $R_2 = 4R_1$). The current through Q_1 is four times the current through the LM317. The thermal shutdown and the short-circuit protection are provided to Q_1. The heat sink for Q_1 must, of course, have four times the capacity of the heat sink for the LM317.

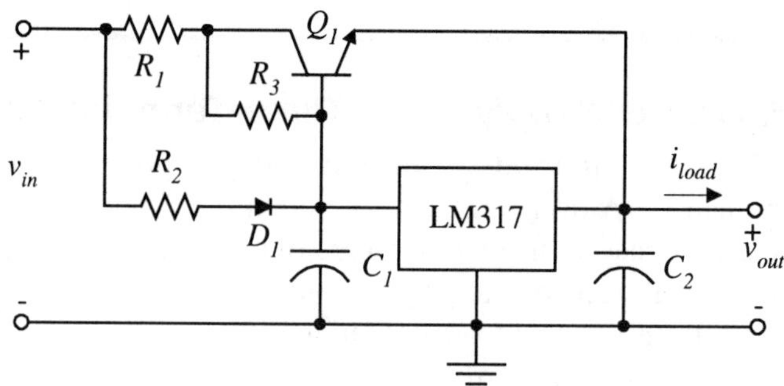

Figure 8.25 – Circuit to increase output current

The transistor in Figure 8.25 acts as a *pass* transistor for the regulator. The resistor, R_3, is added to provide a *dc* bias path. This assures that the transistor will be properly biased.

8.6 SWITCHING REGULATORS

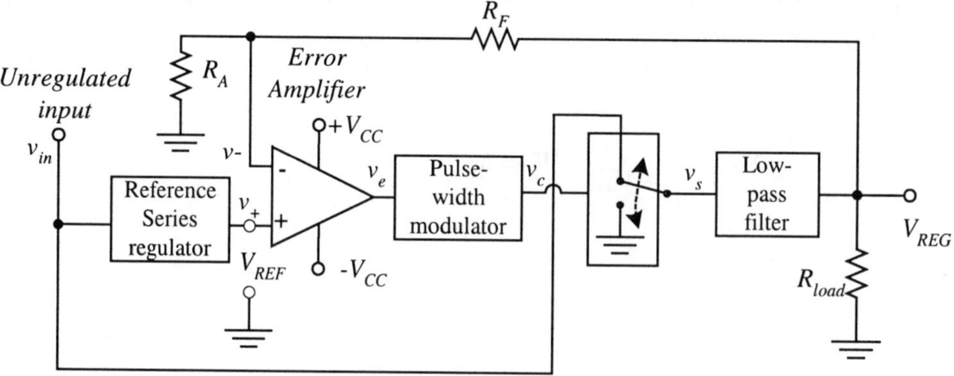

Figure 8.26 – Switching regulator

Discrete or integrated circuit-type series regulators were discussed in the previous sections. Although these regulators are useful, they suffer from several limitations. The most serious difficulty lies in the area of the power generated within the regulator. These series regulators rely on the variable voltage dropped across the series resistor, R_i, of the power transistor. The input voltage must be greater than the regulated output voltage. The difference is dropped across an internal component. The greater the difference, the greater the power dissipated within the regulator.

Because of the inefficiency of the series regulator, power supplies that generate high current output (in excess of 2 amperes) rely upon a switching regulator. The block diagram of a switching regulator is shown in Figure 8.26.

This "feedback" system compares a reference voltage, V_{REF}, with the regulated output voltage, V_{REG}. V_{REF} is obtained from a low-current output series regulator. Since little current (perhaps 20 mA) is required from this reference series regulator, it dissipates little internal power and provides an accurate reference voltage. The regulated output voltage, V_{REG}, is compared to a fraction, $R_A/(R_A+R_F)$, of V_{REF}. The error amplifier is an operational amplifier. The output of the error amplifier, v_e, is applied to a circuit that generates output pulses with widths proportional to the input amplitude (i.e., a *pulse width modulator).* The output of the pulse width modulator, v_c, is used to control the high-current switch. This control voltage, v_c, is a square wave of period T whose duty cycle, σ, is given by

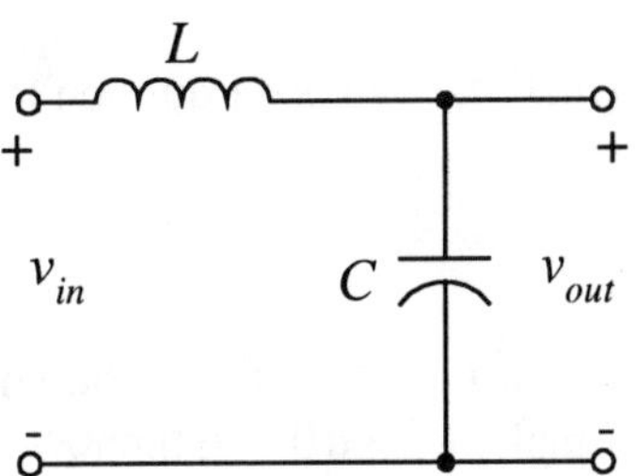

Figure 8.27 – Low-pass filter for switching regulators

$$\sigma = kv \tag{8.59}$$

The high current switch alternately supplies either unregulated voltage or zero volts to the filter. Hence, the voltage at the filter input, v_s, is a square wave with a period T and duty cycle, σ, (just as the control voltage, v_c) but whose low value is zero and whose high value is v_{in}. The voltage, v_s, is passed through the low pass filter to reduce the fundamental frequency, $2\pi/T$, and higher harmonics in V_{REG}. The low-pass filter is shown in Figure 8.27, where $\sqrt{LC}$ must be much larger than $T/2\pi$. The value of V_{REG} is then a constant and is equal to the average value of v_s.

An analysis of this operational amplifier circuit yields the following equations:

$$v_- = \frac{V_{REG} R_A}{R_A + R_F} \tag{8.60}$$

and

$$v_+ = V_{REF} \tag{8.61}$$

v_+ must equal v_- for linear operation of an operational amplifier. Therefore,

$$V_{REG} = V_{REF}\left(1 + \frac{R_F}{R_A}\right) \tag{8.62}$$

Hence, assuming good filtering, the regulated voltage output depends on the accuracy of V_{REF}

and the resistor ratio, R_F/R_A. The output, V_{REG}, does not vary either as a function of input voltage, v_{in}, or load current.

EXAMPLE 8.8 - Switching Regulator Supply

Select values of R_F and R_A for the switching regulator of Fig. 8.26. V_{REG} is to be 12 V and V_{REF} is 5 V.

Solution: We use Equation (8.62) and solve for the ratio, R_F/R_A as follows:

$$\frac{R_F}{R_A} = \frac{V_{REG}}{V_{REF}} - 1 = 1.4$$

Now that the ratio is known, we can simply choose a value for R_A, and solve for R_F. If, for example, R_A is 10 kΩ, then R_F would be equal to 14 kΩ.

We must be certain that $v_i > V_{REG}$ since V_{REG} is the average value of a chopped signal whose maximum value is v_i.

Some portions of the circuit of Figure 8.26 are consolidated onto one IC chip. These include the reference series regulator, the error amplifier and the pulse width modulator. As a result, the design of a switching regulator concentrates on the output circuitry, especially the high current switch and the low pass filter.

8.6.1 Efficiency of Switching Regulators

The output current of a switching regulator comes directly from the unregulated input voltage, v_{in}, through the high-current switch and the filter inductor, L. Thus, if we use a transistor switch with low "ON" voltage drop and a low-loss inductor, conversion efficiency can be high (greater than 90%). The significant saving in this regulator is based upon switching, or *modulating*, the input voltage with the high-current switch. This contrasts with dissipating power across a series resistor or a pass transistor as is the case with other regulators.

SUMMARY

We began this chapter by studying various forms of amplifier biasing. We compared Class A, Class B, Class AB and Class C amplifiers with respect to bias conditions and their use in power amplification. We then applied these various configurations to power amplifying, where we learned techniques for calculating power. We saw the contrasts between inductive coupling and transformer coupling for multi-stage amplifiers.

The important push-pull amplifier was considered next, followed by the Darlington transistor pair. We learned that the Darlington pair has the desirable properties of high input impedance, low output impedance and high current gain, but it also suffers an important disadvantage related to leakage current.

We then turned our attention to power supply design, and learned to design regulated supplies using both discrete components and integrated circuits. The chapter concluded with an examination of the switching regulator power supply.

PROBLEMS

Section 8.2.2

8.1 Determine the output power of an inductively-coupled amplifier as shown in Figure P8.1. Let V_{CC} = 12V, V_{BE} = 0.7V, R_E = 100 Ω, R_{load} = 1kΩ, and β = 60. Also find R_1 and R_2, the power provided by the power supply, the power dissipated in the transistor and the maximum output voltage swing.

8.2 An inductively-coupled amplifier is designed for a current gain of, A_i = -15. Determine the output power when R_{load} =2kΩ, V_{CC} = 12V, β = 200, and V_{BE} = 0.7V. Also determine the power supplied by the power supply, power rating required for the transistor, R_1, R_2, and R_E. Use the circuit of Figure P8.1 except delete the emitter bypass capacitor.

8.3 Use the circuit of Figure P8.1 to obtain a current gain of -60. The power supply is 15V, R_{load} = 1kΩ, V_{BE} = 0.7V and β= 100, and R_E = 100 Ω. Find the values of the circuit elements, power required from the power source, power rating of the transistor, R_1, R_2, and maximum power dissipated in the load resistor?

8.4 Design a CE amplifier for the mid frequencies of the type shown in Figure P8.1 without the bypass capacitor which has a V_{CC} = 20V, R_{load} = 2kΩ and A_v = -20. The transistor has β = 300 and V_{BE} = 0.7V. Consider the inductor ideal at the operating frequencies with R_{in} = 3kΩ. Determine:

(a) R_1 and R_2

(b) Maximum symmetrical undistorted output voltage swing

(c) A_i and P_{out}(undistorted)

(d) Load lines for the amplifier

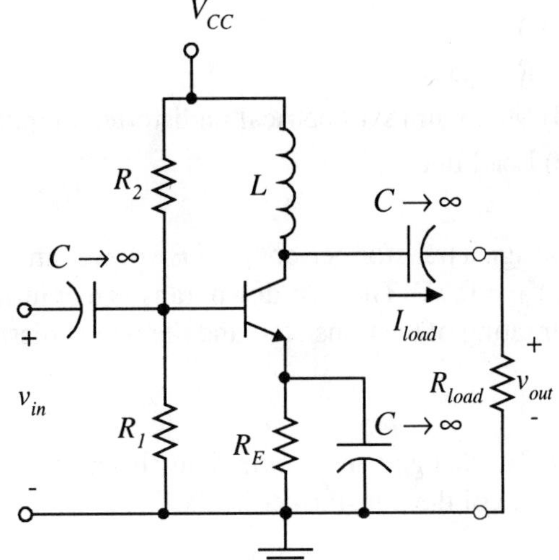

Figure P8.1

8.5 Design a CE amplifier for mid frequencies of the type shown in Figure P8.1 without the bypass capacitor which has a V_{CC} = 20V, R_{load} = 5kΩ, A_v = -20, A_i = -24 and the transistor has a β = 200 and a V_{BE} = 0.6V. Consider the inductor ideal at the operating frequencies. Determine:

(a) R_1 and R_2

(b) Maximum symmetrical undistorted output voltage swing

(c) R_{in} and P_{out}(undistorted)

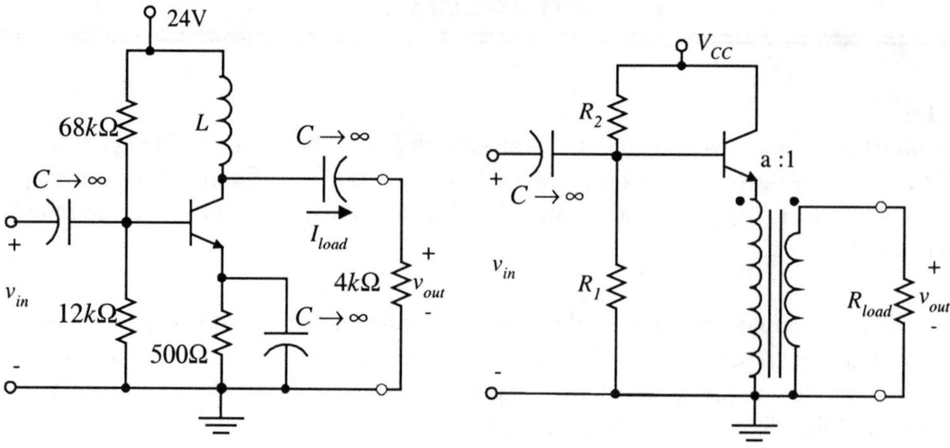

Figure P8.6

Figure P8.7

8.6 Given $\beta = 200$, analyze the inductive-coupled amplifier in Figure P8.6 to determine:

(a) I_{CQ} and V_{CEQ}

(b) A_v

(c) R_{in} and A_i

(d) Maximum symmetrical undistorted output voltage swing

(e) Load lines

8.7 Design a transformer-coupled EF power amplifier to drive a 10Ω load with $A_i = 100$ if $V_{CC} =$ 12V, $V_{BE} = 0.7$V. The step-down transformer turns ratio is 10:1 and $\beta = 50$. Determine R_1, R_2, the power rating of the transistor, and the power dissipated in the load. Refer to the circuit of Figure P8.7.

8.8 What changes are required in the amplifier parameters of Problem 8.7 if the primary resistance of the transformer is 200Ω?

8.9 A Class A transformer-coupled EF power amplifier must deliver an output of 1/2 watt to an 8Ω speaker. What transformer ratio is needed to provide this power if $V_{CC} = 18$V? The transistor has $\beta = 100$ and $V_{BE} = 0.7$V. Assume zero resistance in the transformer. What transistor power rating is needed?

8.10 Design an amplifier of the type shown in Figure P8.7 to have a current gain of 200 to an 8Ω load where $V_{BE} = 0.7$V, $\beta = 100$ with a 20:1 transformer ratio. The transformer primary resistance is 100 Ω. Determine the following when $V_{CC} = 32$V:

(a) R_1 and R_2

(b) Maximum symmetrical undistorted output voltage swing
(c) *dc* power required
(d) *ac* undistorted power output

8.11 Design an EF amplifier of the type shown in Figure P8.7 to have a current gain of 300 to an 8Ω load where $V_{BE} = 0.7$V and $\beta = 200$. The transformer has a 12:1 winding ratio whose primary resistance is 200Ω. Determine the following when $V_{CC} = 24$V.

(a) R_1 and R_2
(b) Maximum symmetrical undistorted output voltage swing
(c) *dc* power required
(d) *ac* undistorted power output

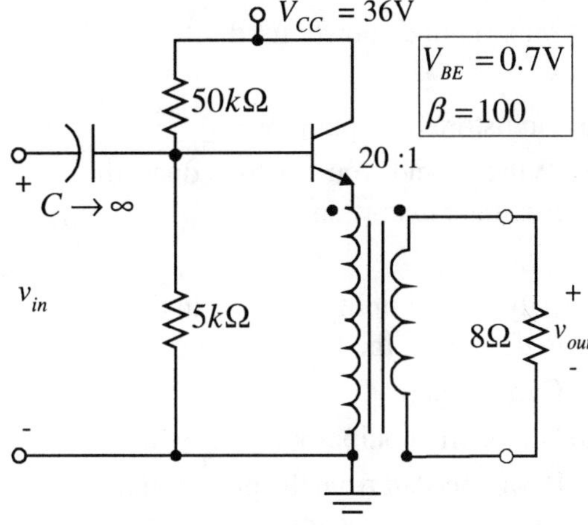

Figure P8.12

8.12 Analyze the amplifier in Figure P8.12 to determine the following (Transformer has a primary resistance of 200Ω):

(a) I_{CQ} and V_{CEQ}
(b) A_i
(c) R_{in}
(d) Maximum symmetrical undistorted output voltage swing.

__Section 8.3.3__

8.13 Design a complementary-symmetry Class B amplifier to drive a 12Ω load. Refer to the circuit shown in Figure P8.13. Assume V_{CC} = 18V, V_{BE} = 0.7V and β = 60. Calculate the total power dissipated in the load, the input resistance, and the power rating of the transistor with a current gain of A_i=20.

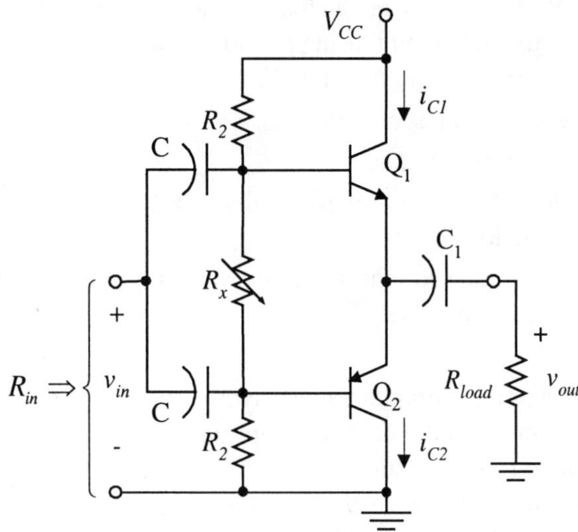

Figure P8.13

8.14 Design a complementary-symmetry Class B amplifier to drive an 8Ω load using $\beta(s) = 60$, $V_{BE}(s) = \pm 0.7$V and V_{CC} = 12V. Use the circuit of Figure P8.13 and a current gain of $A_i = 20$.

(a) Select values for R_2 and R_x.

(b) Determine R_{in}.

(c) Find the maximum power delivered to the load.

8.15 Design a complementary symmetry amplifier of the type shown in Figure P8.13 to obtain a current gain of 40 to a 10Ω load. Use $V_{BE}(s) = \pm 0.7V$ and $\beta(s) = 200$. Determine the following when $V_{CC} = 20V$:

(a) R_2 and R_x

(b) Maximum *dc* power used

(c) R_{in}

(d) Undistorted output power

(e) What would you do to reduce the crossover distortion?

8.16 Analyze the amplifier shown in Figure P8.16 to determine the following:

(a) Current gain

(b) Undistorted output voltage swing

(c) Power needed from the power supply

(d) Power rating of the transistor and P_{out}(undistorted)

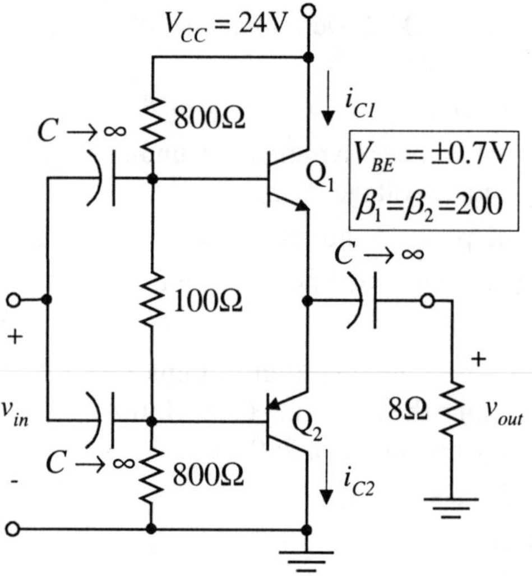

Figure P8.16

8.17 Design a complementary-symmetry diode-compensated Class B amplifier (see Figure P8.17) to drive an 8Ω load providing 8V peak-to-peak output. using $\beta = 80$, $V_{BE} = 0.7V$, $V_{CC} = 16V$, and $R_f = 100\ \Omega$.

(a) Find all quiescent voltages.

(b) Determine R_2 and A_i.

(c) Find the maximum power delivered to the load.

(d) Determine R_{in} and the power rating of the transistors.

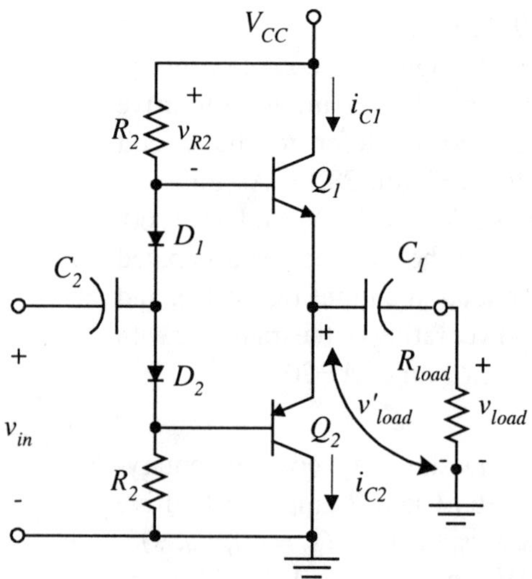

Figure P8.17

8.18 Design a complementary-symmetry diode-compensated Class B amplifier to drive an 8Ω load. Assume $\beta(s) = 80$, peak-to-peak output voltage is 6V, $R_f = 10\Omega$, $V_{CC} = 12V$, and $V_{BE}(s) = \pm 0.7V$. Let $C \to \infty$. Use the circuit of Figure P8.17.

(a) Find the maximum power delivered to the load.

(b) Determine the values of R_2 and R_{in}.

8.19 Design a 5W complementary-symmetry diode-compensated Class B amplifier to drive an 8Ω load. Assume $\beta(s) = 100$, $R_f = 20\Omega$, $V_{CC} = 32V$ and $V_{BE}(s) = \pm 0.7V$. Use the circuit of Figure P8.17.

(a) Find all quiescent voltages at mid-frequency range.

(b) Find the maximum power delivered by the power supply.

(c) Determine R_2, A_i and R_{in}.

8.20 Analyze the amplifier in Figure P8.20 to determine the following when $\beta(s) = 200$, $R_f = 40\ \Omega$, and $V_{BE}(s) = \pm 0.7V$:

(a) Current gain and R_{in}

(b) Undistorted output voltage swing

(c) Power required from power supply

(d) Power rating of the transistors and P_{out}(undistorted)

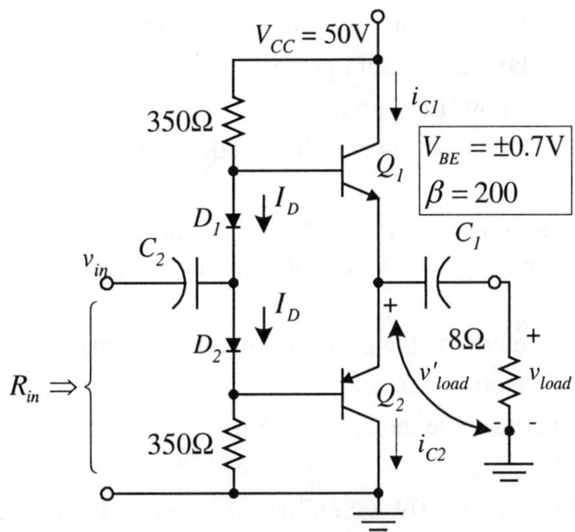

Figure P8.20

8.21 Design an 8W complementary-symmetry diode-compensated Class B amplifier to drive an 8Ω load. Assume $\beta(s) = 100$, $R_f = 20\ \Omega$, $V_{CC} = 32V$ and $V_{BE}(s) = \pm 0.7V$. Use the circuit of Figure P8.17.

(a) Find all quiescent voltages at mid range frequency.

(b) Determine R_2, R_{in}, and A_i.

(c) Find the value of power needed from power supply

(d) Determine the power rating needed for the transistors

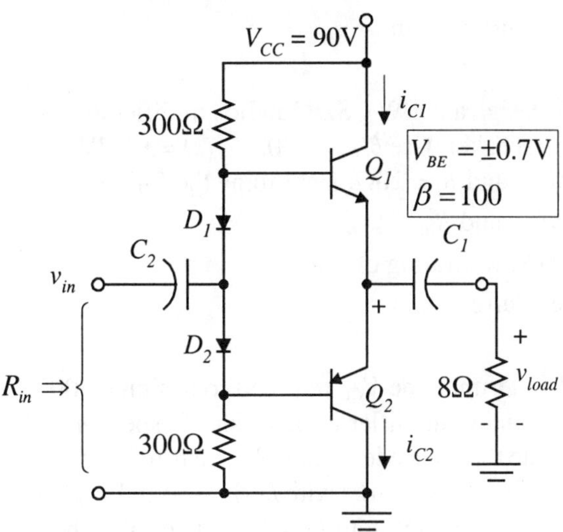

Figure P8.23

8.22 Design a CSDC amplifier of the type shown in Figure P8.17 to obtain 50W output. The diodes have $R_f = 40\ \Omega$ and the transistors have $\beta(s) = 200$ and $V_{BE}(s) = \pm 0.7V$. Determine the following when $V_{CC} = 64V$:

(a) R_2 and R_{in}
(b) A_i
(c) Power rating of transistor required
(d) *dc* power required

8.23 Analyze the amplifier shown in Figure P8.23 to determine the following when $\beta(s) = 100$, $R_f = 20\Omega$, and $V_{BE}(s) = \pm 0.7V$:
(a) Current gain and R_{in}
(b) Maximum undistorted output voltage swing
(c) Maximum output power
(d) *dc* power required
(e) Transistor power rating needed

8.24 Design an 80W CS*DC* audio amplifier to drive an 8Ω speaker. Use $\beta(s) = 200$, $V_{BE}(s) = \pm 0.7V$, and $V_{CC} = 80V$. Use the circuit of Figure P8.17. The diodes have forward resistance of 50Ω.
(a) Determine the power rating of the transistors at low frequency.
(b) Determine R_2 and R_{in}.
(c) Determine the current gain

8.25 Design a 120W CS*DC* audio amplifier to drive an 8Ω speaker. Use $\beta(s) = 100$, $V_{BE}(s) = \pm 0.7V$, $V_{CC} = 120V$, and $R_f = 10\Omega$. Determine the following:
(a) R_2 and $R_{in.}$
(b) Power rating of the transistor
(c) Current gain

8.26 Design a 200W CS*DC* audio amplifier to drive an 8Ω speaker. Use $\beta(s) = 100$, $V_{BE}(s) = \pm 0.7V$, $V_{CC} = 150V$, and $R_f = 20\Omega$. Determine the following:
(a) R_2 and $R_{in.}$
(b) Power rating of transistor
(c) Current gain

8.27 Determine the V_{CC} required to design a 300W CS*DC* audio amplifier to drive an 8Ω speaker and calculate the R_2 needed when R_{in} needs to be at least 220Ω. Using transistors with $\beta(s) = 150$ and $V_{BE}(s) = \pm 0.7V$, and diodes with $R_f = 20\Omega$, determine the A_i of your design.

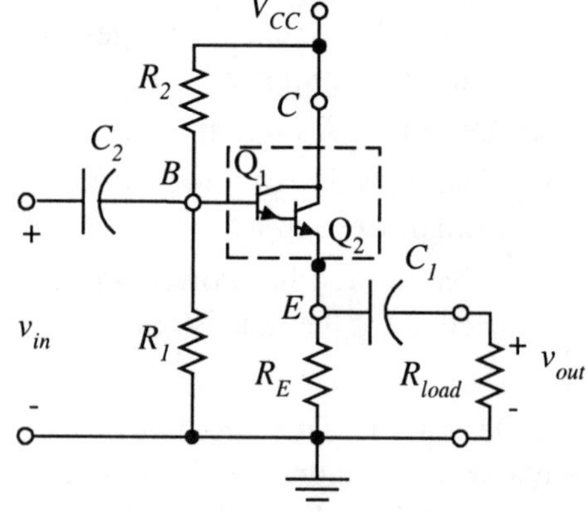

Figure P8.29

8.28 Design a CS*DC* audio amplifier to drive a 100Ω load with a 100V peak-to-peak signal. Use $\beta(s) = 100$, $V_{BE}(s) = \pm 0.7V$, $V_{CC} = 120V$, and $R_f = 20\ \Omega$. Determine the values of R_2, R_{in}, A_i, and P_{out}.

Section 8.4

8.29 Design an EF Class A amplifier using a Darlington transistor pair which has a combined β of 8000 and $V_{BE} = 1.4V$ to an 8Ω load with $R_{in} = 5\ k\Omega$. Determine all the component values and find A_i and P_{out} when $V_{CC} = 24V$. Use the circuit of Figure P8.29.

8.30 Design an EF Class A amplifier using a Darlington transistor pair that has a combined β of 6000 and $V_{BE} = 1.4V$ to drive a 10Ω load. The system requires $A_i = 500$. Use the circuit of Figure P8.29 with $V_{CC} = 12V$. Determine all the component values for the amplifier and P_{out}.

8.31 Analyze the amplifier shown in Figure P8.31 and determine the I_{C2}, R_{in}, A_i, and maximum symmetrical undistorted output voltage swing when the Darlington pairs have combined $\beta = 25{,}000$ and $V_{BE} = 1.2V$.

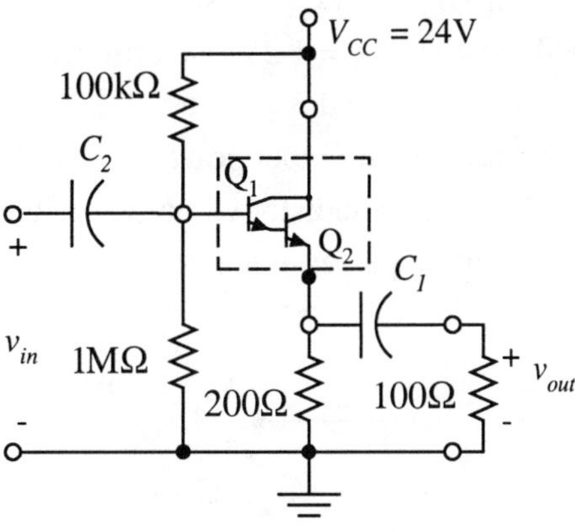

Figure P8.31

8.32 Repeat Problem 8.24 but use Darlington transistor pairs with combined $\beta = 6000$ and $V_{BE} = 1.4V$.

8.33 Design an EF amplifier using a Darlington transistor pair with combined $\beta = 25{,}000$ and $V_{BE} = 1.2V$ to match 100kΩ to 100Ω. Use V_{CC} = 20V and also determine the maximum symmetrical undistorted output voltage swing.

8.34 Design a Darlington pair CE amplifier as shown in Figure P8.34 to provide an A_i of -4000 to a 1kΩ load. Design the amplifier for maximum output voltage swing and determine the value of the required maximum input voltage. $\beta_1 = 100$, $\beta_2 = 200$, V_{BE} for each transistor is 0.6 V and $V_{CC} = 12V$.

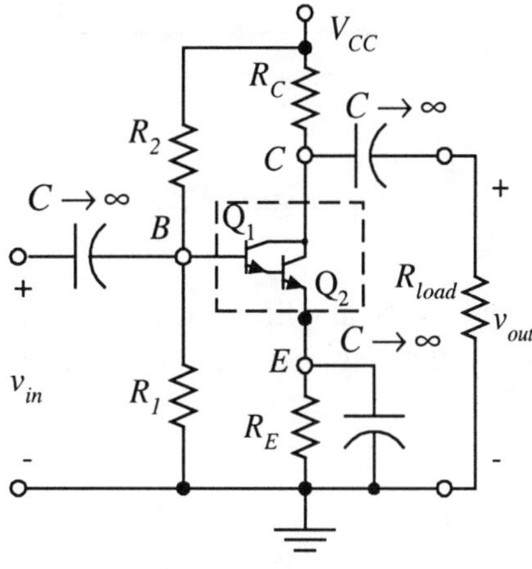

Figure P8.34

8.35 Design a *dc* bias-stable Darlington pair CE

amplifier to provide high input impedance with an A_v = -20 to a 5 kΩ load. Determine all the values of the resistors, R_{in}, A_i, and maximum output voltage swing. Assume a combined β = 30,000, that V_{BE} for each transistor is 0.6V and V_{CC} = 24V.

8.36 Design a CE amplifier as shown in Figure P8.36 for a voltage gain of -100 with R_{in} = 100kΩ. Use Darlington pairs with combined β of 30,000 and V_{BE} = 1.2V. Determine all resistor values and the maximum symmetrical undistorted output voltage swing.

8.37 Design a CE amplifier using Darlington transistor pairs for maximum output voltage swing. The requirements are A_v = -50, A_i = -80, R_{load} = 5kΩ, and V_{CC} = 15V. Assume a combined β = 25000 and that V_{BE} = 1.2V. Determine:

(a) R_E, R_1, R_2, and R_{in}

(b) Undistorted output power

(c) Maximum undistorted output voltage swing

(d) Input *dc* power required

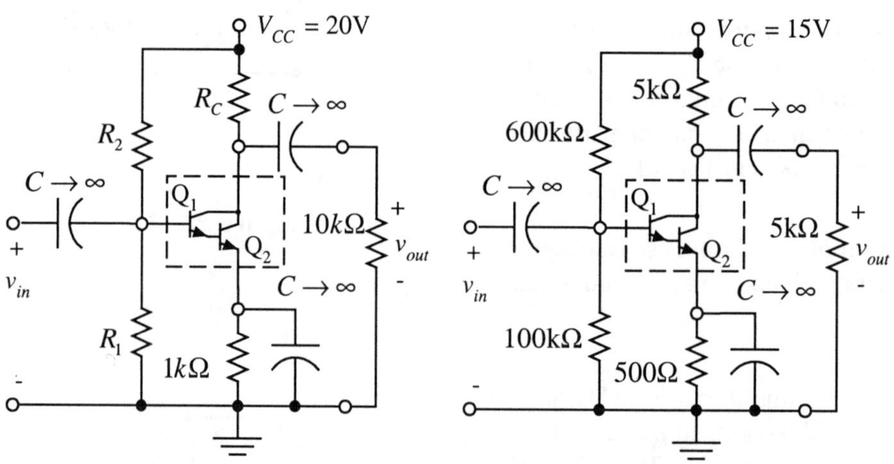

Figure P8.36 **Figure P8.38**

8.38 Analyze the amplifier shown in Figure P8.38 and determine I_{C2}, R_{in}, A_v, and v_{out}(undistorted symmetrical swing) when the Darlington pair has a V_{BE}(combined) = 1.2V and β(combined) = 25,000.

Section 8.5.1

8.39 A power supply is to provide an amplifier with 300 ±50mA of regulated power. Design a power source (see Figure P8.39) that will provide the power to the amplifier if the transformer has a turns ratio of 8:1 to each secondary and a 12V Zener diode is used. Assume the input voltage is 115V at 60Hz and that the forward resistance of the diodes is zero. Use $\beta = 50$ and $V_{BE} = 0.7$V. Select C_F so $\Delta V = 10\%$. Determine C_I, R_i, and the power rating of the diodes and of the power transistor.

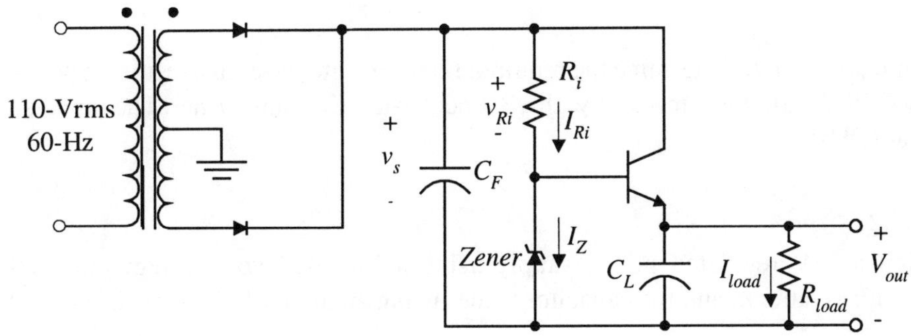

Figure P8.39

8.40 A power supply is to provide an audio amplifier with a 500 ±75mA regulated current. Design a power source (See Figure P8.39) which uses a 20V Zener, and a 5:1 transformer ratio to each secondary. The input voltage is 110 V, 60 Hz, $\beta = 100$, $V_{BE} = 0.7$V, and $\Delta V = 10\%$.

(a) Determine C_I and R_i assuming no diode forward resistance.

(b) Determine the power rating of the Zener diode.

(c) Determine the voltage variation at the load if $R_z = 2\Omega$.

8.41 Design a regulated power supply to obtain an 11.3V output using a power transistor having a $V_{BE} = 0.7$V and $\beta = 100$. The power supply will have an input of 120VRMS 60Hz and a 4:1 center tapped transformer and will be required to provide a load current varying from 500mA to 1A. The only Zener available is a 12V 1/4W Zener is used. (See Figure P8.39) Determine:

(a) I_{zmax} and I_{zmin}

(b) R_i and V_{smin}

(c) C_F

(d) Power requirement of R_i and transistor

(e) Percent voltage regulation

8.42 Design a regulated power supply. The design requirements are the same as those of Problem 8.41, except the input is changed from 120V 60Hz to a varying input of 105V to 125V 60Hz and the transformer is changed to a 3:1 center tapped transformer with a 1W 12V Zener.

8.43 Design a regulated power supply to obtain an output of 5.5V at 500 ±100mA. Use a 1N753 Zener diode. What is the value of R_i, C_F and the power rating of the transistor which has $V_{BE} = 0.7$V and $\beta = 100$. The transformer has a ratio of 5:1 and an input voltage of 110V at 60Hz.

8.44 Design a 11.3V regulated power supply of the type shown in Figure P8.39 to provide voltage to a load varying from 12 to 24Ω. The 12V Zener has an $R_z = 1\Omega$. The power transistor to be used has a $\beta = 200$ and a $V_{BE} = 0.7$V. Input voltage to a 3:1 center tapped transformer. For capacitor sizing use $\Delta V = 40\%$. Determine I_{zmax}, R_i, C_F, and % regulation.

8.45 Given $I_{load\ max} = 1$ A, determine the required filter capacitor size for a regulated power supply using an MC7812, full-wave rectifier with a 3:1 center-tapped transformer. The input is 110V to 120Vrms at 60Hz.

Section 8.5.2

8.46 Design a 12V regulated power supply using a MC7912 voltage regulator. Select the transformer turns ratio, a, and the capacitor values using an input of 120V 60Hz and an 800mA output.

8.47 Design a 10V regulated power supply using an MC7810 voltage regulator. Select the transformer turns ratio, a, and the capacitor values using an input of 120V, 60Hz and 1A output.

8.48 Design a MC7805 IC regulator to generate a 5V output into a load where the resistance varies from 10 to 20Ω. The input is 120V 60Hz. Determine the transformer turns ratio and capacitor size.

Section 8.6

8.49 Determine the values of R_F and R_A of the switching regulator shown in Figure 8.26 when $V_{Reg} = 20$V and $V_{Ref} = 5$V.

8.50 If the switching regulator in Figure 8.26 has a $V_{Reg} = 24$V and $V_{Ref} = 8$V, what values of R_F and R_A are required for the regulator to work correctly?

Chapter 9

Practical Operational Amplifiers

9.0 INTRODUCTION

Ideal op-amps were introduced in Chapter 2. We presented these from the perspective of a systems engineer who would analyze and design an electronic system. In this chapter, we study a variety of component circuits that make up a typical op-amp.

We discuss the internal characteristics of the op-amp. First we analyze the difference or differential amplifier, which is the basic building block. Several other internal circuit groups are then discussed.

The chapter then explores the forms of packaging used for op-amps. A discussion of the 741 general purpose op-amp is included for illustrative purposes.

We then modify the ideal op-amp mathematical model by recognizing the changes required to make the model more closely coincide with the real op-amp. Our design method is refined to account for the necessary modifications from the ideal op-amp.

The chapter concludes with a discussion of power audio op-amps.

When you finish studying this chapter, you will:

- Understand the internal operation of the op-amp so you will appreciate its limitations and the circumstances under which it can no longer be considered using the idealized models of Chapter 2.
- Be able to calculate a variety of parameters relating to circuits containing operational amplifiers.
- Understand the operation and utility of differential amplifiers.
- Be able to design circuits with balanced inputs and outputs.
- Be aware of the coupling considerations when op-amps operate with multiple inputs.
- Be able to design systems using power audio op-amps.

9.1 DIFFERENTIAL AMPLIFIERS

Most operational amplifiers are comprised of a series of transistors, resistors, and capacitors forming a complete system on a single chip. The amplifiers available today are reliable, small in size, and consume very little power.

The input stage of most op-amps is a *differential amplifier* as shown in its simplest form in Figure 9.1.

The differential amplifier is composed of two emitter-coupled common-emitter *dc* amplifiers. It has two inputs, v_1 and v_2, and three outputs, v_{o1}, v_{o2} and v_{out}. The third output, v_{out}, is the difference between v_{o1} and v_{o2}.

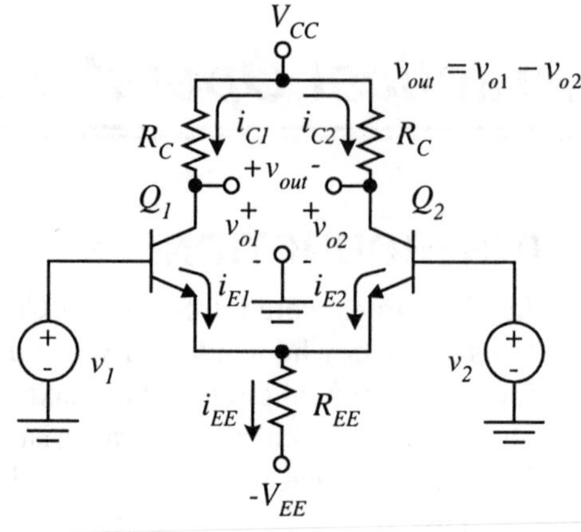

Figure 9.1 – Differential amplifier

9.1.1 dc Transfer Characteristics

The differential amplifier does not operate linearly with large signal inputs. In order to simplify the analysis we assume that R_E is large, that the base resistance of each transistor is negligible and that the output resistance of each transistor is large. Note that we use R_{EE} rather than R_E in the differential amplifier since the resistor used here is large and may be the equivalent resistance of a current source. The large value of R_{EE} keeps the emitter resistor voltage drop nearly constant.

We now solve this circuit for the output voltage. We begin by writing a KVL equation around the base junction loop for the circuit of Figure 9.1.

$$v_1 = v_{BE1} - v_{BE2} + v_2 \tag{9.1}$$

We need to find expressions for the collector currents, i_{C1} and i_{C2}. The base-emitter voltages are given by the equation,

$$v_{BE1} = V_T \ln\left(\frac{i_{C1}}{\beta I_{o1}}\right)$$

$$v_{BE2} = V_T \ln\left(\frac{i_{C2}}{\beta I_{o2}}\right) \tag{9.2}$$

In Equation (9.2) I_{o1} and I_{o2} are the reverse saturation currents for Q_1 and Q_2 respectively. The transistors are assumed to be identical. Combining Equations (9.1) and (9.2) yields

$$v_1 - V_T \ln\left(\frac{i_{C1}}{\beta I_{o1}}\right) + V_T \ln\left(\frac{i_{C2}}{\beta I_{o2}}\right) - v_2 = 0 \tag{9.3}$$

Solving Equation (9.3) for the current ratio, we find,

$$\frac{i_{C1}}{i_{C2}} = \exp\left(\frac{v_1 - v_2}{V_T}\right) = e^{\left(\frac{v_1 - v_2}{V_T}\right)} \quad (9.4)$$

We can assume i_{C1} is approximately equal to i_{E1} and i_{C2} is approximately equal to i_{E2}. Therefore,

$$i_{EE} = i_{E1} + i_{E2} \cong i_{C1} + i_{C2} \quad (9.5)$$

Combining Equations (9.4) and (9.5), we have

$$i_{C1} = \frac{i_{EE}}{1 + \exp\left[-(v_1 - v_2)/V_T\right]}$$

$$(9.6)$$

$$i_{C2} = \frac{i_{EE}}{1 + \exp\left[(v_1 - v_2)/V_T\right]}$$

Note that

$$v_{out} = (i_{C1} - i_{C2})R_C \quad (9.7)$$

An important observation can be made by viewing Equation (9.6). If $v_1 - v_2$ becomes greater than several hundred millivolts, the collector current in transistor 2 becomes small and the transistor is essentially cut off. The collector current in transistor 1 is approximately equal to i_{EE}, and this transistor is saturated. The collector currents, and therefore the output voltage v_{out}, become independent of the difference between the two input voltages.

Linear amplification occurs only for input voltage differences less than approximately 100 mV. In order to increase the linear range of the input voltage, small emitter resistors can be added.

9.1.2 Common-Mode and Differential-Mode Gains

The differential amplifier is intended to respond only to the difference between the two input voltages, v_1 and v_2. However, in a practical op-amp the output depends to some degree on the sum of these inputs. For example, if both inputs are equal, the output voltage should ideally be zero, but in a practical amplifier it is not. We label the case when the circuit responds to the difference as the *differential mode*. If the two inputs are made equal, we say the circuit is in its *common mode*. Ideally we would expect the circuit to produce an output only in the differential mode.

Any two input voltages, v_1 and v_2, can be resolved into a common and a differential part. We define two new input voltages as follows:

$$v_{di} = v_1 - v_2$$

$$v_{ci} = \frac{v_1 + v_2}{2} \quad (9.8)$$

The voltage, v_{di}, is the differential-mode input voltage and it is simply the difference between the two input voltages. The voltage, v_{ci}, is the common-mode input voltage, and it is the average of the two input voltages. The original input voltages can be expressed in terms of these new quantities as follows:

$$v_1 = \frac{v_{di} + 2v_{ci}}{2} = \frac{v_{di}}{2} + v_{ci}$$
$$v_2 = \frac{2v_{ci} - v_{di}}{2} = v_{ci} - \frac{v_{di}}{2} \tag{9.9}$$

If we set the two input voltages equal, we have

$$v_{ci} = v_1 = v_2$$
$$v_{di} = 0 \tag{9.10}$$

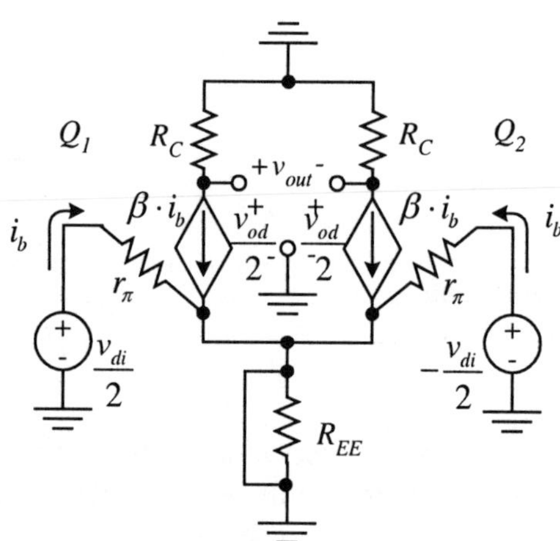

Figure 9.2(a) Differential-mode amplifier equivalent circuit

Since the two inputs are equal, the emitter-base junction voltages are equal (if the transistors are identical). Thus, the collector currents must also be identical.

We now view the equivalent circuit for the differential-mode input voltage as shown in Figure 9.2(a). Note that as the current in the Q_1 circuit increases, the current in the Q_2 circuit decreases at the same rate and amplitude. This is true since the input to Q_2 is equal to that of Q_1 but 180° out of phase. Thus the voltage change across R_{EE} is zero. Since the *ac* signal voltage across R_{EE} is zero, it can be replaced by a short circuit in the *ac* equivalent circuit. Note that placing voltages at each transistor base which are equal in amplitude but 180° out of phase is equivalent to placing a voltage between the two transistor bases of twice the amplitude. The voltages at v_{o1} and v_{o2} are of equal amplitude but opposite phase and the differential-mode gain is

$$A_d = v_{out}\frac{1}{v_{di}} = \frac{-R_C}{2r_e} \tag{9.11}$$

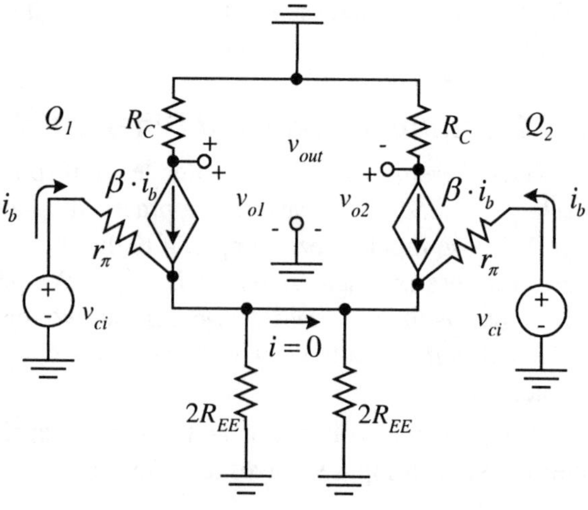

Figure 9.2(b) Common-mode amplifier equivalent circuit

This differential-mode gain is defined at a *single-ended output* since it is taken between one collector and ground. If the output is taken between v_{o1} and v_{o2}, the differential-mode gain is termed a *double-ended output* and is given by

$$A'_d = \frac{v_{o1} - v_{o2}}{v_{di}} = \frac{v_{od}}{v_{di}} = \frac{-R_C}{r_e} \tag{9.12}$$

A similar analysis can be applied to the common-mode equivalent circuit in Figure 9.2(b). If we divide the resistor R_{EE} into two parallel resistors each having double the original resistance, we can find the output by analyzing only half of the circuit. Since the transistors are identical and the common-mode input voltages are equal and in-phase, the voltages across the $2R_{EE}$ resistors are the same. Thus, the current between the two parallel resistors shown for is zero and we need only look at one side of the circuit. The common-mode voltage gain is then

$$A_c = \frac{v_{oc}}{v_{ci}} = \frac{-R_c}{2R_{EE}} \tag{9.13}$$

Equation (9.13) assumes R_{EE} is large and $r_e << R_{EE}$.

We find the double-ended output voltage in terms of the common-mode and differential-mode gain as follows:

$$v_{out} = A_d v_{di} + A_c v_{ci} \tag{9.14}$$

It is desirable for the differential-mode gain to be much larger than the common-mode gain so that the amplifier reacts primarily to the difference between the input voltages. The *common-mode rejection ratio, CMRR*, is defined as the ratio of the differential-mode gain to the common-mode gain. It is usually expressed in dB.

$$CMRR \doteq 20 \log \left(\frac{\left| {-R_C}/{2r_e} \right|}{\left| {-R_C}/{2R_{EE}} \right|} \right) = 20 \log \left(\frac{R_{EE}}{r_e} \right) \quad \text{dB} \tag{9.15}$$

We now determine the input resistance of the amplifier in both the differential mode and the common mode. For the differential mode, we look into the amplifier at the base of both transistors. This results in a complete circuit through the emitter of both transistors, and the input resistance is

$$R_{in}(\text{differential mode}) = 2r_\pi \tag{9.16}$$

Now for the common-mode input, we look into the amplifier in Figure 9.2(b). Thus, the input resistance is

$$R_{in}\,(\text{common mode}) = 2\beta R_{EE} \tag{9.17}$$

These results indicate that the input resistance of the common mode is much higher than that of the differential mode.

Our differential amplifier analysis is based upon BJTs as the transistor building blocks. FETs can also be used in differential amplifiers with the resulting advantages of reduced input bias current and nearly infinite input impedance. The analysis of the differential amplifier using FETs is accomplished in the same way as that of BJT analysis.

Differential amplifiers need matched transistors to insure that the circuit operates correctly. If the differential amplifier is on an integrated circuit, this additional requirement is less of a problem since the two transistors are fabricated at the same time using the same material.

9.1.3 Differential Amplifier with Constant Current Source

It is desirable to make R_{EE} as large as possible in order to reduce the common-mode output. Equation (9.15) shows that to make the CMRR large we must make R_{EE} large. Since large resistances are hard to fabricate on IC chips, we seek an alternate approach. This is accomplished by replacing R_{EE} with a *dc* current source. An ideal current source has infinite impedance, so we investigate the possibility of replacing R_{EE} with such a current source. Figure 9.3 illustrates a differential amplifier where the resistor, R_{EE}, is replaced with a constant-current source.

The closer the source is to the ideal constant-current source, the higher the common-mode rejection ratio. We illustrate a diode-compensated fixed-bias current source. The compensation makes the operation of the circuit less dependent on temperature variations. Diode D_1 and transistor Q_3 are selected so that they have nearly identical characteristics over the range of operating temperatures.

In order to analyze the circuit of Figure 9.3(a) and find the CMRR, we need to determine the equivalent resistance, R_{TH} (the Thevenin equivalent of the constant current source circuit). The equivalent resistance is given by [see Figure 9.3(b)]

$$R_{TH} = \frac{v_1 + v_2}{i_{TH}} \tag{9.18}$$

Writing a KCL equation at node 1, we have

$$i_{TH} = \beta i_B + \frac{v_1}{r_o} \tag{9.19}$$

where r_o is the internal resistance of the transistor at the specified operating point. It is given by

$$r_o = \frac{V_A}{I_C} \tag{9.20}$$

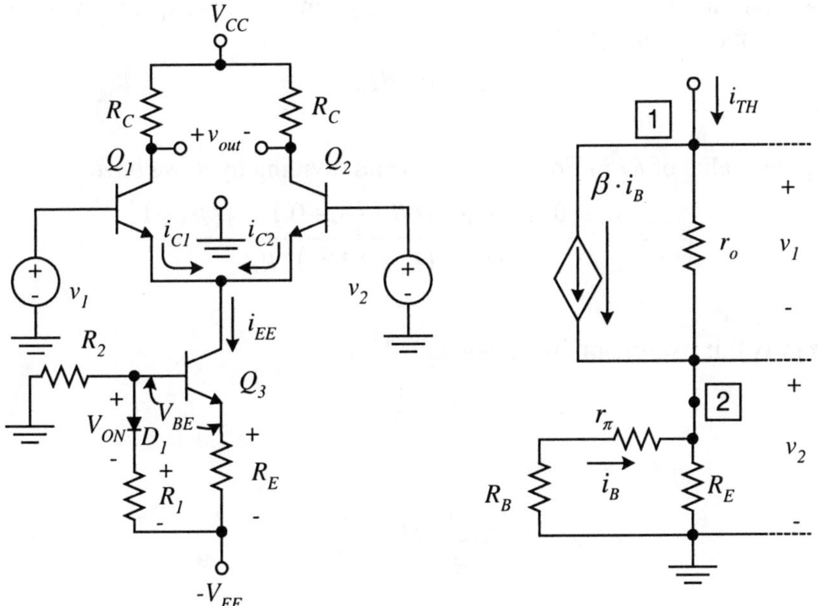

(a) Differential amplifier with current source (b) Equivalent circuit of current source

Figure 9.3 – Differential amplifier with constant-current source

A KCL equation at node 2 yields

$$\beta i_B + \frac{v_1}{r_o} + i_B - \frac{v_2}{R_E} = 0 \tag{9.21}$$

where

$$\begin{aligned} v_1 &= \left(i_{TH} - \beta i_B\right) \cdot r_o \\ v_2 &= -i_B \cdot \left(r_\pi + R_B\right) \end{aligned} \tag{9.22}$$

Substituting v_1 and v_2 into the equation at node 2, we have

$$-i_{TH} = i_B + \frac{r_\pi + R_B}{R_E} i_B = i_B\left(1 + \frac{r_\pi + R_B}{R_E}\right) \tag{9.23}$$

Finally, the Thevenin resistance is given by substituting Equations (9.22) and (9.23) into Equation (9.18).

$$R_{TH} = \frac{r_\pi + R_B + r_o\left[1 + \left(r_\pi + R_B\right)/R_E\right] + \beta r_o}{1 + \left(r_\pi + R_B\right)/R_E} \tag{9.24}$$

We will now make a series of assumptions to greatly simplify this expression. To maintain bias stability, we use the guideline that

$$R_B = 0.1\beta R_E \tag{9.25}$$

Substituting this value of R_B in Equation (9.24) and dividing by β, we have

$$R_{TH} = \frac{r_e + 0.1R_E + r_o\left[1/\beta + (r_e + 0.1R_E)/R_E + 1\right]}{1/\beta + (r_e + 0.1R_E)/R_E} \tag{9.26}$$

We can simplify this expression by noting

$$1 \gg \frac{1}{\beta}$$

$$\frac{r_e + 0.1R_E}{R_E} \gg \frac{1}{\beta} \tag{9.27}$$

We then have

$$R_{TH} = R_E + r_o\left(1 + \frac{R_E}{r_e + 0.1R_E}\right) \tag{9.28}$$

Since the second term in this equation is much greater than the first, so we can ignore R_E to obtain

$$R_{TH} \approx r_o\left(1 + \frac{R_E}{r_e + 0.1R_E}\right) \tag{9.29}$$

This equation can be further simplified if the following condition exists:

$$0.1R_E \gg r_e \tag{9.30}$$

In that case, we have the simple result

$$R_{TH} \approx 11 \cdot r_o \tag{9.31}$$

Hence, if all of the approximations are valid, R_{TH} is independent of β and its value is quite large.

9.1.4 Differential Amplifier with Single-Ended Input and Output

Figure 9.4 shows a differential amplifier where the second input, v_2, is set equal to zero and the output is taken as v_{o1}.

We use a constant current source in place of R_{EE}, as discussed in the previous section. This is known as a *single-ended input and output amplifier with phase reversal.* The amplifier is analyzed by setting $v_2 = 0$ in the earlier equations. The differential input is then simply

$$v_{di} = v_1 - v_2 = v_1 \tag{9.32}$$

so the output is

$$v_{out} = v_{o1} = A_d v_{di} = \frac{-R_C v_1}{2r_e} \tag{9.33}$$

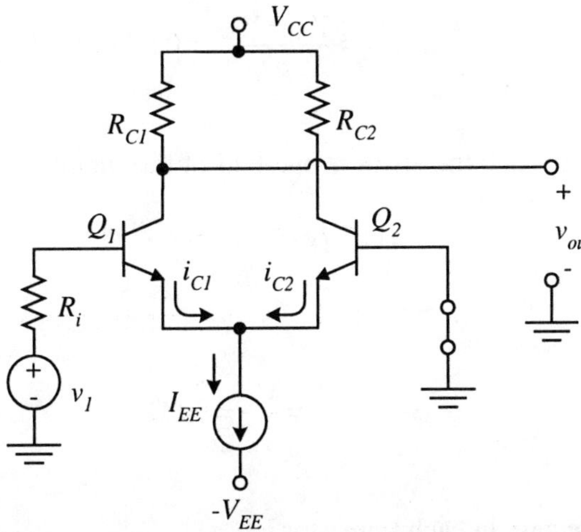

Figure 9.4 – Single-ended input with phase reversal

The minus sign indicates that this amplifier exhibits an 180° phase shift between the output and input. A typical sinusoidal input and output are illustrated in Figure 9.5.

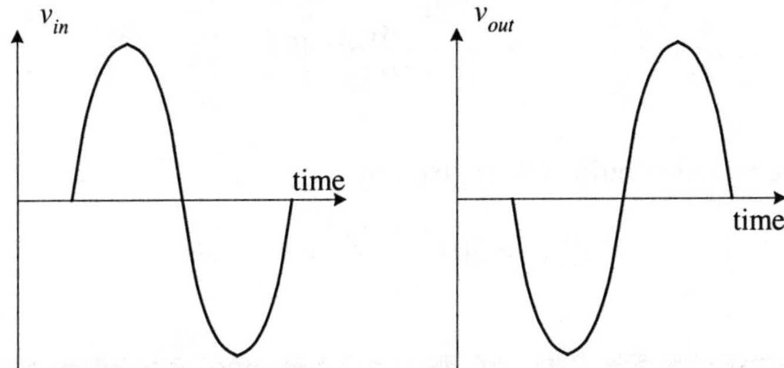

Figure 9.5 – Sinusoidal input and output

If an output signal is to be referenced to ground but a phase reversal is not desired, the output can be taken from transistor Q_2.

EXAMPLE 9.1 - Differential Amplifier (Analysis)

Find the differential voltage gain, the common-mode voltage gain, and the CMRR for the circuit shown in Figure 9.1. Assume that $R_i = 0$, $R_C = 5$ kΩ, $V_{EE} = 15$ V, $V_{BE} = 0.7$ V, $V_T = 26$ mV, and $R_{EE} = 25$ kΩ. Let $v_2 = 0$ and take the output from v_{o2}.

Solution: The current through R_{EE} is found at the quiescent condition. Since the base of Q_2 is grounded, the emitter voltage is $V_{BE} = 0.7$ V, and

$$I_{EE} = \frac{V_{EE} - V_{BE}}{R_{EE}} = 0.57 \text{ mA}$$

The quiescent current in each transistor is one-half of this amount.

$$I_{C1} = I_{C2} = \frac{I_{EE}}{2} = 0.29 \text{ mA}$$

Since

$$r_e = \frac{V_T}{I_C} = 90\ \Omega$$

the differential voltage gain in each transistor is

$$A_d = \frac{-R_C}{2r_e} = -28$$

The common-mode voltage gain is

$$A_c = \frac{-R_C}{2R_{EE}} = -0.1$$

The common-mode rejection ratio is then given by

$$CMRR = 20 \log\left(\frac{A_d}{A_c}\right) = 49 \quad \text{dB}$$

EXAMPLE 9.2

For the differential amplifier described in Example 9.1, design a temperature-compensated fixed-bias current source (Figure 9.3) to replace R_{EE} and determine the new CMRR for the differential amplifier, with $r_o = 105$ kΩ, $V_{BE} = 0.7$ V, and $\beta = 100$. Assume $R_1 = R_2$.

Solution: We place the transistor operating point in the middle of the *dc* load line.

$$V_{CE} = \frac{V_{EE} - V_{BE}}{2} = 7.15\ \text{V} = V_{R1}$$

Then, referring to the current source of Figure 9.3(a),

$$R_E = \frac{7.15\ \text{V}}{0.57\ \text{mA}} = 12.5\ \text{k}\Omega$$

For bias stability,

$$R_B = 0.1\beta R_E = 125\ \text{k}\Omega$$

Then

$$R_1 = R_2 = 250\ \text{k}\Omega$$

Since $0.1R_E >> r_e$ (i.e., 1.25 kΩ >> 26/0.57 Ω), then from Equation (9.31) we have

$$R_{TH} \approx 11 r_o = 11(105\ \text{k}\Omega) = 1.16\ \text{M}\Omega$$

The CMRR is given by

$$CMRR = 20\ \log\left(\frac{R_{TH}}{r_e}\right) = 82.2\ \ \text{dB}$$

EXAMPLE 9.3

Design a circuit to attain the conditions as specified in Figure 9.6 for maximum output voltage swing. The five transistors, Q_1 to Q_5, each have $\beta = 100$ while Q_6 has a β of 200. V_{BE} is 0.6 V for all transistors, $V_T = 26$ mV, and $V_A = 80$ V. Assume all transistors are identical.

Determine,

(a) R_C, R_1, and CMRR.

(b) Common-mode output voltage.

(c) Differential-mode output voltage.

(d) Differential-mode *input* voltage v_{di} for maximum output.

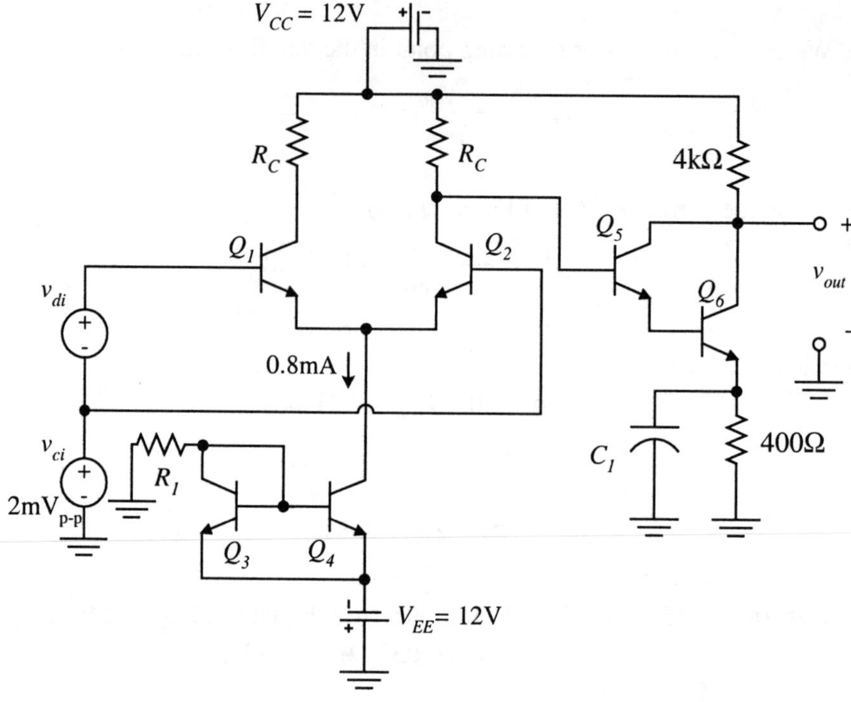

Figure 9.6 – Differential amplifier for Example 9.3

Solution: We shall treat the circuit in three sections:

1. Darlington amplifier.

$$I_C = \frac{12}{4400 + 4000} = 1.43 \text{ mA (for maximum swing)}$$

$$r_e = \frac{26}{1.43} = 18.2\ \Omega$$

$$R_{in}(\text{Darlington}) = R_{load}(\text{differential}) = 2r_{e2}\beta_1\beta_2 = 728\text{ k}\Omega$$

$$V_{out(\text{Darlington})} = 0.9 \times 0.00143 \times 4000 = 5.15 \text{ V (zero to peak)}$$

$$A_v = -\frac{4000}{2(18.2)} = -110$$

2. Differential amplifier

$$I_{C1} = I_{C2} = \frac{I_{EE}}{2} = \frac{0.0008}{2} = 0.4 \text{ mA}$$

$$V_C = 12 - R_C(0.0004) = V_B = 1.2 + 0.00143 \times 400$$

$$R_C = 25.6 \text{ k}\Omega$$

$$r_e(\text{diff}) = \frac{26}{0.4} = 65\ \Omega$$

3. Simple current source

$$R_1 = \frac{12 - 0.6}{0.8 \times 10^{-3}} = 14.25 \text{ k}\Omega$$

$$R_{TH} = \frac{80}{0.8 \times 10^{-3}} = 100 \text{ k}\Omega$$

Now for the total system, we have

$$A_{vd} = \frac{728 \text{ k}\Omega \| 25.6 \text{ k}\Omega}{2 \times 65} \times (-110) = -20.9 \times 10^3$$

$$A_{vc} = \frac{728 \text{ k}\Omega \| 25.6 \text{ k}\Omega}{2 \times 10^5} \times (-110) = 13.6$$

$$CMRR = 20 \log \left(\frac{20.9 \times 10^3}{13.6} \right) = 63.7 \quad \text{dB}$$

$$v_{oc} = 0.002 \times 13.6 = 27.2 \text{ mV p-p}$$

The differential input v_{di} necessary to produce maximum undistorted output voltage swing is

$$v_{di} = \frac{5.15\text{V}_{\text{peak}}}{20.9 \times 10^3} = 0.246 \text{ mV}_{\text{peak}} \quad \text{or} \quad 0.492 \text{ mV}_{\text{peak-to-peak}}$$

EXERCISES

E9.1 What are the differential and common mode gains of the amplifiers of Figure 9.1 if $R_{C1} = R_{C2} = 5$ kΩ and $R_{EE} = 20$ kΩ? Assume that $V_{CC} = 12$ V, $V_{BE} = 0.7$ V, $V_T = 26$ mV, and $V_{EE} = 12$ V.

Answer: $A_c = -0.125$; $A_d = -53.8$

E9.2 What are the differential and common mode gains of the amplifier of Figure 9.4 if $R_{C1} = R_{C2} = 5$ kΩ, $V_{CC} = 15$ V, $V_{EE} = 15$ V, $V_{BE} = 0.7$ V, and $V_T = 26$ mV? Assume that V_{EE}/R_{TH} is a constant-current source with $R_{TH} = 10$ kΩ.

Answer: $A_c = -0.25$; $A_d = -69$

E9.3 For the fixed-bias constant-current source shown in Figure 9.3, determine R_E, R_1, and R_2, where $V_{EE} = 10$ V, $I_{EE} = 2$ mA, and $V_{BE} = 0.7$ V. Also assume that $V_T = 26$ mV and $\beta = 200$.

Answer: $R_E = 2.33$ kΩ; $R_1 = 93$ kΩ; $R_2 = 93$ kΩ

9.2 LEVEL SHIFTERS

Even if the input to an amplifier has an average value of zero volts, the output often has a non-zero average voltage due to biasing effects. These *dc* voltages can cause an undesired offset which adversely affects the operation of a system.

Since the op-amp is a multi-stage *dc* amplifier with high gain, unwanted *dc* voltages can be a source of concern. A small offset in an early stage can saturate a later stage.

Level shifters are amplifiers that add or subtract a known voltage from the input in order to compensate for *dc* offset voltages. Op-amps have level shifters included in their design.

Figure 9.7 illustrates a simple level shifter. We show that this shifter acts as a unit-gain amplifier for *ac* while providing an adjustable *dc* output.

We begin the analysis by using KVL in the input loop of Figure 9.7(a) and letting $v_{in} = 0$ to obtain

$$V_{BB} = I_B R_B + V_{BE} + I_C R_E + V_{out} \tag{9.34}$$

Now since

$$I_B = \frac{I_C}{\beta} \tag{9.35}$$

we solve for the *dc* value of output voltage, V_{out}.

$$V_{out} = V_{BB} - \frac{R_B I_C}{\beta} - I_C R_E - V_{BE} \tag{9.36}$$

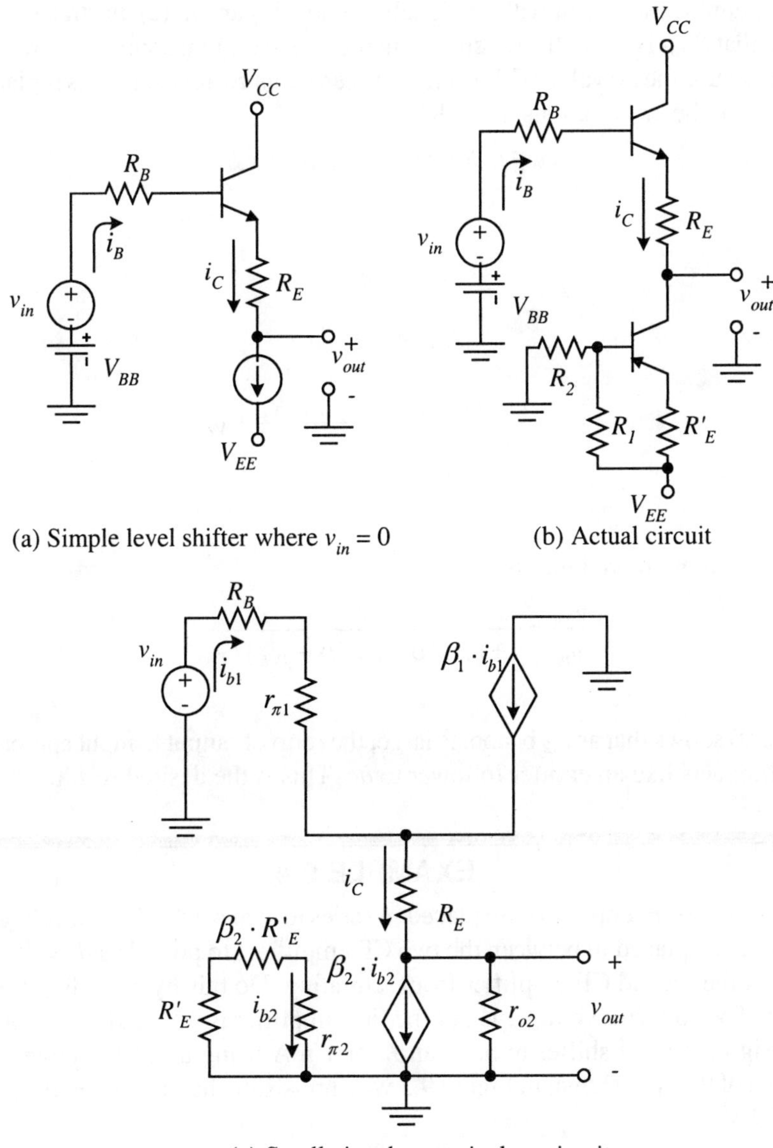

(a) Simple level shifter where $v_{in} = 0$

(b) Actual circuit

(c) Small-signal ac equivalent circuit

Figure 9.7– Level shifter

Equation (9.36) shows that by varying R_E, V_{out} can be set to any desired *dc* level (limited to a maximum of V_{BB}-V_{BE}). Since V_{BB} is the *dc* level acquired from the previous stage, this amplifier is used to shift the level *downward* (to a lower value). If *upward* shifting is required, a similar circuit is used but *pnp* transistors are substituted for the *npn* transistors. A complete circuit with active current source is shown in Figure 9.7(b). Any of the current sources of Section 5.10 can be used.

We now examine the circuit with *ac* signals applied. Figure 9.7(c) illustrates the *ac* equivalent circuit. Note that $\beta_2 i_{b2}$ is the collector current in the active current source, and we assume it to be a constant. Because the *ac* value of the current is zero, this current source is replaced by an open circuit. We write the *ac* equations using KVL.

$$v_{in} = i_{b1}R_B + i_{b1}r_{\pi 1} + i_c R_E + v_{out} \tag{9.37}$$

and

$$v_{out} = i_c r_{o2}$$

$$i_c = \frac{v_{out}}{r_{o2}}$$

$$v_{in} = \frac{v_{out}R_B}{\beta r_{o2}} + \frac{v_{out}r_{\pi 1}}{\beta r_{o2}} + \frac{v_{out}R_E}{r_{o2}} + v_{out} \tag{9.38}$$

The ratio of *ac* output to *ac* input is

$$\frac{v_{out}}{v_{in}} = \frac{1}{1 + \left(R_B/\beta + r_{\pi 1}/\beta + R_E\right)/r_{o2}} \tag{9.39}$$

Equation (9.39) shows that as r_{o2} becomes large, the ratio of output to input approaches unity and the level shifter acts like an emitter follower to *ac*. This is the desired result.

EXAMPLE 9.4

Two direct-coupled CE amplifiers are placed in series to achieve the desired voltage gain. Design a level shifter to be placed in between the two CE amplifiers to provide a *dc* voltage sufficiently low to prevent the second CE amplifier from saturating. Do this by providing a 1 V bias to the second stage. The collector voltage, V_C, of the first amplifier is 4 V, and the R_C of that amplifier is 1 kΩ. Design the level shifter to have an I_C of 1 mA using a ± 10 V power supply. Use a current source of the type shown in Figure 9.3 with transistors having $\beta(s) = 100$, $V_{BE}(s) = 0.7$ V, and $V_{ON} = 0.7$ V.

Solution: The level shifter is shown in Figure 9.7(b). We need to find the values of R_E, R_1, R_2, and R'_E. Since the first amplifier has a V_C of 4 V, the value of V_{BB} for Equation (9.36) is 4 V, whereas the R_B of that formula is 1 kΩ. Note this is using the Thevenin equivalent circuit of the previous amplifier. Equation (9.36) then yields,

$$R_E = 2.29 \text{ k}\Omega$$

Setting the current-source transistor operating point in the middle of the *dc* load line, we have

$$R'_B = R_1 \| R_2 = 0.1\beta R'_E = 55 \text{ k}\Omega$$

and

$$V_{CE} = \frac{10 + 1}{2} = 5.5 \text{ V}$$

$$R_{E'} = \frac{5.5}{10^{-3}} = 5.5 \text{ k}\Omega$$

The voltage across R'_E is 5.5 V. Then

$$V_{R2} = 10 - 5.5 - 0.7 = 3.8 \text{ V}$$

$$V_{R1} = V_{BB} = 0.7 + (0.001\text{mA})\left(\frac{55\text{k}}{100} + 5.5\text{k}\right) = 6.75 \text{ V}$$

We now know the voltages across R_1 and R_2 and the parallel resistance. This yields two equations, where we assume that the base current in the lower transistor of Figure 9.7(b) is negligible.

$$R'_B = \frac{(5.5/I)(3.8/I)}{(5.5/I) + (3.8/I)} = 55 \text{ k}\Omega$$

$$I = 0.041 \text{ mA}$$

and

$$R_1 = 134 \text{ k}\Omega$$

$$R_2 = 93 \text{ k}\Omega$$

The design is therefore complete.

EXERCISE

E9.4 Design a level shifter to change V_C from 6 V to 2 V so the voltage is compatible with a following CE amplifier. Use a CE amplifier which has an $R_C = 5$ kΩ and a current source of 4 mA with $V_{CC} = 15$ V and $V_{EE} = -15$ V. The transistors have $\beta(s) = 200$ and $V_{BE}(s) = 0.7$ V.

Answer: $R_E = 800\ \Omega$; $R'_E = 2.13$ kΩ

$R_1 = 110$ kΩ; $R_2 = 69$ kΩ

9.3 THE TYPICAL OP-AMP

Most operational amplifiers are designed and constructed in accordance with the block diagram shown in Figure 9.8.

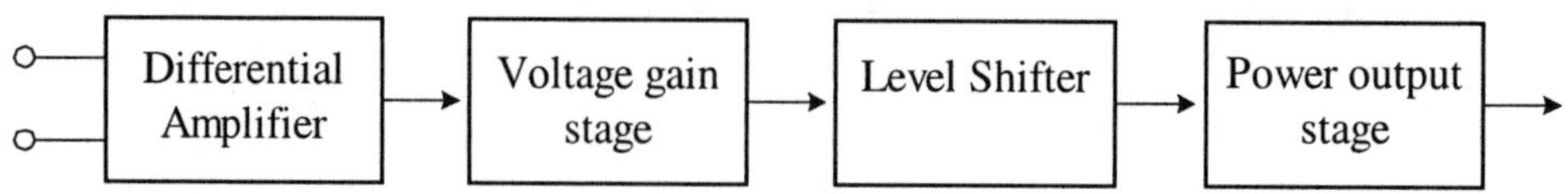

Figure 9.8 – Typical configuration of an op-amp

The differential amplifier and the voltage gain stage are the only stages which provide the voltage gain. The differential amplifier also provides the CMRR which is so important in the op-amp. The output of the differential amplifier is often connected to an emitter follower with a large emitter resistor so as to provide a high impedance load to the differential amplifier in order to obtain a high gain. Remember that a high-gain common-emitter amplifier suffers from much lower input impedance than a moderate gain CE amplifier. This then allows the use of a high gain CE amplifier to provide the additional gain. Linear op-amps are direct coupled to provide *ac* gain. This also eliminates the need for a coupling capacitor that is too large to be placed on an IC chip. Level shifters are required to insure that the output signal does not have any *dc* offset.

9.3.1 Packaging

Op-amp circuits are packaged in standard IC packages, including cans, dual-in-line packages (DIP), and flat packs. Each of these packages has at least eight pins or connections. They are illustrated in Figures 9.9, 9.10, and 9.11.

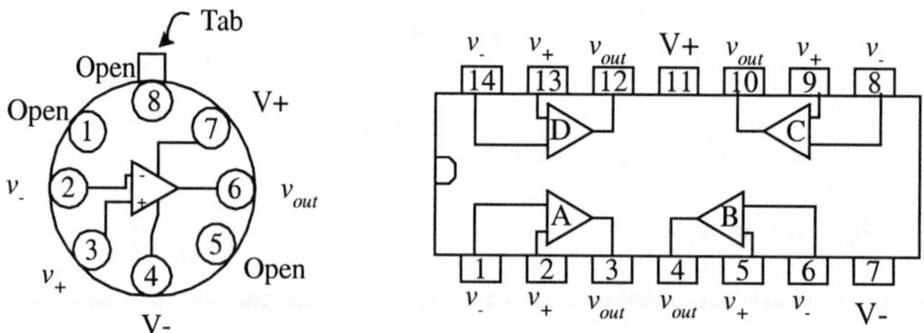

Figure 9.9 – Op-amp connection for can package (top view)

Figure 9.10 - Op-amp connection 14-pin DIP (Top View)

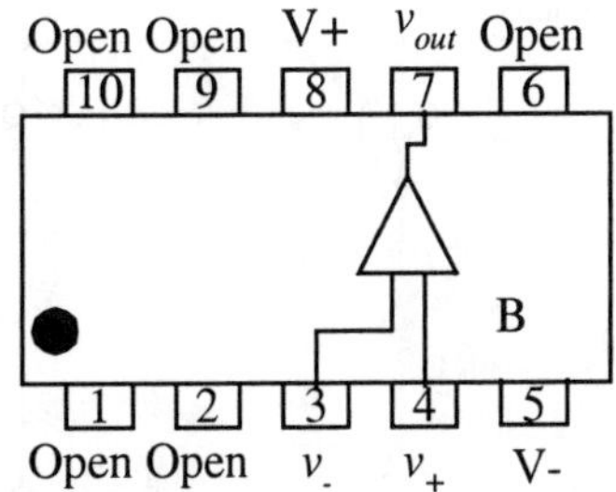

Figure 9.11 – Op-amp connection for for 10-pin flat pack (Top view)

When constructing a circuit, it is important to identify the various leads correctly (they are usually not numbered). The figures illustrate the location of pin 1. In the *can package* of Figure 9.9, pin 1 is identified as the first pin to the left of the tab, and the pins are numbered consecutively counterclockwise looking from the top. In the *dual-in-line package* of Figure 9.10, the top of the package has an indentation to locate pin 1, and the pins are numbered down on the left and up on the right. Note that more than one op-amp (typically 2 or 4) is packaged in one DIP.

In the *flat pack* of Figure 9.11, pin 1 is identified by a dot and the pins are numbered as in the DIP.

9.3.2 Power Requirements

Many op-amps require both a negative and a positive voltage source. Typical voltage sources range from ±5 V to ±25 V. Figure 9.12 shows typical power supply connections to the op-amp.

The maximum output voltage swing is limited by the *dc* voltage supplied to the op-amp. Some operational amplifiers can be operated from a single voltage source. The manufacturer's specifications define the limits of operation in those cases where the op-amp uses only one power supply.

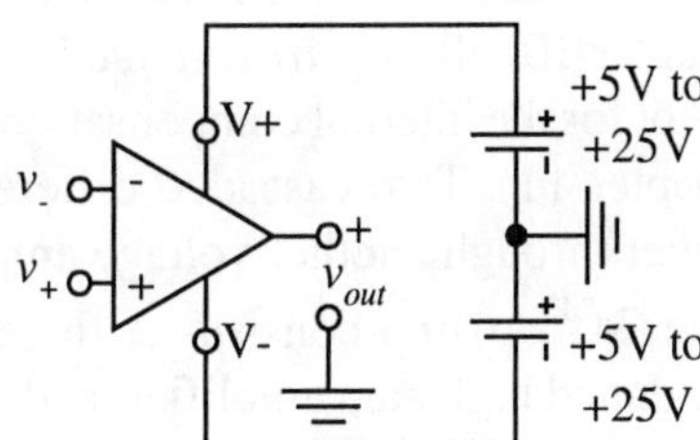

Figure 9.12 – Power supply connections

9.3.3 The 741 Op-amp

The μA741 op-amp is illustrated in the equivalent circuit of Figure 9.13. It has been produced since 1966 by most IC manufacturers, and although there have been many advances since its introduction, the 741 is still widely used.

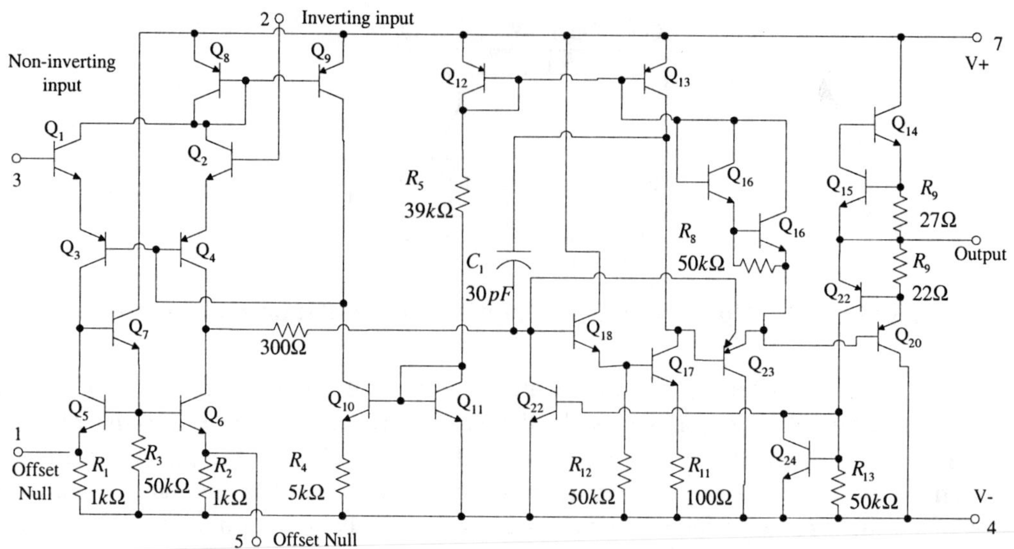

Figure 9.13 – The 741 op-amp

The 741 op-amp has *internal compensation* which refers to the RC network which causes the high-frequency amplitude response to fall off. Because the amplifier has high gain (on the order of 10^4 to 10^5 at low frequencies) and because parasitic capacitances in the transistors (discussed in Chapter 10) allow *parasitic feedback*, the op-amp would become unstable and oscillate if it were not for the internal compensation (we discuss feedback stability and compensation methods in Chapter 11). Two cascaded difference amplifiers drive a complementary symmetry power amplifier through another voltage amplifier.

The 741 op-amp consists of three stages: an input differential amplifier, an intermediate single-ended high gain amplifier, and an output buffering amplifier. Other circuitry important to its operation is a level shifter to shift the *dc* level of the signal so that the output can swing both positive and negative, bias circuits to provide reference currents to the various amplifiers, and circuits that protect the op-amp from short circuits at the output. The 741 is internally compensated by means of an on-chip capacitor-resistor network.

The op-amp is further improved by adding more stages of amplification, isolating the input circuits, and adding more emitter followers at the output to decrease the output impedance. Other improvements result in increased CMRR, higher input impedance, wider frequency response, decreased output impedance and increased power.

Bias Circuits

Several constant sources can be seen in the 741 op-amp of Figure 9.13. Transistors Q_8 and Q_9 are the current source for I_{EE} of the differential amplifier formed by Q_1, Q_2, Q_3, and Q_4. Transistors Q_5, Q_6, and Q_7, are the active loads substituting for the R_C resistors of the differential amplifier. Transistors Q_{10}, Q_{11}, and Q_{12} form the bias network for the differential amplifier current sources. Transistors Q_{10} and Q_{11} form a Widlar current source for this bias network with the other transistors acting as a current mirror.

Short Circuit Protection

The 741 circuit includes a number of transistors that are normally cut off and conduct only in the event that a large current exists at the output. The bias on the output transistors is then changed to reduce this current to an acceptable level. In the circuit of Figure 9.13, this short-circuit protection network consists of transistors Q_{15} and Q_{22} and resistor R_{11}.

Input Stage

The input stage of the 741 op-amp is required to provide voltage gain, level shifting, and a single-ended differential amplifier output. The complexity of the circuitry causes a large offset voltage error. In contrast to this, the standard resistor-loaded differential amplifier causes less offset voltage error. However, the standard amplifier has limited gain which means that more stages would be required to achieve the desired amplification. The resistor-loaded differential amplifiers are used in op-amps which have less voltage drift than the 741.

BJTs used in the input stage require large bias currents, introducing offset current problems. To reduce the offset current error, other op-amp types use MOSFETs in the input stage.

The input stage of the 741 is a differential amplifier with an active load formed by transistors Q_5, Q_6, and Q_7 and resistors R_1, R_2, and R_3. This circuit provides a high resistance load and converts the signal from differential to single-ended with no degradation of gain or common-mode rejection ratio. The single-ended output is taken from the collector of Q_6. The input stage level shifter consists of lateral *pnp* transistors, Q_3 and Q_4, which are connected in a common-base configuration.

Use of the lateral transistors, Q_3 and Q_4, results in an added advantage. They help protect the input transistors, Q_1 and Q_2, against emitter-base junction breakdown. The emitter-base junction of an *npn* transistor will break down when the reverse bias exceeds about 7 V. Lateral transistor breakdown does not occur until the reverse bias exceeds about 50 V. Since the transistors are in series with Q_1 and Q_2, the breakdown voltage of the input circuit is increased.

Intermediate Stage

The intermediate stages in most op-amps provide high gain through several amplifiers. In the 741, the single-ended output of the first stage is connected to the base of Q_{16} which is in an emitter follower configuration. This provides a high input impedance to the input stage which minimizes loading. The intermediate stage also consists of transistors Q_{16} and Q_{17}, and resistors R_8 and R_9. The output of the intermediate stage is taken from the collector of Q_{17}, and provided to Q_{14} through a phase splitter. The capacitor in the 741 is used for frequency compensation which is discussed in subsequent chapters of this text.

Output Stage

The output stage of an op-amp is required to provide high current gain to a low-output impedance. Most op-amps use a complementary symmetry output stage to increase efficiency without sacrificing current gain. The maximum achievable efficiency for the complementary symmetry, class B amplifier is 78% (see Chapter 8). The single-ended output amplifier has a maximum efficiency of only 25%. Some op-amps use Darlington pair complementary symmetry to increase their output capability. The complementary symmetry output stage in the 741 consists of Q_{14} and Q_{20}.

The small resistors, R_6 and R_7, provide current limiting at the output. The Darlington pair, Q_{18} and Q_{19}, is used in place of the diode in the diode-compensated complementary symmetry output stage as described in Chapter 8. The Darlington pair arrangement is favored over the two transistors connected as a diode since it can be fabricated in a smaller area. The current source substituting for the bias resistor in the complementary symmetry circuit is realized by one part of transistor Q_{13}. Transistors Q_{22}, Q_{23}, and Q_{24} are part of a level shifter arrangement which insures that the output voltage is centered around the zero axis.

9.4 MANUFACTURERS' SPECIFICATIONS

Manufacturer's specifications provide the characteristics of the op-amp under various operational conditions. The major parameters are shown either in tabular or graphical form. There may also be manufacturer-recommended typical applications for the op-amp. Other items shown in the specification may include examples of the external circuits required to balance the op-amp, or alter the frequency response. This would be an appropriate time to familiarize yourself with the Appendix where we illustrate examples of specification sheets. The μA741 is included and should be viewed as a typical example.

Op-amps are versatile building blocks for use by the designer. As we explore the various applications of these building blocks, it would be most useful to obtain one of the latest copies of a manufacturer's *linear handbook*. This contains the various specification sheets and other valuable information for a variety of op-amps and related linear ICs.

9.5 PRACTICAL OP-AMPS

Practical op-amps approximate their *ideal* counterparts but differ in some important respects. It is important for the circuit designer to understand the differences between actual op-amps and ideal op-amps, since these differences can adversely affect circuit performance.

Our goal is to develop a detailed model of the practical op-amp - a model that takes into account the most significant characteristics of the non-ideal device. We begin by defining the parameters used to describe practical op-amps. These parameters are specified in listings on data sheets supplied by the op-amp manufacturer.

Table 9.1 lists the parameter values for three particular op-amps, one of the three being the μA741. We use μA741 operational amplifiers in many of the examples and end-of-chapter problems for the following reasons: (1) they have been fabricated by many IC manufacturers, (2) they are found in great quantities throughout the electronics industry, and (3) they are general-purpose internally-compensated op-amps, and their properties can be used as a reference for comparison purposes when dealing with other op-amp types. As the various parameters are defined in the following sections, reference should be made to Table 9.1 in order to find typical values.

Op-Amplifiers:	**Ideal**	**General-Purpose μ741**	**High-speed 715**	**Low-noise 5534**
Voltage gain, G_o	∞	1×10^5	3×10^4	10^5
Output impedance, Z_o	0	75 Ω	75 Ω	0.3 Ω
Input impedance, Z_{in} (open loop)	∞	2 MΩ	1 MΩ	100 kΩ
Offset current, I_{io}	0	20 nA	250 nA	300 nA
Offset voltage, V_{io}	0	2 mV	10 mV	5 mV
Bandwidth, BW	∞	1 MHz	65 MHz	10 MHz
Slew rate, SR	∞	0.7 V/μs	100 V/μs	13 V/μs

Table 9.1 - Parameter values for op-amps

The most significant difference between ideal and actual op-amps is in the voltage gain. The ideal op-amp has a voltage gain that approaches infinity. The actual op-amp has a finite voltage gain that decreases as the frequency increases (we explore this in detail in the next chapter).

9.5.1 Open-Loop Voltage Gain (G)

The open-loop voltage gain of an op-amp is the ratio of the change in output voltage to a change in the input voltage without feedback. Voltage gain is a dimensionless quantity. The symbol G is used to indicate the open-loop voltage gain. Op-amps have high voltage gain for low-frequency inputs. The op-amp specification lists the voltage gain in volts per millivolt or in decibels (dB) [defined as $20\log_{10}(v_{out}/v_{in})$].

9.5.2 Modified Op-amp Model

Figure 9.14 shows a modified version of the idealized op-amp model. We have altered the idealized model by adding input resistance (R_i), output resistance (R_o), and common-mode resistance (R_{cm}).

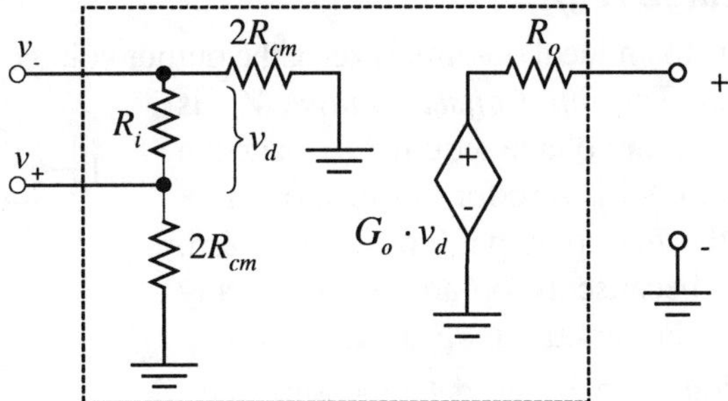

Figure 19.14 – Modified op-amp model

Typical values of these parameters (for the 741 op-amp) are

$R_i = 2\ \text{M}\Omega$

$2R_{cm} = 400\ \text{M}\Omega$

$R_o = 75\ \Omega$

$G_o = 10^5$

We now consider the circuit of Figure 9.15 in order to examine op-amp performance. The inverting and non-inverting inputs of the op-amp are driven by sources that have series resistance. The output of the op-amp is fed back to the input through a resistor, R_F.

The sources driving the two inputs are denoted v_A and v_I, and the associated series resistances are R_A and R_I. If the input circuitry is more complex, these resistances can be considered as Thevenin equivalents of that circuitry.

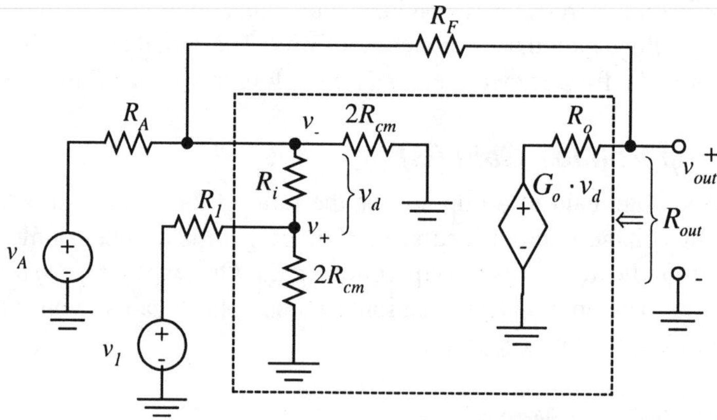

Figure 9.15 – Op-amp circuit

9.5.3 Input Offset Voltage (V_{io})

When the input voltage to an ideal op-amp is zero, the output voltage is also zero. This is not true for an actual op-amp. The *input offset voltage*, V_{io}, is defined as the differential input voltage required to make the output voltage equal to zero. V_{io} is zero for the ideal op-amp. A typical value of V_{io} for the 741 op-amp is 2 mV. A non-zero value of V_{io} is undesirable because the op-amp amplifies any input offset, thus causing a larger output *dc* error.

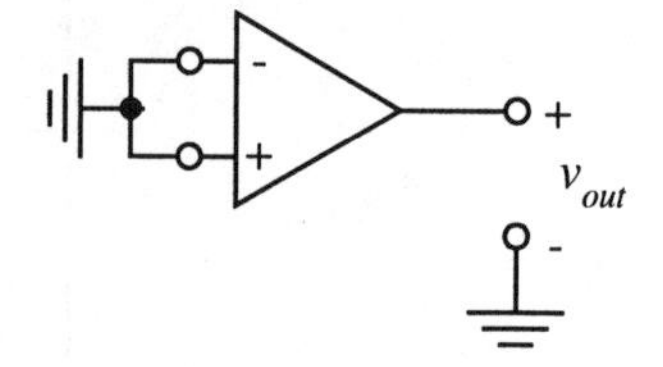

Figure 9.16 – Technique for measuring V_{io}

The following technique can be used to measure the input offset voltage. Rather than vary the input voltage in order to force the output to zero, the input is set equal to zero, as shown in Figure 9.16, and the output voltage is measured.

The output voltage resulting from a zero input voltage is known as the *output dc offset voltage.* The input offset voltage is obtained by dividing this quantity by the open-loop gain of the op-amp.

The effects of input offset voltage can be incorporated into the op-amp model as shown in Figure 9.17.

In addition to including input offset voltage, the ideal op-amp model has been further modified with the addition of four resistances. R_o is the *output resistance.* The *input resistance* of the op-amp, R_i, is measured between the inverting and non-inverting terminals. The model also contains a resistor connecting each of the two inputs to ground.

These are the *common-mode resistances*, and each is equal to $2R_{cm}$. If the inputs are connected together as in Figure 9.16, these two resistors are in parallel, and the combined Thevenin resistance to ground is R_{cm}. If the op-amp is ideal, R_i and R_{cm} approach infinity (i.e., open circuit) and R_o is zero (i.e., short circuit).

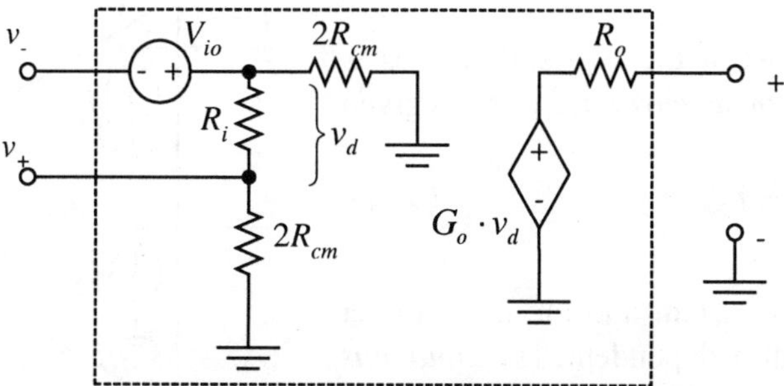

Figure 9.17 – Input offset voltage

The external configuration shown in Figure 9.18(a) can be used to negate the effects of offset voltage. A variable voltage is applied to the inverting input terminal. Proper choice of this voltage cancels the input offset. Similarly, Figure 9.18(b) illustrates this balancing circuit applied to the non-inverting input.

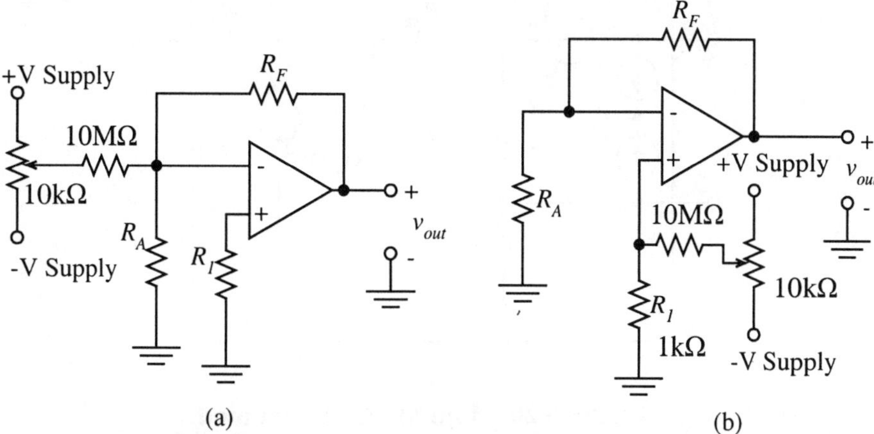

Figure 9.18 - Offset voltage balancing

9.5.4 Input Bias Current (I_{Bias})

Although ideal op-amp inputs draw no current, actual op-amps allow some bias current to enter each input terminal. I_{Bias} is the *dc* current into the input transistor, and a typical value is 2 μA. When the source impedance is low, I_{Bias} has little effect, since it causes a relatively small change in input voltage. However, with high-impedance driving circuits, a small current can lead to a large voltage.

The bias current can be modeled as two current sinks, as shown in Figure 9.19. The values of these sinks are independent of the source impedance. The *bias current* is defined as the average value of the two current sinks. Thus

$$I_{Bias} = \frac{I_{B+} + I_{B-}}{2} \tag{9.40}$$

The difference between the two sink values is known as the *input offset current*, I_{io}, and is given by

$$I_{io} = I_{B+} - I_{B-} \tag{9.41}$$

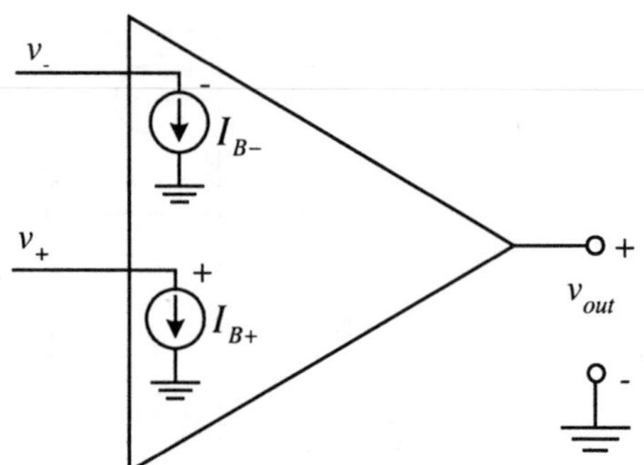

Figure 9.19 – Offset voltage balancing

Both the input-bias current and the input offset current are temperature dependent. The *input bias current temperature coefficient* is defined as the ratio of change in bias current to change in temperature. A typical value is 10 nA/°C. The *input offset current temperature coefficient* is defined as the ratio of the change in magnitude of the offset current to the change in temperature. A typical value is -2nA/°C.

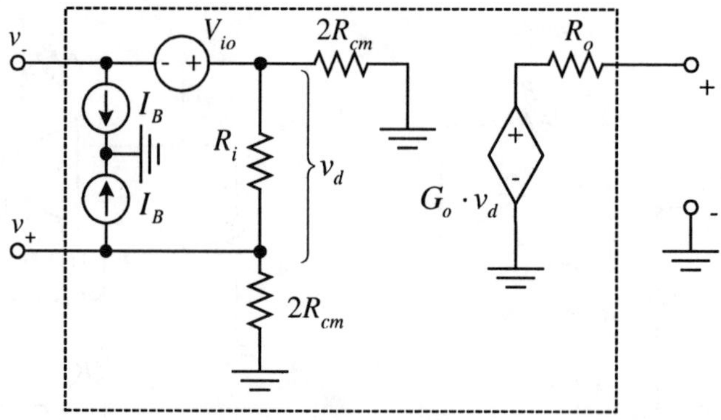

Figure 9.20 – Input bias current model

The input bias currents are incorporated into the op-amp model of Figure 9.20, where we assume that the input offset current is negligible. That is,

$$I_{B+} = I_{B-} = I_B \tag{9.42}$$

We analyze this model in order to find the output voltage caused by the input bias currents.

Figure 9.21(a) shows an op-amp circuit where the inverting and non-inverting inputs are connected to ground through resistances.

The circuit is replaced by its equivalent in Figure 9.21(b), where we have neglected V_{io}. We further simplify the circuit in Figure 9.21(c) by neglecting R_o and R_{load}. That is, we assume $R_F >> R_o$ and $R_{load} >> R_o$. Output loading requirements usually ensure that these inequalities are met.

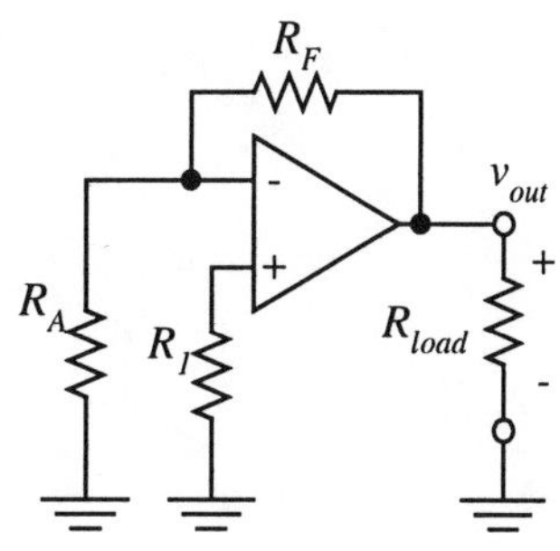

Figure 9.21(a) – The circuit

The circuit is further simplified in Figure 9.21(d) where the series combination of the dependent voltage source and resistor is replaced by a parallel combination of a dependent current source and resistor.

Finally, we combine resistances and change both current sources back to voltage sources to obtain the simplified equivalent of Figure 9.21(e).

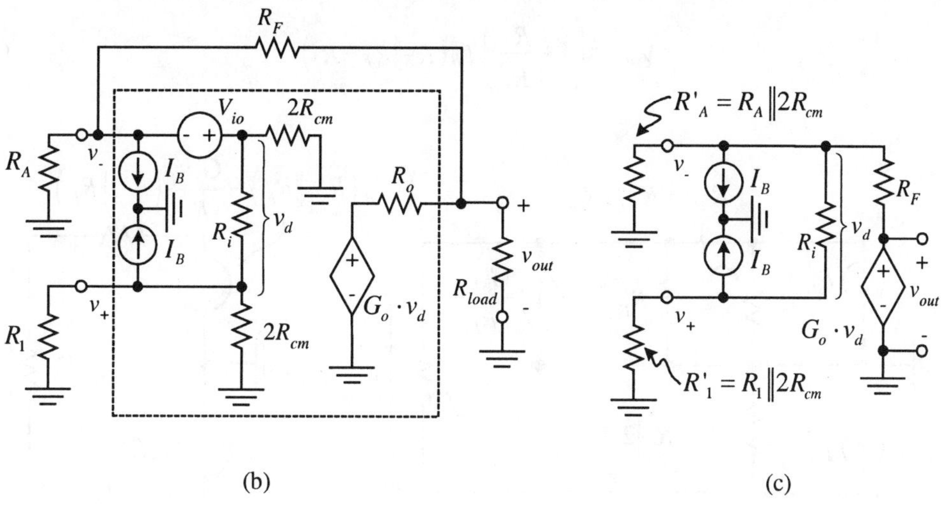

(b) (c)

Figure 9.21(b) and (c) – Input bias effects

We use a loop equation to find the output voltage.

$$V_{out} = G_o V_d = \frac{G_o R'_1 \left(R'_A \| R_F - R'_1\right) I_B \left(R'_A + R_F\right)}{\left(R'_A + R_F\right)\left(R_i + R'_A\right)\|\left(R_F + R'_1\right) + G_o R'_1 R'_A} \tag{9.43}$$

where

$$\begin{gathered} R'_1 = R_1 \| 2R_{cm} \\ R'_A = R_A \| 2R_{cm} \\ R_F \gg R_o \\ R_{load} \gg R_o \end{gathered} \tag{9.44}$$

The common-mode resistance, R_{cm}, is in the range of several hundred megohms for most op-amps. Therefore

$$\begin{gathered} R'_A \approx R_A \\ R'_1 \approx R_1 \end{gathered} \tag{9.45}$$

If we further assume that G_o is large, Equation (9.43) becomes Equation (9.46).

$$V_{out} = \left(1 + \frac{R_F}{R_A}\right) I_B \left(R_A \| R_F - R_1\right) \tag{9.46}$$

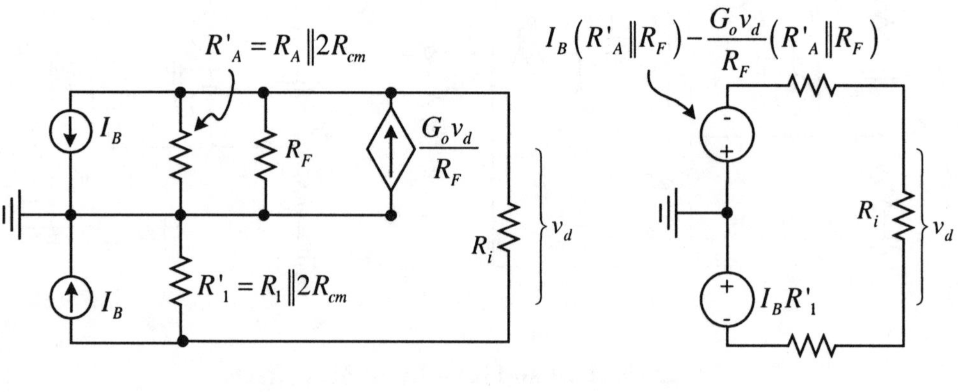

Figure 9.21(d) and (e) – Input bias effects

Note that if the value of R_I is selected to be equal to $R_A \| R_F$, then the output voltage is zero. We conclude from this analysis that the *dc* resistance from V_+ to ground should equal the *dc* resistance from V_- to ground. We use this *bias balance* constraint many times in our designs. It is important that both the inverting and non-inverting terminals have a *dc* path to ground to reduce the effects of input bias current.

EXAMPLE 9.5

Find the output voltage for the configurations of Figure 9.22 where $I_B = 80$ nA $= 8 \times 10^{-8}$ A.

Solution: We use the simplified form of Equation (9.46) to find the output voltages for the circuit of Figure 9.22(a).

$$V_{out} = \left(1 + \frac{10^5}{10^4}\right)(8 \times 10^{-8})(9100 - 10^4) = -0.79 \text{ mV}$$

For the circuit of Figure 9.22(b), we obtain

$$V_{out} = \left(1 + \frac{10^5}{10^4}\right)(8 \times 10^{-8})(9100 - 0) = 8.0 \text{ mV}$$

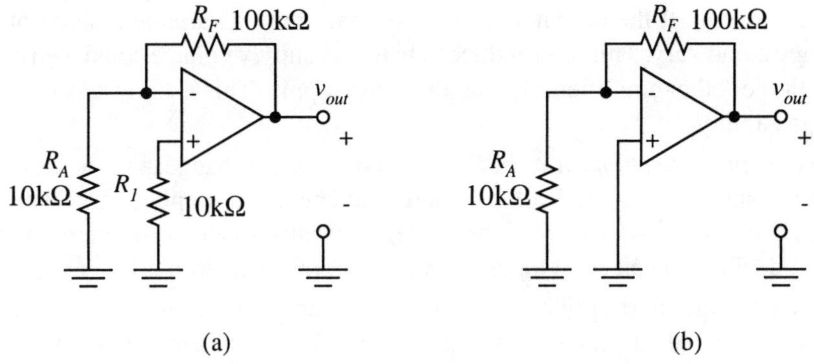

Figure 9.22 - Configurations for Example 9.5

By selecting $R_I = 10$ kΩ rather than 0 Ω, we reduce the output voltage due to I_B by a factor of 10. We therefore balance the bias-current effect by equating the resistances connected between the positive terminal and ground with those connected between the negative terminal and ground.

9.5.5 Common-Mode Rejection

The op-amp is normally used to amplify the difference between two input voltages. It therefore operates in the *differential mode*. A constant voltage added to each of these two inputs should not affect the difference and should therefore not be transferred to the output. In the practical case, this constant, or average value of the inputs *does* affect the output voltage. If we consider only the equal parts of the two inputs, we are considering what is known as the *common mode*.

Let us assume that the two input terminals of an actual op-amp are connected together and then to a common source voltage. This is illustrated in Figure 9.23. The output voltage would be zero in the ideal case. In the practical case, this output is non-zero. The ratio of the non-zero output voltage to the applied input voltage is the *common-mode voltage gain*, G_{cm}. The *common-mode rejection ratio* (CMRR) is defined as the ratio of the *dc* open-loop gain, G_o, to the common mode gain. Thus,

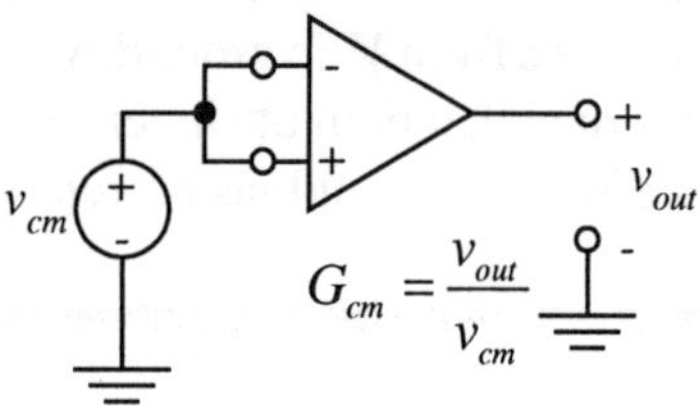

Figure 9.23 – Common mode

$$CMRR = 20\ \log_{10}\left(\frac{|G_o|}{|G_{cm}|}\right) \quad \text{dB} \tag{9.47}$$

Typical values of the CMRR range from 80 to 100 dB. It is desirable to have the CMRR as high as possible.

9.5.6 Power Supply Rejection Ratio

Power supply rejection ratio is a measure of the ability of the op-amp to ignore changes in the power supply voltage. If the output stage of a system draws a variable amount of current, the supply voltage could vary. This load-induced change in supply voltage could then cause changes in the operation of other amplifiers sharing the same supply. This is known as *cross-talk*, and it can lead to instability.

The *power supply rejection ratio* (*PSRR*) is the ratio of the change in v_{out} to the total change in power supply voltage. For example, if the positive and negative supplies vary from ±5 V to ±5.5 V, the total change is 11 - 10 = 1 V. The PSRR is usually specified in microvolts per volt or sometimes in decibels. Typical op-amps have a PSRR of about 30 μV/V.

To decrease changes in supply voltage, the power supply for each group of op-amps should be *decoupled* (i.e., isolated) from those of other groups. This confines the interaction to a single group of op-amps. In practice, each printed circuit card should have the supply lines bypassed to ground via a 0.1-μF ceramic or 1-μF tantalum capacitor. This ensures that load variations will not feed significantly through the supply to other cards.

9.5.7 Output Resistance

As a first step in determining the output resistance, R_{out}, we find the Thevenin equivalent for the portion of the op-amp circuit shown in the box enclosed in dashed lines in Figure 9.24. Note that we are ignoring the offset current and voltage in this analysis.

Since the circuit contains no independent sources, the Thevenin equivalent voltage is zero, so the circuit is equivalent to a single resistor. The value of the resistor cannot be found using resistor combinations. To find the equivalent resistance, assume that a voltage source, v, is applied to the output leads. We then calculate the resulting current, i, and take the ratio v/i. This yields the Thevenin resistance.

Figure 9.25(a) illustrates the applied voltage source. The circuit is simplified to that shown in Figure 9.25(b).

The circuit can be further reduced to that shown in Figure 9.25(c), where we define two new resistances as follows:

$$R'_A = R_A \| 2R_{cm} \qquad R'_1 = R_1 \| 2R_{cm} \tag{9.48}$$

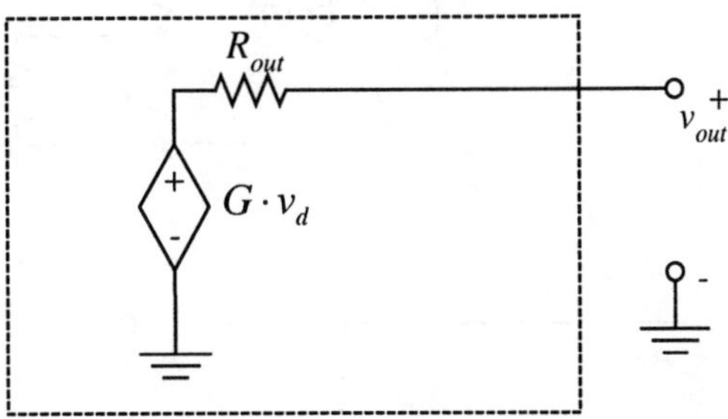

Figure 9.24 – Thevenin equivalent circuit for output resistance R_{out}

We make the assumption that $R'_A << (R'_1 + R_i)$ and $R_i >> R'_1$. The simplified circuit of Figure 9.25(d) results.

The input differential voltage, v_d, is found from this simplified circuit using a voltage divider ratio.

$$v_d = \frac{-R'_A \cdot v}{R'_A + R_F} \tag{9.49}$$

To find the output resistance, we begin by writing the output loop equation.

$$i \cdot R_o = v - G_o v_d = v\left(1 + \frac{G_o R'_A}{R_F + R'_A}\right) \tag{9.50}$$

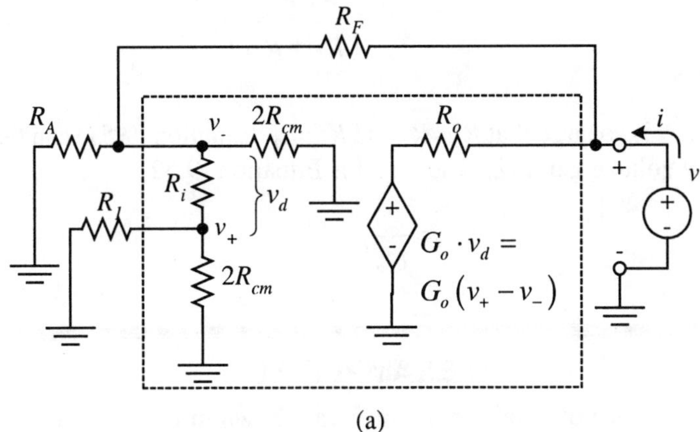

Figure 9.25 (part a) - Thevenin equivalent circuits

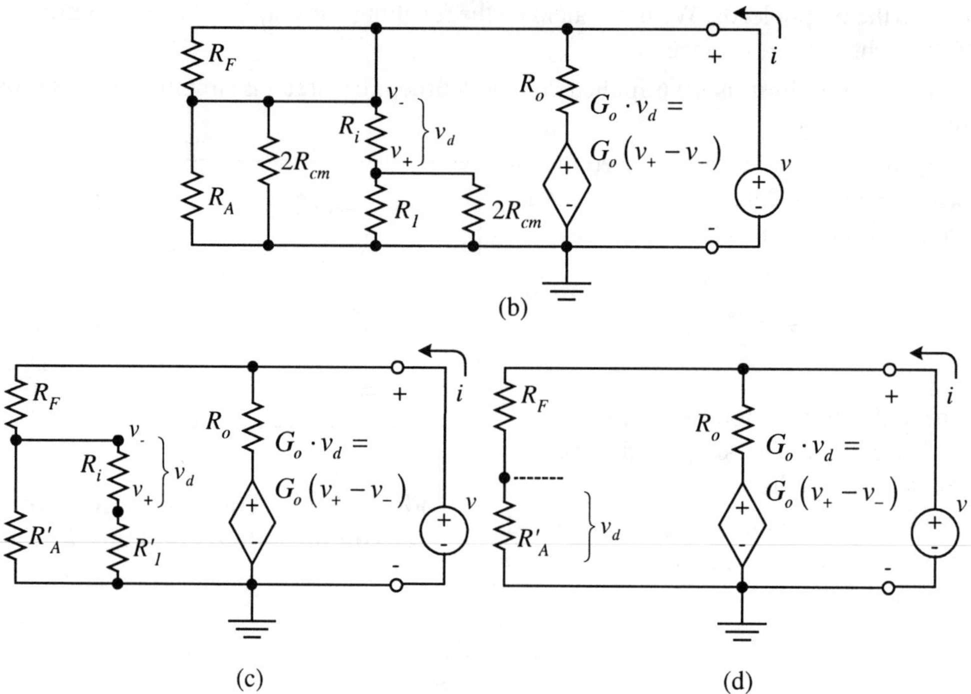

Figure 9.25 (parts c and d) - Reduced Thevenin equivalent circuits

The output resistance is then given by Equation (9.51).

$$R_{out} = \frac{v}{i} = \frac{R_o}{1 + \dfrac{G_o R'_A}{(R_F + R'_A)}} \tag{9.51}$$

In most cases, R_{cm} is so large that $R'_A \approx R_A$ and $R_1' \approx R_1$. Equation (9.51) can be simplified using the zero-frequency voltage gain, G_o. The result is Equation (9.52).

$$R_{out} = \frac{R_o}{G_o}\left(1 + \frac{R_F}{R_A}\right) \tag{9.52}$$

EXAMPLE 9.6

Find the output impedance of a unity-gain buffer as shown in Figure 9.26.

Solution: When the circuit of Figure 9.26 is compared to the feedback circuit of Figure 9.24, we find that

$$R_A \to \infty$$

Therefore,

$$R'_A = \infty \| 2R_{cm} = 2R_{cm}$$

Equation (9.51) cannot be used, since we are not sure that the inequalities leading to the simplification of Figure 9.25(c) apply in this case. That is, the simplification requires that

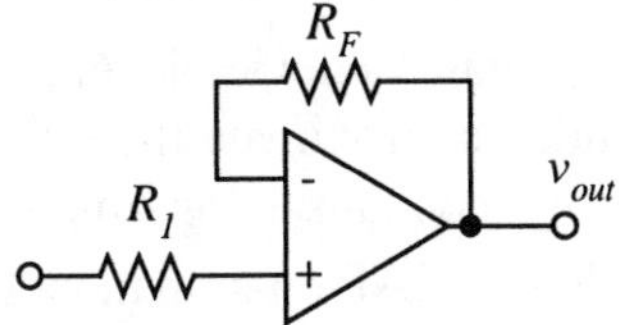

Figure 9.26 – Unity gain buffer

$$2R_{cm} \ll R_I \| (2R_{cm} + R_i)$$

Without this simplification, the circuit takes the form shown in Figure 9.27.

This circuit is analyzed to find the following relations:

$$v_d = \frac{-R_i v}{R'_I + R_i}$$

$$R_o \cdot i = v - G_o v_d = \left(1 + \frac{R_i}{R'_I + G_o R_i}\right) v$$

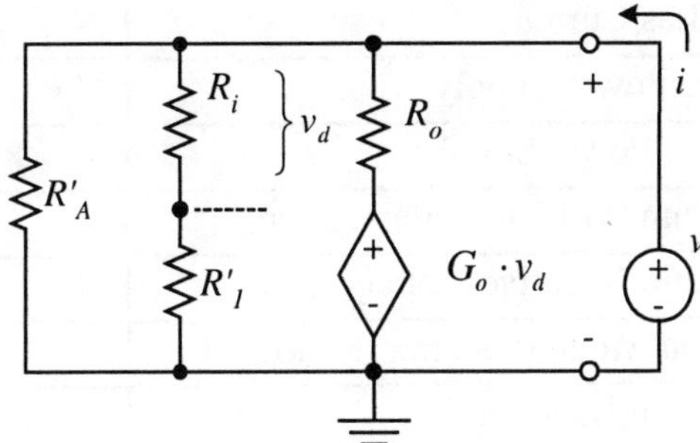

Figure 9.27 – Equivalent circuit for Unity gain buffer

In the first of these equations, we have assumed that $R_o << (R'_I + R_i) << 2R_{cm}$. The output resistance is then given by

$$R_{out} = \frac{v}{i} = \frac{R_o}{1 + R_i G_o / (R'_I + R_i)}$$

Where we again use the zero-frequency voltage gain, G_o.

9.6 COMPUTER SIMULATION OF OP-AMP CIRCUITS

SPICE contains a device-level model for the op-amp. When SPICE is used, a sub-circuit has been included approximate the op-amp. We discuss this in the SPICE Appendix to this text. MICRO-CAP contains an op-amp model, and we discuss that in the current section.

The MICRO-CAP op-amp model contains 20 parameters, as shown in Table 9.2. The symbols are those used by MICROCAP and vary slightly from those of the previous section.

SYMBOL	PARAMETER	UNITS	DEFAULT
LEVEL	Model Level		1
TYPE	1=NPN; 2=PNP; 3=JFET		3
C	Compensation Capacitor	F	30E-12
A	DC Open-loop gain		2E5
ROUTAC	AC Output Resistance	Ω	75
ROUTDC	DC Output Resistance	Ω	125
VOFF	Input Offset Voltage	V	0.001
IOFF	Input Offset Current	A	1E-9
SRP	Maximum Positive Slew Rate	V/S	5E5
SRN	Maximum Negative Slew Rate	V/S	5E5
IBIAS	Input Bias Current	A	1E-7
VCC	Positive Power Supply	V	15
VEE	Negative Power Supply	V	-15
VPS	Maximum Positive Voltage Swing	V	13
VNS	Maximum Negative Voltage Swing	V	-13
CMRR	Common-Mode Rejection Ratio		1E5
GBW	Unity Gain Bandwidth		1E6
PM	Phase Margin	degrees	60
PD	Power Dissipation	Watts	0.025
IOSC	Short Circuit Current	A	0.02

Table 9.2 - MICRO-CAP op-amp parameters

If the *level* is set to 1, the model becomes a simple voltage-controlled current source with finite output resistance and open loop gain. Only three of the parameters are used in the model: the *DC Open-Loop Gain*, the *AC Output Resistance*, and the *DC Output Resistance.*

The Level 2 adds the *slew rates, bandwidth,* and *phase margin* so it contains a two-pole model with slew rate limiting. We discuss these frequency-related topics in the next chapter.

The Level 3 model is the enhanced *Boyle Model*, as is often used in the SPICE sub-circuit models. It includes all of the parameters in Table 9.2. Figure 9.28(a), (b), and (c) show the Level 1, Level 2 and Level 3 equivalent circuits respectively

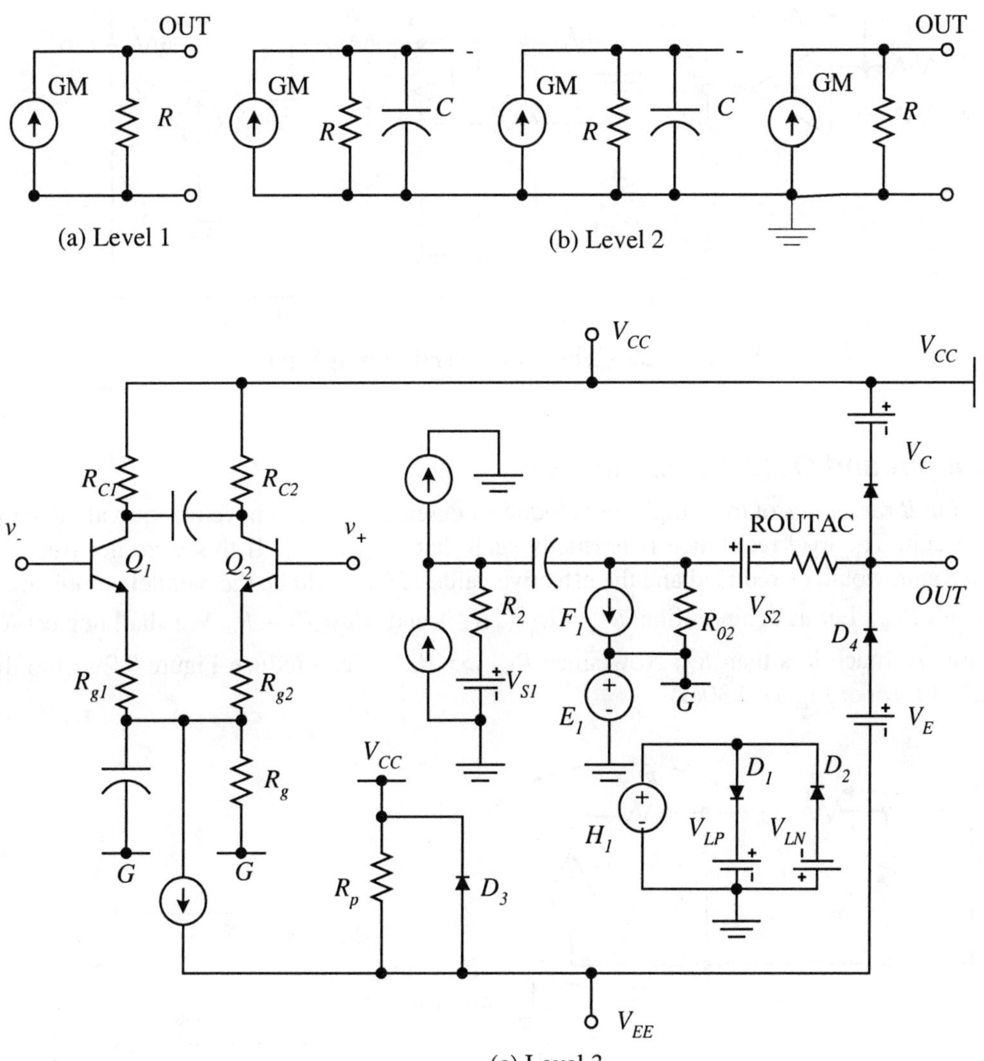

Figure 9.28 - MICRO-CAP op-amp equivalent circuits

9.7 NON-INVERTING AMPLIFIER

Figure 9.29(a) illustrates the *non-inverting amplifier*, and Figure 9.29(b) shows the equivalent circuit.

The input voltage is applied through $R_I \left(\cong R_A \| R_F\right)$ into the non-inverting terminal.

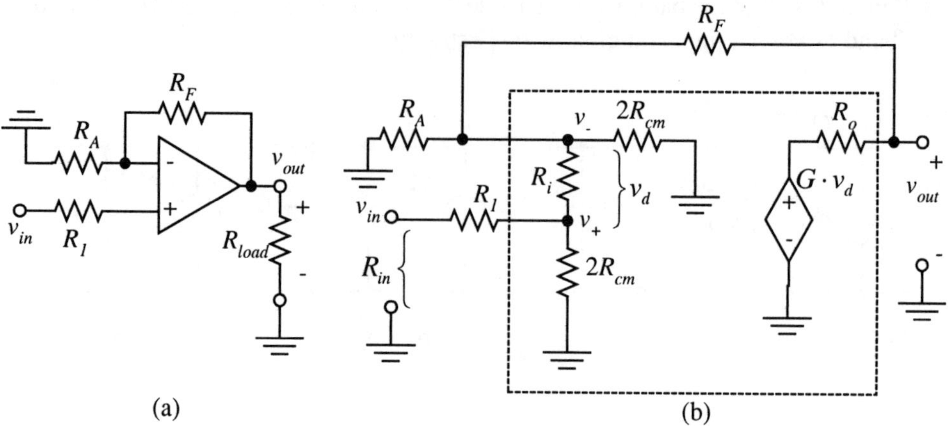

Figure 9.29 - The non-inverting amplifier

9.7.1 Input and Output Resistances

The *input resistance* of this amplifier is found by determining the Thevenin equivalent of the input circuit. The load resistance is normally such that $R_{load} >> R_o$. If this were not true, the effective gain would be reduced and the effective value of R_o would be the parallel combination of R_o with R_{load}. Let us again define $R'_A = R_A \| (2R_{cm})$ and $R'_F = R_F + R_o$. We shall neglect R_1, since it is so much less than R_{in}. Now since $R_{load} >> R_o$, we can reduce Figure 9.29(a) to the simplified form of Figure 9.30(a).

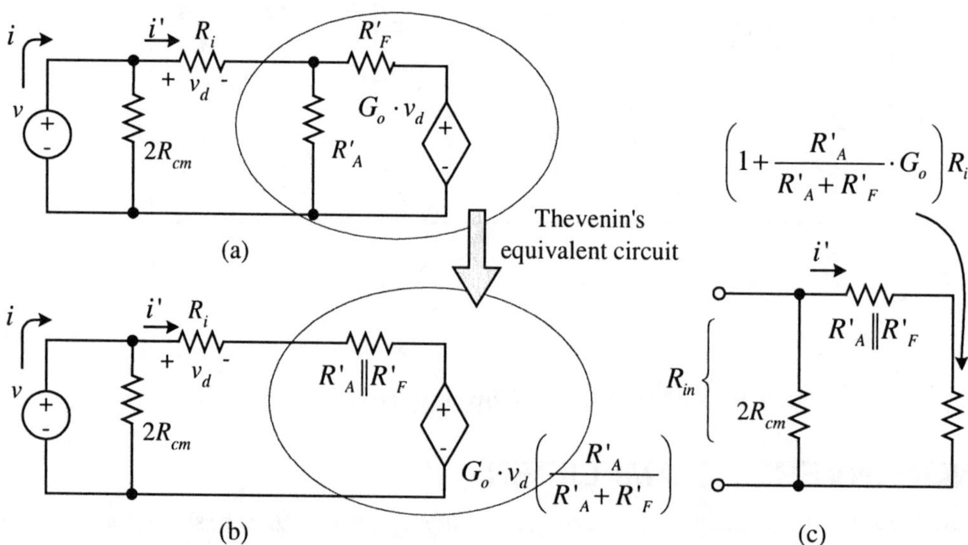

Figure 9.30 - Reduced circuits for input resistance

We find the Thevenin equivalent of the circuit surrounded by the elliptical curve, resulting in Figure 9.30(b). In Figure 9.30(c), the resistance to the right of $2R_{cm}$ is given by v/i'. In order to evaluate this, we write a loop equation to obtain

$$\left(R_i + R'_A \| R'_F\right) \cdot i' = v - \frac{R'_A G_o R_i \cdot i'}{R'_A + R'_F} \tag{9.53}$$

Therefore,

$$\frac{v}{i'} = R'_A \| R'_F + \left(1 + \frac{R'_A \cdot G_o}{R'_A + R_{F'}}\right) R_i \tag{9.54}$$

The input resistance is the parallel combination of this quantity with $2R_{cm}$.

$$R_{in} = 2R_{cm} \left\| \left[R'_A \left\| R'_F + \left(1 + \frac{R'_A G_o}{R'_A + R'_F}\right) \cdot R_i \right. \right] \right. \tag{9.55}$$

Recall that $R'_A = R_A \| 2R_{cm}$, $R'_F = R_F + R_o$, and $R_{load} >> R_o$. If we retain only the most significant terms and note that R_{cm} is large, Equation (9.55) reduces to

$$R_{in} = 2R_{cm} \left\| \frac{R_i \cdot G_o}{1 + \frac{R'_F}{R'_A}} \right. \tag{9.56}$$

where we again use the zero-frequency voltage gain, G_o.

Equation (9.56) can be used to find the input resistance of the 741 op-amp. If we substitute the parameter values as given in Table 9.1, Equation (9.56) becomes

$$R_{in} \approx 400 \text{ M}\Omega$$

The *output resistance* is found using the techniques of Example 9.6. We again use the assumptions that R_{cm} is large, that is $R'_F \approx R_F$ and $R'_A \approx R_A$. Then the output resistance of a 741 op-amp is given by

$$R_{out} = \frac{75(1 + R_F/R_A)}{10^5} \tag{9.57}$$

EXAMPLE 9.7

Calculate the input resistance for the unity-gain follower shown in Figure 9.31(a).

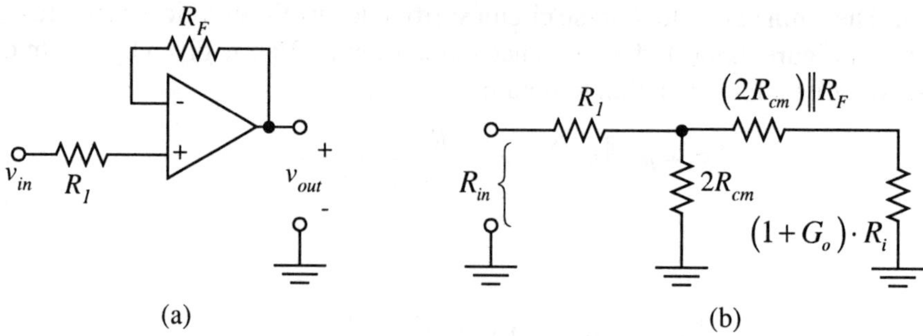

Figure 9.31 - Unity-gain follower - Example 9.6

Solution: The equivalent circuit is shown in Figure 9.31(b). Since we assume the zero-frequency gain, G_o, and the common-mode resistance, R_{cm}, are high, we can neglect the term $(2R_{cm})\|R_F$ compared to $(1+G_o)R_i$. Equation (9.57) cannot be used since $R_A = 0$. The input resistance is then given by

$$R_{in} = 2R_{cm}\|\left[(1+G_o)R_i\right] = 2R_{cm}$$

This is typically equal to 400 MΩ or more, so we can neglect R_I (i.e., set $R_I = 0$).

9.7.2 Voltage Gain

We wish to determine the voltage gain, A_+ for the non-inverting amplifier of Figure 9.32(a). This gain is defined by

$$A_+ = \frac{v_{out}}{v_i} = \frac{v_{out}}{v_+} \tag{9.58}$$

The equivalent circuit is shown in Figure 9.32(b). If we assume $R_F >> R_o$, $R_{load} >> R_o$ and $R'_A = R_A\|2R_{cm}$, the circuit can be reduced to that shown in Figure 9.32(c). If we further define $R'_1 = R_1\|2R_{cm}$, then Figure 9.32(d) results.

The assumed conditions are desirable in order to prevent reduction of the effective gain. The operation of taking Thevenin equivalents modifies the dependent voltage source and the driving voltage source as in Figure 9.32(d). Note that

$$\frac{R'_1}{R_1} = \frac{2R_{cm}}{R_1 + 2R_{cm}} \tag{9.59}$$

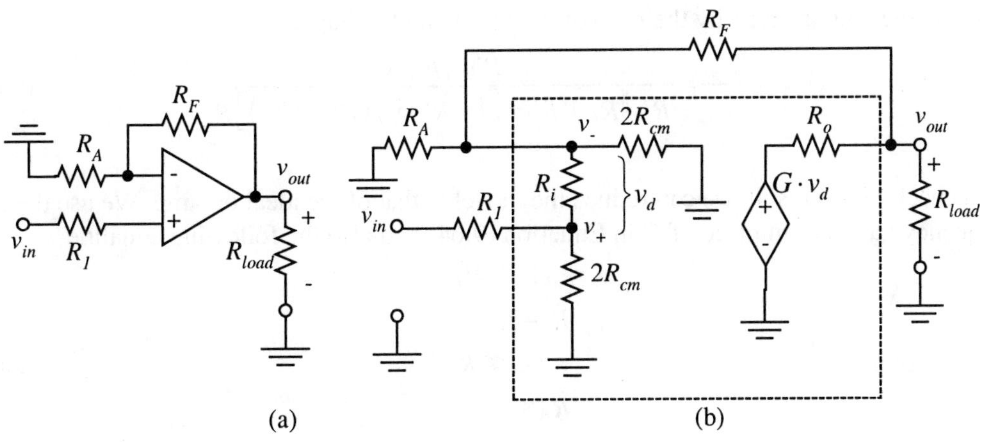

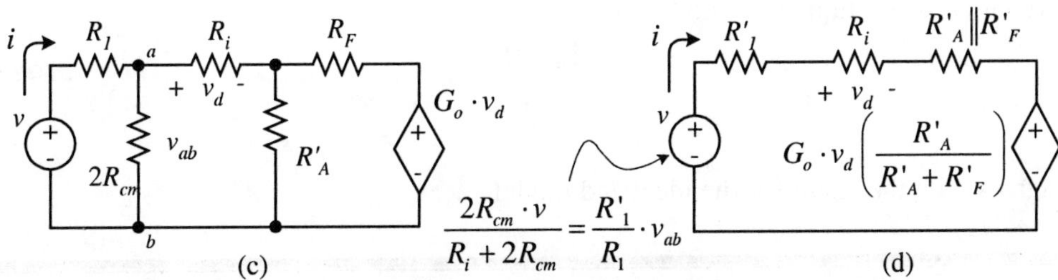

Figure 9.32 – Non-inverting amplifier

The output voltage is given by

$$v_{out} = G_o v_d = R_i G_o \cdot i \tag{9.60}$$

We can find i by applying KVL to the circuit of Figure 9.32(d) to obtain

$$\left(R'_1 + R_i + R'_A \| R_F\right) \cdot i = \frac{R'_1 v_{in}}{R_1} - \frac{R'_A \cdot G_o \, v_d}{R'_A + R_F} \tag{9.61}$$

where

$$v_d = R_i \cdot i \tag{9.62}$$

and $R_F \gg R_o$ implying $R'_F \cong R_F$.

Solving for the current, i, we obtain

$$i = \frac{R'_1 \cdot v_{in} / R_1}{\left(R'_A \| R_F\right) + R'_1 + \left[1 + R'_A G_o / \left(R'_A + R_F\right)\right] R_i} \tag{9.63}$$

The voltage gain is given by the ratio of output to input voltage.

$$A_+ = \frac{v_{out}}{v_{in}} = \frac{R'_1 G_o R_i / R_1}{R'_A \| R_F + R'_1 + \left[1 + R'_A G_o / (R'_A + R_F)\right] R_i} \tag{9.64}$$

As a check of this result, we can reduce the model to that of the ideal op-amp. We use the zero-frequency gain, G_o, in place of G in Equation (9.64) and also the following equalities.

$$\begin{aligned} &R_i G_o \ll R_F \\ &R_1 = R'_1 \\ &R_i G_o \ll R_1 \\ &R_A = R'_A \\ &R_i G_o \ll R_{load} \end{aligned} \tag{9.65}$$

When we let $G_o \rightarrow \infty$, Equation (9.64) becomes

$$A_+ = \frac{R_A + R_F}{R_A} \tag{9.66}$$

which agrees with the result for the idealized model.

EXAMPLE 9.8

Find the gain of the unity-gain follower shown in Figure 9.33.

Solution: In this circuit, $R_A \rightarrow \infty$, $R'_A = 2R_{cm}$, and $R_F << R'_A$. We assume that G_o is large, $R'_1 \approx R_1$, and we set $R_1 = R_F$. Equation (9.64)then reduces to

$$A_+ = \frac{G_o R_i}{2R_F + G_o R_i} \approx \frac{R'_A + R_F}{R'_A} \approx 1 \tag{9.67}$$

so $v_{out} = v_{in}$ as expected.

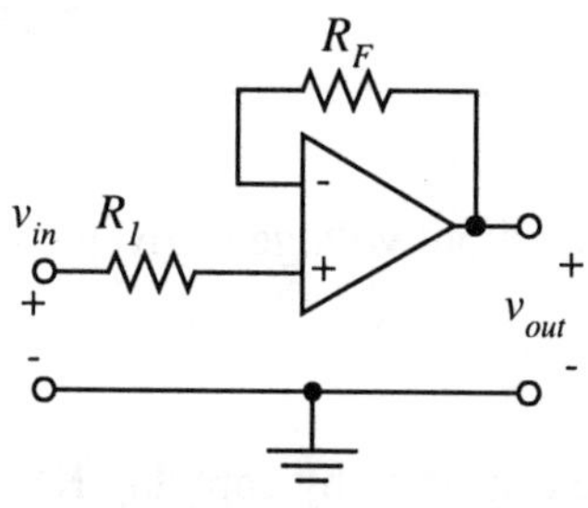

Figure 9.33 – Unity gain follower

9.7.3 Multiple-Input Amplifiers

We extend the previous results to the case of the non-inverting amplifier with multiple voltage inputs. Figure 9.34 shows a multiple-input non-inverting amplifier.

If inputs v_1, v_2, v_3, ..., v_n are applied through input resistances R_1, R_2, R_3, ..., R_n, we obtain a special case of the general result derived in Chapter 2, as follows:

$$v_{out} = \left(1 + \frac{R_F}{R_A}\right)\left[R_1 \| R_2 \| \ldots \| R_n\right] \sum_{k=1}^{n} \frac{v_k}{R_k} \qquad (9.68)$$

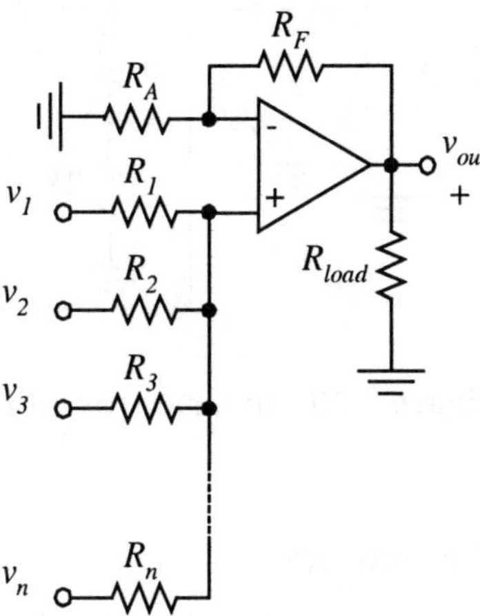

Figure 9.34 – Multiple-input non-inverting amplifier

We choose

$$R_A \| R_F = R_1 \| R_2 \| \cdots \| R_n \qquad (9.69)$$

to achieve bias balance. The output resistance is found from Equation (9.52).

As a specific example, let us determine the output voltage of the two-input summer of Figure 9.35.

The output voltage is found from Equation (9.68), as follows:

$$v_{out} = \left(1 + \frac{R_F}{R_A}\right)\left(\frac{R_2 v_1}{R_1 + R_2} + \frac{R_1 v_2}{R_1 + R_2}\right) \qquad (9.70)$$

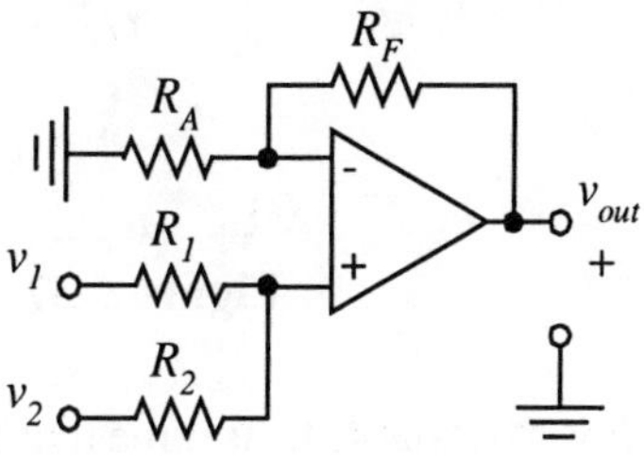

Figure 9.35 – Two-input summer

We choose $R_A \| R_F = R_1 \| R_2$ to achieve bias balance. If we assume $R_F = R_1 = R_2 = R_A$, then Equation (9.70) reduces to $v_{out} = v_1 + v_2$, which is a unity-gain two-input summer.

9.8 INVERTING AMPLIFIER

Figure 9.36(a) illustrates an inverting amplifier. Figure 9.36(b) shows the equivalent circuit using the op-amp model developed earlier in this chapter.

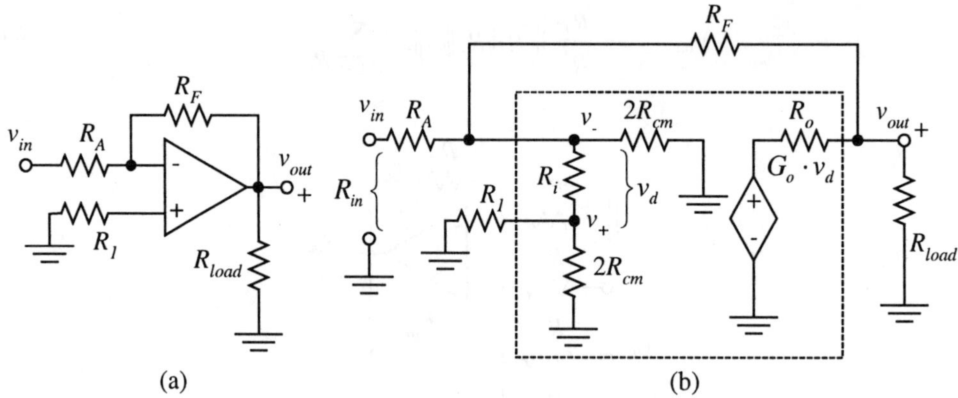

Figure 9.36 - Inverting amplifier

9.8.1 Input and Output Resistance

Figure 9.36(b) is reduced to Figure 9.37(a) if we let $R'_1 = R_1 \| 2R_{cm}$, $R_F >> R_o$, and $R_{load} >> R_o$.

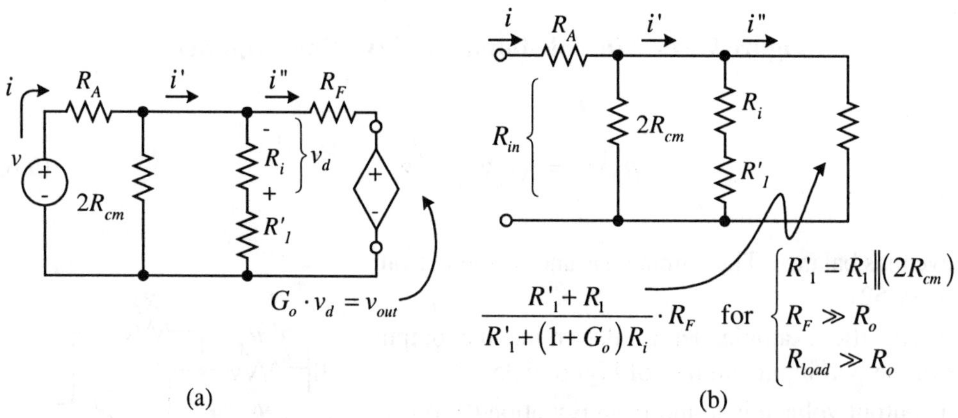

Figure 9.37 – Simplified inverting amplifier model

It is reasonable to assume that these inequalities apply because, were they not true, the output would load the input and the gain would be reduced.

A voltage-divider relationship can be used to yield

$$v_d = \frac{-R_i \cdot v_-}{R_i + R'_1} \tag{9.71}$$

and a loop equation yields

$$R_F \cdot i'' = v_- - G_o v_d = \left(1 + \frac{R_i \cdot G}{R_i + R'_1}\right) \cdot v_- = \frac{R'_1 + (1+G)R_i}{R_i + R'_1} \cdot v_- \tag{9.72}$$

The input resistance, R_{in}, is obtained from Figure 9.37(b), where we have replaced the dependent source with an equivalent resistance. The value of this resistor is v_i/i'' which is found from Equation (9.72). For large G (i.e., $G \rightarrow G_o$), the rightmost resistance in Figure 9.37(b) is approximately zero, and $R_{in} \approx R_A$.

The output resistance of the inverting amplifier is the same as that of the non-inverting amplifier. Thus,

$$R_{out} = \frac{\left(1 + R_F/R_A\right)}{G_o} \cdot R_o \tag{9.73}$$

9.8.2 Voltage Gain

We use the equivalent circuits of Figure 9.36(b) and Figure 9.37(a) to determine the voltage gain. The inverting input gain, $A_- = v_{out}/v_{in}$, is obtained from the circuit of Figure 9.37(a) by again making the same assumptions that we made in finding the output resistance.

These assumptions reduce the circuit to that shown in Figure 9.38(a), where we have changed the voltage source in series with a resistance to a current source in parallel with a resistance. The resistors can then be combined to yield the circuit of Figure 9.38(b). Finally, the current source is converted back to the voltage source to yield the simplified circuit of Figure 9.38(c).

The loop equation for this circuit is given by

$$v_d = \frac{-R_i}{R_i + R'_I + R'_A \| R_F}\left[\left(R'_A \| R_F\right) \cdot \frac{v_{in}}{R_A} + \frac{R'_A \cdot G_o}{R'_A + R_F} \cdot v_d\right] \tag{9.74}$$

Since $v_{out} = G_o v_d$, the inverting voltage gain is

$$A_- = \frac{v_{out}}{v_{in}} = -\frac{G_o R'_A R_i R_F / R_a}{\left(R_i + R'_I\right)\left(R'_A + R_F\right) + R'_A R_F + R_i R'_A G_o} \tag{9.75}$$

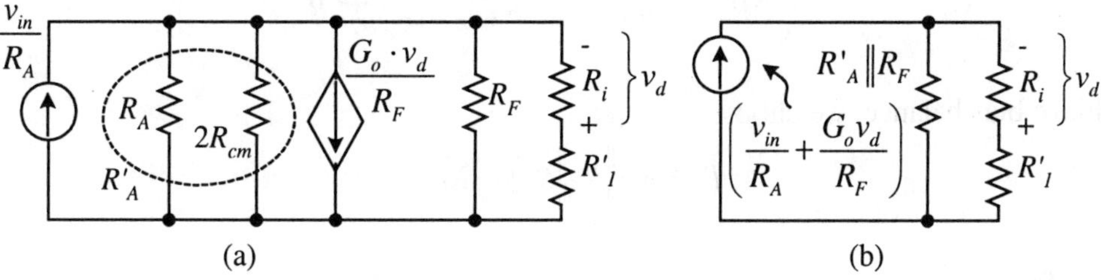

Figure 9.38 (parts a and b)- Inverting input gain

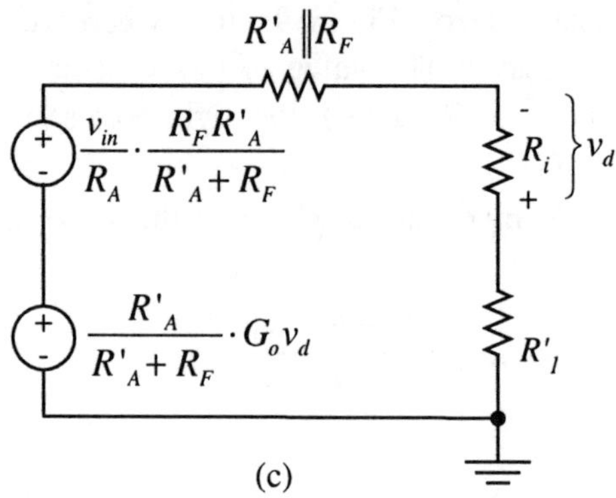

Figure 9.38 (part c)- Inverting input gain

We can verify this result relative to the gain of the ideal op-amp by making the approximations: $R_A << 2R_{cm}$ and $G >> 1$. Then

$$R'_A = R_A \| 2R_{cm} = R_A$$

$$A_- = -\frac{R_F}{R_A} \tag{9.76}$$

This is the same as the result found earlier for the simplified model.

9.8.3 Multiple-Input Amplifiers

If the voltages v_a, v_b, ... , v_m are applied to the summing junction (inverting input to op-amp) through resistors R_a, R_b, ..., R_m, respectively, as shown in Figure 9.39, the output voltage is

$$v_{out} = -\frac{R_F v_a}{R_a} - \frac{R_F v_b}{R_b} \cdots - \frac{R_F v_m}{R_m} = -R_F \sum_{j=a}^{m} \frac{v_j}{R_j} \tag{9.77}$$

To achieve bias balance, we choose

$$R_1 = R_F \| R_a \| R_b \| \cdots \| R_m \tag{9.78}$$

Let us define

$$R_A = R_a \| R_b \| \cdots \| R_m \tag{9.79}$$

The output resistance is then

$$R_{out} = \frac{R_o(1 + R_F/R_A)}{G_o} \tag{9.80}$$

Suppose now that only two inputs are used. The output voltage is then

$$v_{out} = -\frac{R_F v_a}{R_a} - \frac{R_F v_b}{R_b} \tag{9.81}$$

The input resistance at v_a is approximately equal to R_a, and the input resistance at v_b is approximately R_b. We can make this circuit a unity-gain two-input summer with an output voltage of

$$v_{out} = -v_a - v_b \tag{9.82}$$

by setting $R_F = R_a = R_b$. The resistance from the non-inverting input terminal to ground is chosen to achieve bias balance. Thus, $R_1 = R_F/3$, and we have

$$1+\frac{R_F}{R_A} = 1+\frac{R_F}{R_a \| R_b} = 3 \tag{9.83}$$

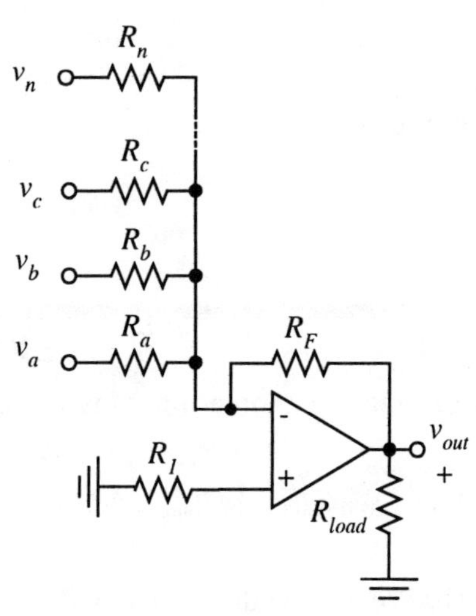

Figure 9.39 – Multiple-input inverting amplifier

An equal-gain (i.e., not unity) two-input summer is obtained by setting $R_a = R_b = R$ and $R_1 = (R_F \| R)/2$. In this case, the output voltage is

$$v_{out} = -\left(\frac{R_F}{R}\right)(v_a + v_b) \tag{9.84}$$

The input resistance is approximately R. Since $R_A = R/2$,

$$1+\frac{R_F}{R_A} = 1+\frac{2R_F}{R} \tag{9.85}$$

If m inputs are summed through equal resistors (say R), the output voltage is

$$v_{out} = -\frac{R_F}{R}\sum_{j=a}^{m} v_j \tag{9.86}$$

For this equal-gain multiple-input inverting summer, the input resistance to each input is approximately R. Since $R_A = R/m$,

$$1+\frac{R_F}{R_A} = 1+\frac{m \cdot R_F}{R} \tag{9.87}$$

and

$$R_1 = R_F \left\| \frac{R}{m} \right. \tag{9.88}$$

The output resistance is

$$R_{out} = \frac{R_o}{G_o}\left(1 + \frac{m \cdot R_F}{R}\right) \tag{9.89}$$

EXAMPLE 9.9

Design and analyze a three-input inverting amplifier using a 741 op-amp where

$$v_{out} = -4v_a - 2v_b - 3v_c$$

and the input resistance is $R_{min} = 8\ \text{k}\Omega$.

Solution: We use the design method of Chapter 2 to find $X = 0$, $Y = 9$, $Z = -10$. Then

$$R_F = 10 \times 8\ \text{k}\Omega = 80\ \text{k}\Omega$$

$$R_a = 80\text{k}\Omega/4 = 20\ \text{k}\Omega$$

$$R_b = 80\ \text{k}\Omega/2 = 40\ \text{k}\Omega$$

$$R_c = 80\ \text{k}\Omega/3 = 26.7\ \text{k}\Omega$$

$$R_x = 80\ \text{k}\Omega/\text{-}(-10) = 8\ \text{k}\Omega$$

$$R_A = R_a \| R_b \| R_c = 8.9\ \text{k}\Omega$$

The gain multiplier of the amplifier is $1+R_F/R_A = 10$. We find the input resistance as follows:

$$R_{in}(v_a) = 20\ \text{k}\Omega$$

$$R_{in}(v_b) = 40\ \text{k}\Omega$$

$$R_{in}(v_c) = 26.7\ \text{k}\Omega$$

The output resistance is approximately $75(10)/10^5 = 7.5\ \text{m}\Omega$. To achieve bias balance, we set

$$R_x = R_a \| R_b \| R_c \| R_F = 8\ \text{k}\Omega$$

9.9 DIFFERENTIAL SUMMING

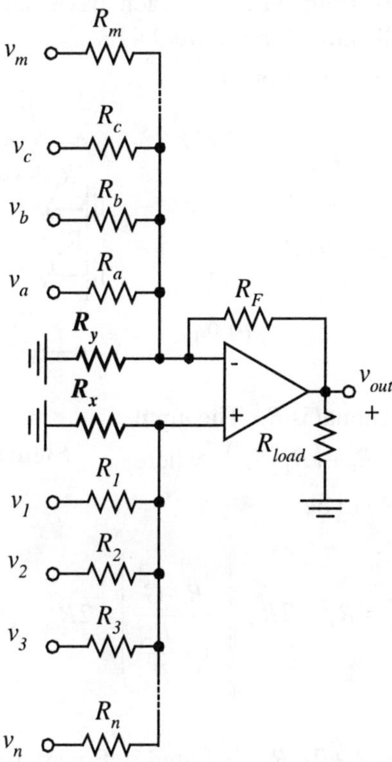

Figure 9.40 – Differential summing

We have seen that an op-amp can be configured to produce an output that is a weighted sum of multiple inputs. If the sum includes both positive and negative signs, *differential summing* results.

The op-amp configuration of Figure 9.40 produces an output voltage, v_{out}, given by

$$v_{out} = \left(1 + \frac{R_F}{R_A}\right)\left[R_1 \| R_2 \| R_3 \| \ldots \| R_n \| R_x\right] \sum_{i=1}^{n} \frac{v_i}{R_i} - R_F \sum_{j=a}^{m} \frac{v_j}{R_j} \tag{9.90}$$

where

$$R_A = R_a \| R_b \| R_c \| \ldots \| R_m \| R_y \tag{9.91}$$

We choose the resistors to achieve bias balance, as follows:

$$R_1 \| R_2 \| R_3 \| \cdots \| R_x = R_F \| R_a \| R_b \| R_c \| \cdots \| R_y \tag{9.92}$$

The input resistance for each inverting input, v_j, is R_j.

If the inverting and non-inverting terminals each have only one input, the result is a *differencing amplifier.* This is illustrated in Figure 9.41.

The output voltage for this configuration is

$$v_{out} = \left(1 + \frac{R_F}{R_A}\right) \frac{R_x}{R_1 + R_x} \cdot v_1 - \frac{R_F}{R_A} \cdot v_a \tag{9.93}$$

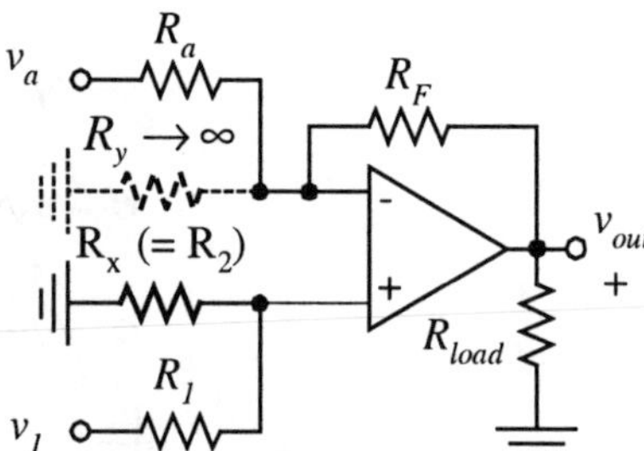

Figure 9.41 – Differencing amplifier

Note that RA = Ra [see Equation (9.91)].

To achieve bias balance, we choose

$$R_1 \| R_x = R_A \| R_F \tag{9.94}$$

The input resistance for the v_a terminal is R_A. The input resistance for the v_1 terminal is $R_1 + \left(R_2 \| R_{in}\right)$, where R_{in} is found from Equation (9.56) to be

$$R_{in} = R_{in} = 2R_{cm} \left\| \left(\frac{R_i \cdot G}{1 + \dfrac{R_F}{R_A}} \right) \right. \approx 2R_{cm} \tag{9.95}$$

Then R_{in}(at V_1) is approximately R_1+R_2. R_{out} is found in Equation (9.52) and is equal to

$$R_{out} = \frac{R_o\left(1 + R_F/R_A\right)}{G_o} \tag{9.96}$$

To achieve unit-gain differencing, where the output is given by $v_{out} = v_1 - v_a$ we set $R_A = R_F = R_1 = R_x$. If a 741 op-amp is used, a typical value for these four resistors is 10 kΩ. The input resistance into v_{out} is then 10 kΩ and into the v_1 terminal the resistance is 20 kΩ.

Suppose that equal-gain differencing is desired but that the gains need not be unity. We then set $R_1 = R_A$ and $R_x = R_F$. The output voltage is then

$$v_{out} = \frac{R_F\left(v_1 - v_a\right)}{R_A} \tag{9.97}$$

The input resistance into the v_a terminal is R_A, and into the non-inverting terminal it is $R_A + \left(R_F \| R_{in}\right)$, which is approximately $R_A + R_F$ since $R_{in} >> R_F$. Values for input resistance and

R_{out} are easily determined with the use of Equations (9.95) and (9.96).

A useful modification of the differencing amplifier configuration of Figure 9.41 is the *sign switcher* as shown in Figure 9.42.

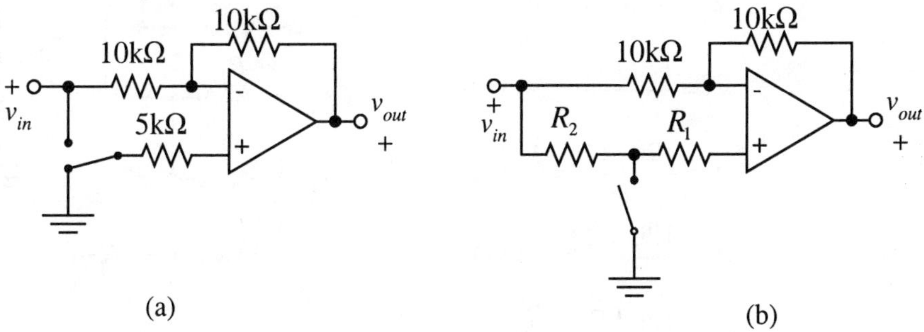

Figure 9.42 - Sign switcher

With the switch in the position shown in Figure 9.42(a), $v_{out} = -v_{in}$, and for the opposite switch position, $v_{out} = 2v_{in} - v_{in} = v_{in}$. The input resistance is 10 kΩ for each position, and the bias is balanced in each position. Figure 9.42(a) shows a single-pole double-throw switch. Sign switching can also be accomplished with a single-throw switch as shown in Figure 9.42(b). However, for this implementation, the bias and input resistances are not equal in the two switch positions.

EXAMPLE 9.10

Determine the output resistance and the input resistance at each of the inputs of a multiple input 741 amplifier which has an output of

$$V_{out} = 3V_1 + 4V_2 + 2V_3 - 5V_4 - 6V_5$$

Assume that the value of the resistance at the + and - terminals is 10 kΩ.

Solution: Using the larger of X and $(Y+1)$ yields the multiplying factor for determining R_F.

$$X = 9$$

$$Y + 1 = 12$$

Then

$$Z = 9 - 12 = -3$$

The circuit is shown in Figure 9.43.

$$R_F = 12 \times 10\ \text{k}\Omega = 120\ \text{k}\Omega$$

$$R_1 = \frac{120\ \text{k}\Omega}{3} = 40\ \text{k}\Omega$$

$$R_2 = \frac{120\ \text{k}\Omega}{4} = 30\ \text{k}\Omega$$

$$R_3 = \frac{120\ \text{k}\Omega}{2} = 60\ \text{k}\Omega$$

$$R_4 = \frac{120\ \text{k}\Omega}{5} = 24\ \text{k}\Omega$$

$$R_5 = \frac{120\ \text{k}\Omega}{6} = 20\ \text{k}\Omega$$

$$R_x = \frac{120\ \text{k}\Omega}{-(-3)} = 40\ \text{k}\Omega$$

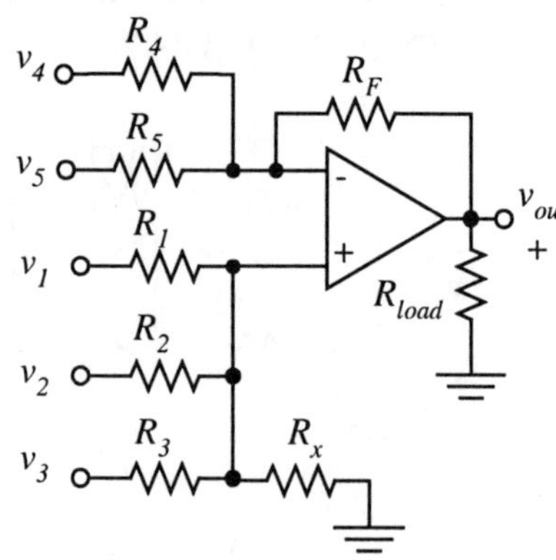

Figure 9.43 – Circuit for Example 9.10

$$R_o = 75 \times \frac{12}{10^6} = 0.9\ \text{m}\Omega$$

$$R_{in}(\text{ at } V_1) = 40\ \text{k}\Omega + 30\ \text{k}\Omega \| 60\ \text{k}\Omega \| 40\ \text{k}\Omega = 53.3\ \text{k}\Omega$$

$$R_{in}(\text{ at } V_2) = 30\ \text{k}\Omega + 40\ \text{k}\Omega \| 60\ \text{k}\Omega \| 40\ \text{k}\Omega = 45\ \text{k}\Omega$$

$$R_{in}(\text{ at } V_3) = 60\ \text{k}\Omega + 30\ \text{k}\Omega \| 40\ \text{k}\Omega \| 40\ \text{k}\Omega = 72\ \text{k}\Omega$$

$$R_{in}(\text{ at } V_4) = 24\ \text{k}\Omega$$

$$R_{in}(\text{ at } V_5) = 20\ \text{k}\Omega$$

EXERCISES

E9.5 Find the gain and input resistance for the 741 op-amp of Figure 9.36 with $R_F = 10\ \text{k}\Omega$ and $R_A = 1\ \text{k}\Omega$.

Answer: $A_v = -10$

E9.6 Find the input resistance for the differencing amplifier of Figure 9.41 using the 741 op-amp. $R_F = R_2 = 10\ \text{k}\Omega$ and $R_A = R_1 = 1\ \text{k}\Omega$.

Answer: $R_{in}(V_1) = 11\ \text{k}\Omega$; $R_{in}(V_a) = 1\ \text{k}\Omega$

E9.7 Determine the input resistance at each of the inputs of a multiple input amplifier which has an output of

$$V_1 + 2V_2 + 3V_3 - 4V_4 - 5V_5$$

and a resistance of 10 kΩ at the inverting and non-inverting inputs.

Ans: $R_{in}(V_1) = 120\ k\Omega$; $R_{in}(V_2) = 75\ k\Omega$; $R_{in}(V_3) = 66.7\ k\Omega$; $R_{in}(V_4) = 25\ k\Omega$; $R_{in}(V_5) = 20\ k\Omega$

9.10 AMPLIFIERS WITH BALANCED INPUTS OR OUTPUTS

The op-amp systems presented so far in this text are driven by voltages where one side of the source is grounded. Numerous op-amp applications require that we deal with voltages that are balanced; that is, neither side of the voltage source can be grounded. Op-amps are useful for converting a balanced input to a grounded (or unbalanced) output.

Figure 9.44 illustrates various configurations of balanced inputs and outputs. These configurations use the second method of balancing, that of cascading two op-amps.

As an example, in the configuration shown in Figure 9.44(b) if v_{in} is supplied from a high-impedance source, the 5kΩ resistors are no longer useful. Bias current may not be balanced in each amplifier. However, the effects of equal offsets due to unbalanced bias currents in the two input amplifiers should cancel one another. The alternative arrangement shown in the figure avoids this problem.

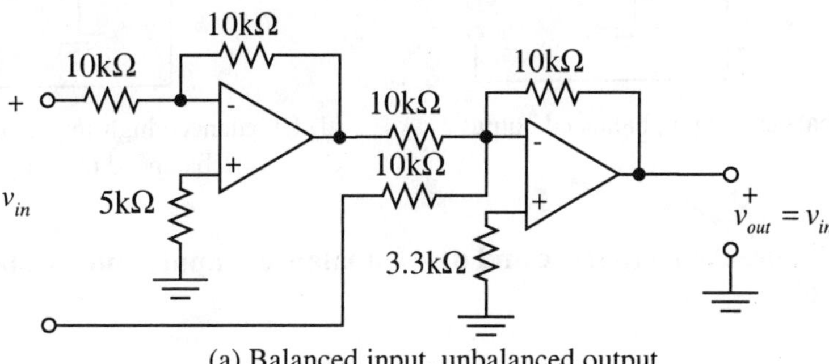

(a) Balanced input, unbalanced output

Figure 9.44 (part a) - Balanced input and output

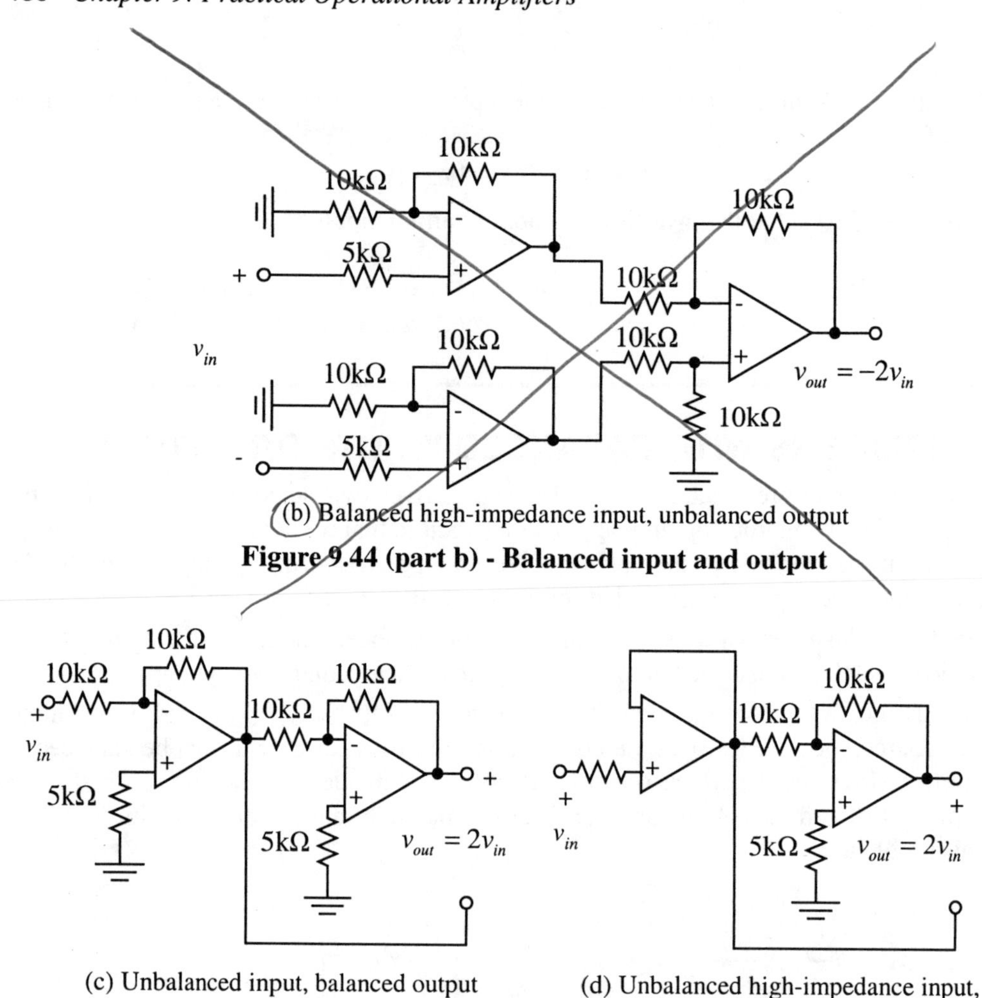

(b) Balanced high-impedance input, unbalanced output

Figure 9.44 (part b) - Balanced input and output

(c) Unbalanced input, balanced output

(d) Unbalanced high-impedance input, balanced output

Figure 9.44 – (parts c and d) – Unbalanced inputs and outputs

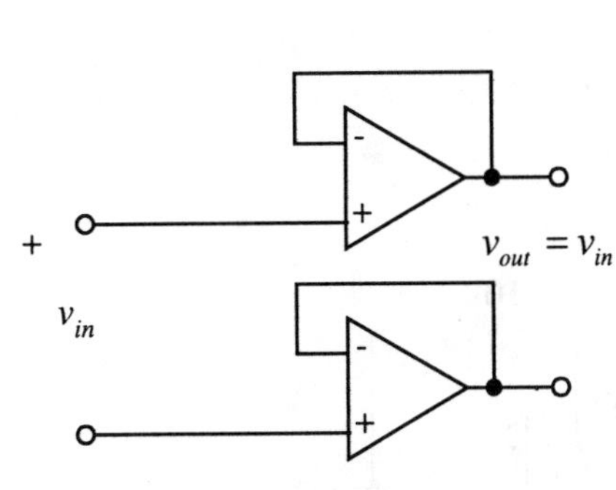

(e) Balanced high-impedance input, balanced output

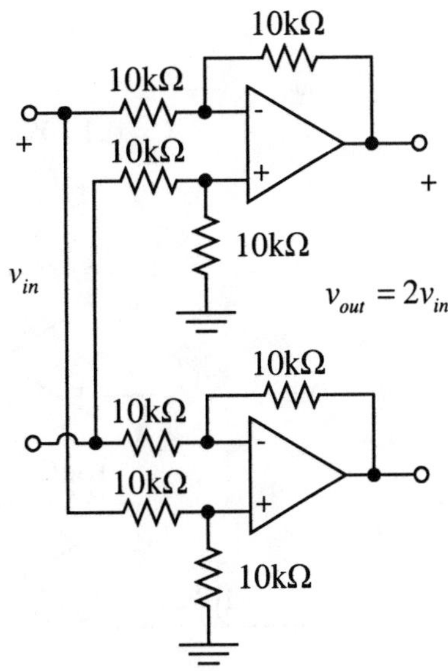

(f) Balanced input, balanced output

Figure 9.44 (parts e and f) - Balanced inputs and outputs

EXAMPLE 9.11

Design an op-amp system to monitor one of the line-to-line voltages on the three-phase Δ-power system that operates at 60 Hz, as shown in Figure 9.45.

The voltages,

$$V_{21}| = |V_{32}| = |V_{13}|$$
$$= 190 \text{ V rms}$$

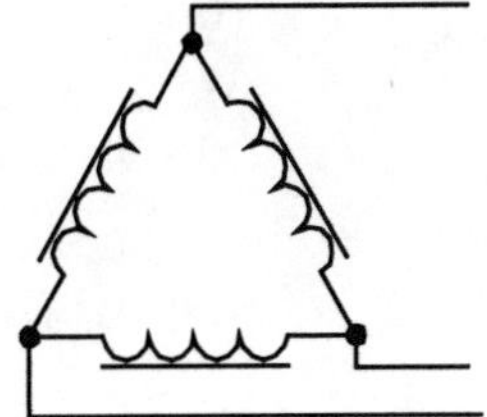

Figure 9.45 – Three-phase power system

Let us design an op-amp system to monitor V_{21} (defined as V_2-V_1) and deliver an unbalanced output given by

$$V_{out} = 0.1 V_{21} \quad \text{rms}$$

Solution: We cannot use an op-amp system of the type shown earlier because, in those systems, one terminal is grounded. In this example it is clearly impossible to ground any of the three-phase power lines. Let us use 741 op-amps and be sure that the input impedances to the instrumentation system are greater than 50 MΩ. We connect a non-inverting buffer to each input, v_1 and v_2, with the buffered outputs feeding into a differential op-amp system with a gain of 0.1. We use the design method of Section 2.6.

$$v_{out} = 0.1 v_{21} = 0.1(v_2 - v_1)$$

$$X = 0.1,\ \ Y = 0.1,\ \ Z = X - Y - 1 = -1$$

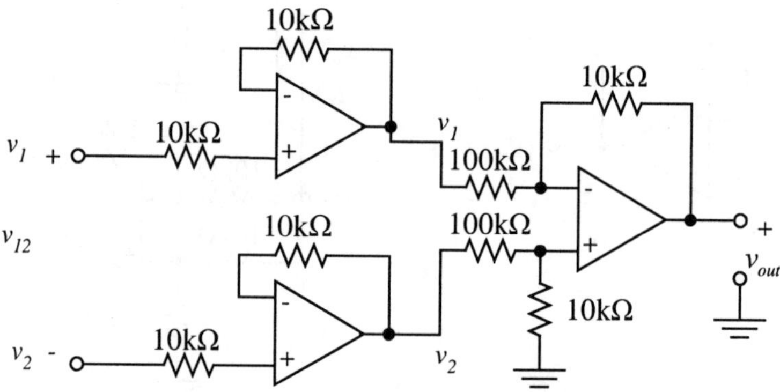

Figure 9.46 – System for Example 9.11

Let us choose $R_F = 10\ \text{k}\Omega$.

$$R_y \rightarrow \infty$$

$$R_x = \frac{R_F}{1} = 10\text{k}\Omega$$

$$R_2 = \frac{R_F}{0.1} = 100\text{k}\Omega$$

$$R_1 = \frac{R_F}{0.1} = 100\text{k}\Omega$$

The system is as shown in Figure 9.46. As a practical consideration, it is necessary to use an opto-coupler to isolate the instrumentation from the power lines.

9.11 COUPLING BETWEEN MULTIPLE INPUTS

When more than one input signal is connected to either the inverting or the non-inverting input to the op-amp, coupling between the inputs can result. This is frequently a disturbing problem, since a variation in one channel can produce an unwanted input into an adjoining channel. Consider the dual-input, non-inverting op-amp of Figure 9.47(a), where each channel is driven with a voltage source in series with a source resistance (the internal resistance of the voltage source).

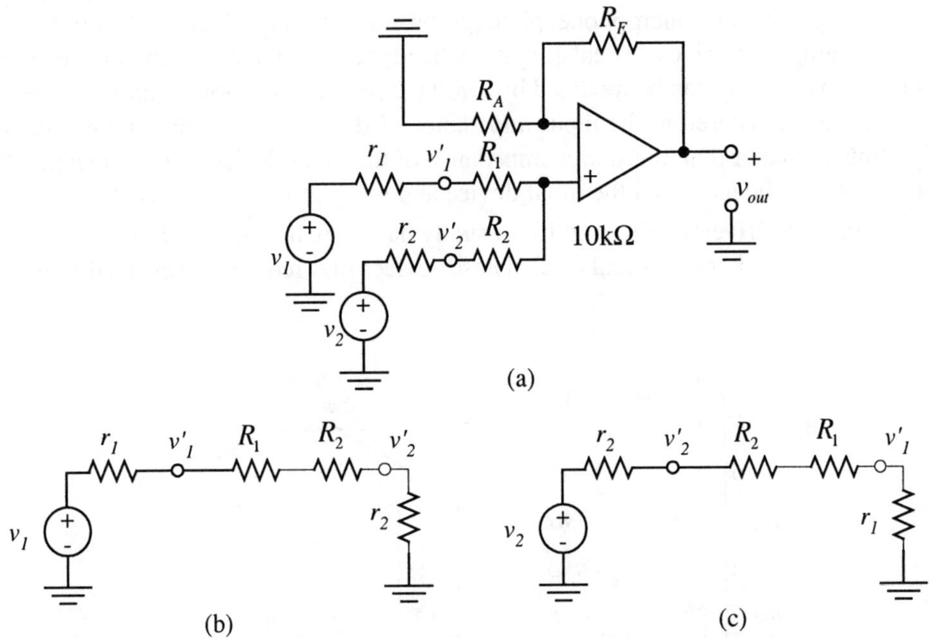

Figure 9.47 - Coupling between multiple inputs

The ideal source voltages, v_1 and v_2, have series resistances, r_1 and r_2 respectively. We begin by writing the equations for the effective voltages, v'_1 and v'_2, into the summing amplifier. We assume that zero current enters the op-amp. With v_2 set equal to zero, as shown in Figure 9.47(b), the voltage into the op-amp, v'_2, is

$$v'_2 = \frac{r_2}{r_1 + r_2 + R_1 + R_2} \cdot v_1 \tag{9.98}$$

When $v_1 = 0$, the v'_1 voltage is [see Figure 9.47(c)],

$$v'_1 = \frac{r_1}{r_1 + r_2 + R_1 + R_2} \cdot v_2 \tag{9.99}$$

Notice that the v'_2 voltage comes from v_1 and the v'_1 voltage comes from v_2. This coupling effect produces undesirable *cross-talk* between the two inputs. The effect can be eliminated by designing a system with r_1 and r_2 approaching zero. Hence, to eliminate coupling, each non-inverting multiple input should be driven with an op-amp that has zero (or very low) output impedance.

9.12 POWER AUDIO OP-AMPS

A common use for linear amplifiers is to provide gain for audio systems. An *audio amplifier* receives an input signal from a microphone, phonograph cartridge, tape deck, or AM/FM tuner. The output of the amplifier drives a speaker system, headphones, or a tape recorder. The input devices named above usually can be modeled by a voltage source with a low output voltage and high source impedance. Therefore the input impedance of the amplifier following this device must be high (much greater than the source impedance of the input device). In this manner, the amplifier does not significantly load the input device and the gain is not decreased.

The devices that are driven by the amplifier usually have low impedance. For example, the impedance of a single speaker is normally 8 Ω. These devices may require powers on the order of 1 to 10 W.

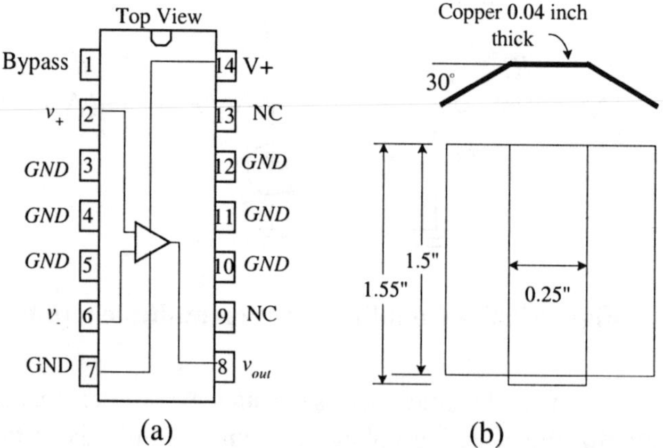

Figure 9.48 – The LM380 audio chip and optional heat sink

A variety of integrated circuit audio power op-amps, with different output powers, are available to the electronic design engineer. As an example, we present the LM380 audio power amplifier[1] which is used in such consumer applications as phono and tape deck amplifiers, intercoms, line drivers, alarms, TV sound systems, AM/FM radios, small servo drivers, and power converters. It has an internally fixed gain of 50 (34 dB) and an output that centers itself around one half of the supply voltage. Inputs can be either referenced to ground or balanced. The output stage is protected with both short circuit current limiting and thermal shutdown circuitry. The amplifier is packaged in a 14-pin DIP package as shown in Figure 9.48(a).

The output current is rated at 1.3 A peak. Since the device shuts down at junction temperatures above 150 °C, a heat sink [See Figure 9.48(b)] should be soldered to the unit. Maximum output power (with a heat sink) is 3.7 watts. The device is internally biased.

[1]The data and circuits are printed with the permission of the manufacturer, National Semiconductor Corp. The student is urged to use the data books when designing equipment with power op-amps.

Figure 9.49 shows the circuit configuration of a complete phono amplifier. A volume and tone control has been included in this circuit.

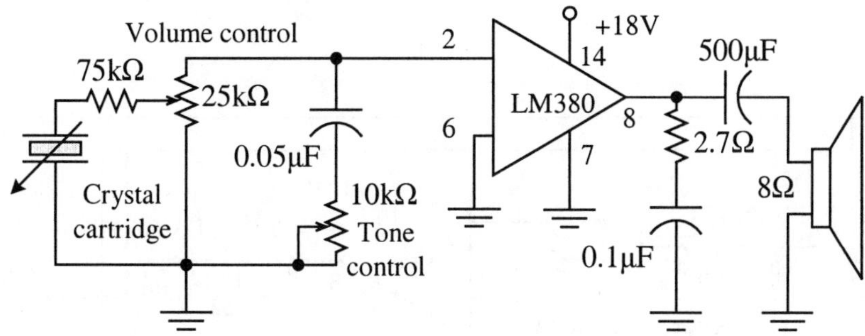

Figure 9.49 – Phono amplifier using LM380

9.12.1 Bridge Power Op-amp

If a particular application requires more power than can be obtained from a single power op-amp, we can use the bridge configuration of Figure 9.50.

Since this system provides twice the voltage swing across the load as the single-device system, the power capability is theoretically increased by a factor of 4 over the single amplifier (for a given power supply voltage). Since heat dissipation is the limiting concern in this design, we usually design the system conservatively and only double the output power.

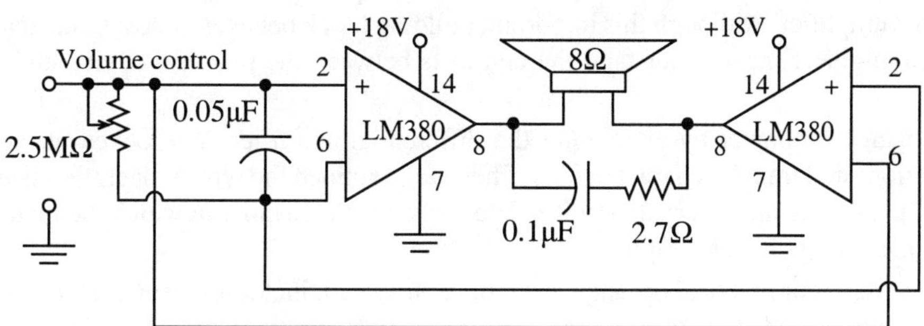

Figure 9.50 – Bridge configuration for high power

9.12.2 Intercom

Figure 9.51 shows an intercom incorporating a power op-amp and a few external components. With the dual two-position switch (S1A-S1B) in the talk position (as shown in the figure), the speaker of the master station performs the function of a microphone, driving the power op-amp through a step-up transformer. The remote speaker is driven from the output of the power op-amp.

Switching S1A-S1B to the listen position reverses the role of master and remote. Now the *remote* speaker plays the role of the microphone, and it drives the power amplifier through a step-up transformer. The master speaker is now driven from the output of the power op-amp. The student should trace the wiring with S1A-S1B in the listen position to verify this. A step-up transformer with a turns ratio of 1:25 can be used, and the potentiometer, R_v, acts as the volume control.

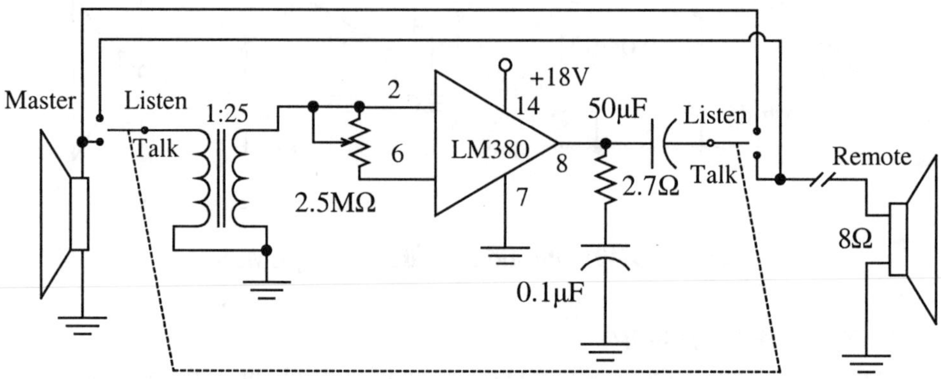

Figure 9.51 - Intercom

SUMMARY

This chapter built on the material presented in Chapter 2, where we focused on the ideal operational amplifier. Although this important building block behaves almost as ideal amplifier, the design engineer must understand the contrasts between the practical device and the ideal model.

We began the chapter by examining the differential amplifier. We looked at the various configurations and transfer characteristics. Then we examined the typical operational amplifier, including packaging and internal circuitry. We looked at the manner in which the manufacturer specifies parameters for the amplifier.

Characteristics of practical op-amps were then presented, including gain, offset voltage, bias current, common-mode rejection, and power supply rejected ratio. Computer simulation models were next considered, followed by a detailed analysis of non-inverting and inverting amplifiers.

The chapter concluded with a variety of design considerations and examples. We examined balanced inputs and outputs and coupling between inputs. We also looked at power audio op-amps, including an example of an intercom circuit.

PROBLEMS

Section 9.1

9.1 What are the differential and common mode gains for the amplifier of Figure 9.1 if $R_{C1} = R_{C2} = 10\ \mathrm{k}\Omega$, $R_{EE} = 10\ \mathrm{k}\Omega$ and $V_{CC} = 15$ V? Assume that V_{EE}/R_{EE} is a constant-current source and that $V_{BE} = 0.7$ V, $V_T = 26$ mV and $V_{EE} = 15$ V.

9.2 What are the differential and common-mode gains of the amplifier of Figure 9.1 if $R_{EE} = 5\ \mathrm{k}\Omega$, $R_{C1} = R_{C2} = 5\ \mathrm{k}\Omega$, $V_{CC} = V_{EE} = 15$ V? Assume that $V_{BE} = 0.7$ V, $V_T = 26$ mV and $\beta = 100$.

9.3 Find the differential voltage for the circuit of Figure 9.1 if $v_1 = 0.6$ V and $v_2 = 0.55$ V. Let $R_C = 5\ \mathrm{k}\Omega$, $R_{EE} = 5\ \mathrm{k}\Omega$ and $I_{EE} = 2.6$ mA.

9.4 A manufacturer lists the voltage gain of a differential amplifier as 200 and the CMRR as 80 dB. If a differential signal of 2 mV is applied to the input along with an unwanted common-mode signal of 10 mV, what is the amplitude of each signal at the output?

9.5 The differential amplifier of Figure 9.3 has $A_d = 200$, a differential voltage input of 3 mV, a common-mode voltage of 15 mV and a CMRR of 95 dB. Calculate the differential voltage and the common-mode voltage at the output.

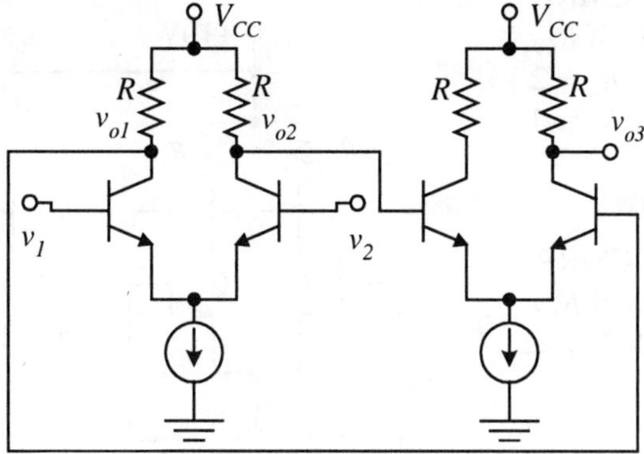

Figure P9.6

9.6 Calculate v_{o1}, v_{o2} and v_{o3} in terms of the input v_1 and v_2 for the circuit of Figure P9.6. Assume the differential voltage gain, A_d, (double-ended output to double-ended input) is 100 and that the common mode voltage gain, A_c, is -0.5 for each stage. All transistors can be assumed to be identical.

9.7 Calculate v_{o3} in terms of the inputs, v_1 and v_2 for the circuit of Figure P9.7. The differential and common-mode voltage gains for the first stage are the same as those in Problem 9.6. For transistor Q_3, $\beta = 100$, $R_C = 10\ \text{k}\Omega$, $R = 50\ \text{k}\Omega$ and $r_E = 200\ \Omega$.

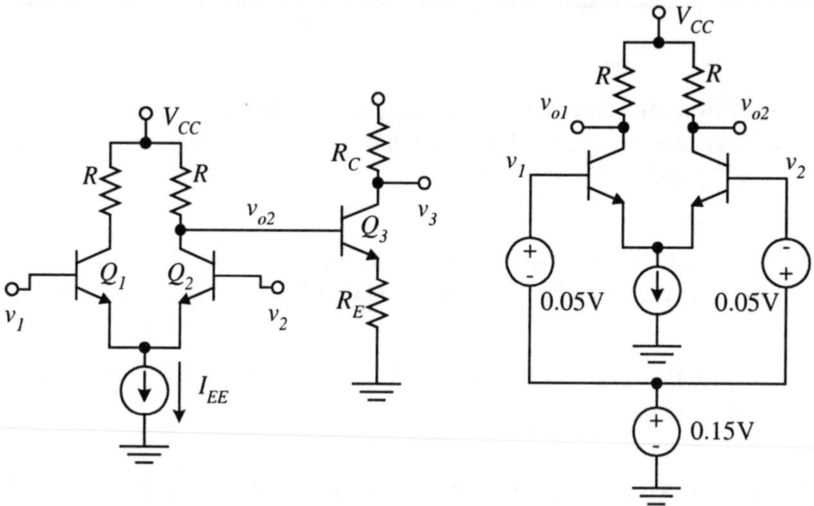

Figure P9.7 **Figure P9.8**

9.8 Calculate v_{o1} and v_{o2} for the input voltages as shown in Fig. P9.8. A_d and A_c are the same as those in Problem 9.6.

9.9 Find A_c, A_d and the CMRR for the circuit of Figure 9.3 if $R_{C1} = R_{C2} = 3\ \text{k}\Omega$, $I_{EE} = 4\text{mA}$, $R_E = 2\ \text{k}\Omega$, $V_A = 60\ \text{V}$, $V_{CC} = 12\ \text{V}$ and $V_{EE} = 12\ \text{V}$.

9.10 Find A_c, A_d and the CMRR of the circuit of Figure 9.1 if $R_{C1} = R_{C2} = 4\ \text{k}\Omega$, $I_{EE} = 3\ \text{mA}$, $V_{CC} = V_{EE} = 12\ \text{V}$, $R_{EE} = 40\ \text{k}\Omega$.

9.11 Find A_c, A_d and the CMRR for the circuit of Figure P9.7 when R(current source) $= 50\ \text{k}\Omega$, $R = 6\ \text{k}\Omega$, V_2 is grounded, $I_{EE} = 2\ \text{mA}$, $V_{CC} = 8\ \text{V}$, $R_C = 2\ \text{k}\Omega$, $R_E = 500\ \Omega$ and $\beta = 200$.

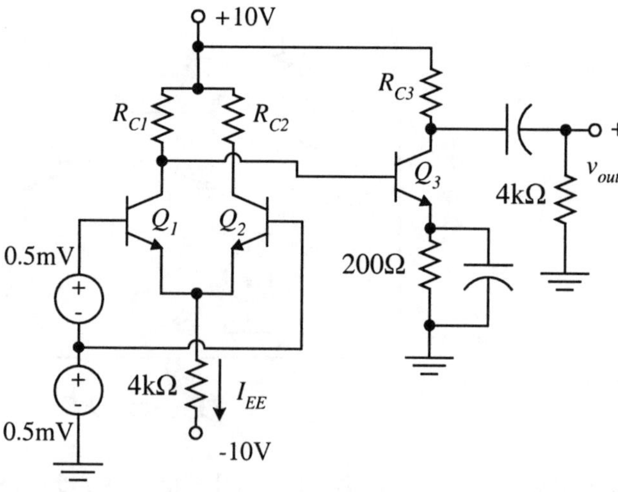

Figure P9.14

9.12 In the current source shown in Figure 9.3, determine the values of R_1 and R_2 if $V_{EE} = 10$ V, $I_{EE} = 2$ mA and $\beta = 200$. Make sure that V_{on} can be used to balance out the temperature variations of V_{BE}.

9.13 If the current source shown in Figure 9.3 has $R_1 = 20$ kΩ, $R_2 = 18$ kΩ, $V_{EE} = 15$ V, $R_E = 10$ kΩ, and $\beta = 200$, what is the value of I_{EE} for the circuit? What are the values of I_{C1} and I_{C2} if the differential amplifier is balanced? Assume that $V_{BE} = V_{on}$.

9.14 For the circuit shown in Figure P9.14, determine R_{C1}, R_{C2}, I_{EE}, A_c, A_d, v_{out} and the CMRR. Assume $V_{BE} = 0.7$ V and $\beta = 200$.

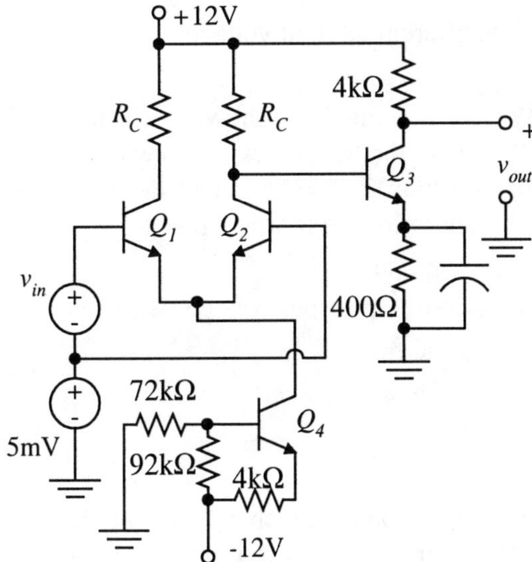

Figure P9.18

9.15 If the CE bypass capacitor is removed from the circuit in Problem 9.14, would A_c, A_d and CMRR change? If so, by how much?

9.16 If R_{EE} in Problem 9.14 were replaced with a temperature-compensated fixed-bias current source as shown in Figure 9.3, what would be the value of all the resistors and the CMRR of the circuit? Let $V_A = 100$ V and $V_{BE} = V_{on} = 0.7$ V.

9.17 If R_{EE} in Problem 9.14 were replaced with a simple current source [$V_A = 80$ V] what is the new CMRR? Determine the value for R_{ref}.

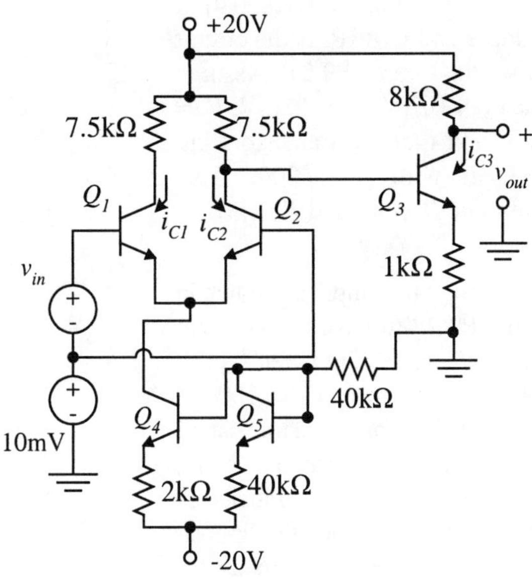

Figure P9.19

9.18 Design the amplifier shown in Figure P9.18 to have a maximum swing. Transistors have betas of 400, $V_{BE}(s) = 0.7$ V, $V_A = 100$ V, and $V_T = 26$ mV. Determine:

(a) R_C and CMRR

(b) Common-mode output voltage
(c) Differential output voltage
(d) Differential input voltage

9.19 Given the amplifier shown in Figure P9.19 where the transistors have betas of 200, $V_T = 26$ mV, $V_A = 50$ V, and $V_{BE}(s) = 0.7$ V, determine the following:

(a) I_{C1}, I_{C2}, and I_{C3}
(b) Maximum output voltage swing
(c) A_c and A_d
(d) $v_{in}(dm)$ and $v_{out}(cm)$
(e) CMRR(dB)

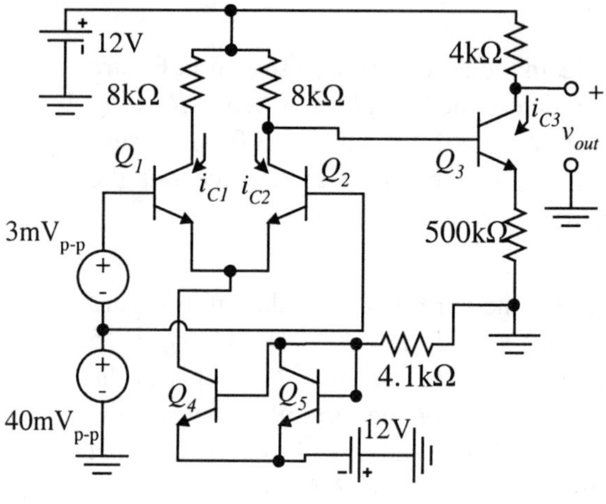

Figure P9.21

9.20 What would the change be in the CMRR of Problem 9.19 if a simple current mirror was designed to replace the more complicated fixed-bias transistor current source? Also what would the value of the reference resistor be?

9.21 Determine the differential-mode and common-mode output voltages and CMRR of the circuit shown in Figure P9.21. Assume that $V_{BE} = 0.7$ V, $V_T = 26$ mV, $V_A = 60$ V and that the transistors are identical with $\beta = 200$. Also determine $R_{in}(dm)$ and $R_{in}(cm)$.

9.22 Design the amplifier shown in Figure P9.22 to have a maximum output voltage swing when $I_{EE} = 2$ mA, $V_T = 26$ mV, $V_A = 100$ V, $V_{BE}(s) = 0.7$ V for single transistors and 1.2 V for Darlington pairs, $\beta(s) = 300$ for single transistors and 20,000 for the Darlington pairs, and $v_{cut} = 2$ mV peak-to-peak. Determine the following:

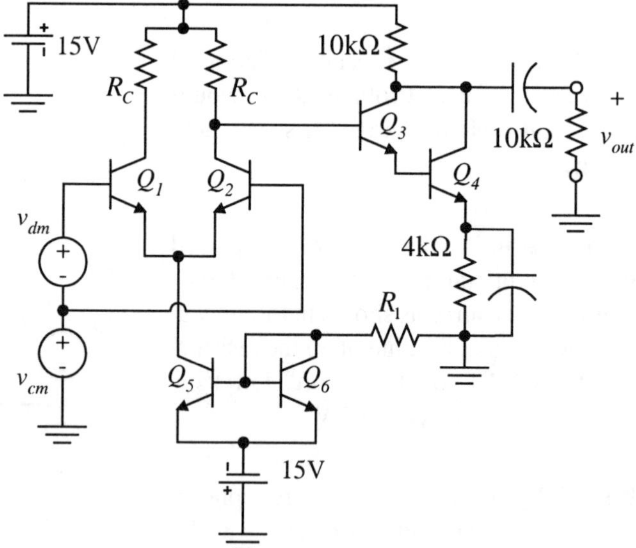

Figure P9.22

(a) R_C and R_1
(b) A_c, A_d, and CMRR
(c) Maximum undistorted output voltage swing

(d) Maximum input voltage swing

(e) Maximum common-mode output voltage swing

9.23 Design the amplifier shown in Figure P9.23 to have a maximum output swing when $I_{EE} = 2$ mA, V_T = 26 mV, V_A = 100 V, $V_{BE}(s)$ = 0.7 V, $\beta(s)$ = 300 and v_c = 2 mV. Determine the following:

(a) R_C and R_1

(b) A_c, A_d, and CMRR

(c) Maximum undistorted output voltage swing

(d) Maximum input voltage swing

(e) Maximum common mode output voltage swing

9.24 For the amplifier shown in Figure P9.24, determine R_1, R_2, R_3, A_c, A_d, R_{c1}, R_{c2}, and CMRR when $\beta(s) = 100$ and $V_{BE}(s) = 0.7$ V for the single transistors and $\beta = 10{,}000$ and $V_{BE} = 1.4$ V for the Darlington pair.

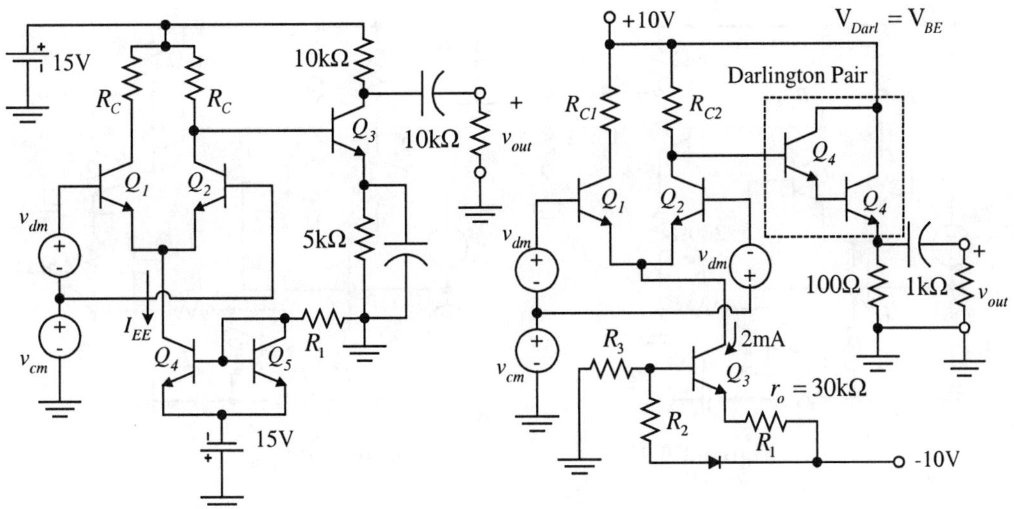

Figure P9.23 **Figure P9.24**

9.25 Design a Widlar current source for $I_{ref} = 20$ mA to be used in the circuit of Problem 9.14 when $R_{EE} = 40$ kΩ, $\beta = 200$, and $V_A = 50$ V. Determine the resistor values and change in CMRR.

9.26 Change the current source in Problem 9.23 to a Widlar current source using I_{ref} as 100 mA and determine the resistor values and the change in the CMRR when using the same type of transistors.

9.27 Design the amplifier as shown in Figure P9.27 to have a maximum output voltage swing when $I_{EE} = .5$ mA, $V_T = 26$ mV, $V_A = 50$ V, $V_{BE} = 0.7$ V, $\beta = 300$, and $v_{cut} = 20$ mV.

(a) R_C and R_2

(b) A_d, A_c, and CMRR

(c) Maximum undistorted output voltage swing

(d) Maximum input voltage swing

(e) Maximum common-mode output voltage swing

9.28 Analyze the amplifier shown in Figure P9.28 when the transistors Q_1 has βs of 200 and transistor Q_2 has a $\beta = 100$, $V_T = 26$ mV, $V_A = 60$ V, $V_{BE} = 0.6$ V, $v_{in}(dm) = .1$ mV, and $v_{in}(cm) = 5$ mV. Determine the following:

(a) I_C and I_{C1}

(b) A_c and A_d

(c) v_{out}(dm) and v_{out}(cm)

(d) CMRR (dB)

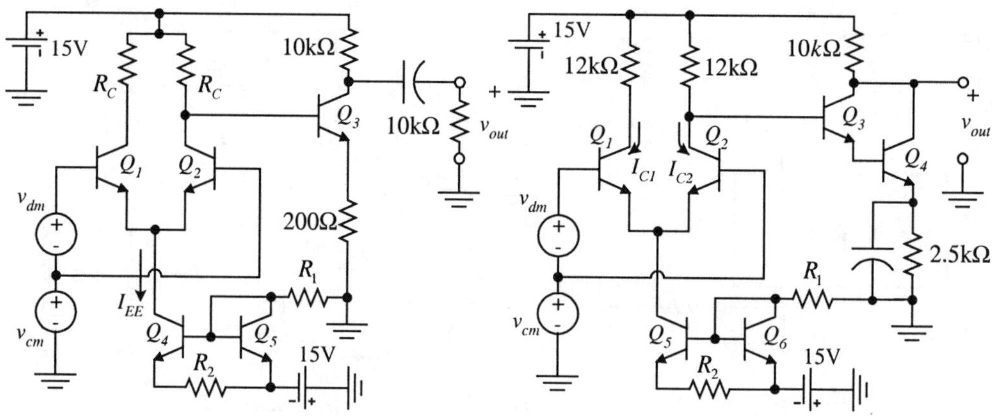

Figure P9.27 **Figure P9.28**

9.29 For the circuit in Problem 9.14, design a Wilson current source to provide I_{EE} to the differential amplifier. Assume $V_{BE} = 0.6$ V, $V_T = 26$ mV, $V_A = 60$ V, and $\beta = 200$. Also determine the change in the CMRR.

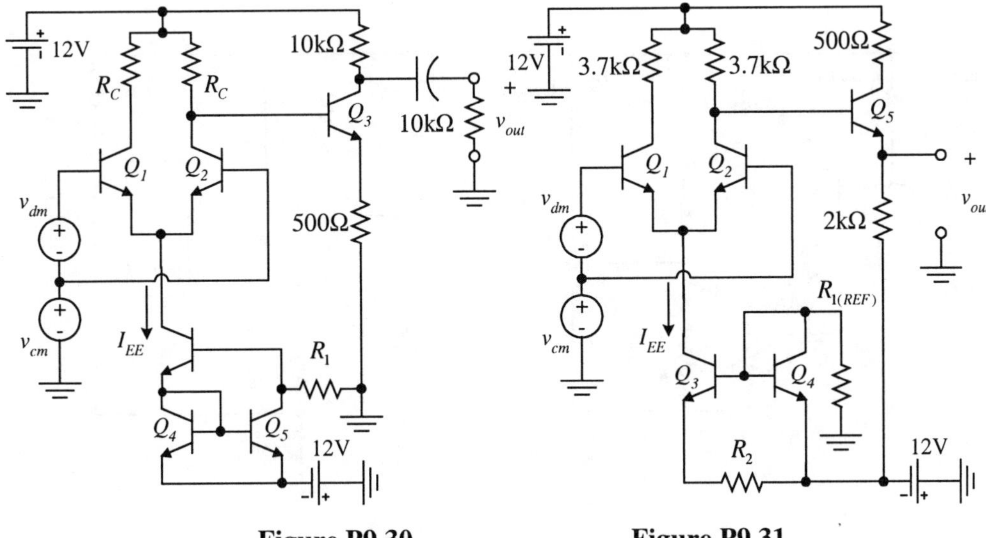

Figure P9.30 **Figure P9.31**

9.30 Design the amplifier shown in Figure P9.30 to have a maximum output voltage swing when I_{EE} = 1 mA. V_T = 26 mV, V_A = 50 V, V_{BE} = 0.7 V, β = 200 and v_c = 20mV. Determine the following:

(a) R_c and R_1

(b) A_c and A_d

(c) Maximum undistorted output swing

(d) Maximum v_{in}

(e) Maximum common-mode output voltage

9.31 Find the *dc* offset (when v_{in} = 0), A_d, A_c, and the CMRR of the circuit shown in Figure P9.31. Assume that β = 300 for all transistors, V_T = 26 mV, V_A = 80 V, and V_{BE} = 0.7 V. Determine the value of R_{Ref} and R_2 for I_{EE} = 2 mA and I_{Ref} = 50 mA.

Section 9.2

9.32 What is the output of the level shifter of Figure 9.7(a) if V_{BB} = 8 V, R_B = 5 kΩ, V_{CC} = 10 V, the current source provides 4 mA, R_E = 800 Ω, V_{BE} = 0.7 V and β = 100?

9.33 Design a level shifter to attain a 4 V offset using the circuit of Figure 9.7(a). Assume that R_B = 4 kΩ, V_{BB} = 8 V, V_{CC} = 12 V, V_{EE} = -12 V, β = 100, and V_{BE} = 0.7 V. Use a fixed-bias current source which provides 6 mA.

9.34 A direct-coupled multistage amplifier has a common-emitter amplifier for its last stage. The V_C for the CE amplifier is 6 V with an R_C of 5 kΩ. Design a level shifter to follow the CE amplifier and provide an *ac* output. The parameter values are V_{CC} = 10 V, V_{EE} = -10 V, V_{BE} = 0.7 V and β = 100. Design the current source to have a 5 mA output.

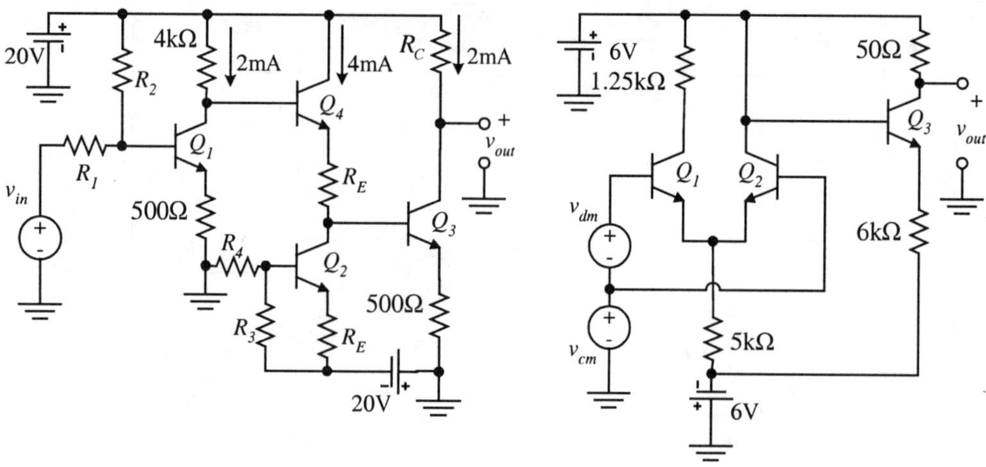

Figure P9.35 Figure P9.36

9.35 An amplifier has cascaded common-emitter amplifiers but to get the second amplifier to be biased correctly, a level shifter has to be placed between the amplifiers as shown in Figure P9.35. In this circuit, transistors Q_1 and Q_3 are the CE amplifiers while transistors Q_2 and Q_4 make up the level shifter. Design the level shifter to provide 1.7 V *dc* bias to the second CE amplifier and operate at $I_C = 4$ mA. The I_C values of the CE amplifiers are 2 mA. All transistors have betas of 200 and $V_{BE} = 0.7$ V. Determine the resistor values of the level shifter.

9.36 In the unbalanced emitter-coupled amplifier shown in Figure P9.36, determine the following when $\beta(Q_1 \text{ and } Q_2) = 200$, $\beta(Q_3) = 300$, $V_{BE}(Q_1 \text{ and } Q_2) = 0.7$ V, $V_{BE} = -0.6$ V, and $V_T = 26$ mV:

(a) A_d and A_c

(b) $R_{in}(dm)$ and $R_{in}(cm)$

(c) CMRR (dB) and R_o

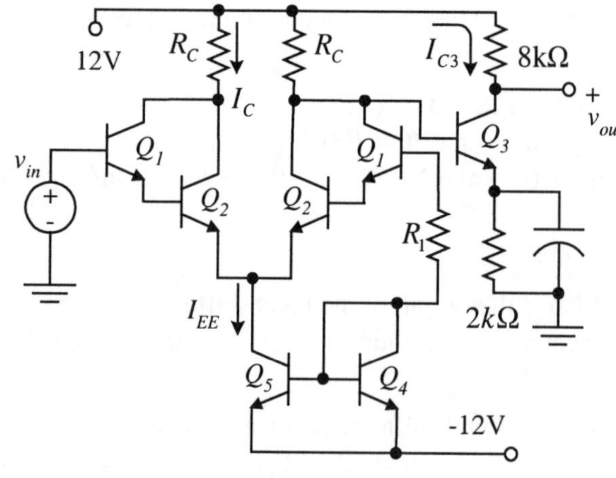

Figure P9.37

9.37 For the Darlington compound differential amplifier shown in Figure P9.37, design the amplifier for a maximum output voltage swing. Assume $V_T = 26$ mV, $V_{BE}(s) = 0.6$ V, $V_{BE}(\text{Darl}) = 1.2$ V, β(s) = 200, β (Darlington)= 20,000, $V_A = 75$ V, and $I_{EE} = 1$ mA. Determine:

(a) R_1 and R_C

(b) Undistorted output voltage swing

(c) A_d, A_C, and CMRR

(d) v_{in}(Maximum peak-to-peak)

(e) R_{in} to Darlington

9.38 Analyze the circuit shown in Figure P9.37 when $R_C = 15\ \text{k}\Omega$, $R_1 = 9\ \text{k}\Omega$, $\beta = 200$, β(Darl) = 20,000, V_{BE}(Darl)= 1.2 V, $V_{BE} = 0.6$ V, $V_T = 26$ mV, and $V_A = 60$ V. Determine the following:

(a) I_C and I_{C1}

(b) A_d, A_C, and CMRR

(c) Undistorted output voltage swing

(d) v_{in} (Maximum peak-to-peak)

(e) R_{in} (Darlington)

Section 9.5

9.39 Consider the modified op-amp model with $G = 10^5$; $R_i = 1\ \text{M}\Omega$; $R_{cm} = 200\ \text{M}\Omega$. Solve the network of Figure P9.39 for the resistance, R_o.

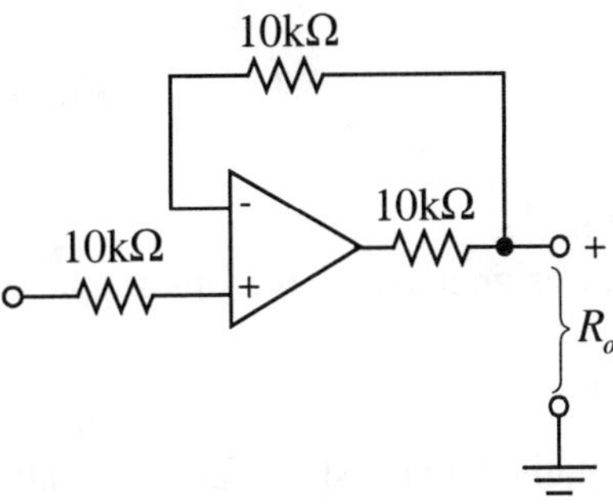

Figure P9.39

9.40 In each of the op-amp circuits of Figure P9.40, V_{io} = 10 mV, the input offset voltage temperature coefficient is 10 μV/°C, the temperature is 50°C, and R_i = 1 MΩ. Find the largest possible offset in v_{out} due to V_{io}.

9.41 For each of the circuits of Figure P9.40, the op-amp input bias current is 800 nA, the bias offset is 20 nA, the input bias current temperature coefficient is -10 nA/°C, and the input offset bias current temperature coefficient is -2 nA/°C. Find:

(a) The largest possible offset in v_{out} due to average bias current effects.

(b) The largest possible offset in v_{out} due to bias offset effects.

(c) The largest possible offset in v_{out} due to voltage offset bias current and bias offset combined.

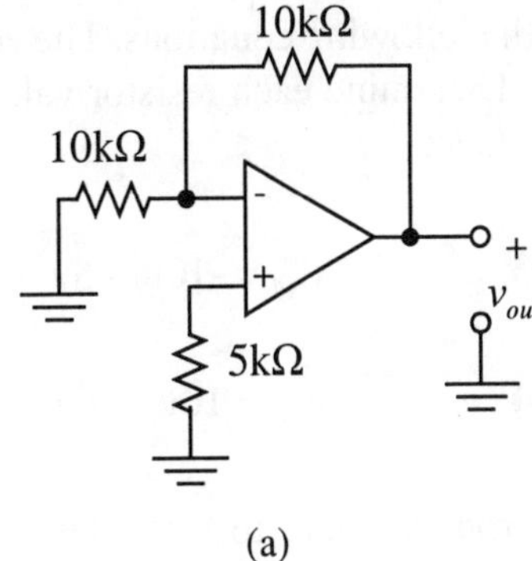

(a)

Figure P9.40 (part a)

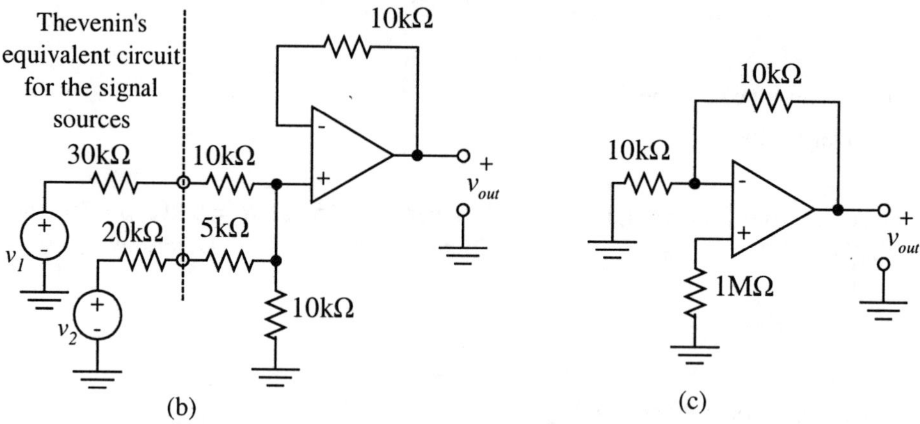

Figure P9.40 (parts b and c)

Section 9.9

9.42 Design a single 741 op-amp amplifier which will yield an output given by the equation,

$$v_{out} = 10\,v_1 + 6v_2 + 4v_3$$

The equivalent resistance at the negative and positive terminals is 10 kΩ. Determine each resistor value, the input resistance of each amplifier input, and the output resistance.

In Problems 9.43 and 9.44, design a single 741op-amp amplifier which will yield an output given by the following equations. The equivalent resistance at the negative and positive terminals is 10 kΩ. Determine each resistor value, the input resistance at each amplifier input, and the output resistance.

9.43 $v_{out} = -10v_1 - 5v_2 - 4v_3$

9.44 $v_{out} = 10v_1 + 6v_2 - 3v_3 - 4v_4$

In Problems 9.45 to 9.50, design single 741 op-amps that will generate the indicated output voltage, v_o, when the equivalent resistance at the negative and positive terminals are as shown in each of the problems. Determine each resistor value, input resistance at each of the amplifier inputs, and the output resistance. Draw the schematic and show the resistor values.

9.45 $v_{out} = 12v_1 - 10v_2 - 5v_3 + 6v_4$
$R_{eq} = 10\ \text{k}\Omega$

9.46 $v_{out} = 10v_1 - 6v_2 - 5v_3 + 4v_4$
$R_{eq} = 20\ \text{k}\Omega$

9.47 $v_{out} = 8v_1 - 7v_2 - 4v_3 + 4v_4$
$R_{eq} = 20\text{ k}\Omega$

9.48 $v_{out} = 4v_1 - 5v_2 - 6v_3 + 3v_4$
$R_{eq} = 20\text{ k}\Omega$

9.49 $v_{out} = 5v_1 + 4v_2 - 10v_3 + 2v_4$
$R_{eq} = 12\text{ k}\Omega$

9.50 $v_{out} = 3v_1 + 5v_2 - 8v_3 - 6v_4$
$R_{eq} = 8\text{ k}\Omega$

Section 9.10

9.51 Design a circuit using 741 op-amps which, from the differential voltages, v_1 and v_2, develops an output voltage,

$$v_{out} = 100v_1 + 50v_2$$

Input resistances should be balanced to ground and should be in excess of 100 MΩ. The maximum gain per stage will be limited to 20.

9.52 Design a circuit using 741 op-amps which, from voltages v_1 and v_2, develops a "balanced" output voltage,

$$v_{out} = 100v_1 - 50v_2$$

The output resistances should be less than 1 Ω.

9.53 Design a circuit using 741 op-amps which has a balanced input, a balanced output, a gain of 100, input impedance greater than 100 MΩ and output impedance less than 1 Ω.

9.54 Two differential voltages, v_A and v_B, each of which are balanced with respect to ground, are available as inputs. The v_A source has a Thevenin resistance between 10 kΩ and 210 kΩ, whereas the v_B source has a Thevenin resistance between 50 kΩ and 150 kΩ. Design a multiple 741 circuit to generate the voltage, with respect to ground without coupling between the two input sources. The bias current balance should be as good as is possible.

$$v_{out} = 10(v_A - v_B)$$

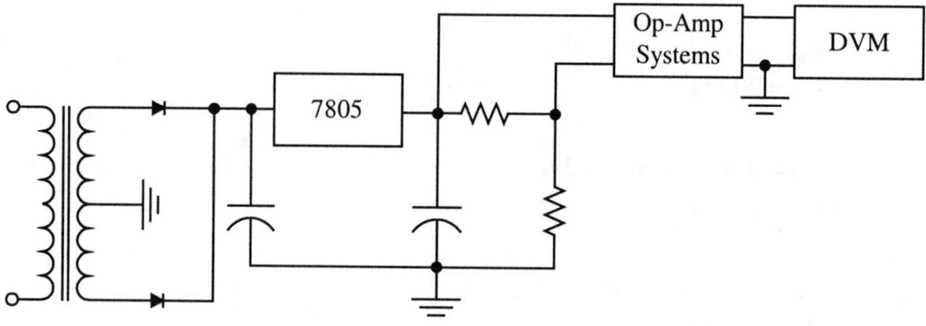

Figure P9.55

9.55 Design an op-amp system to measure the output current of a power supply, as shown in Figure P9.55 The voltage across a precision 1 Ω resistor is used to measure the current out of the power supply. This output current varies from 75 mA to 125 mA. The digital voltmeter (DVM) input must be in the range of 0.75 V to 1.25 V.

9.56 A balanced 3-phase WYE power system operates at 50 Hz. The magnitude of the line-to-line voltages is $V_{21} = V_{32} = V_{13} = 110$ V rms. Design an instrumentation system to monitor the voltage, V_{21}, as shown in Figure P9.56 and to yield an output voltage, V_o, given by the equation,

$$V_{out} = 0.1V_{21}$$

Use 741 op-amps and R_{in} must be greater than 100 MΩ. Select the proper value of V_{CC} for the 741 op-amps.

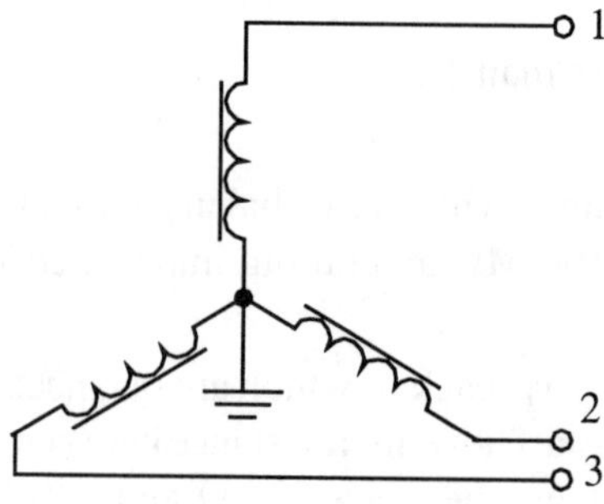

Figure P9.56

Chapter 10

Frequency Behavior of Transistor Amplifiers

We have examined a number of transistor amplifiers in the earlier chapters of this book. Unfortunately, life is not quite as simple as we have made it seem. During our earlier studies, we did not have to consider the frequency of the input. This was true for two reasons: Our transistor models did not contain any frequency-sensitive components (i.e., capacitors and inductors), and the capacitors in our circuits were assumed to be large enough to act as short circuits.

If we use proper terminology, we would say that up to now we have been concentrating on the *midband* range of frequencies for operation of amplifiers. We have done this so that the general nature of the amplifiers could be observed without the complications of frequency dependence. We now will consider the frequency-related behavior of these circuits.

When you finish studying this chapter, you will have the following knowledge and tools:

- Methods for determining the low and high cutoff frequencies for the various amplifier configurations.
- Low-frequency performance of the common-emitter, common-source, emitter-resistor, source-resistor, common-base, emitter-follower and source-follower discrete-component amplifiers.
- Modified models for BJTs and FETs that account for high-frequency effects.
- The Miller effect and its impact on the high-frequency performance of CE, CS, and differential-pair amplifiers.
- High-frequency performance of common-emitter, common-source, emitter-resistor, source-resistor, common-base, emitter-follower, source-follower, cascode and differential-pair amplifiers.

10.0 INTRODUCTION

We did not have to worry about frequency behavior in our earlier studies because we assumed that all frequency-dependent components were either open or short circuits. We now relax this assumption.

There are two types of capacitance which are intentionally placed in amplifier circuits: (1) *coupling* and (2) *bypass capacitors*. The reasons for placing these capacitors in systems are to couple stages together, isolate the *dc*, and reduce the effects of resistors in the emitter circuit. The desired condition for all of these types of capacitors is to be a short circuit for the entire frequency range of the applied signals. These capacitors are intended to be open circuits for *dc* bias voltages but allow all signal components to pass through them without attenuation.

Capacitors do not suddenly switch from a short circuit condition to an open circuit condition as the frequency approaches zero. Instead they gradually start acting like an open circuit as the frequency gets smaller. For this reason, system performance is degraded as the input frequency decreases.

In addition to the capacitances we intentionally place in the circuit, a second type of capacitance is present unintentionally. Whenever two conductors are separated by any non-conducting material, capacitance exists. Internal capacitance exists within semiconductors, between contacts, and between the conductors of the circuit configuration. As frequencies increase, these capacitances tend to "short out" the signal and decrease the gain. Most of these capacitances are very small and only affect the high frequency cutoff.

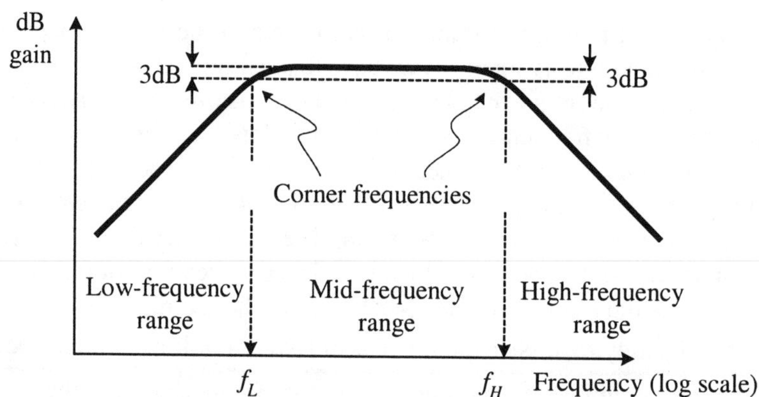

Figure 10.1 – Gain versus frequency

Amplifiers are analyzed as linear systems. The frequency response can be described by a complex function representing a magnitude and phase shift for each input frequency. In our analysis, we concentrate on a simple method, know as the *Bode plot*, which permits drawing frequency plots almost by inspection.

The typical frequency response for an *RC*-coupled amplifier is similar to that shown in Figure 10.1. Note that the maximum gain occurs for a *midrange* of frequencies and that the gain decreases at both low and high frequencies. At low frequencies, the coupling and bypass capacitors start to open and decrease the gain. At high frequencies, the "unintentional" capacitors start shorting out the signal.

The low and high limits of the midrange, f_L and f_H, are know as the *corner frequencies.* You could also show them as ω_L and ω_H if you wanted to use radian frequency (radians/sec) instead of linear frequency (Hz). These corner frequencies are defined as the points at which the current or voltage gain drops to 0.707 ($1/\sqrt{2}$) of its midrange value. This represents the frequency at which the output power decreases to one-half of its midrange value and is know as the *half power point.* The cutoff frequencies are also known as the *3dB cutoff frequency* since at these frequencies, the voltage or current amplitude has dropped 3 dB from the peak value.

If we tried to develop the equation for the frequency response of an amplifier, we would probably end up with a 5th or 6th order equation which is almost impossible to solve in closed form without the aid of a computer. This happens because we have to include all the internal capacitances in the transistor itself. Capacitors create poles in the transfer function of the system.

Although computer simulation programs such as Pspice or MICRO-CAP solve these higher-order equations, in performing a design you often need a more thorough understanding of the effects of each one of these capacitors. Luckily, we have the ability to break up the analysis in separate steps. For example we can break up the analysis into the low and high frequency regions. Then we can break those up into input and output circuits.

The transistor models used in Chapters 4 and 6 can be applied to the low- and mid-frequency ranges. By separating the low-frequency analysis and the high-frequency analysis, we can determine the frequency response. In the high frequency analysis, we will have to develop transistor models which include the capacitances between each pair of external contacts. We will show how these models are developed later in this chapter.

When you do "pencil and paper" analysis (as contrasted with computer simulation), you certainly want to simplify as much as possible without compromising the accuracy of the result. For example, suppose we were to examine the location of the various poles (roots of the denominator) of the transfer function. In examining the location of the poles affecting the *low-frequency* response, we look for wide separations. Assume, for example, that the separation between the highest-frequency pole and its nearest neighbor is two to three decades. In this case, the highest-frequency pole is considered the *dominant pole*, and we could eliminate the other poles from the *low-frequency* response analysis. These other poles would have little or no effect on the low frequency response. You will see examples of this shortly. This same approach can be used for the high frequency response, provided a dominant pole exists.

In analyzing the effects of the capacitances on the circuit, the location of each pole is determined by the time constant associated with that pole. We explore this concept in the problems at the back of this chapter. For now, we discuss techniques for estimating the low and high frequency cutoffs based on the various time constants.

If poles are widely separated, the effects of these poles can be considered separately. As an example, suppose there were two low-frequency poles, one at 10 Hz and the second at 200 Hz. Suppose we set the input frequency to 200 Hz. The pole at that frequency has the effect of cutting the amplitude to 0.707 of its midband value. The effect of the other pole is negligible at this frequency since the poles are so widely separated. The low-frequency cutoff is then determined only by the pole at 200 Hz.

If the poles are not widely separated, their effects interact and we need to combine the equations to find the cutoff frequency. Let's look at the actual procedure for estimating the cutoff.

First, find the time constant associated with each capacitor: When finding time constants, we begin by setting all independent sources to zero (i.e., short circuit voltage sources and open current sources). Then select one of the capacitors and eliminate all other capacitors in the circuit. The manner in which you eliminate these other capacitors depends on whether the capacitors are in series or parallel. For the low-frequency analysis, capacitors in series are short circuited (these are typically large coupling capacitors), and those in parallel are open circuited (these are typically small intrinsic capacitors).

Now that you have a circuit with only one capacitor and a combination of resistors, you need only find the Thevenin (equivalent) resistance across the capacitor terminals. The product of the resistance with the capacitance gives the time constant.

Determine cutoff frequencies from the time constants: The reciprocal of each time constant represents the frequency associated with that pole. In determining the low frequency cutoff, we examine the various frequencies associated with the series capacitors. If the frequencies are widely separated, the low-frequency cutoff is approximately equal to the highest of these frequencies. If the frequencies are not widely separated, the effects of the poles will interact and the low-frequency cutoff will be higher than the highest of these frequencies. For example, if one pole is at 90 Hz and another at 100 Hz, the response will be down by more than 3 dB at 100 Hz (i.e., the pole at 100 Hz contributes -3dB while the pole at 90 Hz contributes an additional attenuation). To a first approximation, the low-frequency cutoff can be found by taking the square root of the sum of the squares of the two highest poles. For the 90 Hz-100 Hz example, the cutoff is at 134 Hz. (We explore the validity of this approximation in the problems at the back of this chapter).

A similar approach is used for the high-frequency cutoff. If the poles associated with the parallel capacitors are widely separated, the high-frequency cutoff is approximately equal to the lowest frequency associated with the poles. If the frequencies are not widely separated, the analysis is more complex. The cutoff will be below the lowest of the frequencies. There is *no simple approximation* comparable to that for the low-frequency cutoff.

EXAMPLE 10.1

Determine the low-frequency cutoff and the high-frequency cutoff for the circuit shown in Figure 10.2.

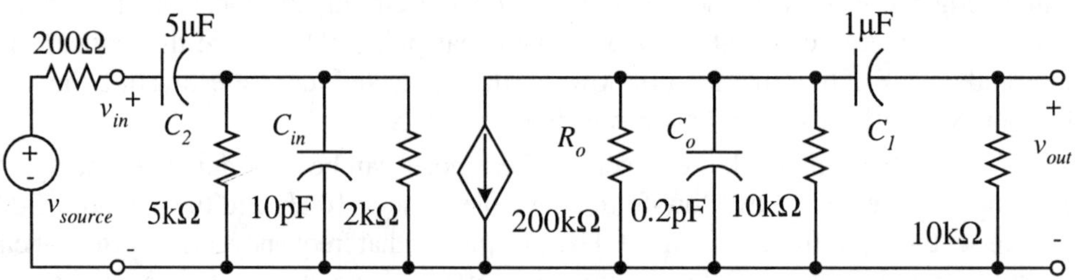

Figure 10.2 – Circuit for Example 10.1

Solution: We first find the various time constants. We short out the voltage input source and then we identify the capacitors in the circuit. C_1 and C_2 are series capacitors in the signal loop while capacitors C_{in} and C_o are shunt (parallel) capacitors. While looking at C_1, we short C_2 and open C_{in} and C_o. The resistance in the discharge path of C_1 is $200\text{k}\Omega \| 10\text{k}\Omega + 10\text{k}\Omega = 19.5\text{k}\Omega$. Then the time constant is $RC = 19.5\text{ k}\Omega \times 1\mu\text{F} = 19.5$ msec. This corresponds to 8.16 Hz. To find the time constant associated with C_2, we short C_1 and open C_{in} and C_o. The resistance in the discharge path for C_2 is $200\Omega + 5\text{k}\Omega \| 2\text{k}\Omega = 1.63\text{k}\Omega$. The time constant is $RC = 1.63\text{ k}\Omega \times 5\mu\text{F} =$ 8.15 msec. The frequency is then 19.5 Hz. Since these two frequencies are within one decade of each other we need determine the low frequency cutoff by taking the square root of the sum of the squares:

$$f_L = \sqrt{19.5^2 + 8.16^2} = 21.1 \quad \text{Hz}$$

For the high-frequency cutoff of the circuit, we start by shorting all the series capacitors and opening the capacitors that we are not working with. Thus, to find the frequency of the pole for C_{in}, we short out C_1 and C_2 and open C_o. The resistance in the discharge path of C_{in} is $200\Omega \| 5k\Omega \| 2k\Omega = 175\Omega$. The time constant is $175\Omega \times 10pF = 0.00175$ μsec and the frequency is 90.8 MHz. Now looking at C_o, we have to open C_{in} and short C_1 and C_2. The resistance in the discharge path of C_o is $200k\Omega \| 10k\Omega \| 10k\Omega = 4.87k\Omega$. Then the time constant is $0.2pF \times 4.87k\Omega$ = 0.000974 μsec, and the frequency is 163 MHz. We can only say in this case that the high-frequency cutoff is less than 90.8 MHz since the second pole is within one decade of the first. This causes interaction between the poles resulting in the cutoff frequency to be slightly lower than the lowest of the high frequencies. This approach to determining the frequencies is a very good way to get the approximate cutoff frequencies of a circuit. We will see later in our frequency evaluations that in some circuits this technique is quite accurate.

10.1 LOW-FREQUENCY RESPONSE OF AMPLIFIERS

Coupling capacitors in multistage amplifiers are used in order to avoid the problems of the interaction of the *dc* levels of one stage controlling the biasing of the next stage. These capacitors isolate the *dc* voltages from one stage to the next while passing the *ac* signal. Other amplifiers have direct coupling between amplifier stages and do not have coupling capacitors. These types of amplifiers are more difficult to design due to the interaction of the biasing levels - they are usually only found on integrated circuits. This is due to the fact that capacitors take up too much space on an integrated circuit. Amplifiers without coupling capacitors have no series capacitors in the signal loop. Therefore the low-frequency cutoff is zero - the Bode plot is flat all the way to zero.

10.1.1 Low-Frequency Response of Emitter-Resistor Amplifier

Figure 10.3(a) shows an emitter-resistor amplifier with coupling capacitors C_1 and C_2. The equivalent circuit is shown in Figure 10.3(b). As the frequency decreases toward zero, both of the coupling capacitors approach open-circuit conditions and the input signal is attenuated. We shall find the voltage and current gains for the entire circuit (including the capacitors). The input impedance is found directly from Figure 10.3(b):

$$Z_{in} = R_{source} + \frac{1}{sC_2} + R_{in} = R_{source} + \frac{1}{sC_2} + R_B \| \left[r_\pi + (1+\beta) R_E \right] \tag{10.1}$$

Where

$$R_B = R_1 \| R_2 \tag{10.2}$$

Note that the current in R_E is $(1+\beta)i_B$. That is why the resistor value must be scaled. In the following equations, we will approximate $1+\beta$ with β. The input current is the ratio of voltage to impedance:

$$I_{in} = \frac{V_{in}}{R_{in} + 1/sC_2 + R_{source}} \tag{10.3}$$

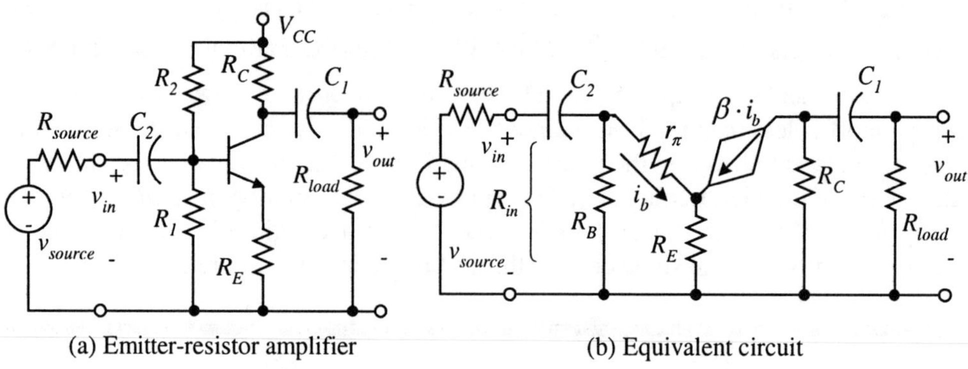

(a) Emitter-resistor amplifier (b) Equivalent circuit

Figure 10.3 - Emitter-resistor amplifier

We use a current divider ratio to find the base current.

$$I_B = \frac{V_{in}}{R_{in} + 1/sC_2 + R_{source}} \cdot \frac{R_B}{R_B + r_\pi + \beta R_E}$$

$$= \frac{V_{in}}{R_{in} + 1/sC_2 + R_{source}} \cdot \frac{R_{in}}{r_\pi + \beta R_E} \tag{10.4}$$

The last equality in Equation (10.4) results from recognizing that R_{in} is the parallel combination of R_B with $(r_\pi+\beta R_E)$. We can simplify the expression of Equation (10.4) by defining a time constant for the base resistor-capacitor combination. Calling this time constant τ_2, we have

$$\tau_2 = (R_{in} + R_{source})C_2$$

$$I_B = \frac{V_{in}}{r_\pi + \beta R_E} \cdot \frac{R_{in}C_2}{\tau_2} \cdot \frac{s}{s + 1/\tau_2} \tag{10.5}$$

Now that we have an expression for the base current, we can proceed to find the output voltage. We use current division at the output to find,

$$V_{out} = \frac{-\beta I_B R_C R_{load}}{R_C + R_{load} + 1/sC_1} \tag{10.6}$$

As in the case of the base current, we can simplify this expression by defining a time constant, τ_1, for the *RC* output loop. Thus,

$$\tau_1 = C_1\left(R_C + R_{load}\right)$$

(10.7)

$$V_{out} = -\beta I_B\left(R_C \| R_{load}\right)\frac{s}{s + 1/\tau_1}$$

We are now in a position to find the voltage gain for the amplifier. We combine Equations (10.7) and (10.5).

$$A_v = \frac{V_{out}}{V_{in}} = \frac{-R_C \| R_{load}}{r_\pi + R_E} \cdot \frac{R_{in}C_2 s^2}{\tau_2\left(s + 1/\tau_1\right)\left(s + 1/\tau_2\right)} \tag{10.8}$$

The current gain is found in a similar manner. We use two current dividers to find,

$$I_B = \frac{R_B I_{in}}{R_B + r_\pi + \beta R_E}$$

(10.9)

$$I_{out} = -\beta I_B \frac{R_C}{R_C + R_{load} + 1/sC_1}$$

The current gain is found by taking the ratio of output to input current. The equation has been rewritten so we could incorporate the previously defined time constant, τ_1.

$$A_i = \frac{I_{out}}{I_{in}} = -\frac{R_B}{R_B/\beta + r_e + R_E} \cdot \frac{s}{s + 1/\tau_1} \cdot \frac{R_C}{R_C + R_{load}} \tag{10.10}$$

Equations (10.8) and (10.10) are the desired results. We will be able to evaluate the low frequency performance by plotting these gains as a function of frequency. However, before plotting these results, we will take a moment to simplify the form of the equations. We define the *midrange gain* as the value of gain when the external capacitors are short circuits. This is the value to the right of the lower corner frequency on the gain plot. We need not go back and analyze the circuit with the capacitors shorted - we can derive the results directly from the final equations. If we let s approach infinity, the effects of the capacitors disappear. Equations (10.8) and (10.10) then become,

$$A_{v\,midband} = \frac{-\left(R_C \| R_{load}\right)R_{in}C_2}{\left(R_E + r_e\right)\tau_2} = \frac{-\left(R_C \| R_{load}\right)R_{in}}{\left(R_E + r_e\right)\left(R_{in} + R_{source}\right)}$$

(10.11)

$$A_{i\,midband} = \frac{-R_B}{R_B/\beta + r_e + R_E} \cdot \frac{R_C}{R_C + R_{load}}$$

$$A_{v\ midband} = \frac{-(R_C \| R_{load}) R_{in} C_2}{(R_E + r_e)\tau_2} = \frac{-(R_C \| R_{load}) R_{in}}{(R_E + r_e)(R_{in} + R_{source})}$$

(10.11)

$$A_{i\ midband} = \frac{-R_B}{R_B/\beta + r_e + R_E} \cdot \frac{R_C}{R_C + R_{load}}$$

We can now simplify the final expressions for the gains by dividing by the midrange gain (i.e., normalizing). This yields the simple results,

$$\frac{A_v}{A_{v\ midband}} = \frac{s^2}{(s + 1/\tau_1)(s + 1/\tau_2)}$$

(10.12)

$$\frac{A_i}{A_{i\ midband}} = \frac{s}{s + 1/\tau_1}$$

The frequency dependence is now obvious. The expression for normalized voltage gain has a second-order zero at the origin, and two poles. The expression of normalized current gain only has a first-order zero at the origin, and one pole.

EXAMPLE 10.2

Draw a Bode plot of the low-frequency voltage gain and current gain for the amplifier shown in Figure 10.4. Assume zero source resistance, R_{source}.

Solution: We need to find the Q point in order to find r_e. From the circuit, we find

$$V_{BB} = \frac{2200 \times 10}{2.2 \times 10^4} = 0.991 \text{ V}$$

$$R_B = 2.2 \text{ k}\Omega \| 20 \text{ k}\Omega = 1.98 \text{ k}\Omega$$

$$I_{CQ} = \frac{0.991 - 0.7}{1980/200 + 100} = 2.65 \text{ mA}$$

$$r_e = \frac{26 \text{ mV}}{2.65 \text{ mA}} = 9.8\ \Omega$$

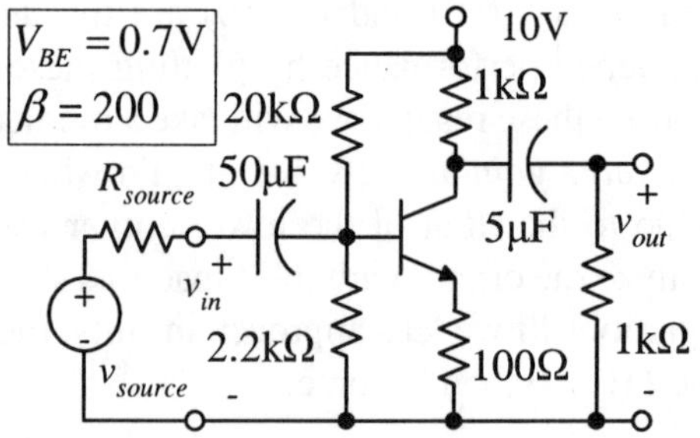

Figure 10.4 – Amplifier for Example 10.2

The input resistance and time constants are found next.

If the internal impedance R_{source} of the voltage source was significant, it would have to be added to the resistance, R_{in}, to determine the correct value of ω_2.

The midrange gains are now given by Equation (10.11).

$$A_{v\ midband} = -4.55$$

$$A_{i\ midband} = -7.65$$

Finally, the normalized gains are given by

$$\frac{A_v}{A_{v\ midband}} = \frac{s^2}{(s+100)(s+11)}$$

$$\frac{A_i}{A_{im}} = \frac{s}{s+100}$$

The voltage amplitude Bode plot starts at a slope of +40 dB/decade due to the second order zero at the origin. At the first corner frequency of $\omega = 11$, the slope decreases to 20 dB/decade. At the second corner frequency of $\omega = 100$, the slope changes to 0 dB/decade. The amplitude remains constant to the right of this point. This is shown in Figure 10.5. The actual curve deviates from the straight-line asymptotic Bode approximation by 3 dB at the corner frequencies.

The phase curve starts at 180° with respect to the normalized value. Starting at one-tenth of the first corner frequency (1.1 rad/s) the curve follows a -45°/decade asymptote until it reaches one-tenth of the second corner frequency, or 10 rad/s. At this point, the slope increases to a value of -90°/decade. At the second pole location (100 rad/s), the effect of the first pole disappears and the asymptotic curve has a slope of -45°/decade until we reach a frequency of 1000. Thereafter, the slope of the phase curve is 0°/decade.

The current plot is simpler than the voltage plot. The amplitude starts at a slope of 20 dB/decade because of the first-order zero at the origin. At the corner frequency of 100 rad/s, the slope decreases to 0 dB/decade, and the amplitude remains constant at 0 dB (note this is the normalized amplitude). The phase shift curve starts at -90° at low frequency. At 10 rad/s, the slope becomes -45°/decade until a frequency of 100 rad/s. To the right of this point, the phase shift goes to zero.

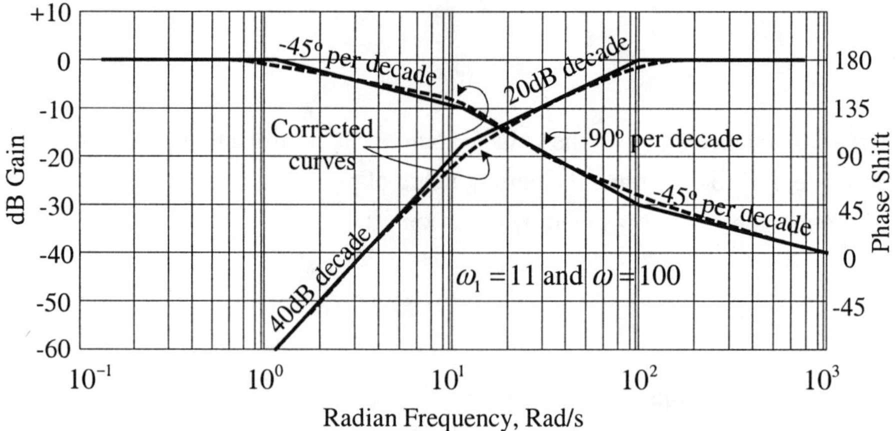

Figure 10.5 – Normalized Bode plot for Example 10.2

10.1.2 Design for a Given Frequency Characteristic

The previous section explored methods of *analyzing* the low-frequency response of an emitter-resistor amplifier. In this section, we explore techniques for *designing* an amplifier to achieve a specified cutoff frequency. The approaches we develop are applicable to any type of amplifier.

In designing for a specified low-frequency cutoff frequency, if the amplifier has only one corner frequency (i.e., pole of the gain function), we simply equate that pole location to the specified cutoff. In most cases, we will have two corner frequencies that interact with each other, so the design is more complex. We present three different design approaches. The specific approach applied in a particular design depends on the degree of separation of the two corner frequencies.

Approach 1: We let one pole produce the entire 3dB drop and set the other pole one decade lower in frequency (so it has little effect at the corner frequency). Thus, as frequency is reduced toward zero, the 3dB design requirement is achieved before the second pole takes effect.

Approach 2: In cases where the input and output resistances are approximately equal, we set the two pole corner frequencies equal. We allow each of the two poles to decrease the magnitude by 1.5dB at the specified frequency. The total decrease is therefore 3dB, as required by the design.

The normalized voltage gain is

$$\frac{A_v}{A_{v\,midband}} = \left|\frac{s^2}{(s+1/\tau_l)^2}\right| = \left|\frac{s^2}{(s+\omega_c)^2}\right| \tag{10.13}$$

The 3dB point occurs when this normalized magnitude drops to 0.707. Thus, with ω_c

representing the frequency associated with each pole (i.e., $1/\tau$) and ω_o the desired 3dB frequency, we have

$$\frac{\omega_o^2}{\omega_o^2+\omega_c^2}=0.707$$

$$\omega_c=\frac{\omega_o}{1.55} \tag{10.14}$$

Note that the actual pole corner frequencies are below the specified 3dB design frequency. If we were to set both poles to the design corner frequency, the drop at that frequency would be 6 dB instead of 3 dB.

Approach 3: Approach 1 separates the corner frequencies sufficiently so that the lower frequency can be ignored. Approach 2 sets the two frequencies equal. In contrast to these first two approaches, Approach 3 chooses equal capacitor values. This allows for interchanging of components, and often represents an efficient design approach.

Setting the normalized gain equal to 0.707 at the specified corner frequency, ω_o,

$$\frac{A_v}{A_{v\,midband}}=\left|\frac{(j\omega)^2}{(j\omega+1/\tau_1)(j\omega+1/\tau_2)}\right|_{\omega=\omega_o}$$

$$=\frac{\omega_o^2}{\sqrt{\omega_o^2+(1/\tau_1)^2}\sqrt{\omega_o^2+(1/\tau_2)^2}}=\frac{1}{\sqrt{2}} \tag{10.15}$$

Solving for ω_o yields

$$\omega_o^4=\omega_o^2\left(\frac{1}{\tau_1}\right)^2+\omega_o^2\left(\frac{1}{\tau_2}\right)^2+\left(\frac{1}{\tau_1}\right)^2\left(\frac{1}{\tau_2}\right)^2 \tag{10.16}$$

If both $1/\tau_1$ and $1/\tau_2$ are less than ω_o, we can neglect the last term in this equation, and solve for ω_o.

$$\omega_o=\sqrt{\left(\frac{1}{\tau_1}\right)^2+\left(\frac{1}{\tau_2}\right)^2}=\sqrt{\frac{1}{C_1^2(R_C+R_{load})^2}+\frac{1}{R_{in}^2C_2^2}} \tag{10.17}$$

We have substituted the earlier derived expressions for the time constants. If we now set the capacitors equal to a constant, C, as specified in this approach, we can solve for this capacitor to find,

$$C=\frac{1}{\omega_o R_{in}(R_C+R_{load})}\sqrt{R_{in}^2+(R_C+R_{load})^2} \tag{10.18}$$

where

$$R_1 = R_{source} + R_{in}$$
$$R_2 = R_C + R_{load}$$

Equation (10.18) is the desired result. Once again, if the source resistance, R_{source}, is significant in comparison to R_{in}, we will have to replace R_{in} with $R_{source}+R_{in}$ in the equations.

EXAMPLE 10.3

An emitter-resistor amplifier has $R_C = R_{load} = 2\ \text{k}\Omega$, $R_{in} = R_B = 5\ \text{k}\Omega$, and $R_{source} << R_{in}$. Determine the capacitor sizes that will yield a low-frequency cutoff at 20 Hz. Verify your result using a computer simulation program.

Solution: We illustrate the three approaches, but show the computer simulation only for the first.

Approach 1: We place one pole at the given frequency and the second pole one decade lower. Thus,

$$C_1 = \frac{1}{2\pi f\left(R_{load} + R_C\right)} = 2\ \mu\text{F}$$

$$C_2 = \frac{1}{2\pi\left(f/10\right)\left(R_{in} + R_{source}\right)} = 15.9\ \mu\text{F}$$

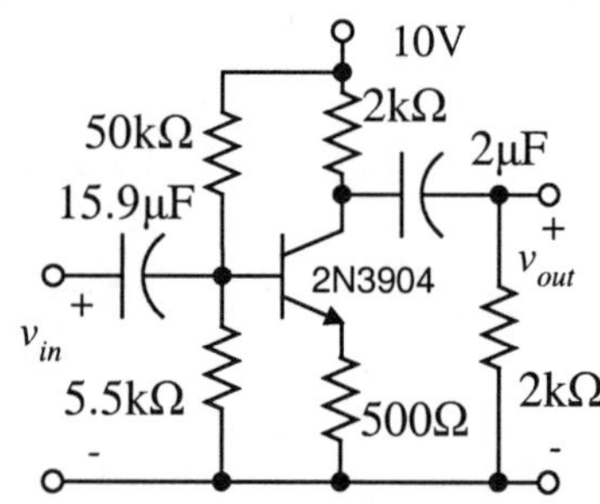

Figure 10.6(a) – Circuit for Example 10.3

We now perform the computer simulation to verify this result. Our first job is to configure the circuit from the given parameters. This involves choosing the resistor values not specified in the problem statement. To save time, we shall modify the bias circuitry used in Example 10.2 (see Figure 10.4) and scale the base resistor network by a factor of 2.5 to achieve the specified input resistance. We also select the 2N3904 transistor since this is a general purpose *npn* transistor in the computer library. The resulting circuit is shown in Figure 10.6(a).

We now perform an *ac* analysis using a range of frequencies surrounding the expected break point of 20 Hz. The result is shown in Figure 10.6(b). Note that the gain reaches a mid-frequency value of about 5.3 dB. The curve crosses the 3dB point, 2.3 dB, at 20 Hz, thus verifying the design.

Approach 2: We set both corner frequencies to the same value.

$$f_c = \frac{20}{1.55} = 12.9\ \text{Hz}$$

The capacitors are then found from the equations,

$$C_1 = \frac{1}{2\pi f\left(R_{load} + R_C\right)} = 3.08\ \mu\text{F}$$

$$C_2 = \frac{1}{2\pi f\left(R_{in} + R_{source}\right)} = 2.46\ \mu\text{F}$$

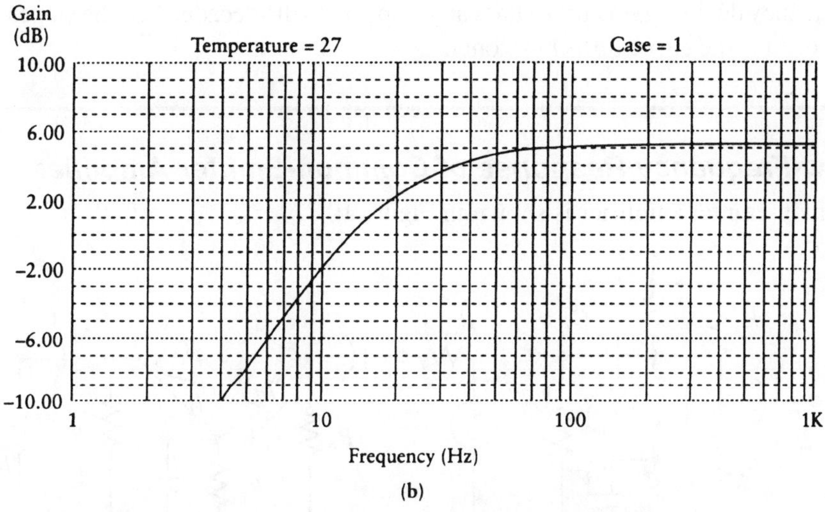

Figure 10.6(b) – Computer analysis

Approach 3: We set both capacitors equal in value. From the equation,

$$C = \frac{1}{2\pi f R_{in}\left(R_C + R_{load}\right)} \cdot \sqrt{R_{in}^2 + \left(R_C + R_{load}\right)^2} = 2.55\ \mu\text{F}$$

The two corner frequencies are given by

$$\frac{1}{2\pi\tau_1} = \frac{1}{2\pi C\left(R_C + R_{load}\right)} = 15.6\ \text{Hz}$$

$$\frac{1}{2\pi\tau_2} = \frac{1}{2\pi C\left(R_{in} + R_{source}\right)} = 12.5\ \text{Hz}$$

EXERCISE

E10.1 Determine the low-frequency response for the amplifier of Figure 10.3 when $C_1 = 4\ \mu F$, $C_2 = 2\ \mu F$, $R_1 = 10\ k\Omega$, $R_2 = 90\ k\Omega$, $R_C = 1\ k\Omega$, $R_E = 200\ \Omega$, $R_{load} = 2\ k\Omega$, $\beta = 100$, $V_{BE} = 0.7$ V, $V_{CC} = 20$ V, and $R_{source} << R_{in}$.

Answer: $\tau_1 = 0.012$ s; $f_1 = 13.3$ Hz
$\tau_2 = 0.0125$ s; $f_2 = 12.7$ Hz

The low-frequency decibel gain curve starts at a slope of 40 dB/decade. At f_1 the slope changes to 20 dB/decade. At f_2 the curve turns horizontal.

10.1.3 Low-Frequency Response of Common-Emitter Amplifier

The common-emitter amplifier is shown in Figure 10.7.

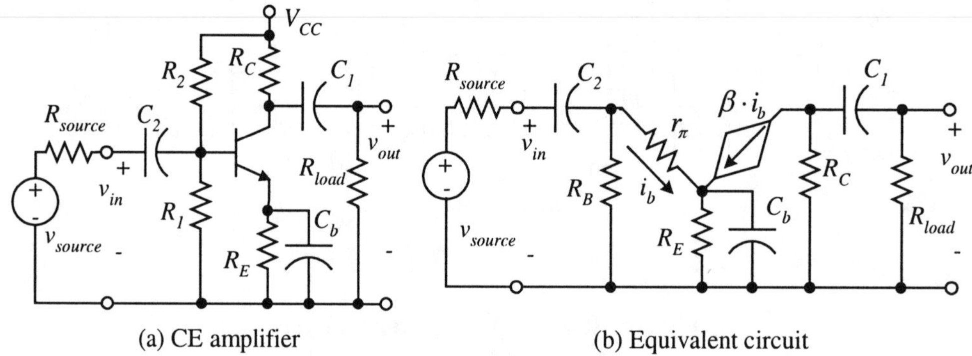

(a) CE amplifier (b) Equivalent circuit

Figure 10.7 - CE amplifier

A common-emitter amplifier can be thought of as an emitter-resistor amplifier where the value of the emitter resistor goes to zero. We can therefore adapt the equations of the previous section without having to re-derive them. Since the τ_1 and τ_2 equations do not include the emitter resistor, these equations for the CE amplifier are the same as those of the emitter-resistor amplifier.

$$\tau_2 = C_2(R_{in} + R_{source})$$
$$\tau_1 = C_1(R_C + R_{load}) \qquad (10.19)$$

Note that since R_E is zero, the value of R_{in} is

$$R_{in} = R_B \| r_\pi \qquad (10.20)$$

By referring to Example 10.1, we see that the time constants of the low-frequency end of the CE amplifier can be determined by looking at the equivalent circuit and determining the discharge paths of the capacitors.

One difference between the emitter-resistor and the CE amplifier is that the CE has an additional capacitor, the emitter resistor bypass capacitor. The effects of this additional capacitor are evaluated by letting C_1 and C_2 be replaced by short circuits (i.e., $C \to \infty$). To evaluate the frequency-dependent effects of the bypass capacitor, we solve for the voltage gain. The base current and output voltage are given by

$$I_b = \frac{V_{in}}{\beta\left(r_e + R_E \| (1/sC_b)\right)}$$

$$V_{out} = -\beta I_b \left(R_{load} \| R_C\right) \tag{10.21}$$

The voltage gain is given by the ratio of output to input voltage.

$$A_v = \frac{V_{out}}{V_{in}} = \frac{-\left(R_{load} \| R_C\right)\left(1 + 1/sR_E C_b\right)}{r_e\left(1 + 1/sR_E C_b\right) + R_E/sR_E C_b} \tag{10.22}$$

Note that we could have used h_{ib} instead of r_e since these two terms are identical.

Equation (10.22) can be considerably simplified by defining a midband gain and normalizing the expression, just as we did in the previous section. This will make the frequency dependence more obvious.

Letting s go to infinity, we find the midband gain to be

$$A_{v\,midband} = \frac{-\left(R_{load} \| R_C\right)}{r_e} = -g_m\left(R_{load} \| R_C\right) \tag{10.23}$$

In the final equality in Equation (10.23), we have recognized the fact that r_e is $1/g_m$. We can now divide Equation (10.22) by Equation (10.23) to find the normalized gain.

$$\frac{A_v}{A_{v\,midband}} = \frac{s + 1/\tau_a}{s + 1/\tau_b} \tag{10.24}$$

where the time constants are defined by

$$\tau_a = R_E C_b$$

$$\tau_b = \frac{R_E C_b}{1 + R_E/r_e} = \left(R_E \| r_e\right) C_b \tag{10.25}$$

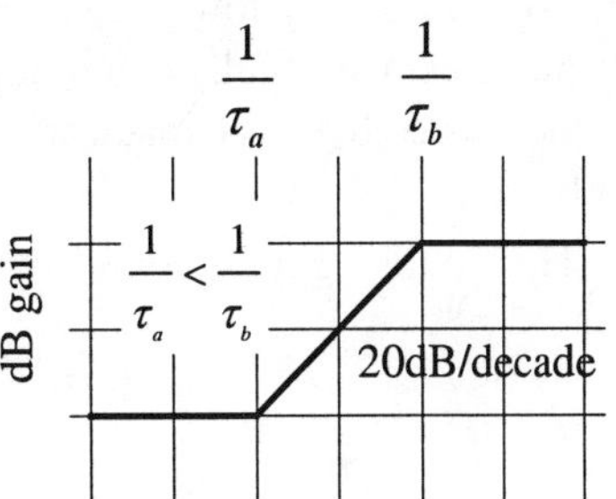

Figure 10.8 – Bode plot of CE amplifier gain

You can see from Equation (10.25) that τ_a is greater than τ_b. The Bode plot of the normalized gain in Equation (10.24) has two corner frequencies. The lower of these is due to the zero of the function. We illustrate the plot in Figure 10.8.

At low frequency, the plot starts as a horizontal line. At the corner frequency of the zero, $1/\tau_a$, the curve turns upward at a slope of +20 dB/decade. When the pole corner frequency is reached, the curve once again turns horizontal.

Before we combine these results with the effects of the coupling capacitors, we take a moment to observe that we could have found τ_b almost by inspection. We find the time constant associated with C_b using the technique established at the beginning of this chapter. The Thevenin resistance across this capacitor is given by

$$R_{TH} = R_E \left\| \left(r_e + \frac{R_{source} \| R_B}{\beta} \right) \right. \tag{10.26}$$

so the time constant is

$$\tau_b = C_b \left(R_E \| r_e \right) \tag{10.27}$$

just as we found in Equation (10.25).

The combined effect of the three capacitors, C_1, C_2 and C_b is three corner frequencies. Since one end of C_b is usually at ground potential and the working voltage is small, we can use a chemical capacitor (tantalum or electrolytic) which can be quite large in value. Therefore, we can easily place this pole one decade below the desired corner frequency, and the corner frequency is determined primarily by the effects of C_1 and C_2. In such cases, the analysis and design are identical to that of the emitter-resistor amplifier of the previous section.

10.1.4 Low-Frequency Response of Common-Source Amplifier

Rather than analyze each separate circuit configuration of the FET amplifier, we will begin with the most complicated configuration. In this way we can determine all the time constants. To apply the results to simpler configurations, we will only have to eliminate some of the time constants. The detailed configuration is shown in Figure 10.9. The value of the time constants does not depend on the type of FET. For purposes of analysis, we will use the JFET.

Since the input impedance of a FET amplifier is high, the input time constant is high thus resulting in a very low corner frequency. Since we are concerned with the highest of the low frequencies, we usually can ignore this input pole. The low frequency performance is determined by the source bypass capacitor, C_2, by the output coupling capacitor, C_1, or by a combination of both.

The voltage gain is found from a current-divider relationship as follows:

$$A_v = \frac{V_{out}}{V_{in}} = -\frac{R_{load} R_D}{R_{load} + R_D + 1/sC_1} \cdot \frac{V_{gs}\, g_m}{V_{in}} \tag{10.28}$$

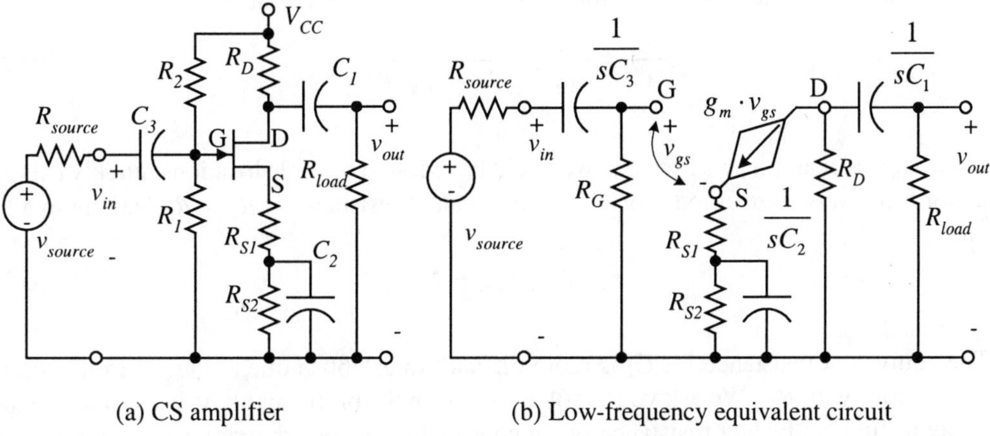

(a) CS amplifier (b) Low-frequency equivalent circuit

Figure 10.9 – Single-stage FET amplifier

Writing a loop equation around the gate-to-source loop yields (neglecting i_{in}),

$$V_{gs} = V_{in} - g_m V_{gs}\left(R_{S1} + R_{S2} \| (1/sC_2)\right)$$

$$= \frac{V_{in}}{1 + g_m\left(R_{S1} + R_{S2} \| (1/sC_2)\right)} \tag{10.29}$$

Combining Equations (10.28) and (10.29) yields the complicated-looking expression,

$$A_v = \frac{-R_{load}\, R_D\, sC_1}{sC_1\left(R_{load} + R_D\right) + 1} \cdot \frac{g_m}{1 + g_m R_{S1} + \dfrac{g_m R_{S2}}{sC_2 R_{S2} + 1}} \tag{10.30}$$

We can simplify this by normalizing and defining three time constants. The midband gain [which is found either directly from the circuit by shorting capacitors, or from Equation (10.30) by letting s approach infinity] and time constants are given by

$$\begin{aligned} A_{v\,midband} &= \frac{-g_m\left(R_D \| R_{load}\right)}{1 + g_m R_{S1}} \\ \tau_1 &= C_1\left(R_{load} + R_D\right) \\ \tau_2 &= C_2 R_{S2} \\ \tau_3 &= C_2\left(R_{S2} \left\| \left[R_{S1} + \frac{1}{g_m}\right]\right.\right) \end{aligned} \tag{10.31}$$

The normalized gain then reduces to the simpler expression of Equation (10.32).

$$\frac{A_v}{A_{vm}} = \frac{\tau_1 \tau_3}{\tau_2} \cdot \frac{s}{\tau_1 s + 1} \cdot \frac{\tau_2 s + 1}{\tau_3 s + 1} \qquad (10.32)$$

Before doing an example, we note that we could have found the pole locations quickly using the capacitor time constant method. For C_1, the equivalent resistance is $R_{load}+R_D$ leading to a time constant,

$$\tau_1 = C_1 (R_{load} + R_D) \qquad (10.33)$$

The equivalent resistance for C_2 is more difficult to establish due to the controlled current source in series with R_{S1}. We ask you to solve for this in the problems at the back of the chapter. One way to find equivalent resistance when controlled sources are present is to impose a test voltage source, measure the resulting current, and take the ratio.

In most designs, C_3 is chosen to set the corner frequency one decade below the design frequency so that it does not affect the response. This is done since the input circuit has a large resistance ($R_{source}+R_{in}$).

EXAMPLE 10.4

For the FET amplifier of Figure 10.9, select capacitor values so that the low-frequency 3dB point is at 20 Hz. The parameter values are given as: $R_{S1} = 100\ \Omega$, $R_{S2} = 200\ \Omega$, $R_D = 3\ \text{k}\Omega$, $R_{load} = 40\ \text{k}\Omega$, $R_1 = 1\ \text{M}\Omega$, R_2 approaches infinity, $I_D = 3.33$ mA, $V_{GS} = -1$ V, $V_{DS} = 10$ V, and $g_m = 2\times10^{-3}\ (\Omega)^{-1}$. Assume $R_{source} << R_{in}$.

Solution: We solve for the three time constants using Equation (10.31).

$$\tau_1 = C_1(43\ \text{k}\Omega)$$

$$\tau_2 = C_2(200\ \Omega)$$

$$\tau_3 = C_2(150\Omega)$$

We have a lot of leeway in designing this amplifier. There are two zeros and two poles in the response characteristic, and only the low frequency cutoff is specified. Since we have so many possible choices, let's simplify the design by letting one of the zeros cancel one of the poles. That is, we let

$$\tau_1 = \tau_2$$

$$C_2(200\ \Omega) = C_1(43\ \text{k}\Omega)$$

This is one equation in two unknown capacitors. The normalized gain then reduces to

$$\frac{A_v}{A_{v\,midband}} = \frac{\tau_3 s}{\tau_3 s + 1}$$

Setting the corner frequency to 20 Hz yields,

$$\frac{1}{\tau_3} = 2\pi \times 20$$

$$C_2 = \frac{1}{150(2\pi)(20)} = 53\ \mu\text{F}$$

$$C_1 = \frac{C_2(200\ \Omega)}{43\ k\Omega} = 0.25\ \mu F$$

In order to find the remaining capacitor value, we look at the input circuitry. Setting the associated corner frequency to one decade below 20 Hz yields,

$$10^6 C_3 = \frac{1}{4\pi}$$

$$C_3 = \frac{10^{-6}}{4\pi} = 0.08\ \mu\text{F}$$

The design is now complete.

10.1.5 Low-Frequency Response of Common-Base Amplifier

The common-base amplifier is shown in Figure 10.10.

To evaluate the frequency response, we can either determine the time constants which affect the low-frequency response or we can perform the detailed circuit analysis. Using the simpler time constant approach, we start with C_1. The discharge path is through $R_C + R_{load}$ so

$$\tau_1 = C_1\left(R_C + R_{load}\right) \tag{10.34}$$

At C_2, the time constant is given by

$$\tau_2 = C_2\left[R_{source} + R_E \,\Big\|\, \left(r_e + {R_B}/{\beta}\right)\right] \tag{10.35}$$

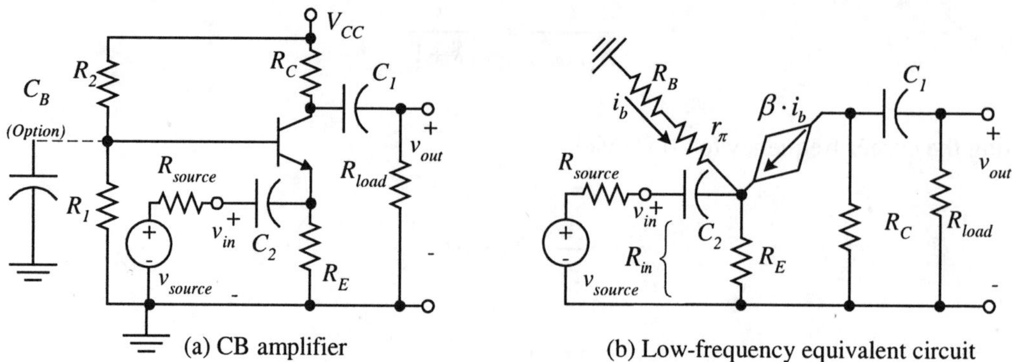

Figure 10.10 Common-base amplifier

τ_1 is usually larger than τ_2. Therefore we allow the 3dB point to occur at the input circuit to keep the capacitor sizes reasonable. Remember the input resistance of the CB amplifier is relatively small. It is therefore reasonable to expect the low-frequency cutoff of the amplifier to be controlled by the input. In design, we decrease the effect of the output circuit by setting its corner frequency to one decade below the specified lower frequency limit. When R_B is bypassed, R_B drops out of Equation (10.35) making τ_2 much easier to calculate. However, we have to now size the bypass capacitor. The new equation can be determined from the circuit as follows:

$$\tau_3 = C_B\left\{R_B \left\| \left[r_\pi + \beta\left(R_{source} \| R_E\right)\right]\right.\right\} \qquad (10.36)$$

10.1.6 Low-Frequency Response of Emitter-Follower Amplifier

The low-frequency characteristic of the EF amplifier is similar to the CB amplifier - there are two time constants but one has a much smaller resistance associated with it than the other. Figure 10.11(a) shows the EF amplifier circuit and Figure 10.11(b) shows the equivalent circuit.

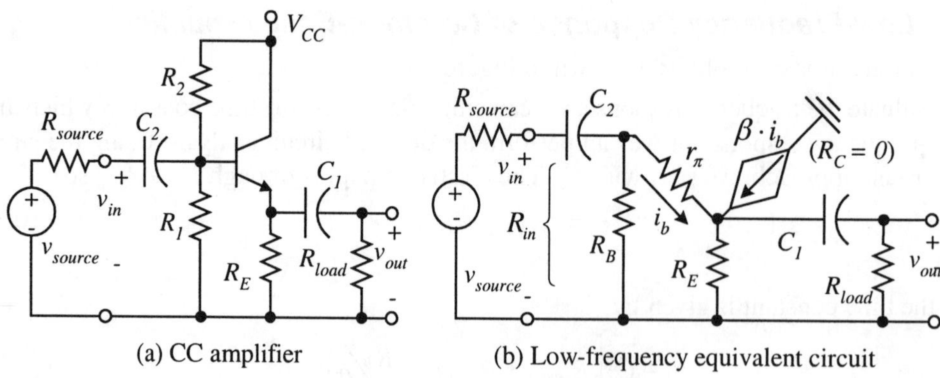

Figure 10.11 – EF amplifier

From this circuit we identify the discharge path for C_1 to find the time constant

$$\tau_1 = C_1\left\{R_{load} + R_E \middle\| \left[r_e + \left(R_B \| R_{source}\right)/\beta\right]\right\} \tag{10.37}$$

For C_2, the discharge path is through $R_{source} + R_{in}$, so the time constant is

$$\tau_2 = C_2\left(R_{source} + R_{in}\right) \tag{10.38}$$

In an EF amplifier, R_{in} is much larger than the output resistance. The input time constant is therefore larger than the output time constant so we can allow the 3dB loss to be determined by the output circuit. That is, the break frequency due to the input circuit occurs at a lower frequency than that of the output circuit. The design limitation (i.e., lowest useable frequency) is then set by the output circuitry. This approach results in capacitor sizes that are as low as possible. We design the input capacitor-resistor combination to reflect no loss at the corner frequency. We do this by setting the input corner frequency one decade lower than the output corner frequency.

10.1.7 Low-Frequency Response of Source-Follower (Common-Drain) Amplifier

The source-follower (SF) amplifier is shown in Figure 10.12.

As was the case with its BJT counterpart (the EF amplifier) the SF amplifier has two time constants. Only one of these is of concern because the other is much larger (leading to a lower frequency break point). The input time constant is quite large due to the high input impedance of the SF amplifier and is given by

$$\tau_2 = C_2\left(R_G + R_{source}\right) \tag{10.39}$$

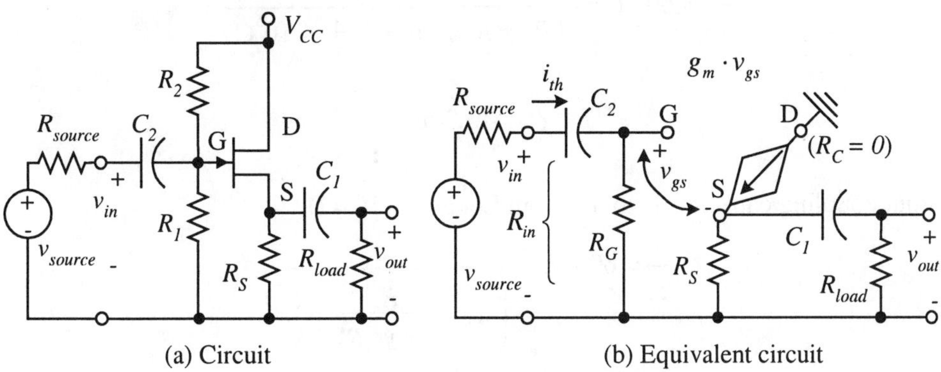

Figure 10.12 – SF amplifier

The equivalent resistance at C_1 is more difficult to evaluate. Since the controlled current source is connected to R_S, we cannot directly combine resistors in either parallel or series. We replace the capacitor by a Thevenin voltage and solve for the ratio of the Thevenin voltage to Thevenin current.

The loop equations for the input and output loops are given by

$$V_{gs}+\left(g_m V_{gs}+I_{TH}\right)R_S=0$$

$$V_{TH}-I_{TH}R_{load}-\left(g_m V_{gs}+I_{TH}\right)R_S=0 \tag{10.40}$$

The equivalent resistance is the ratio of voltage to current, so

$$R_{TH}=\frac{V_{TH}}{I_{TH}}=R_{load}+\frac{R_S}{1+g_m R_S} \tag{10.41}$$

The input time constant is then given by

$$\tau_l=C_l\left(R_{load}+\frac{R_S}{1+g_m R_S}\right) \tag{10.42}$$

EXAMPLE 10.5:

Determine the size of the coupling capacitors for a CD amplifier to produce a low-frequency cutoff of 300 Hz. The amplifier parameters are: $R_{source}=100$ kΩ, $R_{load}=1$ kΩ, $R_S=800$ Ω, $g_m=2$ m(Ω)$^{-1}$, and $R_G=300$ kΩ.

Solution: We design the input circuitry to have a cutoff one decade below the specified frequency (so it has virtually no effect on the amplifier cutoff). Thus, we set

$$\frac{1}{\tau_2}=60\cdot\pi=-\frac{1}{\left(R_G+R_{source}\right)C_2}=\frac{1}{4\times 10^5 C_2}$$

$$C_2=13.3 \text{ nF}$$

The output coupling capacitor is found from Equation (10.42).

$$\frac{1}{\tau_l}=600\cdot\pi=\frac{1}{\left(R_L+\frac{R_S}{1+g_m R_S}\right)C_l}$$

$$C_l=0.41\,\mu\text{F}$$

10.2 HIGH-FREQUENCY TRANSISTOR MODELS

The low-frequency response of transistor circuits depends on the *external* capacitors used for coupling and bypass. The high frequency response depends on the *internal* capacitance of the wiring and of the transistor. These capacitances are modeled as shunt capacitance in the signal loop. We will enhance the simplified transistor models studied in Chapters 4, 5 and 6 by adding these capacitances.

The capacitances which affect the high-frequency response, exist between the terminals of the device. We can view the capacitance as being in series with the equivalent (Thevenin) resistance of the associated circuitry.

We begin by examining the simple RC circuit of Figure 10.13.

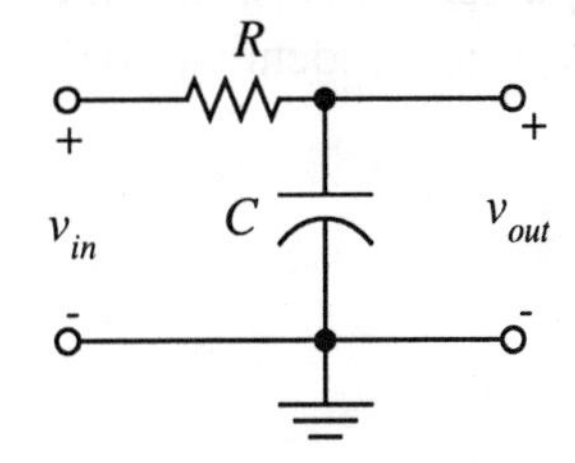

Figure 10.13 – RC circuit

As the frequency of the input increases, the output signal decreases in amplitude at -20 dB/decade. The input-output relationship is given by

$$\frac{V_{out}}{V_{in}} = \frac{1}{j\omega RC + 1} = \frac{1}{j\omega\tau + 1} \tag{10.43}$$

In Equation. (10.43), τ is the time constant and is given by RC. The equation only reflects the high-frequency performance. The coupling and bypass capacitors are not considered here since they are assumed to be short circuits at high frequency.

10.2.1 Miller Theorem

In developing the high frequency equivalent circuits for the transistors, we will find Miller's Theorem to be very useful. This theorem indicates that the equivalent capacitance of a circuit can be considerably higher than the actual capacitor values present in the circuit. To see this important result, we will examine Figure 10.14.

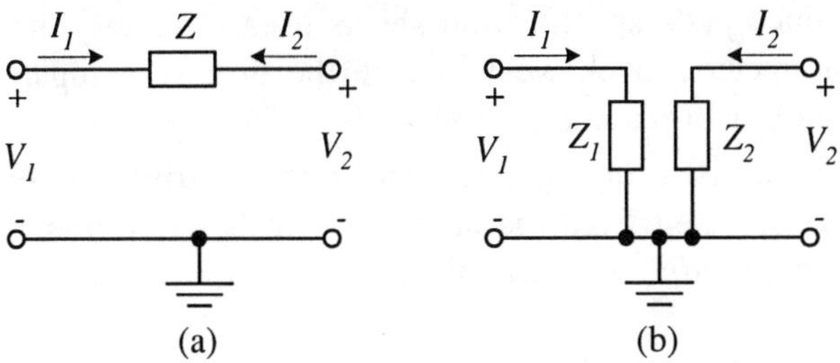

Figure 10.14 – Miller theorem

By appropriately selecting the values of the impedances, Z_1 and Z_2, in the circuit of Figure 10.14(b), we can make the two circuits behave identically. Thus, we can transform the element connecting input and output (as found in the hybrid-π model) into input and output elements. This simplifies the analysis. Let us first write the equation for I_1 of Figure 10.14(a).

$$I_1 = \frac{V_1 - V_2}{Z} = \frac{V_1}{Z}\left(1 - \frac{V_2}{V_1}\right) = \frac{V_1(1 - A_v)}{Z} \qquad (10.44)$$

In Equation (10.44), A_v is the voltage gain, given by the ratio V_2/V_1. Now for the circuit of Figure 10.14(b) to be identical to that of Figure 10.14(a), we set the currents equal. Thus,

$$I_1 = \frac{V_1}{Z_1} = \frac{V_1(1 - A_v)}{Z}$$

$$Z_1 = \frac{Z}{1 - A_v} \qquad (10.45)$$

In a similar manner, we solve for the current in the first circuit,

$$I_2 = \frac{V_2 - V_1}{Z} = \frac{V_2}{Z}\left(1 - \frac{V_1}{V_2}\right) = \frac{V_2}{Z}\left(1 - \frac{1}{A_v}\right) \qquad (10.46)$$

Setting the two currents equal and solving for Z_2 yields,

$$Z_2 = \frac{Z}{1 - 1/A_v} \qquad (10.47)$$

We will refer to the results of Equations (10.45) and (10.47) in the following analysis.

10.2.2 High-Frequency BJT Model

We evaluate high-frequency response of BJT amplifier using the hybrid-π model of Figure 10.15. Note that we have included the small capacitors which were ignored in the earlier low-frequency analysis. Since parts specification sheets usually specify the parameter values by referring to the h-parameter model, we will take the time to compare the hybrid-π model parameters with those of the h-parameter model.

The symbol B' in Figure 10.15(a) represents an internal (intrinsic) base terminal that does not exist physically. It is separated from the actual physical base terminal, B, by a distributed resistance, $r_{bb'}$, the *base spreading resistor*. We now define the resistances and relate them to the h parameters.

Base Spreading Resistance: The base spreading resistance, $r_{bb'}$ is related to h-parameter, h_{ie}, which is the input resistance with the output shorted. In the hybrid-π model, this is often referred as r_π. If we apply a short circuit between the emitter and the collector, we will get

$$h_{ie} \doteq r_\pi = r_{b'b} + r_{b'e} \| r_{b'c} \approx r_{b'b} + r_{b'e} \qquad (10.48)$$

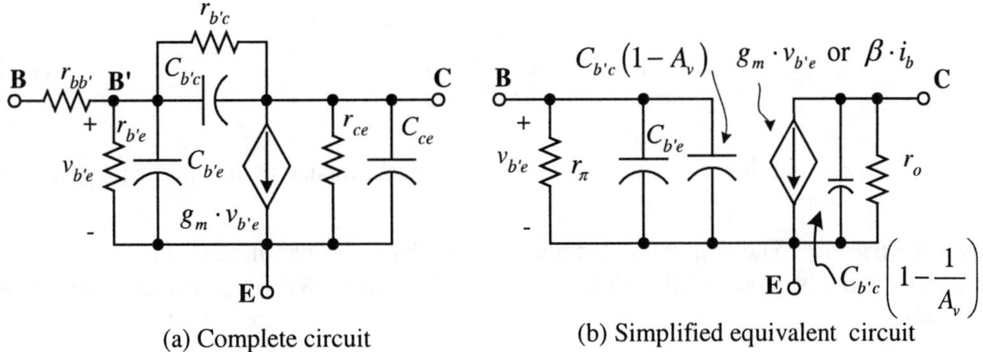

(a) Complete circuit (b) Simplified equivalent circuit

Figure 10.15 – High-frequency BJT equivalent circuit

The last approximation in Equation (10.48) is justified since $r_{b'c} >> r_{b'e}$. Note that the base-to-collector junction is reverse-biased; thus the resistance is large. Looking from the base, $r_{b'c}$ is typically on the order of $10\beta r_o$. The value of $r_{bb'}$ depends on the current but it is usually around 100 Ω or less.

Input Resistance: The input resistance, $r_{b'e}$ (r_π in the hybrid model) is approximated by the ratio

$$r_\pi \approx \frac{v_{b'e}}{i_b} \tag{10.49}$$

The short-circuit collector current, i_c, is found from Figure 10.15 by short circuiting the collector and emitter and obtaining

$$i_c = g_m v_{b'e} \approx g_m r_\pi \cdot i_b = \beta \cdot i_b = h_{fe} \cdot i_b \tag{10.50}$$

Solving this equation for r_π, we obtain

$$r_\pi = \frac{i_c}{g_m i_b} = \frac{h_{fe}}{g_m} = \frac{\beta}{g_m} = \frac{\beta \times 26 \times 10^{-3}}{I_C} = \frac{\beta V_T}{I_C} = \beta r_e \approx h_{ie} \tag{10.51}$$

Now let's turn our attention to g_m.

$$g_m \approx \frac{1}{h_{ib}} \approx \frac{1}{r_e} \approx \frac{I_C}{26 \times 10^{-3}} = \frac{I_C}{V_T} \tag{10.52}$$

Finally, the input resistance to the transistor is approximately

$$R_{in} \approx r_\pi \approx h_{ie} = r_{bb'} + r_{b'e} \tag{10.53}$$

Feedback resistance: The feedback resistance, $r_{b'c}$ is related to h_{re}, the reverse voltage gain as follows:

$$h_{re}=\frac{v_{b'e}}{v_{ce}}=\frac{r_{b'e}}{r_{b'e}+r_{b'c}}\approx\frac{r_{b'e}}{r_{b'c}} \tag{10.54}$$

Finally $r_{b'c} >> r_{b'e}$ and therefore $r_{b'c}$ is very large - in most transistors, it is in the megohm range.

Output Resistance: The output conductance is given by h_{oe} (h-parameter) in the manufacturer's data sheets, and it is determined with the input open-circuited. We see from the circuit of Figure 10.15 that

$$h_{oe}=\frac{i_c}{v_{ce}}=\frac{1}{r_o} \tag{10.55}$$

where r_o is V_A/I_C.

The hybrid-π model as used in Chapter 4 can be used to evaluate the high frequency performance of BJTs if three capacitances are added, as shown in Figure 10.15(a). The capacitance, $C_{b'c}$, is small (typically in the range of 0.5 to 5 pF). The *collector-junction capacitance* is the capacitance of the collector-base junction. Although it is a varying capacitance, it is usually considered as constant over a particular transistor operating region. The value of this capacitance appears in the manufacturer's data sheets as C_{ob}. The capacitance, $C_{b'c}$ varies depending on the voltage that appears across the junction. Most of the manufacturer's data sheets have graphs of the capacitance versus the voltage across the junction. (An example of this can be seen in Figure 16 of the data sheets for the 2N3904 in the Appendix).

The output capacitance, C_{ce}, is usually small. In many cases it is ignored since the input capacitance is so much larger.

The third capacitance shown in Figure 10.15 is $C_{b'e}$, which is the *base-emitter capacitor*. The value of this capacitor appears in data sheets as C_{ib}. This capacitance is the sum of the emitter diffusion capacitance and emitter junction capacitance. Because the former capacitor is the larger of the two, $C_{b'e}$ is approximately equal to the diffusion capacitance (also known as the *base-charging capacitance*). The value of $C_{b'e}$ is typically in the range of 1 to 200pF. We can estimate the value of $C_{b'e}$ as

$$C_{b'e}\approx\frac{g_m}{2\pi f_T}=\frac{1}{2\pi f_T\, r_e}=\frac{|I_{CQ}|}{52\pi f_T\times 10^{-3}}=\frac{|I_{CQ}|}{2\pi f_T V_T} \tag{10.56}$$

In Equation (10.56), f_T is the frequency at which the CE short circuit current gain is 0 dB. The *gain-bandwidth product* is approximately constant as the input bandwidth varies. When the gain is unity, the gain-bandwidth product is simply the bandwidth. Therefore, we estimate the value of f_T to be the same as the gain-bandwidth product. The value of the capacitance of $C_{b'c}$ between the base and emitter and the value of $C_{b'c}$ between the collector and emitter by using Miller's theorem as follows:

$$C_{M1} = C_{b'c}(1 - A_v) \quad \text{(input circuit)}$$

$$C_{M2} = C_{b'c}\left(1 - \frac{1}{A_v}\right) \quad \text{(output circuit)} \tag{10.57}$$

10.2.3 High-Frequency FET Model

The high-frequency equivalent circuit for a FET is obtained by adding three capacitors to the model developed in Chapter 6. This is shown in Figure 10.16.

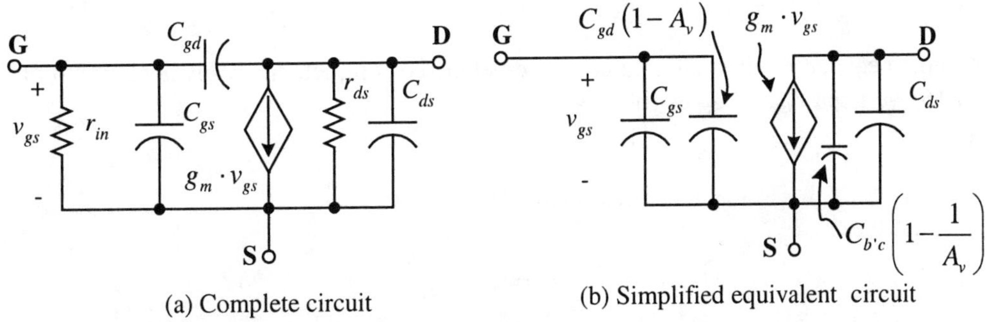

(a) Complete circuit (b) Simplified equivalent circuit

Figure 10.16 – High-frequency FET equivalent circuit

The capacitors are defined as follows:

C_{gs} is the capacitance between gate and source.

C_{gd} is the capacitance between gate and drain.

C_{ds} is the capacitance between drain and source.

We simplify the model in Figure 10.16(a) to obtain Figure 10.16(b). To derive this simplified model, we used Miller's theorem on C_{gd} and open-circuited r_{in} and r_{ds}, where r_{in} is the resistance between the gate and the source of the FET. r_{in} is usually around 1 to 10 MΩ for JFETs and even larger for MOSFETs so we usually consider the input resistance of FETs to be infinity so it can be ignored. The value of r_{ds} is usually much larger than the drain and load resistances connected to the drain so the value of r_{ds} has little effect on circuit performance.

We will now investigate how to determine these capacitances from the manufacturer's data sheets. The equivalent input capacitance, forward transfer capacitance, reverse transfer capacitance, and output capacitance as shown on the data sheets are

$$C_{is} = C_{gs} + C_{gd}$$
$$C_{fs} = C_{gd}$$
$$C_{rs} = C_{gd} \tag{10.58}$$
$$C_{os} = C_{gd} + C_{ds}$$

The input and reverse capacitors, C_{is} and C_{rs}, are usually shown in the manufacturer's data sheets as C_{iss} and C_{rss}. The second "s" is used to indicate that one of the ports is short-circuited.

The capacitors of Figure 10.16(b) can be approximately related to C_{rss} and C_{iss} by

$$C_{gd} = C_{rss}$$
$$C_{gs} = C_{iss} - C_{rss} \tag{10.59}$$

As noted earlier, C_{ds} is small and may be deleted. To complete the equivalent circuit of Figure 10.16, we need r_{ds} and g_m as follows:

$$r_{ds} = \frac{1}{\text{Re}(Y_{os})}$$

$$g_m = \text{Re}(Y_{fs}) \tag{10.60}$$

where

$$C_{M1} = C_{gd}(1 - A_v) \text{ (input circuit)}$$

$$C_{M2} = C_{gd}\left(1 - \frac{1}{A_v}\right) \text{ (output circuit)} \tag{10.61}$$

10.3 HIGH-FREQUENCY RESPONSE OF AMPLIFIERS

Now that we have developed the high-frequency transistor models, we can analyze the high-frequency response of all types of amplifiers.

10.3.1 High-Frequency Response of Common-Emitter Amplifier

Figure 10.17(a) shows the CE amplifier. We substitute the transistor equivalent circuit of Figure 10.15 to obtain the equivalent circuit of Figure 10.17(b). C_{ce} is very small and will be neglected

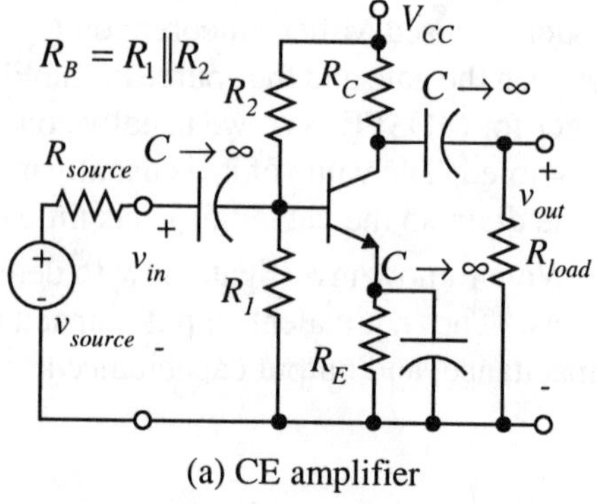

(a) CE amplifier

Figure 10.17(part a) CE amplifier

here.

We can make several simplifications as follows:

$r_{ce} >> \left(R_{load} \| R_C\right)$ so r_{ce} is deleted

$r_{b'c} >>$ other resistors so $r_{b'c}$ is deleted

$r_{bb'} << r_{b'e}$ so $r_{bb'}$ is deleted

We use Miller's theorem to reflect $C_{b'c}$ to the input (C_{M1}) and the output (C_{M2}). We further simplify the circuit by combining R_B and $r_{b'e}$ into a single resistance as follows:

$$r_{b'e} \approx h_{ie} \approx r_\pi \tag{10.62}$$

Then

$$R_{in} = R_B \| r_\pi \tag{10.63}$$

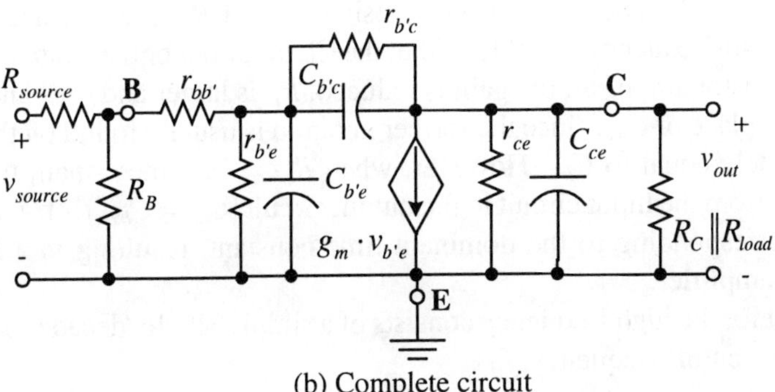

(b) Complete circuit

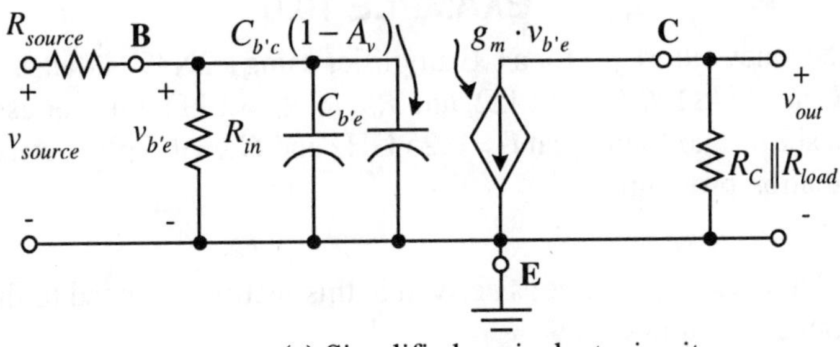

(c) Simplified equivalent circuit

Figure 10.17(parts b and c) - CE amplifier

We find that there are two RC time constants in the transfer function - one in the base circuit and the other in the collector circuit. The base circuit dominates because the input capacitance is so large (it is multiplied by A_V). This results from the fact that $|A_V|$ is usually greater than unity and the output capacitance is approximately equal to $C_{b'c}$. We can then ignore the output capacitance since the input capacitance is so much larger.

Looking at the input, we combine the two capacitors into a total capacitance, C_{in}, using the Miller capacitance, as follows:

$$C_M = C_{b'c}(1 - A_v)$$
$$C_{in} = C_{b'e} + C_M \tag{10.64}$$

The high-frequency cutoff, f_H, is determined from the input resistance and capacitance where the resistance is $R_{source} \| R_{in}$ the capacitance, C_{in}. Using the same technique as was used in Example 10.1, the high-frequency cutoff is the reciprocal of the RC time constant as follows:

$$f_H = \frac{1}{2\pi(R_{source} \| R_{in})C_{in}} \tag{10.65}$$

Since we generalized the above equation by using A_v and R_{in}, we can use this equation for determining the high-frequency cutoff for either the CE amplifier or the emitter-resistor amplifier. For the emitter-resistor amplifier, the gain is reduced, R_{in} is larger and the bandwidth is greater. We can use C_{ob} in place of $C_{b'c}$, since the former notation is usually found on the data sheets and C_{ob} is approximately equal to $C_{b'c}$. However, when R_{source} becomes small, the dominant time constant changes from the input circuit to the output circuit [$C_{M2} = C_{b'c}(1 - 1/A_v)$]. This then raises the frequency corresponding to the dominant time constant, resulting in a higher frequency capability of the amplifier.

The Bode plot for the high frequency consists of a simple -20 dB/decade roll off starting from the high frequency cutoff frequency, f_H.

EXAMPLE 10.6

Find the high-frequency cutoff, f_H, for a CE amplifier using a 2N3904 transistor. Assume that $\beta = 200$, $I_C = 10$ mA, $R_B = 5$ kΩ, $R_{source} = 1$ kΩ, and $R_{load} = R_C = 1$ kΩ. Further assume that you have checked the data sheets and found that $f_T = 0.25$ GHz and $C_{ob} = 4.5$ pF. Verify your results using a computer simulation program.

Solution: In order to use the equations derived in this section, we need to find h_{ie}, R_{in}, $C_{b'e}$, and C_M. These are found as follows:

$$h_{ie} \approx r_\pi = 26 \times 10^{-3} \frac{\beta}{I_{CQ}} = 520\ \Omega$$

$$R_{in} = R_B \| r_\pi = 5\ \text{k}\Omega \| 520\ \Omega = 471\ \Omega$$

$$C_{b'e} = \frac{|I_{CQ}|}{52\pi f_T \times 10^{-3}} = 245\ \text{pF}$$

To find C_M, we first need A_v. Thus,

$$A_v = \frac{-R_{load} \| R_C}{r_\pi / \beta} = -192$$

$$C_M = C_{b'c}(1 - A_v) = 869\ \text{pF}$$

where $C_{b'c} = C_{ob}$. Finally, the cutoff frequency is given by

$$f_H = \frac{10^{12}}{2\pi \times 320 \times (245 + 869)} = 446\ \text{kHz}$$

Equation (10.65) indicates that the high-frequency cutoff can be increased by lowering R_{source} and R_{in}, by lowering the voltage gain of the stage, or by selecting a high-frequency transistor with lower capacitance values. For example, suppose we recalculate f_H assuming the source impedance, R_i, is reduced from 1 kΩ to 250 Ω. We find the new cutoff frequency.

$$R_{source} \| R_{in} = 250\Omega \| 471\Omega = 163\ \Omega$$

$$f_H = 874\ \text{kHz}$$

Hence, by reducing the source impedance, we have nearly doubled the high-frequency cutoff.

We now perform the computer simulation. The circuit was entered into the computer when we solved Example 10.2. We therefore call the circuit from memory (of course, you always save your circuits in meaningfully-labeled files), modify the resistor values, and add a bypass capacitor across R_E. We must also set the bias circuitry and source voltage to achieve the required bias conditions. Note that the supply voltage must be increased beyond 10 V since the specified value of I_C is 10 mA and the quiescent voltage drop across R_C is 10 V. We have performed this type of design many times, so we ask you to fill in the details. The resulting *ac* analysis plot is shown as Figure 10.18.

The mid-frequency gain is approximately 36.3 dB, so the high-frequency cutoff occurs at a gain of 33.3 dB. This corresponds to a frequency of about 530 kHz. The theoretical solution is 446 kHz, so we must explain this discrepancy. If we view the equation for f_H, we see that this parameter increases beyond the theoretical value of 446 kHz if one or more of the following four changes occur:

1. The parallel combination of R_{source} and R_{in} is less than 320 Ω. This quantity is approximately equal to R_B, which is fixed when the resistor values in the base bias circuitry are specified. This parameter varies if the resistor model in the computer contains a tolerance other than 0%
2. $C_{b'e}$<245 pF. This capacitance depends on g_m and f_T, both of which vary from those values assumed in our "paper" design as the current changes.
3. C_{ob}<4.5 pF. This capacitance is a transistor parameter that varies from the value assumed in our "paper" design as the current increases.
4. $|A_v|$<192. The midrange gain, A_v, deviates from the calculated value of -192 due to variation in r_π and in β. The computer varies these parameters away from their nominal values as a function of the operating point. Note that the simulated midband gain is 192 rather than 62 (36.3 dB). The 36.3 dB calculated earlier represents overall gain and includes the input source resistor, R_{source}. If we take the voltage-divider ratio of R_{source} with R_{in} into account, the simulated gain of 192 reduces by a factor of 471/1471, and the two answers match closely.

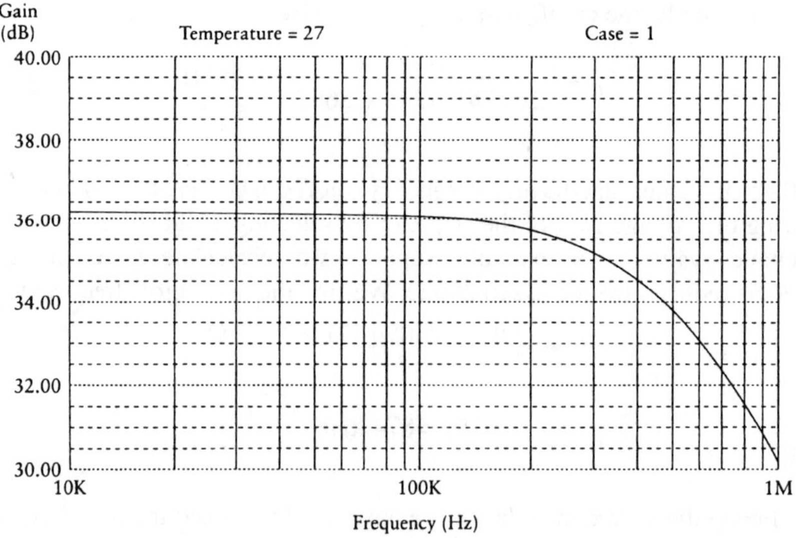

Figure 10.18 – Computer simulation for Example 10.6

EXERCISE

E10.2 Determine the high-frequency cutoff for the CE amplifier of Figure 10.17. The transistor parameters are $f_T = 0.4$ GHz, $C_{oB} = 2$ pF, $\beta = 200$, $r_\pi = 400\ \Omega$, $I_C = 13$ mA, $R_{source} = 270\ \Omega$, $R_B = 10$ kΩ, $R_E = 65\ \Omega$, and $R_C = R_{load} = 670\ \Omega$.

Answer: $R_{in} = 385\ \Omega$; $C_{b'e} = 199$ pF; $C_M = 338$ pF
$f_H = 2.29$ MHz

10.3.2 High-Frequency Response of Common-Source Amplifier

The common-source amplifier is shown in Figure 10.19(a). We use the equivalent circuit developed in Section 10.2.3 to develop the equivalent of Figure 10.19(b).

The output resistance of the FET, r_{ds}, normally can be neglected because it is usually larger than R_D_R_L. Using the Miller theorem, we can further simplify the equivalent circuit as follows:

$$C_{in} = C_{gs} + C_{gd}\left(1 - A_v\right) \tag{10.66}$$

In Figure 10.20, we show the simplified equivalent circuit where C_{ds} and C_{gd} are neglected.

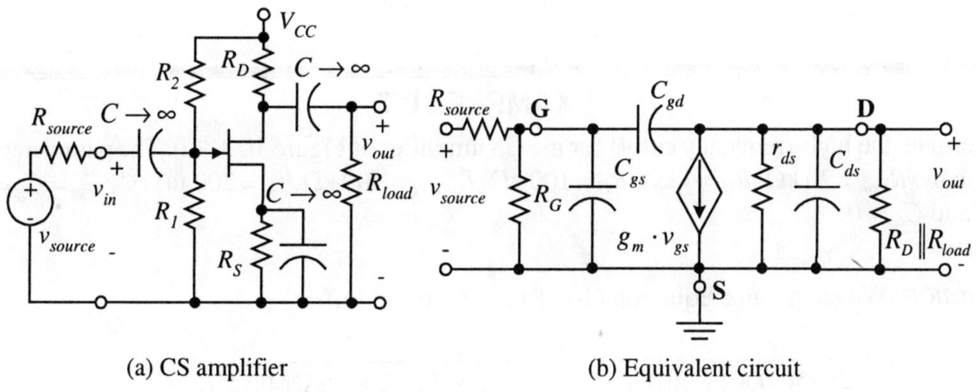

(a) CS amplifier (b) Equivalent circuit

Figure 10.19 – CS amplifier high-frequency model

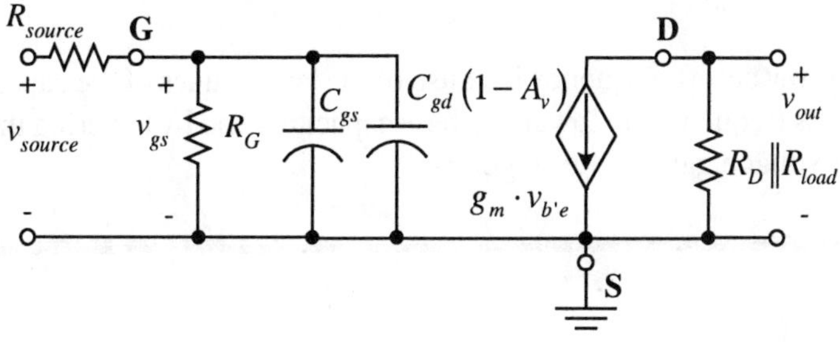

Figure 10.20 – Simplified high-frequency equivalent circuit

The dominant time constant is normally determined by the input characteristics of the amplifier due to the Miller effect at the input. However, if R_{source} is small, we may not be able to ignore the output capacitance as it may become the dominant time constant or the lowest cutoff frequency. If this is the case, then the output capacitance is given by

$$C_o = C_{ds} + C_{gd}\left(1 - \frac{1}{A_v}\right) \tag{10.67}$$

We use the technique of Example 10.1 to determine reciprocal of the RC time constant.

$$f_H = \frac{1}{2\pi\left(R_G \| R_{source}\right)C_{in}} \tag{10.68}$$

where C_{in} is given by

$$\begin{aligned} C_{in} &= C_{gs} + C_{gd}\left(1 - A_v\right) \\ &= C_{gs} + C_{gd}\left[1 + g_m\left(R_{load} \| R_D\right)\right] \end{aligned} \tag{10.69}$$

EXAMPLE 10.7

Determine the high-frequency cutoff for the CS amplifier of Figure 10.19(a). The parameters are given by: $R_{load} = 20$ kΩ, $R_D = 4$ kΩ, $R_G = 100$ kΩ, $R_{source} = 100$ kΩ, $g_m = 200\ \mu(\Omega)^{-1}$, $C_{gs} = C_{gd} = 16$ pF, and $C_{ds} = 0$.

Solution: We simply use Equation (10.68) to find the cutoff.

$$f_H = \frac{1}{2\pi\times 50{,}000\{16\times10^{-12} + 16\times10^{-12}[1 + (0.002)(20\text{k}\Omega \| 4\text{k}\Omega)]\}}$$

$$= 22.9 \text{ kHz}$$

This is a relatively low cutoff frequency because of the large values of the capacitors, C_{gs} and C_{gd}. We can increase this frequency by lowering these capacitors and by lowering the input resistor, or by decreasing the voltage gain of the stage.

EXERCISE

E10.3 Determine the high-frequency cutoff, f_H, for the FET amplifier of Figure 10.19 with $C_{gs} = C_{gd} = 3$ pF, $C_{ds} = 0$, $R_L = 20$ kΩ, $R_D = 4$ kΩ, $R_G = R_{source} = 10$ kΩ and $g_m = 2000\ \mu(\Omega)^{-1}$.

Answer: $f_H = 1.22$ MHz

10.3.3 High-Frequency Response of Common-Base Amplifier

The common-base amplifier has a low input resistance and a high output resistance. It is used in wide bandwidth applications. The circuit is shown in Figure 10.21(a) with its equivalent circuit shown in Figure 10.21(b).

We can use the equivalent circuit to determine the time constants of the circuit and its respective poles. For the CE amplifier, the Miller effect increased the capacitance thereby decreasing the high-frequency cutoff. In the case of the CB amplifier, the Miller effect does not exist and there is no multiplying factor for $C_{b'c}$. This is shown in the equivalent circuit of Figure 10.21(b). Notice that the capacitor at the left side of Figure 10.21(a) effectively shorts the base to ground.

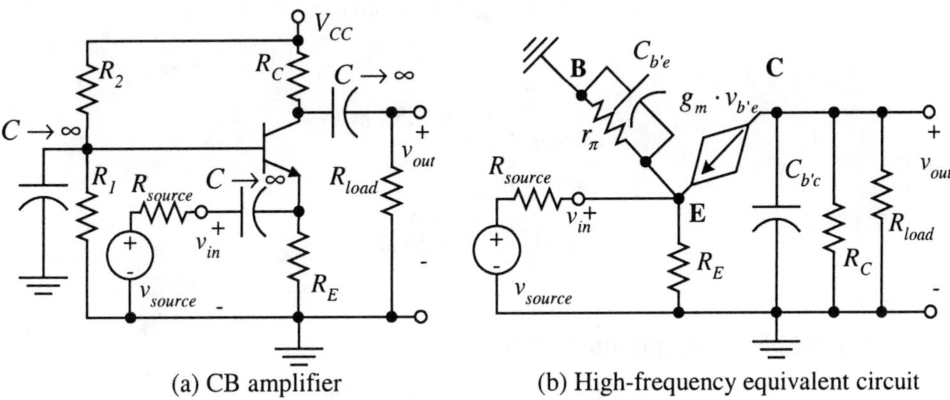

Figure 10.21 CB amplifier

As with most amplifiers, the CB amplifier response has two time constants. These can be found, as in Example 10.1, by observing the discharge path for the two capacitors. For the output circuit, the discharge path is through $R_C \| R_{load}$, so

$$\tau_{out} = C_{b'c}\left(R_C \| R_{load}\right) \tag{10.70}$$

At the input, the time constant is

$$\tau_{in} = C_{b'e}\left(\frac{r_\pi}{\beta}\Big\|R_E\Big\|R_{source}\right) = C_{b'e}\left(r_e\|R_E\|R_{source}\right) \tag{10.71}$$

The dominant pole will normally be at the input circuit so the high-frequency cutoff is

$$f_H = \frac{1}{2\pi C_{b'e}\left(r_e\|R_E\|R_{source}\right)} \tag{10.72}$$

Note that the high-frequency cutoff would be considerably higher if R_B were not bypassed.

EXAMPLE 10.8

Determine the frequency response of the CB amplifier of Figure 10.21 with the following parameters: $V_{CC} = 12$ V, $V_{BE} = 0.7$ V, $\beta = 100$, $R_{source} = 600\ \Omega$, $R_E = 200\ \Omega$, $R_{load} = R_C = 2\ \text{k}\Omega$, $C_{oB} = 2$ pF, and $f_T = 100$ MHz. The amplifier is biased for maximum output swing.

Solution: We first determine the Q-point location for maximum output swing.

$$I_{CQ} = \frac{V_{CC}}{R_{ac} + R_{dc}} = \frac{12}{\left(R_C\|R_{load} + R_{source}\|R_E\right) + \left(R_C + R_E\right)}$$

$$= \frac{12}{1150 + 2200} = 3.58 \text{ mA}$$

Then

$$r_e = \frac{26}{3.58} = 7.26\ \Omega$$

Since $C_{b'c} = C_{ob} = 2$ pF, the output time constant is

$$\tau_{out} = \left(R_{load}\|R_C\right)(2\text{ pF}) = 2 \text{ ns}$$

We now find $C_{b'e}$ using Equation (10.56) as follows:

$$C_{b'e} = \frac{I_C}{52\times 10^{-3}\pi f_T} = 219 \text{ pF}$$

The input time constant can now be found.

$$\tau_{in} = C_{b'e}\left(r_e\|R_E\|R_{source}\right) = 1.52 \text{ ns}$$

The high-frequency breakpoints are the reciprocals of the time constants. Stating these in Hz, we find

$$f_H(input) = \frac{1}{2\pi \times 1.52 \times 10^{-9}} = 105 \text{ MHz}$$

$$f_H(output) = \frac{1}{2\pi \times 2 \times 10^{-9}} = 80 \text{ MHz}$$

10.3.4 High-Frequency Response of Emitter-Follower Amplifier

The emitter-follower (EF) amplifier is a current gain amplifier which has a voltage gain of unity. It is shown in Figure 10.22(a) with its equivalent circuit in Figure 10.22(b). Figure 10.22(c) is a modification showing the Miller effect.

The load for the EF amplifier is small and is often capacitive in nature, so we will include the load capacitor, C_{load}, in our models. Since the gain is close to unity and positive, both $C_{b'e}(1 - A_V)$ and $C_{b'e}(1 - 1/A_V)$ are close to zero. We again find the time constants by determining the equivalent resistance in the discharge paths of the two capacitors.

For C_{load}, the discharge path is through $R_{load} \| R_E$ so the output time constant is

$$\tau_{out} = C_{load}\left(R_{load} \| R_E\right) \tag{10.73}$$

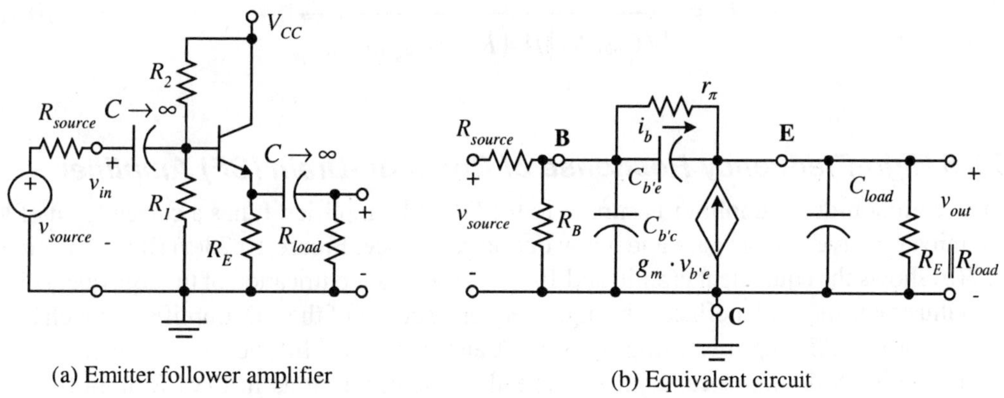

(a) Emitter follower amplifier

(b) Equivalent circuit

Figure 10.22(parts a and b) – EF amplifier

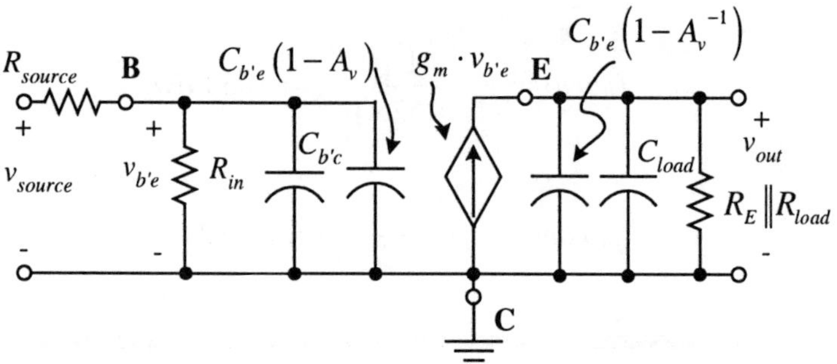

(c) Equivalent circuit using Miller's Theorem

Figure 10.22(part c) – EF amplifier

For $C_{b'c}$ (or C_{ob}), the discharge path is through $R_{in} \| R_{source}$, so the input time constant is

$$\tau_{in} = C_{ob}\left(R_{in} \| R_{source}\right) \tag{10.74}$$

where

$$R_{in} = R_B \| \left[\beta\left(R_E \| R_{load}\right)\right] \tag{10.75}$$

If C_{load} is approximately equal to C_{ob}, then $\tau_{in} >> \tau_{out}$ and the high-frequency cutoff is limited by τ_{in}, Thus, the high-frequency cutoff is

$$f_H = \frac{1}{2\pi C_{ob}\left[R_B \| \beta \cdot \left(R_E \| R_{load}\right) \| R_{source}\right]} \tag{10.76}$$

10.3.5 High-Frequency Response of Common-Drain (SF) Amplifier

The common-drain amplifier is similar to the BJT EF amplifier. It has a current gain of less than unity, positive voltage gain and a low output resistance. Figure 10.23(a) shows the circuit, 10.23(b) shows the equivalent circuit, and 10.23(c) shows a modification of the equivalent circuit which illustrates the Miller effect. The high-frequency cutoff of the CD amplifier is much higher than that of the CS amplifier using the same transistor. The Miller effect, as seen in Figure 10.23(c), reduces the input capacitance instead of increasing it as in the CS amplifier. This reduces the effect of the input time constant, thus, raising the high-frequency cutoff. The input and output time constants are found by observing the discharge path for the corresponding capacitors, with the result

$$\begin{aligned} \tau_{in} &= \left(R_G \| R_{source}\right)\left[C_{gd} + C_{gs}\left(1 - A_v\right)\right] \\ \tau_{out} &= \left[C_{ds} + C_{gs}\left(1 - 1/A_v\right)\right]\left(R_s \| R_{load}\right) \end{aligned} \tag{10.77}$$

The high-frequency cutoff, f_H, is found by inverting the time constant. The dominant pole could be either at the input or the output depending on the values of the components.

$$f_H = \frac{1}{2\pi\tau} \tag{10.78}$$

τ could be either τ_{in} or τ_{out}.

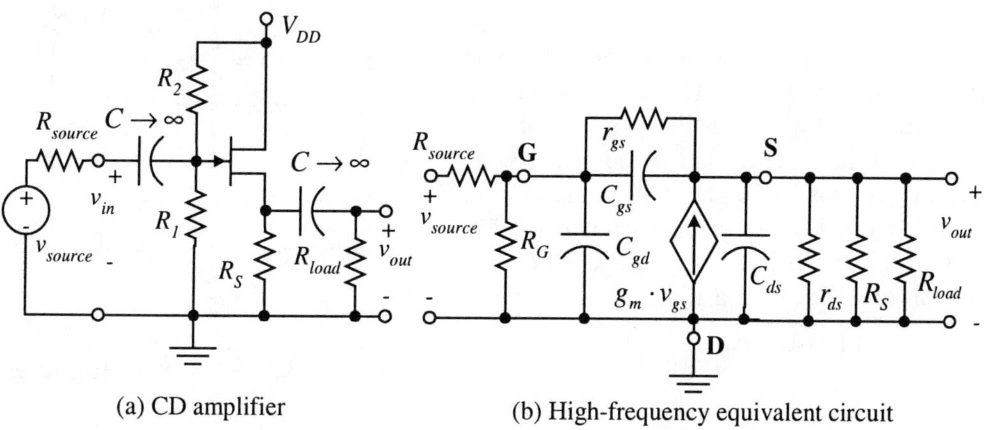

(a) CD amplifier

(b) High-frequency equivalent circuit

(c) Equivalent circuit using Miller's Theorem

Figure 10.23 – CD amplifier

10.3.6 Cascode Amplifiers

The cascode amplifier was introduced in Chapter 5. This configuration was developed to increase the bandwidth of voltage amplifiers. It exhibits a much higher cutoff frequency than is experienced with the conventional cascaded CE or emitter-resistor amplifiers using the same type of transistor. The cascode configuration is a CE amplifier driving a CB amplifier as shown in Figure 10.24.

Since the CE amplifier (Q_1) sees the low input resistance of the CB amplifier, the gain of the CE amplifier is approximately equal to -1. This reduces the effect of the capacitance between the base and collector. Since this capacitance is the source of the dominant high frequency pole, the Miller effect, $C_{b'c}(1 - A_V)$, is greatly diminished and the pole occurs at a higher frequency. The CB amplifier (Q_2) is not affected by the Miller effect of the capacitance of the junction and already has a wide bandwidth. It has a high voltage gain and compensates for the low voltage gain of the CE amplifier. This results in a high voltage gain, wide bandwidth amplifier with a high input resistance and high output resistance.

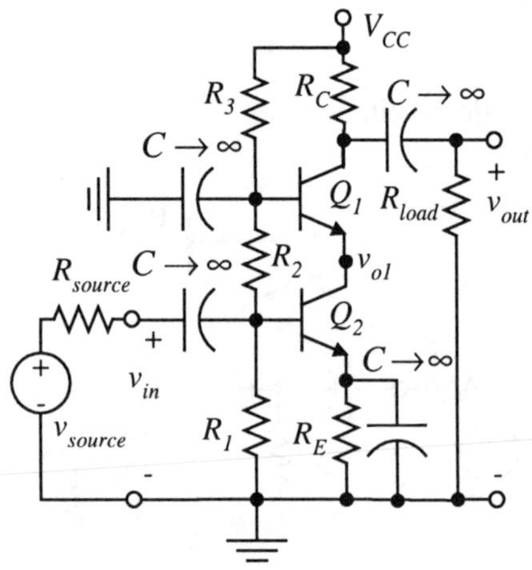

Figure 10.24 – Cascode amplifier

10.4 HIGH-FREQUENCY AMPLIFIER DESIGN

In the previous sections, we learned to analyze specific amplifier configurations to determine the high-frequency cutoff point. For any new amplifier configuration, the equivalent circuit can be developed and reduced (taking into account the Miller effect). The time constants are then determined by finding the equivalent resistance through which each capacitor discharges. The series capacitors are shorted at the high frequency and affect only the low-frequency cutoff.

In designing an amplifier, the high-frequency cutoff point is determined by the particular transistor type selected, circuit parameters, and the amplifier configuration used. If the resulting high-frequency cutoff is not as high as desired, the designer has some options:

- Reduce the gain per stage to reduce the Miller effect.
- Select a transistor that has a higher frequency capability.
- Use an amplifier circuit configuration that is not as frequency sensitive, such as the common-base configuration.

Changing any of the above parameters requires that a new high-frequency analysis be performed. Since this is time consuming, it represents an ideal application for computer simulation programs. Computer simulations not only model transistors more accurately but also permit iterative analysis. Using the iteration feature present in many of the SPICE-based programs allows you to view a family of output curves representing different temperature and/or different component values chosen from within their tolerance limits. You can then select the best designs for your application.

10.5 FREQUENCY RESPONSE OF OP-AMP CIRCUITS

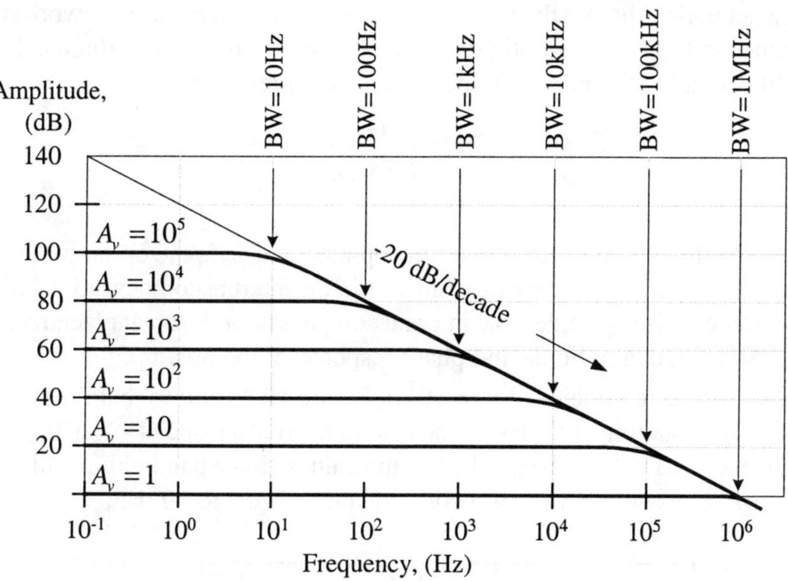

Figure 10.25 Op-amp open-loop gain characteristics

Now that we have explored the frequency response of discrete amplifier circuits, we turn our attention to the frequency analysis of op-amp circuits. A typical open-loop (i.e., break the feedback connection) op-amp amplitude versus frequency characteristic is shown in Figure 10.25, where we illustrate a family of curves, each corresponding to a different closed-loop gain, A_v. The closed-loop (i.e., with feedback) gain for each curve is indicated on the figure.

The numbers are typical of a general purpose single roll-off op-amp such as the 741. The 741 op-amp includes *fixed compensation*, which is a technique of modifying the open-loop frequency response characteristic for the purpose of improving performance. Compensation is used in numerous feedback systems. One of the simplest forms of frequency compensation is provided by the introduction of an RC network as shown in Figure 10.26.

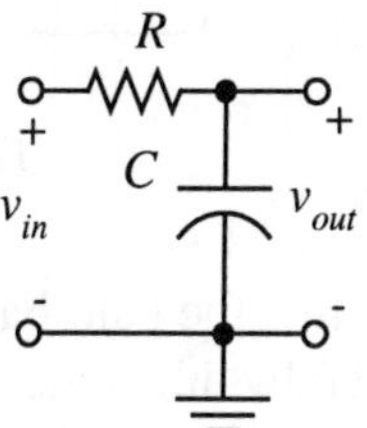

Figure 10.26 – RC compensation network

The transfer function for this network is

$$\frac{V_{out}(j\omega)}{V_{in}(j\omega)} = \frac{1}{j\omega RC + 1} = \frac{1}{j\omega\tau + 1} \tag{10.79}$$

where the time constant, τ, is RC. This network has a single pole at a frequency of $1/\tau$. When the

RC network is inserted into an op-amp, the gain decreases at a slope of -20 dB/decade for frequencies greater than the corner frequency, $\omega_H = 1/\tau$. The 741 op-amp has a fixed compensation network built into the device. This *internal compensation* network causes the 741 op-amp response to follow the amplitude-frequency response shown in Figure 10.25. We can approximate this family of curves with the following expression:

$$G(s) = \frac{G_o}{1 + s/\omega_o} \tag{10.80}$$

The constant G_o is the *dc* open-loop gain of the op-amp and ω_o is the op-amp corner frequency. This amplitude-frequency characteristic results from the internal compensation built into the op-amp. The curve shown is for single-pole internal compensation. The manufacturer's specification sheets usually show both amplitude and phase response of the op-amp.

Examination of the curve labeled $A_v = 10^5$ in Figure 10.25 shows that the gain is 100 dB at low frequency. Then starting at $f = 10$ Hz the gain falls off at a slope of -20 dB/decade, reaching 0 dB at a frequency of 10^6 Hz. The product of the gain with the bandwidth, which is defined as the *gain-bandwidth product (GBP)*, is a constant and is equal to 10^6 Hz.

A_v	BW	GBP
10^5	10^1	10^6
10^4	10^2	10^6
10^3	10^3	10^6
10^2	10^4	10^6
10^1	10^5	10^6
10^0	10^6	10^6

Table 10.1-Gain Bandwidth Product

We verify that the gain-bandwidth product is constant by referring to the curves in Figure 10.25. The bandwidth is the corner frequency (the frequency beyond which the amplitude response falls at a slope of -20 dB/decade). We tabulate the gain (A_v), the bandwidth (BW), and the gain-bandwidth product (GBP) in Table 10.1.

Notice that for this first-order compensation network, the product of gain and bandwidth is a constant, 10^6.

Figure 10.27 shows a typical non-inverting amplifier configuration.

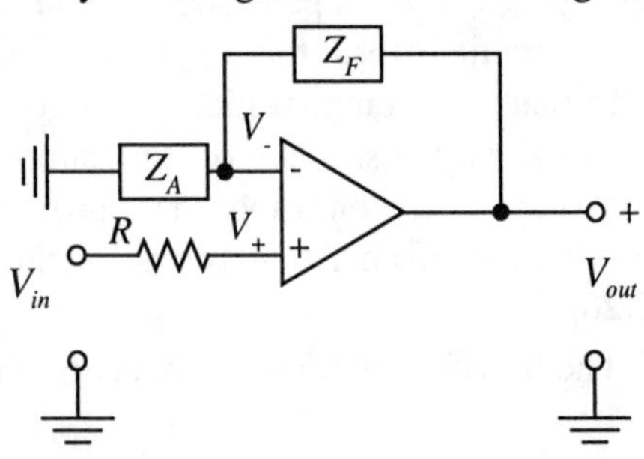

Figure 10.27 – Circuit configuration for non-inverting op-amp

We now find the closed-loop gain for this non-inverting amplifier. The closed-loop gain is found by writing the nodal equations at V_+ and V_- as follows:

$$V_+ = V_{in}$$
$$\frac{V_-}{Z_A} = \frac{V_{out} - V_-}{Z_F} \tag{10.81}$$

Solving for the inverting voltage input, we obtain

$$V_- = V_{out} \frac{Z_A}{Z_A + Z_F} \tag{10.82}$$

We use the open-loop gain relationship to solve for the output voltage.

$$V_{out} = G_o(V_+ - V_-) = G_o\left(V_{in} - V_{out}\frac{Z_A}{Z_A + Z_F}\right)$$
$$= \frac{G_o V_{in}}{1 + G_o Z_A/(Z_A + Z_F)} \tag{10.83}$$

When we let

$$\gamma = \frac{Z_A}{Z_A + Z_F} \tag{10.84}$$

the voltage gain reduces to

$$A_{v\,(closed\ loop)} = \frac{V_{out}}{V_{in}} = \frac{G_o}{1 + G_o\gamma} \tag{10.85}$$

If the open-loop op-amp gain, G_o, is large, the closed-loop amplifier gain approaches

$$A_{v\ (closed\ loop)} = \frac{V_{out}}{V_{in}} \rightarrow \frac{1}{\gamma} \tag{10.86}$$

The quantity $1/\gamma$ is the closed-loop gain of the non-inverting op-amp system at low frequencies. We substitute G, which is the function of frequency given by Equation (10.80), into Equation (10.85) to obtain

$$A_v = \frac{G_o}{1 + G_o\gamma + s/\omega_o} \tag{10.87}$$

If the *dc* gain is large, we can assume that $\gamma G_o >> 1$. Equation (10.87) then reduces to

$$A_v = \frac{1}{\gamma} \cdot \frac{1}{1 + s/\gamma G_o \omega_o} \tag{10.88}$$

If the impedances are purely resistive, $Z_A = R_A$ and $Z_F = R_F$, and

$$\frac{1}{\gamma} = 1 + \frac{R_F}{R_A} \tag{10.89}$$

The closed-loop gain under this purely resistive condition is

$$A_v = \frac{1}{\dfrac{1}{1 + R_F/R_A} + \dfrac{s}{G_o \omega_o}} \tag{10.90}$$

This gain equation contains a single pole. Therefore, the Bode plot starts at $20\log(1+R_F/R_A)$ and has a corner frequency at

$$\omega_c = \frac{G_o \omega_o}{1 + R_F/R_A} \tag{10.91}$$

Note that if we form the product of $A_{v\,(closed)}$ (the closed-loop non-inverting gain at low frequency) with the bandwidth (the corner frequency ω_c) the resulting gain bandwidth product is

$$A_{v\,(closed)} \times \omega_c = \left(1 + \frac{R_F}{R_A}\right) \cdot \frac{G_o \omega_o}{1 + R_F/R_A} = G_o \omega_o \tag{10.92}$$

Hence we again see that for single-pole compensation, the gain bandwidth product is constant for the inverting configuration. We can show that the bandwidths for the non-inverting and inverting configurations are identical.

As the closed-loop gain increases, the corner frequency (i.e., bandwidth) must decrease so that their product remains constant. This is also verified in Table 10.1. The inverse relationship between gain and bandwidth is an important trade-off in design considerations.

10.5.1 Open-Loop Op-Amp Response

In Chapter 11, we discuss stability of systems using the frequency response methods. We will present concepts involving feedback loops, and will refer to the open-loop function. In this section, we consider a generalized approach to evaluating the open-loop frequency response for op-amp systems. We start with a non-inverting op-amp system as shown in Figure 10.27. The circuit response is found as before, by writing the node equations for V_- and V_+. For convenience, we repeat Equation (10.83) as Equation (10.93).

$$\frac{V_{out}}{V_{in}} = \frac{G_o}{1 + G_o Z_A/(Z_A + Z_F)} \tag{10.93}$$

The *open-loop response* is the product of all the transmittance functions around the loop. To find the open-loop response for Equation (10.85), we obtain

$$G(s)H(s) = G\frac{Z_A}{Z_A + Z_F} \tag{10.94}$$

The Bode plot is useful for determining stability of electronic systems. For this application we construct a Bode plot of the open-loop response, not the closed-loop response. For this reason, Equation (10.94) is useful in determining stability.

It is important to notice that the open-loop response for the *inverting* op-amp is also given by Equation (10.94).

EXAMPLE 10.9

Find the open-loop function for the op-amp system of Figure 10.28.

The op-amp gain is

$$G(s) = \frac{G_o}{0.001s + 1}$$

Solution: In this system, $Z_A = 1/sC$ and $Z_F = sL+R$. The open-loop function is given by Equation (10.94).

$$\frac{G Z_A}{Z_A + Z_F} = \frac{G(1/LC)}{s^2 + (R/L)s + (1/LC)}$$

We insert values for R, L, and C to obtain

$$\frac{G Z_A}{Z_A + Z_F} = \frac{G}{[s/(1.13\times10^3) + 1]\,[s/(8.9\times10^3) + 1]}$$

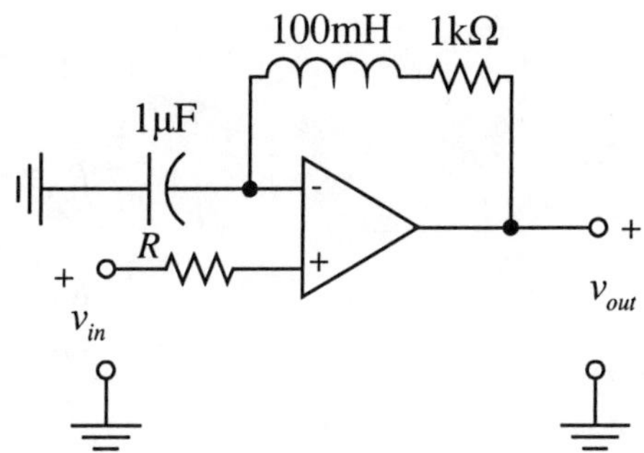

Figure 10.28 – Op-amp system for Example 10.9

We substitute for G to find the open loop function,

$$G(s)H(s) = \frac{G_o}{[s/10^3 + 1]\,[s/(1.13\times10^3) + 1]\,[s/(8.9\times10^3) + 1]}$$

The open-loop function is used to construct the Bode plot and hence to determine the system stability.

EXAMPLE 10.10

Design a 741 op-amp to have the following characteristics:

$$V_{out} = 5V_1 + 2V_2 + 3V_3 - 4V_4$$

The resistance to any of the input terminals will be at least 10 kΩ. Determine R_{in} at the non-inverting and inverting terminals, the output resistance and the bandwidth of the op-amp.

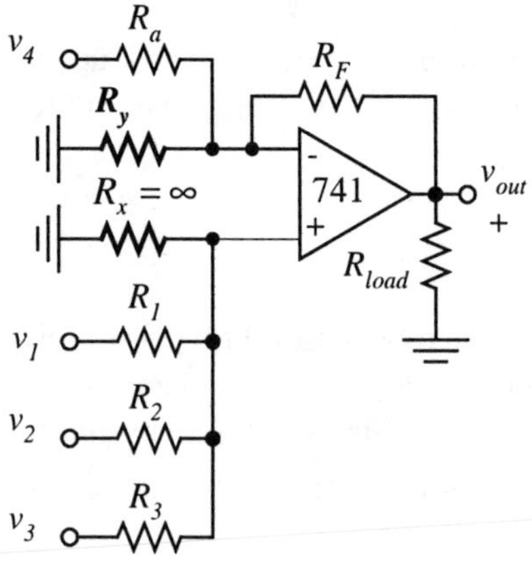

Figure 10.29 – Circuit for Example 10.10

Solution: Since

$$R_{min} = 10\ \text{k}\Omega$$
$$Z = 10 - 4 - 1 = 5$$

then R_F is 10 kΩ × 5 = 50 kΩ and

$$R_1 = \frac{50\ \text{k}\Omega}{5} = 10\ \text{k}\Omega$$

$$R_2 = \frac{50\ \text{k}\Omega}{2} = 25\ \text{k}\Omega$$

$$R_3 = \frac{50\ \text{k}\Omega}{3} = 16.7\ \text{k}\Omega$$

$$R_a = \frac{50\ \text{k}\Omega}{4} = 12.5\ \text{k}\Omega$$

$$R_Y = \frac{50\ \text{k}\Omega}{5} = 10\ \text{k}\Omega$$

The input resistance at the inverting and non-inverting terminals is given by

$$R_{in} = 12.5\ \text{k}\Omega \| 10\ \text{k}\Omega \| 50\ \text{k}\Omega\ = 10\ \text{k}\Omega \| 25\ \text{k}\Omega \| 16.7\ \ \text{k}\Omega\ = 5\ \text{k}\Omega$$

The output resistance and bandwidth are given by

$$R_o = \frac{6.6 \times 75}{10^5} = 4.175\ \text{m}\Omega$$

$$BW = \frac{10^6}{1 + R_F / R_A} = 152.5\ \text{kHz}$$

The resulting circuit is shown in Figure 10.29.

10.5.2 Phase Shift

If a sinusoidal signal forms the inverting input to an *ideal* op-amp, the output is 180° out of phase with this input. However, with *practical* op-amps, the phase shift between input and output signals is not exactly 180°. The angle decreases as the frequency of the input signal increases. At high frequencies, the phase difference approaches zero and a portion of the output signal is fed back in phase. This changes the feedback from *negative* to *positive*, and the amplifier can exhibit behavior characteristics of an oscillator.

Op-amp manufacturers often prevent this situation by including an internal filter. This is done in a manner such that the op-amp has a gain of less than unity at frequencies where the phase difference between output and input approaches zero. Oscillation will not occur with positive feedback as long as the gain is less than unity. This modification of the op-amp is known as *internal frequency compensation.* If the manufacturer does not provide for this internal compensation, an external capacitor can be added to accomplish the same result.

10.5.3 Slew Rate

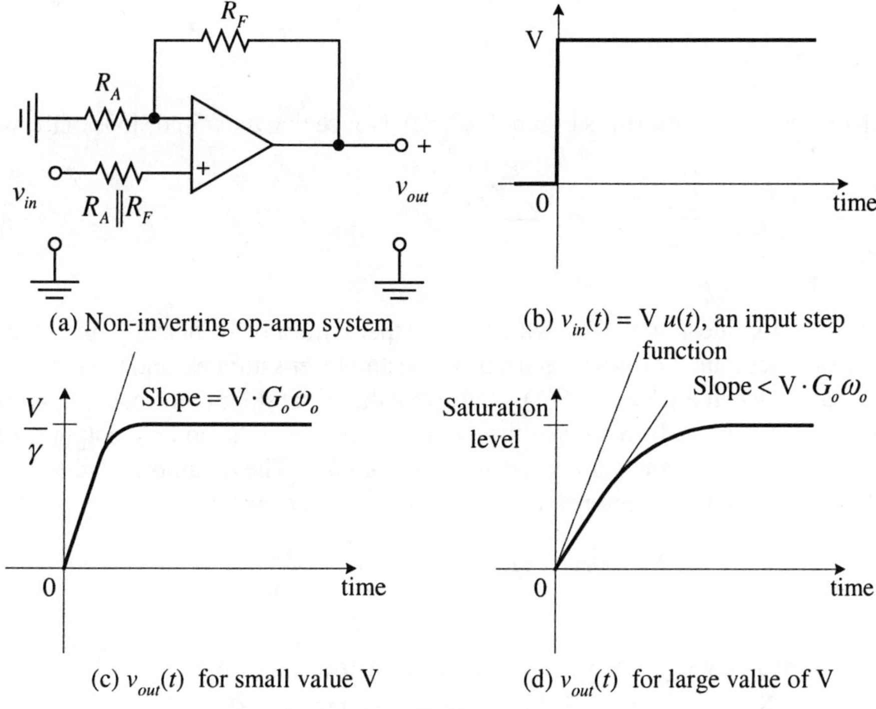

Figure 10.30 – Slew rate limiting

Because a practical op-amp has a response that is frequency dependent, the output due to a step input is not a perfect step function. This characteristic of op-amps, which is termed *slew rate limiting*, causes distortion of the output signal. We analyze slew rate limiting by referring to equation (10.88) for the closed-loop gain, A_v, of the non-inverting op-amp systems [see Figure 10.30(a)]. For convenience, we repeat this equation as Equation (10.95).

$$A_v = \frac{1}{\gamma} \cdot \frac{1}{1 + s/\gamma G_o \omega_o} \tag{10.95}$$

The circuit includes resistors, R_A and R_F, so the low frequency gain, $1/\gamma$, is $1+R_F/R_A$. The gain-bandwidth product is $G_o\omega_o$, which for the 741 op-amp is 10^6 Hz.

We apply the step function shown in Figure 10.30(b) at the input to the op-amp system of Figure 10.30(a). We can use Laplace transform methods to find the output.

$$V_{out}(s) = \frac{V}{s} \cdot \left(\frac{1}{\gamma} \frac{1}{1 + s/\gamma G_o \omega_o} \right) \tag{10.96}$$

where the Laplace transform of the input step is V/s. The output time response is found using partial fraction expansions with the result

$$v_{out}(t) = \frac{V}{\gamma}\left(1 - e^{-t\gamma G_o \omega_o}\right) \tag{10.97}$$

We sketch this output waveform as Figure 10.30(c). Notice that the initial slope of the waveform is

$$\left.\frac{dv_{out}(t)}{dt}\right|_{t=0} = \frac{V\gamma\, G_o\omega_o}{\gamma} \cdot \left. e^{-t\gamma G_o \omega_o}\right|_{t=0} = VG_o\omega_o \tag{10.98}$$

These results are for linear operation, which means that V must be sufficiently small such that the op-amp does not saturate. For large values of V, the amplifier saturates, and the output response resembles that shown in Figure 10.30(d). Notice that the initial slope of the output response curve is lower than that predicted by the linear theory. This inability of the op-amp output to rise as fast as the linear theory predicts is defined as *slew rate limiting*. The op-amp is said to be *slewing*, and the initial slope of the output response is defined as the *slew rate*:

$$\text{Slew rate} = \text{SR} = \text{maximum of } \frac{dv_{out}}{dt} \tag{10.99}$$

An op-amp begins slewing when the initial slope of the v_{out}(t) response is less than $VG_o\omega_o$.

The value of SR is usually specified in the manufacturer's data sheets in volts per microsecond at unity-gain (see Appendix). The equations derived for Figure 10.30 can be applied to a unity gain buffer by letting $R_A \to \infty$ since this makes $1/\gamma$ equal to unity.

Slew rate is related to the *power bandwidth*, f_p, which is defined as the frequency at which a sine wave output, *at rated* output voltage, begins to exhibit distortion. For example, if the output signal is

$$v_{out} = V \sin\left(2\pi\, f_p\, t\right) \tag{10.100}$$

then the rate of change of this curve is

$$\frac{dv_{out}}{dt} = V \cdot 2\pi f_p \cos\left(2\pi\, f_p\, t\right) \tag{10.101}$$

and the maximum value of this slope occurs at t = 0:

$$\left.\frac{dv_{out}}{dt}\right|_{max} = 2\pi\, f_p\, V \tag{10.102}$$

Now if $2\pi f_p V > SR$, the output response is distorted. The *power bandwidth* is found from the slew rate at the point where the distortion begins. That is,

$$f_p = \frac{SR}{2\pi\, V_r} \tag{10.103}$$

where V_r is the rated op-amp output voltage. Note that if the output voltage is lower than V_r, slew rate distortion begins at a frequency that is higher than f_p.

EXERCISES

E10.4 If the slew rate for a unity-gain inverting 741 op-amp is 0.5 V/μs, how long will it take for the output to change by 5 V?

Answer: 10 μs

E10.5 For an op-amp with SR = 0.6 V/μs, find f_p for a peak undistorted output voltage of (a) 1 V and (b) 10 V.

Answer: (a) 95.5 kHz ; (b) 9.6 kHz

E10.6 For a 741 op-amp with SR = 0.5 V/μs, find f_p with a peak output voltage of 13 V.

Answer: 6.1 kHz

10.5.4 Designing Amplifiers Using Multiple Op-Amps

We now have knowledge of the external electrical characteristics of the op-amp and are able to use this knowledge as a building block in the design of amplifiers requiring more than one op-amp. The specified input resistance at each terminal is important to the designer, as are the characteristics of bandwidth and output resistance. Other characteristics that aid in selecting the correct op-amp type include CMRR, PSRR, and the slew rate.

The first step in designing multiple op-amp circuits is to determine the amount of gain per stage. This is accomplished by dividing the gain-bandwidth product of the selected op-amp by the required bandwidth.

The next step is to determine which inputs are negative and which are positive. This determines whether connections should be made to the negative or positive terminal of the op-amp.

If the required input resistance is above the value of the coupling resistor, the input voltage must be fed to the non-inverting terminal of the op-amp. Recall that the input resistance to the inverting terminal is equal to the value of the coupling resistance used, and this is considerably less than 1 MΩ. There are other considerations in the design, such as isolation of various sources from each other and phase relationships. Having previously presented some simple examples, we now tie these concepts together through the following design examples.

EXAMPLE 10.11

Design a system to yield the following output voltage function using μA741 op-amps.

$$v_{out} = -400v_I$$

The input resistance must be greater than 100 MΩ and the bandwidth must be greater than 20 kHz. Calculate the output resistance of the system.

Solution: Referring to Equation (10.91), we write an expression for the bandwidth of the op-amp using the fact that the gain-bandwidth product for the 741 op-amp is 10^6.

$$BW = \frac{G_o\,\omega_o}{1 + R_F/R_A} = \frac{10^6}{1 + R_F/R_A}$$

Since the gain-bandwidth product is 10^6 and the required bandwidth is 20 kHz, the maximum attainable gain for any stage is

$$A_{\max} = \frac{10^6}{BW} = 50$$

Therefore, in order to attain a gain of 400, at least two op-amps are required. Suppose we select a gain of 20 for each of two stages. The first stage should consist of a noninverting amplifier with a gain of 20. We use a non-inverting amplifier for the first stage (rather than the second) to obtain a high value for input resistance. The second stage consists of an inverting amplifier with a gain of -20. Thus we provide the specified overall negative value of gain. The

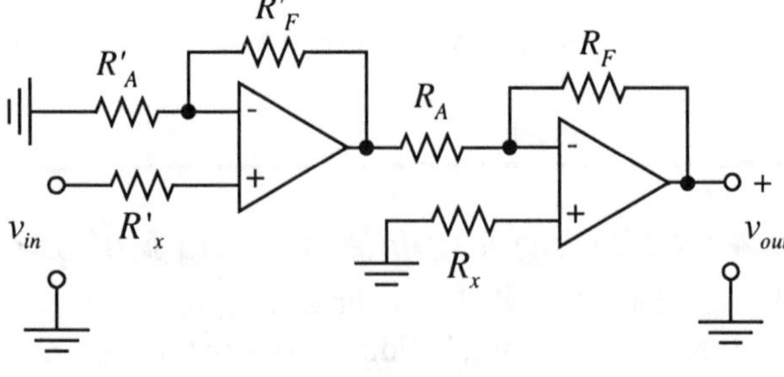

Figure 10.31 – Configuration for Example 10.11

configuration is shown in Figure 10.31.

For the first stage,

$$A = 20 = 1 + \frac{R'_F}{R'_A}$$

Since we have one equation in two unknowns and there are no additional design constraints in this problem, let us select a value for R'_A of 10 kΩ. The feedback resistor is then given by

$$R'_F = 190 \text{ k}\Omega$$

$$R'_x = R'_A \| R'_F = 9.5 \text{ k}\Omega$$

A similar approach for the second stage yields $R_A = 10$ kΩ, $R_F = 200$ kΩ and $R_x = 9.5$ kΩ. The input resistance is then approximately 400 MΩ and the output resistance is given by

$$R_o = \frac{75 \times 21}{10^5} = 15.8 \text{ m}\Omega$$

The bandwidth is

$$BW = \frac{10^6}{21} = 47.6 \text{ kHz}$$

which meets the specifications.

EXAMPLE 10.12 MULTIPLE OP-AMP (DESIGN)

Design an amplifier that is composed of 741 op-amps in order to obtain a gain of 800 with an input impedance of at least 20 MΩ. The amplifier must respond to a frequency of 40 kHz. Determine all resistor values, the output resistance, the input resistance, and the bandwidth. Check the gain of your design using a computer simulation program.

Solution: The maximum gain per stage is determined by the gain-bandwidth product for the 741 op-amp and the specified bandwidth. Thus,

$$A_{max} = \frac{1 \text{ MHz}}{40 \text{ kHz}} = 25$$

In order to achieve an overall gain of 800, we therefore need at least three stages of amplification. To achieve the high input impedance, the input to the first op-amp must be connected to the non-inverting input. The overall gain must be split among the three stages, so one possible choice is to design two of the stages with gains of 10 each and the third with a gain of 8. All stages are non-inverting.

When selecting the gain per stage, it is normally preferable to balance the stages - that is, to have all of the individual stage gains approximately equal in magnitude. This is true since the bandwidth is limited by the highest stage gain.

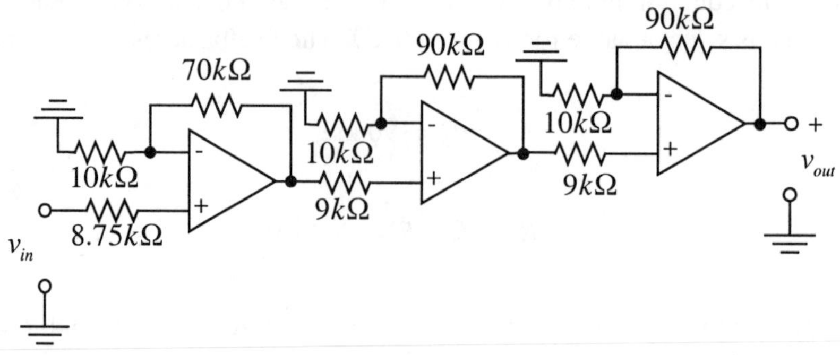

(a)

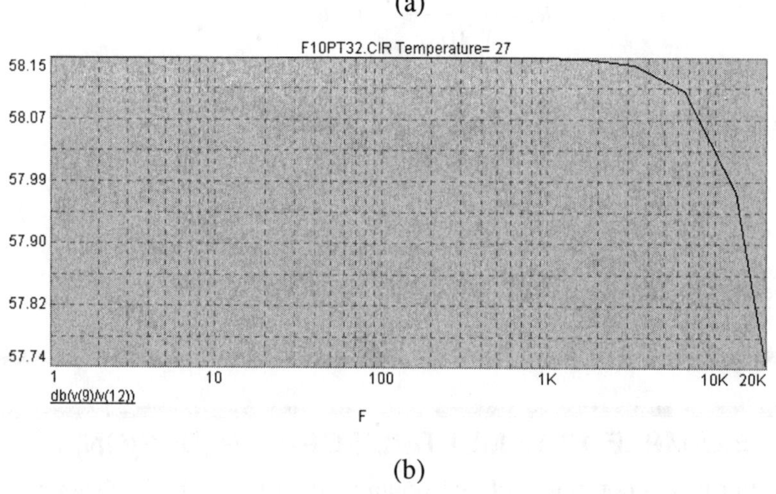

(b)

Figure 10.32 – Solution for Example 10.12

In designing single op-amp stages in earlier sections of this text, we found that usually not enough information is given to specify all of the design parameters. We must choose the value of one or more resistors before proceeding with the design. The same is true in this case, and if the procedures are followed, one possible set of resistor values for the op-amps with gains of 10 is

$$R_F = 90\text{ k}\Omega,\quad R_A = 10\text{ k}\Omega,\quad R_1 = 9\text{ k}\Omega$$

For the op-amp requiring a gain of 8, we can use

$$R_F = 70\text{ k}\Omega,\quad R_A = 10\text{ k}\Omega,\quad R_1 = 8.75\text{ k}\Omega$$

The resulting design is shown in Figure 10.32(a).

The bandwidth of the amplifier is the smallest of the three individual bandwidths of the various stages. For the stage with gain of 10, the bandwidth is given by

$$BW = \frac{1\,\text{MHz}}{10} = 100\ \text{kHz}$$

which exceeds the requirement. The input resistance is approximately 400 MΩ which also exceeds the requirement. The output resistance is found to be

$$R_o = \frac{75(1 + R_F/R_A)}{10^5} = 7.5\ \text{m}\Omega$$

We now verify our design using a computer simulation program. We used MICRO-CAP, but any SPICE-based program can be used. The circuit of Figure 10.32(a) is entered, and the LM741 op-amp is used as it appears in the program library. We can verify the overall gain as well as the required upper frequency response by running an *ac* analysis from a low frequency (say 1 Hz) to 20 kHz.

Running the program produces a plot of gain as a function of frequency, as shown in Figure 10.32(b). The curve starts at a gain of 58.15 dB for low frequency and decreases to 57.74 dB for a frequency of 20 kHz. A gain factor of 800 is equivalent to about 58 dB, so our system is yielding a gain of almost exactly 800 at low frequency. At high frequency, the gain is changing by -0.3 dB, which is equivalent to 0.966. We thus see a decrease of less than 3.5% in the gain at the high frequencies. This verifies our design.

EXAMPLE 10.13 MULTIPLE OP-AMP (DESIGN)

Design an amplifier that is composed of 741 op-amps to obtain an output of

$$v_{out} = 20v_1 - 40v_2 - 45v_3$$

The amplifier must respond to frequencies up to 50 kHz. Determine all resistor values, the output resistance, the input resistance, and the bandwidth of the amplifier.

Solution: The maximum gain in any one stage is checked using the GBP and the bandwidth requirements as follows:

$$A_{\max} = \frac{GBP}{BW} = \frac{1\ \text{MHz}}{50\ \text{kHz}} = 20$$

Thus, we can achieve the required gain of the v_1 channel with one amplification stage. If the gain of any channel is greater than 20, we obtain that gain with more than one amplifier in series.

We must use two amplifiers to achieve the required gain for v_2 and v_3. Suppose the first of each set of amplifiers multiplies v_2 by 4 and v_3 by 5. The main amplifier stage must then solve the modified equation

$$v_{out} = 20v_1 - 10v'_2 = 9v'_3$$

We design the main amplifier stage using the procedure of Section 2.6.

$$X = 20;\ Y = 19;\ Z = 0$$

so

$$R_x = R_y \to \infty$$

We choose $R_F = 180$ kΩ and then solve for the other resistor values:

$$R_1 = \frac{180\ \text{k}\Omega}{20} = 9\ \text{k}\Omega$$

$$R_2 = \frac{180\ \text{k}\Omega}{10} = 18\ \text{k}\Omega$$

$$R_3 = \frac{180\ \text{k}\Omega}{9} = 20\ \text{k}\Omega$$

The first voltage, v_1, is connected directly to the noninverting terminal, yielding an input resistance of approximately 400 MΩ. The amplification of v_2 by 4 is achieved with a stage using

$$R_A = 10\ \text{k}\Omega$$
$$R_F = 30\ \text{k}\Omega$$
$$R_1 = 7.5\ \text{k}\Omega$$

The amplification of v_3 by 5 is achieved with a stage using

$$R_A = 10\ \text{k}\Omega$$
$$R_F = 40\ \text{k}\Omega$$
$$R_1 = 8\ \text{k}\Omega$$

The output resistance is given by

$$R_o = \frac{75[1 + R_F / (R_2 \| R_3)]}{10^5} = 15\ \text{m}\Omega$$

The bandwidth for the system is determined by the amplifier with the largest gain ($20v_1$),

$$BW = \frac{1\ \text{MHz}}{1 + R_F / (R_2 \| R_3)} = 50\ \text{kHz}$$

The resulting amplifier is shown in Figure 10.33.

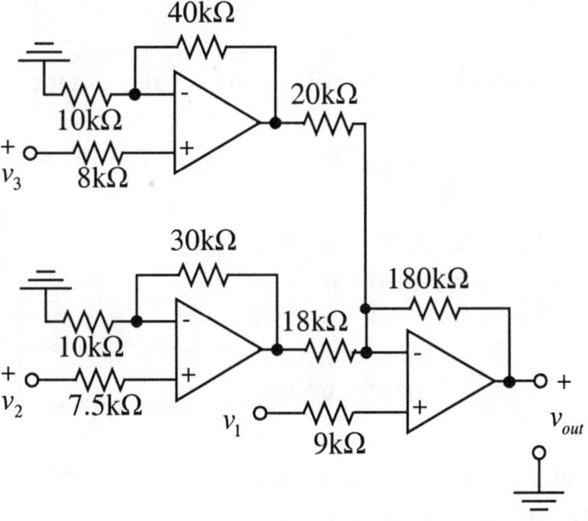

Figure 10.33 – Solution for Example 10.13

EXERCISES

E10.7 Find the input resistance and bandwidth of the 741 op-amp circuit of Figure E10.1. Let $R_A = R_F = R_{load} = 10$ kΩ.

Answer: $R_{in} = 400\ M\Omega$, $BW = 0.5\ MHz$

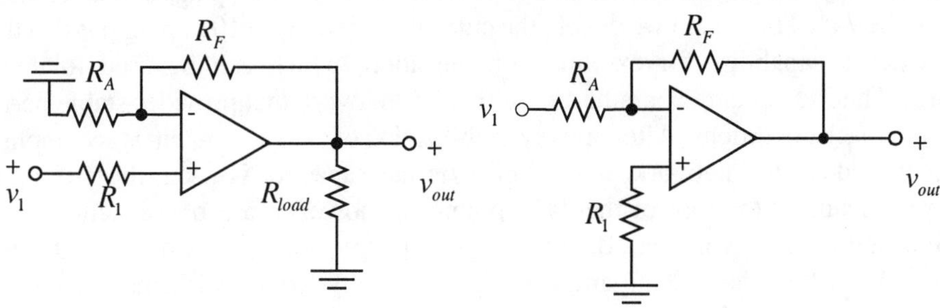

Figure E10.1 **Figure E10.2**

E10.8 Calculate the output resistance, R_{out}, for the amplifier of Figure E10.1. Use a 741 op-amp with $R_A = R_F = R_{load} = 10\ k\Omega$.

Answer: 1.5 mΩ

E10.9 Find the voltage gain and bandwidth of the 741 op-amp circuit of Figure E10.1. Let $R_F = 10\ k\Omega$, $R_1 = R_A = 1\ k\Omega$.

Answer: $A_v = 11$; *BW = 91 kHz*

E10.10 Find the gain and bandwidth for the 741 op-amp of Figure E10.2 with $R_F = 100\ k\Omega$, $R_A = 10\ k\Omega$, and $R_1 = 9\ k\Omega$.

Answer:
$A_v = -10$; *BW = 91 kHz*

E10.11 Find the bandwidth and input resistance for the differencing amplifier of Figure E10.3 using the 741 op-amp, $R_F = R_2 = 100\ k\Omega$ and $R_A = R_1 = 10\ k\Omega$.

Answer: $R_{in}(v_1) = 11\ k\Omega$; *BW = 91 kHz;*
$R_{in}(v_a) = 10\ k\Omega$

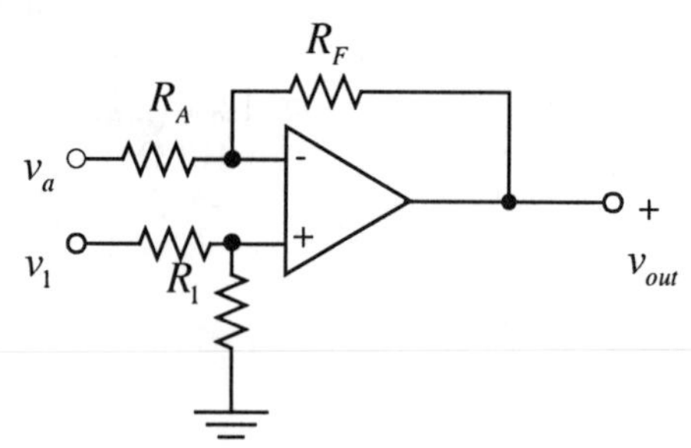

Figure E10.3

10.5.5 The 101 Amplifier

In Chapter 9, we presented the 741 as an example of a basic operational amplifier. We saw that it is internally compensated to enhance stability. The 101 op-amp has characteristics similar to those of the 741. The reason we devote the current section to the 101 op-amp is that this device also provides a capability for external compensation, which can be used to increase the bandwidth. The 741 op-amp contains an internal RC network that provides stable performance for most feedback conditions. Alternatively, stabilization of the 101 op-amp is accomplished with an externally added RC network. If a 30-pF external capacitor is used, the 101 op-amp has characteristics similar to those of the 741 op-amp. If, however, a 3-pF capacitor is externally added, the break point is moved 10 times higher in frequency, providing a 10 times wider bandwidth. With this change, the amplifier is stable only for a low-frequency gain of 10 or greater.

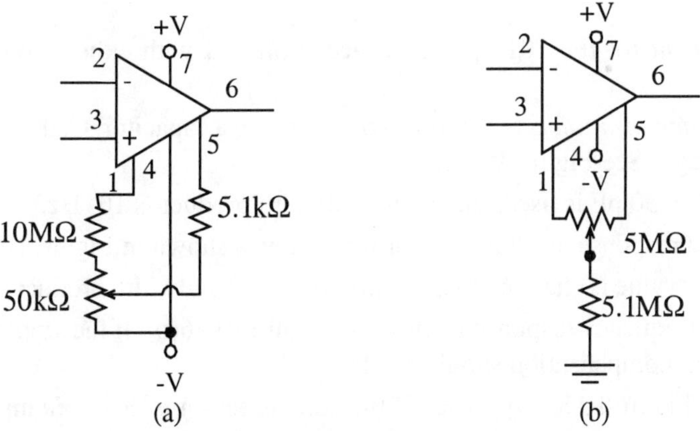

Figure 10.34 - Input offset adjustment

The principal characteristics of the 101 op-amp are

$R_i = 2$ MΩ $\qquad R_o = 100$ Ω

$R_{cm} = 200$ MΩ $\qquad G_o = 10^5$ (externally compensated)

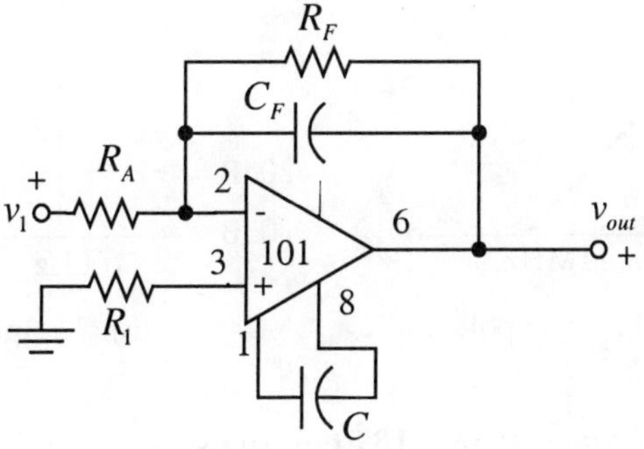

(a) Single-pole compensation

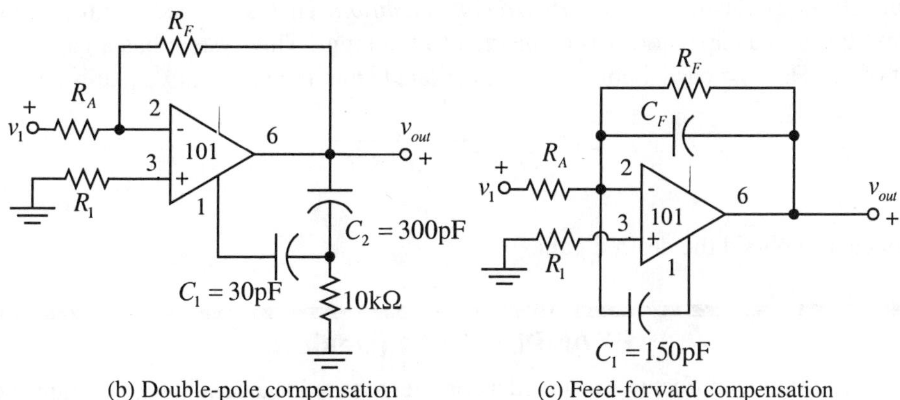

(b) Double-pole compensation

(c) Feed-forward compensation

Figure 10.35 – Op-amp 101 compensation

Offset adjustment for the 101 op-amp is accomplished with either arrangement shown in Figure 10.34.

Single-pole compensation is accomplished by placing a capacitor, C, between pins 1 and 8 of the op-amp package [See Figure 10.35(a)].

If a value of $C = 30$ pF is used, the gain-bandwidth product is 10^6 Hz.

The amplitude response as a function of frequency is shown in Figure 10.36(a).

If the capacitor value is changed to $C = 3$ pF, the gain-bandwidth product increases to 10^7 Hz.

The resulting frequency response is shown in Figure 10.36(b). If the amplifier has a gain less than +20 dB, 3-pF compensation should not be used.

The circuit of Figure 10.35(b) is used if the compensation is *two-pole* instead of *one-pole*. The frequency response drops with frequency at twice the slope (-40 dB per decade) as is the case with one-pole compensation.

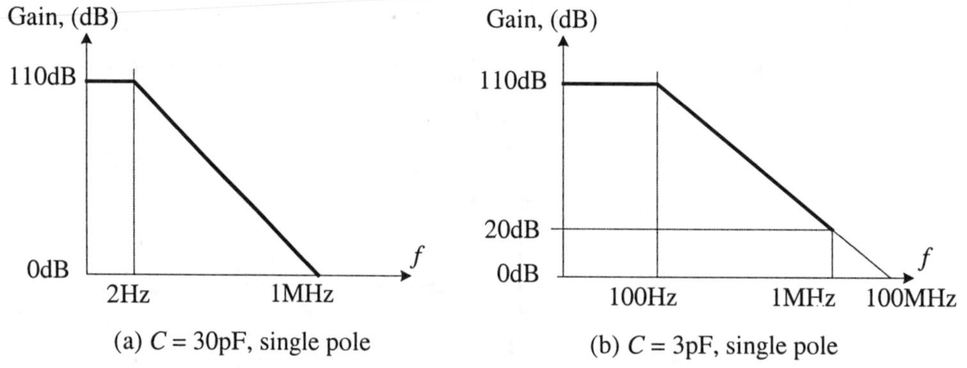

(a) $C = 30$pF, single pole (b) $C = 3$pF, single pole

Figure 10.36 – 101 compensation, single pole

Figure 10.35(c) illustrates *feed-forward compensation*. That is, instead of pin 1 being tied to the output through a capacitor, it is connected to the input. This system has a gain bandwidth product of 10^7 Hz. The capacitance, C_F, is calculated from the following equation.

$$C_F = \frac{1}{2\pi \times 3 \times 10^6 \times R_F} \qquad (10.104)$$

R_F is selected to obtain the desired gain.

EXAMPLE 10.14 (Design)

An instrumentation manufacturer received a contract to provide a certain type of transducer with maximum output of 0.8 mV. Its output is to be connected to an instrumentation transmitter which has a 0 to 5 V input. This transducer has a maximum variation of change of 20 kHz. The input impedance of the amplifier has to be at least one MΩ to avoid loading the transducer. A ±15 V power source is available for the design.

Solution: First the engineer has to select the most economical method of amplification. Since a ±15 V power source is available, the op-amp is a prime candidate. The op-amp is also capable of providing a high input impedance. Since only the frequency range is defined in the problem, a general purpose low-cost op-amp (such as the 741) could be used.

The amount of gain needed is 5V/0.8mV = 6250. The 741 op-amp gain per stage at 20 kHz is $10^6/20\times10^3 = 50$. This would then require the use of at least three op-amps in series to get the desired result. The last two op-amps could be set for a gain of 20, leaving the first op-amp with a required gain of 15.6 to achieve the overall 6250 factor.

To be assured that the input impedance to the first op-amp is high, the input is connected to the + terminal through a balancing resistor. For the first and second op-amps, we would use 5 kΩ for R_A and a feedback resistor of $R_F = 19R_A = 95$ kΩ. This is true since $1 + R_F/R_A = 20$. The balancing resistor, R_I, would be the parallel combination of 95 kΩ with 5 kΩ, or 4.76 kΩ. The final stage would have $R_A = 5$ kΩ, $R_F = 14.6$ kΩ and $R_A = 73$ kΩ. Then R_I is the parallel combination of 5 kΩ with 73 kΩ, or 4.68 kΩ. The final design is shown in Figure 10.37.

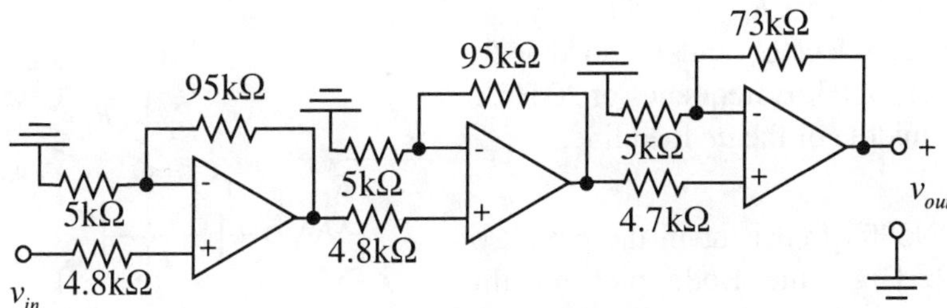

Figure 10.37 – Design for Example 10.14

SUMMARY

We began this chapter by dividing the response of an electronic amplifier into three broad frequency ranges: low frequency, mid frequency and high frequency. We then explored methods for determining the boundaries of these regions for the various configurations of BJT and FET amplifiers. We found that capacitors (bypass, coupling and internal) played a major role in establishing the frequency response of an amplifier.

We modified the transistor models to include small internal capacitors which affect high-frequency performance. We also examined the Miller effect which proved very useful in high-frequency analysis.

Throughout the chapter, we treated both analysis and design. We developed multiple techniques for designing an amplifier with a specified frequency response.

PROBLEMS

Section 10.1

10.1 Construct Bode plots for v_{out}/v_{in} for the circuits of Figure P10.1 and determine the lower and upper 3dB frequencies.

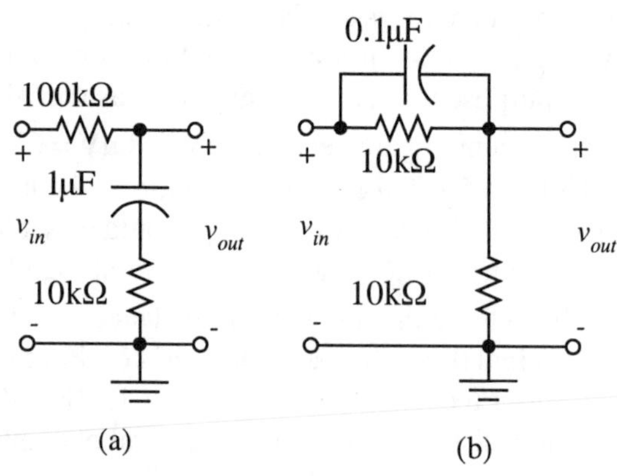

Figure P10.1

10.2 A 2N3903 transistor is incorporated in the circuit of Figure P10.2. Calculate the lower corner 3dB frequency and draw the Bode plot for this amplifier. Let $R_{load} = R_C = 1$ kΩ, $C_1 = 0.1$ μF, $R_E = 100$ Ω, $R_1 = 1.5$ kΩ, $R_2 = 10$ kΩ, $C_2 = 0.01$ μF, and $V_{CC} = 12$ V.

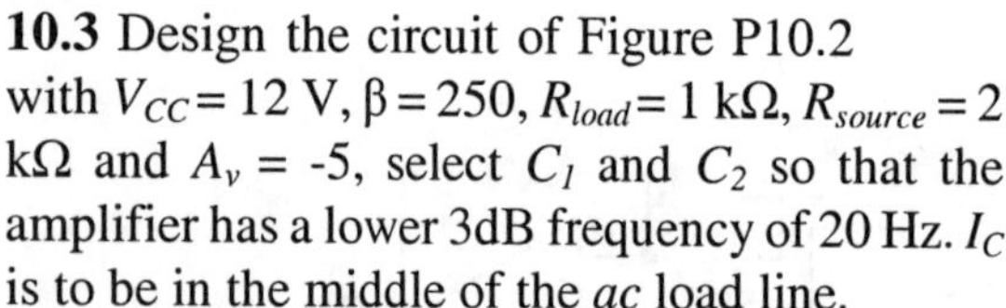

10.3 Design the circuit of Figure P10.2 with $V_{CC} = 12$ V, $\beta = 250$, $R_{load} = 1$ kΩ, $R_{source} = 2$ kΩ and A_v = -5, select C_1 and C_2 so that the amplifier has a lower 3dB frequency of 20 Hz. I_C is to be in the middle of the *ac* load line.

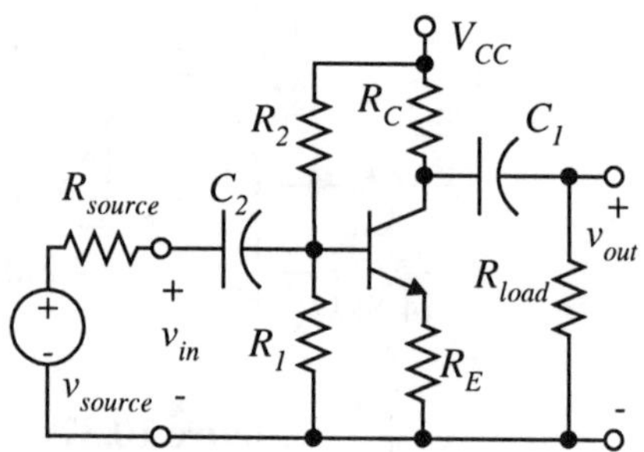

Figure P10.2

10.4 Use a 2N3903 transistor in the circuit of Figure P10.2. Draw the Bode plot for this amplifier when $R_1 = 1$ kΩ, $R_2 = 9$ kΩ, $R_{load} = R_C = 1$ kΩ, $R_E = 100$ Ω, $C_2 = 0.01$ μF and $C_1 = 0.1$ μF.

10.5 Given R_{source} = 5 kΩ, design an emitter-resistor amplifier with $R_{in} = 15$ kΩ, $A_v = -10$, R_{load} = 10 kΩ, and a low-frequency cutoff of 40 Hz. Use a transistor with β = 200, V_{BE} = 0.7 V and $V_{CC} = 12$ V. What are the values of C_1 and C_2 for the following cases?

(a) the poles are one decade apart?

(b) both poles are identically located?

(c) $C_1 = C_2 = C$.

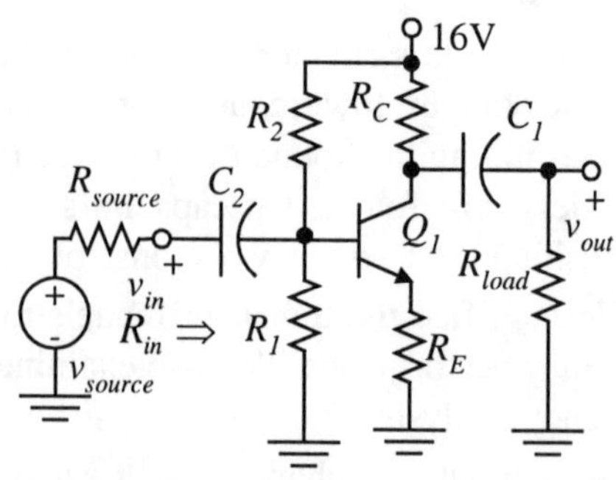

Figure P10.6

10.6 Design an amplifier of the type shown in Figure P10.6 with R_{in} = 4 kΩ, R_{source} = 1 kΩ, R_{load} = 5 kΩ, A_v = -10, and β = 200 for a 3 dB drop at 40 Hz. Use $V_T = 26$ mV and $V_{BE} = 0.7$ V.

(a) Determine all resistor values.

(b) Find values of C_1 and C_2 when the poles are 1 decade apart.

(c) Find values of C_1 and C_2 when the poles are identical.

(d) Determine a common value of C for the 3dB point and identify the frequency of each pole.

10.7 The emitter resistor is bypassed in the amplifier of Problem 10.5. What value is required for the bypass capacitor if the cutoff frequency is 40 Hz?

10.8 Design an amplifier with $R_{in} = 5$ kΩ, $A_v = -20$, $R_{load} = 8$ kΩ, $R_{source} = 2$ kΩ, $V_{CC} = 16$ V, $\beta = 200$, $f_L = 100$ Hz, $V_T = 26$ mV and $V_{BE} = 0.7$ V. Use the circuit of Figure P10.2.

(a) Determine all resistor values.

(b) Find the value of C_1 and C_2 assuming that the time constants are one decade apart.

(c) Find the values of C_1 and C_2 assuming that the time constants are identically located.

(d) Find the value of C when using $C_1 = C_2$.

10.9 Determine the low-frequency cutoff of the amplifier shown in Figure P10.6 when $R_{in} = 4$ kΩ, $R_C = R_{load} = 6$ kΩ, $R_E = 300$ Ω, $R_{source} = 2$ kΩ, and $C_1 = C_2 = 0.2$ μF.

10.10 Given the FET amplifier of Figure P10.10 with a 3N128 MOSFET and $V_{DD} = 12$ V, $R_{in} = 50$ kΩ.

(a) Design the amplifier to have a midrange voltage gain of -2 when $R_{load} = 3$ kΩ. Use $g_m = 5$ mS, $V_{DS} = 7.5$ V and $I_D = 2$ mA.

(b) Select C_1, C_2 and C_3 so that the lower 3dB frequency is 10 Hz.

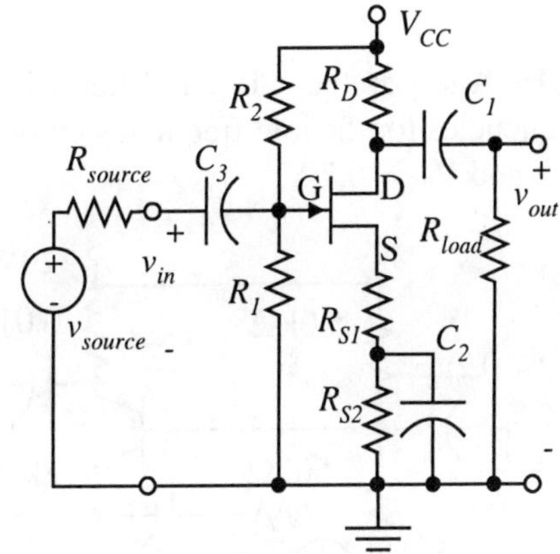

Figure P10.10

10.11 Design a JFET amplifier for $A_v = -10$, $R_{in} = 50$ kΩ, and $R_{load} = 20$ kΩ, using $V_{CC} = 20$ V. The Q-point is selected at $V_{DS} = 7$ V, $V_{GS} = -0.35$ V, $I_D = 1.3$ mA, and $g_m = 1.6$ mΩ^{-1}. Select C_1, C_2 and C_3 for a lower 3dB frequency of 20 Hz.

10.12 In the amplifier of Problem 10.11, the transistor is replaced by a MOSFET which has $g_m = 3333$ μΩ^{-1} at a Q-point of $V_{DS} = 6$ V, $I_D = 1$ mA and $V_{GS} = 2$ V.

(a) Design the amplifier.

(b) Select C_1, C_2 and C_3.

10.13 Design a JFET CS amplifier for a 3dB lower frequency cutoff of 40 Hz for $A_v = -2$ and $R_{in} = 100$ kΩ. The Q-point is selected at $V_{DS} = 6$ V, $V_{GS} = -1$ V, $I_D = 0.5$ mA and $g_m = 2$ mΩ^{-1}. Determine each of the following.

(a) All resistor values when $V_{CC} = 12$ V and $R_{load} = 10$ kΩ.

(b) τ values.

(c) Values of C_1, C_2, and C_3.

10.14 Design a CB amplifier for maximum output voltage swing. The amplifier must have a voltage gain of 10 into 4 kΩ load. Let $\beta = 100$, $V_{BE} = 0.7$ V, $V_{CC} = 18$ V, $R_{source} = 100$ Ω, and $R_E = 500$ Ω. Choose the capacitors for a 3dB corner frequency of 50 Hz.

10.15 Using the equivalent circuit for a common-base amplifier, determine the equation for the time constant of the base capacitor and input capacitor when the source resistor is significant.

10.16 Analyze the CB amplifier as shown in Figure P10.16 to determine the break frequencies for the low-frequency cutoff and the low-frequency cutoff. Use $V_T = 26$mV, $\beta = 200$, and $V_{BE} = 0.7$ V.

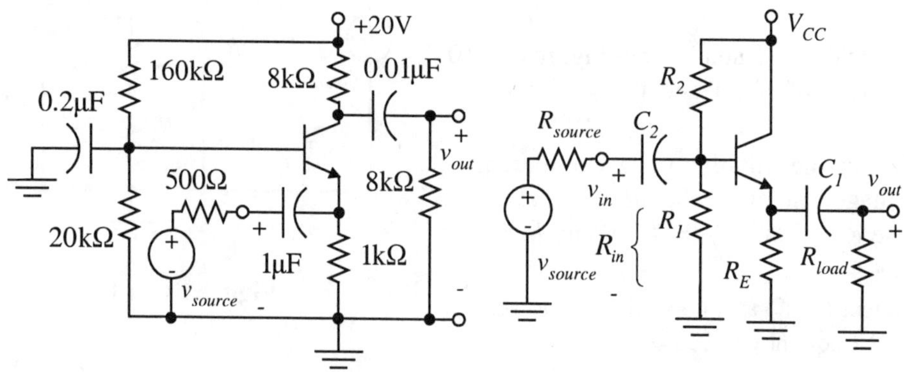

Figure P10.16 **Figure P10.17**

10.17 An EF amplifier of Figure P10.17 has $R_1 = 20$ kΩ, $R_2 = 2$ kΩ, $R_{load} = 100$ Ω, $R_E = 50$ Ω, $R_{source} = 1$ kΩ, $C_1 = 100$ μF and $C_2 = 3.3$ μF. Draw the Bode plots for this amplifier if $V_{CC} = 10$ V, $\beta = 200$, and $V_{BE} = 0.7$ V.

10.18 Design an EF amplifier with $R_{source} = 1$ kΩ, $A_i = 10$, $R_{load} = 20$ Ω and a low-frequency cutoff of 20 Hz. Use $V_{CC} = 10$ V and a transistor with $\beta = 80$ and $V_{BE} = 0.7$ V. What are the values of C_1 and C_2 if:

(a) The poles are one decade apart.

(b) Both poles are identically located.

(c) $C_1 = C_2$.

Section 10.3

10.19 Determine the low- and high-frequency response for the circuit shown in Figure P10.19. The transistor has a $C_{ob} = 2$ pF, $f_T = 2 \times 10^8$, $V_{BE} = 0.7$ V, $\beta = 100$, and $V_T = 26$ mV. Also show the break frequencies.

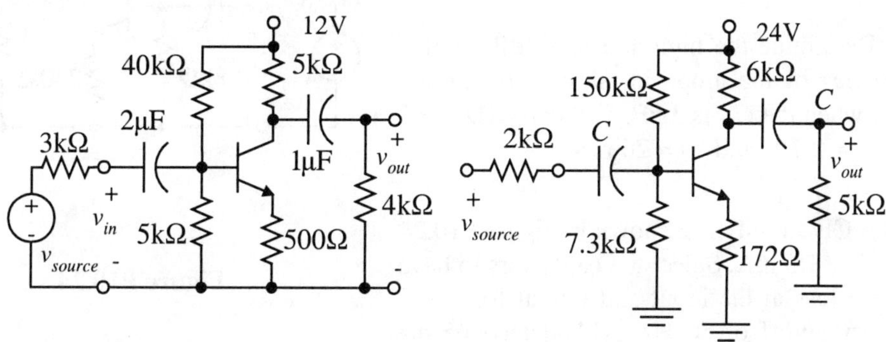

Figure P10.19 **Figure P10.21**

10.20 Design a CE amplifier for a low-frequency response of 50 Hz and an overall stage voltage gain of -7. Assume $V_{BE} = 0.7$ V, $\beta = 200$, $V_T = 26$ mV, $C_{ob} = 2$ pF and $f_T = 2 \times 10^8$. The specifications for the circuit are $R_{in} = R_{source} = 4$ kΩ, $R_{load} = 5$ kΩ and $V_{CC} = 15$ V. Design the amplifier such that the time constants are identical. Determine all resistor and capacitor values, and high-frequency cutoff.

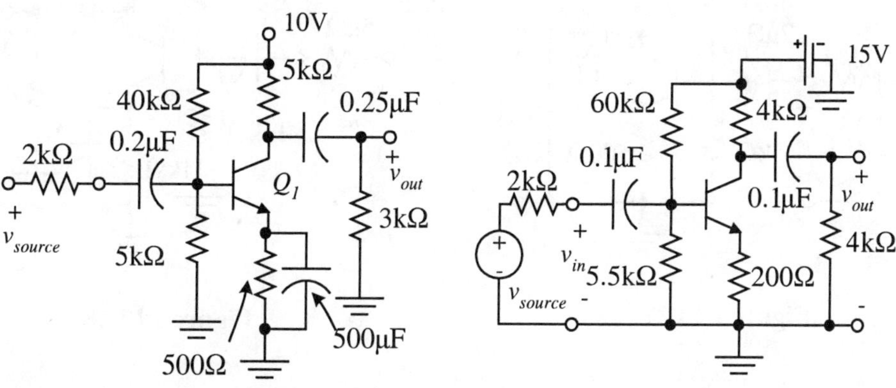

Figure P10.22 **Figure P10.23**

10.21 The circuit shown in Figure P10.21 has an $A_v = -15$ at mid frequency when $I_C = 2.64$ mA. Determine the value of C to allow $C_1 = C_2$ at 40 Hz and the high-frequency cutoff. The transistor has a $C_{ob} = 5$ pF, $f_T = 2 \times 10^8$, $V_{BE} = 0.7$ V and $\beta = 250$.

10.22 Determine the high and low frequency response for the circuit shown in Figure P10.22. The transistor has a $C_{ob} = 2$ pF, $f_T = 2 \times 10^8$, $V_{BE} = 0.7$ V, $\beta = 100$ and $V_T = 26$ mV. Also indicate the break frequencies.

10.23 Determine the high and low 3dB cutoff frequencies of the amplifier shown in Figure P10.23 when the C_{ob} is 3 pF, $f_T = 4 \times 10^8$ Hz, $\beta = 100$, $V_{BE} = 0.7$ V and $V_T = 26$ mV.

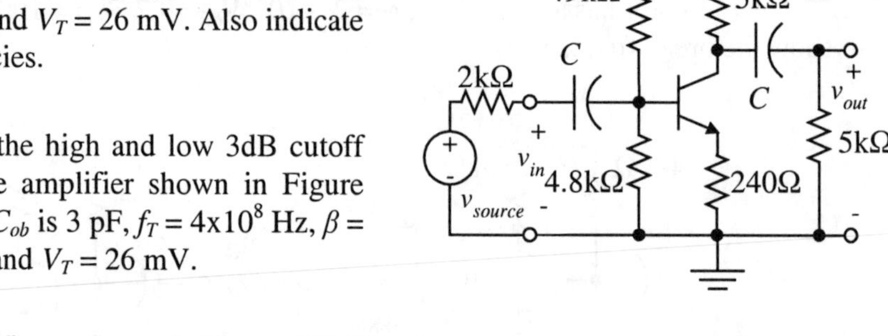

10.24 A CE amplifier as shown in Figure P10.24 has an $I_C = 1.5$ mA. Select the capacitors to have the same loss at the input and output for a low frequency cutoff of 50 Hz. Also determine the high-frequency cutoff when $C_{ob} = 6$ pF and $f_T = 3 \times 10^8$.

Figure P10.24

10.25 Using a 2N3904 transistor with the circuit of Figure P10.23, determine the upper 3dB frequency and construct the Bode plot. Let $R_{load} = R_C = 10$ kΩ, $C_1 = 0.1$ μF, $R_E = 100$ Ω, $R_1 = 1.5$ kΩ, $R_2 = 21$ kΩ, $R_{source} = 500$ Ω, $C_2 = 0.01$ μF, $V_{CC} = 12$ V, $C_{ob} = 4.5$ pF, $f_T = 200$ MHz and $\beta = 100$.

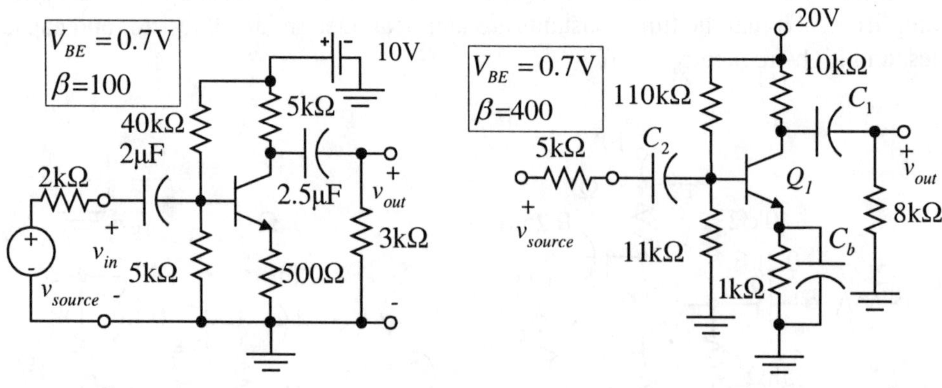

Figure P10.27

Figure P10.28

10.26 Design a CE amplifier for a low-frequency response of 50 Hz which has an overall stage gain of -10 when using a transistor having a $V_{BE} = 0.7$ V, $\beta = 200$, $C_{ob} = 2$ pF, $V_T = 26$ mV and $f_T = 2 \times 10^8$ Hz. The specification R_{in} (at the capacitor input) = $R_{source} = 4$ kΩ, $R_{load} =$ 5 kΩ, and $V_{CC} = 15$ V. Design the amplifier for a $C_{in} = C_{out}$. Determine all resistor and capacitor values, high-frequency cutoff and sketch the magnitude plot. Note that this means to design the transistor stage for $A_v = -20$ because of the voltage division at the input.

10.27 Determine the high and low 3dB cutoff frequencies for the circuit shown in Figure P10.27 and sketch the Bode magnitude plot of the response. The transistor has $C_{ob} = 2$ pF and $f_T = 2 \times 10^8$ Hz, $V_{BE} = 0.7$ V, $V_T = 26$ mV, and $\beta = 100$.

10.28 The circuit shown in Figure P10.28 was designed for an $I_C = 1.09$ mA. Determine the value of C_1 and C_2 to allow 1.5 dB loss at input and output at 100Hz, value of C_B for no loss, and the high-frequency cutoff when $V_T = 26$ mV, $C_{ob} = 3$ pF, and $f_T = 3 \times 10^8$.

10.29 Calculate the f_H for a junction transistor CE amplifier with the following values: $f_T =$ 500 MHz, $h_{fe} = 400$, $C_{ob} = 0.5$ pF, $I_C = 5$ mA, $R_{load} = R_C = 7$ kΩ and $R_B = 20$ kΩ, and $R_{source} =$ 2 kΩ.

10.30 The specifications for a particular FET show that at 200 MHz, $C_{iss} = 6$ pF, and $C_{rss} =$ 2.5 pF. Determine the capacitor values needed in the model shown in Figure 10.20 when the gain is 2.

10.31 Determine the parameters of the model of Figure 10.19(b) from the information for the 3N128 given in the Appendix. Use a frequency of 200 MHz at $V_{DS} = 15$ V and $I_D = 5$mA. Assume the capacitor values are the same for 1 MHz as for 200 MHz and ignore the series resistors in the gate and source.

10.32 Design a CS JFET amplifier and find the high-frequency cutoff of the amplifier when $A_v = -2$, $R_{in} = 100$ kΩ, $R_{load} = 5$ kΩ, $R_{source} = 10$ kΩ and $V_{DD} = 20$ V. The transistor used has $I_{DSS} = 10$ mA, $V_p = -6$ V, $C_{gs} = 5$ pF, $C_{gd} = 2$ pF, $C_{ds} = 1$ pF. Use $I_D = 0.4\, I_{DSS}$ and $V_{DS} = 10$ V.

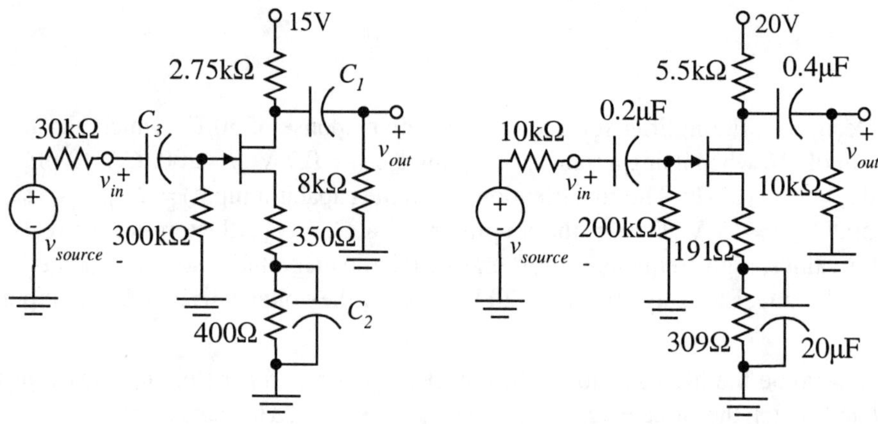

Figure P10.33

Figure P10.34

10.33 Determine the size of all capacitors in the amplifier shown in Figure P10.33 for a low-frequency cutoff of 80 Hz and determine the high frequency cutoff when C_{ds} = 1 pF, C_{gs} = 5 pF, and C_{gd} = 4 pF. The g_m for the operating point of the *n*-channel JFET is 3 mΩ^{-1}.

10.34 Determine the high- and low-frequency response for the circuit shown in Figure P10.34 when g_m = 2.5 mΩ^{-1}, C_{iss} = 10 pF and C_{rss} = 4 pF. Sketch the amplitude Bode plot of the amplifier and show the break frequencies.

10.35 The high-frequency equivalent for a FET amplifier has been selected as shown in Figure P10.35. Determine the following:

(a) Mid-frequency voltage gain.

(b) High frequency voltage gain in terms of *s*. Show how you derived the transfer function.

(c) Normalized voltage gain, A_v/A_{vmid}.

(d) If R_{source} approaches zero, what is the normalized gain equation?

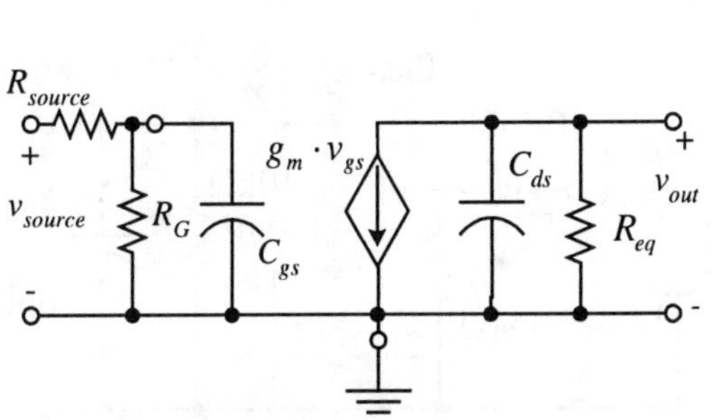

Figure P10.35

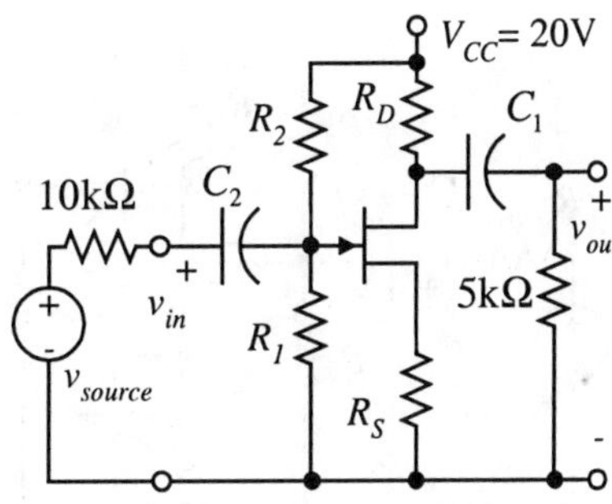

Figure P10.36

10.36 Design a CS FET amplifier and find the high-frequency cutoff of the amplifier for A_v = -3, R_{source} = 10 kΩ, and R_{in} = 100 kΩ. The transistor used has I_{DSS} = 10 mA, V_p = -5 V, C_{iss} = 7 pF, and C_{rss} = 2 pF. Use the circuit of Figure P10.36.

10.37 Determine the high and the low frequency response for the circuit shown in Figure P10.37 when $g_m = 2.5\ \text{m}\Omega^{-1}$, C_{iss} = 12 pF, and C_{rss} = 4 pF. Sketch the amplitude Bode plot and show the break frequencies.

10.38 Analyze the circuit shown in Figure P10.38. The transistor used is a JFET with V_p = -4 V, I_{DSS} = 8 mA, C_{gd} = 3 pF, C_{ds} = 0, C_{gs} = 10 pF and $1/r_{ds}$ = 0. The transistor is operating at 3.2 mA. Determine all the time constants and break frequencies of the circuit.

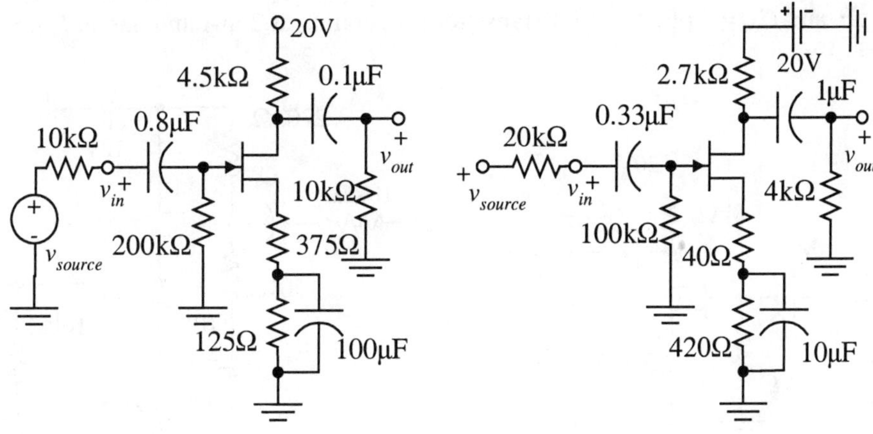

Figure P10.37

Figure P10.38

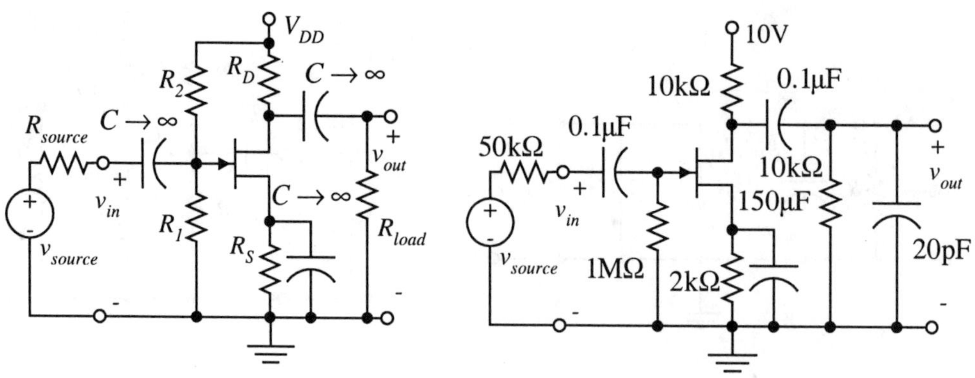

Figure P10.39 **Figure P10.40**

10.39 For the circuit of Figure P10.39 develop the high frequency portion of the Bode plot for an amplifier when $R_{source} = 2$ kΩ, $R_{load} = 4$ kΩ, $R_D = 3$ kΩ, $R_G = 20$ kΩ, $r_{ds} = 10$ kΩ, $C_{gs} =$ 5 pF and $C_{ds} = 1.1$ pF, $C_{gd} = 2$ pF and $g_m = 0.002\ \Omega^{-1}$.

10.40 Determine the frequency response for the FET amplifier shown in Figure P10.40 where $r_{ds} = 100$ kΩ, $g_m = 2.5$ mΩ^{-1}, $C_{gd} = 2$ pF, $C_{gs} = 10$ pF and $C_{ds} = 2$ pF.

10.41 For the circuit shown in Figure P10.41, determine the size of all the capacitors for a low frequency cutoff of 50 Hz and also calculate the high frequency cutoff when $C_{ds} = 1$ pF, $C_{gs} = 5$ pF, and $C_{gd} = 2$ pF. The FET transistor is operating at 2 mA and has an $I_{DSS} = 5$ mA and $V_p = -3$ V.

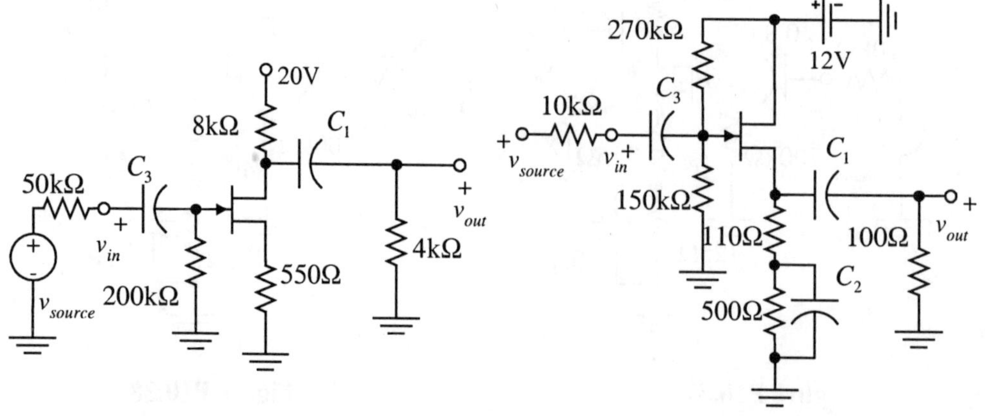

Figure P10.41 **Figure P10.42**

10.42 For the circuit shown in Figure P10.42, determine the high-frequency response when $C_{gd} = 4$ pF and $C_{gs} = 3$ pF and the transistor is operating at 10 mA. The transistor parameters are $V_p = -6$ V and $I_{DSS} = 20$ mA.

10.43 Determine the high-frequency response for the amplifier shown in Figure P10.43 when $R_{source} = R_E = 500\ \Omega$, $I_C = 1$ mA, and $R_{laad} = R_C = 10$ kΩ. The transistor has a $\beta = 100$, $f_T = 2 \times 10^8$ Hz, $C_{ob} = 2$ pF, and $V_T = 26$ mV.

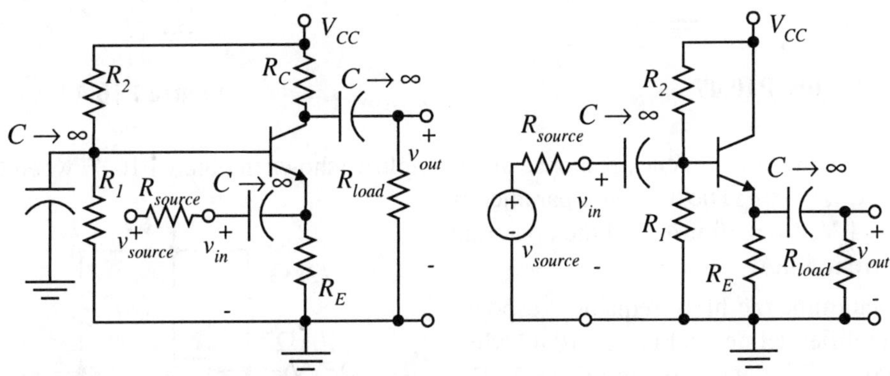

Figure P10.43 **Figure P10.46**

10.44 Derive the equation for the high-frequency response for the amplifier shown in Figure P10.43 when the base capacitor is removed.

10.45 Design a CB amplifier for maximum output swing and determine its high-frequency response when $f_T = 2 \times 10^7$ Hz, $\beta = 200$, $V_{BE} = 0.7$ V, $C_{ob} = 4$ pF, $R_{source} = 50\ \Omega$, $R_E = 400\ \Omega$, $R_{load} = 5$ kΩ and $V_{CC} = 12$ V. The low-frequency cutoff must be at 20 Hz. Use the circuit shown in Figure P10.43.

10.46 Determine the high-frequency response for the amplifier shown in Figure P10.46 when $R_{source} = 3$ kΩ, $R_1 = R_2 = 5$ kΩ, and $R_E = R_{load} = 500\ \Omega$. The transistor has a $\beta = 100$ and $C_{ob} = 3$ pF.

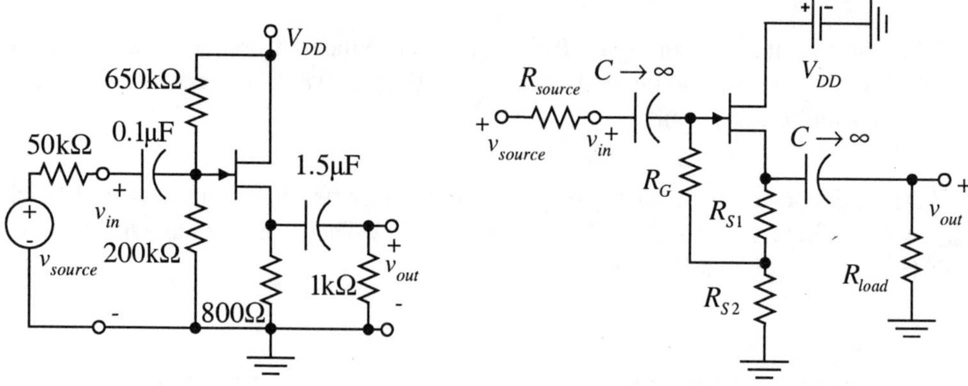

Figure P10.47

Figure P10.49

10.47 Determine the frequency response of the amplifier shown in Figure P10.47 when C_{iss} = 9 pF and C_{rss} = 5 pF. The transistor parameters are V_p = -4 V, I_{dss} = 10 mA, and the operating point current 5 mA.

10.48 Determine the high frequency response of the amplifier defined in Figure P10.47 when g_m = 0.002 mΩ^{-1}, C_{rss} = 3 pF and C_{iss} = 7 pF.

10.49 Derive the equation for the high-frequency response of the SF bootstrap amplifier shown in Figure P10.49.

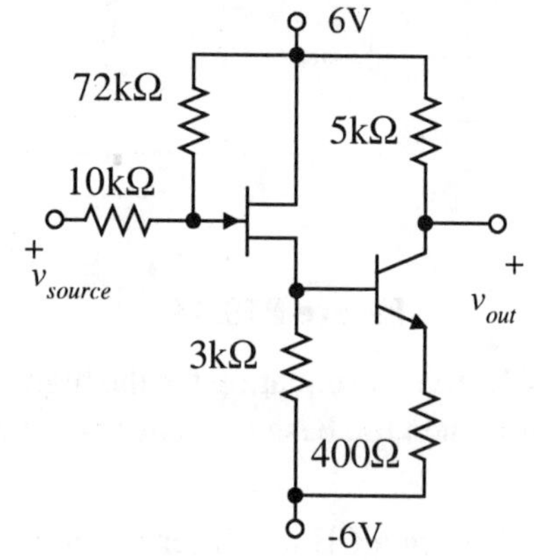

Figure P10.50

10.50 What is the frequency response of the circuit shown in Figure P10.50 when the FET is operating at 2.4 mA. The FET parameters are C_{iss} = 6 pF, C_{rss} = 3 pF, V_p = -4 V, and I_{dss} = 6 mA. The BJT parameters are β = 200, V_{BE} = 0.7 V, C_{ob} = 4 pF, V_T = 26 mV, and $f_T = 3 \times 10^8$ Hz.

Section 10.5

In Problems 10.51 to 10.60, design 741 op-amp circuits which will generate the indicated output voltage, v_o, input voltages v_1, v_2, and v_3. Be sure to balance the bias currents in each design. For each design, find the input resistance for each input, the output resistance and the bandwidth. The input resistance must be at least 100 MΩ and the bandwidth must be greater than 20 kHz. It may be necessary to use more than one op-amp in some of these designs.

10.51 $v_{out} = 700v_1$

10.52 $v_{out} = v_1/700$

10.53 $v_{out} = -700v_1$

10.54 $v_{out} = -v_1/700$

10.55 $v_{out} = v_1 - v_2$

10.56 $v_{out} = 10v_1 - v_2$

10.57 $v_{out} = v_1 - 10v_2$

10.58 $v_{out} = v_1 + 700v_2$

10.59 $v_{out} = -(v_1 + 700v_2)$

10.60 $v_{out} = v_1 - 2v_2 + 3v_3$

In Problem 10.61 to 10.67, design a circuit which is composed of one or more 741 op-amps to obtain the output as indicated in each problem with at least the bandwidth shown. The input resistances will be in excess of 100 megohms when using the minimum number of op-amps and all op-amps need to be *dc* biased balanced. Determine the output resistance and draw schematic with resistor values.

10.61 $v_{out} = 50v_1 - 190v_2 - 200v_3$ BW = 20 kHz

10.62 $v_{out} = 50v_1 - 180v_2 - 400v_3$ BW = 20 kHz

10.63 $v_{out} = 40v_1 - 190v_2 - 400v_3$ BW = 25 kHz

10.64 $v_{out} = 8v_1 - 14v_2$ BW = 50 kHz

10.65 $v_{out} = 20v_1 - 45v_2 - 120v_3$ BW = 50 kHz

10.66 $v_{out} = 10v_1 - 20v_2 - 7v_3$ BW = 100 kHz

10.67 $v_{out} = 25v_1 - 400v_2$ BW = 40 kHz

In Problems 10.68 to 10.73, design multiple 741 op-amp circuits to develop the indicated output voltage, v_{out}, from the input voltages, v_1, v_2 and v_3 using the minimum number of op-amps. The input resistance to each input must be 100 MΩ or greater, and the inputs should not be directly coupled to one another. For each design, find R_{in}, R_{out}, and the bandwidth. A minimum bandwidth of 50 kHz must be achieved.

10.68 $v_{out} = 3(v_1 + v_2)$

10.69 $v_{out} = 3(v_1 - v_2)$

10.70 $v_{out} = 1000v_1 - 300v_2$

10.71 $v_{out} = 500v_1 - 50v_2$

10.72 $v_{out} = 70v_1 - (1/7)v_2$

10.73 $v_{out} = 100v_1 + 50v_2$

In Problems 10.74 to 10.79, design an amplifier circuit composed of a minimum number of op-amps needed to provide the gain and bandwidth as shown in each problem. The input resistance will be in excess of 100 MΩ and the op-amps will be *dc* biased balanced. Determine the output resistance and draw the schematic with resistor values.

10.74 Gain = 4000 Bandwidth = 100 kHz

10.75 Gain = -8500 Bandwidth = 40 kHz

10.76 Gain = 9000 Bandwidth = 50 kHz

10.77 Gain = -10,000 Bandwidth = 40 kHz

10.78 Gain = 200,000 Bandwidth = 20 kHz

10.79 Gain = 600,000 Bandwidth = 20 kHz

In Problems 10.80 to 10.83, design single-amplifier 101 circuits that will generate the indicated output voltage, v_{out}, from the input voltages, v_1 and v_2. Use a 3-pF compensating capacitor wherever possible. Be sure to balance the bias currents in each input. Calculate R_{in}, R_{out}, and the bandwidth has to be at least 20 kHz.

10.80 $v_{out} = 700v_1$

10.81 $v_{out} = 10v_1 - v_2$

10.82 $v_{out} = 20v_1 + 30v_2$

10.83 $v_{out} = v_1 - 15v_2$

In Problems 10.84 to 10.86, design multiple 101 operational amplifier circuits to develop the voltage, v_{out}, from the input voltages, v_1 and v_2. The input resistance into each input must be at least 100 MΩ and the inputs should not be directly coupled to one another. The bandwidth must be greater than 20kHz using 30 pF or 3 pF 101 compensation.

10.84 $v_{out} = 10(v_1 + v_2)$

10.85 $v_{out} = 10v_1 - v_2$

10.86 $v_{out} = 1000v_1 - 300v_2$

Chapter 11
Feedback and Stability

11.0 INTRODUCTION

Feedback exists when the output of a system is connected to the input in such a way that waveforms appearing at the output affect the input signal. We have already seen several forms of feedback. Transistor amplifiers often include an emitter resistor. If that emitter resistor is left unbypassed, a form of feedback occurs. This is true since a part of the output voltage is subtracted from the input voltage thereby affecting the base-to-emitter voltage.

Previous chapters dealt with op-amp circuits, most of which include feedback between output and input. This feedback has the desirable effect of reducing the sensitivity of the overall amplifier to changes in the op-amp parameters. Most notably, the gain of the open-loop op-amp (without feedback) varies significantly with changes in frequency, whereas the overall gain of the *feedback amplifier* is much less sensitive to frequency changes.

The advantages of feedback are summarized as follows:

1. Closed-loop gain, although usually lower than that without feedback, is less sensitive to variations of device parameters.
2. Input and output resistances of the closed-loop system are controlled.
3. Amplifier bandwidth is increased.
4. Nonlinearities and distortion are reduced.
5. Unwanted internal-generated noise signals are reduced.

In our initial discussion, we consider *negative feedback*. This occurs when the portion of the output that is fed back to the input has the effect of reducing the magnitude of the input. *Positive feedback*, in which the signal is fed back from the output in a manner that increases the input magnitude, is frequently used in electronic circuits. Such feedback is intentionally introduced in the design of *oscillators*. The amplifier becomes unstable and, even in the absence of an input signal, begins to oscillate, producing a periodic output signal.

This chapter develops the mathematical tools for analyzing the effects of feedback on electronic systems. After studying this material, you will understand the following concepts:

- The different types of feedback.
- How amplifier stability can be controlled.
- The use of unstable amplifiers as oscillators.
- The effects of capacitive loading.

11.1 FEEDBACK AMPLIFIER CONSIDERATIONS

Figure 11.1 shows a model of a feedback system.

This model can be used to represent an amplifier or any other system with feedback. The circle denotes a summing operation. The signal leaving the circle, $\varepsilon(s)$, is equal to the difference between the two signals entering. Thus,

$$\varepsilon(s) = R(s) - Y(s) \tag{11.1}$$

Each of the parameters in the above equation can represent a time function, a Laplace transform, or a complex phasor as used in the case of sinusoidal inputs. For the present analysis, we use Laplace transform notation.

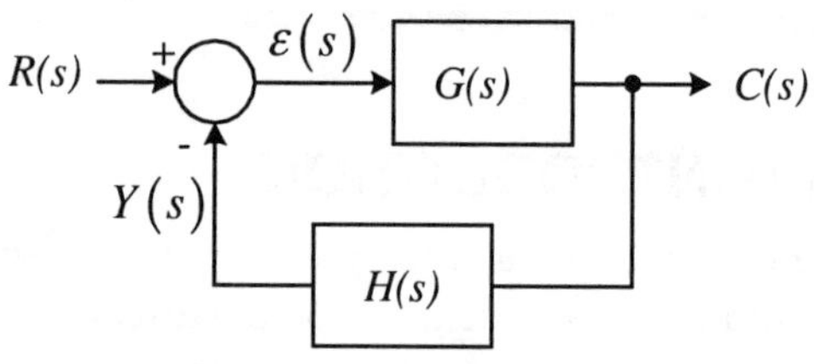

Figure 11.1 – Typical closed loop system

The system of Figure 11.1 is a *negative-feedback* system since the signal driving the forward loop block, $G(s)$, is equal to the input signal, $R(s)$, *minus* some function of the output signal, $C(s)$. These quantities are functions of the Laplace transform variable, s, so are frequency dependent. In this case,

$$Y(s) = H(s)C(s)$$

$$C(s) = G(s)\varepsilon(s) \tag{11.2}$$

$H(s)$ and $G(s)$ are *transfer functions*, which represent the ratio of the Laplace transform of the output of a given block to the Laplace transform of the input to that block. The *closed-loop* transfer function, $C(s)/R(s)$, is derived from the following equations (taken directly from the system diagram):

$$\varepsilon(s) = R(s) - H(s)C(s)$$

$$C(s) = G(s)\varepsilon(s) = G(s)R(s) - G(s)H(s)C(s) \tag{11.3}$$

$$\frac{C(s)}{R(s)} = \frac{G(s)}{1 + G(s)H(s)}$$

11.2 TYPES OF FEEDBACK

Feedback exists when a portion of the output is connected to the input through a circuit. The output voltage can be fed back to the input in the form of a voltage signal that then subtracts from the input voltage signal. Similarly, either or both of these voltage parameters can be replaced with current parameters. This gives rise to the four forms of feedback shown in Figure 11.2 and summarized in Table 11.1. We have included impedance characteristics.

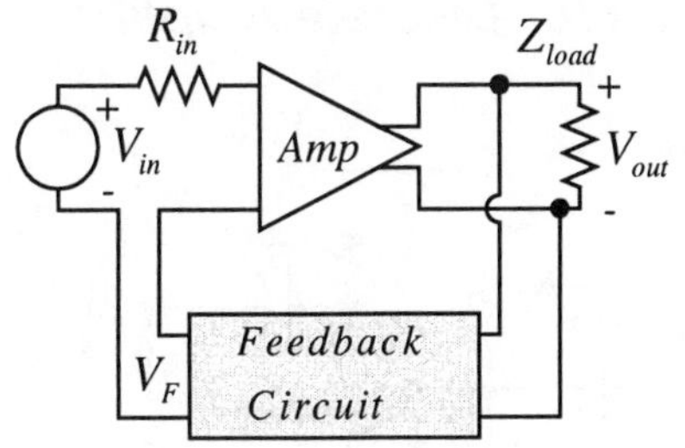

(a) Voltage feedback - voltage subtraction

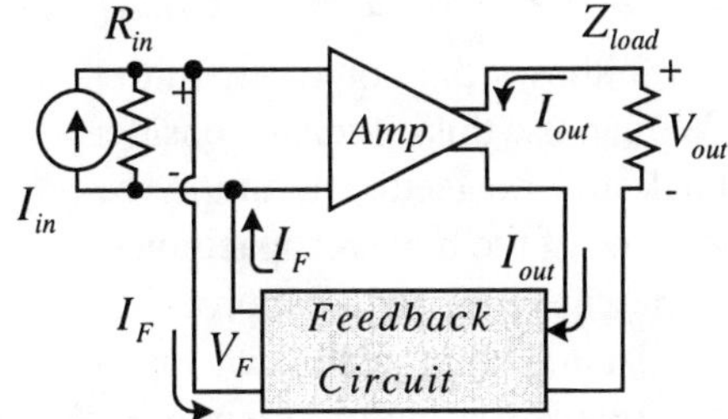

(b) Current feedback - current subtraction

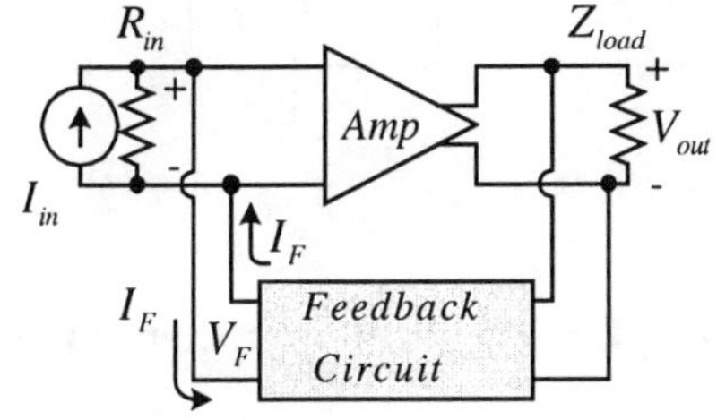

(c) Voltage feedback - current subtraction

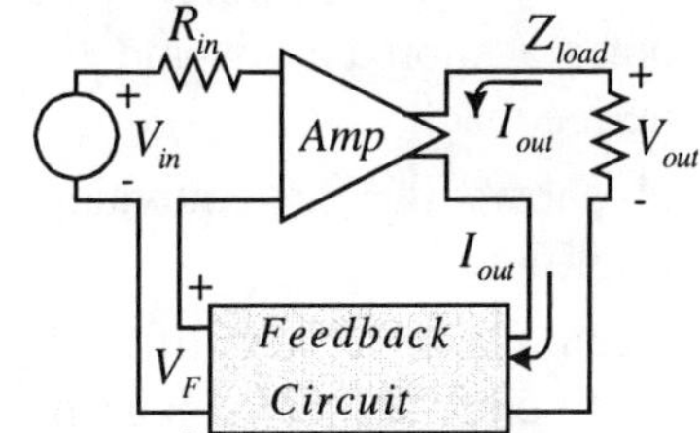

(d) Current feedback - voltage subtraction

Figure 11.2 - Four types of feedback

Type of Feedback	Input	Output	Input Impedance	Output Impedance
Voltage Feedback-Voltage subtraction	Voltage	Voltage	High	Low
Current Feedback-Current subtraction	Current	Current	Low	High
Voltage Feedback-Current subtraction	Current	Voltage	Low	Low
Current Feedback-Voltage subtraction	Voltage	Current	High	High

Table 11.1 - Types of Feedback

11.3 FEEDBACK AMPLIFIERS

In this section, we discuss examples of both voltage and current feedback. In most cases the amplifier networks consist of active elements and the feedback networks consist of passive elements. The feedback networks can be either resistive or frequency dependent. In frequency-dependent feedback networks, the amount of feedback is determined by the frequency of the input signals. As the frequency changes, the amount of feedback changes.

11.3.1 Current Feedback - Voltage subtraction for Discrete Amplifiers

Figure 11.3 shows the common-emitter amplifier. We can use this circuit to consider both feedback and no feedback simply by varying the value of the bypass capacitance. That is, as the capacitor value approaches zero, the capacitor approaches an open circuit and we have the feedback situation (i.e., the emitter-resistor amplifier). As the capacitance approaches infinity, the capacitor becomes a short circuit and the amplifier has no feedback.

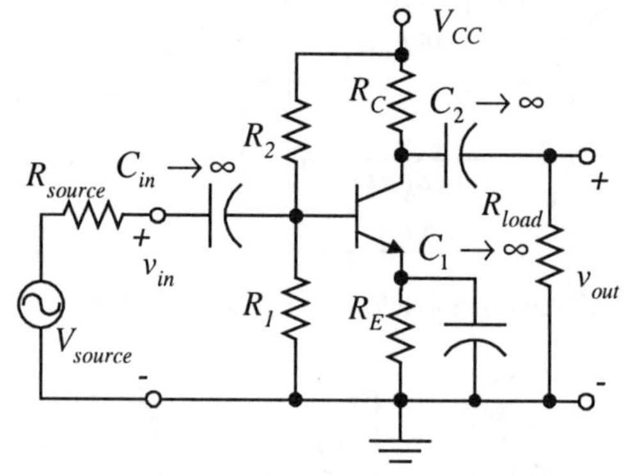

Figure 11.3 – Common-emitter stage

Figure 11.4 shows the *ac* equivalent circuit of the amplifier.

The voltage gain for the CE amplifier is calculated from this equivalent circuit as in Chapter 5. We present the result of the derivation in Equation (11.4).

$$A_v = \frac{V_{out}}{V_{in}} = \frac{-\beta\left(R_C \| R_{load}\right)}{r_\pi + \beta\left(R_E \| 1/sC\right)} = \frac{-\left(R_C \| R_{load}\right)}{r_e + \left(R_E \| 1/sC\right)} \tag{11.4}$$

The voltage gain with feedback (the emitter-resistor amplifier) is known as the *closed-loop gain* and is found by letting C approach zero in Equation (11.4). To simplify the result, let us also assume that $R_E >> r_e$. Equation (11.4) for the closed-loop gain then reduces to

$$A_{v\,(closed\ loop)} = \frac{-\left(R_C \| R_{load}\right)}{R_E} \tag{11.5}$$

The voltage gain without feedback is known as the *open-loop gain*, $A_{v\,(open\ loop)}$, and is found by letting C approach infinity in Equation (11.4).

$$A_{v\,(open\ loop)} = \frac{-\left(R_C \| R_{load}\right)}{r_e} = \frac{-\beta\left(R_C \| R_{load}\right)}{r_\pi} \tag{11.6}$$

As an example, let us calculate the open-loop and closed-loop gain for this amplifier with the following component values: $R_C = R_{load} = 1\ \text{k}\Omega$, $R_E = 100\ \Omega$, $r_\pi = 600\ \Omega$, and $\beta = 300$. The gain with and without feedback (open loop) are given by

$$A_{v\,(closed\,loop)} = \frac{-\left(R_C \| R_{load}\right)}{R_E} = -5$$

(11.7)

$$A_{v\,(open\,loop)} = \frac{-\beta\left(R_C \| R_{load}\right)}{r_\pi} = -250$$

$A_{v\,(closed\,loop)}$ is much smaller than $A_{v\,(open\,loop)}$. The feedback considerably reduces the gain. Also note that the equation for gain with feedback does not include any transistor parameter values. Thus, the gain with feedback depends only on the ratio of resistance values. This is often desirable. The higher gain, obtained when the capacitance approaches infinity, is dependent on the transistor parameters β and r_π. In Chapter 7 we showed that these parameters may vary considerably.

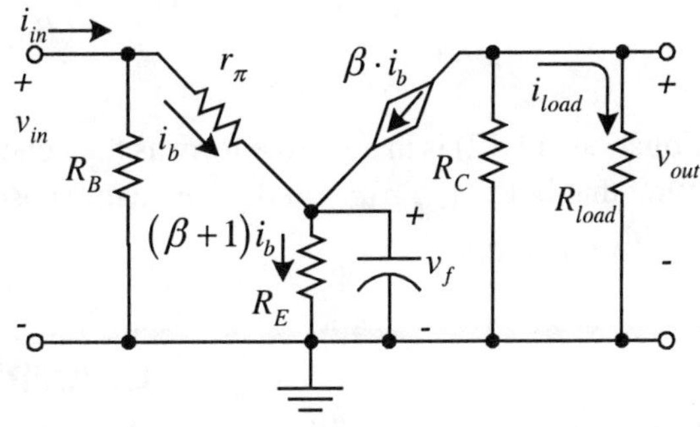

Figure 11.4 – Equivalent circuit for CE amplifier

It may not be obvious that this circuit fits the feedback model. To highlight the negative feedback, let us write the voltage around the base-emitter loop of Figure 11.4. The voltage, v_{be}, is given by

$$v_{be} = v_{in} - i_c R_E \qquad (11.8)$$

Equation (11.8) shows that the voltage driving the transistor, v_{be}, is reduced by a signal proportional to the output current, i_c. We now return to Equation (11.4) and rewrite it in a form that emphasizes the feedback, that is,

$$A_{v\,(closed\,loop)} = \frac{-\left(R_C \| R_{load}\right)}{r_e} \cdot \frac{1}{1+\left(R_E \| 1/sC\right)/r_e} \qquad (11.9)$$

To put this into the feedback model format, we define γ as the ratio of feedback voltage to the output voltage. The feedback voltage, V_f, is the voltage across the parallel combination of R_E and $1/sC$. The *feedback attenuation factor, γ,* corresponds to *H(s)* in Figure 11.1. The symbol β is often used for the feedback factor. We have chosen γ so as not to confuse this with the current gain of a transistor. The gain without feedback is found by letting *C* approach infinity in Equation (11.9). This yields

$$A_{v\,(open\,loop)} = A_{vo} = \frac{-\left(R_C \| R_{load}\right)}{r_e} \qquad (11.10)$$

The feedback attenuation factor is

$$\gamma = \frac{V_f}{V_{out}} = \frac{-R_E \| (1/sC)}{(R_C \| R_{load})} \tag{11.11}$$

We can now write an equation for closed-loop in terms of the open-loop gain and the feedback attenuation factor.

$$A_{v\,(closed\ loop)} = A_{vo}\left[\frac{1}{1+(R_C \| R_{load})\gamma / r_e}\right] = \frac{A_{vo}}{1+\gamma A_{vo}} \tag{11.12}$$

Equation (11.12) is in the same form as the general feedback equation, Equation (11.1). Keep in mind that both $A_{v\,(open\ loop)}$ and γ are negative, so the denominator in Equation (11.12) contains positive quantities.

EXAMPLE 11.1

In a given feedback amplifier, A_{vo} = -80 and the ratio of feedback voltage to output voltage is γ = -0.1. What is the closed-loop voltage gain of the amplifier? Now suppose that the gain without feedback increases by 25%. Find the new overall gain.

Solution: The closed-loop gain is given by Equation (11.12).

$$A_v = \frac{-80}{1 + 0.1 \times 80} = -8.89$$

We now let A_{vo} change from -80 to -100. The new closed-loop gain is

$$A_v = \frac{-100}{1 + 0.1 \times 100} = -9.09$$

Thus, a 25% change in the open-loop gain results in only a 1.1% change in the closed-loop gain.

Example 11.1 considers a specific example of the *sensitivity* of an amplifier to changes in gain. This sensitivity is determined by differentiating Equation (11.12)

$$\frac{dA_v}{dA_{vo}} = \frac{1}{(1+\gamma A_{vo})^2} \tag{11.13}$$

with respect to the open-loop gain. Thus, if we now divide this derivative by A_v [from Equation (11.12)], we have

$$\frac{dA_v}{A_v} = \frac{1}{1+\gamma A_{vo}} \cdot \frac{dA_{vo}}{A_{vo}} \approx \frac{1}{\gamma A_{vo}} \cdot \frac{dA_{vo}}{A_{vo}} \quad (11.14)$$

The final approximation in Equation (11.14) assumes $\gamma A_{vo} >> 1$.

The expression on the left side of Equation (11.14) is the fractional change in closed-loop gain. The equation shows this is approximately equal to the fractional change in open-loop gain divided by γA_{vo}. Since γA_{vo} is usually a large number, the variation in closed-loop gain is greatly reduced for a given variation in open-loop gain.

EXERCISE

E11.1 Calculate the feedback attenuation factor, γ, for the amplifier stage of Example 11.1.

Answer: $\gamma = -0.2$

11.3.2 Voltage Feedback-Current Subtraction for a Discrete Amplifier

Figure 11.5(a) illustrates an amplifier in which the output voltage is fed back to the input through a resistor, R_F. Since we are dealing with voltage feedback-current subtraction, the source should be a current source. The figure shows a voltage, v_{source}, in series with a source resistance, R_{source}. This represents the Thevenin equivalent of the current source, where $v_{source} = i_{in}R_{source}$.

The *ac* equivalent circuit is shown in Figure 11.5(b). Note that R_E is bypassed with a large capacitor so we don't have the type of feedback seen in section 11.3.1.

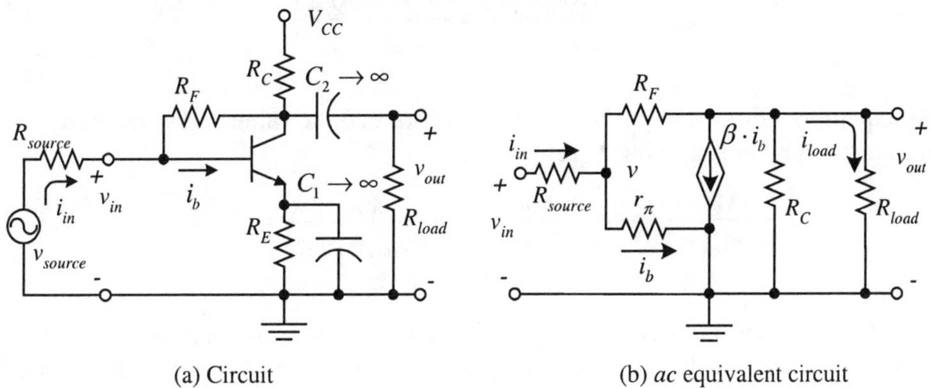

(a) Circuit

(b) *ac* equivalent circuit

Figure 11.5 – Voltage feedback – current subtraction

We wish to develop equations for the gain of this circuit which clearly show the effect of feedback. We find the output voltage by assuming that the current through R_F is negligible with respect to βi_b. Thus,

$$v_{out} = -(R_C \| R_{load})\beta \cdot i_b \tag{11.15}$$

The current, i_b, can be found by writing a node equation at the node labeled v in Figure 11.5(b).

$$i_b = \frac{v_{in} - v}{R_{source}} + \frac{v_{out} - v}{R_F} = \frac{v_{in}}{R_{source}} + \frac{v_{out}}{R_F} - \frac{v}{R_{source} \| R_F} \tag{11.16}$$

Now since $i_b = v/r_\pi$, we can simplify this to

$$i_b = \frac{v}{r_\pi} = \frac{v_{in}/R_{source} + v_{out}/R_F}{\alpha} \tag{11.17}$$

In Equation (11.17), we have simplified the algebra by defining a constant, α, given by

$$\alpha = 1 + \frac{r_\pi}{R_{source} \| R_F} \tag{11.18}$$

We now combine Equations (11.17) and (11.15) to find the gain, A_v.

$$A_v = \frac{v_{out}}{v_{in}} = \frac{-\beta(R_C \| R_{load})/\alpha R_{source}}{1 + \beta(R_C \| R_{load})/R_F \alpha} \tag{11.19}$$

If we remove the feedback by letting R_F approach infinity, the gain becomes

$$A_{vo} = \frac{-\beta(R_C \| R_{load})}{\alpha R_{source}} = \frac{-\beta(R_C \| R_{load})}{R_{source} + r_\pi} \tag{11.20}$$

In the last equality of Equation (11.20), we have substituted the value of α when R_F approaches infinity. Equation (11.19) can now be rewritten as

$$A_v = \frac{A_{vo}(R_{source} + r_\pi)/\alpha R_{source}}{1 - A_{vo}(R_{source} + r_\pi)/\alpha R_F} \approx \frac{A_{vo}}{1 - R_{source} A_{vo}/R_F} = \frac{A_{vo}}{1 + \gamma A_{vo}} \tag{11.21}$$

We have done two things in Equation (11.21). First, we approximated α by its value for infinite R_F since R_F is typically much larger than R_{source}. Second, we have defined $\gamma = -R_{source}/R_F$.

Equation (11.21) is in the form of the basic feedback equation. As A_{vo} becomes large, A_v approaches $1/\gamma = -R_F/R_{source}$ which is the closed-loop gain of the amplifier.

EXAMPLE 11.2

In the single-stage amplifier of Figure 11.5(a), let $R_C = R_{load} = 1\ \text{k}\Omega$, $R_E = 100\ \Omega$, $r_\pi = 800\ \Omega$, $\beta = 300$, $R_{source} = 1\ \text{k}\Omega$, and $R_F = 10\ \text{k}\Omega$. Determine the open- and closed-loop voltage gain of this amplifier.

Solution: We need simply apply Equations (11.20) and (11.21) to find the open- and closed-loop gain. We first solve for α.

$$\alpha = 1 + \frac{r_\pi}{R_{source}} = 1.8$$

Now from Equation (11.20) we find the open-loop gain to be $A_{vo} = -83.3$. This is the voltage gain for no feedback (open loop). The gain with feedback (closed loop) is given by Equation (11.21).

$$A_v = \frac{-83.3}{1 - (1000/10^4)(-83.3)} = -8.93$$

A_v is much less than A_{vo}. The feedback has reduced the sensitivity to a change in A_{vo} by a factor of 0.11 as can be seen from the following sensitivity expression.

$$\frac{dA_v}{A_v} = \frac{1}{1 + (10^3/10^4)\,8.3} \cdot \frac{dA_{vo}}{A_{vo}} = 0.11 \frac{dA_{vo}}{A_{vo}}$$

11.4 MULTISTAGE FEEDBACK AMPLIFIERS

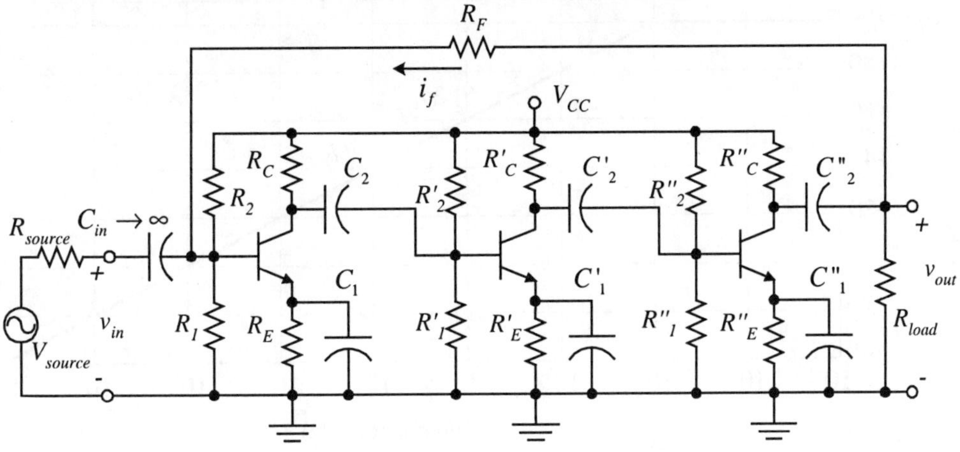

Figure 11.6 (a) – Multistage feedback amplifier

The performance of an amplifier can be altered by the use of feedback. If we desire negative feedback, the number of negative-gain amplifier stages must be odd (so there is an odd number of polarity changes).

An example of a feedback amplifier with an odd number of polarity changes (3) is shown in Figure 11.6(a).

Increasing the number of stages before feedback does not pose a major analysis problem since we can represent the amplifier of many stages as a single amplifier. Of course, we must be careful to monitor the number of phase reversals in the overall amplifier.

The open-loop gain of the circuit in Figure 11.6(a) is large (on the order of 10^4). Figure 11.6(b) shows an equivalent circuit using a single op-amp.

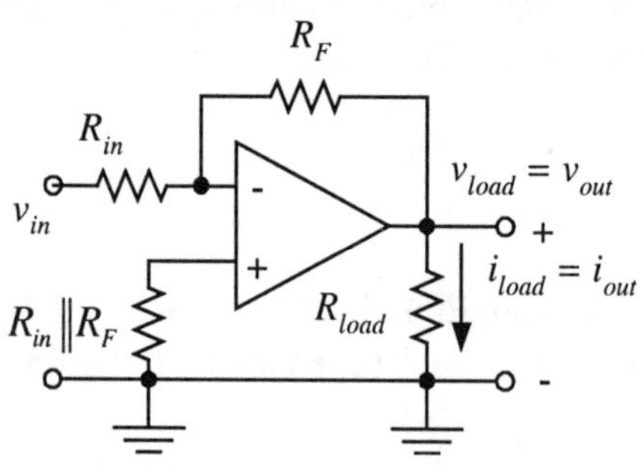

Figure 11.6 (b) – Multistage feedback amplifier equivalent circuit

11.5 FEEDBACK IN OPERATIONAL AMPLIFIERS

The gain of a practical op-amp is high at *dc* and it decreases as frequency increases. This frequency dependence is built into the op-amp by the manufacturer. Many op-amps permit the engineer to select *external compensation networks*, which change the shape of the Bode plot to improve performance.

Figure 11.7 shows the open-loop gain for a μA741 op-amp as a function of frequency.

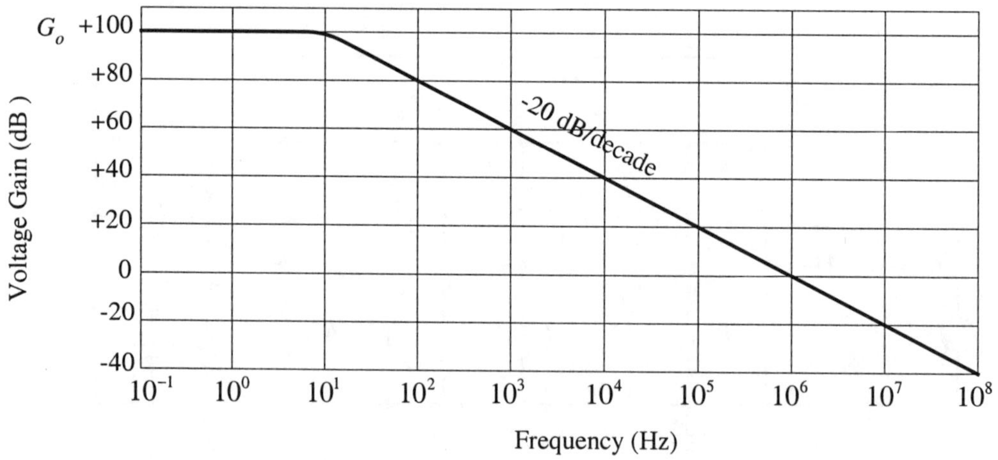

Figure 11.7 – Typical op-amp open-loop gain response

For this case, the corner frequency, ω_o, is 20π radians per second (10 Hz). The zero-frequency gain, G_o, is 100 dB, or 10^5. The analytic expression representing a single-pole op-amp that decays at the slope of -20 dB/decade is

$$G(s) = \frac{G_o}{1 + s/\omega_o} \tag{11.22}$$

For a μA741 op-amp, we simply substitute $\omega_o = 20\pi$ radians per second and $G_o = 10^5$.

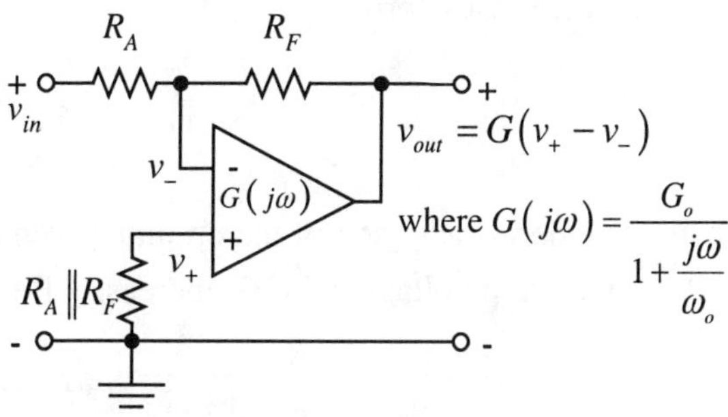

Figure 11.8(a) – Inverting amplifier

Just as in the case of discrete amplifiers, op-amps exhibit less sensitivity when feedback is employed. To calculate the error due to gain variations, we assume that all characteristics of the op-amp are ideal except for the gain variation with frequency. We use the inverting amplifier circuit of Figure 11.8(a) for the analysis and begin by finding the effect of the output voltage on the op-amp input.

This effect is characterized by the ratio v_{in}/v_{out}. We assume that $v_{in} = 0$ since we are finding only that portion of v_- due to v_{out}. Once again, γ is defined as the feedback attenuation factor and $1/\gamma$ is the low-frequency gain of the non-inverting op-amp.

$$\gamma = \frac{v_{in}}{v_{out}} = \frac{R_A}{R_A + R_F} = \frac{1}{1 + R_F/R_A} \tag{11.23}$$

This function represents the fraction of the output voltage, v_{out}, that is fed back to the inverting terminal with $v_{in} = 0$ (grounded). In order to find v_-, we write the nodal equation at v_- of Figure 11.8(a) and solve for v_- to obtain

$$v_- = v_{out}\frac{R_A}{R_A + R_F} = v_{out}\frac{1}{1 + R_F/R_A} = \gamma v_{out} \tag{11.24}$$

To find the closed-loop gain, we write a nodal equation at the inverting terminal of the amplifier of Figure 11.8(a) as follows:

$$\frac{v_- - v_{in}}{R_A} + \frac{v_- - v_{out}}{R_F} = 0 \tag{11.25}$$

Now since $v_+ = 0$,

$$v_{out} = -Gv_-$$
$$v_- = \frac{-v_{out}}{G} \tag{11.26}$$

Substituting Equation (11.26) into Equation (11.25), we obtain the closed-loop gain.

$$A_{v\ (closed\ loop)} = \frac{v_{out}}{v_{in}} = \frac{-R_F}{R_A}\frac{1}{1 + (1 + R_F/R_A)/G} \tag{11.27}$$

We use the feedback attenuation factor definition of Equation (11.23) to obtain the expression in standard feedback form,

$$\frac{v_{out}}{v_{in}} = -\frac{R_F}{R_A} \cdot \frac{G\gamma}{1+G\gamma} \tag{11.28}$$

where G is the voltage gain of the op-amp given by Equation (11.22).

As the op-amp voltage gain, G, increases, Equation (11.28) approaches $A_{v\infty}$ as given by

$$\frac{v_{out}}{v_{in}} = -\frac{R_F}{R_A} \cdot \frac{G\gamma}{1+G\gamma}\bigg|_{G\to\infty} = A_v\big|_{G\to\infty} \doteq A_{v\infty} = -\frac{R_F}{R_A} \tag{11.29}$$

This means that as the op-amp gain approaches infinity, A_v becomes independent of the specific value of G. It is a function only of the two resistor values, R_F and R_A. This is the same result as obtained in Chapter 2 for an ideal op-amp.

We now perform a similar analysis for a *non-inverting* op-amp as shown in Figure 11.8(b). We assume that the op-amp is ideal except that the gain, G, depends on frequency given by Equation (11.22). We find the closed-loop gain in a manner similar to that above. We write the node voltages for the inverting and the non-inverting inputs as follows:

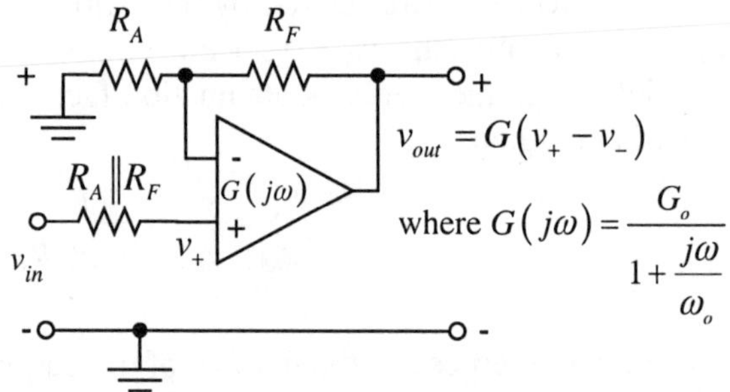

Figure 11.8(b) – Non-inverting amplifier

$$v_- = v_{out}\frac{R_A}{R_A + R_F}$$

$$v_+ = v_{in} \tag{11.30}$$

The output voltage is

$$v_{out} = G(v_+ - v_-) = G\left(v_{in} - v_{out}\frac{R_A}{R_A + R_F}\right) \tag{11.31}$$

We use the definition of γ as given in Equation (11.23) to find the closed-loop voltage gain.

$$A_{v\ (closed\ loop)} = \frac{v_{out}}{v_{in}} = \frac{G}{1+\gamma G} = \left(1+\frac{R_F}{R_A}\right) \cdot \frac{\gamma G}{1+\gamma G} \tag{11.32}$$

For large G, this reduces to the ideal op-amp expression,

$$A_v\big|_{G\to\infty} \doteq A_{v\infty} = \frac{1}{\gamma} = 1 + \frac{R_F}{R_A} \tag{11.33}$$

The two gain expressions, Equations (11.28) and (11.33), can be *normalized* by dividing by $A_{v\infty}$, the gain for infinite G. After normalizing, the same expression results for both the inverting and the non-inverting amplifier, as follows:

$$\boxed{\frac{A_v}{A_{v\infty}} = \frac{G\gamma}{1+G\gamma}} \tag{11.34}$$

$G\gamma$ is the *open-loop gain.* This is the gain obtained by tracing a loop through the amplifier and feedback path back to the starting point. Note that the loop gain of both amplifiers is identical.

To determine the sensitivity of the closed-loop gain, A_v, to changes in the open-loop gain, $G\gamma$, we differentiate Equation (11.34) to obtain,

$$\frac{dA_v}{d(G\gamma)} = \frac{A_{v\infty}}{(1+G\gamma)^2} \tag{11.35}$$

We can then divide by A_v to obtain the sensitivity.

$$\frac{dA_v}{A_v} = \frac{1}{1+G\gamma}\frac{d(G\gamma)}{G\gamma} \tag{11.36}$$

Equation (11.36) applies to both the inverting and the non-inverting amplifier. It clearly shows the effect of feedback. A variation in open-loop gain, $G\gamma$, is divided by $1+G\gamma$ to yield a much smaller variation in closed-loop gain. As an example, if the open-loop gain, $G\gamma$, starts at 1000 (60 dB), a 10% variation in this gain will result in only a 0.01% variation in A_v.

EXERCISE

E11.2 Find the closed loop voltage gain, A_v, for the op-amp circuit of Figure E11.1. $R_F = 200$ kΩ and $R_{source} = 10$ kΩ. Also find the sensitivity, dA_v/A_v, at zero frequency. Note that

$$G(s) = \frac{10^5}{1+s/20\pi}$$

Answer: $\dfrac{dA_v}{A_v} = 0.01\%$, $\dfrac{d(G\gamma)}{G\gamma} = 50\%$

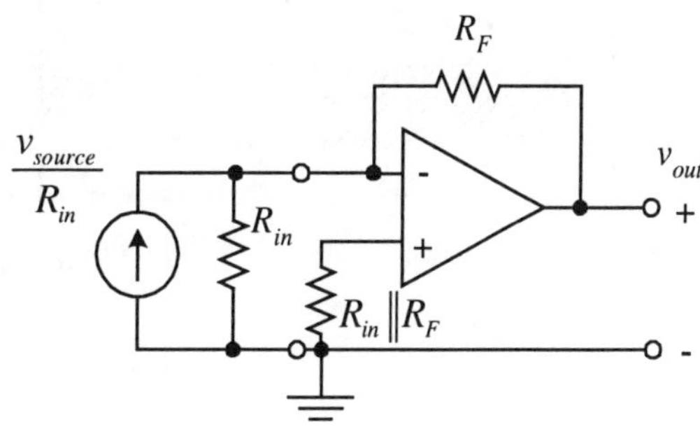

Figure E11.1

11.6 STABILITY OF FEEDBACK AMPLIFIERS

Negative feedback improves performance by making an amplifier less sensitive to parameter variations. Negative feedback requires that a portion of the output signal be subtracted from the input signal. Although we might design a system to provide such perfect subtraction, phase shifts may make the subtraction less than perfect when frequencies vary away from the midrange. In particular, a phase shift of 180° could occur at certain frequencies. The subtraction changes to an addition and *negative* feedback changes to *positive* feedback! This can make the system unstable.

Although the output of an unstable system may be bounded (i.e., real parameters cannot reach infinity), it no longer depends on the input value. In designing amplifiers, it is therefore important to make sure that the circuit is stable for all operating frequencies.

Amplifier stability depends only on the properties of the system and not on the driving function. Hence, if a system is unstable, *any* excitation causes the system to operate in an unstable manner. Alternatively, if a system is stable, *any* bounded excitation causes a bounded response.

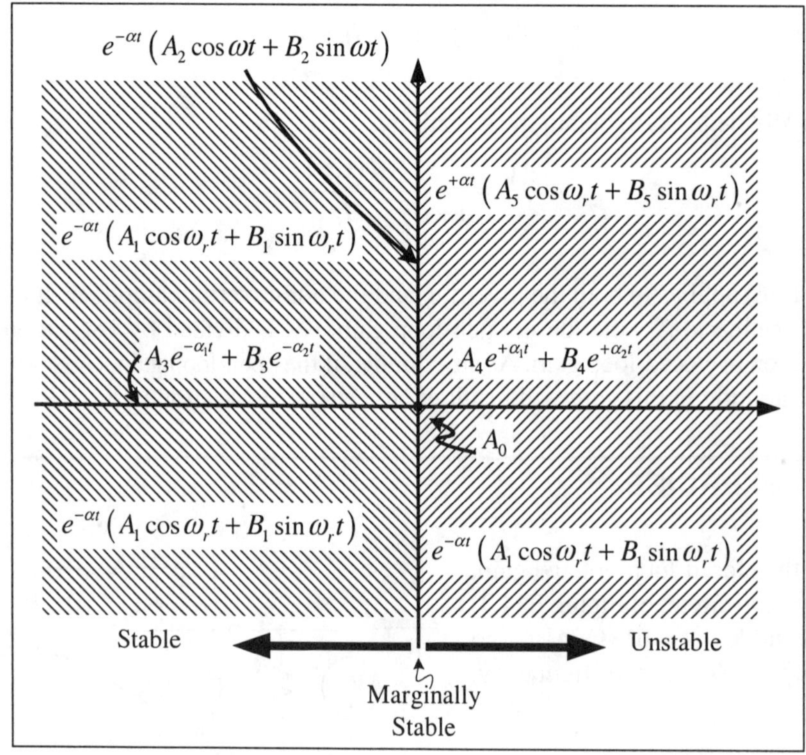

Figure 11.9 – Root plane and location of roots

If the transient time response of a system to an impulse input decays as time approaches infinity, the system is stable. For example, suppose the following time response, *h(t)*, is the result of applying an impulse function to the input of some system:

$$h(t)= Ae^{-a_1 t} + e^{-a_2 t}\left(B\cos\omega_r t + C\sin\omega_r t\right) \qquad (11.37)$$

As *t* approaches infinity, *h(t)* approaches zero and the system is stable. Although stability analysis can be performed by examining *h(t)*, it is often easier to use Laplace transforms.

We begin with a review of the basic concepts. The Laplace transform of Ae^{-at} is $A/(s+a)$. The root of the denominator falls at s = $-a$. When the root of the denominator (i.e., the pole) lies in the left half-plane, the exponent of the associated time function is negative and the function decays to zero.

The location of typical roots in the s-plane and the corresponding time functions are shown in Figure 11.9.

Table 11.1 illustrates the relationship between the location of the roots and the time function.

Root Location	**Form of solution**
Single roots along the negative real axis, such as $-\alpha_1$ and $-\alpha_2$ where α_1 and $\alpha_2>0$	$A_3e^{-\alpha_1 t} + B_3e^{-\alpha_2 t}$
Single roots along the positive real axis, α_1 and α_2 where α_1 and $\alpha_2>0$	$A_4e^{+\alpha_1 t} + B_4e^{+\alpha_2 t}$
A single complex conjugate pair of roots, $\pm j\omega$, along the imaginary or *j* axis.	$A_3\cos\omega t + B_3\sin\omega t$
One simple pair of complex roots, $-\alpha\pm j\omega$, in the left half plane ($\alpha>0$)	$e^{-\alpha t}\left(A_1\cos\omega_r t + B_1\sin\omega_r t\right)$
A simple pair of complex roots, $\alpha\pm j\omega$, in the right half plan ($\alpha>0$).	$e^{+\alpha t}\left(A_5\cos\omega_r t + B_5\sin\omega_r t\right)$
Double roots of the characteristic equations occurring at one point on the real axis, in the left half of the *s* plane assuming both roots at $-\alpha$.	$\left(A_6 + B_6\right)e^{-\alpha t}$
A single root at the origin.	A_0
A double root at the origin.	$A_7 + B_7t$

Table 11.1 - Root location and form of solution

The nature of stability can now be stated in terms of the location of the roots of the characteristic equation [$1+G(s)H(s)=0$]. This is the denominator of Equation (11.3). *A system is stable* if *all* roots lie in the left half-plane. *A system is unstable* if

(a) any of the roots lie in the right half-plane, or

(b) any multiple (double, triple, etc.) complex pairs of roots lie along the j axis, or

(c) any multiple real roots lie at the origin.

A system is *marginally stable* if

(a) any single pair of conjugate roots lies along the j axis or

(b) a single root lies at the origin and all other roots lie in the left half-plane.

A system is conditionally stable if all roots lie in the left half-plane only for some particular condition of the system parameters. The system is often stable for a limited range of some parameters (e.g., loop gain constant).

Roots that lie in the right half-plane result in responses that increase with time, and such systems are unsuitable for practical use. Single conjugate pairs of roots that lie on the imaginary axis (other than at the origin) result in an undamped sinusoidal (oscillatory) response term. If all other roots lie in the left half-plane (except possibly a single root at the origin), this system may be considered an oscillator. This is the limiting case between stable and unstable systems.

11.6.1 System Stability and Frequency Response

A designer is interested in knowing whether any system roots lie in the right half-plane since this indicates an unstable system. Amplitude and phase plots are often readily available, whereas considerable analytical effort would be required to determine the location of system roots. This is particularly true if sPICE-based computer simulations are used. These programs generate frequency curves directly from the circuit. We therefore would like to be able to make stability determinations directly from frequency response plots.

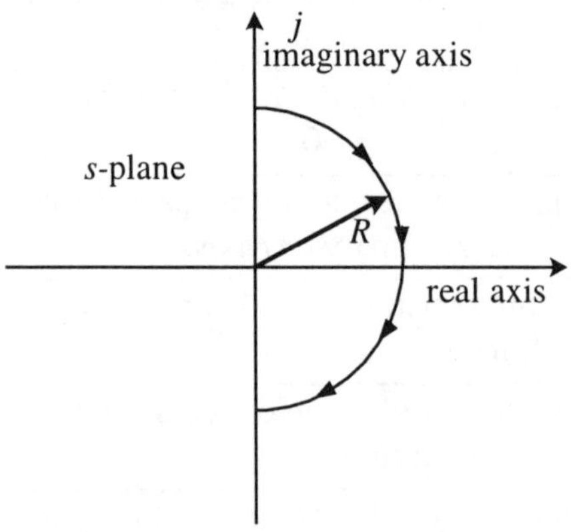

Figure 11.10 – Contour enclosing the right half plane

In order to extend stability criteria from the s-plane to the frequency response curves, we need to invoke concepts from advanced calculus – in particular, contour integration. We will present this material in a manner that does not require that you have an extensive background in advanced calculus.

To determine whether any roots of $1+G(s)H(s)=0$ are in the right half-plane, we examine the contour shown in Figure 11.10.

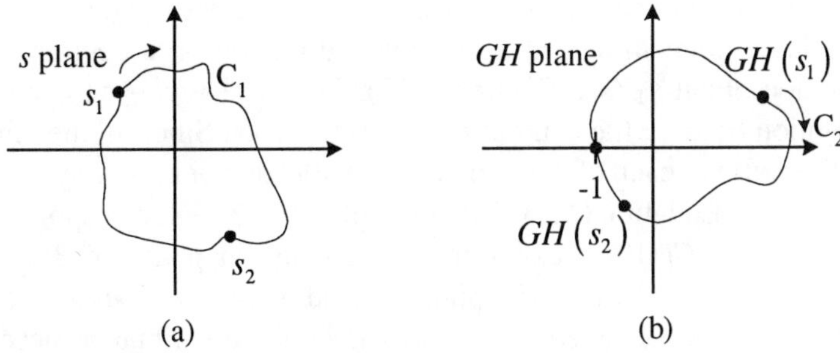

Figure 11.11 – Contour C_1 in the s-plane mapped into the contour C_2 in the GH-plane

R is made so large that all possible roots in the right half-plane are included. This is usually done by considering the limiting case of *R* approaching infinity. Stability depends on whether any roots fall within the closed contour.

The plot of $G(s)H(s)$ as s follows the contour of Figure 11.10 yields the *mapping* of this contour located in the s plane into a contour in the *GH* plane. A closed curve, C_1, such as that shown in the s plane of Figure 11.11(a), maps into a closed curve, C_2, in the *GH* plane, as shown in Figure 11.11(b).

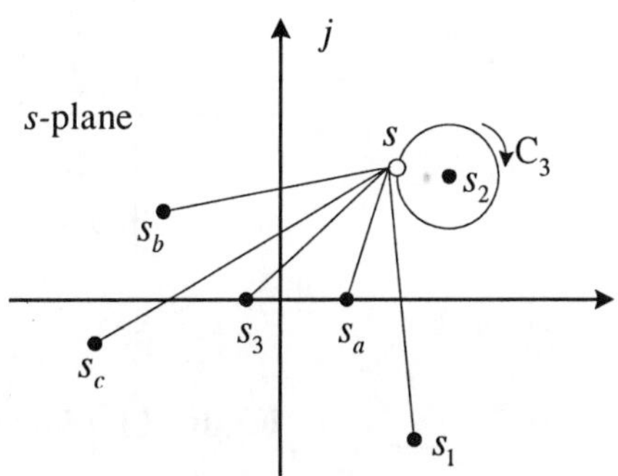

Figure 11.12 – Encirclement of a root in the s-plane

For single-valued functions, a one-to-one correspondence exists between a point on C_1 (the curve in the s plane) and a point on C_2 (the map in the *GH* plane). If a point is moved along C_1 in the direction of the arrow (clockwise), the mapped point moves along C_2 in a direction that depends on the *GH* function.

Let s_j denote a root of $1+G(s)H(s) = 0$. Now suppose the contour C_1 passes through the point s_j in the s plane, as shown in Figure 11.11(a). If s_j is a root, then $G(s_j)H(s_j) + 1 = 0$; thus for $s = s_j$, $G(s_j)H(s_j) = -1$. That is, the contour C_2 in the *GH* plane passes through the point $GH = -1$.

The characteristic function for a closed-loop system can be written in factored form, as shown in Equation (11.38).

$$1+G(s)H(s)= K_1 \cdot \frac{(s + s_1)(s + s_2)...(s + s_r)}{(s + s_a)(s + s_b)...(s + s_p)} \tag{11.38}$$

$-s_1$, $-s_2$, ... $-s_r$ are the zeros and $-s_a$, $-s_b$,... $-s_p$ are the poles. For simplicity, we will examine $G(s)H(s)$ instead of $1+G(s)H(s)$. Poles of $G(s)H(s)$ are also poles of $1+G(s)H(s)$ since substitution of the pole in either equation makes the expression approach infinity.

Once a value is assumed for s, each factor in Equation (11.38) is a complex number and hence can be represented by a vector, as shown in Figure 11.12.

The vectors extend from the fixed points, s_1, s_2, s_3, and poles s_a, s_b, s_c, to the variable point s. Suppose the variable point moves in a clockwise direction on a contour so as to make one complete revolution about s_2 (see Figure 11.12). Then the vector $s+s_2$ makes one complete clockwise revolution because the contour encircles this root. Since all the other roots and poles are external to the contour, each of the remaining vectors do *not* make any complete revolutions. Since the factor $s+s_2$ in Equation (11.38) changes phase by 360° (corresponding to one complete revolution about s_2), $1+G(s)H(s)$ experiences a change in phase of 360°. Hence, a vector representing $1+G(s)H(s)$ [in the (1+*GH*)-plane] would make one clockwise encirclement of the origin [see Figure 11.13(a)]. The remaining roots and poles contribute no net change to the phase of $1+G(s)H(s)$.

Because the roots are in the numerator of Equation (11.38), one clockwise rotation about s_2 results in one clockwise encirclement of the origin in the (1+*GH*) plane, which is related to the *GH* plane as shown in Figure 11.13(b). One clockwise encirclement of the origin in the (1+*GH*) plane is equivalent to one clockwise encirclement of the -1+j0 point in the *GH* plane.

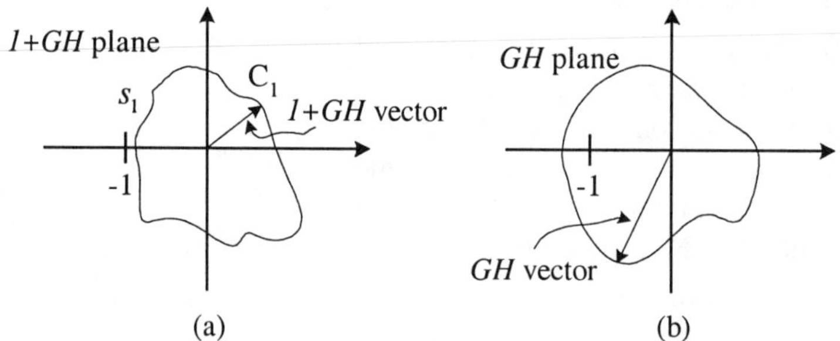

Figure 11.13 – (1+GH)-plane and the GH-plane

Suppose the closed contour in the *s* plane is made to encircle both a root and a pole in the clockwise direction, as shown in Figure 11.14.

In this case both the vector from s_2 to *s* and that from s_a to *s* rotate through one complete clockwise revolution, or 360°. The factor, $s+s_2$, corresponding to the root s_2, contributes +360° to the change in phase of $1+G(s)H(s)$ since it is in the numerator of Equation (11.38). The factor $s+s_a$, contributes -360° to the change in phase since it is in the denominator. Hence the net change in phase of $1+G(s)H(s)$ is zero, and the resulting map in the *GH* plane *does not* encircle the -1 point (See Figure 11.15).

If the closed contour in the *s* plane is enlarged to include s_1, s_2 and s_a, the net change in phase of $1+G(s)H(s)$ is 360°. A clockwise encirclement of a root causes a clockwise encirclement of the -1 point in the *GH* plane. A clockwise encirclement of a pole causes a counterclockwise encirclement of the -1 point in the *GH* plane.

We now summarize these results. We define n_N as the number of clockwise encirclements of the -1 point, n_R as the number of roots located within the contour in the *s* plane and n_P as the number of poles located within this contour. Then a clockwise encirclement of a region in the *s* plane causes $n_N = n_R - n_P$ clockwise encirclements of the -1 point in the *GH* plane. n_N is positive if $n_R > n_P$ in the right half-plane. In this case the -1 point is encircled in the same direction (clockwise) as the contour in the *s* plane. n_N is zero if $n_R = n_P$ and the -1 point is not encircled. n_N is negative if $n_R<n_P$ and the -1 point is encircled in the direction opposite (counter clockwise) to the contour in the s plane (clockwise).

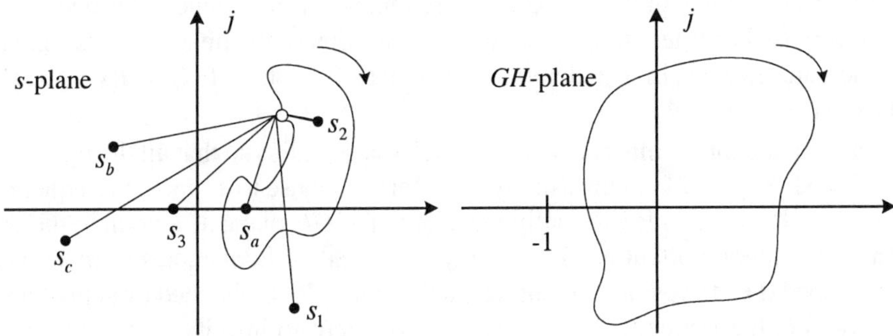

Figure 11.14 – Enclosing a root and a pole

Figure 11.15 – No encirclement of the –1 point in the *GH*-plane

11.6.2 Bode Plots and System Stability

A closed-loop system is unstable if the roots of the characteristic equation, $1+G(s)H(s)=0$, lie in the right half of the s plane. Suppose the contour of Figure 11.10 is made large enough to include the entire right half of the s plane. If this contour is mapped on the *GH* plane, the number of clockwise encirclements of the -1 point of the resulting map yields information regarding the stability of the closed-loop system.

The stability criterion can be stated as follows: the open-loop transfer function, $G(s)H(s)$ is expressed as the ratio of two factored polynomials in the variable s and written in the form

$$G(s)H(s)=\frac{K(s\tau_1+1)(s\tau_3+1)}{s^n(s\tau_2+1)(s\tau_4+1)} \tag{11.39}$$

As s travels a closed contour comprising the imaginary axis from $-j\infty$ to $+j\infty$ and then the right-hand semicircle from $s=Re^{j\pi/2}$ to $s=Re^{-j\pi/2}$ as R approaches infinity, the polar plot of $G(s)H(s)$ encircles the -1+j0 point in a clockwise direction n_N times. n_N is given by

$$n_N=n_R-n_P \tag{11.40}$$

n_N is the number of clockwise encirclements of the point -1 (a negative n_N corresponds to counter clockwise encirclements), n_P is the number of poles of $G(s)H(s)$ in the right half plane, and n_R is the number of roots of $1+G(s)H(s)$ which lie in the right half-plane. $G(s)$ is the forward-loop transfer function, and $H(s)$ is the feedback-loop transfer function. (These functions are indicated in Figure 11.1.) As noted earlier, the poles of $G(s)H(s)$ are also poles of $1+G(s)H(s)$.

A somewhat simpler contour than that shown in Figure 11.10 is used in practice. Since systems considered in this text have characteristic equations with constant real coefficients, the roots of the characteristic function must either be real or occur in complex conjugate pairs. As a result, the map of the upper half of the $j\omega$ axis and the upper half of the infinite semicircle is the mirror image of the lower half of the $j\omega$ axis and the lower half of the infinite semicircle. Further, the pole and zero structures in these two areas are mirror images. Hence, it is necessary only to plot the simple closed contour comprising the upper portion of the imaginary axis and the upper portion of the semi-infinite circle to determine whether any roots of $1+G(s)H(s)=0$ lie in the right half of the s-plane.

The semicircular contour must have an infinitely-large radius so that all the right half of the s plane is encircled. Physical systems usually have zero response to an infinite frequency; hence, the large semicircle in the *s* plane usually maps onto the *GH* plane as a point at the origin. We therefore arrive at the important result that only real, positive frequencies from zero to infinity need to be mapped (i.e., the positive imaginary axis). This plot is obtained by applying sinusoidal inputs and varying the frequency of the signals from zero to infinity. We have succeeded in relating the s-plane analysis to a frequency response analysis.

The stability criterion gives information regarding the difference between the number of roots and the number of poles of $1+G(s)H(s)$. $G(s)H(s)$ can be expressed as the ratio of factored polynomials (and often it occurs naturally in this form). Since the poles of $1+G(s)H(s)$ are identical to the poles of $G(s)H(s)$, the number of poles of $G(s)H(s)$ in the right half of the *s* plane can be found by inspection of Equation (11.39). Hence, under the conditions just stated, the number of poles with positive real parts can easily be determined. The number of clockwise encirclements n_N of the point -1+j0 in the *GH* plane is found from the *GH*-plane plot. Then both n_N and n_P in Equation (11.41) are known. The number of roots of $1+G(s)H(s)$ in the right half of the *s* plane can then be found from Equation (11.41).

$$n_R = n_N + n_P \qquad (11.41)$$

The stability criterion can be applied to the Bode plot of decibel gain and phase shift. It is necessary only to find the -1 point on this Bode format. This is easy, since in complex form

$$-1 = e^{-j\pi} \qquad (11.42)$$

so the -1 point occurs when the gain is 0 dB at -180° phase shift.

We can determine system stability as follows:

Examine the *perfected* Bode plot (a plot where corrections have been made to the straight-line asymptotes) and determine the frequency at which the phase shift crosses -180°. If the dB gain at this frequency is

(1) Less than 0 dB, the system is stable.

(2) Equal to 0 dB, the system is marginally stable; that is, the response neither builds up nor dies out.

(3) Greater than 0 dB, the system is unstable.

EXAMPLE 11.3

A three-stage amplifier is shown in Figure 11.16(a). Each identical stage has a gain, $-K$, and an input RC network which approximates the RC time constant within each stage. Plot the Bode diagram for $RC = 10^{-5}$ sec and determine the gain, K, that will produce *marginal stability* (This is the point where the phase shift is -180° and the gain is 0 dB.).

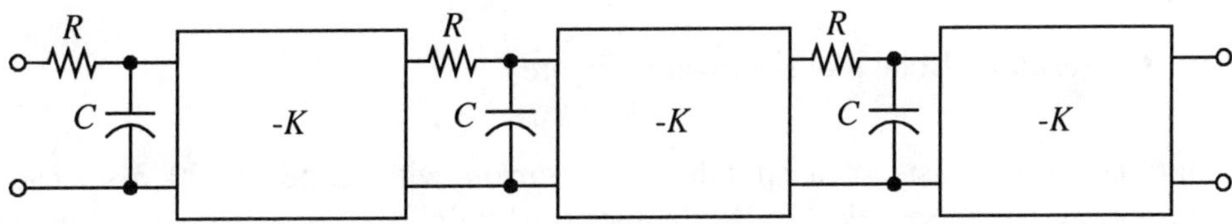

Figure 11.16(a) - Three-stage amplifier

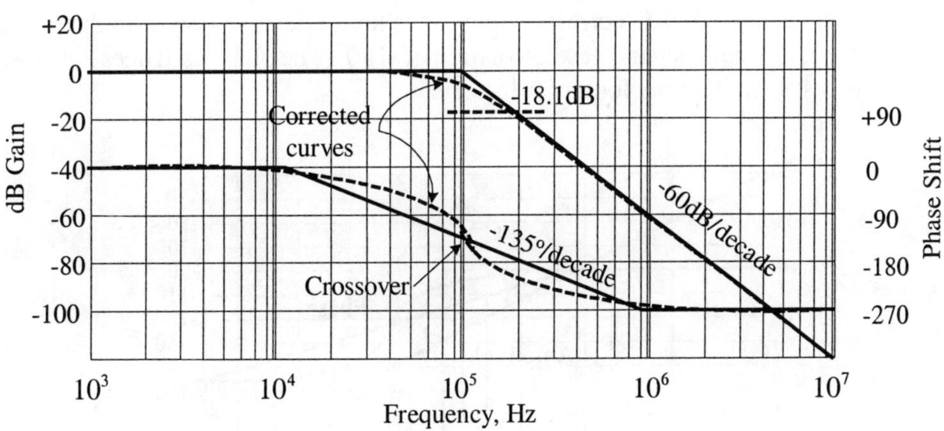

Figure 11.16(b) Bode diagram for Example 11.3

Solution: The Bode diagram is plotted in Figure 11.16(b). The frequency at which the phase shift crosses -180° is 1.73×10^5 rad/sec, or 27.53 kHz. At this frequency, the gain is -18.1 dB, which indicates that we can raise the combined gain, K^3, by 18.1 dB or

$$K^3 = 8.04$$

so

$$K = 2.$$

EXAMPLE 11.4

Examine the stability of the system with s = 0.1 sec and the following *G(s)H(s)* function.

$$G(s)H(s)=\frac{A}{s(s\tau+1)}$$

Solution: The resulting Bode plot is shown in Figure 11.17.

The amplitude plot consists of a straight line segment with slope of -20 dB/decade for frequencies below 10 rad/sec. For $\omega>10$, the plot is a straight-line segment with slope of -40 dB/decade. The curve is plotted for A = 1. A different value of A would result in a vertical translation of the amplitude curve.

The phase curve starts at -90°, corresponding to the term 1/jω resulting from the pole at the origin. It decreases as frequency increases, to a limit of -180°. The phase shift does not cross the -180° line, so this system is stable for any value of A.

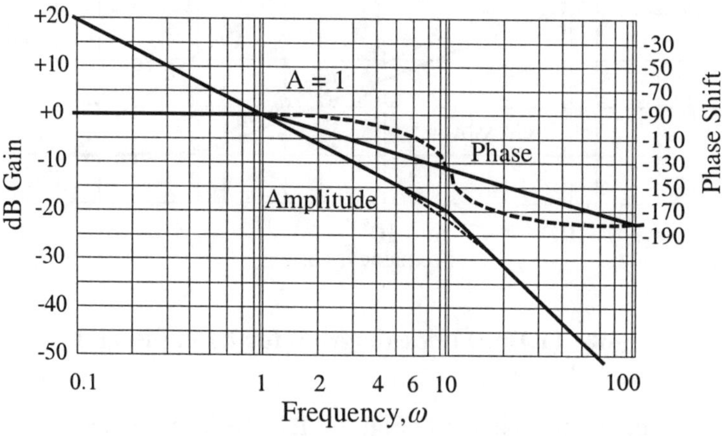

Figure 11.17 – Bode plot for Example 11.4

EXAMPLE 11.5

Examine the stability of a system with the following *G(s)H(s)* function:

$$G(s)H(s)=\frac{A}{s(s+1)(0.5s+1)}$$

Solution: The Bode plot is constructed with the asymptotic approximations as shown in Figure 11.18.

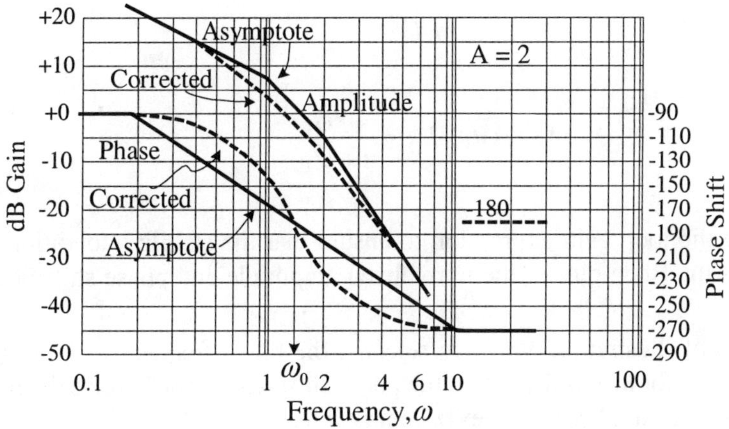

Figure 11.18 – Bode plot for Example 11.5

As a starting point, we have illustrated the Bode plot for $A = 2$. To determine stability, we look for the point where the phase shift curve crosses the -180° line. At this frequency, we examine the corrected dB gain curve. Note that at the frequency where the phase is -180°, the gain curve is below 0 dB (approximately -4 dB). Hence the system is stable with a gain of $A = 2$. However, if the gain increases by 4 dB (i.e., A increases to 3.16), the amplitude curve shifts upward and reaches 0 dB at the -180° phase shift point. Further increases in A move the system into instability.

11.7 FREQUENCY RESPONSE - FEEDBACK AMPLIFIER

The stability of a negative-feedback system is dependent on the loop gain being less than 0 dB when the phase shift crosses -180°. If the system has -180° of phase shift when the gain is 0 dB, the system is unstable and can oscillate. In other words, an output will exist even when no input signal is applied.

11.7.1 Single-Pole Amplifier

Let us return to the basic feedback system of Figure 11.1 and assume that $G(s)$ is a polynomial with one pole. We further assume that $H(s)$ is a constant. That is,

$$G(s) = \frac{-G_o}{1 + s/\omega_o}$$

$$H(s) = -\gamma \tag{11.43}$$

$$G(s)H(s) = \frac{\gamma G_o}{1 + s/\omega_o}$$

We examine the loop gain expression to ensure that the stability condition is met. Figure 11.19 illustrates the Bode plot of the normalized amplitude and phase shift of the single-pole system.

For purposes of illustration, we have selected the break frequency to be ω_o=4 rad/sec. A necessary condition for instability is that the phase shift reach -180°. Since the maximum phase shift is only -90°, this amplifier can never be unstable.

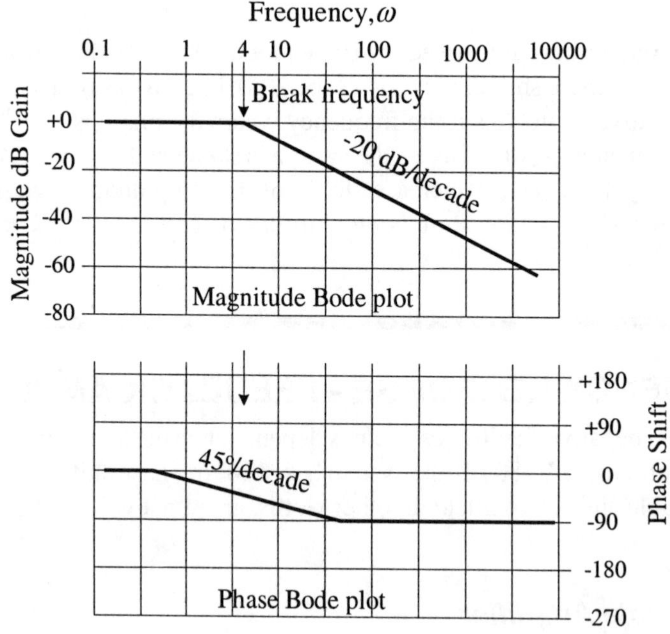

Figure 11.19 – Bode plot for single-pole amplifier

The single-pole amplifier has a closed-loop gain, $T(s)$, given by

$$T(s)=\frac{G(s)}{1+G(s)H(s)}$$

$$=\frac{G_o}{1+G_o\gamma}\frac{1}{1+\dfrac{s}{(1+G_o\gamma)\omega_o}} \tag{11.44}$$

The 3-dB point for the closed-loop gain characteristic is at a frequency of

$$\omega=(1+\gamma G_o)\omega_o \tag{11.45}$$

Since γG_o>>1 and the closed-loop gain is approximately given by Equation (11.46) and the 3dB frequency is $\gamma G_o\omega_o$.

$$T(s)=\frac{-1}{\gamma}\frac{1}{1+\dfrac{s}{G_o\gamma\omega_o}} \tag{11.46}$$

11.7.2 Two-Pole Amplifier

Let us now assume that $G(s)$ has two poles at the same location (We again assume that $H(s)$ is a constant). Thus,

$$G(s)=\frac{G_o}{(1+s/\omega_o)^2}$$

$$H(s)=-\gamma \tag{11.47}$$

$$G(s)H(s)=\frac{\gamma G_o}{(1+s/\omega_o)^2}$$

In order to examine the response, let us set ω_o = 60 rad/sec, γ = 0.1 and $G_o = 10^5$. The function becomes,

$$G(s)H(s)=\frac{10^4}{(1+s/60)^2} \tag{11.48}$$

with Bode plot as shown in Figure 11.20.

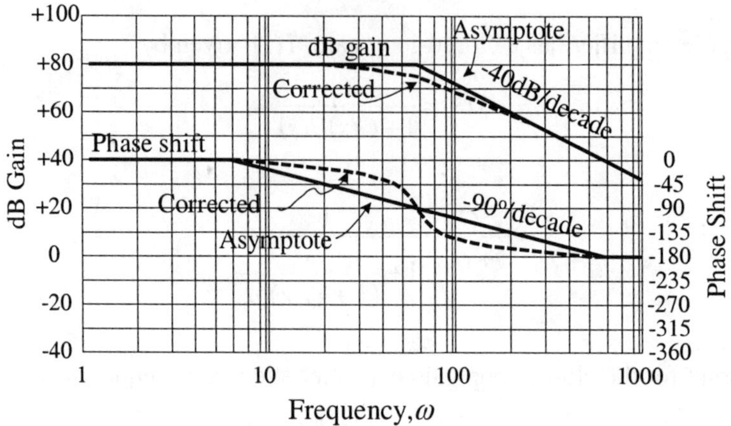

Figure 11.20 – Bode plot for two-pole amplifier

Since the phase shift curve does not cross the -180° point, the system is stable for any value of gain. We really did not need to plot this function since we will see that *any* two-pole amplifier is stable.

We will now examine the gain in more detail. The closed-loop gain function, $T(s)$, is given by

$$T(s)=\frac{G(s)}{1+G(s)H(s)}$$

$$=\frac{G_o}{1+\gamma G_o}\frac{1}{\dfrac{s^2}{\omega_o^2(1+\gamma G_o)}+\dfrac{2s}{\omega_o(1+\gamma G_o)}+1} \tag{11.49}$$

This can be written in a more useful form using the following two definitions:

$$\omega_n=\omega_o\sqrt{1+\gamma G_o}$$

$$\xi=\frac{1}{\sqrt{1+\gamma G_o}} \tag{11.50}$$

ω_n is the *undamped natural radian frequency* and ξ is the *damping ratio*. The gain function of Equation (11.49) can now be written as

$$T(s)=\frac{G_o}{1+\gamma G_o}\cdot\frac{1}{\dfrac{s^2}{\omega_n^2}+\dfrac{2\xi s}{\omega_n}+1} \tag{11.51}$$

EXAMPLE 11.6

Determine the stability of the op-amp circuit shown in Figure 11.21. Assume the op-amp has a gain function given by

$$G(s) = \frac{G_o}{1 + s/\omega_o}$$

with $G_o = 10^5$ and $\omega_o = 20\pi$.

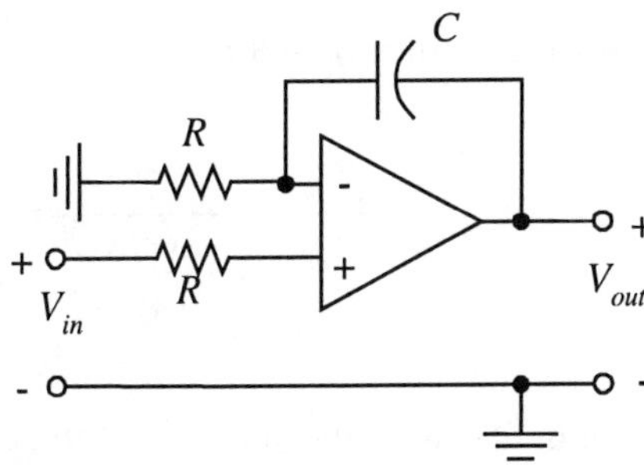

Figure 11.21(a) – Amplifier for Example 11.6

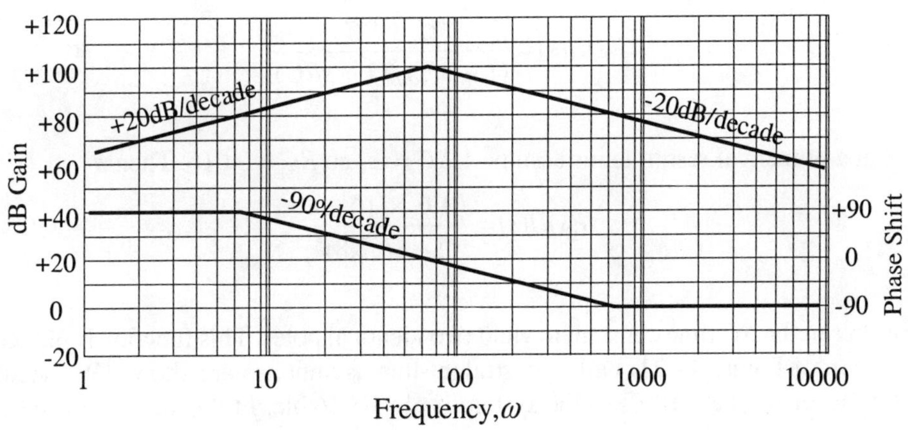

Figure 11.21 - Amplifier for Example 11.6

Solution: We write the node equation at the inverting op-amp input.

$$\frac{V_-}{R} + \frac{V_- - V_{out}}{1/sC} = 0$$

Solving for V_- yields

$$V_- = \frac{s\,R\,C\,V_{out}}{1 + sRC}$$

At the non-inverting input, the node equation is $V_+ = V_{in}$. We use the op-amp equation,

$$V_{out} = G(V_+ - V_-) = G\left(V_{in} - \frac{s\,R\,C\,V_{out}}{1 + sRC}\right)$$

to solve for the closed-loop gain.

$$\frac{V_{out}}{V_{in}} = \frac{G}{1 + \dfrac{GsRC}{1 + sRC}} = \frac{\dfrac{G_o}{1 + s/\omega_o}}{1 + \dfrac{G_o sRC}{(1 + s/\omega_o)(1 + sRC)}}$$

In the last equality, we have substituted the given function for G. This is now in the form of

$$\frac{G(s)}{1 + G(s)H(s)}$$

The Bode diagram is a plot of the $G(s)H(s)$ function, which is seen to be (compare the previous two equations)

$$G(s)H(s) = \frac{G_o\, s\, RC}{(1 + s/\omega_o)(1 + sRC)}$$

To arrive at a numerical result, let us assume $1/RC = \omega_o$ so $RC = 0.016$. Then

$$G(s)H(s) = \frac{1.6 \times 10^3\, s}{(1 + s/62.8)^2}$$

We have chosen the RC time constant to yield two identical poles. This function is plotted in the Bode diagram of Figure 11.21. Only the straight-line asymptotes are shown. We see that the phase shift never reaches -180°, so the system is always stable. In this case, we need look no further than the straight-line approximations.

EXAMPLE 11.7

Determine the stability of the op-amp system of Figure 11.22. The op-amp gain function is given by

$$G(s) = \frac{G_o}{(1 + s/20\pi)^2}$$

Let $R = 100$ kΩ and $C = 0.1$ μF.

Solution: We again write the node equation at the op-amp inputs.

$$V_{-} = V_{out} \frac{1}{1 + s\,RC}$$

$$V_{+} = V_{in}$$

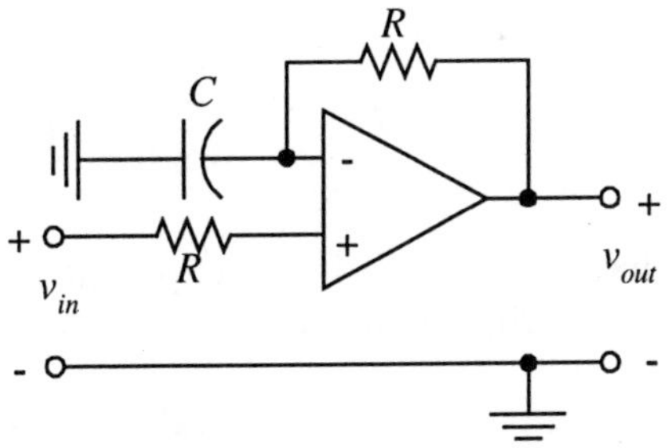

Figure 11.22(a) – Amplifier for Example 11.7

The output voltage is $V_{out} = G(V_{+} - V_{-})$, so combining terms we obtain

$$V_{out} = G\left(V_{in} - \frac{V_{out}}{1 + s\,RC} \right)$$

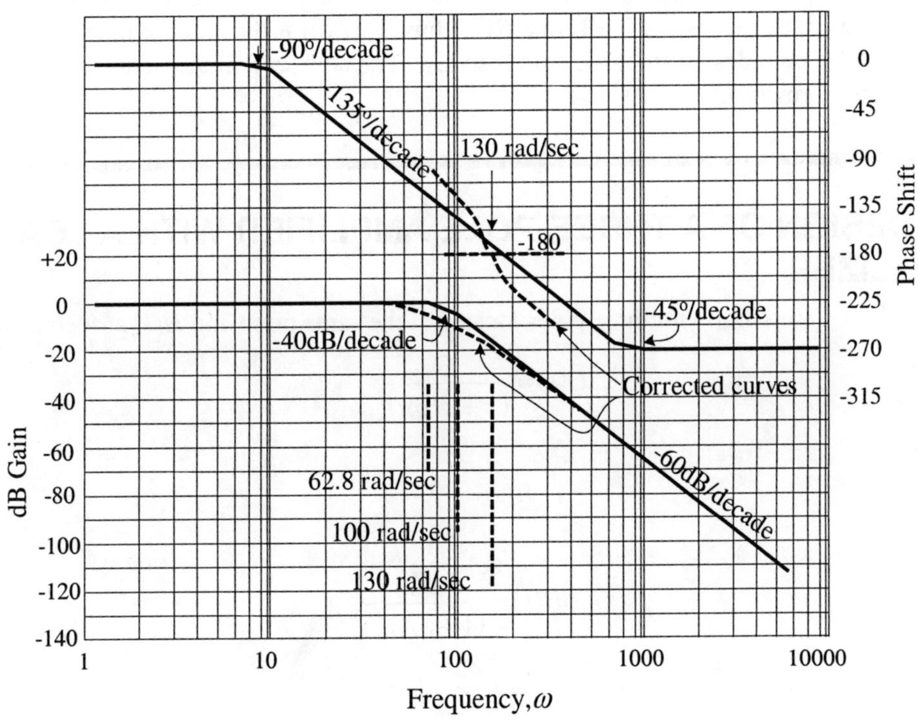

Figure 11.22(b) – Bode plot for Example 11.7

The closed-loop gain is

$$\frac{V_{out}}{V_{in}} = \frac{G(s)}{1 + G(s)/(1 + sRC)} = \frac{G(s)}{1 + G(s)H(s)}$$

and the $G(s)H(s)$ function is given by

$$G(s)H(s) = \frac{G_o}{(1 + sRC)(1 + s/20\pi)^2}$$

where we have substituted in the expression for $G(s)$. Let us substitute the given component values and start with a gain, $G_o = 1$. The resulting function is

$$G(s)H(s) = \frac{1}{(1 + s/100)(1 + s/62.8)^2}$$

This is shown in Figure 11.22(b). The straight-line asymptotes are first plotted, and the curves are corrected in the vicinity of the frequency where the phase shift is -180°. From this corrected plot, we can see that the phase shift curve intersects the -180° line at a frequency of 130 rad/sec, and the gain at this frequency is -18.7 dB (or 8.61). Thus, 18.7 dB is the gain for marginal stability. This would be a poor design since the gain is so low. The next section considers one method for improving performance.

11.8 DESIGN OF A THREE-POLE AMPLIFIER WITH A LEAD EQUALIZER

Consider an amplifier with three poles located at the same point and $H(s)$ as a constant.

$$G(s) = \frac{G_o}{(1 + s/\omega_o)^3}$$

$$H(s) = -\gamma \tag{11.52}$$

$$G(s)H(s) = \frac{\gamma G_o}{(1 + s/\omega_o)^3}$$

Figure 11.23 illustrates the Bode plot for the loop transfer function, $G(s)H(s)$, where we have let γG_o be normalized to 1. For purposes of illustration, we have selected a corner frequency of $\omega_o =$ 10 rad/sec.

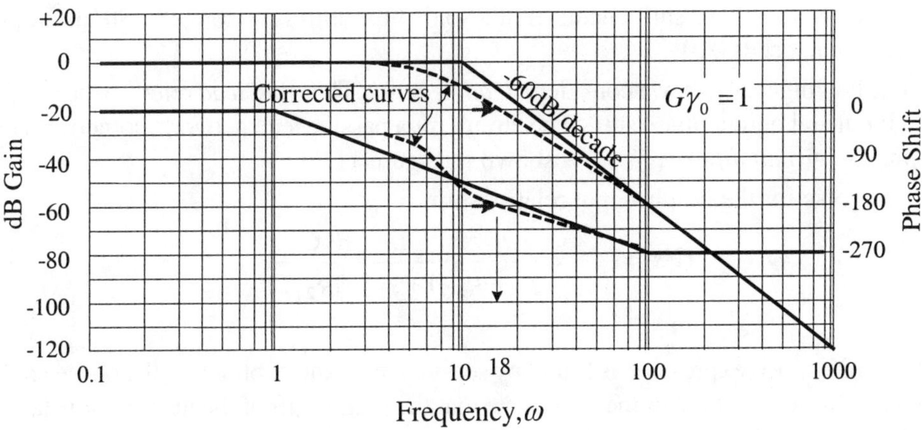

Figure 11.23 – Bode plot for three-pole amplifier

As before, we determine the stability of the amplifier system with the loop transfer function rather than with the closed-loop gain of the amplifier system. We check for instability by seeing whether the $G(s)H(s)$ function has an amplitude of unity when its phase shift is -180°. We note that the phase shift reaches -180° at a frequency of 18 rad/sec. The amplitude at this point is -18 dB, but recall that we have normalized the function by dividing it by γG_o. Thus, if the loop gain, γG_o, reaches +18 dB, the overall gain reaches 0 dB and the system becomes unstable. A gain of +18 dB is relatively low, so this particular amplifier would probably be of little use in a practical application.

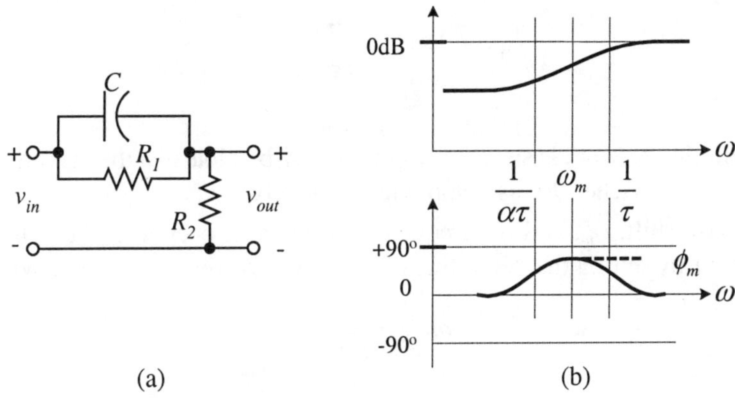

Figure 11.24 – Passive circuit lead network and Bode plots

This leaves us only two options. We must either abandon the amplifier since it becomes unstable at low gain, or change it so that the instability does not occur. Fortunately, it is not difficult to alter the amplifier to reduce the chances of instability. *Compensation networks* (or *equalizers*) are used to alter the gain-phase characteristics in order to prevent instabilities. These networks change the phase shift characteristic so that the shift is no longer -180° at frequencies where the gain exceeds 0 dB.

In the following analysis, we consider a *lead network.* The word *lead* refers to the relationship between input and output phase shift. The circuit for a passive lead network, sometimes referred to as a *passive circuit differentiator*, is shown in Figure 11.24.

We first solve for the output-input relationship,

$$G(s) = \frac{V_{out}}{V_{in}} = \frac{R_2}{R_1 + R_2} \cdot \frac{1 + s R_1 C}{1 + s\left(R_1 \| R_2\right)C} \tag{11.53}$$

The phase shift of this expression is found by setting $s = j\omega$ and subtracting the phase shift of the denominator from that of the numerator. Note that the phase shift of the numerator is larger than that of the denominator since

$$R_1 C > \left(R_1 \| R_2\right)C \tag{11.54}$$

Therefore the overall phase shift of this expression is positive, and the output phase shift leads the input phase. Equation (11.53) can be simplified by defining

$$\begin{aligned} \alpha &= 1 + \frac{R_1}{R_2} \\ \tau &= \frac{R_1 R_2 C}{R_1 + R_2} \end{aligned} \tag{11.55}$$

With these two definitions, the transfer function becomes

$$G(s) = \frac{V_{out}}{V_{in}} = \frac{\alpha \tau s + 1}{\alpha(\tau s + 1)} \tag{11.56}$$

The Bode plot for this network is shown in Figure 11.24(b). Note that the maximum phase lead is a function of α. It approaches 90° as α approaches infinity.

The peak phase shift, φ_m, and the frequency at which it occurs, ω_m, can be related to the parameters α and τ by setting the derivative of the phase expression to zero. We obtain

$$\begin{aligned} \omega_m &= \frac{1}{\sqrt{\alpha \tau}} \\ \phi_m &= \sin^{-1}\left(\frac{\alpha - 1}{\alpha + 1}\right) \end{aligned} \tag{11.57}$$

We obtain the output-input relationship,

$$\frac{V_{out}}{V_{in}} = \frac{CR_2 s + 1}{C(R_1 + R_2)s + 1} \tag{11.58}$$

Since R_1+R_2 is greater than R_2, the phase shift of the output lags the phase shift of the input. That is, the phase of the denominator in Equation (11.58) is larger than the phase of the numerator, so the overall phase shift is negative.

EXAMPLE 11.8

Select a lead network with τ = 1/40 and α = 4 to adequately compensate a three-pole op-amp summing amplifier.

Solution: The transfer function for the lead network is

$$G(s) = \frac{0.1s + 1}{4(s/40 + 1)}$$

Figure 11.25 illustrates the gain and phase curves for the function that results when this is multiplied by the transfer function of the three-pole system.

Shown in Figure 11.25 is a repeat of the three-pole amplitude and phase curves from Figure 11.23. When the compensation network is placed in cascade with this system, we add the Bode plots (both dB gain and phase) for the uncompensated amplifier to those of the compensation network. Thus note that the amplitude curve has a slope that increases by 20 dB/decade between a frequency of 10 and 40, and then decreases by 20 dB/decade to return to a slope of -60 dB/decade. These two changes are due to the zero and pole of the compensation network function at frequencies of 10 and 40 respectively. The phase curve is similarly modified at the break frequencies of 1/10 and 10 times the two corner frequencies (10 and 40).

We now view the point at which the compensated phase curve crosses a phase shift of -180°. At this frequency (approximately 35 rad/sec), the compensated gain is -34 dB. The system can therefore have any gain below 34 dB and still be stable. This is the overall gain including the compensation network. Since the compensation network has a gain (attenuation) of 1/4 (-12 dB), the gain of the op-amp can be as high as

$$G_o = 34 \text{ dB} + 12 \text{ dB} = 46 \text{ dB}$$

Without compensation, the allowable gain is about 20 dB. Thus, an improvement of approximately 26 dB is realized. The system can be further improved if we vary the location of the zero and pole.

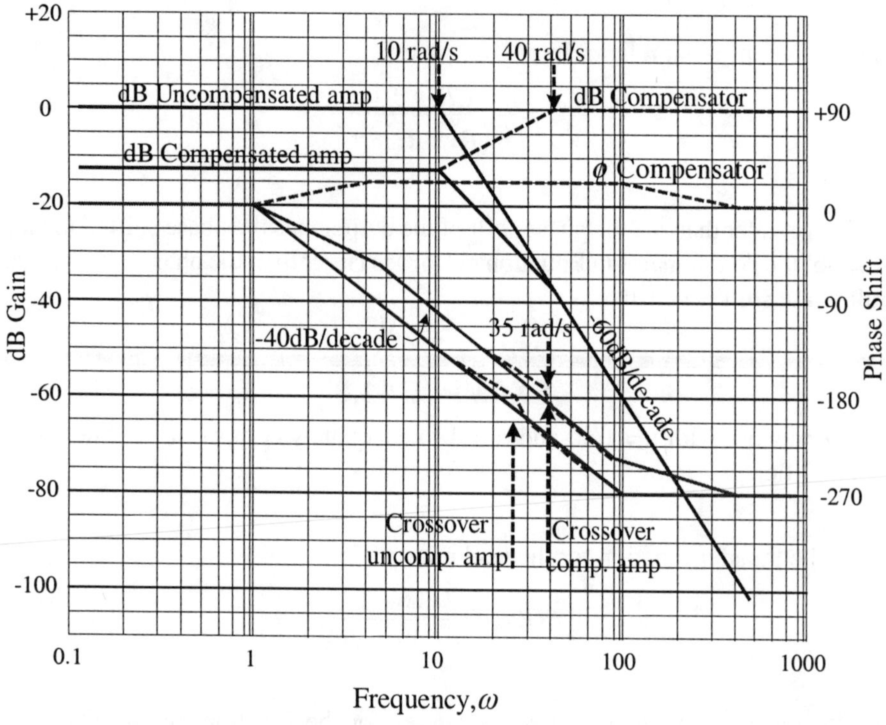

Figure 11.25 - Bode plots for Example 11.8

In the previous example, we found that the compensated gain is -34 dB at a frequency where the phase is -180°. The term *gain margin* is used for the difference between 0-dB and the actual gain when the phase is 180°. Thus, the gain margin is the amount that the gain can increase before the system is unstable.

Alternatively, we can view how much the phase can change at a frequency where the gain is 0 dB. This is known as the *phase margin.* (Note that since we did not assign an amplifier gain to the previous example, the concept of phase margin does not apply because the gain is always less than 0 dB).

EXAMPLE 11.9

Consider the negative-gain op-amp system of Figure 11.26(a). Investigate the stability of this three-pole amplifier.

Solution: The equivalent circuit of the amplifier is shown in Figure 11.26(b), where v_d is the differential op-amp input voltage. The closed-loop gain, V_{out}/V_{in}, is found using Equation (11.27) which is repeated here for convenience.

$$\frac{V_{out}}{V_{in}} = \frac{-G\gamma R_F / R_A}{1 + G\gamma}$$

where

$$\gamma = \frac{1}{1 + R_F/R_A}$$

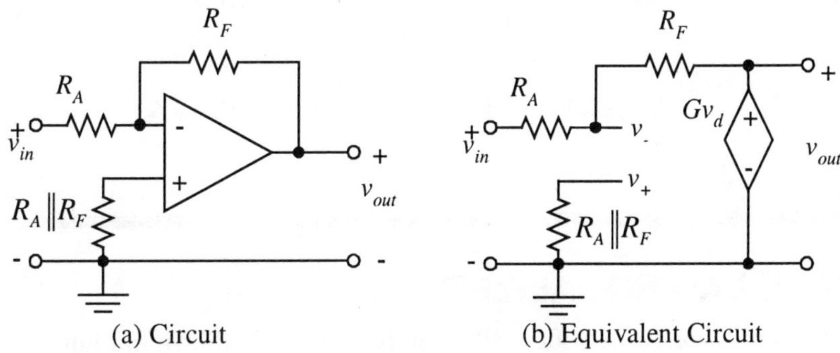

Figure 11.26 – Amplifier for Example 11.9

The amplifier has the following third-order transfer function:

$$G = \frac{G_o}{s(1 + s/\omega_o)^3}$$

where

$$\omega_o = 10$$

The Bode plot for this system is shown in Figure 11.27.

Notice that we construct the Bode plot for the loop gain, $G_o\gamma$, where we set $G_o\gamma = 1$. The phase shift reaches -180° at a frequency of 10 rad/sec, and the associated gain is -26 dB. The straight line asymptotes account for -20 dB, and the additional -6 dB is due to the correction to the straight-line asymptote. Thus, the design allows for a gain of 26 dB before instability is experienced.

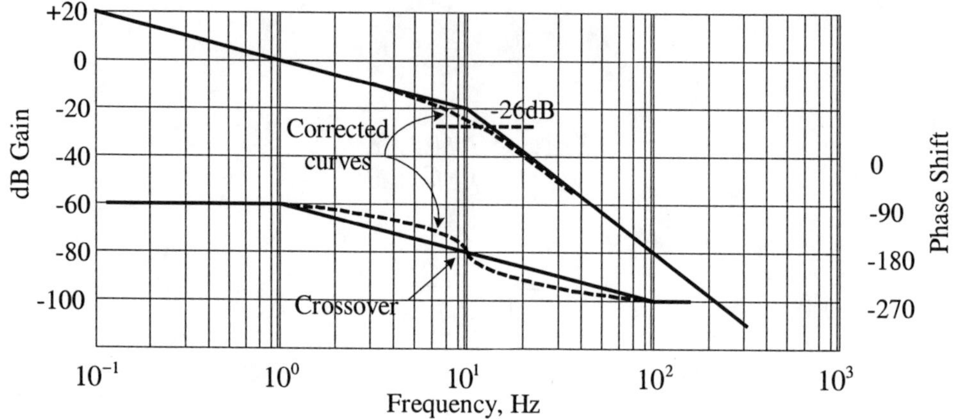

Figure 11.27 – Bode plot for Example 11.9

11.9 PHASE-LAG EQUALIZER

A *passive phase-lag network*, often called an *integrator*, is shown in Figure 11.28.

We can simplify the transfer function by defining two constants,

$$\alpha = 1 + \frac{R_1}{R_2}$$
$$\tau = R_2 C \tag{11.59}$$

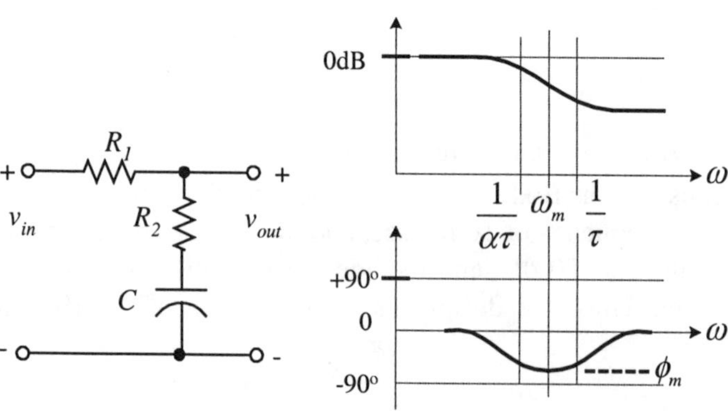

Figure 11.28 – Passive circuit lag network

The transfer function then becomes

$$\frac{V_{out}}{V_{in}} = G(s) = \frac{1}{\alpha} \cdot \frac{s + 1/\tau}{s + 1/\alpha\tau} \tag{11.60}$$

The Bode plot for this expression is shown in Figure 11.28. We rely on the attenuation of the dB gain curve to improve the stability. Note that the maximum phase lag increases as α increases, and it approaches 90° as α approaches infinity. The frequency, ω_m, at which the maximum occurs decreases with increasing α. We insert this network in the feedback path of the op-amp to improve stability.

Lag networks possess certain disadvantages when contrasted with other forms of compensation. If the time constant of the lag network is too large, a large root occurs in the system function, which can lead to transients that die out very slowly.

11.10 EFFECTS OF CAPACITIVE LOADING

The op-amp transfer function includes the effects of output capacitance and chip capacitance. A capacitive load lowers the corner frequency (i.e., a longer time constant leads to lower frequency). This is troublesome for capacitor values of more than about 100 pF in a typical circuit configuration [see Figure 11.29(a)]. The effect can be reduced by addition of a series resistance as shown in Figure 11.29(b). This resistance adds attenuation and

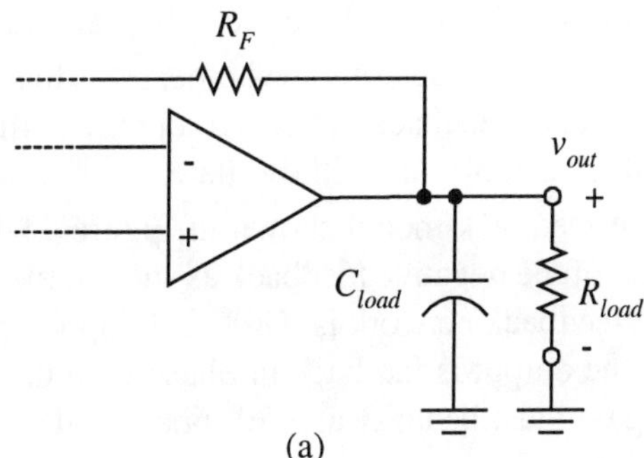

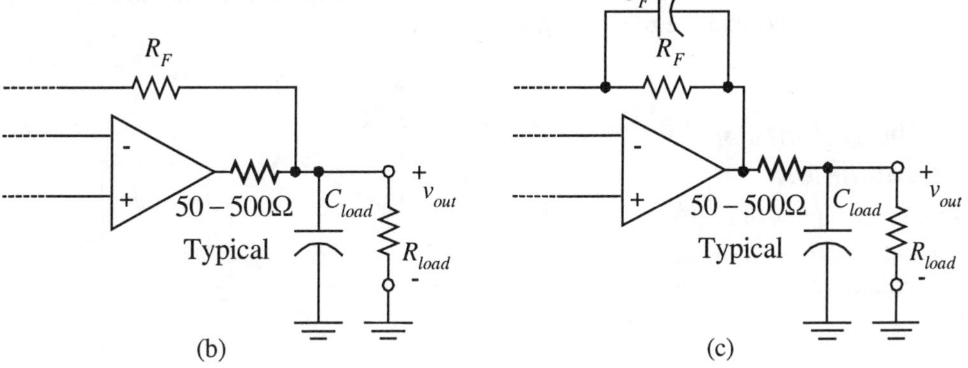

Figure 11.29 – Capacitive loading

modifies the gain-phase characteristic.

Input impedance is frequently modeled as a capacitor, C_i, in parallel with a resistor, R_i. This R_iC_i network accounts for another of the poles of $G(s)$ and leads to a phase shift at high frequencies. Additional external capacitance across the input is a problem when R_F is large because it lowers the corner frequency. Additional compensation in the form of a capacitor, C_F, in parallel with R_F is often used as a cure [see Figure 11.29(c)]. Typical values for C_F are 3 to 10 pF. This is known as *Miller-effect compensation*. The compensating circuit contributes one zero and one pole. The pole is far from the origin because of the Miller effect, which multiplies the capacitance value by the gain. The circuit parameters are chosen to place the zero at the same location as the original circuit pole. The pole and zero then cancel each other. The result is a much higher corner frequency. This approach is used extensively for internal compensation.

11.11 OSCILLATORS

Sinusoidal driving sources are the building blocks of many systems. A feedback system oscillates if the loop-transfer function reaches unity amplitude (0 dB) when the phase shift is or becomes -180°. Such a system produces an output with no input. In a sense, it "chases its tail," with the signal constantly recirculating and regenerating itself.

We can easily determine whether a feedback circuit will oscillate. We examine the loop gain of a negative-feedback system. If a phase shift of -180° occurs where the loop gain is 0 dB, the circuit is unstable and will oscillate.

The feedback model shown in Figure 11.1 is a good starting point for oscillator analysis. Instead of the negative feedback as shown, the feedback is positive. This occurs if the phase shift of the feedback network is -180°. The input signal can be removed without changing the output since the output is fed back in phase with the input. If the circuit is to sustain oscillations, the loop gain must be unity at -180° phase shift.

While the basic concept of instability and positive feedback is common to all oscillators, there are a number of variations on the basic design. Common oscillators include the *Colpitts*, the *Hartley*, the *Wien bridge*, and the *phase shift* oscillators.

11.11.1 The Colpitts and Hartley Oscillators

We begin by analyzing the circuit shown in Figure 11.30. Several of the standard oscillators can be modeled in this manner.

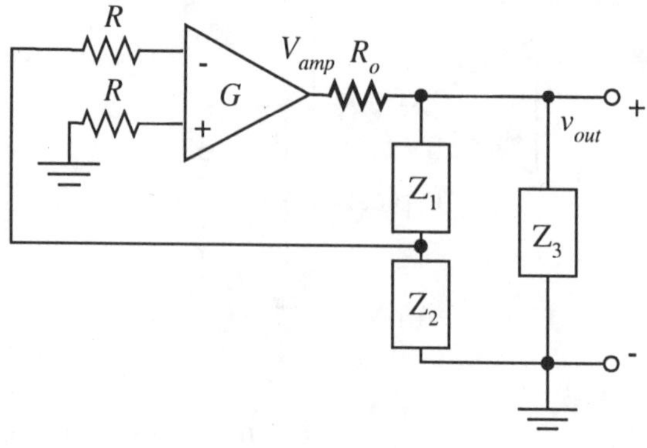

Figure 11.30 – Oscillator circuit

Colpitts Oscillator

If Z_1 and Z_2 are capacitors and Z_3 is an inductor, the circuit is known as a *Colpitts oscillator*. The equivalent impedance between the output terminal and ground is

$$Z_L = Z_3 \| (Z_1 + Z_2) = sL \left\| \left(\frac{1}{sC_1} + \frac{1}{sC_2} \right) \right. \tag{11.61}$$

We expand Equation (11.61) to find

$$Z_L = \frac{sL}{\dfrac{s^2 C_1 C_2 L}{C_1 + C_2} + 1} \tag{11.62}$$

The denominator of Equation (11.62) has poles on the imaginary axis which results in oscillation. We can find the resonant frequency of the Colpitts oscillator by substituting s = $j\omega$ and solving for the pole.

$$\omega_o = \sqrt{\frac{C_1 + C_2}{C_1 C_2 L}} \tag{11.63}$$

Hartley Oscillator

Now suppose that in the circuit of Figure 11.30, Z_1 and Z_2 are inductors and Z_3 is a capacitor. The circuit is then a *Hartley oscillator*. The impedances are given by $Z_1 = sL_1$; $Z_2 = sL_2$; and $Z_3 = 1/sC$ and

$$Z_L = \frac{1}{sC} \| (sL_1 + sL_2) = \frac{sL_1 + sL_2}{s^2 C (L_1 + L_2) + 1} \tag{11.64}$$

Again, the denominator of Z_L has two poles on the imaginary axis, so the resonant frequency is

$$\omega_o = \frac{1}{\sqrt{C(L_1 + L_2)}} \tag{11.65}$$

11.11.2 Wien Bridge Oscillator

The Wien bridge oscillator is shown in Figure 11.31. We analyze this circuit by writing equations for V_+ and V_- as follows:

$$V_+ = V_{out} \cdot \frac{Z_1}{Z_1 + Z_F} = \frac{RC \cdot sV_{out}}{s^2 (RC)^2 + 3sRC + 1}$$

$$V_- = \frac{V_{out}}{1 + R_F / R_A}. \tag{11.66}$$

We equate V_+ and V_- and let $s = j\omega$ and $RC = \tau$ to get

$$\frac{1}{1+R_F/R_A} = \frac{-\omega\tau}{j(1-\omega^2\tau^2)-3\omega\tau} \tag{11.67}$$

This complex equality represents two equations since both the imaginary and real parts of the two expressions must be equal. The two equations are

$$1-\omega^2\tau^2=0$$

$$\frac{1}{1+R_F/R_A} = \frac{-\omega\tau}{-3\omega\tau} = \frac{1}{3} \tag{11.68}$$

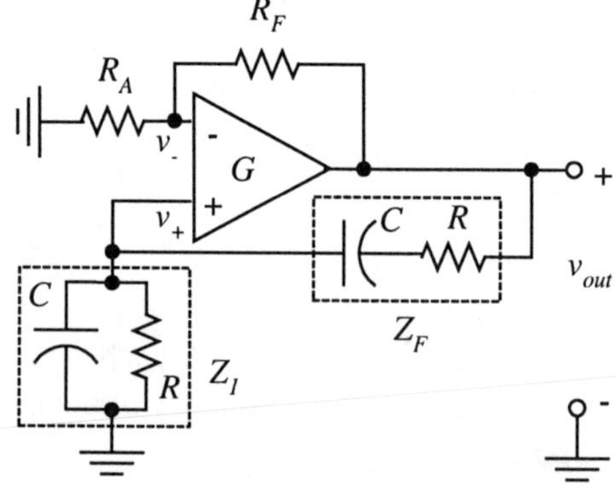

Figure 11.31 Wien bridge oscillator

We can solve these to find the resonant frequency and the relationship between R_F and R_A.

$$\omega_o = \frac{1}{\tau} = \frac{1}{RC} \tag{11.69}$$
$$R_F = 2R_A$$

11.11.3 The Phase Shift Oscillator

The *phase shift oscillator* is shown in Figure 11.32. It includes three identical *RC* networks. Each provides a -60° phase shift, resulting in the required -180° total phase shift.

To achieve oscillation, the loop gain (the product of the op-amp gain, *A*, and the transfer function, V_+/V_o) must satisfy the oscillation criterion. That is, the phase shift must be -180° when the gain is 0 dB. This yields the design equation for this oscillator. We solve the circuit by writing three node equations.

$$V_1\left(2sC+\frac{1}{R}\right)+V_2(-sC)=V_{out}\cdot sC$$

$$V_1(-sC)+V_2\left(2sC+\frac{1}{R}\right)+V_+(-sC)=0 \tag{11.70}$$

$$V_2(-sC)+V_+\left(sC+\frac{1}{R}\right)=0$$

Equations (11.70) are solved for the transfer function, V_+/V_{out}, and τ is substituted for RC to obtain

$$\frac{V_+}{V_{out}}(s)=\frac{s^3\tau^3}{s^3\tau^3+6s^2\tau^2+5s\tau+1}$$

$$\frac{V_+}{V_{out}}(j\omega)=\frac{(\omega\tau)^3}{(\omega\tau)^3-5\omega\tau+j\left[1-6(\omega\tau)^2\right]} \tag{11.71}$$

To determine the frequency of oscillation, we set the phase shift of Equation (11.71) to -180°:

$$Phase\ shift=\tan^{-1}\left(\frac{1-6(\omega\tau)^2}{\omega\tau[(\omega\tau)^2-5]}\right)=-180^\circ \tag{11.72}$$

Solving for ω [set the numerator of Equation (11.72) to zero since the tangent of -180° is zero], we find

$$\omega=\frac{1}{\sqrt{6}RC} \tag{11.73}$$

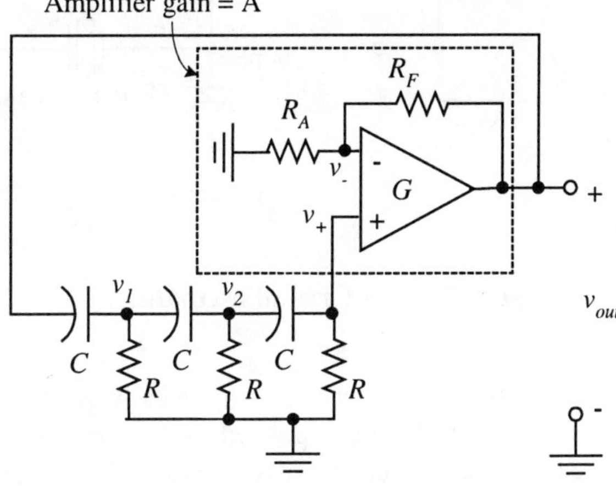

Figure 11.32 – Phase-shift oscillator

To determine the value of the gain, we find the magnitude of Equation (11.71) at the frequency found in Equation (11.73). The magnitude is given by

$$\left|\frac{V_+}{V_{out}}(j\omega)\right|\Bigg|_{\omega=\frac{1}{\sqrt{6}RC}} = \frac{(\omega\tau)^3}{\sqrt{\left[(\omega\tau)^3 - 5\omega\tau\right]^2 + \left[1 - 6(\omega\tau)^2\right]^2}}\Bigg|_{\omega=\frac{1}{\sqrt{6}RC}} = \frac{1}{29} \tag{11.74}$$

For the loop gain to be 0 dB (unit amplitude), the amplifier gain must be at least 29.

This oscillator uses no inductors, is relatively easy to operate, and is inexpensive. However, the oscillator frequency is not accurately controlled, since it depends on the values of R and C. Similar accuracy problems exist for the Colpitts, Hartley, and Wien bridge oscillators. The next section presents a more precise oscillator.

11.11.4 The Crystal Oscillator

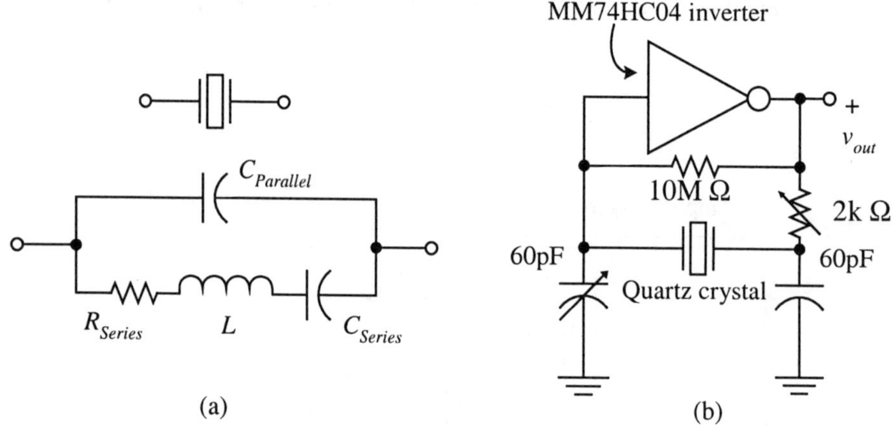

Figure 11.33 – Crystal oscillator

When a voltage is applied across a piezoelectric crystal (usually quartz), the crystal oscillates in a stable and accurate manner. Electrodes are deposited on the opposite faces of the crystal so that the crystal can be excited. The frequency of oscillation is determined by the crystal dimensions. The sharpness of the frequency response curve (i.e., the Q of the resonant circuit) is much higher for a crystal than for other tuned circuits.

Since the crystal is a resonant circuit, it can be used in conjunction with discrete or integrated circuits. Crystal oscillators achieve accurate frequency control. Stabilities in the range of several parts per million in frequency variation can be achieved. Commercial quartz crystals are readily available with frequencies from a few kHz to a few hundred MHz and with extremely high values of Q (10^4 to 10^5).

The equivalent circuit for a crystal is shown in Figure 11.33(a). Since the Q is so high, we can neglect R_{Series}. We write the equation for impedance as

$$Z(s) = \frac{1}{s\,C_{Parallel}} \cdot \frac{s^2 + 1/LC_{Series}}{s^2 + \dfrac{1/C_{Series} + 1/C_{Parallel}}{L}} \tag{11.75}$$

Two frequencies exist, one for the double zero and one for the double pole.

$$\omega_z = \frac{1}{\sqrt{LC_{Series}}}$$

$$\omega_p = \sqrt{\frac{1}{L}\left(\frac{1}{C_{Series}} + \frac{1}{C_{Parallel}}\right)} \tag{11.76}$$

$C_{Parallel}$ is much larger than C_{Series}, so the two frequencies are approximately equal.

A crystal can replace the tuned inductance-capacitance circuit in a wide variety of oscillators. The oscillator frequency is determined by the crystal rather than by the remaining part of the circuit.

A simple crystal oscillator can be designed using a CMOS inverter that is biased to operate as an *ac* amplifier. The square-wave oscillator, which is shown in Figure 11.33(b), provides a fixed frequency, which is determined by the crystal frequency. By placing a 10 MΩ resistor from the output to the input of the MM74HC04 CMOS inverter, we cause it to operate as an *ac* amplifier. This 10-MΩ negative-feedback resistor biases the inverter to operate at one-half of the supply voltage, with a gain of several thousand. The MM74HC04 inverter can produce a gain of 10^4. The loop gain can be adjusted with R, which is set to about 2 kΩ. The variable capacitor (approximately 60 pF) provides for small adjustments in frequency. The capacitors also prevent the crystal from oscillating at any frequency other than the fundamental. The higher harmonics are filtered out with the RC network around the crystal.

11.11.5 Touch-Tone Generator

We present this generator both as a practical example of an oscillator application, and because you might incorporate this generator in other designs. *Touch-tone dialing* permits a standard telephone keypad to be used for dialing a telephone number by generating a pair of frequencies or tones for each key pressed. The TP5087DTMF tone generator, which is shown in Figure 11.34 (please see next page), supplies four row frequencies, R_i, and four column frequencies, C_i, as shown below.

R_1	697 Hz	C_1	1209 Hz
R_2	770 Hz	C_2	1336 Hz
R_3	852 Hz	C_3	1477 Hz
R_4	941 Hz	C_4	1633 Hz

The block at the left of the figure indicates the tone combinations. For example, when the number 7 is pressed, the two sinusoidal frequencies of 852 Hz (R_3) and 1209 Hz (C_1) are simultaneously generated by the IC.

The basic frequency is generated from a low-cost 3.579545 MHz crystal (a standard NTSC TV color burst crystal), which feeds the IC. The row and column inputs, which are energized when a key is pressed, are decoded to develop the high-frequency tone and the low-frequency tone. The two tones are summed in a mixing amplifier and power amplified in an *npn* emitter follower. Some of the circuits shown in Figure 11.34 (i.e., dividers, counters, and D/A) are covered in more detail in later chapters. For now, we note that the tones are derived by dividing the reference frequency by fixed numbers. For example, 697 Hz results from dividing the reference by 5136, and 1633 Hz results if we divide by 2192.

SUMMARY

Feedback, where the output of an electronic amplifier combines with the input, is an important concept for the system designer. It can be used to improve the stability of a system and to decrease the sensitivity of the system to changes in parameters. It can also be used to create an oscillator.

We began this chapter with a thorough examination of the types of feedback, including positive and negative as well as current and voltage. We then applied these principles to both single-stage and multistage amplifiers. We saw how feedback is used in operational amplifiers to significantly decrease the effects of frequency variations.

Next, we examined roots and poles of transfer functions and their effect on stability. This theory was applied to develop Bode plots showing amplitude and phase response. We briefly discussed equalizers and their utility for controlling stability. The chapter concluded with a study of various types of oscillators, and a discussion of the *touch-tone* generator integrated circuit.

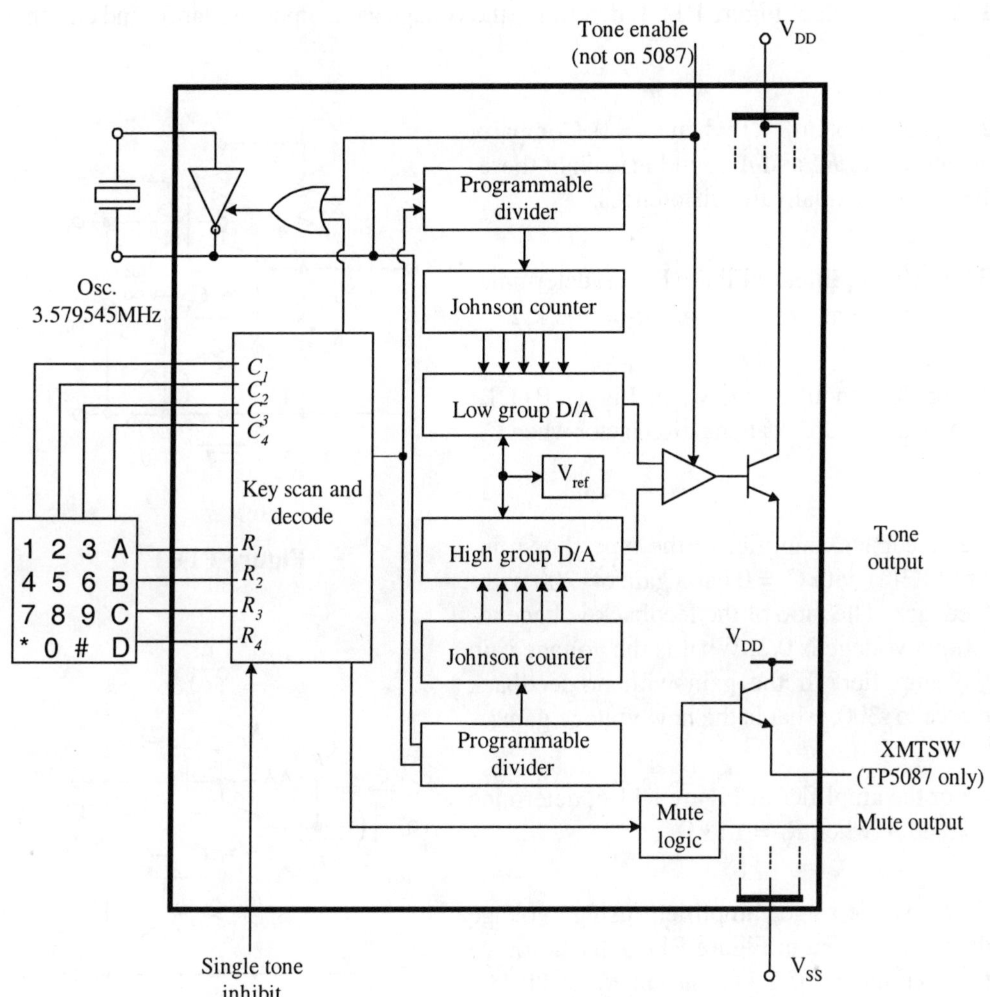

Figure 11.34 – TP50-87DTMF tone generator

PROBLEMS

Section 11.4

11.1 For the circuit of Figure P11.1, determine the voltage gain, input resistance, and current gain when $C_I \to \infty$.

11.2 Repeat Problem 11.1 when $C_I = 0$. Compare the values of A_v, R_{in} and A_i found in each of these problems, and explain any differences.

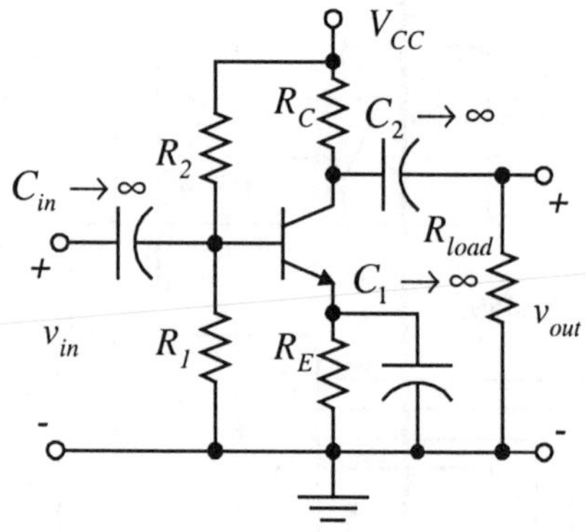

Figure P11.1

11.3 For the amplifier of Figure P11.1, determine A_v, R_{in}, and A_i when $R_I \to \infty$ and $R_2 = 200$ kΩ.

11.4 For the amplifier shown in Figure P11.1, determine the feedback attenuation factor when $C_I = 0$.

11.5 A feedback amplifier of the type shown in Figure 11.3(a) with $C_I = 0$ has a gain of -200 with no feedback. The ratio of the feedback voltage to the output voltage is 0.2. What is the voltage gain of the amplifier? If the gain with no feedback increases to -300, what is the new voltage gain?

11.6 For the amplifier of Figure P11.6, determine A_v, R_{in} and A_i when $R_F = 14$ kΩ.

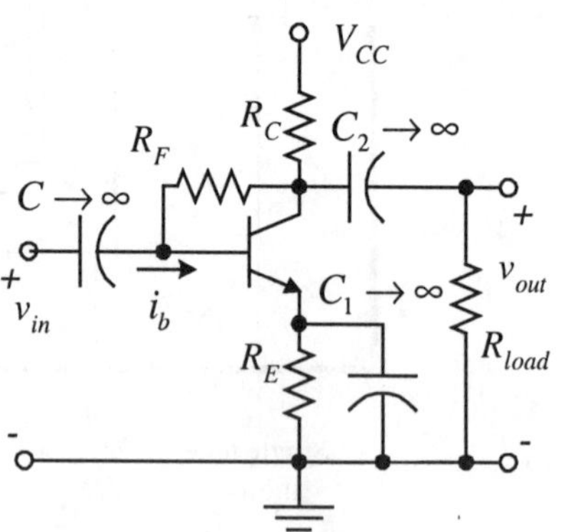

Figure P11.6

11.7 A single-stage amplifier using voltage feedback, as shown in Figure P11.6, has a source voltage resistance of 2 kΩ and an R_F of 20 kΩ. Determine the open-loop and closed-loop gain of the amplifier.

11.8 Using the same amplifier as in Problem 11.7, select the value of R_F to make the amplifier bias stable and determine the closed-loop gain.

Section 11.5

11.9 Draw the amplitude and phase Bode plots for the operational amplifier of Figure P11.9. Let $G_o = 120$ dB and $\omega_c = 2\pi$ rad/s in the equation

$$G = \frac{G_o}{1 + s/\omega_c}$$

Use the following values of resistor ratios:

(a) $R_F/R_A = 10^3$
(b) $R_F/R_A = 10$
(c) $R_F/R_A = 1$

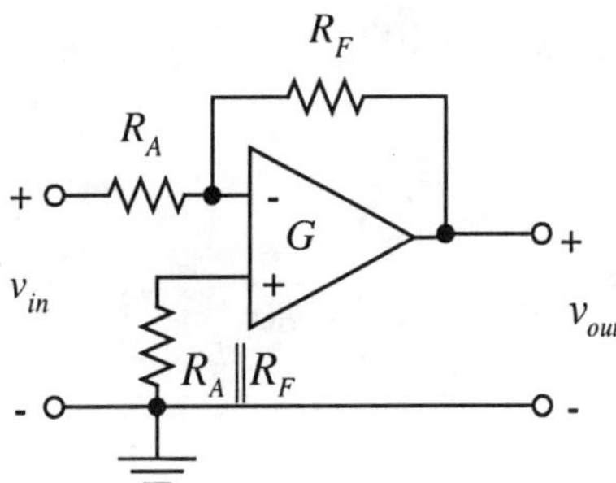

Figure P11.9

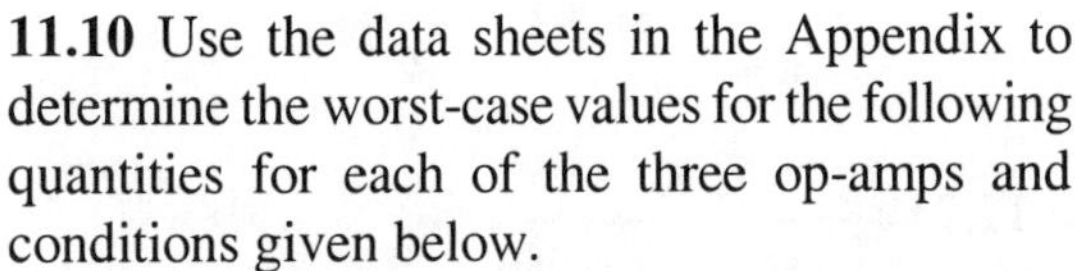
11.10 Use the data sheets in the Appendix to determine the worst-case values for the following quantities for each of the three op-amps and conditions given below.

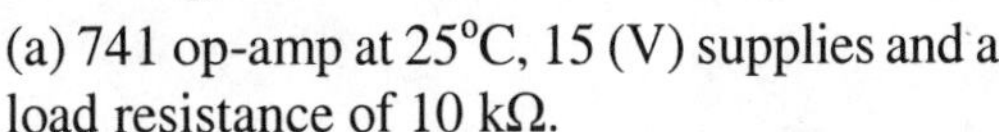
(a) 741 op-amp at 25°C, 15 (V) supplies and a load resistance of 10 kΩ.
(b) 741 op-amp at 50°C, 20 (V) supplies and a load resistance of 2 kΩ.
(c) 101 op-amp at 50°C, 15 (V) supplies and a load resistance of 5 kΩ.

(i) Gain (smallest is worst case)
(ii) Input resistance (smallest is worst case)
(iii) Input offset voltage (largest is worst case)
(iv) Input bias current (largest is worst case)
(v) Input offset current (largest is worst case)
(vi) Output resistance (largest is worst case)
(vii) Output voltage swing (smallest is worst case)
(viii) Gain-bandwidth product (smallest is worst case)
(ix) Power supply current (largest is worst case)

11.11 For the op-amp inverting amplifier shown in Figure 11.8(a), what is the percent error if the open-loop gain is only 50,000? Use $R_F = 200$ kΩ and $R_A = 10$ kΩ.

Section 11.7

In Problems 11.12 through 11.23, sketch decibel gain and phase curves for each function, and discuss the stability of each system as a function of K.

11.12 $\dfrac{K}{s(s + 10)}$

11.13 $\dfrac{K}{s^2(s + 10)}$

11.14 $\dfrac{K(s+1)}{s^2(s+10)}$

11.15 $\dfrac{K}{s(s+1)(s+100)}$

11.16 $\dfrac{K(s+1)}{s^3(s+100)}$

11.17 $\dfrac{K}{s(s^2+20s+100)}$

11.18 $\dfrac{K}{s(s+10)(s+80)}$

11.19 $\dfrac{K}{s(s+30)(s+100)}$

11.20 $\dfrac{K}{s(s+10)(s+50)}$

11.21 $\dfrac{K}{s(s+5)(s+40)}$

11.22 $\dfrac{K(s+100)}{s(s+10)(s+500)}$

11.23 $\dfrac{K}{s(s+10^3)(s+10^4)}$

11.24 The op-amp system of Figure 11.22(a) has a gain function which is

$$G(s) = \frac{G_o}{1 + s/2\pi}$$

$R = 100$ kΩ and $C = 0.1$ μF. Determine the open- and closed-loop functions.

11.25 For the op-amp system of Problem 11.24, plot a Bode diagram with $G_o = 1$. Determine the stability for this system.

11.26 For the op-amp system of Figure 11.21(a), use

$$G(s) = \frac{G_o}{(1 + s/20\pi)^2}$$

$R = 160$ kΩ and $C = 0.1$ μF. Note the square in the op-amp gain function. Determine the open- and closed-loop functions.

11.27 For the op-amp system of Problem 11.26, plot a Bode diagram with $G_o = 1$. Determine the stability of the system.

For the expressions in Problems 11.28 through 11.37, sketch Bode plots and discuss stability of each amplifier as a function of *K*.

11.28 $\frac{K}{s(s^2 + s + 25)}$ **11.29** $\frac{K}{s^2(s^2 + s + 25)}$

11.30 $\frac{Ks}{s^2 + s + 25}$ **11.31** $\frac{K}{s(s + 100)^2}$

11.32 $\frac{K}{s(s + 20)^2}$ **11.33** $\frac{K(s + 1))}{s(s + 40)^2}$

11.34 $\frac{K}{s(s^2 + 2s + 100)}$ **11.35** $\frac{K}{s(s^2 + 5s + 100)}$

11.36 $\frac{K}{s(s^2 + 2s + 64)}$ **11.37** $\frac{K}{s(s^2 + 10s + 1000)}$

11.38 Determine the value of gain, *K*, for which the system with

$$G(s)H(s) = \frac{K}{s(0.1s + 1)^2}$$

has a phase shift of -180° at a dB gain of 0 dB (i.e., marginal stability).

11.39 A zero is added to the system function of Problem 11.38 to improve performance. The new system has an open-loop function given by

$$G(s)H(s) = \frac{K(0.125s + 1)}{s(0.1s + 1)}$$

Find the value of *K* for which the system is marginally stable.

11.40 Plot a Bode diagram for the op-amp system of Figure P11.40. For what values of the gain, K, is the system stable? Perfect the critical point before determining the value of K. Let $C = 1\ \mu F$, $L = 100$ mH, $R = 1\ k\Omega$. The op-amp gain function is given by

$$G(s) = \frac{K}{0.001s + 1}$$

11.41 Determine the stability of the integrator shown in Figure P11.41. The op-amp gain function is

$$G(s) = \frac{K}{(1 + s/20\pi)^3}$$

and $RC = 200$ ms. Find the value of K for marginal stability.

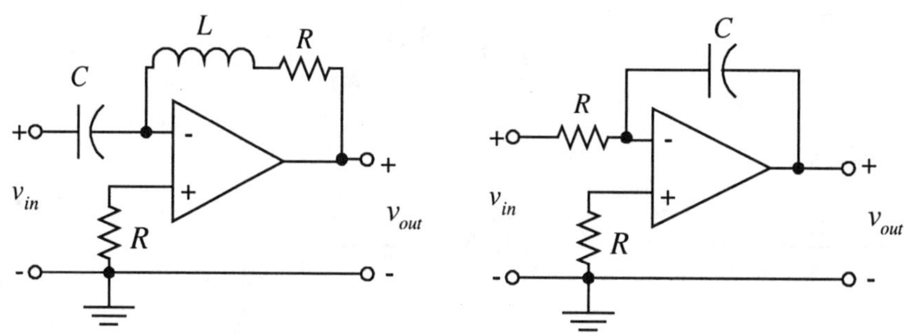

Figure P11.40

Figure P11.41

11.42 Determine the stability of the differentiator of Figure P11.42. The op-amp gain function is

$$G(s) = \frac{K}{(1 + s/40)^2}$$

and $RC = 250$ ms. Find K for marginal stability; (i.e., 0-dB gain when the phase is -180°). Be sure to perfect the critical point.

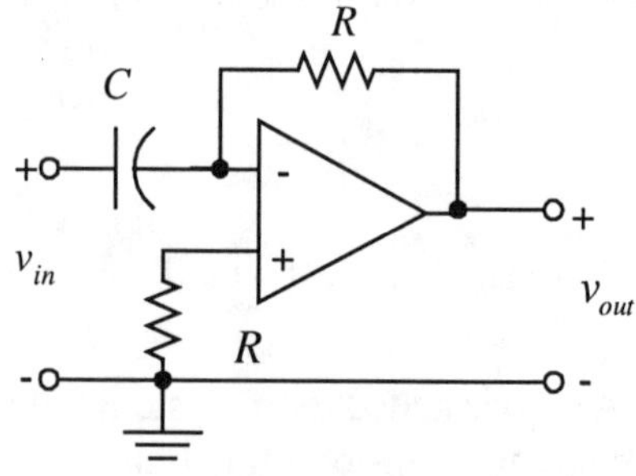

Figure P11.42

Section 11.11

11.43 What is the frequency in Hertz of a Colpitts oscillator when $C_1 = .1\ \mu F$, $C_2 = .05\ \mu F$, and $L = 0.5$ mH?

11.44 Determine the size of the capacitor in a Colpitts oscillator for a frequency of 1.5 MHz when $L = 5$ μH.

11.45 What is the frequency in Hertz of a Hartley oscillator when $C = .001$ μF, $L_1 = 0.5$ μH, and $L_2 = 0.2$ μH?

11.46 Determine the value of C for a frequency of 3.5 MHz when $L_1 = 5.0$ μH and $L_2 = 3$μH.

11.47 Determine the ratio of R_F to R_A to meet the condition for oscillations of the Wien Bridge Oscillator shown in Figure P11.47 and determine the formula for frequency of oscillation.

11.48 Design a phase shift oscillator using a FET transistor as shown in Figure P11.48. Let $g_m =$ 5 mS, $r_d = 50$ kΩ and the feedback resistors, $R = 20$ kΩ. Select the value of C for the oscillator to operate at 10 kHz. Make sure the gain of the amplifier is at least -50 to compensate for loading.

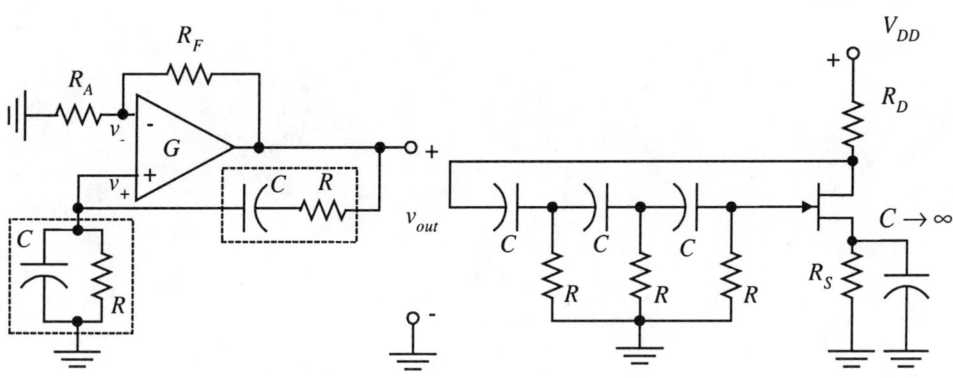

Figure P11.47 **Figure P11.48**

11.49 Design a phase shift oscillator, as shown in Figure 11.32 to operate at 100 kHz. Let $C =$ 100 pF and select appropriate values for R, R_F, and R_A.

11.50 In Problem 11.47, design the Wien Bridge oscillator to oscillate at 100 MHz using $R = 10$ kΩ.

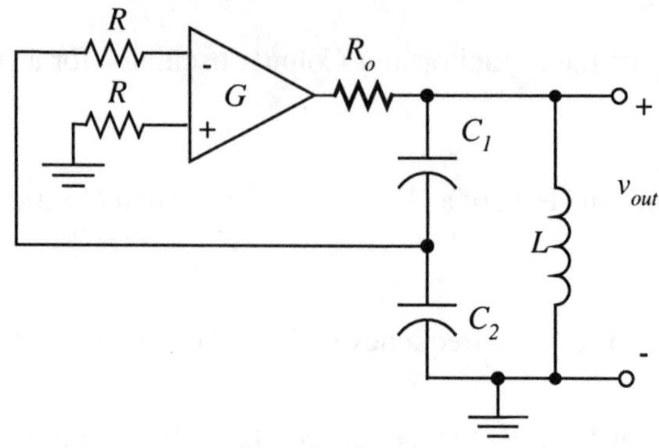

Figure P11.51

11.51 Determine the value of the capacitor needed in the Colpitts oscillator of Figure P11.51 if a 0.001 mH inductor were the only value inductor available. The frequency of oscillation is specified to be 500 kHz.

Chapter 12

Active Filters

Suppose that you are employed by a company which designs and manufactures video games. The company has started a new generation of games coupling compact disc technology with microprocessor-controlled video games. The pioneer entry in this market is a game, "The Colonization of Mars". This couples actual footage of film taken on the surface of Mars with images of the player of the game. The FCC (Federal Communications Commission) must license the game since video signals from the player are transmitted by a small remote camera to the game module. Unfortunately, the FCC refused approval due to spurious signals. The commission claimed your transmitter was interfering with signals in adjacent frequency bands. Your employer has given you a small budget to eliminate the problem as quickly as possible since firm orders for the game (at fixed price) must be filled within 30 days.

Having taken undergraduate courses in network synthesis, you muster your knowledge and design a filter which meets the FCC specifications for reducing out of band transmissions. However, the specifications are so stiff that your filter requires a large number of components. Since components are inexpensive, this did not bother you until you became aware of the "real estate" problem. That is, the serious problem is finding space to house components. Alas, after searching your storehouse of experience and knowledge, you cannot come up with a solution. Another engineer working for the same company asks you if you considered active filters. Indeed, you had not. The current chapter will give you the tools to solve the problem described above.

After studying this material, you will be able to:

- Analyze active networks.
- Design first-order active filters.
- Verify filter design using computer simulation.
- Design Butterworth low-pass and high-pass filters.
- Design Chebyshev low-pass and high-pass filter.
- Design IC filters.

12.0 INTRODUCTION

A *filter* is a system designed to achieve a desired transfer characteristic. That is, it operates on an input signal in a predetermined manner. *Passive linear filters* are normally considered as part of a study of circuits, networks or linear systems. They are composed of combinations of resistors, inductors and capacitors. While it is possible to achieve a wide variety of transfer characteristics using only these elements, a large number of components is often required. This leads us to explore alternatives to passive filters.

Active filters contain amplifiers, which permit the design of a wide range of transfer functions (within some broad restrictions relating to the properties of the transfer function).

12.1 INTEGRATORS AND DIFFERENTIATORS

A simple two-element passive circuit can approximate an integrator or differentiator. For example, a series *RC* circuit can perform this function.

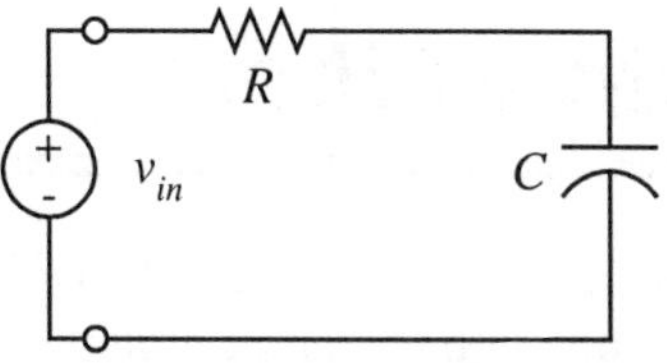

Figure 12.1 – RC circuit

Figure 12.1 illustrates an *RC* circuit with a voltage source applied. Since the current in a capacitor is proportional to the derivative of the voltage across the capacitor, the circuit can act as a differentiator. This happens if the resistance, *R*, is made small compared to the capacitive impedance, $1/\omega C$, at the frequencies of interest. The capacitor voltage is then almost equal to the input voltage since the voltage across *R* is small. The current is therefore approximately equal to the derivative of the input voltage. The output, which is taken across the resistor, is then approximately proportional to the derivative of the input voltage.

In order to approximate an integrator, the opposite approach is used. That is, we want the *current* in the circuit to be proportional to the input voltage. This is achieved by making the resistance predominate over the capacitive impedance. Since the voltage across a capacitor is proportional to the integral of the current through it, the output is taken across the capacitor.

This passive circuit approximates the operations of differentiation and integration, and the approximation gets better as the impedance of one of the elements is made much smaller than that of the other. Unfortunately, as this impedance gets smaller, the magnitude of the output voltage also gets smaller.

Considerable performance improvement is possible if we switch from passive to active circuits. Let us begin our study with the basic op-amp of Figure 12.2(a).

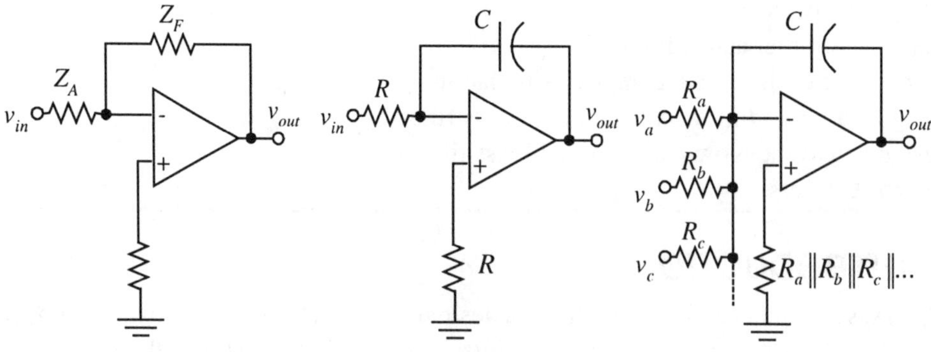

Figure 12.2 - Op-amp circuit

The gain of this ideal op-amp circuit is given by Equation (12.1) where Z_F is the impedance in the feedback path and Z_A is the impedance between the source and the inverting input terminal.

$$\frac{V_{out}}{V_{in}} = -\frac{Z_F}{Z_A} \tag{12.1}$$

The Laplace transform operator notation for an integrator is $1/s$. Therefore, if we choose impedances which make the right side of Equation (12.1) proportional to $1/s$, we have accomplished integration. For example, if Z_F is the impedance of a capacitor, and Z_A is that of a resistor, the gain takes the desired form. Alternatively, Z_F can be the impedance of a resistor and Z_A that of an inductor. Figure 12.2(b) shows one form of the integrator. The behavior of this circuit is described by the following equation, where we present both the Laplace transform and time function version of the equation.

$$V_{out}(s) = -\left(\frac{1}{sRC}\right)V_{in}(s)$$

$$v_{out}(t) = -\left(\frac{1}{RC}\right)\int_0^t v_{in}(\tau)\,d\tau \tag{12.2}$$

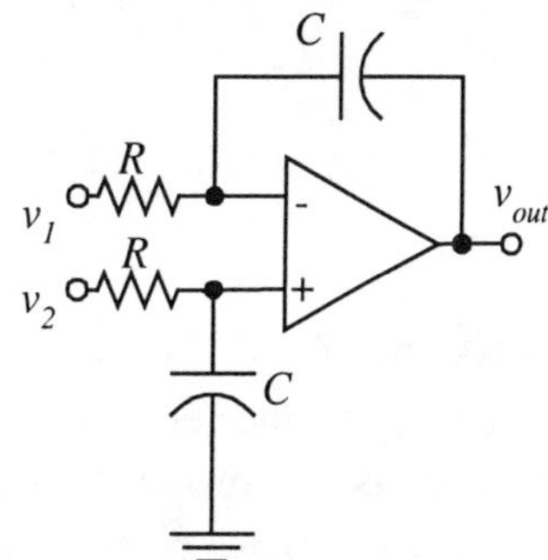

Figure 12.3 – Differencing integrator

The above analysis makes the active filter appear to be a perfect integrator. Of course we are using the ideal model for the op-amp, so the real circuit is still an approximation. However, this active circuit yields a much better approximation to an integrator than can be achieved with passive circuits.

Another advantage of using op-amps is their ability to easily sum inputs. A *summing inverting integrator* is illustrated in Figure 12.2(c). This configuration yields the following equations:

$$V_{out}(s) = -\frac{1}{s}\left(\frac{V_a(s)}{R_a C} + \frac{V_b(s)}{R_b C} + \ldots\right)$$

$$v_{out}(t) = -\int_0^t \left(\frac{v_a(\tau)}{R_a C} + \frac{v_b(\tau)}{R_b C} + \ldots\right) d\tau \tag{12.3}$$

It is easy to form differences between input signals when op-amps are used in circuits. A *differencing integrator* is shown in Figure 12.3. The equations for the voltages at the op-amp inputs are obtained as follows:

$$V_- = \frac{RC \cdot sV_{out} + V_1}{RCs + 1}$$

$$V_+ = \frac{V_2}{RCs + 1} \tag{12.4}$$

Note that we are using upper-case notation since the voltages are functions of *s*. Since *G* approaches infinity, $V_+ = V_-$. Solving for the output voltage, we have

$$V_{out} = \frac{V_2 - V_1}{RC\, s}$$

$$v_{out}(t) = \frac{1}{RC}\int_0^t \left[v_2(\tau) - v_1(\tau)\right] d\tau \tag{12.5}$$

The components *R* and *C* are chosen to achieve the required *dc* gain.

If the capacitor and resistor of the previous circuit are interchanged, the result is the *basic differentiator*, as is shown in Figure 12.4(a).

Since $V_+ = V_- = 0$, we write a node equation at the inverting terminal of the op-amp and solve for the output voltage.

$$V_{out} = -RC \cdot sV_{in}$$

$$v_{out}(t) = -RC \cdot \frac{dv_{in}(t)}{dt} \tag{12.6}$$

Differentiation circuits are not often used. One of the reasons for this is the effect the circuit has upon random noise. Integration is a smoothing process while differentiation is the opposite. For example, if noise spikes are present, differentiation leads to higher spikes because of the presence of large slopes in the noise voltage waveform. A second reason to avoid differentiator circuits is that these circuits are more seriously affected by op-amp bandwidths. This is true since the differentiator accentuates higher frequencies.

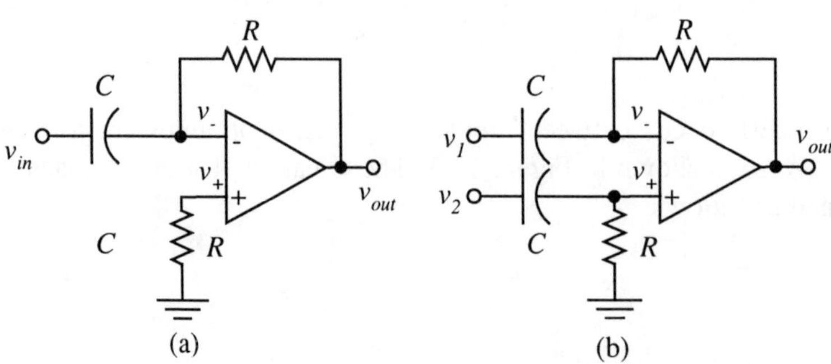

Figure 12.4 - Differentiator

As with integrators, we can either sum or take the difference between inputs. A *differencing differentiator* is shown in Figure 12.4(b). The equations describing its operation are derived from the basic op-amp relationships, as follows:

$$V_+ = \frac{V_2 RCs}{RCs+1}$$
$$V_- = \frac{V_{out} + RCsV_1}{RCs+1} \tag{12.7}$$

Since G approaches infinity, $V_+ = V_-$, and we obtain

$$V_{out} = (V_2 - V_1)RCs$$
$$v_{out}(t) = RC\frac{d\left[v_2(t) - v_1(t)\right]}{dt} \tag{12.8}$$

As previously noted, the process of differentiation accentuates high-frequency components. That is, taking the derivative of a sinusoid multiplies the amplitude by the frequency of the waveform. For this reason, if differentiators are used they are often combined with filters whose transfer function attenuates high frequencies. In reality, the op-amp frequency limitations often provide this attenuation without the need for additional circuitry. Thus, at low frequency, the transfer function approaches a multiple of s, while at high frequencies, the function approaches either a constant or zero. Examples of typical composite transfer functions are:

$$H_1(s) = \frac{100s}{s+100}$$
$$H_2(s) = \frac{100s}{s^2+20s+100} \tag{12.9}$$

Both of these functions approximate $H(s) = s$ at low frequencies (i.e., $s = j\omega \to 0$).

12.2 ACTIVE NETWORK DESIGN

Network synthesis is the process of starting with a desired transfer function and translating this into a practical circuit implementation. The addition of an amplifier to the passive circuit results in a transfer function that has the form of a ratio of two polynomials. The constant multiplier (overall gain) may be changed, but the form of the transfer function remains the same.

The general form of the active network is repeated as Figure 12.5.

A number of advantages are associated with using active networks as compared to passive networks. We list a few of these below.

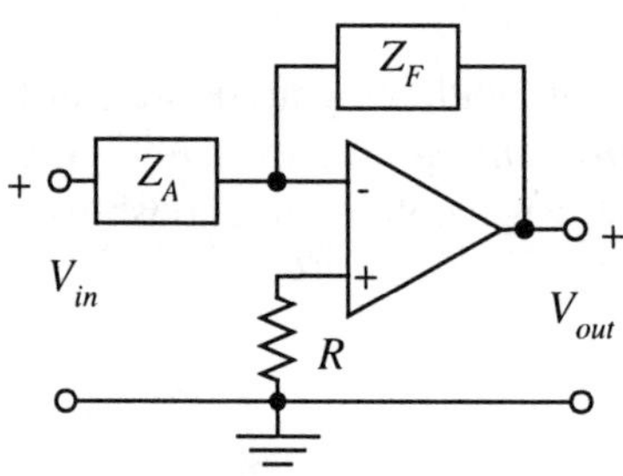

Figure 12.5 – Op-amp used for active network synthesis

- *Low Cost:* In low-frequency applications, inductors can be quite large and expensive. Active filters using op-amps usually do not require inductors.
- *Cascadeability*: Because of good isolation, complex filters can be broken down into a series of simple sections. Each filter section can be separately designed and then cascaded with other sections so that the total transfer function becomes the product of the individual section functions.
- *Gain*: Active filters can produce gain as needed to suit system or filter requirements.

Along with these advantages are some limitations.

- *Supply Power*: A power supply is needed for all active filters, while passive filters do not require any supply.
- *Amplitude Limits:* The op-amp inherently has definite signal amplitude limits beyond which nonlinear operation occurs.
- *Frequency limits:* The op-amp cannot respond at high frequencies. It may have a cutoff frequency too low to permit use in a particular application.

One of the most direct methods of active network design is based on Equation (12.1), which we repeat as Equation (12.10).

$$\frac{V_{out}}{V_{in}} = -\frac{Z_F}{Z_A} \qquad (12.10)$$

The impedances, Z_F and Z_A need not represent single elements. In fact, they can be any achievable two-terminal functions resulting from combinations of elements. Table 12.1 illustrates some common two-terminal configurations and their associated impedance functions.

EXAMPLE 12.1:

Design a network to achieve the following transfer function:

$$\frac{V_{out}}{V_{in}} = \frac{-(s+30)^2}{(s+50)(s+10)}$$

Solution: We use the circuit of Figure 12.5. Comparing Equation (12.8) with Equation (12.10) and solving for the two-terminal impedance functions, we find one possible implementation.

$$Z_F = \frac{s+30}{s+50}$$

$$Z_A = \frac{s+10}{s+30}$$

Reference to Table 12.1 indicates several two-terminal networks that will satisfy these equations. In particular, entries (b) or (e) can be used.

C_1, R, C

$$\frac{s+\frac{1}{RC}}{sC_1\left(s+\frac{1}{R}\cdot\frac{C_1+C}{C_1\cdot C}\right)}$$

(a)

R_1, R, C

$$\frac{R_1R\left(s+\frac{1}{RC}\right)}{(R_1+R)\left(s+\frac{1}{C(R_1+R)}\right)}$$

(b)

R, C

$$\frac{sRC+1}{sC}$$

(c)

R, C, C_1

$$\frac{(C+C_1)\left[s+\frac{1}{R(C+C_1)}\right]}{sCC_1\left[s+\frac{1}{RC}\right]}$$

(d)

R, C, R_1

$$\frac{R_1\left(s+\frac{1}{C}\cdot\frac{R_1+R}{R_1R}\right)}{\left(s+\frac{1}{RC}\right)}$$

(e)

R, C

$$\frac{1}{C\left(s+\frac{1}{RC}\right)}$$

(f)

Table 12.1

EXERCISE

E12.1 Design an active network to generate the following transfer function.

$$\frac{V_{out}}{V_{in}} = -\frac{(s+4)^2}{s(s+20)^2}$$

Use no inductors and only one op-amp.

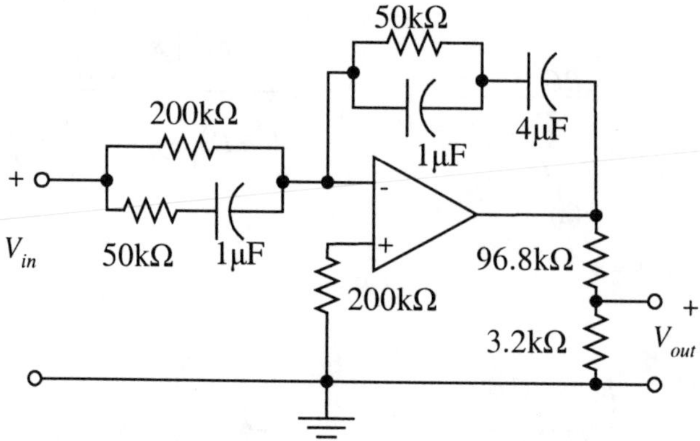

Figure E12.1

Answer: Use circuit (b) from Table 12.1 for Z_A and circuit (d) for Z_F. The result is shown in Figure E12.1 (please see next page).

12.3 ACTIVE FILTERS

The word *filter* refers to the removal of an undesired portion of the frequency spectrum. It was originally applied to systems that eliminated undesired frequency components from a time waveform. The word is now used in a much more general way to include systems which simply weight the various frequency components of a function in a desired manner. Four of the most commonly-encountered classes of filters are low-pass, high-pass, band-pass and band-stop.

Ideal *low-pass* filters allow frequencies up to a given limit to pass. They attenuate frequencies above that limit. Ideal *high-pass* filters are just the reverse of low-pass in that they pass frequencies above the limit and attenuate those below. Ideal *band-pass* filters allow only a particular band of frequencies to pass and attenuate the remaining frequencies. Ideal *band-stop* filters are just the reverse of band-pass in that they pass frequencies outside of the particular band and reject those frequencies within the band.

Active filters produce gain and usually consist only of resistors and capacitors along with integrated circuits. The op-amp, when combined with resistors and capacitors, can simulate the performance of passive inductive-capacitive filters. For high-order filters, the active configurations are simpler than the passive ones.

Constraints are usually imposed in the design of a circuit or system. Meeting the desired specifications is the heart of the design. Specifications can include the *roll-off* (the rate of attenuation of a signal outside of the pass band), the *corner* (or *cutoff*) frequency and the *peaking* (amount of gain produced at the resonant frequency of the circuit). These are frequency domain requirements. Time domain requirements are usually also important since they affect the transient response. These are commonly expressed in terms of *rise time*, *overshoot*, and *settling time* for prescribed inputs (usually step functions).

Often one constraint can be met only at the expense of another. In these situations, the engineer is forced to make a trade off between the desired parameter and its unwanted counterpart.

12.3.1 Filter Properties and Classification

We first consider single-input, single-output linear time-invariant systems. Figure 12.6 illustrates a general system and summarizes the notation. The transfer function, $H(s)$, is the ratio of the Laplace-transformed output, $Y(s)$, to the Laplace transformed input, $R(s)$, with all initial conditions set equal to zero. Note that since we are talking about general systems rather than specific circuits, we use the more general notation of $r(t)$ for the input and $y(t)$ for the output. For specific circuits, these become the voltages $v_{in}(t)$ and $v_{out}(t)$. The Laplace transform of the impulse response of the system is also the transfer function. This is true since the Laplace transform of an impulse is unity.

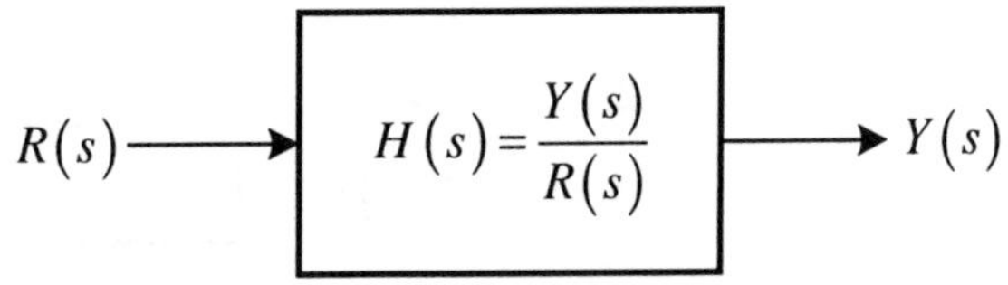

$$R(s) \longrightarrow \boxed{H(s)=\frac{Y(s)}{R(s)}} \longrightarrow Y(s)$$

Figure 12.6 – Definition of the transfer function

The output and input for a linear time-invariant system are related by a differential equation as follows:

$$\frac{d^n y}{dt^n}+a_{n-1}\frac{d^{n-1}y}{dt^{n-1}}+\ldots+a_1\frac{dy}{dt}+a_0 y=$$
$$b_m\frac{d^m r}{dt^m}+b_{m-1}\frac{d^{m-1}r}{dt^{m-1}}+\ldots+b_1\frac{dr}{dt}+b_0 r \qquad (12.11)$$

The corresponding transfer function is then given by Equation (12.12).

$$H(s)=\frac{b_m s^m+b_{m-1}s^{m-1}+\ldots+b_1 s+b_0}{s^n+a_{n-1}s^{n-1}+\ldots+a_1 s+a_0} \qquad (12.12)$$

EXAMPLE 12.2:

Determine the transfer function of the system described by the following differential equation.

$$\frac{d^2y}{dt^2}+2\frac{dy}{dt}+10y=6\frac{d^2r}{dt^2}$$

Solution: We take the Laplace transform of the equation with zero initial conditions to obtain

$$H(s)=\frac{Y(s)}{R(s)}=\frac{6s^2}{s^2+2s+10}$$

The transfer function can be obtained from the impulse response, as indicated in Figure 12.7.

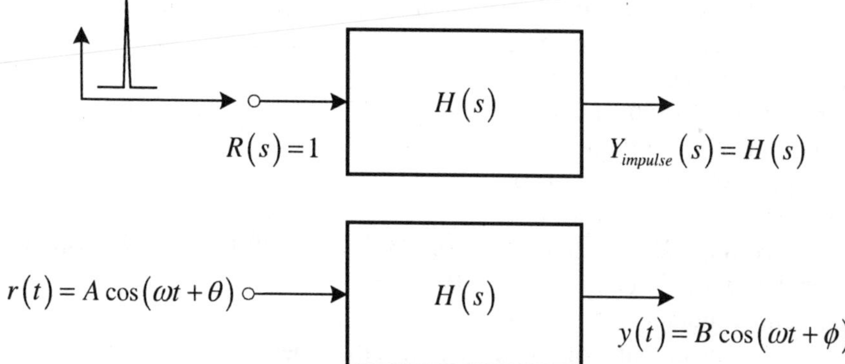

Figure 12.7 – Impulse and frequency response

If an impulse function is applied as the system input, the system output has a Laplace transform equal to the system transfer function. The system impulse response is thus the inverse Laplace transform of the transfer function.

The transfer function can also be determined from the sinusoidal steady state response shown in Figure 12.7. If a sinusoidal signal forms the input to a system, the ratio of output magnitude to input magnitude is the magnitude of the transfer function evaluated at $s = j\omega$. The difference in phase between output and input is the phase of the transfer function at this frequency.

EXAMPLE 12.3:

Describe the frequency response of a system with transfer function

$$H(s)=\frac{10}{s+2}$$

Solution: The gain is given by

$$|H(j\omega)| = \sqrt{\frac{100}{\omega^2 + 4}}$$

This is equal to 5 at ω = 0, and declines at -20 dB/decade for frequencies larger than the corner frequency of ω=2 rad/sec. This is a low-pass filter.

We now examine the frequency response of the general classifications of filters. A *low-pass* filter has a frequency response which is non-zero for $\omega = 0$ and approaches zero as ω approaches infinity, as shown in Figure 12.8(a). Note we are considering amplitude only and ignoring phase. A *high-pass* filter has a magnitude characteristic that is zero for ω = 0 and non-zero, approaching a constant, as ω approaches infinity, as shown in Figure 12.8(b).

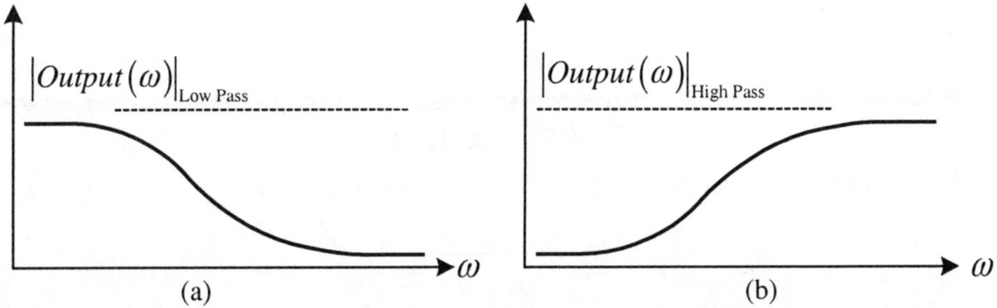

Figure 12.8 – Low-pass and high-pass filter characteristics

EXAMPLE 12.4:

Describe the frequency response of a system with transfer function

$$H(s) = \frac{s}{s + 2}$$

Solution: The gain is given by,

$$|H(j\omega)| = \sqrt{\frac{\omega^2}{\omega^2 + 4}}$$

The zero at the origin yields a zero magnitude as ω approaches zero. The magnitude approaches a constant, 1, for ω approaches infinity. This is a high-pass filter.

A *band-pass* filter has a magnitude characteristic which is zero for $\omega = 0$ *and* for ω approaching infinity, but has a non-zero magnitude for a band of frequencies between these extremes. This is illustrated in Figure 12.9(a).

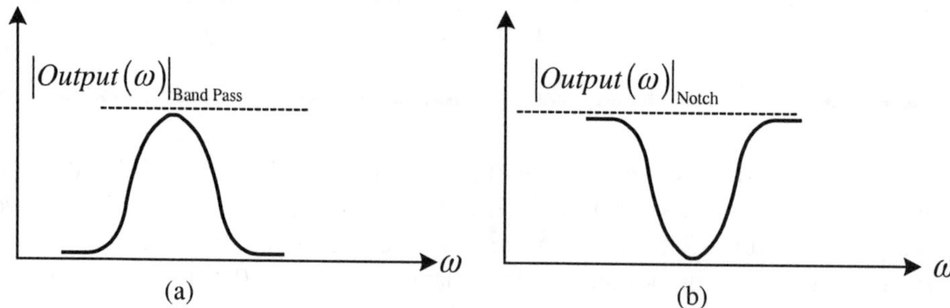

Figure 12.9 – Amplitude response of band-pass and band-stop (notch filter)

EXAMPLE 12.5:

Describe the frequency response of a system with transfer function,

$$H(s) = \frac{s}{s^2 + s + 20}$$

Solution: The gain is given by

$$|H(j\omega)| = \sqrt{\frac{\omega^2}{\omega^2 + (20 - \omega^2)^2}}$$

The zero at the origin leads to a magnitude of zero for $\omega = 0$. The higher-order denominator causes the magnitude to be zero for ω approaches infinity. For $\omega = \sqrt{20}$, the gain is unity. This is a band-pass filter.

A *band-stop* or *notch* filter has a magnitude characteristic which is non-zero for $\omega = 0$ and the same non-zero value for ω approaches infinity. The amplitude is zero (or nearly zero) over some range of values of frequency. This is shown in Figure 12.9(b).

EXAMPLE 12.6

Describe the frequency response of a system with transfer function,

$$H(s) = \frac{3s^2 + 60}{s^2 + s + 20}$$

Solution: The gain is given by

$$|H(j\omega)| = \sqrt{\frac{(60 - 3\omega^2)^2}{\omega^2 + (20 - \omega^2)^2}}$$

The numerator of this transfer function is zero for $\omega = \sqrt{20}$ (i.e., $s = j\sqrt{20}$) and the constant term and the highest power terms have the same ratio, in this case, 3:1. This is a notch filter.

A nontrivial filter for which the magnitude is constant (or near constant) is termed an *all-pass* filter or *delay equalizer*. A magnitude characteristic plot for such a filter is shown in Figure 12.10. Only the magnitude is shown in the figure.

The following two examples show typical forms of the transfer functions for an all-pass filter.

$$H(s) = \frac{s - 10}{s + 10}$$

$$H(s) = \frac{s^2 - 3s + 20}{s^2 + 3s + 20} \tag{12.13}$$

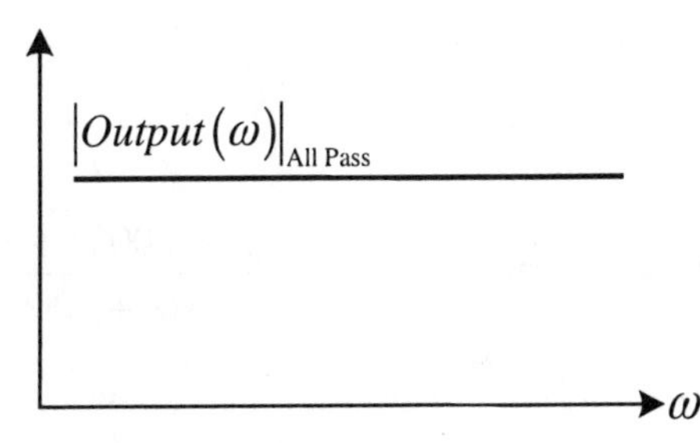

Figure 12.10 – All-pass network

It is not possible to achieve a phase which is identically zero, (i.e., $\varphi(\omega) = 0^{\circ}$). In fact, if the phase were zero, the filter would be "trivial". That is, the resulting circuit would not produce any change in a signal. The closest approximation for many applications is to let the phase shift be proportional to frequency, as follows:

$$\phi(j\omega) = -\tau\omega$$

where τ is a constant corresponding to a constant *time delay* of signals passing through the filter. The delay is τ seconds if φ is expressed in radians.

EXERCISES

Find the transfer function, $H(s)$, for the circuits shown in Figures E12.2 to E12.4. Let all resistors, R_1, R_2, R_3 and R_4 be 100 kΩ. Also let $C_1 = 10$ μF; $C_2 = 0.01$ μF.

E12.2 *Answer:* $-\dfrac{s + 2000}{s + 1000}(s + 1)$

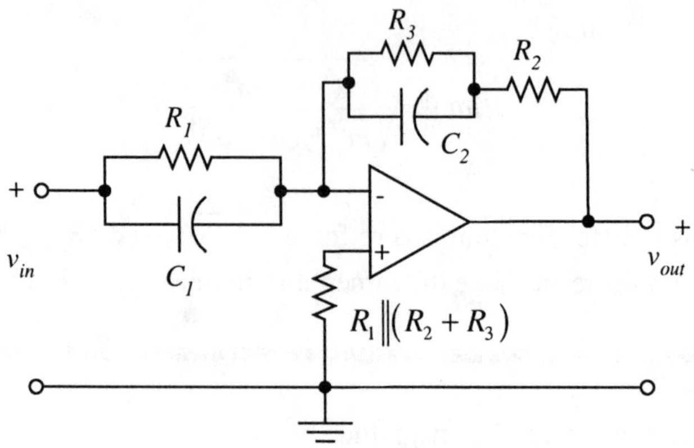

Figure E12.2

E12.3 *Answer:* $-\dfrac{s^2 + 2000s + 1000}{s(s + 1000)}$

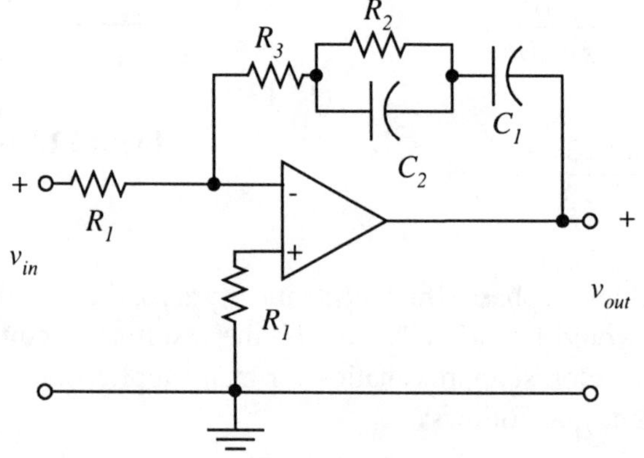

Figure E12.3

E12.4 *Answer:* $\dfrac{10^3(s + 1)}{s(s + 2)}$

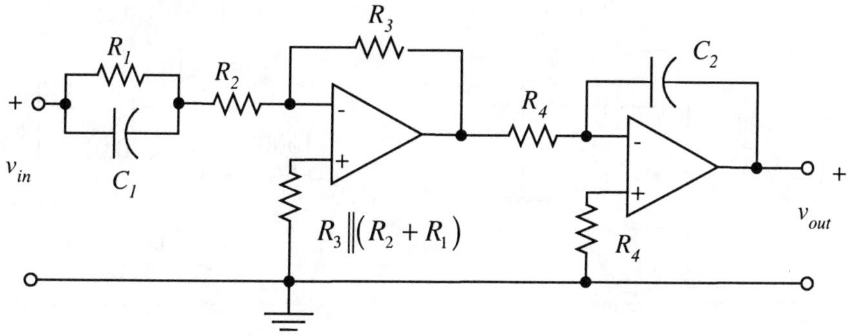

Figure E12.4

E12.5 What type of filter does the following transfer function describe?

$$H(s) = \frac{5s - 10}{s^2 + s + 200}$$

Answer: Low-pass filter

12.3.2 First-Order Active Filters

An active *RC* low-pass filter is shown in Figure 12.11(a).

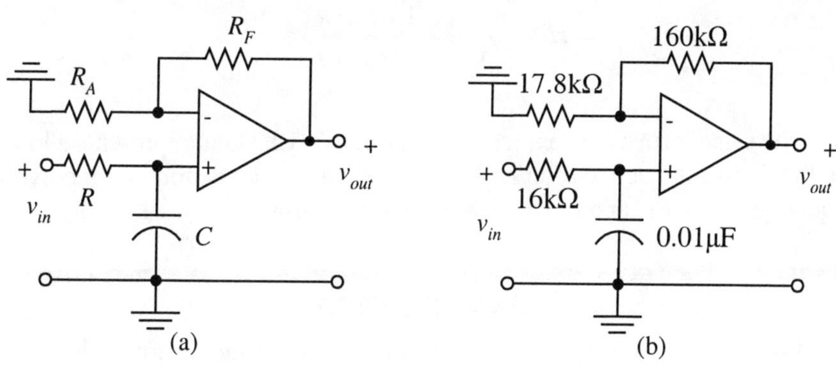

Figure 12.11 (parts a and b) – The low-pass filter

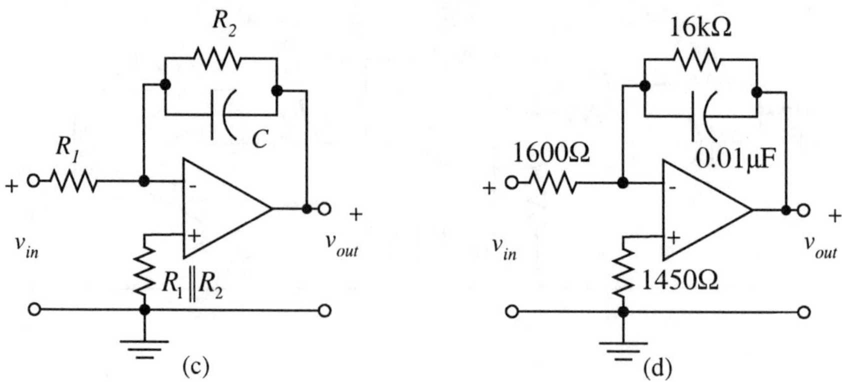

Figure 12.11 (parts c and d) – The low-pass filter

The voltages for the two op-amp inputs are as follows:

$$V_+ = \frac{V_{in}}{RsC+1}$$

$$V_- = \frac{R_A V_{out}}{R_A + R_F} \tag{12.14}$$

Setting $V_+ = V_-$ (we consider an ideal op-amp) and solving for the transfer function yields,

$$H(s) = \frac{V_{out}}{V_{in}} = \frac{1 + R_F/R_A}{sRC+1} \tag{12.15}$$

This is of the same form as the expression in Example 12.3, and represents a low-pass filter. Notice that this first-order active filter has one pole (a first-order denominator polynomial). The corner frequency is at $1/RC$ and the *dc* gain (found by setting $s = 0$) is $1+R_F/R_A$.

EXAMPLE 12.7:

Design a first-order active low-pass filter with a *dc* gain of 10 and a corner frequency of 1 kHz.

Solution: There are four unknown variables (R, R_A, R_F and C) and only three equations: the *dc* gain, the corner frequency and the equation for bias current balance. (If we had specified the input impedance, we would have four equations in four unknowns). We therefore are free to choose one element value at will. In practice, we choose this to put all component values into reasonable ranges (e.g., It would be senseless to solve the equations and find that a 100 farad capacitor is needed! It is preferable to keep component values in a range that permits use of "off the shelf" components). Let us choose C as the specified component, and use a 0.01 μF capacitor. We use the equation for corner frequency in order to solve for R; that is:

$$\omega = 2\pi f = 6280 = \frac{1}{RC}$$

Therefore,

$$R = 16 \text{ k}\Omega$$

If bias current balance is to be achieved,

$$R_A \| R_F = R = 16 \text{ k}\Omega$$

The *dc* gain specification gives a second equation in R_A and R_F.

$$H(0) = 1 + \frac{R_F}{R_A} = 10$$

Solving these two equations yields

$$R_F = 160 \text{ k}\Omega$$

$$R_A = 17.8 \text{ k}\Omega$$

The design is complete. The resulting circuit is shown in Figure 12.11(b).

An alternate form of low-pass filter is shown in Figure 12.11(c). The transfer function is derived in the same manner as was done in the previous circuit. That is, we set $V_- = V_+$ to obtain

$$H(s) = \frac{-R_2}{R_1} \frac{1}{R_2 Cs + 1}$$

The *dc* gain is R_2/R_1 and the corner frequency is at $1/R_2C$.

EXAMPLE 12.8:

Design a first-order active filter with a *dc* gain of 10 and a corner frequency of 1 kHz. Use the circuit of Figure 12.11(c). Verify that your design meets the specifications using a computer simulation program.

Solution: From the equation for corner frequency, we find

$$\omega = 2\pi f = 6280 = \frac{1}{R_2 C}$$

The *dc* gain equation yields,

$$H(0) = -\frac{R_2}{R_1} = -10$$

There is one more unknown than the number of constraints. Suppose we choose $C = 0.01\ \mu F$. Then

$$R_2 = 16\ k\Omega$$
$$R_1 = 1.6\ k\Omega$$

The complete filter is shown in Figure 12.11(d).

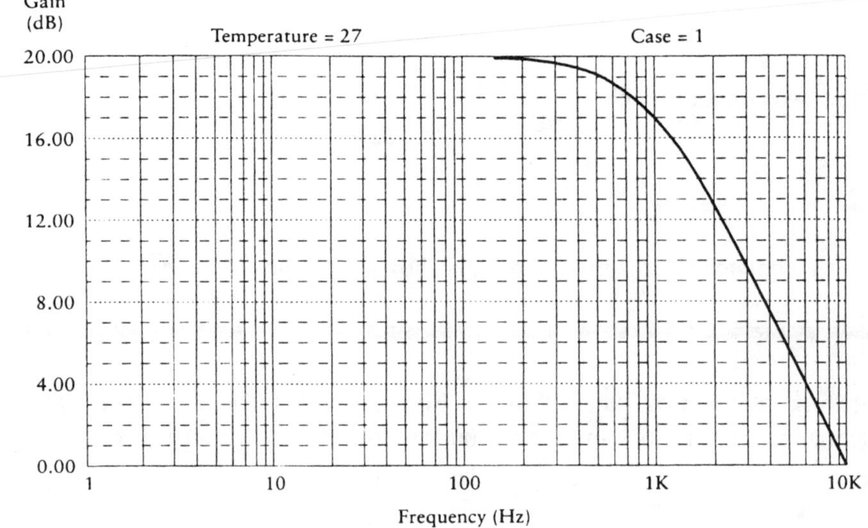

Figure 12.12 – Computer simulation result for Example 12.8

We now enter the circuit of Figure 12.11(d) using MICRO-CAP or any other SPICE-based computer simulation program. We chose a 741 op-amp for our simulation. However, since practical op-amps behave in a manner closely approximating ideal op-amps (for relatively low frequency), the result is not highly dependent upon the choice of op-amp. The resulting *ac* response curve is shown in Figure 12.12.

The response starts at 20 dB which corresponds to an amplitude factor of 10. The 3 dB point (17 dB gain on the curve) falls at 1 kHz as expected. The design is therefore verified.

One advantage of active filters is that it is often quite simple to vary parameter values. As an example, a first-order low-pass filter with adjustable corner frequency is shown in Figure 12.13.

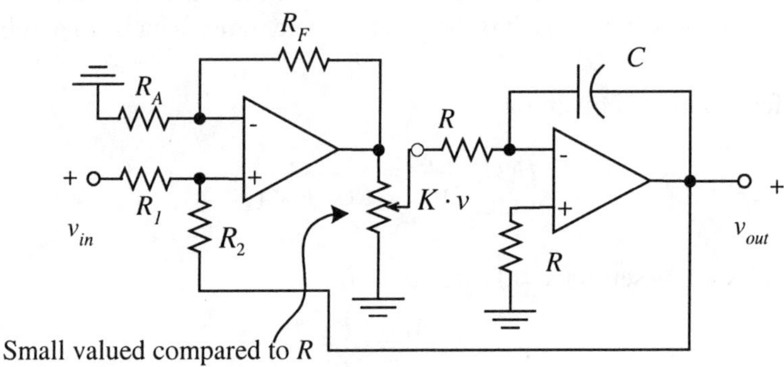

Figure 12.13 – Low-pass filter with adjustable corner frequency

The voltages at the op-amp inputs are given by

$$v_- = \frac{v_1 R_A}{R_A + R_F}$$

$$v_+ = \frac{R_2 v_{in}}{R_1 + R_2} + \frac{R_1 v_{out}}{R_1 + R_2} \tag{12.16}$$

Setting $v_+ = v_-$ we obtain the voltage, v_1, as follows:

$$v_1 = \left(1 + \frac{R_F}{R_A}\right)\left(\frac{R_2}{R_1 + R_2} \cdot v_{in} + \frac{R_1}{R_1 + R_2} \cdot v_{out}\right)$$

$$= A_1 v_{in} + A_2 v_{out} \tag{12.17}$$

where

$$A_1 = \frac{(1 + R_F/R_A) R_2}{R_1 + R_2}$$

$$A_2 = \frac{(1 + R_F/R_A) R_1}{R_1 + R_2}$$

The second op-amp acts as an inverting integrator, and

$$V_{out} = -\frac{KV_1}{RCs} = \frac{-K(A_1V_{in} + A_2V_{out})}{RCs} \tag{12.18}$$

Note that we use upper case letters for the voltages since these are functions of s. K is the fraction of V_1 sent to the integrator. That is, it is the potentiometer ratio, which is a number between 0 and 1.

The transfer function is given by

$$H(s) = \frac{V_{out}}{V_{in}} = \frac{-KA_1}{RCs + KA_2} \tag{12.19}$$

The *dc* gain is found by setting $s = 0$ (i.e., $j\omega = 0$).

$$-\frac{A_1}{A_2} = -\frac{R_2}{R_1} \tag{12.20}$$

The corner frequency is at KA_2/RC. Thus, the frequency is adjustable and is proportional to K. Without use of the op-amp, we would normally have a corner frequency which is inversely proportional to the resistor value. With a frequency proportional to K, we can use a *linear taper* potentiometer. The frequency is then linearly proportional to the setting of the potentiometer.

EXAMPLE 12.9:

Design a first order adjustable low-pass filter with a *dc* gain of 10 and a corner frequency adjustable from near 0 to 1 kHz.

Solution: There are six unknowns in this problem (R_A, R_F, R_1, R_2, R and C) and only three equations (gain, frequency and bias balance). This leaves three parameters open to choice. Suppose we choose the following values:

$$C = 0.1\ \mu\text{F}$$
$$R = 10\ \text{k}\Omega$$
$$R_1 = 10\ \text{k}\Omega$$

The ratio of R_2 to R_1 is the *dc* gain, so with a given value of $R_1 = 10$ kΩ, R_2 must be 100 kΩ. We solve for A_1 and A_2 in order to find the ratio, R_F/R_A.

The maximum corner frequency occurs at $K = 1$, so this frequency is set to $2\pi \times 1000$. Since R and C are known, we find $A_2 = 6.28$. Since A_2 and A_1 are related by the *dc* gain, we determine $A_1/A_2 = 10$ and $A_1 = 62.8$. Now, substituting the expression for A_2, we find

$$A_2 = \frac{(1 + R_F/R_A)(R_1)}{R_1 + R_2} = 6.28 \tag{12.21}$$

and since

$$\frac{R_1}{R_1 + R_2} = \frac{1}{11}$$

we find $R_F/R_A = 68$. R_A is chosen to achieve bias balance. The impedance attached to the non-inverting input is

$$10\ \text{k}\Omega \| 100\ \text{k}\Omega \approx 10\ \text{k}\Omega$$

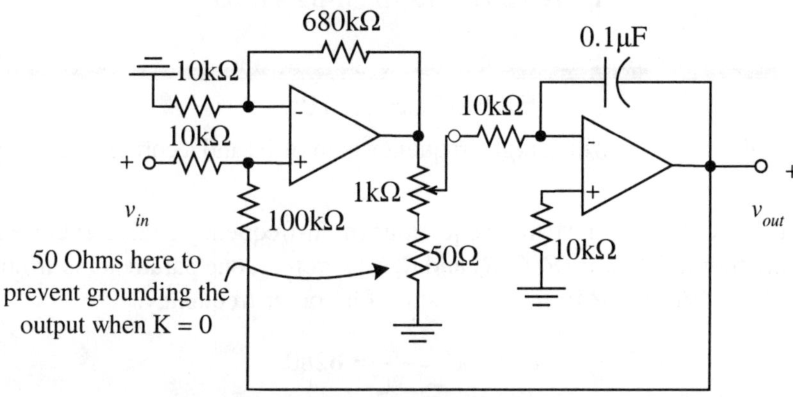

Figure 12.14 – Filter for Example 12.9

If we assume that R_F is large compared with R_A (we can check this assumption after solving for these resistors), the parallel combination will be close to the value of R_A. We therefore can choose $R_A = 10\ \text{k}\Omega$. With this choice of R_A, R_F is found to be 680 kΩ and bias balance is achieved. The complete filter is shown in Figure 12.14.

An *RC high-pass filter* is shown in Figure 12.15(a). Once again, we solve for V_+ and V_-, and then set these equal to each other to find the transfer function.

$$H(s) = \left(1 + \frac{R_F}{R_A}\right) \cdot \frac{s}{s + 1/RC} \tag{12.22}$$

The high-frequency gain is $1+R_F/R_A$ and the corner frequency is at $1/RC$.

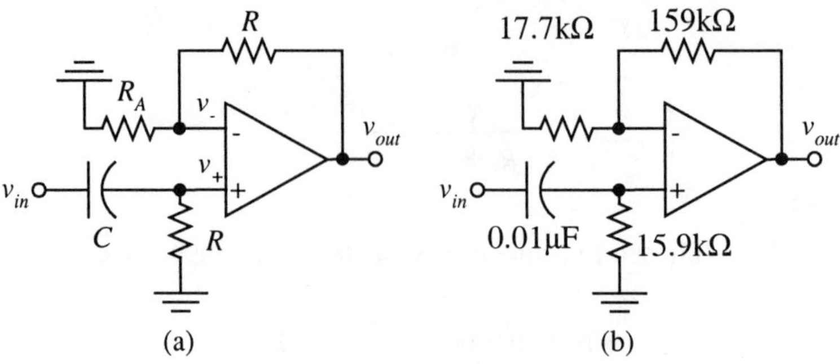

Figure 12.15 – RC high-pass filter

EXAMPLE 12.10:

Design an *RC* high-pass filter with a high-frequency gain of 10 and a corner frequency of 1 kHz.

Solution: In this problem we have three equations (high-frequency gain, corner frequency and bias balance) and four unknowns (R, C, R_A and R_F). Therefore, one parameter is arbitrary. Let us choose $C = 0.01$ μF. We find R from the equation for corner frequency.

$$\omega = 2\pi f = \frac{1}{RC} = 6280$$

$$R = \frac{1}{6280 \cdot C} = 15.9 \text{ k}\Omega$$

The high-frequency gain equation yields

$$1 + \frac{R_F}{R_A} = 10$$

This represents one equation in two unknowns, R_F and R_A. We derive a second equation from the bias balance relationship,

$$R_A \| R_F = R = 15.9 \text{ k}\Omega$$

Solving these two equations yields,

$$R_F = 159 \text{ k}\Omega$$

$$R_A = 17.7 \text{ k}\Omega$$

The complete circuit is shown in Figure 12.15(b).

EXERCISE

E12.6 What is the *dc* gain and corner frequency of the circuit shown in Figure E12.5? What type of circuit is this?

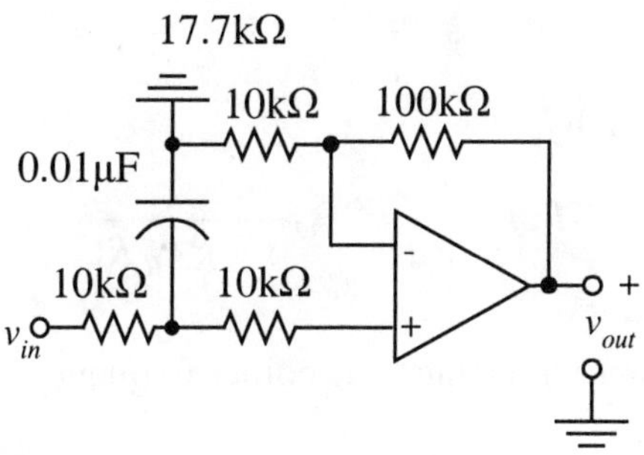

Figure E12.5

Answer: dc gain = 11, Corner frequency is 10^4 rad/sec. This circuit is a low-pass filter.

A variation of the high-pass filter is the *adjustable* high-pass filter. Figure 12.16 combines an amplifier for signal summing with a second amplifier for low-pass summing. We analyze the circuit to find the following equations:

$$V_{out} = \frac{(1 + R_F/R_A)R_I V_I}{R_I + R_2} - \frac{R_F V_{in}}{R_A} \tag{12.23}$$

$$= A_I V_I - A_2 V_{in}$$

where

$$A_I = \frac{(1 + R_F/R_A)R_I}{R_I + R_2}$$

$$A_2 = \frac{R_F}{R_A}$$

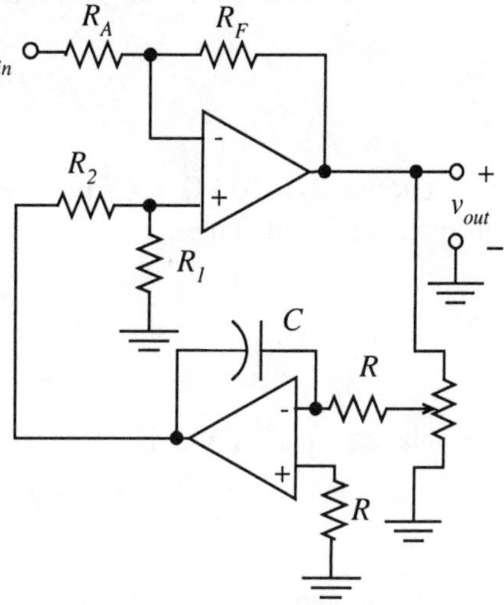

Figure 12.16 – Adjustable high-pass filter

If K is the potentiometer attenuation then

$$V_1 = -\frac{KV_{out}}{RCs}$$
$$V_{out} = \frac{-KA_1V_{out}}{RCs} - A_2V_{in} \tag{12.24}$$

The transfer function is given by

$$H(s) = \frac{V_{out}}{V_{in}} = -A_2\frac{s}{s + KA_1/RC} \tag{12.25}$$

The result is a high-pass filter with adjustable corner frequency.

EXAMPLE 12.11:

Design a high-pass filter with a high-frequency gain of 10 and a corner frequency adjustable from 100 Hz to 400 Hz. Verify that your design meets the specifications using a computer simulation program.

Solution: We have three equations and six unknowns, so we choose values for three variables: R_A, A_1 and C. We start with the high-frequency gain equation,

$$A_2 = \frac{R_F}{R_A} = 10$$

If we now choose $R_A = 10\ \text{k}\Omega$, we find $R_F = 100\ \text{k}\Omega$. We select $A_1 = 1$ to achieve unity gain for the non-inverting input. Then,

$$A_1 = \frac{(1 + R_F/R_A)R_1}{R_1 + R_2} = 1$$

The bias balance equation yields

$$R_1 \| R_2 = R_A \| R_F = 10\ \text{k}\Omega \| 100\ \text{k}\Omega$$

We thus have two equations in R_1 and R_2. Solving these yields

$$R_1 = 10\ \text{k}\Omega$$
$$R_2 = 100\ \text{k}\Omega$$

Since K cannot exceed unity, we design for the maximum corner frequency at $K = 1$ to yield

$$\frac{A_I}{RC} = \frac{1}{RC} = \omega = 2\pi f = 2512 \text{ rad/s}$$

If we now choose $C = 0.01$ μF, we find

$$R = \frac{10^8}{2512} = 40 \text{ k}\Omega$$

Adjusting K from 0.25 to 1 yields the desired frequency range of 100 Hz to 400 Hz. This is accomplished using a 4-kΩ potentiometer with a limiting tab or by placing a 1kΩ fixed resistor between ground and the 3kΩ potentiometer. This latter approach is shown in the input of the feedback op-amp in the circuit of Figure 12.17(a).

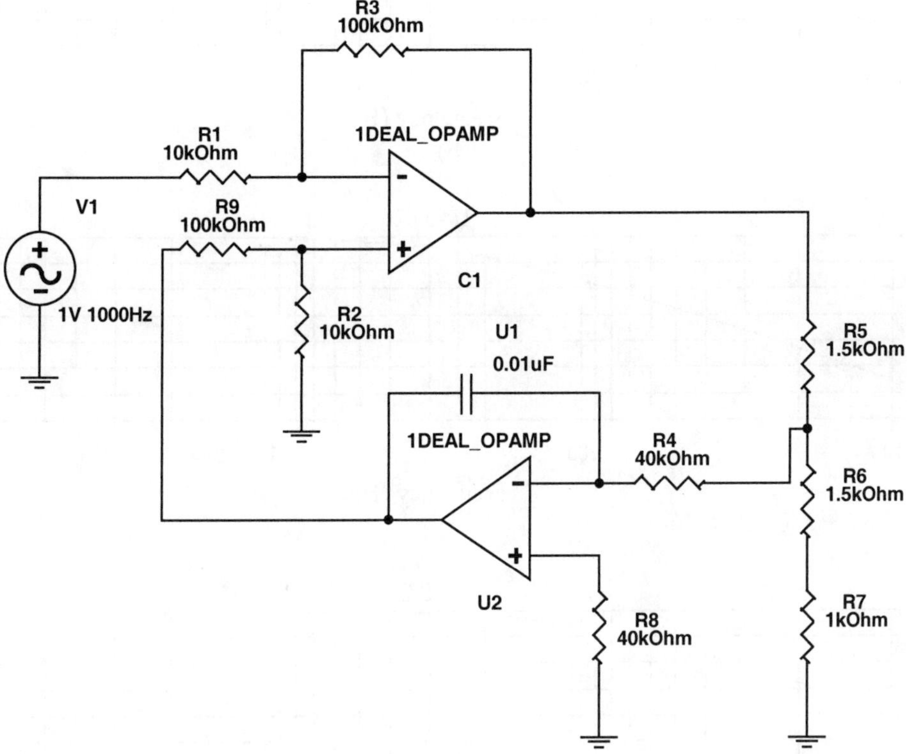

Figure 12.17(a) – Circuit for Example 12.11

We now use a computer simulation to check our result. The circuit shown in Figure 12.17(a) is the graphical representation of the Electronics Workbench input file used for the computer simulation. Since the simulation we used does not provide for potentiometers, we broke the 3 kΩ potentiometer into two 1.5 kΩ. In this manner, we were able to achieve values of $K = 0.25$, $K = 0.625$ and $K = 1$ by varying the point at which the right side of the 40 kΩ is connected. The resulting frequency plots are shown in Figures 12.17(b), (c), and (d) for the three values of K. Note that for $K = 1$ (Figure 12.17(b)), the 3dB break point occurs at 400 Hz. For $K = 0.625$ (Figure 12.17(c)), the break is at 230 Hz and for $K = 0.25$ (Figure 12.17(d)), it occurs at 100 Hz. Note the triangle shaped frequency makers above the plots in Figures (b), (c), and (d), locating the cut-off frequencies, 400 Hz, 245 Hz, and 100Hz, respectively. At these frequencies we see the circuit output voltage drop 3 dB from the nominal value of 20 dB to 17 dB. We have therefore verified the design.

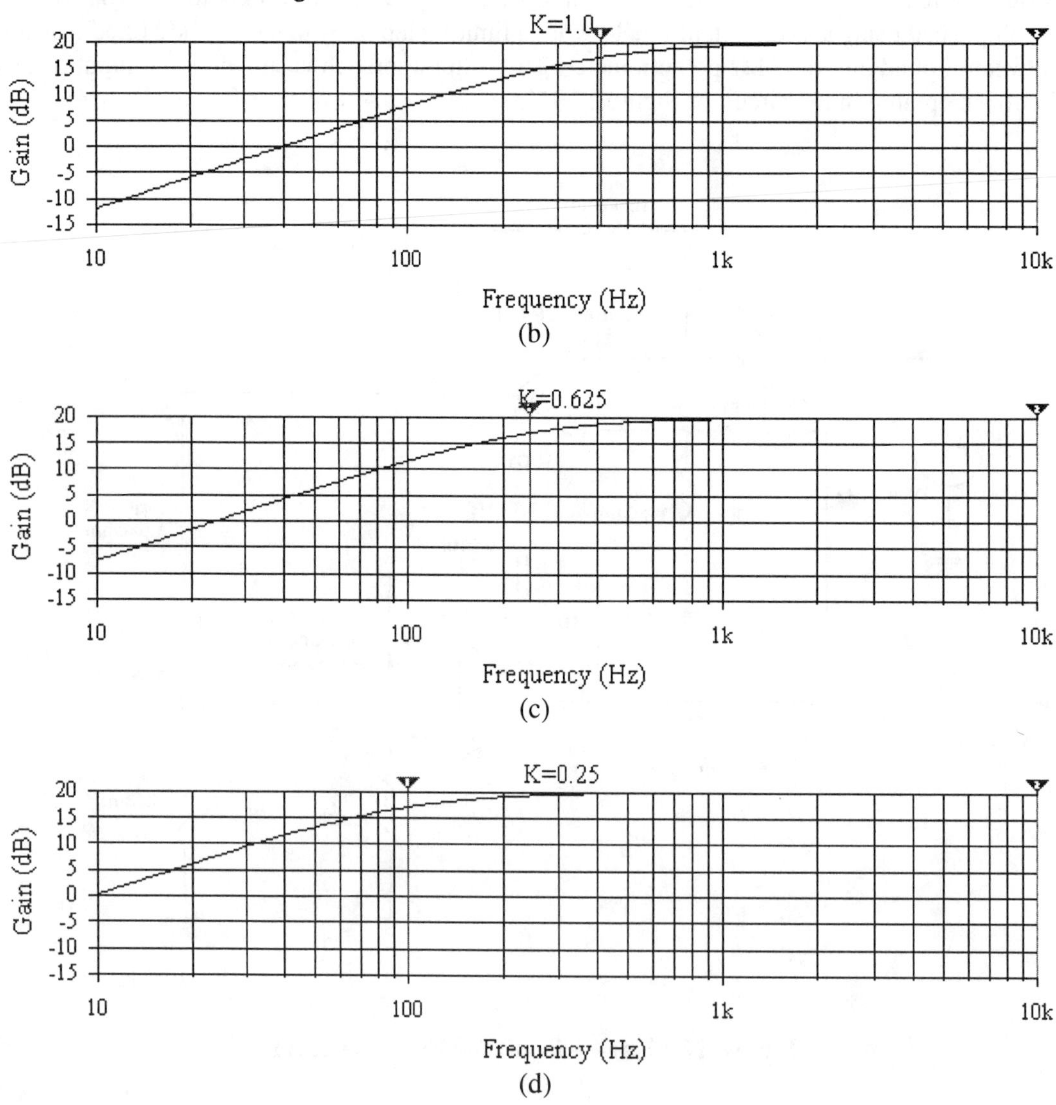

Figure 12.17 Parts (b), (c), and (d)

EXERCISE

E12.7 What is the gain and the adjustable frequency range for the circuit shown in Figure E12.6?

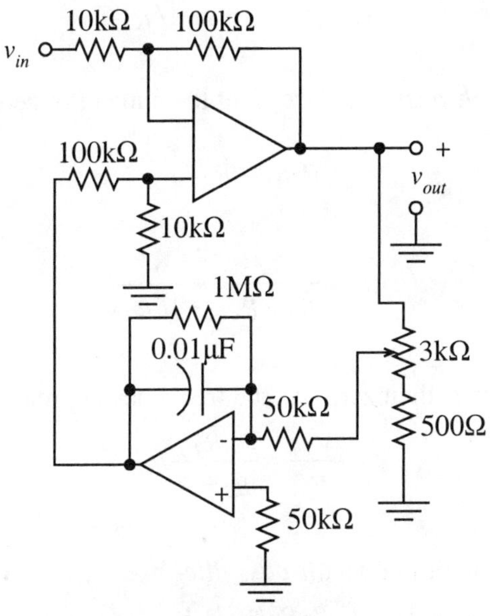

Figure E12.6

Answer: $A_I = 1$. Range of frequencies is 28.6 Hz to 200 Hz.

12.4 SINGLE AMPLIFIER - GENERAL TYPE

We considered the low-pass and high-pass filters in the previous sections. These filters are specific in form. In this section, we consider a "general type" first-order filter. The circuit diagram for the single op-amp filter is shown in Figure 12.18.

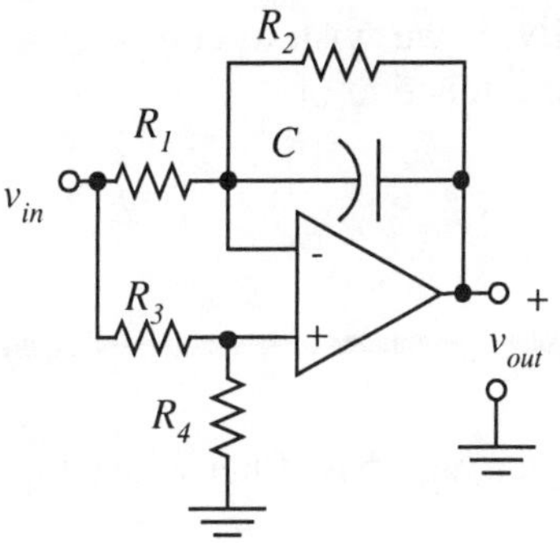

Figure 12.18 – Single op-amp general filter

This one circuit can be configured to produce the following first-order filters:

- High-pass, when $R_1R_4 = R_2R_3$
- All-pass, when $R_2R_3 = 2R_1R_4$
- Low-pass, when R_3 approaches infinity

If we assume that the op-amp is ideal (i.e., $V_- = V_+$), the transfer function, $H(s)$, is found to be

$$H(s)=\frac{R_4}{R_3+R_4}\frac{s+\left(\frac{1}{R_1 C}\right)\left(\frac{R_1}{R_2}-\frac{R_3}{R_4}\right)}{s+1/R_2 C} \tag{12.26}$$

In order to make this a *high-pass filter*, we want the numerator zero to be at the origin. We therefore let,

$$R_1R_4=R_2R_3 \tag{12.27}$$

Then

$$H(s)=\frac{R_4}{R_3+R_4}\frac{s}{s+1/R_2 C} \tag{12.28}$$

The gain at zero frequency is then zero. As the frequency approaches infinity, the gain is

$$\frac{V_{out}}{V_{in}}=\frac{R_4}{R_3+R_4} \tag{12.29}$$

If we wish to make this circuit into an *all-pass filter*, we set

$$R_2R_3=2R_1R_4 \tag{12.30}$$

The transfer function is

$$H(s)=\frac{R_4}{R_3+R_4}\frac{s-1/R_2 C}{s+1/R_2 C} \tag{12.31}$$

Finally, if we wish to construct a *low-pass filter*, we let R_3 approach infinity. This yields a transfer function of

$$H(s)=\frac{-1/R_1 C}{s+1/R_2 C} \tag{12.32}$$

EXAMPLE 12.12:

Design a high-pass filter with a high-frequency gain of 1/2 and a corner frequency of 4 kHz.

Solution: The unknowns are R_1, R_2, R_3, R_4 and C. We have equations for gain, corner frequency, bias balance and the high-pass constraint. This leaves one unknown which we can select. Let us choose a reasonable value for C, 0.01 μF. Then from the corner frequency specification, we have

$$\frac{10^8}{R_2} = 2\pi f = 25{,}130 \text{ rad/s}$$

Therefore, $R_2 = 4$ kΩ. For a high-frequency gain of 1/2, we find $R_3 = R_4$. The high-pass resistor constraint yields $R_1R_4 = R_2R_3$ and hence $R_1 = R_2 = 4$ kΩ. To achieve bias balance, we choose $R_3 = R_4 = 4$ kΩ.

EXAMPLE 12.13:

Design an all-pass filter with a gain of 1/2 and a corner frequency of 4 kHz.

Solution: Since we have fewer equations than unknowns, let us again choose $C = 0.01$ μF. From the corner frequency equations, we have

$$\frac{1}{R_2 C} = \frac{10^8}{R_2} = 2\pi f = 25{,}130 \text{ rad/s}$$

so $R_2 = 4$ kΩ. To achieve a gain of 1/2, $R_3 = R_4$. The all-pass constraint yields $R_2R_3 = 2R_1R_4$, but since $R_3 = R_4$, we have

$$R_1 = \frac{R_2}{2} = 2 \text{ k}\Omega$$

The parallel combination of R_1 and R_2 has a resistance of 1.33 kΩ, so to achieve bias balance, we require

$$R_3 = R_4 = 2.67 \text{ k}\Omega$$

12.5 CLASSICAL ANALOG FILTERS

In cases where the filter specification requires a roll-off of only -20 dB/decade, the first order single-amplifier filter is the proper choice. However, if a faster roll-off is required, a higher-order filter must be designed. The balance of this chapter is directed toward the design of higher-order filters.

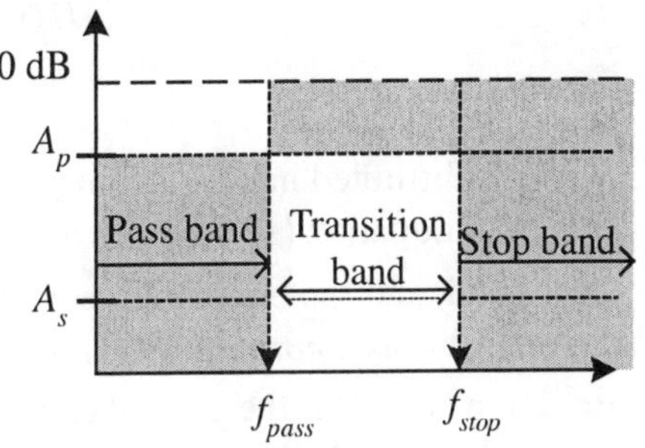

Figure 12.19 – Filter characteristics

There are many types of filters, each of which exhibits special characteristics. *Butterworth* filters produce no ripple in the pass band and attenuate unwanted frequencies outside of this band.

Chebyshev filters attenuate unwanted frequencies while requiring fewer components than Butterworth filters, but they exhibit ripple in the pass band.

Specifications of filters are often presented by use of a modified amplitude versus frequency characteristic diagram. Figure 12.19 is a diagram of the characteristics of a low-pass filter. The *pass band* of the filter extends from zero frequency to a maximum frequency of f_{pass}. The range of frequencies between f_{pass} and f_{stop} is known as the *transition band*, and the range above f_{stop} is the *stop band*. The magnitudes shown on the diagram are in dB. Within the pass band, the unshaded region at the top indicates that the magnitude must be above A_p throughout that band. Some filters, such as the Chebyshev, have a *ripple* in the pass-band. Nonetheless, the minimum magnitude is greater than A_p. Within the transition band, attenuation occurs as the frequency increases, with the magnitude at f_{stop} (the upper frequency) equal to A_s.

The standard form of the transfer function of a filter is often given in the following form:

$$|H(j\omega)|^2 = \frac{1}{1+e^2 s_n^2(\omega)} \qquad (12.33)$$

In this equation, $s_n(\omega)$ is an nth order polynomial and e is related to the ripple in the pass-band. We explore several specific examples in the following sections.

12.5.1 Butterworth Filters

Butterworth filters are also known as *maximally flat magnitude (MFM)* filters. The transfer function is chosen so that the magnitude response curve is as flat as possible within the pass band of the filter. This is accomplished by setting as many derivatives of the function as possible equal to zero at the center of the pass band (zero frequency for a low-pass filter).

The Butterworth transfer function is found by setting $s_n = \omega^n$ and $e = 1$ in Equation (12.33). The magnitude squared transfer function of the nth order Butterworth filter is then given by

$$|H(j\omega)|^2 = \frac{1}{1+\omega^{2n}} \qquad (12.34)$$

For example, the transfer function for a second order Butterworth filter is given by

$$H(s) = \frac{1}{s^2 + \sqrt{2}s + 1} \qquad (12.35)$$

If $s = j\omega$ is substituted into Equation (12.35), the magnitude of the resulting complex function is that given in Equation (12.34) with $n = 2$. The magnitude of the transfer function is unity within the pass band, and the break frequency (i.e., the frequency where $H(j\omega) = 1/\sqrt{2}$) is also unity. We refer to this as a *normalized filter*.

Equation (12.34) is the general expression for the magnitude-squared transfer function of the Butterworth filter. As the order of the filter, n, increases, the roll-off in the transition region becomes steeper. In fact, the roll-off is $20n$ dB/decade where n is the filter order. This observation allows us to find the required order of the filter when the roll-off is specified.

Suppose that the specifications give the magnitude of the characteristic at two points, that is, the magnitude is $|H_1|$ at a frequency of ω_1 and $|H_2|$ at a frequency of ω_2. We find the required order of the filter from Equation (12.34). Substituting the two values into this equation, we find

$$\left(\frac{\omega_2}{\omega_1}\right)^n = \sqrt{\frac{|H_2|^{-2}-1}{|H_1|^{-2}-1}}$$

$$n \geq \frac{\log\left(\sqrt{\frac{|H_2|^{-2}-1}{|H_1|^{-2}-1}}\right)}{\log(\omega_2/\omega_1)} \tag{12.36}$$

The transfer function of the Butterworth filter is expressed as the reciprocal of a polynomial in s [see Equation (12.35) for a second-order example]. If $H(s)$ is the transfer function and $B_n(s)$ is the polynomial for the nth order filter, we obtain,

$$H(s) = \frac{1}{B_n(s)} \tag{12.37}$$

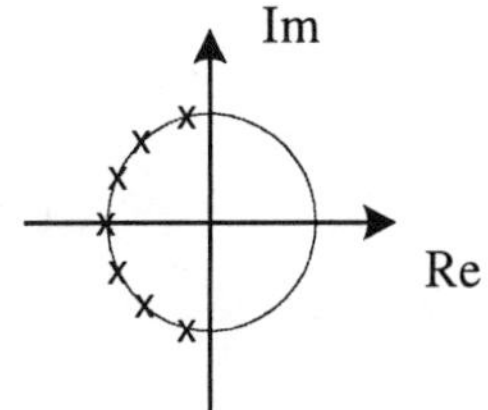

Figure 12.20 – Poles for Butterworth filter

The transfer function for a normalized filter has a corner frequency at $\omega = 1$. The magnitude at this corner frequency is 0.707.

The normalized polynomials for Butterworth filters are as follows:

$$\begin{aligned}
B_1(s) &= s+1\\
B_2(s) &= s^2+1.414s+1\\
B_3(s) &= s^3+2s^2+2s+1\\
B_4(s) &= s^4+2.61s^3+3.41s^2+2.61s+1\\
B_5(s) &= s^5+3.24s^4+5.24s^3+5.24s^2+3.24s+1\\
B_6(s) &= s^6+3.86s^5+7.46s^4+9.14s^3+7.46s^2+3.86s+1
\end{aligned} \tag{12.38}$$

Note that in Equation (12.35) we used the order 2 polynomial, $B_2(s)$.

For each value of n, the poles of $H(s)$ are in the left-half s plane on the unit circle. The poles are symmetrically spaced as shown in Figure 12.20.

EXAMPLE 12.14:

Determine the transfer function for a third order Butterworth low-pass filter with a Bode plot is as shown in Figure 12.21.

Solution: We begin with the transfer function of a normalized Butterworth low-pass filter.

$$H(s)=\frac{1}{s^3+2s^2+2s+1}$$

We now scale the function to account for the *dc* gain, and we scale *s* to provide for a cut-off frequency different from unity. The resulting third-order Butterworth low-pass filter with a *dc* gain of 10 and a cut-off frequency of 1000 Hz is given by

$$H(s)=\frac{10}{\left(\frac{s}{2\pi}\times 1000\right)^3+2\left(\frac{s}{2\pi}\times 1000\right)^2+2\left(\frac{s}{2\pi}\times 1000\right)+1}$$

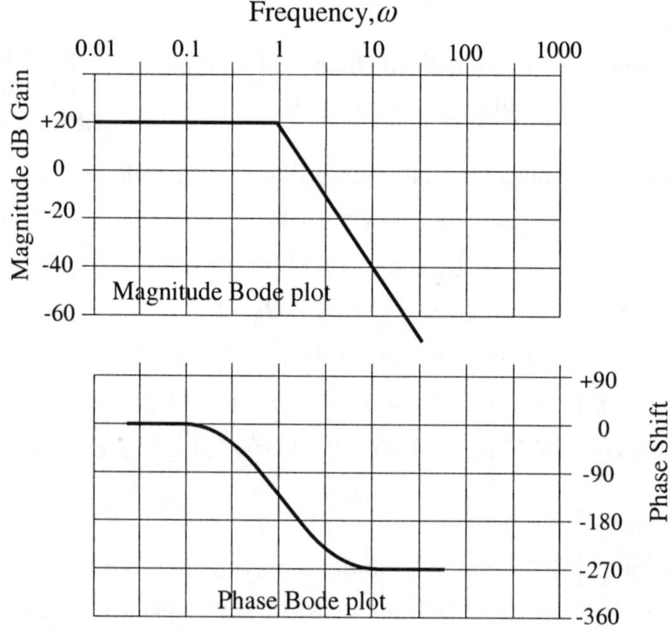

Figure 12.21 – Bode plot for Example 12.14

12.5.2 Chebyshev Filters

The Chebyshev low-pass filter has a transfer function built around a Chebyshev polynomial. The polynomials are sketched in Figure 12.22 and are given by the following equations:

$$\begin{aligned} C_0 &= 1 \\ C_1(x) &= x \\ C_2(x) &= 2x^2 - 1 \\ C_3(x) &= 4x^3 - 3x \\ C_4(x) &= 8x^4 - 8x^2 + 1 \\ C_5(x) &= 16x^5 - 20x^3 + 5x \\ C_6(x) &= 32x^6 - 48x^4 + 18x^2 - 1 \end{aligned} \tag{12.39}$$

and in general

$$c_{n+1}(x) = 2xc_n(x) - c_{n-1}(x) \tag{12.40}$$

Chebyshev filters exhibit ripple in the pass band. However the same specification can frequently be met with a lower order Chebyshev filter than with a Butterworth filters. At the higher frequencies, both filter characteristics have the same asymptotic slope. The magnitude of the transfer function is

$$|H^2(\omega)| = \frac{1}{1+\varepsilon^2 C_n^2(\omega)} \tag{12.41}$$

where C_n is the nth order polynomial. The constant, ε, which is less than 1, determines the ripple magnitude.

Since the polynomials are bounded by ±1, the ripple in the magnitude-squared transfer function is bounded by

$$|Ripple|^2 \leq \frac{1}{1+\varepsilon^2} \tag{12.42}$$

As an example, for $\varepsilon = 0.5$, the ripple is bounded by 0.894.

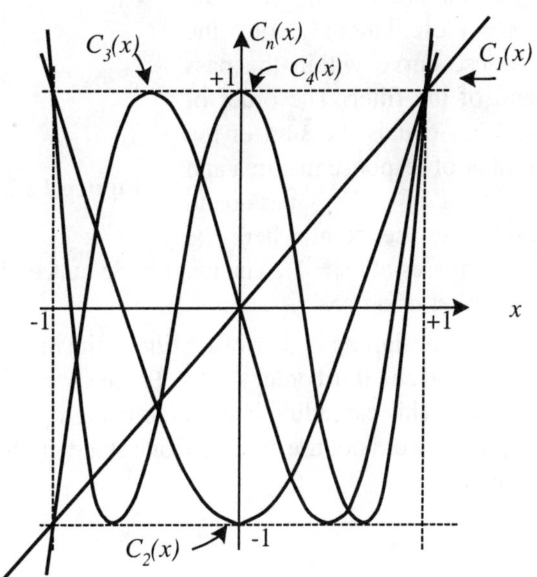

Figure 12.22 – Chebyshev polynominals

The transfer function is found by substituting the value of the Chebyshev polynomial into the general expression. For $\varepsilon = 0.5$, this becomes

$$|H^2(\omega)| = \frac{1}{1+(0.5)^2 C_2^2(\omega)} = \frac{1}{1+0.25(2\omega^2-1)^2} = \frac{1}{\omega^4-\omega^2+1.25} \tag{12.43}$$

Letting $s = j\omega$ yields

$$H^2(s) = \frac{1}{s^4+s^2+1.25} = \frac{1}{(s^2+0.5)^2+0.5} \tag{12.44}$$

In the last term of Equation (12.44), we have completed the square.

If the filter order is odd, the response curve starts at $|H(j\omega)|$ = 1 (0 dB). If the filter order is even, the curve starts at the magnitude of the ripple. The higher the order of the filter, the more "oscillations" of the response curve within the pass band of the filter. The order of the filter equals the sum of the number of response maxima and minima in the pass-band (excluding the point where the curve crosses at $\omega_p = 1$). The magnitude curve of Figure 12.23 would thus result from an even order filter of order 4.

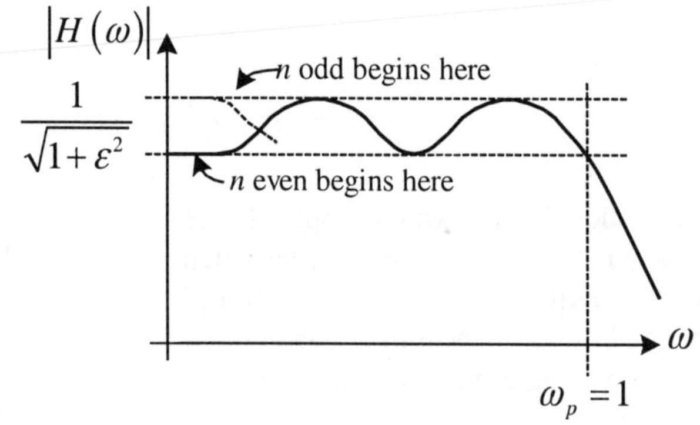

Figure 12.23 – Example of Chebyshev filter

When designing higher-order filters, the most convenient approach is to break the function up into second and third order stages. These successive stages are then combined to yield the desired response. This cascading is possible using op-amps because of the isolation between adjacent stages. If we did not use op-amps, one stage might load another stage and cascading would not be possible.

12.6 TRANSFORMATIONS

There is a close relationship among the various classifications of filters. Once a design is completed for one type, it is often possible to easily modify the design to change the filter into one of a different classification. In this manner, lengthy redesigns may be avoided.

12.6.1 Low-Pass to High-Pass Transformation

Substituting s for $1/s$ converts a normalized low-pass transfer function to a high-pass transfer function. This transformation has the effect of interchanging the resistors with the capacitors.

EXAMPLE 12.15:

Transform a third-order Butterworth low-pass filter into a high-pass filter.

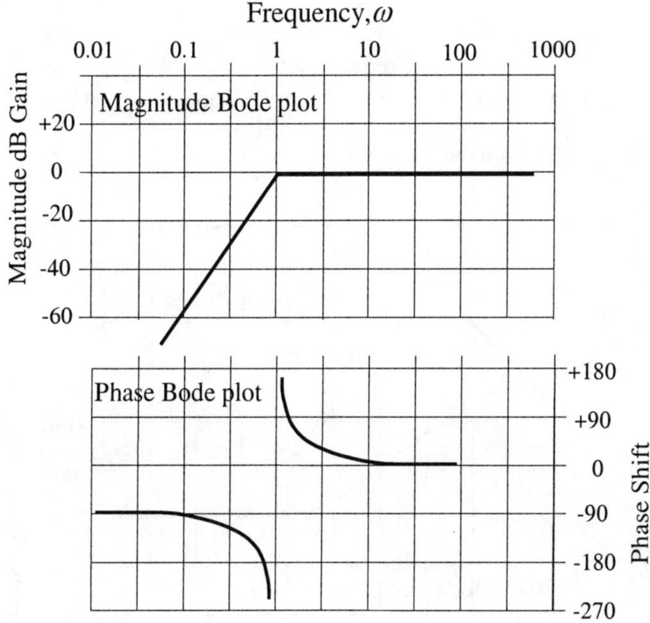

Figure 12.24 – Bode plot of transformed Butterworth filter

Solution: The low-pass transfer function is given by

$$H_{LP}(s) = \frac{1}{s^3 + 2s^2 + 2s + 1}$$

We now replace s by $1/s$ to yield

$$H_{HP}(s) = \frac{1}{(1/s)^3 + 2(1/s)^2 + 2(1/s) + 1} = \frac{s^3}{s^3 + 2s^2 + 2s + 1}$$

The amplitude and phase for this transformed Butterworth network are shown in Figure 12.24.

EXAMPLE 12.16:

Transform a second-order Chebyshev low-pass filter into a high-pass filter.

Solution: We start with the low-pass transfer function,

$$H_{LP}(s) = \frac{1}{(s+0.84)^2 + (0.87)^2} = \frac{1}{s^2 + 1.7s + 1.47}$$

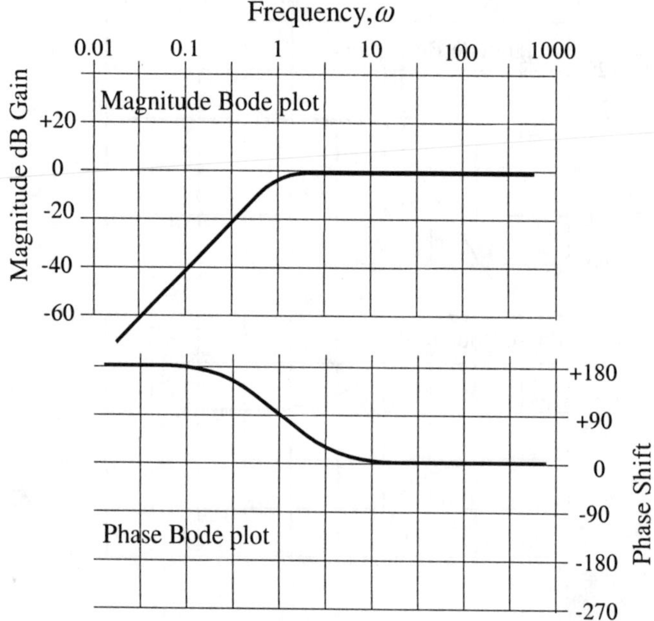

Figure 12.25 – Bode plot for transformed Chebyshev filter

We now replace s by $1/s$ to yield

$$H_{HP}(s) = \frac{s^2}{1.47s^2 + 1.7s + 1}$$

The Bode plot for this transformed Chebyshev network is shown in Figure 12.25.

12.6.2 Low-Pass to Band-Pass Transformation

We can convert a normalized low-pass transfer function into a normalized band-pass transfer function by making the substitution

$$\frac{s^2+1}{s} \text{ in place of } s$$

The order of the band-pass filter is twice that of the original low-pass filter.

EXAMPLE 12.17:

Transform a third-order Butterworth low-pass filter into a band-pass filter.

Solution: We start with the low-pass transfer function,

$$H_{LP}(s) = \frac{1}{s^3 + 2s^2 + 2s + 1}$$

Replacing s with $(s^2+1)/s$ yields

$$H_{BP}(s) = \frac{s^3}{s^6 + 2s^5 + 5s^4 + 5s^3 + 5s^2 + 2s + 1}$$

12.7 DESIGN OF BUTTERWORTH AND CHEBYSHEV FILTERS

In this section, we examine a constant-resistance or constant-capacitance approach toward design of Butterworth and Chebyshev filters up to tenth order. The higher-order filters are formed by combining second and third order filters. This design approach assumes 1-Ω values for the resistors in the two-pole and three-pole low-pass filters shown in Figure 12.26.

If we interchange the capacitors and resistors of a low-pass design, the result is a high-pass filter. In a high-pass filter, the capacitors are all of equal value (instead of the resistors as is the case in low-pass filters). We set the capacitances to 1 F. The two-pole and three-pole high-pass filters are shown in Figure 12.27.

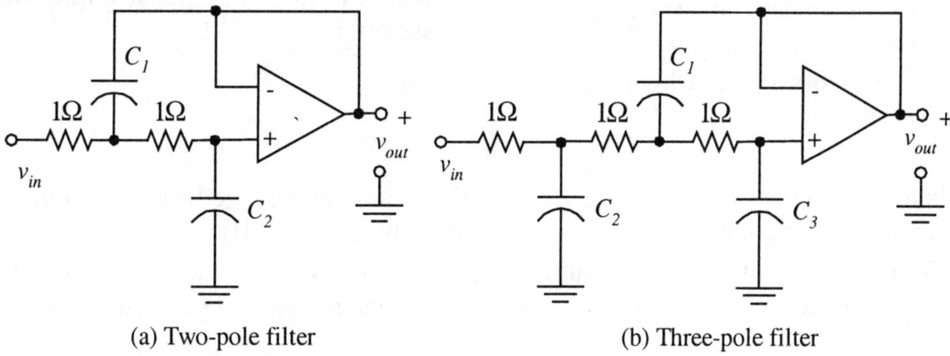

Figure 12.26 – Unity-*R* active low-pass filter

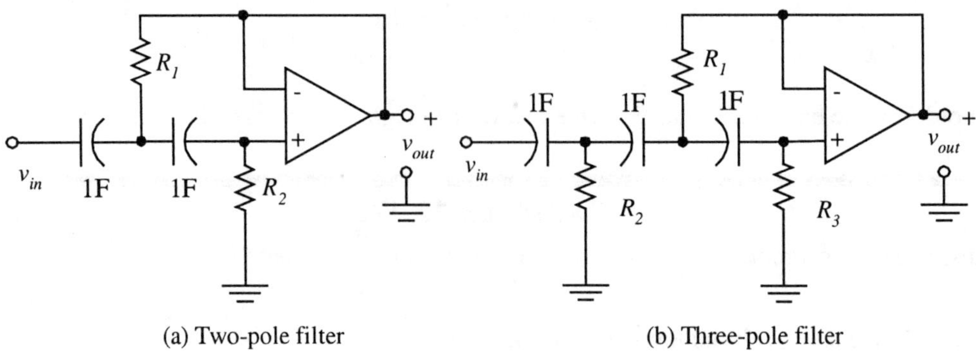

(a) Two-pole filter (b) Three-pole filter

Figure 12.27 – Unity-*C* active high pass filter

The circuit configuration for the Chebyshev filter is identical to that of the Butterworth filter. Only the component values are different.

12.7.1 Low-Pass Filter Design

Four parameters must be specified in the design of Butterworth or Chebyshev filters. These four parameters can be given in various ways. One set of choices is shown in Figure 12.28 and the parameters are listed below.

A_p = dB attenuation in the pass-band

A_s = dB attenuation in the stop-band

f_p = frequency at which A_p occurs

f_s = frequency at which A_s occurs

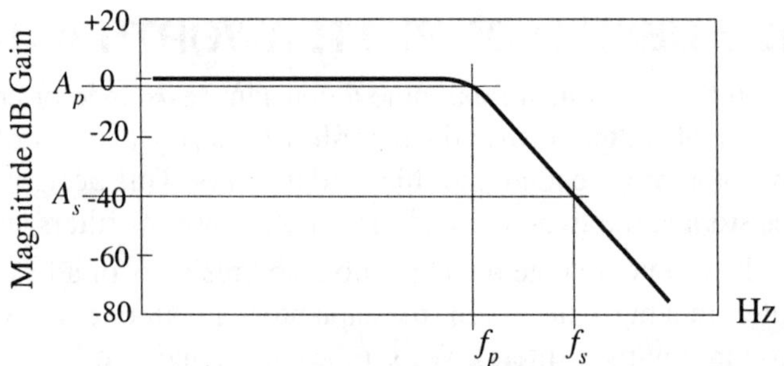

Figure 12.28 – Frequency response requirements for low-pass filter

In the case of the Chebyshev filter, one additional parameter is specified. This parameter is the maximum ripple permitted in the pass-band, ε (usually given in dB).

The design procedure is divided into two parts. We first find the required *order* of the filter, and then find the *scale factor* that must be applied to the normalized parameter values.

12.7.2 Filter Order

We first determine what order filter is needed to satisfy the specification for A_p (at f_p) and A_s

(at f_s). Notice that A_p and A_s are magnitudes, so we need not be concerned with the sign. We denote the filter order by n_B for the Butterworth filter and n_C for the Chebyshev filter. We use Equation (12.36) where $|H_1|$ is A_p, ω_1 is ω_p, $|H_2|$ is A_s and ω_2 is ω_s. Since A_p is the number of dB *below* 0 dB, the value of $|H_1|$ is $10^{-A_p/20}$. Other quantities are similarly transformed. Thus,

$$|H_1|^{-2} = 10^{+0.1A_p} \tag{12.45}$$

Therefore, the equation for the Butterworth order, n_B, is

$$n_B = \frac{\log(\varepsilon_2/\varepsilon_1)}{\log(f_s/f_p)} \tag{12.46}$$

where

$$\varepsilon_1 = \sqrt{10^{0.1A_p} - 1}$$

$$\varepsilon_2 = \sqrt{10^{0.1A_s} - 1} \tag{12.47}$$

Sets of equations exist for finding the required order of a Chebyshev filter. However, the application of these equations is somewhat difficult for the following reason. We have been using the 3dB point to define the corner of the pass band. In the case of the Chebyshev filter, this leads to contradictions since the maximum ripple within the pass band is specified. Thus, for example, a 0.1 dB Chebyshev filter has a maximum ripple of 0.1 dB within the pass band. The 3dB point is not within the pass band of the filter. The *3dB bandwidth* and the *filter pass band* are not the same, and caution must be exercised in applying any formula based upon pass-band properties.

We avoid these ambiguities by using a normalized response curve in order to find the required filter order, n_C. Figure 12.29 illustrates normalized Chebyshev low-pass filter curves for a 1dB filter. Other ripple limits would result in slight deviations from these curves, but the asymptotic slopes depend only on the order regardless of the ripple values. Because of these slight variations, if a set of specifications places us close to the borderline between two choices of filter order, it may be wise to either choose the higher order or perform a simulation of the resulting circuit to assure that the specifications are met.

We shall see how to apply the curves of Figure 12.29 in the following examples.

EXAMPLE 12.18:

Select the order for a low-pass filter which has the following specifications:

$A_p = 3$ dB at $f_p = 1$ kHz
$A_s = 40$ dB at $f_s = 5$ kHz

This filter characteristic is shown as Figure 12.28.

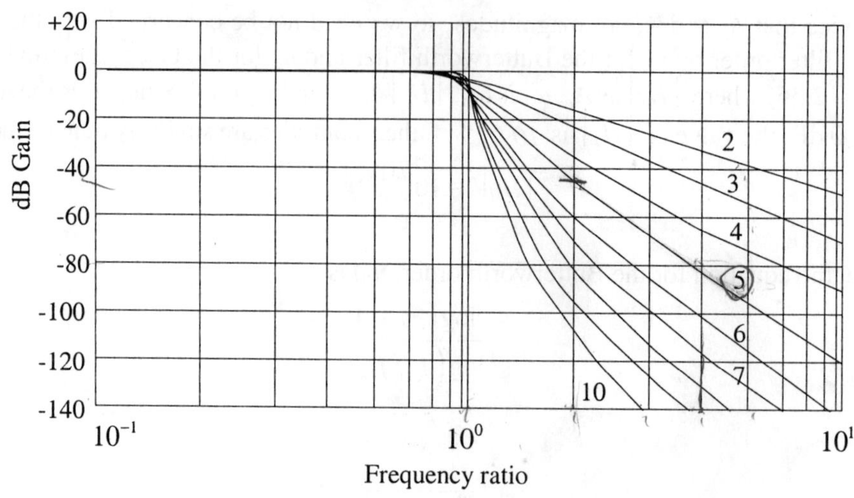

Figure 12.29 – Normalized 1-dB Chebyshev low-pass filter

Solution: Using Equations (12.46) and (12.47), we obtain

$$\varepsilon_1 = \sqrt{10^{0.1\times 3)} - 1} = 1$$

$$\varepsilon_2 = \sqrt{10^{0.1\times 40} - 1} = 100$$

$$n_B = \frac{\log(\varepsilon_2/\varepsilon_1)}{\log(f_s/f_p)} = \frac{\log(100)}{\log(5000/1000)} = 2.86$$

so we use $n = 3$.

We refer to the normalized curves of Figure 12.29 to find the required order of a Chebyshev filter. The two frequencies specified in this example are 1 kHz and 5 kHz. We must first normalize these by dividing by 1000. We are therefore looking for a filter with a 3dB point at 1 Hz and an attenuation of at least 40 dB at 5 Hz. Figure 12.29 indicates that a second-order filter has an attenuation of about 32 dB at 5 Hz while a third-order filter has an attenuation of about 50 dB. We would therefore have to choose the third-order filter.

Even though the required order of the Butterworth and Chebyshev turned out to be equal, we will find in the following examples that the Chebyshev filter provides greater rejection in the stop band than does the Butterworth.

12.7.3 Parameter Scale Factor

Now that we know the required order for the filter, we need to choose the component values.

Various synthesis methods are available to design filters. The constant resistance/constant capacitance technique developed here provides a direct and suitable method to easily design these filters. Once we know the order of the filter, we can use Table 12.2 to select the capacitor coefficients for the Butterworth filter or Table 12.3, *a* through *e*, for design of the Chebyshev filter[1].

Table 12.2 lists capacitor ratios for normalized Butterworth low-pass filters, and resistor ratios for high-pass filters. For the low-pass filter, the resistors are assumed to be 1Ω in value. Thus, as an example, viewing the first row of the table yields a second-order Butterworth filter design. We use one second-order stage with $C_1/C = 1.41$ and $C_2/C = 0.707$. For orders greater than 3, the table contains more than one row. The reason is that we build these filters using second- and third-order stages, so for order greater than 3, more than one stage is required. The table is configured for unit corner frequency, that is, $\omega_p = 1$.

Order, n	C_1/C or R/R_1	C_2/C or R/R_2	C_3/C or R/R_3
2	1.414	0.7071	
3	3.546	1.392	0.2024
4	1.082	0.9241	
	2.613	0.3825	
5	1.753	1.354	0.4214
	3.235	0.3090	
6	1.035	0.9660	
	1.414	0.7071	
	3.863	0.2588	
7	1.531	1.335	0.4885
	1.604	0.6235	
	4.493	0.2225	
8	1.020	0.9809	
	1.202	0.8313	
	1.800	0.5557	
	5.125	0.1950	
9	1.455	1.327	0.5170
	1.305	0.7661	
	2.000	0.5000	
	5.758	0.1736	
10	1.012	0.9874	
	1.122	0.8908	
	1.414	0.7071	
	2.202	0.4540	
	6.390	0.1563	

Table 12.2 - Butterworth active low-pass values

[1]These tables appeared in the *Electronic Filter Design Handbook*, by A. B. Williams, McGraw-Hill publishing, 1981.

Order, n	C_1/C or R/R_1	C_2/C or R/R_2
2	1.4826	0.7042
4	1.4874 3.5920	1.1228 0.2985
6	1.8900 2.5820 7.0522	1.5249 0.5953 0.1486
8	2.3652 2.7894 4.1754 11.8920	1.9493 0.8197 0.3197 0.08672

Table 12.3a - 0.01 dB Chebyshev active values

Order, n	C_1/C or R/R_1	C_2/C or R/R_2	C_3/C or R/R_3
2	1.638	0.6955	
3	6.653	1.825	0.1345
4	1.900 4.592	1.241 0.2410	
5	4.446 6.810	2.520 0.1580	0.3804
6	2.553 3.487 9.531	1.776 0.4917 0.1110	
7	5.175 4.546 12.73	3.322 0.3331 0.08194	0.5693
8	3.270 3.857 5.773 16.44	2.323 0.6890 0.2398 0.06292	
9	6.194 4.678 7.170 20.64	4.161 0.4655 0.1812 0.04980	0.7483
10	4.011 4.447 5.603 8.727 25.32	2.877 0.9756 0.3353 0.1419 0.04037	

Table 12.3b - 0.1 dB Chebyshev active values

To design a practical Butterworth filter, we obtain the capacitor or resistor ratios from the table and scale the values to practical sizes. That is, if the corner frequency is anything other than 1 rev/s, and/or the resistors are any value other than 1Ω, the capacitor values from the table must be appropriately scaled. Since the product, *RC*, is inversely proportional to the frequency, *R* and *C* are themselves inversely related for a given frequency. If, for example, we double *R*, we halve *C*. Thus, to use resistor values other than 1Ω, the capacitor ratios from the table are scaled. Likewise, if a corner frequency other than one rev/s is used, the capacitor values are again scaled. The resistor values which are shown as 1Ω in Figures 12.26 and 12.27 are raised to a more practical value. The capacitor values are also raised to a practical value.

Order, n	C_1/C or R/R_1	C_2/C or R/R_2	C_3/C or R/R_3
2	1.778	0.6789	
3	8.551	2.018	0.1109
4	2.221 5.363	1.285 0.2084	
5	5.542 8.061	2.898 0.1341	0.3425
6	3.044 4.159 11.36	1.875 0.4296 0.09323	
7	6.471 5.448 15.26	3.876 0.2839 0.06844	0.5223
8	3.932 4.638 6.942 19.76	2.474 0.6062 0.2019 0.05234	
9	7.766 5.637 8.639 24.87	4.891 0.3983 0.1514 0.04131	0.6919
10	4.843 5.368 6.766 10.53 30.57	3.075 0.7725 0.2830 0.1181 0.03344	

Table 12.3c - 0.25 dB Chebyshev active values

Order, n	C_1/C or R/R_1	C_2/C or R/R_2	C_3/C or R/R_3
2	1.950	0.6533	
3	11.23	2.250	0.0895
4	2.582 6.233	1.300 0.1802	
5	6.842 9.462	3.317 0.1144	0.3033

6	3.592 4.907 13.40	1.921 0.3743 0.07902	
7	7.973 6.446 18.07	4.483 0.2429 0.05778	0.4700
8	4.665 5.502 8.237 23.45	2.547 0.5303 0.1714 0.04409	
9	9.563 6.697 10.26 29.54	5.680 0.3419 0.1279 0.03475	0.6260
10	5.760 6.383 8.048 12.53 36.36	3.175 0.6773 0.2406 0.09952 0.02810	

Table 12.3d - 0.5 dB Chebyshev active values

Order, n	C_1/C or R/R_1	C_2/C or R/R_2	C_3/C or R/R_3
2	2.218	0.6061	
3	16.18	2.567	0.06428
4	3.125 7.546	1.269 0.1489	
5	8.884 11.55	3.935 0.09355	0.2540
6	4.410 6.024 16.46	1.904 0.3117 0.06425	
7	10.29 7.941 22.25	5.382 0.1993 0.04684	0.4012
8	5.756 6.702 10.15 28.94	2.538 0.4435 0.1395 0.03568	
9	12.33 8.281 12.68 36.51	6.853 0.2813 0.1038 0.02808	0.5382
10	7.125 7.897 9.952 15.50 44.98	3.170 0.5630 0.1962 0.08054 0.02269	

Table 12.3e - 1 dB Chebyshev active values

We first select a value for all resistors, that is $R_1 = R_2 = R_3 = R$. The actual capacitor values are found by using the scaling equation,

$$C_n = \frac{C_i}{2\pi f_p R} \tag{12.48}$$

where R is the chosen resistor value and C_i are read from the table.

EXAMPLE 12.19:

Find component values for the design of Example 12.18. In that example, we specify

$A_p = 3$ dB at $f_p = 1$ kHz

$A_s = 40$ dB at $f_s = 5$ kHz

Verify your result using a computer simulation program.

Solution: Refer to Table 12.2 for the Butterworth filter of order $n_B = 3$. The capacitor ratios are read as follows:

$$\frac{C_1}{C} = 3.546, \ \frac{C_2}{C} = 1.392, \ \frac{C_3}{C} = 0.2024$$

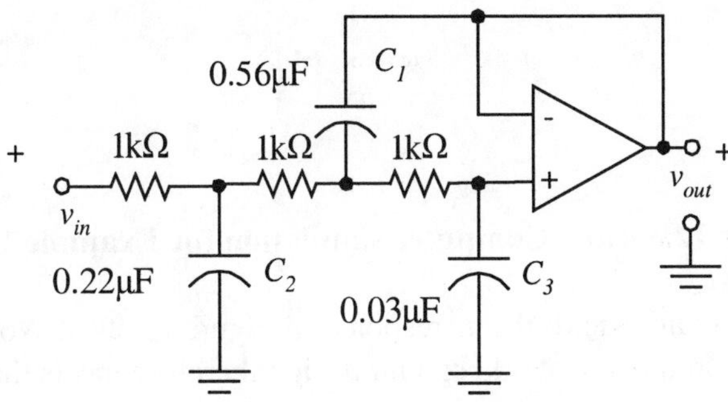

Figure 12.30(a) – 3-pole Butterworth filter for Example 12.19

These values must be scaled inversely with the frequency and the selected resistor value. Suppose we choose resistors of value 1 kΩ. The scaling factor is then

$$\frac{1}{2\pi f_p R} = \frac{1}{2\pi \times 10^3 \times 10^3} = 0.16 \times 10^{-6}$$

This yields capacitors of value

$$C_1 = (0.16)(3.546)\ \mu F = 0.56\ \mu F$$
$$C_2 = (0.16)(1.392)\ \mu F = 0.22\ \mu F$$
$$C_3 = (0.16)(0.2024)\ \mu F = 0.03\ \mu F$$

The complete filter is shown in Figure 12.30(a). All resistor values are equal to 1 kΩ. If the derived capacitor values were not practical because of size or availability, we could select a new value for R and recalculate the capacitor values.

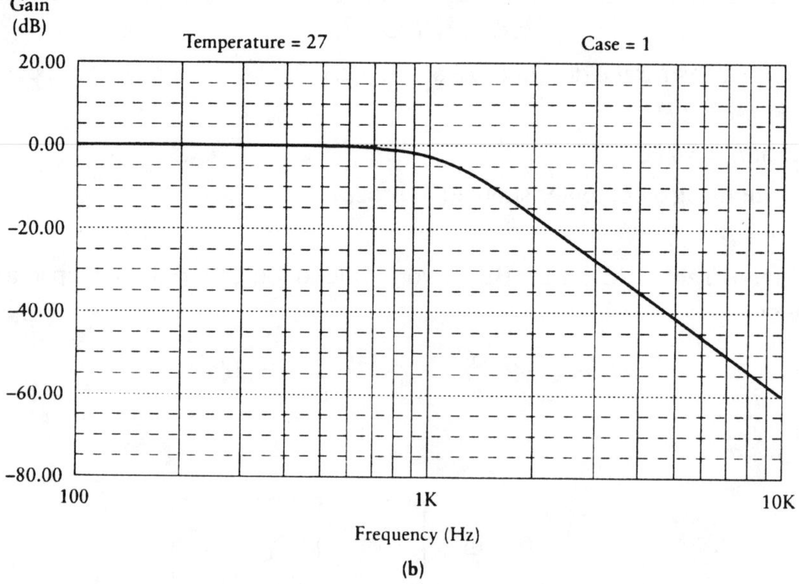

Figure 12.30(b) – Computer simulation for Example 12.19

The computer simulation yields the *ac* response of Figure 12.30(b). Note that the amplitude is down over 42 dB at a frequency of 5 kHz. Our design therefore meets the specifications.

EXAMPLE 12.20:

Derive the 0.1dB Chebyshev filter for the specifications of Example 12.19.

Solution: Let us again select $R = 1$ kΩ and use the capacitor coefficients for a Chebyshev low-pass filter of order 3 (recall that $n_C = 3$ from Example 12.18). These coefficients are taken from Table 12.3b since the maximum ripple is specified as 0.1 dB. Therefore,

$$\frac{C_1}{C} = 6.653,\ \frac{C_2}{C} = 1.825,\ \frac{C_3}{C} = 0.1345$$

Using the scaling technique described above, we find the scale value to be

$$\frac{1}{2\pi f_p R} = 0.16 \times 10^{-6}$$

We thus obtain

$$C_1 = (0.16)(6.653)\ \mu\text{F} = 1.061\ \mu\text{F}$$
$$C_2 = (0.16)(1.825)\ \mu\text{F} = 0.292\ \mu\text{F}$$
$$C_3 = (0.16)(0.1345)\ \mu\text{F} = 0.0215\ \mu\text{F}$$

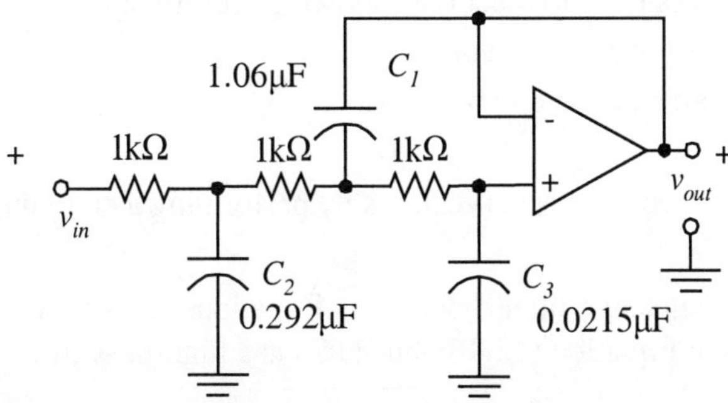

Figure 12.31(a) Chebyshev filter for Example 12.20

The filter is shown in Figure 12.31(a).

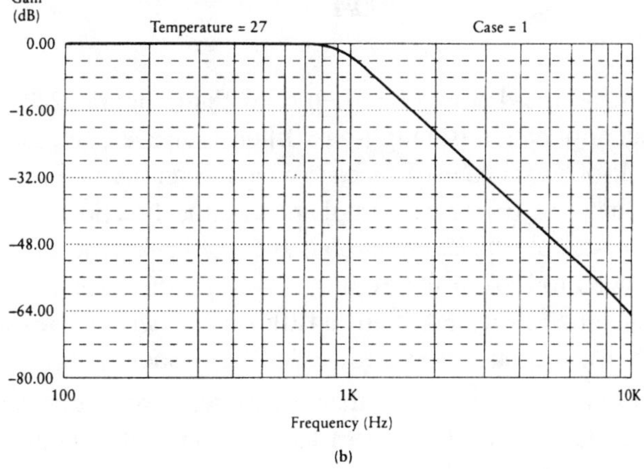

Figure 12.31(b) – Computer simulation for Example 12.20

Figure 12.31(b) illustrates the results of the computer simulation. The attenuation at 5 kHz is approximately 47 dB. Our design therefore exceeds the specifications by a considerable amount.

12.7.4 High-Pass Filter

The circuits for a high-pass filter are shown in Figure 12.27. The two-pole filter is in Figure 12.27(a) and the three-pole filter is shown in Figure 12.27(b). When calculating the order for a high-pass filter, f_p and f_s are interchanged and all of the capacitors are of the same value. We use the ratio of R/R_i in the tables rather than C_i/C.

EXAMPLE 12.21

Design an active high-pass filter to meet the following requirements:

$$A_p = 3 \text{ dB at } f_p = 100 \text{ Hz}$$
$$A_s = 75 \text{ dB at } f_s = 25 \text{ Hz}$$

Verify that your design meets the specifications by performing a computer simulation.

Solution: We first calculate the filter order using Equations (12.46) and (12.47). Note that we have reversed f_p and f_s in Equation (12.46) since this is a high-pass filter.

$$\varepsilon_1 = \sqrt{10^{(0.1\times3)} - 1} = 1$$
$$\varepsilon_2 = \sqrt{10^{7.5} - 1} = 5623$$

$$n_B = \frac{\log 5623}{\log(100/25)} = 6.25$$

so we use $n_B = 7$.

We now need to find the required order of a Chebyshev filter. Figure 12.29 applies to the low-pass filter, and our current application is a high-pass filter. However, since roll-off depends on relative frequency (i.e., roll-off is stated in dB/decade which means a certain dB decrease for each change in frequency by a factor of 10) we can simply reverse the direction and talk about division of frequency by 10. In this example, the attenuation is specified at a frequency which is 1/4 of the corner frequency, so we need to look at the point, $f = 4$ in Figure 12.29. A fourth-order filter achieves about 65 dB of attenuation at $f = 4$, while a fifth-order filter achieves about 80 dB. Since the specification is for 75 dB, we must use a fifth-order Chebyshev filter.

Since the Chebyshev filter has a lower order than the Butterworth, we select this type of filter. We use the data for a 0.5 dB Chebyshev filter from Table 12.3d. Note that the ratios in this table are *resistor* ratios, R/R_i, for a high-pass filter. They are *capacitor* ratios for the low-pass filter. Hence, for this fourth-order filter, we obtain,

First Stage:

$$R/R_1 = 6.842,\ R/R_2 = 3.317,\ R/R_3 = 0.3033$$

Second Stage:

$$R/R'_1 = 9.462,\ R/R'_2 = 0.1144$$

Let us choose $C = 0.015\ \mu F$. The scaling factor is now calculated:

$$R = \frac{1}{2\pi f_p C} = \frac{1}{2\pi(100)(15 \times 10^{-9})} = 1.06 \times 10^5$$

We obtain the following resistor values:

$$R_1 = \frac{R}{6.842} = 15.5\ k\Omega$$

$$R_2 = \frac{R}{3.317} = 32\ k\Omega$$

$$R_3 = \frac{R}{0.3033} = 349\ k\Omega$$

$$R_{1'} = \frac{R}{9.462} = 11.2\ k\Omega$$

$$R_{2'} = \frac{R}{0.1144} = 927\ k\Omega$$

The circuit is shown in Figure 12.32(a). We have placed the third-order filter in front of the second-order filter. We could have reversed the order and obtained the same response.

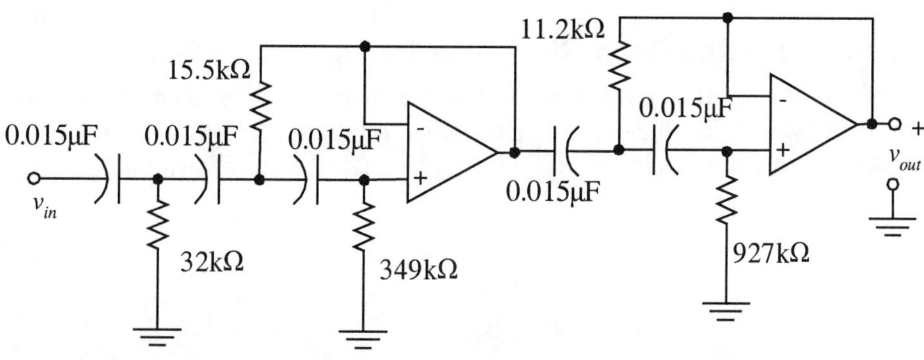

Figure 12.32(a) – High-pass Chebyshev filter for Example 12.21

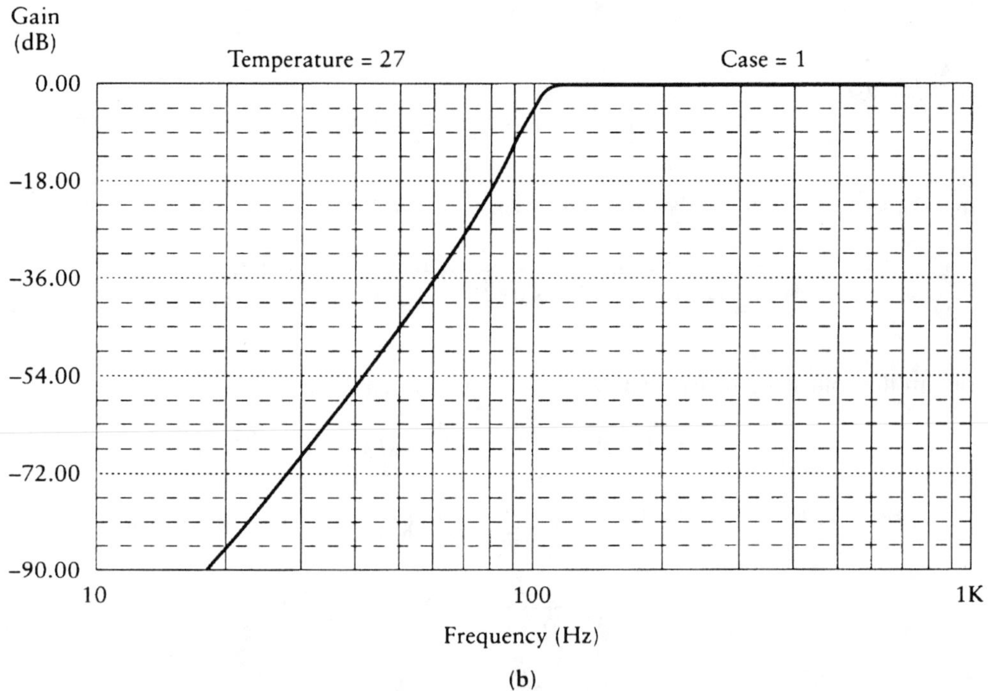

Figure 12.32(b) – Computer simulation of the design Example 12.21

The computer simulation result is shown in Figure 12.32(b). Note that the simulation achieves an attenuation of about 77 dB at 25 Hz, thereby meeting the specifications.

12.7.5 Band-Pass and Band-Stop Filter Design

The band-pass and band-stop filters are each formed from low-pass and high-pass filters. The frequency response for the band-pass filter is shown in Figure 12.33(a). We form this type of filter by placing a low-pass filter in series with a high-pass filter, as shown in Figure 12.33(b).

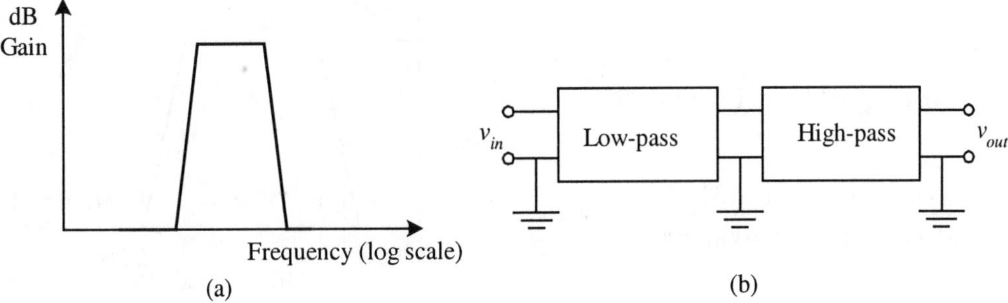

Figure 12.33 – Band-pass filter

The frequency response for the band-stop filter is shown in Figure 12.34(a). We form this filter by placing a low-pass filter in parallel with a high-pass filter, as shown in Figure 12.34(b). We use a summing amplifier to develop the output for the band-stop filter.

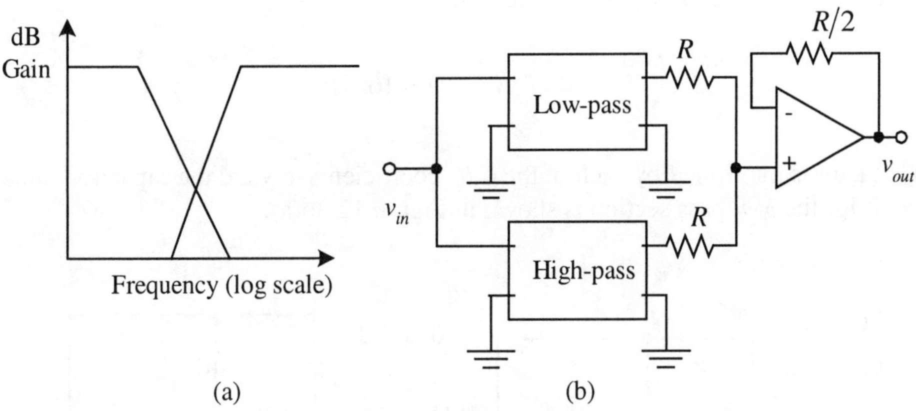

Figure 12.34 – Band-stop filter

EXAMPLE 12.22

Design a band-pass Butterworth filter which has a frequency response as shown in Figure 12.35. Verify that your design meets the specifications by using a computer simulation program.

Solution: This filter is designed using a low-pass filter in series with a high-pass filter, as shown in Figure 12.33(b). We start the design of the low-pass filter by using Equations (12.46) and (12.47) as follows:

$$\varepsilon_1 = \sqrt{10^{(0.1\times 3)} - 1} = 1$$

$$\varepsilon_2 = \sqrt{10^{(0.1\times 30)} - 1} = 31.6$$

$$n_B = \frac{\log(\varepsilon_2/\varepsilon_1)}{\log(f_s/f_p)} = \frac{\log(31.6)}{\log(8000/4000)} = 4.98$$

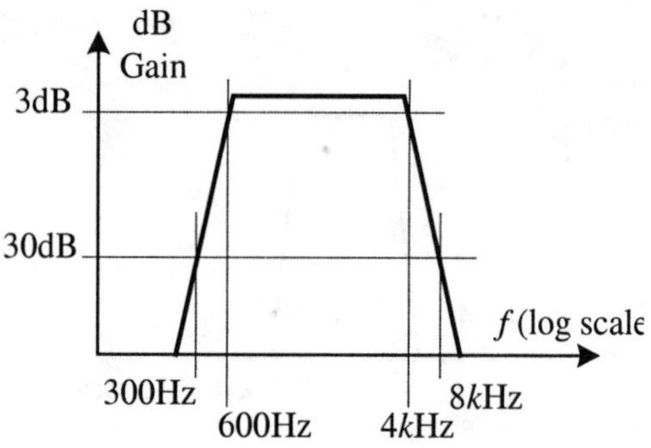

Figure 12.35 – Band-pass filter response for Example 12.22

We therefore choose $n_B = 5$. We obtain the C_i/C coefficients from Table 12.2 as follows:

1.753 1.354 0.4214
3.235 0.309

The scaling factor, C, is found, for a choice of R = 10 kΩ, to be

$$C = scaling\ factor = \frac{1}{2\pi f_p R} = \frac{1}{2\pi(4\times10^3)(10^4)} = 3.98\times10^{-9}\ \text{F}$$

The scale factor is multiplied by each of the C_i/C coefficients to yield the capacitor values. The final circuit for the low-pass section is shown in Figure 12.36(a).

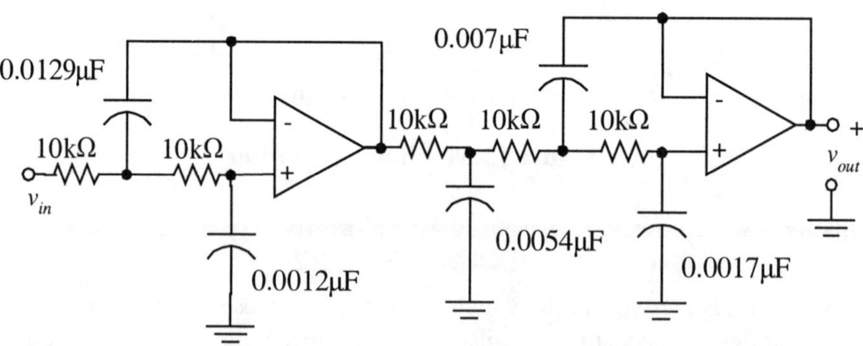

Figure 12.36(a) – Low-pass filter for Example12.22

It makes no difference whether the third-order filter is before or after the second-order filter.

The second part of the filter comprises the design of the high-pass section. Equations (12.46) and (12.47) are used as follows:

$$\varepsilon_1 = \sqrt{10^{(0.1\times3)} - 1} = 1$$
$$\varepsilon_2 = \sqrt{10^{(0.1\times30)} - 1} = 31.6$$

and $n_B = 5$ just as for the low-pass filter. The coefficients for the high-pass filter are the ratio of R/R_i, but have the same numerical values as for the C_i/C ratios. Thus, they are given by:

1.753 1.354 0.4214
3.235 0.309

Let us choose $C = 0.05$ μF yielding the scaling factor, R, as

$$R = \textit{scaling factor} = \frac{1}{2\pi(600)(0.5\times10^{-7})} = 5.305\ \text{k}\Omega$$

The resistor values, R_i, are found by dividing the coefficients into the scaling factor, R, as follows:

$$R_1 = \frac{5305}{1.753} = 3.03\ \text{k}\Omega$$
$$R_2 = \frac{5305}{1.354} = 3.92\ \text{k}\Omega$$
$$R_3 = \frac{5305}{0.4214} = 12.59\ \text{k}\Omega$$
$$R_4 = \frac{5305}{3.235} = 1.64\ \text{k}\Omega$$
$$R_5 = \frac{5305}{0.309} = 17.17\ \text{k}\Omega$$

The final circuit for the high-pass section is shown in Figure 12.36(b).

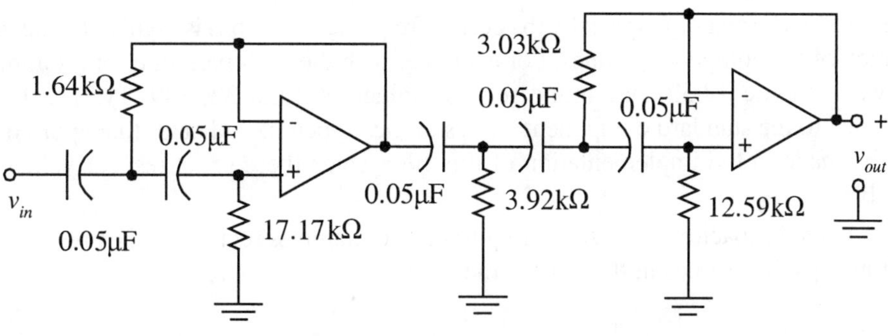

Figure 12.36(b) High-pass filter for Example 12.22

The complete circuit is formed by placing the low-pass section of Figure 12.36(a) in series with the high-pass section of Figure 12.36(b).

The results of the computer simulation are shown in Figure 12.37. This figure shows that the design meets the specifications given at the beginning of this example.

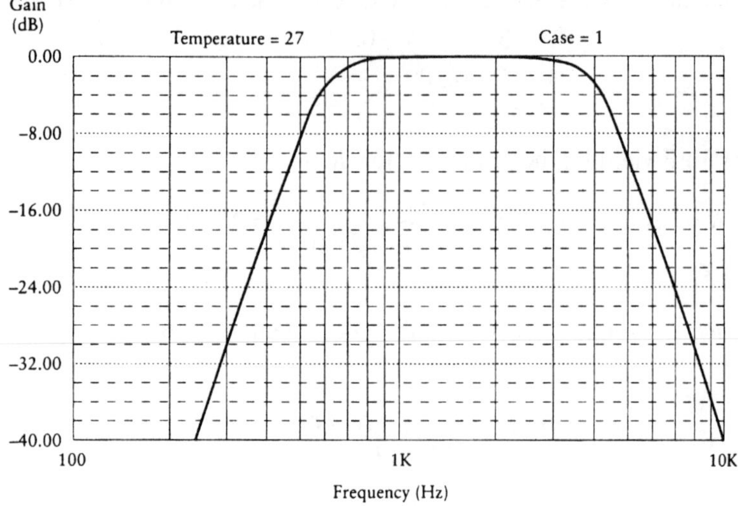

Figure 12.37 – Simulation result for Example 12.22

12.8 INTEGRATED CIRCUIT FILTERS

If we attempt to produce the filter designs presented in the first part of this chapter in monolithic integrated circuit form, we encounter the following problems:

- The filter performance (especially the corner frequency location) is highly dependent on the accuracy of the component values. For example, with the high-pass filter of Example 12.21 (shown in Figure 12.32), we found resistor values of 15.5, 32, 349, 11.2, and 927 kΩ. Reference to the standard component values in the Appendix indicates that approximations must be made in the implementation of this filter since these exact resistor values are not available.
- Large-valued capacitors are usually required. The examples set forth in the previous sections result in capacitor values in the microfarad range.

One technique that avoids these problems is use of the *switched-capacitor filter*. Several manufacturers produce IC filters based upon this technique. We first consider the theory of switched-capacitor filters and then we consider the method of designing IC switched capacitor filters.

12.8.1 Switched-Capacitor Filters

A capacitor is switched between two circuit nodes at a high switching frequency. The result is that this circuit is equivalent to a resistor whose value can be accurately determined by the period of the switching operation.

An active RC integrator is shown in Figure 12.38(a).

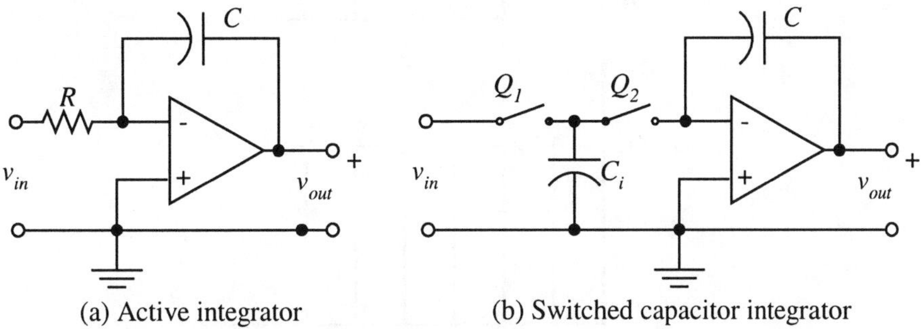

Figure 12.38 – Switched capacitor filter

This network was discussed in Section 12.1. The input resistance, R, to the integrator is changed to a switched-capacitor in the circuit of Figure 12.38(b). The two CMOS switches, Q_1 and Q_2, are driven by a non-overlapping, two-phase clock of period T, as shown in Figure 12.39.

The frequency of the clock, $f = 1/T$, is chosen to be much higher than the highest frequency component of the integrator input. The CMOS switch is closed when the applied clock signal is high and open when the applied clock signal is low. The two-phase clock signals must not overlap since the two switches must never be closed or open at the same instant of time. When Q_1 is closed, Q_2 must be open and when Q_1 is open, Q_2 must be closed.

We now consider the theory of operation of the switched capacitor filter. The input capacitor, C_i, charges to v_{in} during the first half of the clock period. The charge on this capacitor is

$$Q = C_i v_{in} \tag{12.49}$$

Since the frequency of the clock is so much higher than the frequency being filtered, v_{in} does not change while C_i is being charged. During the second half of the clock period, the charge, $C_i v_i$, is transferred to the feedback capacitor since $v_- = v_+ = 0$. The total transfer of charge in one clock cycle is then

$$Q = C_i v_{in} \tag{12.50}$$

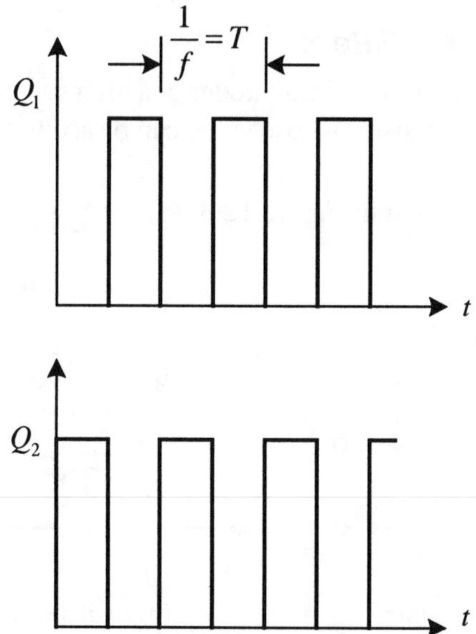

Figure 12.39 – Clock for switched-capacitor filter

Current is charge per unit time so the average input current is

$$I_i = \frac{Q}{T} = \frac{C_i V_{in}}{T} = C_i V_{in} f \qquad (12.51)$$

where f is the clock frequency. The equivalent input resistor R can be expressed as

$$R = \frac{v_{in}}{i_{in}} = \frac{1}{C_i f} \qquad (12.52)$$

The equivalent RC time constant for the switched capacitor filter is

$$RC = \frac{C}{C_i f} \qquad (12.53)$$

Hence the RC time constant that determines the integrator frequency response is determined by the clock frequency, f, and the capacitor ratio, C/C_i. The clock frequency can be set with an accurate crystal oscillator. The capacitor ratios are accurately fabricated on an IC chip (typical tolerances equal 0.1%). We need not accurately set an absolute value of C since only the ratio, C/C_i, affects the time constant. We use small values of capacitance, such as 0.1 pF, in order to reduce the area on the IC devoted to the capacitors.

EXAMPLE 12.23

A switched-capacitor integrator has a frequency, $f = 50$ kHz. The capacitors are given by,

$$\frac{C}{C_i} = \frac{1\,\text{pF}}{0.1\,\text{pF}} = 10$$

Find the resulting RC time constant of the integrator.

Solution: We apply Equation (12.53) to find the time constant.

$$RC = 2 \times 10^{-4}\ \text{s} = 0.2\ \text{ms}$$

Note that we are using small capacitors in order to obtain a time constant of the order of a msec. Hence, we can obtain relatively large time constants, suitable for audio applications, with small areas on the IC.

12.8.2 Sixth-Order Switched-Capacitor Butterworth Low-Pass Filter

Of the numerous IC filters produced by National Semiconductor Corp, we select the MF6, a sixth-order switched-capacitor Butterworth low-pass filter, as a representative model. The block diagram of this filter is shown in Figure 12.40(a).

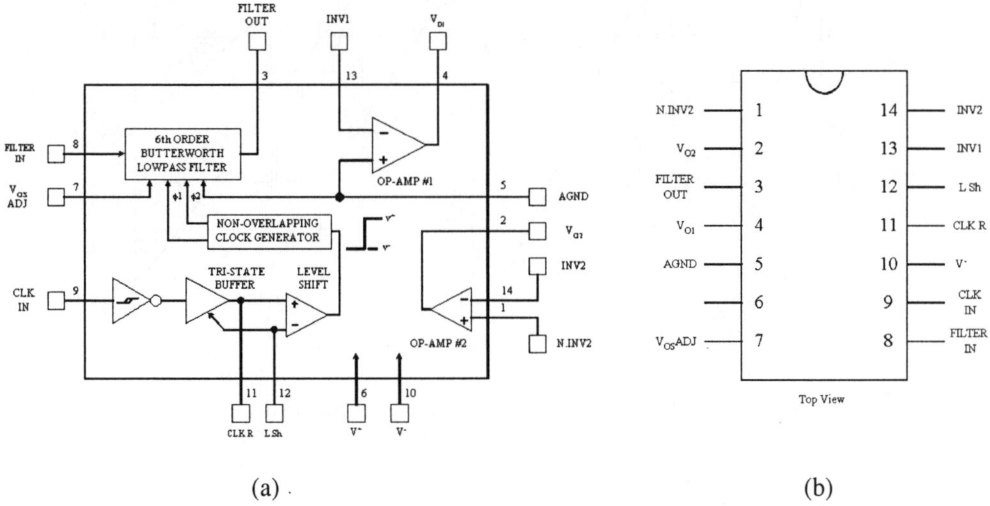

(a) (b)

Figure 12.40 – MF6 low-pass filter

The block diagram contains a Butterworth filter, a clock generator, and a number of op-amps performing level shifting and buffer functions. The non-overlapping clock generator is discussed in Chapter 14, and level shifters were discussed in Chapter 9. The buffer can be thought of as a power amplifier. The ratio of the clock frequency to the low-pass cutoff frequency is internally set to 100 to 1 (MF6-100). For example, to obtain a cutoff frequency of 10 kHz, the clock frequency is 1 MHz. Two clock options are available:

1. With self-clocking, an external resistor and capacitor are used to set the clock frequency. This option is used for standard applications.
2. An external clock can be connected to the filter when more accurate frequency control is needed. This external clock must be compatible with the internal circuitry, so either a TTL- or CMOS-compatible clock is needed.

The filter is maximally flat (Butterworth) and produces a unity gain. Since the gain is unity, filters can be cascaded without worrying about exceeding proper input ranges.

The filter is packaged as a 14-pin DIP (dual in-line package) as shown in the connection diagram of Figure 12.40(b). The frequency response of this filter approximates that of the ideal Butterworth low-pass characteristic, as we can see from the amplitude response shown in Figure 12.41.

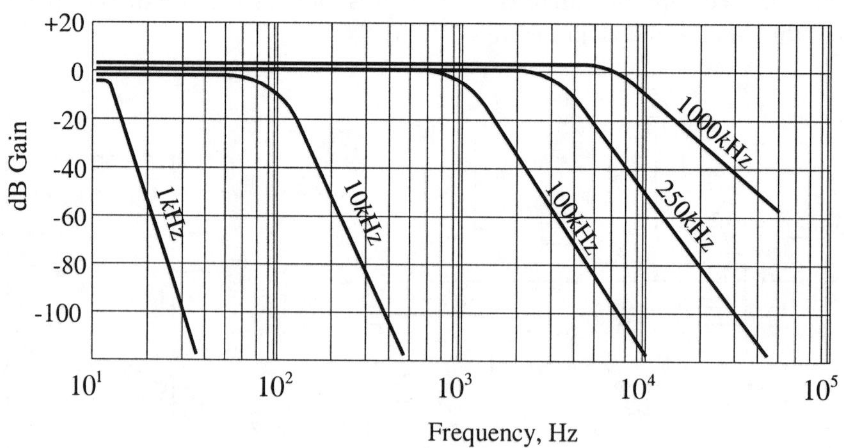

Figure 12.41 – Response of MF6 low-pass filter

EXAMPLE 12.24

Design an IC Butterworth filter to satisfy the following amplitude specifications:

$$A_p = 3 \text{ dB} \qquad f_p = 1 \text{ kHz}$$
$$A_s = 35 \text{ dB} \qquad f_s = 2 \text{ kHz}$$

Solution: From Equations (12.46) and (12.47) we have

$$\varepsilon_1 = \sqrt{10^{0.3} - 1} = 1$$

$$\varepsilon_2 = \sqrt{10^{3.5} - 1} = 56.23$$

$$n_B = \frac{\log(56.23)}{\log(2)} = 5.81$$

We therefore use a sixth-order filter.

We can use the MF6 to implement this. We select $f = 100 \times (1.0 \text{ kHz}) = 100 \text{ kHz}$

12.9 CONCLUDING REMARKS

In the introduction to this chapter, we posed the problem of designing a filter to reduce out of band power output to the level required by the FCC. This design was to be accomplished quickly in order to bring the video game to market in a timely manner. Because the filter was to be designed and manufactured quickly, it is probably not wise to attempt a custom design. The requirement for significant reduction outside of the pass band leads us to consider the Butterworth or Chebyshev design. Since the selling price of our game was calculated without considering the filter, the cost must be held to an absolute minimum. Example 12.18 illustrates that the same level of out of band attenuation could be accomplished with fewer stages using a Chebyshev as compared to a Butterworth filter. For this reason, we would probably select the Chebyshev band-pass filter of the order necessary to meet the FCC specification. One precaution is necessary here. The ripple within the pass-band of the Chebyshev filter normally would not cause great difficulty. In particular, if audio signals are involved, the listener would probably not hear any distortion. However, with video signals, this ripple could lead to ghost images on the monitor screen. Given the tight time schedule, it would probably be best to build a prototype Chebyshev filter and test it in the game. If objectionable results occur, we could switch to a higher-order Butterworth filter.

SUMMARY

We began this chapter with a look at some basic active networks that perform elementary operations such as integration and differentiation. We then turned our attention to the design of active networks to meet specifications that included the desired transfer functions.

With this as an introduction, we were able to understand the operation of active filters. We made extensive use of op-amps in our designs, and also used computer simulations to verify the results.

Following a review of classical analog filters (Butterworth and Chebyshev), we turned our attention to the active implementation of these important filters. We presented a comprehensive design procedure that allows the engineer to meet pass-band ripple and roll-off specifications. The chapter concluded with an examination of integrated circuit filters and the important switched-capacitor filter.

PROBLEMS

Section 12.1

In Problems 12.1-12.6, design active networks to provide the given V_{out}/V_{in} transfer function.

12.1 $H(s)=\dfrac{-10}{s}$

12.2 $H(s)=\dfrac{10}{s^2}$

12.3 $H(s)=\dfrac{-s}{s+10}$

12.4 $H(s)=\dfrac{-10(s+10)}{s+1}$

12.5 $H(s)=\dfrac{10}{s(s+1)}$

12.6 $H(s)=\dfrac{-(s+1)^2}{s(s+10)}$

Sections 12.2 and 12.3

In Problems 12.7-12.8, design a single-amplifier summing integrator to achieve the output voltage V_{out} related to input voltages, V_1, V_2, and V_3 as indicated.

12.7 $V_{out}=\dfrac{-(V_1+10V_2+0.53V_3)}{s}$

12.8 $V_{out}=\dfrac{V_1-V_2-2V_3}{s}$

12.9 Design a multiple-amplifier integrator using a single capacitor that achieves the input-output relationships of Problems 12.7 and 12.8.

12.10 Design a single-input integrator circuit having a switch that will reset the integrator output voltage to +10 (V) when thrown. When integrating, the output voltage should be the negative of the integral of the input voltage. A multiple-pole switch may be used if necessary.

12.11 Design a single amplifier summing differentiator with the following relationship between output voltage, V_{out}, and input voltages, V_1, V_2, and V_3.

$$V_{out}=-s(V_1+10V_2+0.5V_3)$$

12.12 Design a 741 low-pass filter with a *dc* gain of 1/2 and a roll-off frequency of 10 kHz.

12.13 Design a 741 low-pass filter with a *dc* gain of 1000 and a roll-off frequency of 0.4 Hz.

12.14 Design a 741 low-pass filter with a roll-off frequency that adjusts between 10 Hz and 100 Hz. The frequency adjustment should be made with a potentiometer. You may assume that $A_1 = A_2 = 1$.

12.15 Design a 741 low-pass filter which has an independently-adjustable *dc* gain and roll-off frequency. Gain should be adjustable between 0 and 10, and the frequency from near zero to 100 Hz. In addition, this system should have an input impedance greater than 50 MΩ.

12.16 Design a 741 high-pass filter with a high frequency gain of 1/2 and a roll-off frequency of 20 Hz.

12.17 Design a 741 filter having both a low-pass and a high-pass output. Gain of the low-pass (at *dc*) and of the high-pass (at high frequency) should each be 10. Roll-off frequency for each is to be 200 Hz.

12.18 Repeat the design of Problem 12.14 making the roll-off frequency adjustable in the range between 500 Hz and 1500 Hz.

12.19 Design a 741 filter with transfer function,

$$H(s) = \frac{3s - 10}{s + 100}$$

12.20 Design a 741 filter with transfer function,

$$H(s) = \frac{-10s + 5}{3s + 40}$$

12.21 Derive Equation (12.17) from Figure 12.20.

12.22 Design an *RC* low-pass filter with a *dc* gain of 10 and a corner frequency of 2 kHz.

12.23 Design a first-order active filter with a *dc* gain of 20 and a corner frequency of 1 kHz.

12.24 Design a low-pass filter with adjustable roll-off frequency between 500 Hz and 1 kHz and a *dc* gain of 5.

12.25 Design a high-pass filter with a high-frequency gain of 20 and a corner frequency of 500 Hz.

12.26 Design an all-pass filter with the *dc* gain of 0.5 and the corner frequency at 100 Hz.

12.27 Design an adjustable high-pass filter with a high-frequency gain of 20 and a corner frequency adjustable from 200 Hz to 600 Hz.

12.28 Design an adjustable high-pass filter with a high-frequency gain of 10 and a corner frequency adjustable from 100 Hz to 200 Hz.

12.29 Design an all-pass filter with a gain of 10 and a corner frequency of 100 Hz.

12.30 Using the single amplifier of the general type, design a filter with a high-frequency gain of 1 and a corner frequency of 3 kHz.

12.31 Design a second-order single amplifier low-pass filter to obtain the transfer function,

$$H(s)= \frac{5000}{5s^2 + 50s + 5000}$$

[HINT: Refer to circuit shown in Chapter 2, Figure P2.46]

12.32 Design a second-order single amplifier high-pass filter to achieve the following transfer function,

$$H(s)= \frac{s^2}{s^2 + 25s + 2500}$$

[HINT: Refer to circuit shown in Chapter 2, Figure P2.47]

12.33 Design a second order single amplifier band-pass filter to achieve the following transfer function,

$$H(s)= \frac{-s}{s^2 + 25s + 2500}$$

[HINT: Refer to circuit shown in Chapter 2, Figure P2.48]

Section 12.5

12.34 Design a Butterworth low-pass filter with the following specifications:

$f_p = 500$ Hz $\qquad A_p = 3$dB

$f_s = 3 \qquad A_s = 50$dB

12.35 Repeat Problem 12.34 using a Chebyshev filter with a 0.5dB ripple.

12.36 Repeat Problem 12.35 but with a 1.0dB ripple.

12.37 Design a Butterworth high-pass filter with the following specifications:

3 dB at 1 kHz

45 dB at 300 Hz

12.38 Repeat Problem 12.37 using a 0.25dB ripple Chebyshev filter.

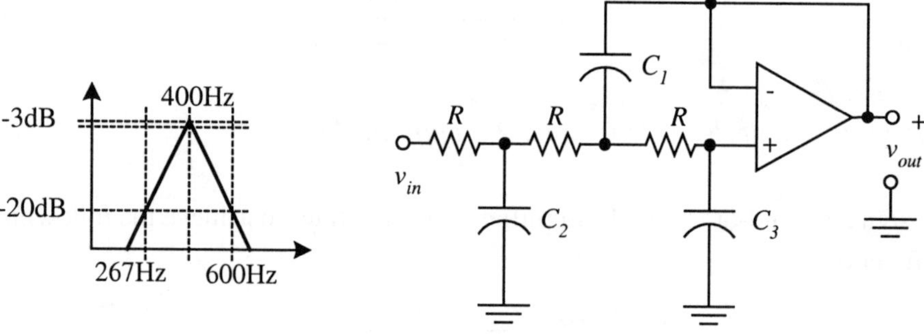

Figure P12.39 **Figure P12.40**

12.39 Design a "crossover" network to distribute the high frequencies of an audio signal into a high-frequency speaker, and the low frequencies into a low-frequency speaker. This is shown in Figure P12.39. Choose either a Butterworth or Chebyshev filter, whichever requires fewer components. If you choose a Chebyshev filter, choose a maximum ripple of 0.25 dB. Draw the filter diagrams.

12.40 Determine the transfer function, V_{out}/V_{in}, for the ideal op-amp circuit shown in Figure P12.40. Since the op-amp is ideal, $V_+ = V_-$. The parameter values are

$C_1 = 3.546C$; $C_2 = 1.392C$; $C_3 = 0.2024C$; $RC = 1.0$

Solve this problem in two steps. First find the equations, then solve them using determinants. Construct a Bode plot for this network.

12.41 Design a Butterworth band-pass filter that has the amplitude characteristics shown in Figure P12.41.

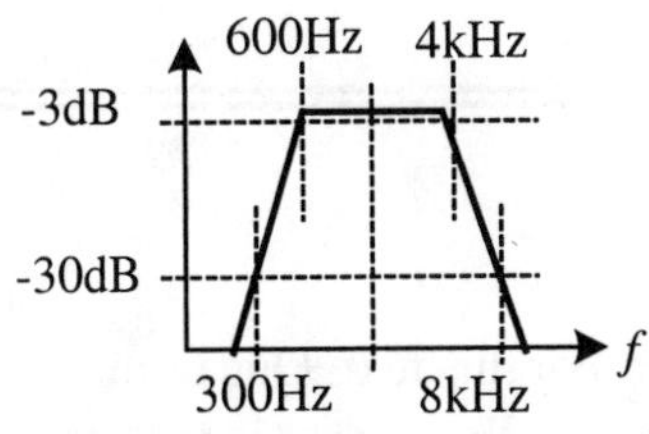

Figure P12.41

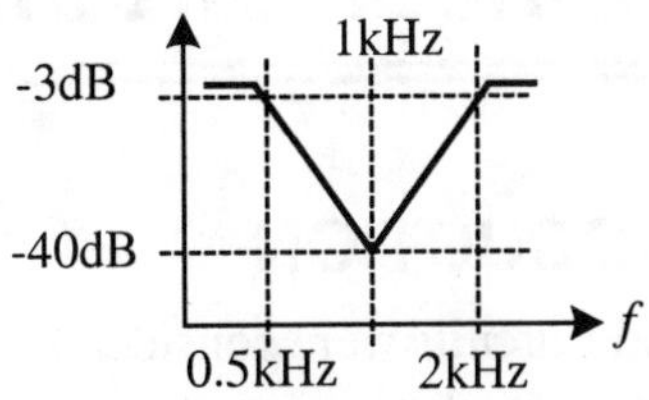

Figure P12.42

12.42 Design a Chebyshev band-stop filter that has the amplitude characteristics shown in Figure P12.42. Set the maximum ripple at 1 dB.

12.43 Design two high-pass filters to satisfy the dB gain plot of Figure P12.43. One filter is a Butterworth and the other is a 0.1dB Chebyshev. Compare the response of the two filters.

12.44 Design a telephone filter to develop the frequency response shown in Figure P12.44. Use a Chebyshev 1dB filter with "reasonable" capacitor and resistor values.

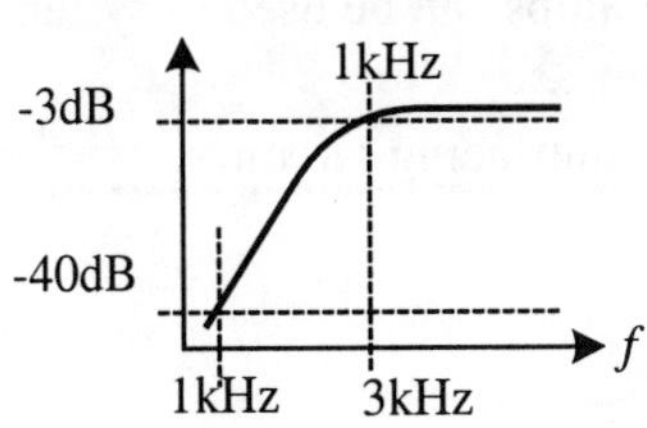

Figure P12.43

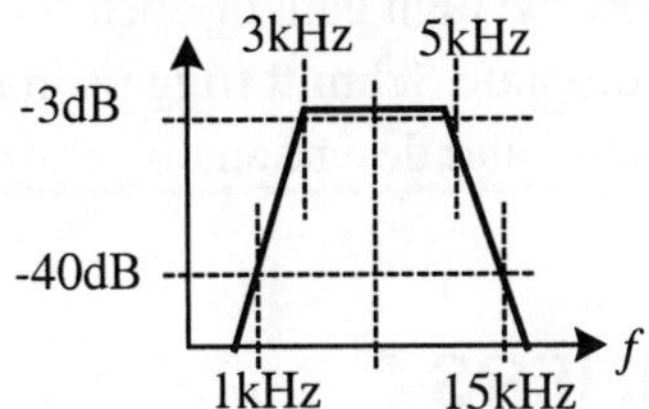

Figure P12.44

12.45 Use the MF6-100 IC Filter to satisfy the specification for the low-pass filter of Problem 12.34.

Chapter 13

Quasi-Linear Circuits

13.0 INTRODUCTION

Several diode circuits were considered in Chapter 3 of this text. One of the examples was the power supply circuit which converts an *ac* signal into *dc*. We also analyzed various clipping and clamping configurations which are used to either chop off a portion of a time-varying signal or to change its *dc* level. In the current chapter, we combine diodes with op-amps in various circuit configurations. The advantage of this approach is that the diodes are able to operate more closely to their ideal characteristics. In many cases, the effects of the forward voltage drop across the diodes are virtually eliminated because of the high open-loop gain of the op-amp. We consider rectifiers, limiters, comparators, and Schmitt triggers. Our objective is to be able to design systems that achieve specified instantaneous nonlinear output-to-input voltage transfer characteristics. We conclude the chapter with a study of the circuits which create the interface between the analog and digital domains.

After studying this material, you will

- Know how to design rectifiers using operation amplifiers.
- Be able to design limiter circuits to obtain quasi-linear outputs.
- Understand how the high gain of open-loop op-amps can be used in systems.
- Be able to incorporate Schmitt triggers in systems.
- Be able to analyze and design analog to digital interfacing circuitry.

13.1 RECTIFIERS

The *rectifier* is one of the most basic and useful nonlinear circuits. Rectifiers operate on an input signal in a manner that depends upon the sign of the instantaneous input voltage. They can be designed to chop off either the negative or positive part of the signal, or to yield an output which is the mathematical absolute value of the input.

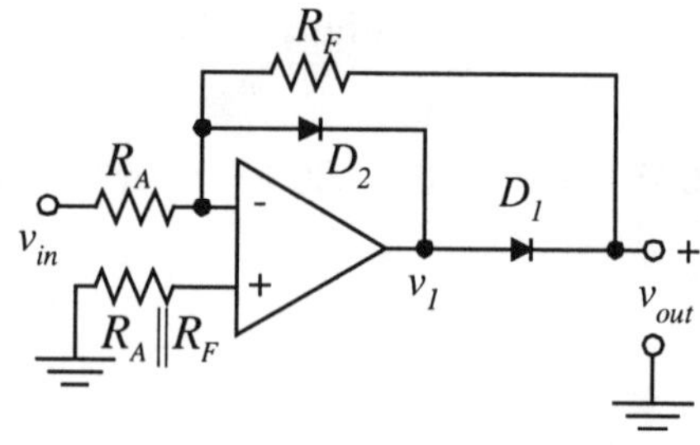

Figure 13.1 – Inverting half-wave rectifier

For illustration, we use the μA741 general purpose op-amp in the circuits presented in this chapter. However, any internally-compensated op-amp can be used in these circuits.

The circuit shown in Figure 13.1 is known as

an *inverting half-wave rectifier*. Since a diode can operate in either of two states, we analyze the rectifier as two separate circuits. Which of the two separate circuits applies depends upon the sign of the op-amp output voltage, v_1.

If we assume the op-amp to be ideal, then the inverting and non-inverting input voltages are zero.

$$v_- = v_+ = 0 \tag{13.1}$$

For positive v_{in}, the op-amp output voltage, v_1, is less than zero. Diode D_2 *conducts* and it can therefore be replaced by a small resistor, R_f. This small diode forward resistance acts as a feedback resistor, thus leading to lowered amplifier gain. Diode D_1 acts as an open circuit under this condition, so

$$v_{out} = v_- = 0 \tag{13.2}$$

Alternatively, when the op-amp output voltage, v_1, is positive, D_2 is *non-conducting* (OFF) and D_1 is *conducting* (ON). Figure 13.2(a) repeats the circuit of Figure 13.1 where the diodes are replaced by their equivalents for the situation when v_1 is positive.

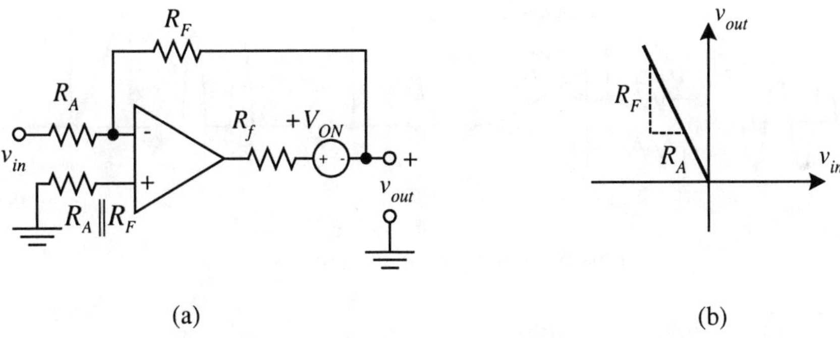

(a) (b)

Figure 13.2 Inverting half-wave rectifier with positive input

That is, D_1 is replaced by a forward resistance, R_f, in series with the diode forward voltage drop, V_{ON}. D_2 is open-circuited. The node equations for the op-amp inputs are found from Figure 13.2(a) as follows:

$$\begin{gathered} v_+ = 0 \\ (v_-)\cdot\left(\frac{1}{R_A}+\frac{1}{R_F}\right)-\frac{v_{in}}{R_A}=\frac{v_{out}}{R_F} \end{gathered} \tag{13.3}$$

Since $v_- = v_+ = 0$, we solve for the output voltage to find

$$v_{out} = -\frac{R_F}{R_A}v_{in} \tag{13.4}$$

The expression in Equation (13.4) does not depend upon the diode forward voltage, V_{ON}. Thus, because of the high open-loop gain of the op-amp, the feedback acts to cancel the diode turn-on (forward) voltage. This leads to improved performance since the diode more closely approximates the ideal device (don't forget we are assuming an ideal op-amp with amplification of infinity). The transfer characteristic of Equation (13.4) is shown in Figure 13.2(b).

The half-wave rectifier is one of the simplest nonlinear circuits. There are a number of variations of the basic circuit. Some of these alternate forms are illustrated in Table 13.1. We recommend that you not proceed beyond this point until you review (and understand) the operation of each circuit in the table.

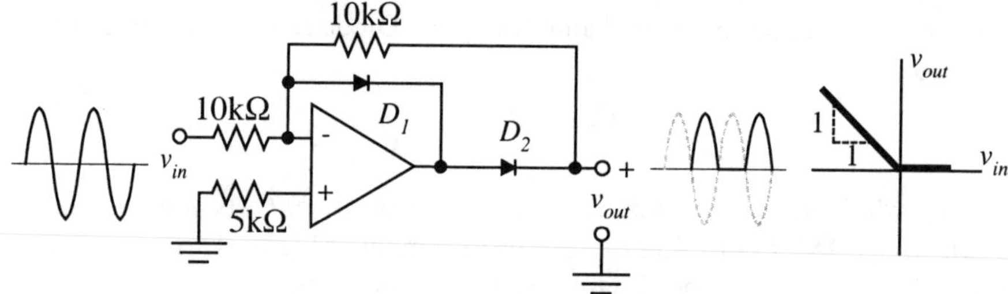

1. Basic, positive going output, inverting

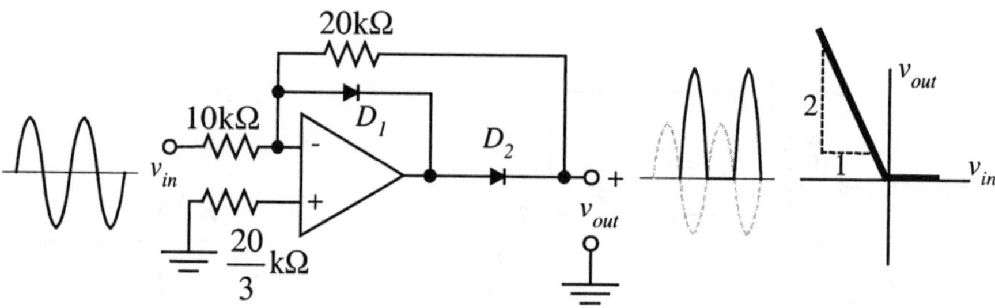

2. Positive going output, inverting with gain

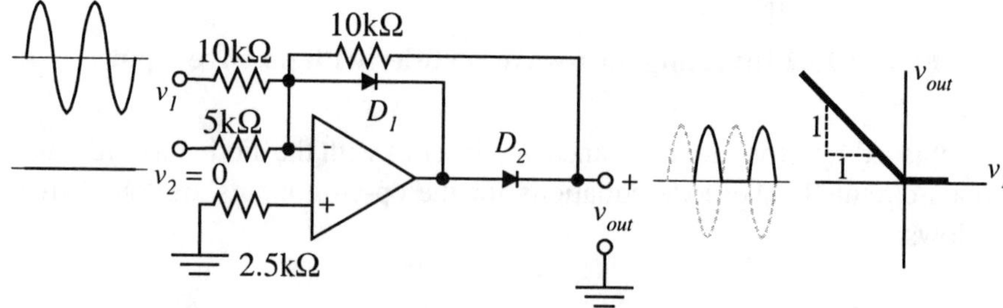

3. Positive going output, inverting with unity gain, and summing

Table 13.1 (parts 1, 2, and 3) - Half-wave rectifier configurations

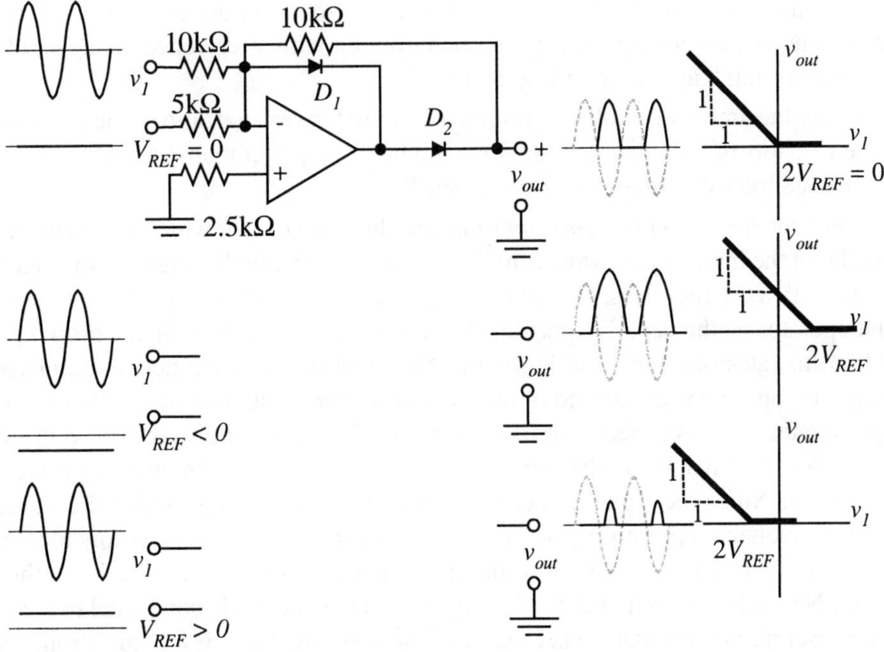

4. Positive going output, inverting with unity gain, and summing

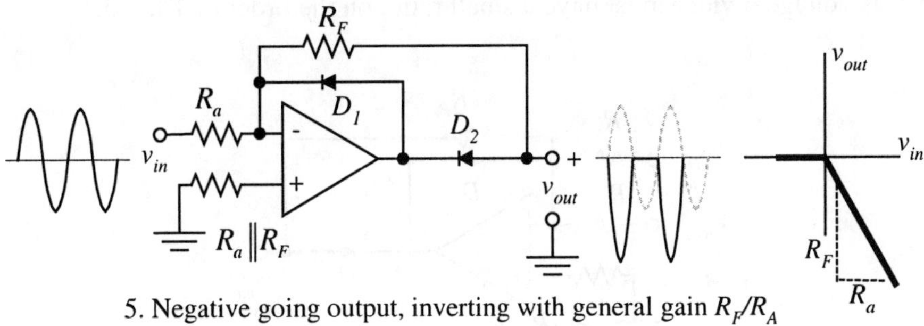

5. Negative going output, inverting with general gain R_F/R_A

Table 13.1(parts 4 and 5) – Half-wave rectifier configurations (continued)

The half-wave rectified output waveform can be shifted along the v_I (or v_{in}) axis. This is done by using a reference voltage added to the input voltage of the rectifier circuit, as shown in Figure 13.3. This is termed *axis shifting*. It adds or subtracts a fixed *dc* voltage to the input signal. This process shifts the diode turn-on voltage point. If a negative reference voltage, V_{REF}, is applied to the circuit of Figure 13.3, the diode turns on when the input voltage is still positive. This shifts the v_{out}/v_{in} transfer function to the right. If a positive reference voltage is applied, the v_{out}/v_{in} transfer function shifts to the left. These shifted characteristic curves are shown in Figure 13.3. Accuracy is improved generating V_{REF} using a well-regulated, low-current power supply from which almost no current is drawn.

The input-output voltage characteristics can also be shifted up or down. This is termed *level shifting* and is accomplished by adding a second op-amp with a reference voltage added to the negative input terminal, as shown in Figure 13.4.

We can vary the amount of voltage shift by adjusting the resistor ratio of the second op-amp, R'_F/R'_b. The resistors of the second op-amp should be made larger than those of the first op-amp to reduce attenuation (by voltage division) when D_2 is off.

A *full-wave rectifier*, or *magnitude operator*, produces an output which is the absolute value, or magnitude, of the input signal waveform. One method of accomplishing full-wave rectification is to use two half-wave rectifiers. One of these operates on the positive portion of the input and the second operates on the negative portion. The outputs are summed with the proper polarities. Figure 13.5 illustrates one such configuration. Note that the resistive network attached to the output summing op-amp is composed of resistors of higher value than those attached to the op-amp that generates v_1. This is necessary since for negative v_{in}, v_2 follows the curve shown above the node labeled v_2. That is, as the input increases in a negative direction, v_2 increases in a positive direction. Since the input impedance to the non-inverting terminal of the summing op-amp is high, the voltage, v_+ is simply one-half of v_2 (i.e., the two 100 kΩ resistors form a voltage divider). The voltage at the negative summing terminal, v_-, is the same as v_+, and therefore is equal to $v_2/2$. Now when v_{in} is negative, D_2 is open, and the node v_1 is connected to the inverting input of the first op-amp through a 5 kΩ resistor. The inverting input is a virtual ground since the non-inverting input is tied to ground through a resistor. The result is that the voltage appearing on the inverting terminal of the summing op-amp also affects v_1 through the voltage divider formed by the 100 kΩ and 5 kΩ resistors. In order to achieve a characteristic resembling that shown in the figure, this voltage divider must have a small ratio, on the order of 1 to 20.

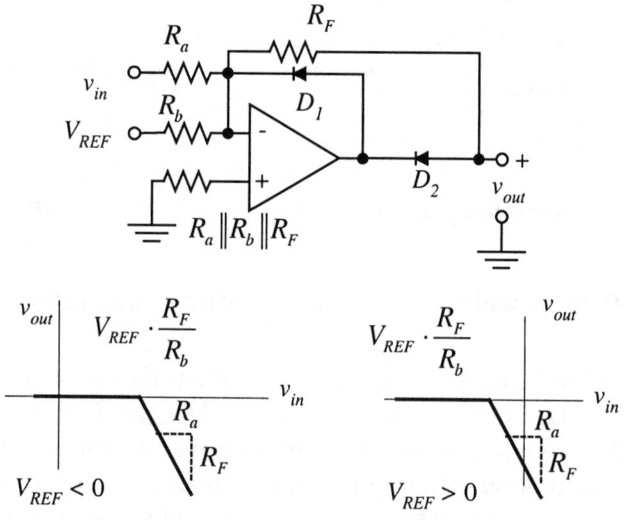

Figure 13.3 – Axis shifting

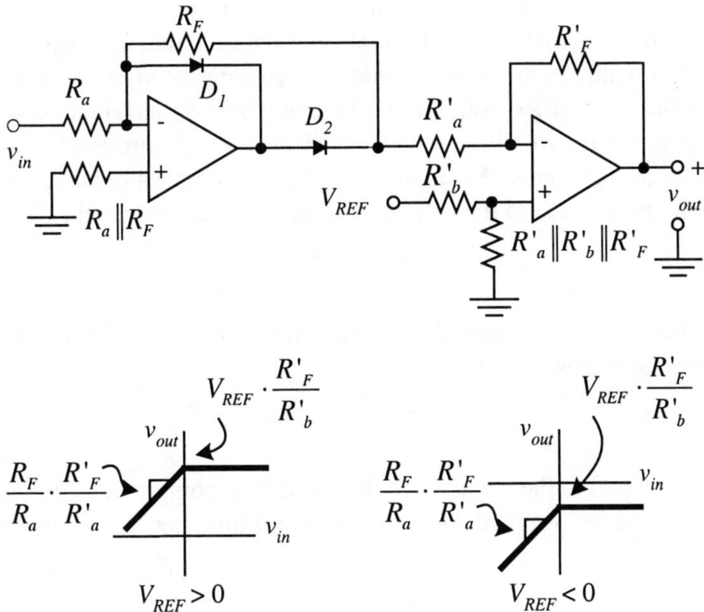

Figure 13.4 – level shifting

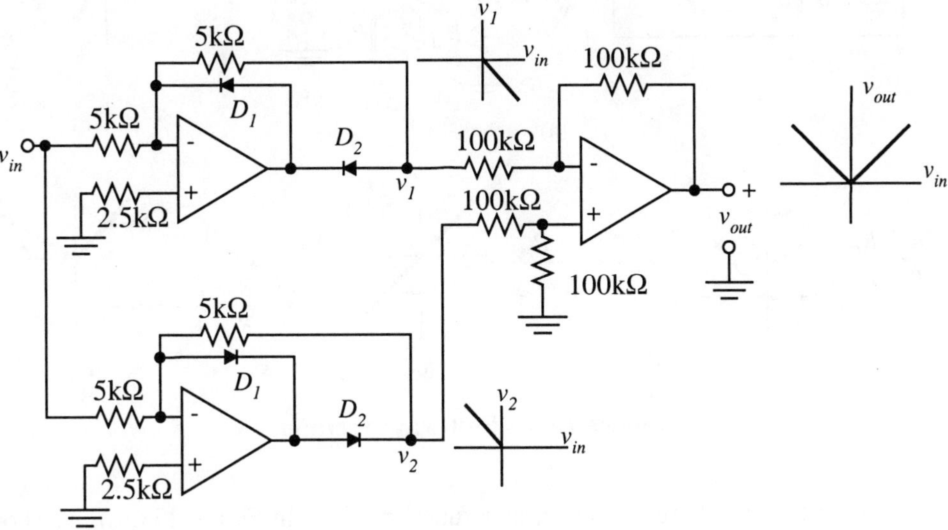

Figure 13.5 – Full-wave rectifier

This method of full-wave rectification requires three separate amplifiers. One simpler approach follows from an arithmetic observation. First note that the mathematical operation of taking the absolute value is the same as that of reversing the sign of the negative part of the signal. If the *half-wave* rectified output is doubled and the original signal is subtracted from this, the result is the full-wave rectified waveform. This is easily proven by considering the two operating conditions separately. First, suppose that the input is positive. Then the half-wave output is equal to the input, and the difference described above becomes

$$2v_{in} - v_{in} = v_{in} \tag{13.5}$$

Thus, the output is equal to the input. Now if the input is negative, the half-wave output is zero, and the difference becomes

$$2 \times 0 - v_{in} = -v_{in} \tag{13.6}$$

Thus, the output is equal to the negative of the input. The composite output is then the absolute value of the input. The full-wave rectifier that performs this operation is shown in Figure 13.6(a).

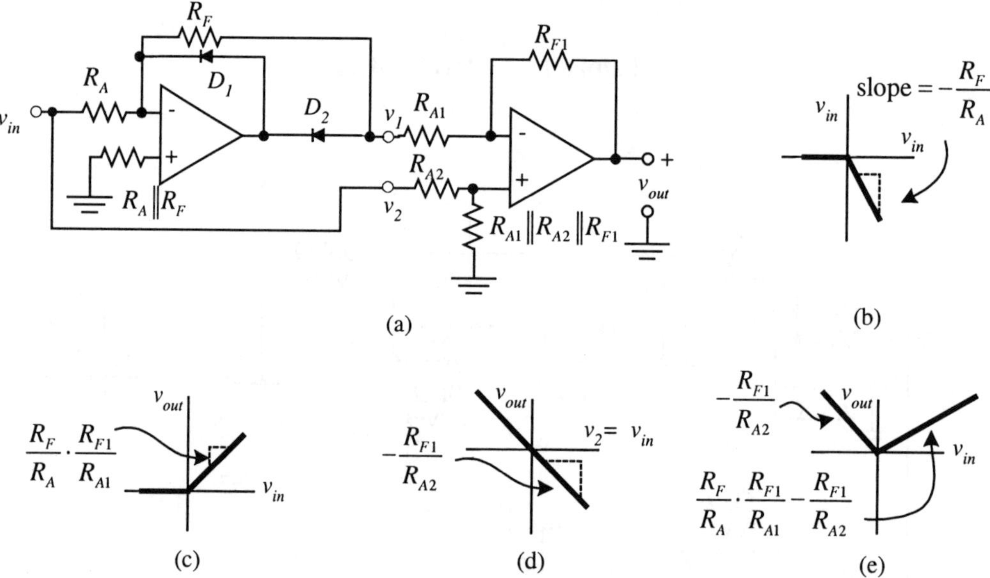

Figure 13.6 – Full-wave rectifier

The curve of Figure 13.6(b) shows v_1 as a function of v_{in}. In Figure 13.6(c), we show the output voltage due to v_{in} through the upper connection. Figure 13.6(d) shows the output voltage as a function of v_{in} through the lower connection. This is given by

$$v_{out}\Big|_{v_{in}=0} = -\frac{R_{F1}}{R_{A2}} \cdot v_2 \tag{13.7}$$

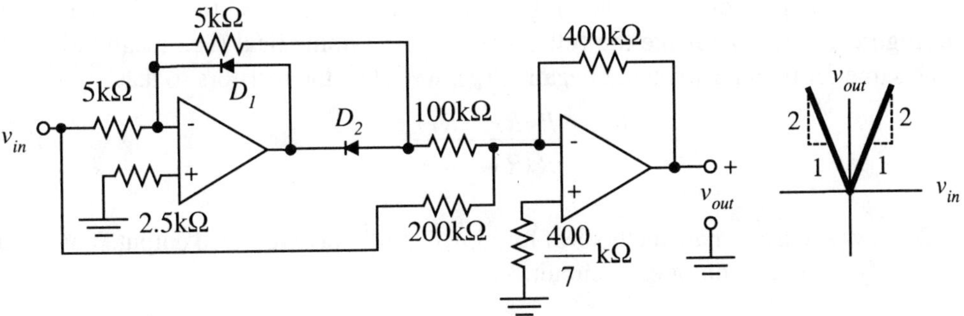

1. Standard full-wave rectifier with minimum number of op-amps

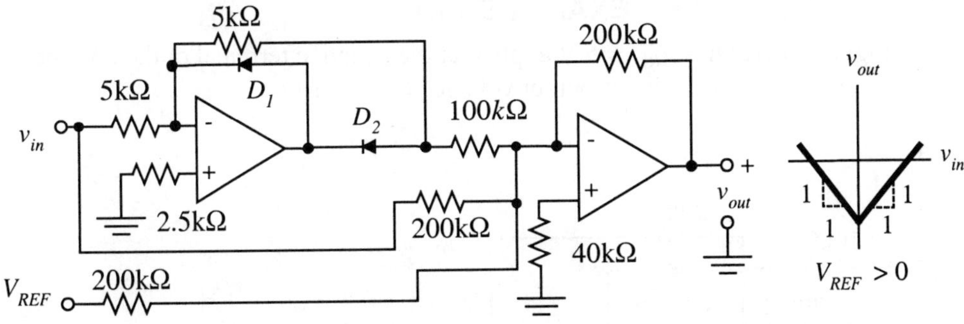

2. Full-wave rectifier with level shifting

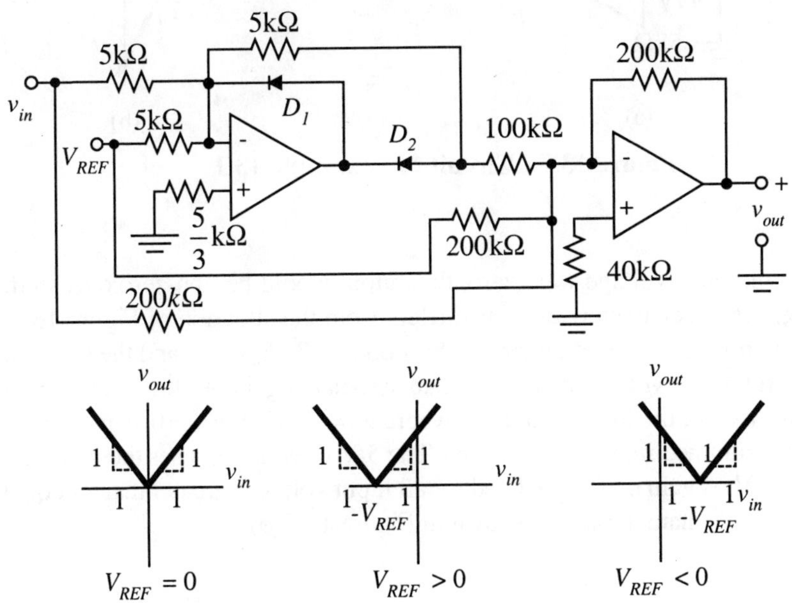

3. Full-wave rectifier with both level shifting and axis shifting

Table 13.2 – Full-wave rectifiers

To obtain the total output voltage, we add Figure 13.6(c) and Figure 13.6(d) to obtain the curve shown in Figure 13.6(e). To make the full-wave rectifier symmetrical (i.e., magnitude of the slope is the same for both positive and negative v_{in}), we select the resistors so that

$$\frac{R_{F1}}{R_{A2}} = \frac{R_F R_{F1}}{R_A R_{A1}} - \frac{R_{F2}}{R_{A2}} \tag{13.8}$$

Table 13.2 shows some alternate methods of forming the full-wave rectified output. You should be able to verify the operation of each circuit.

EXAMPLE 13.1

The circuit of Figure 13.7(a) has $V_{REF} = 5$ V applied at the negative terminal of the op-amp fed through a 20 kΩ resistor. Find the input-output voltage characteristic.

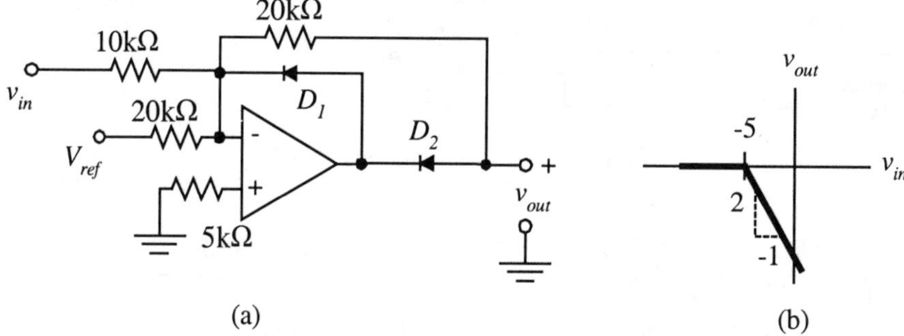

Figure 13.7 - Circuit for Example 13.1

Solution: If the reference voltage were zero, the output would be non-zero only in the fourth quadrant of the v_{out} vs. v_{in} characteristic. This differs from the situation of Figure 13.1 by 180° since the diodes are reversed. In that quadrant, the slope is $-R_F/R_a$ or -2, and the curve intercepts the origin. With a reference voltage of +5 V and an associated gain of unity (based on the given resistor values), the axis of the line is moved to where $v_{in} = -5$ when $v_{out} = 0$. That is, v_{in} must be -5 V in order for the summed input to equal zero. The 5 V reference causes the diode to conduct when v_{in} is above -5 V. A gain of -2 is realized for all input voltages greater than or equal to -5 V. The resulting v_{out} vs. v_{in} characteristic is shown in Figure 13.7(b).

EXAMPLE 13.2

Design an op-amp circuit to provide the transfer characteristic as shown in Figure 13.8(a). Use a minimum number of op-amps.

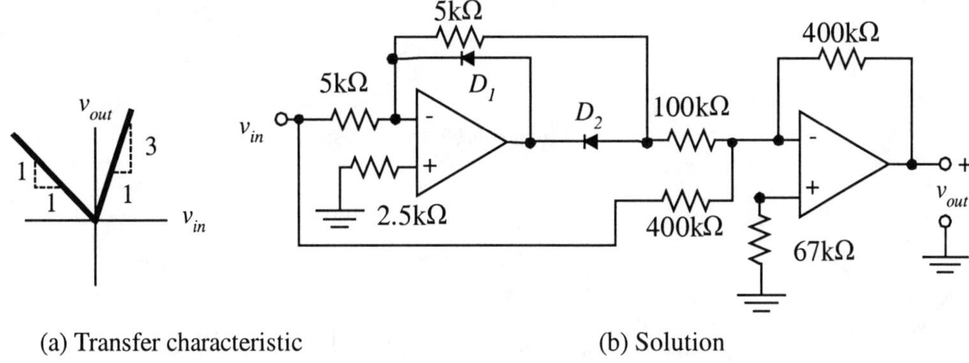

(a) Transfer characteristic (b) Solution

Figure 13.8 – Characteristics and solution for Example 13.2

Solution: The design requirement calls for a minimum number of op-amps and the output is in the form of a full-wave rectified version of the input. We choose the circuit of Figure 13.6 since it only requires two op-amps. We establish two equations from Figure 13.6(e) and the required slopes as follows:

$$\frac{-R_{F1}}{R_{A2}} = -1 \quad \text{so } R_{F1} = R_{A2}$$

$$\frac{R_F R_{F1}}{R_A R_{A1}} - \frac{R_F}{R_{A2}} = +3$$

We have five unknown variables, R_A, R_F, R_{A1}, R_{A2} and R_{F1}, and only two equations, so we can choose three resistor values. Suppose we choose $R_F = R_A = 5$ kΩ, and $R_{A1} = 100$ kΩ (twenty times the other resistors to reduce attenuation). Then the above equations yield $R_{F1} = R_{A2} = 400$ kΩ. The design is complete, and the circuit is as shown in Figure 13.8(b).

EXERCISES

E13.1 and 13.2: Design op-amp circuits with transfer characteristics as shown in the figures. Assume that the reference supply available is ± 10 V and that $V_{ON} = 0.7$ V and $R_f = 100$ Ω. The solutions are shown in Figures E13.1 and E13.2.

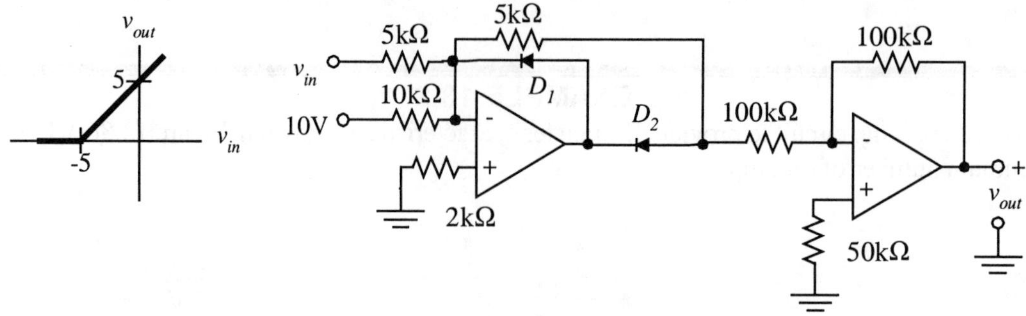

Figure E13.1

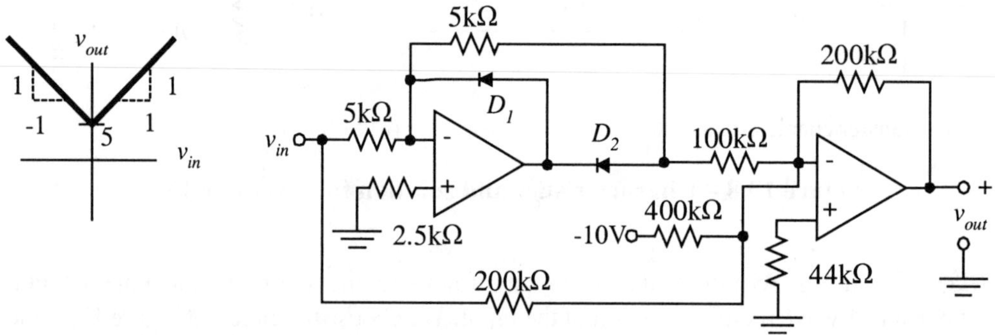

Figure E13.2

E13.3 and 13.4: Find approximate relationships between the input voltages, v_1 and v_2, and the output voltage, v_{out}, for each of the circuits shown. Assume that $V_{ON} = 0.7$ V and that $R_f = 100\ \Omega$. The solutions are shown in Figures E13.3 and E13.4.

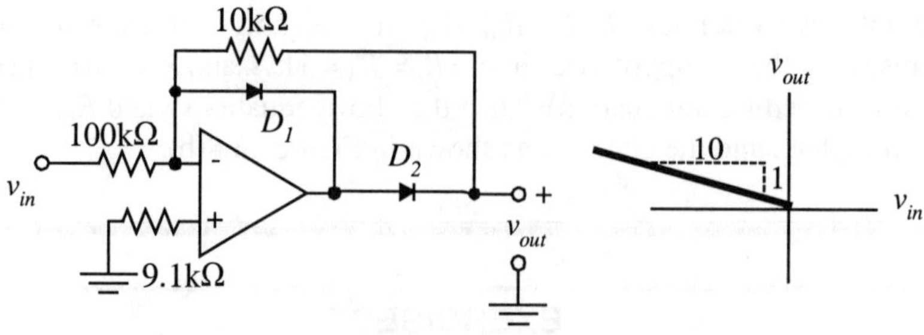

Figure E13.3

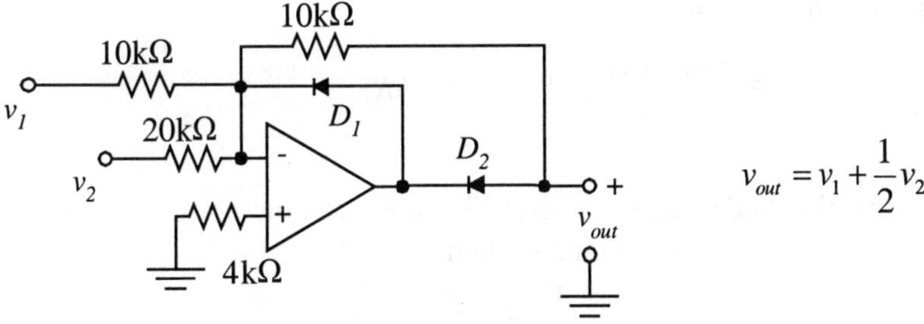

Figure E13.4

3.2 FEEDBACK LIMITERS

An ideal *limiter* constrains a signal to be below (or above) a particular specified value (the *breakpoint)*. The output signal is proportional to the input below (or above) this breakpoint and is constant for inputs above (or below) this value.

There are many varied configurations of the basic limiter circuit. In fact, any characteristic composed of two straight lines intersecting at a point can be considered as a form of limiter. These characteristics can be realized by using a diode in the feedback path of an op-amp.

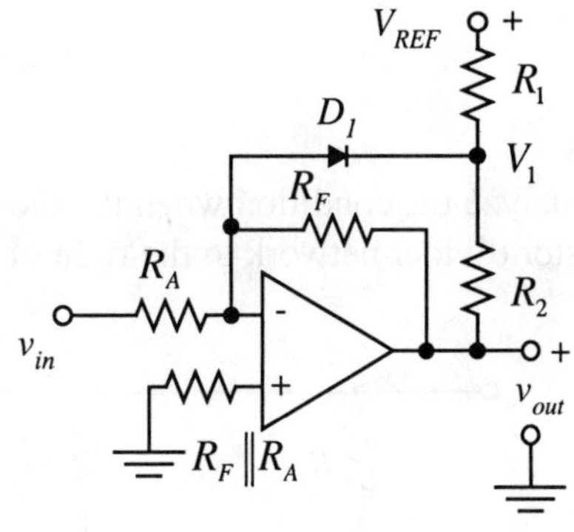

Figure 13.9 – Feedback limiter

As an example, consider the system of Figure 13.9. The circuit is analyzed by considering the two diode-states separately. That is, the diode is first assumed to be an open circuit, and the circuit is solved. The circuit is again solved for the case when the diode is a short circuit. Note that when the diode conducts, the gain of the op-amp is greatly reduced. Analysis simply requires that we find the location of the breakpoint between the two regions.

When the diode of Figure 13.9 is not conducting (i.e., open), the circuit operates as an inverting amplifier with the output given by

$$v_{out} = - v_{in} \frac{R_F}{R_A} \tag{13.9}$$

The gain is $-R_F/R_A$.

The break point occurs when the voltage across the diode reaches V_{ON}. To find that break point, we solve for v_I under one of the two diode assumptions. Since it is easier to solve the circuit with the diode open, we'll assume that condition first. Solving for v_I using a simple voltage divider relationship, we find

$$v_I = \frac{V_{REF} - v_{out}}{R_1 + R_2} R_2 + v_{out} = (R_1 \| R_2)\left(\frac{V_{REF}}{R_1} + \frac{v_{out}}{R_2}\right) \tag{13.10}$$

At the break point, the diode current is zero. The diode conducts when v_I tries to go below V_{ON}. (Note that $v_- = v_+ = 0$). That is, it conducts when

$$v_I = \frac{R_2 V_{REF} + R_1 v_{out}}{R_1 + R_2} < V_{ON} \tag{13.11}$$

Setting $v_I = -V_{ON}$, we solve for v_{out} at the breakpoint.

$$v_{out} = \frac{-(R_1 + R_2)}{R_1} \cdot V_{ON} - \frac{R_2}{R_1} \cdot V_{REF} \tag{13.12}$$

The relative sizes of the terms in Equation (13.12) depend on the resistor values and the relationship between V_{REF} and V_{ON}. The first term is often much less than the second, so we will approximate the output as

$$v_{out} \approx \frac{-R_2 \cdot V_{REF}}{R_1} \tag{13.13}$$

To analyze the condition when the diode is conducting, we find the Thevenin equivalent of the resistor divider network to the right of the diode as shown in Figure 13.10.

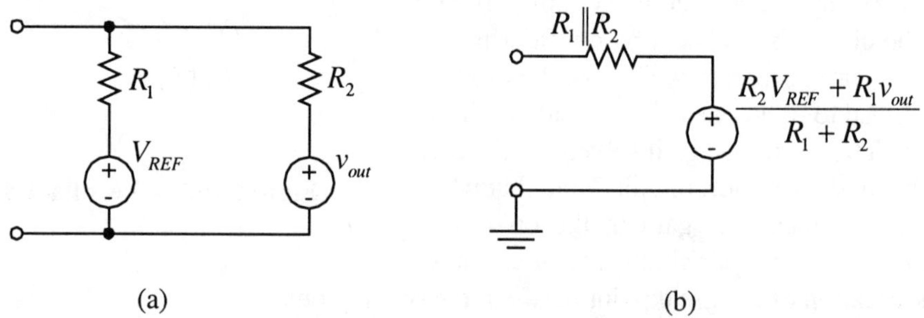

Figure 13.10 - Thevenin equivalent for feedback limiter output circuit

The two voltage sources with series resistors of Figure 13.10(a) reduce to the Thevenin equivalent of Figure 13.10(b). The equivalent resistance is the parallel combination of R_1 with R_2, and the open-circuit voltage is found either using loop or nodal analysis.

When the diode is on, it is replaced by a "turn-on" voltage generator, V_{ON}, and a forward resistance, R_f. The circuit of Figure 13.9 then takes the form shown in Figure 13.11.The voltage, v_{out}, is determined from the circuit as follows:

$$v_{out} = \frac{R_F}{R_A} v_{in} - \frac{R_F}{R_1 \| R_2 + R_f} \left(\frac{R_2 V_{REF} + R_1 v_{out}}{R_1 + R_2} + V_{ON} \right) \tag{13.14}$$

The gain is found by collecting terms in Equation (13.14) and finding the derivative,

$$\frac{dv_{out}}{dv_{in}} = -\left(\frac{1}{R_A}\right)\left(1 + \frac{R_2}{R_1}\right)\left(R_1 \| R_2 + R_f\right) \tag{13.15}$$

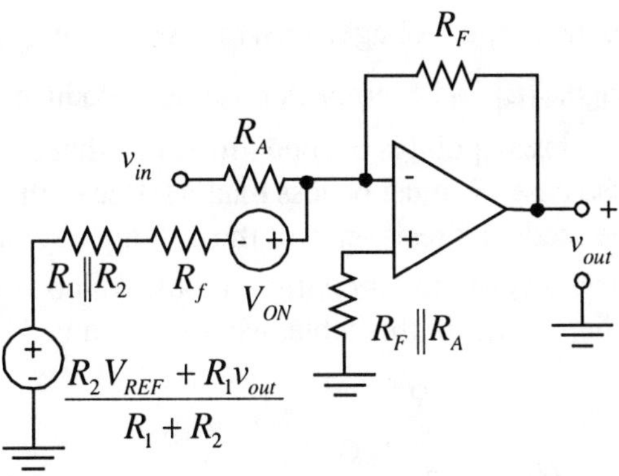

Figure 13.11 – Feedback limiter with diode ON

If $R_f \ll R_1 \| R_2$, the expression for the gain in Equation (13.15) reduces to

$$\frac{dv_{out}}{dv_{in}} = -\frac{R_2}{R_A} \tag{13.16}$$

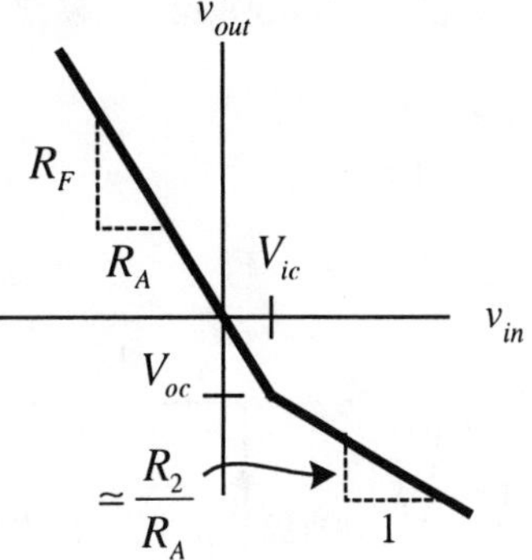

Figure 13.12 – Limiter characteristics

Figure 13.12 shows the resulting characteristic curve. The slope changes from $-R_F/R_A$ to approximately $-R_2/R_A$ as v_{in} increases beyond the break point. If $V_{REF} < 0$, the break in the characteristic curve occurs at a positive value of v_{out}.

R_2 must be much smaller than R_A if good limiting is to be achieved. That is, if the limiter is to have a slope near zero beyond the breakpoint, then $R_2/R_A \ll 1$.

The values of v_{out} and v_{in} when the slope changes (defined as V_{oc} and V_{ic} respectively) are given by the following equations (we are assuming that R_F is much larger than $R_1 \| R_2 + R_f$).

$$V_{oc} = \frac{-R_2 V_{REF}}{R_1} - \left(1 + \frac{R_2}{R_1}\right) V_{ON} \approx \frac{R_2}{R_1} V_{REF}$$

(13.17)

$$V_{ic} = \frac{R_A}{R_F}\left[\frac{R_2 V_{REF}}{R_1} + \left(1 + \frac{R_2}{R_1}\right) V_{ON}\right] \approx \frac{R_A R_2}{R_F R_1} V_{REF}$$

The last approximation is valid if V_{ON} approaches zero.

Note that the value of the output voltage when the slope changes, $|V_{oc}|$, must be less than the op-amp saturation voltage, $|E|$. The amplifier cannot produce a voltage greater than the saturation voltage, so if the break point is beyond this value, that point will never be reached. If $E = V_{REF}$, as is frequently the case, R_2 must be less than R_1. Recall that R_f is the forward resistance of the diode and R_F is the feedback resistance of the op-amp circuit.

Table 13.3 presents a variety of limiter configurations. We hope you will study these carefully before proceeding. For the circuits in this table, we have assumed $R_f = 100\Omega$ and $V_{ON} = 0.7$ V.

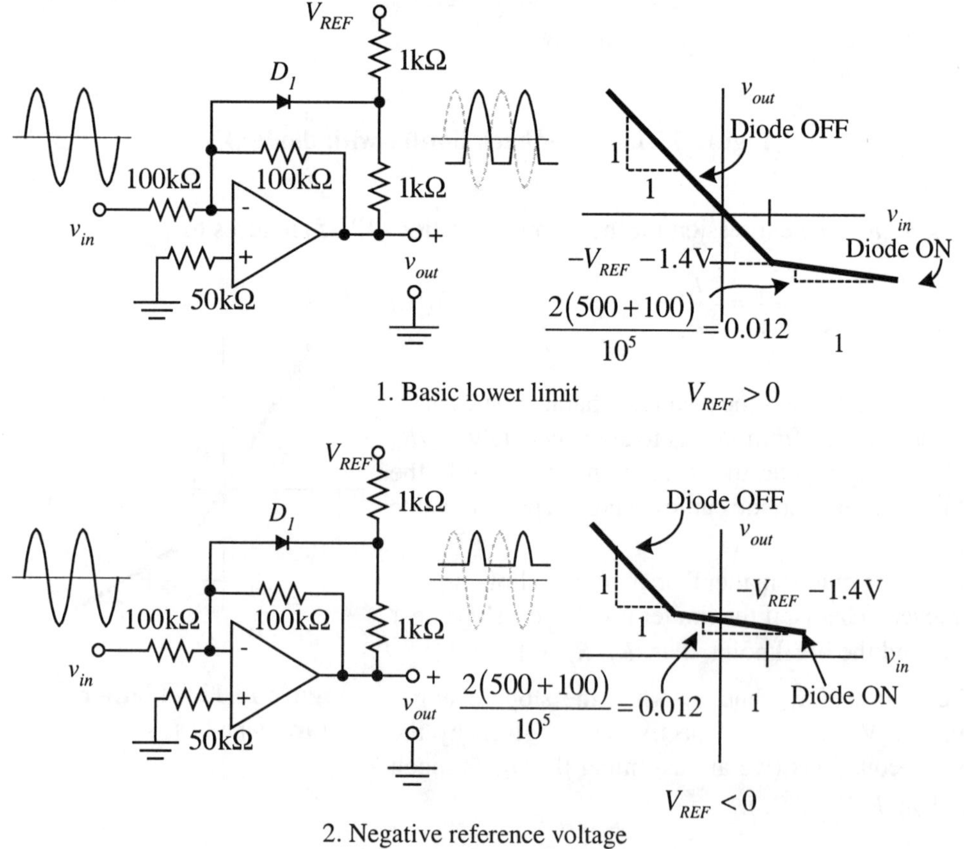

Table 13.3 (parts 1 and 2) - Limiter configurations

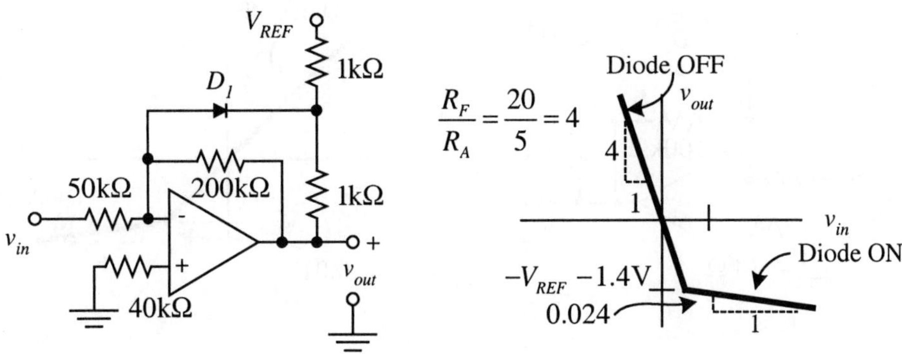

3. Lower limit with gain

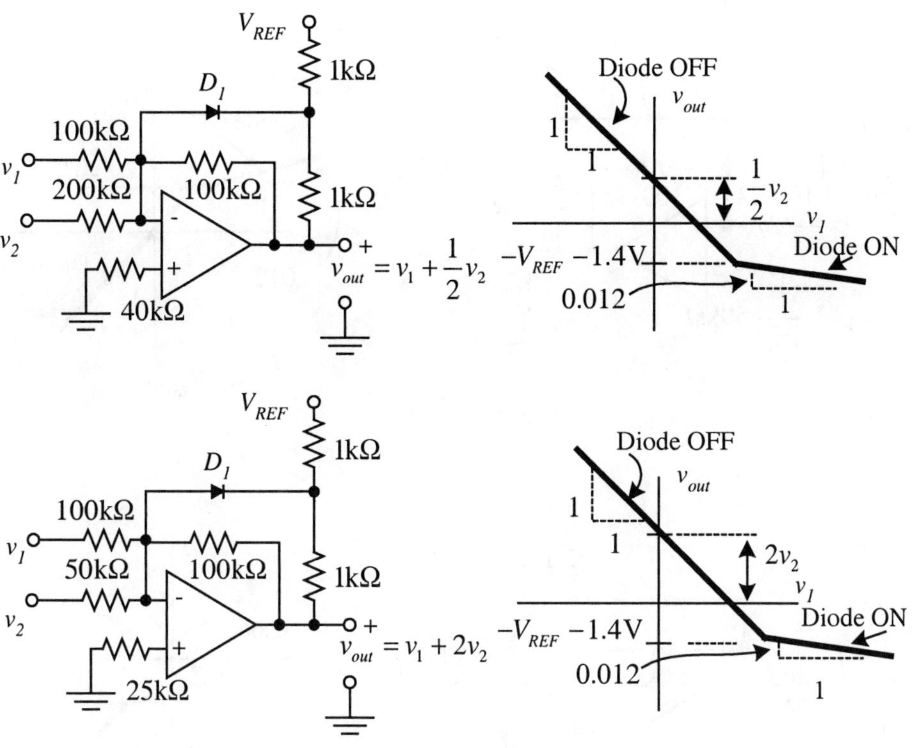

4. Summation and lower limit

Table 13.3 (parts 3 and 4) - Limiter configurations

V_{REF}
D_1
1kΩ
100kΩ
100kΩ
2kΩ
v_{in}
50kΩ
v_{out}
+
Diode OFF
v_{out}
1
1
v_{in}
$-2 \cdot V_{REF} - 2.1V$
Diode ON
0.012
1

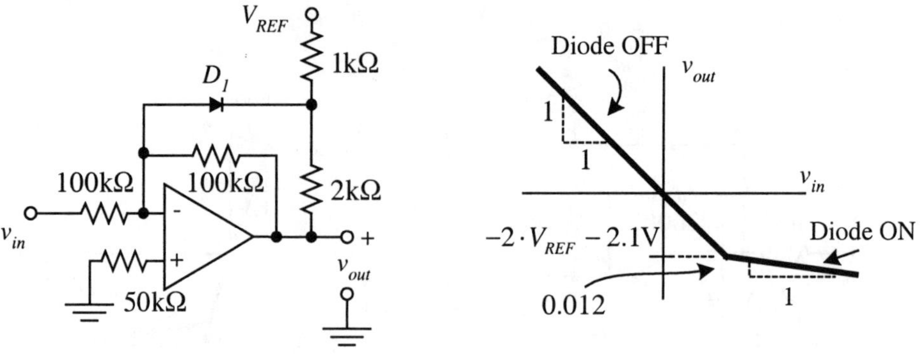

5. Unequal divider resistances

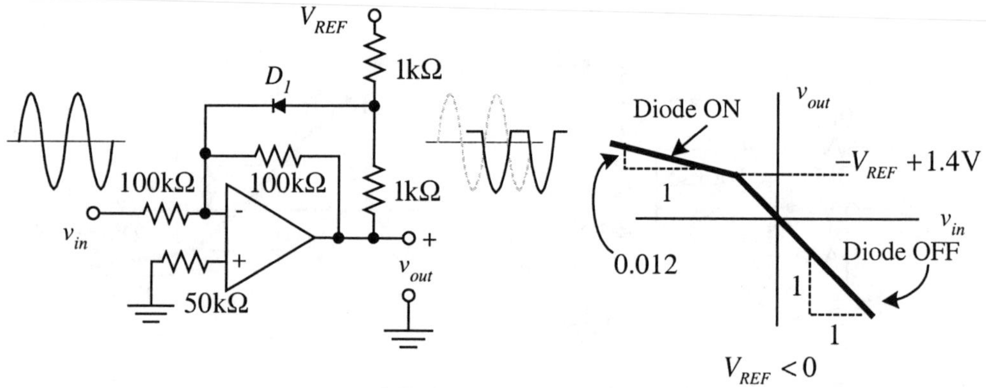

V_{REF}
D_1
1kΩ
100kΩ
100kΩ
1kΩ
v_{in}
50kΩ
v_{out}
+
Diode ON
v_{out}
$-V_{REF} + 1.4V$
1
v_{in}
0.012
Diode OFF
1
1
$V_{REF} < 0$

6. Basic upper limit

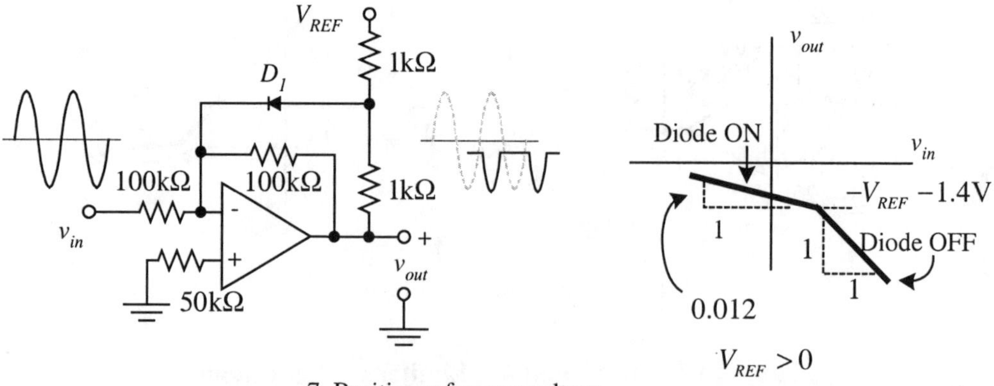

V_{REF}
D_1
1kΩ
100kΩ
100kΩ
1kΩ
v_{in}
50kΩ
v_{out}
+
v_{out}
Diode ON
v_{in}
$-V_{REF} - 1.4V$
1
1
Diode OFF
1
0.012
$V_{REF} > 0$

7. Positive reference voltage

Table 13.3 (parts 5, 6, and 7) - Limiter configurations

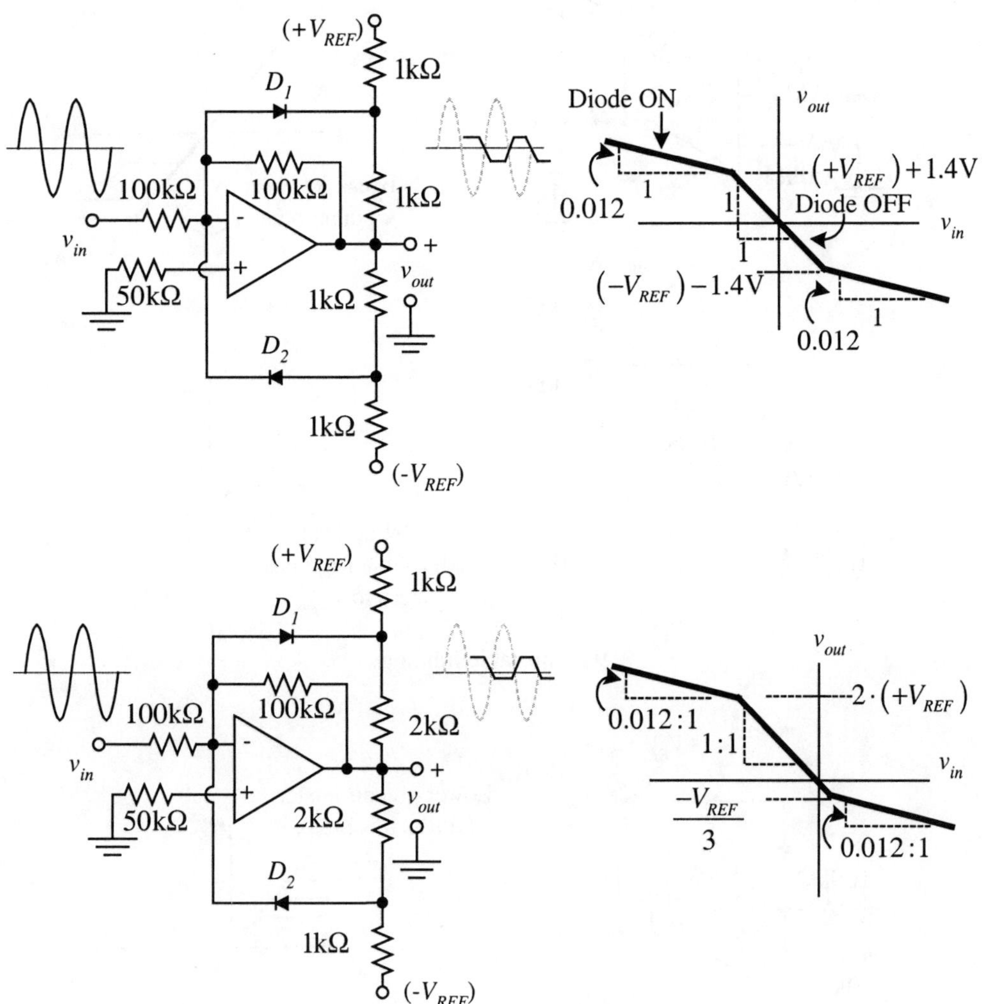

8. Upper and lower limiting

Table 13.3 (part 8) - Limiter configurations

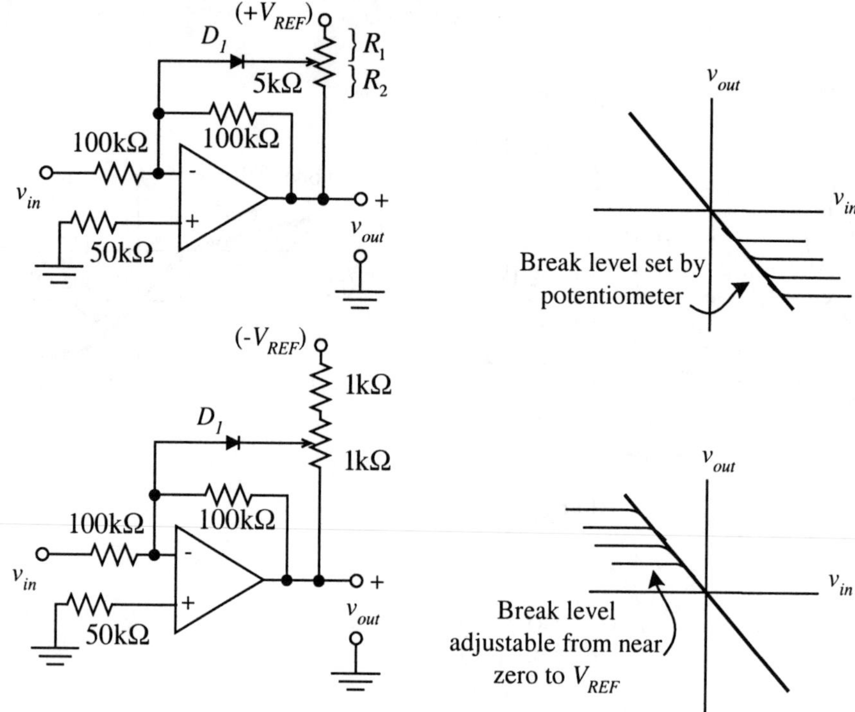

9. Adjustable limiting

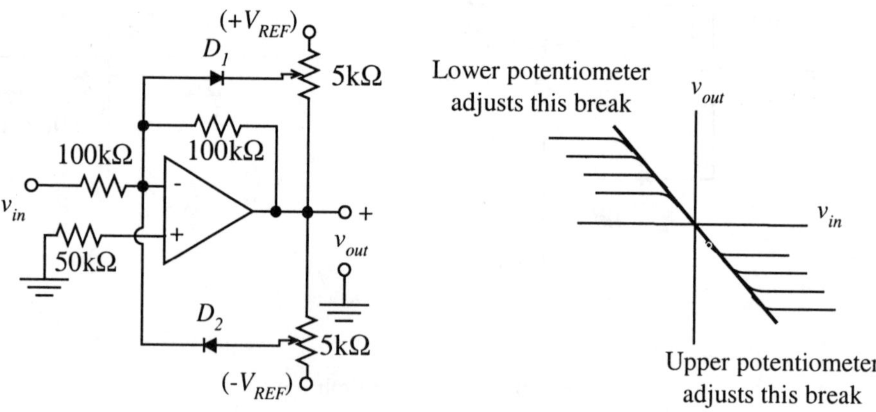

10. Upper and lower adjustable limiting

Table 13.3 (parts 9 and 10) - Limiter configurations

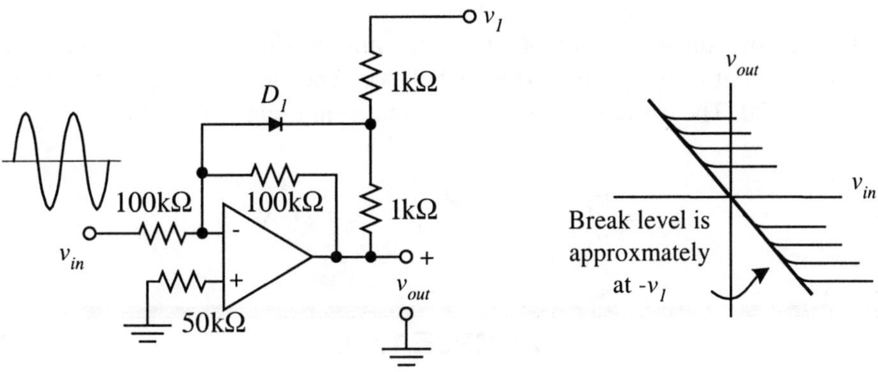

11. Voltage controlled limiting

Table 13.3 (part 11)- Limiter configurations

An important constraint in the design of limiters is that R_1 and R_2 be kept large enough to draw little current from the reference voltage source. A practical guideline is to limit the current from the reference voltage source to less than 1 mA. When two inputs are provided to a limiter as shown in Circuit 4 of Table 13.3, one input can be selected as the reference. The input voltage, v_{in}, will then be equal to the one input plus a fraction of the second input as shown, where $v_{in} = v_1 + 0.5v_2$. A *dc* reference voltage can also be added to the input of the limiter in order to shift the input-output characteristics.

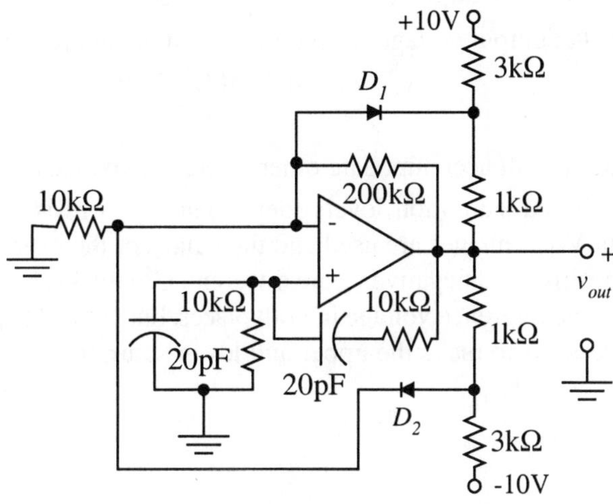

Figure 13.13 – Oscillator amplitude limiting

Figure 13.13 shows an application of a balanced limiter. Here we use a balanced limiter to provide amplitude control of a Wien bridge oscillator. The slope (R_2/R_A) in the range where limiting occurs is -20. The break voltage, V_{oc} is found from Equation (13.17).

$$V_{oc} = \frac{R_2}{R_1} \cdot 10 + \left(1 + \frac{R_2}{R_1}\right) \cdot 0.7 = 4.27 \text{ V} \tag{13.18}$$

EXAMPLE 13.3:

A feedback limiter, as shown in Figure 13.9, has $R_A = 10$ kΩ, $R_F = 20$ kΩ, $R_1 = 4$ kΩ, $R_2 = 2$ kΩ, $V_{REF} = 10$ V, $V_{ON} = 0.7$ V and $R_f = 50$ Ω. Determine where the characteristic of v_{out} vs. v_{in} changes slope and also find the slope in the saturation region (diode ON).

Solution: From the equations for the break point, Equation (13.17), we find $V_{oc} = -6.05$ and $V_{ic} = 3.02$. The slope is given by Equation (13.15) to be -0.21.

The circuits and v_{out} vs. v_{in} characteristics of selected additional limiter applications are sketched in Table 13.4, shown on the following two pages.

We now comment on these circuits. The TTL interface shown in Circuit 1 provides an output voltage of 4.23 V if v_{in} is negative, and 0 V if v_{in} is positive. The break voltage at v_I is calculated from Equation (13.14) to be $v_I = 4.93$ V.

Diode D_3 prevents the output voltage from going negative and reduces it to

$$v_{out} = v_I - 0.7 = 4.23 \text{ V}$$

Other values of R_1 and R_2 will accommodate other reference voltages.

Circuit 2 provides fixed saturation levels (dependent upon resistor and reference source values). Two different V_{REF} voltages are used and the values of the resistors are unequal, so the saturation levels for positive and negative v_{in} are different. Circuit 3 is a modification of Circuit 2 using the same magnitude reference voltage in both places, but with 5 kΩ potentiometers in place of the resistors. The result is to make the upper and lower saturation voltages variable.

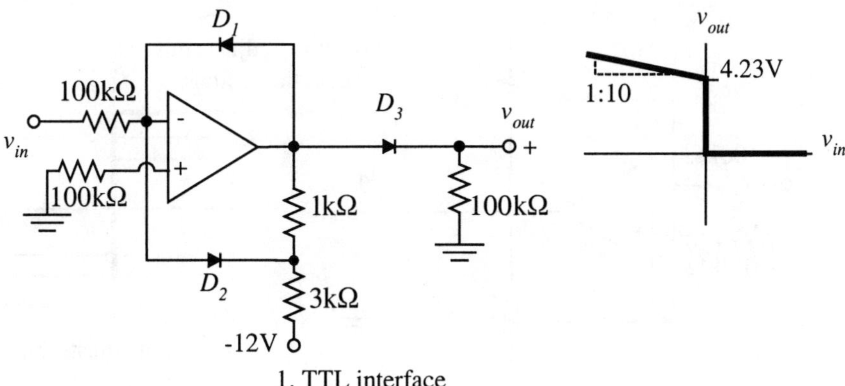

1. TTL interface

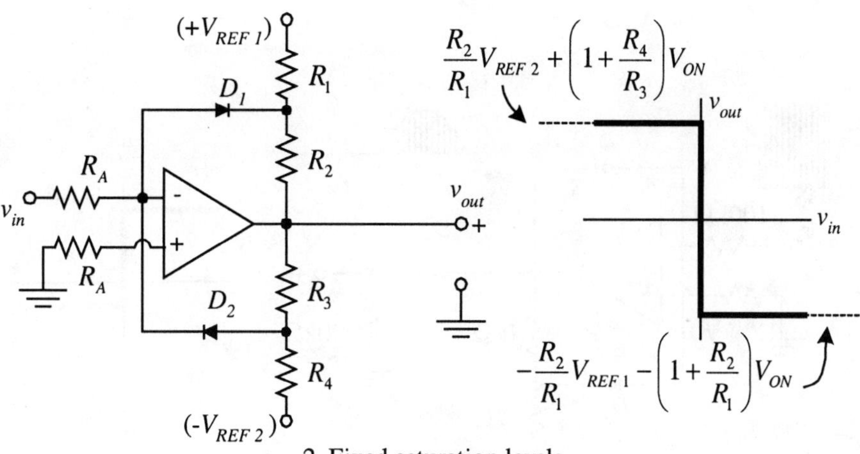

2. Fixed saturation levels

Table 13.4 (parts 1 and 2) – Limiter applications

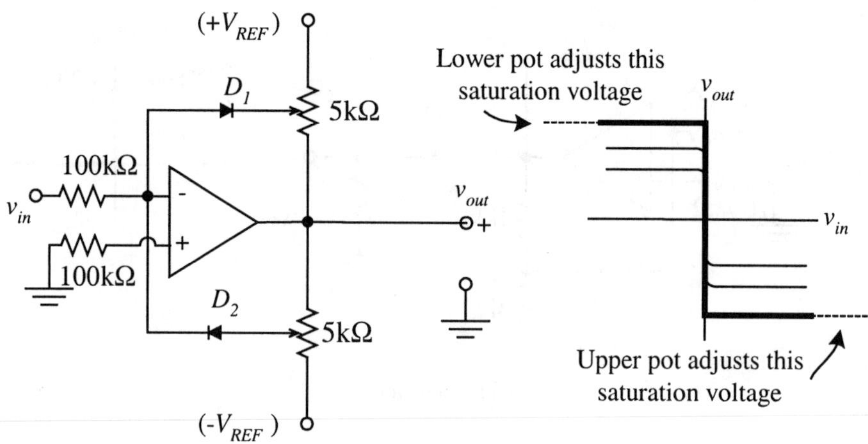

3. Adjustable saturation levels

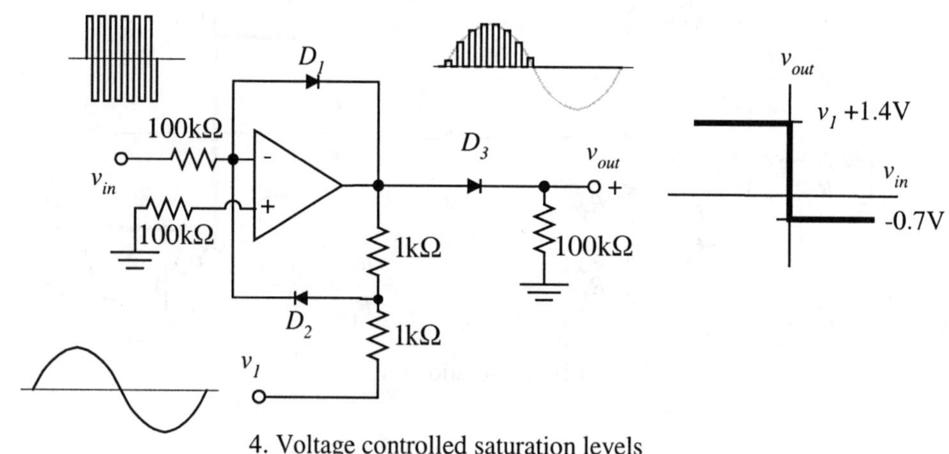

4. Voltage controlled saturation levels

Table 13.4 (parts 3 and 4) – Limiter applications

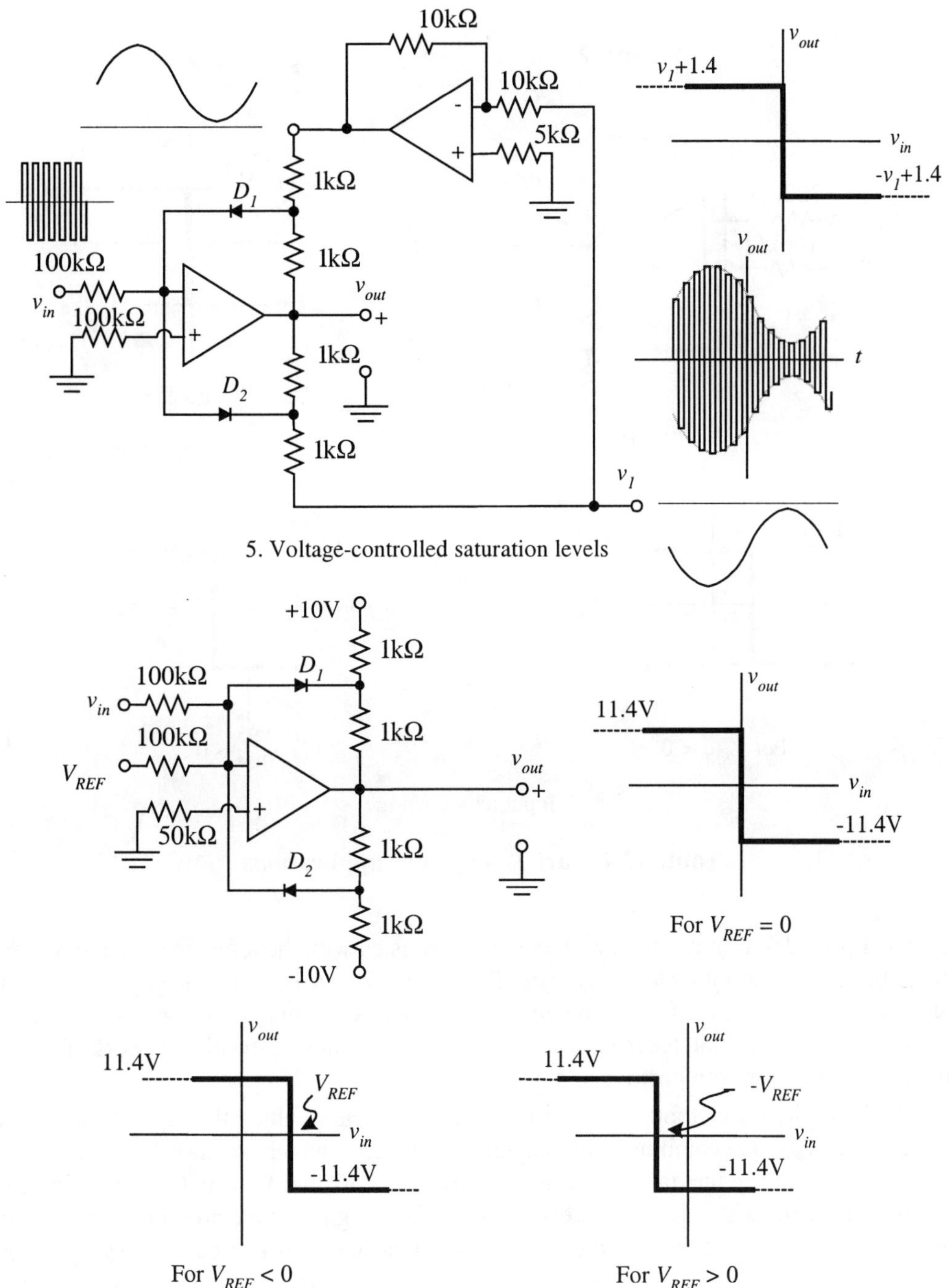

5. Voltage-controlled saturation levels

6. Input axis shifting

Table 13.4 (parts 5 and 6) – Limiter applications

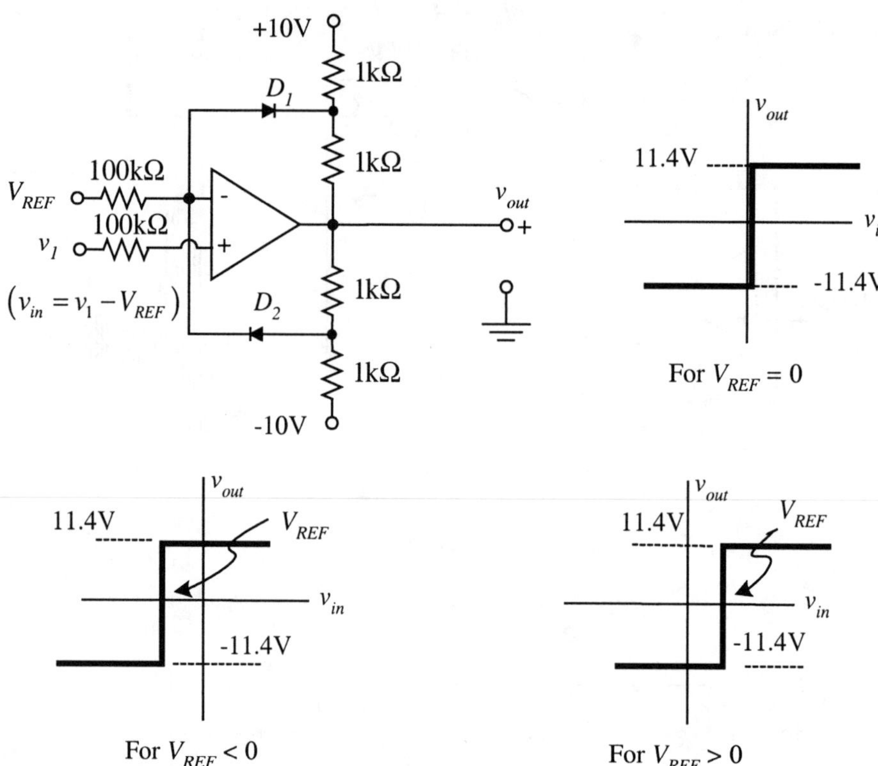

7. Input axis shifting

Table 13.4 (part 7) – Limiter applications

Circuit 4 provides a saturation level that can be adjusted with the reference voltage, v_1. As v_1 is varied, the output saturation level changes. The output voltage is determined by the ratio of the two 1 kΩ resistors. Circuit 5 behaves much like Circuit 4 except that the second op-amp inverts the reference voltage, v_1, and feeds v_2 (which is $-v_1$) to the top half of the bias network. The result is output saturation for both positive and negative values of v_{in}.

Circuit 6 provides a method of shifting the saturation curve along the input axis. The two voltages, v_1 and V_{REF}, are combined into one input voltage, v_{in} which equals $v_1 + V_{REF}$. The three curves show the shifting that takes place for $V_{REF} = 0$, $V_{REF}>0$, and $V_{REF}<0$. Circuit 7 provides a similar type of input-axis shifting. However, since v_1 is brought into the non- inverting terminal of the op-amp, the saturation curves are the mirror images of those of Circuit 6. The input signal is now $v_{in} = v_1 - V_{REF}$ and the saturation curves are shifted as shown for $V_{REF} = 0$, $V_{REF}>0$ and $V_{REF}<0$.

EXAMPLE 13.4:

Design a limiter which will provide limiting at $v_{out} = 6$ V with a gain of -4 and a slope in the saturation region of -1/25. Assume that $V_{REF} = 10$ V, $V_{ON} = 0.7$ V and $R_f = 100\ \Omega$.

Solution: The number of constraints is one less than the number of unknown component values. Let us select $R_A = 100\ \text{k}\Omega$. If this leads to unreasonable values of other components, we will return and revise our selection. We now solve for the other parameters. Since the gain is -4,

$$\frac{R_F}{R_A} = 4$$

$$R_F = 4R_A = 400\ \text{k}\Omega$$

$$V_{oc} = 6 = \frac{R_2 \cdot V_{REF}}{R_1} + \left(1 + \frac{R_2}{R_1}\right) V_{ON}$$

We solve this last equation to find

$$\frac{R_2}{R_1} = 0.495$$

which represents one equation in R_1 and R_2. The slope is -1/25. We obtain (from Figure 13.12),

$$-\frac{1}{25} = -\left(1 + \frac{R_2}{R_1}\right) \cdot \frac{R_1 \| R_2 + R_f}{R_A}$$

This is a second equation in R_1 and R_2, which we solve for the resistor values to find,

$$R_2 = 3.85\ \text{k}\Omega \qquad R_1 = 7.78\ \text{k}\Omega$$

The final circuit is of the type shown in Table 13.3 for "Upper and Lower Limiting" (Circuit 8).

EXAMPLE 13.5

Design a feedback limiter to provide the transfer characteristics as shown in Figure 13.14(a). Assume $V_{REF} = 10$ V, $R_f = 100\ \Omega$ and $V_{ON} = 0.7$ V.

Solution: This is a balanced limiter so we will solve for R_1 and R_2 and use these same values for R_3 and R_4.

When the diodes are off, the gain is

$$\frac{R_F}{R_A} = 2, \qquad \text{so let } R_A = 200\ \text{k}\Omega \quad R_F = 400\ \text{k}\Omega$$

We substitute values into Equation (13.17) to obtain,

$$V_{ic} = -\frac{200\ \text{k}\Omega}{400\ \text{k}\Omega}\left[\frac{R_2}{R_1}(10) + \left(1 + \frac{R_2}{R_1}\right)0.7\right] = -3.5$$

$$\frac{R_2}{R_1} = 0.589$$

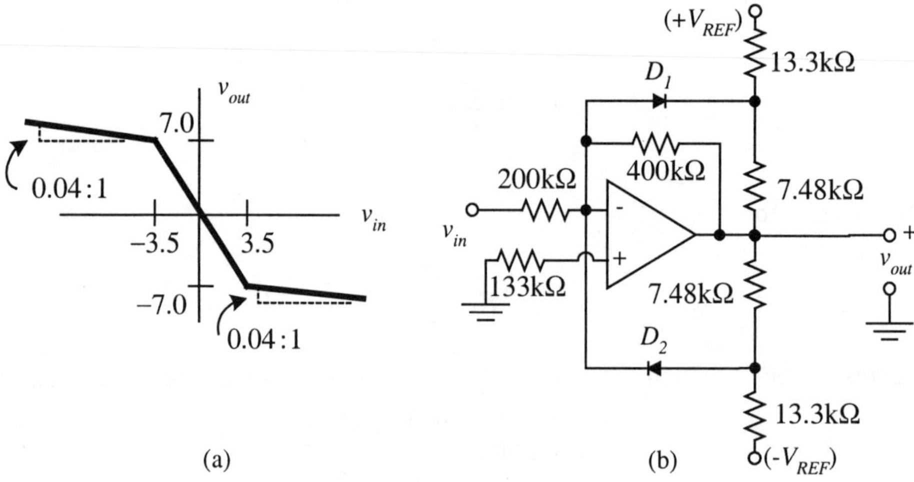

Fig. 13.14 - Characteristics and solution for Example 13.5

When the diodes are on, the slope is given by Equation (13.15) and we obtain,

$$0.04 = \frac{1}{200\ \text{k}\Omega}\left[1.589\left(\frac{R_2}{1 + 0.589} + 100\right)\right]$$

We solve this to find $R_2 = 7.84\ \text{k}\Omega$ and $R_1 = 13.3\ \text{k}\Omega$. The complete circuit is shown in Figure 13.14(b).

EXERCISES

E13.5 Design op-amp circuits with the approximate transfer characteristics shown in Figures E13.5 and E13.6. Available reference supply voltages are ± 10 V. Op-amp supply voltages are ± 15 V. Assume that V_{ON} = 0.7 V. The solutions are shown on the figures.

E13.6 Find approximate relationships between the input voltage, v_I, and the output voltage, v_{out}, for the circuits shown in Figures E13.7 and E13.8. Assume that V_{ON} = 0.7 V. The solutions are shown on the figures.

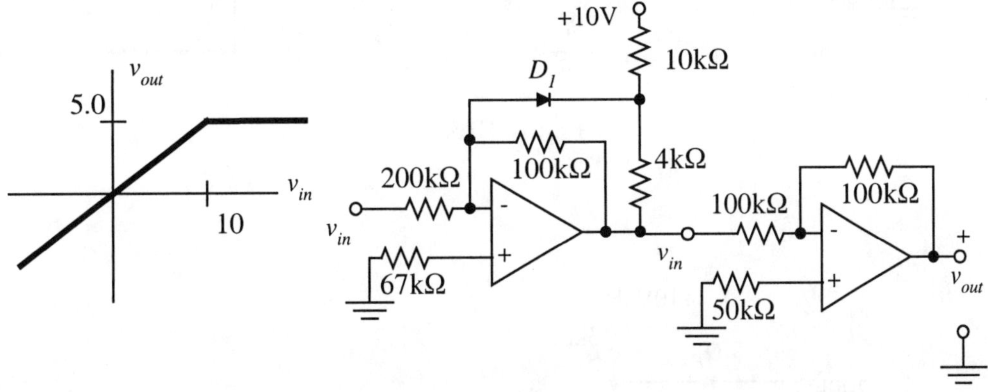

Figure E13.5

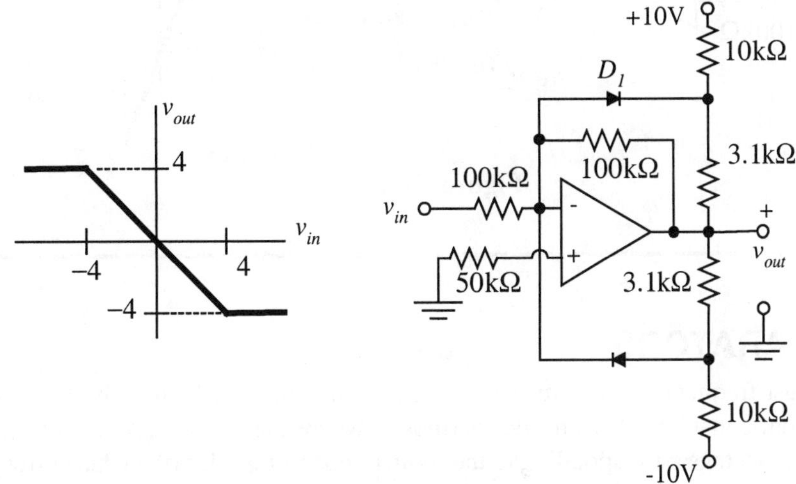

Figure E13.6

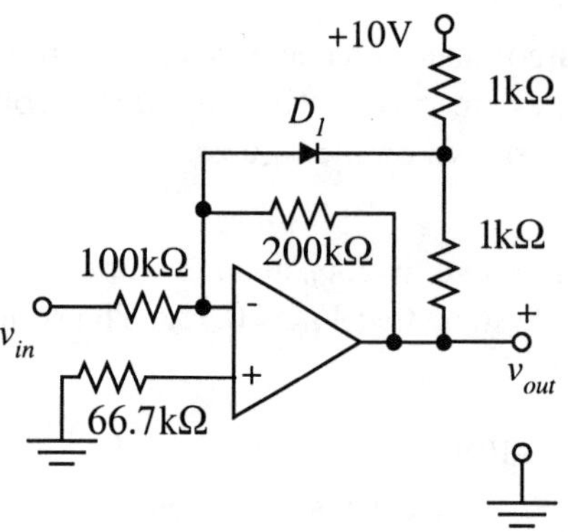

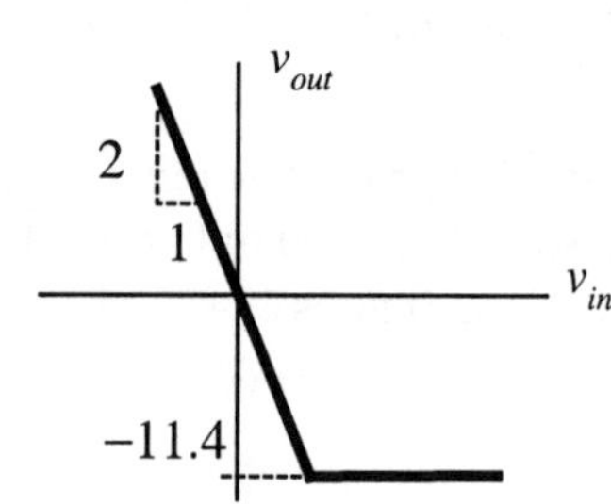

Figure E13.7

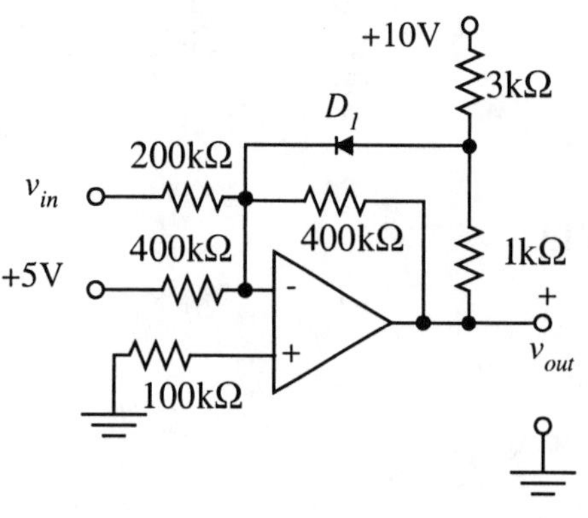

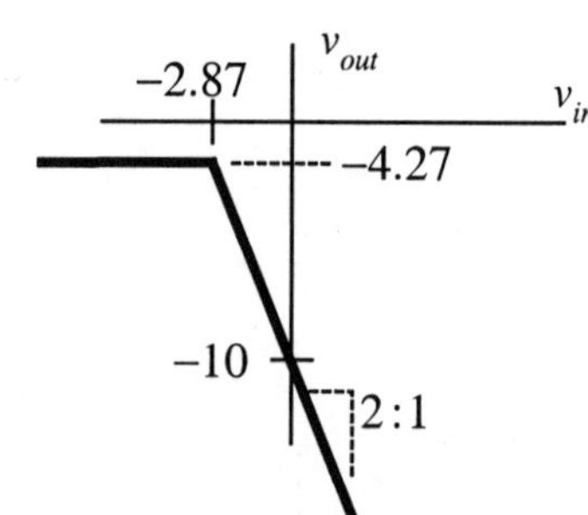

Figure E13.8

13.3 COMPARATORS

Designers must frequently compare two voltages to determine which is the larger. As one simple application, consider an electronic thermostat where the temperature is converted to a voltage. When the voltage corresponding to the room temperature is less than that corresponding to the desired temperature (i.e., the setting of the thermostat), the system should produce a signal that turns on the heater. As a more complex application, consider one form of digital communication called *delta modulation*. It requires that a continuous time signal be replaced by a staircase approximation. At each sampling point, the decision of whether the approximation should step up or step down is based on a comparison of the staircase approximation with the original continuous function.

Feedback control systems usually operate on the difference between two signals (inverting and non-inverting). Comparators are ideally suited to these applications.

The output of the comparator in Figure 13.15(a) is positive when the circuit voltage, v_{in}, is greater than V_{REF} and negative when v_{in} is less than V_{REF}. If the gain of the circuit is large, the output saturates. That is, as soon as v_{in} becomes slightly above V_{REF}, the output rapidly changes to the positive supply voltage. Likewise, the voltage saturates at the negative supply voltage for any value of v_{in} less than V_{REF}. Thus, the output takes on only one of two possible values: positive or negative.

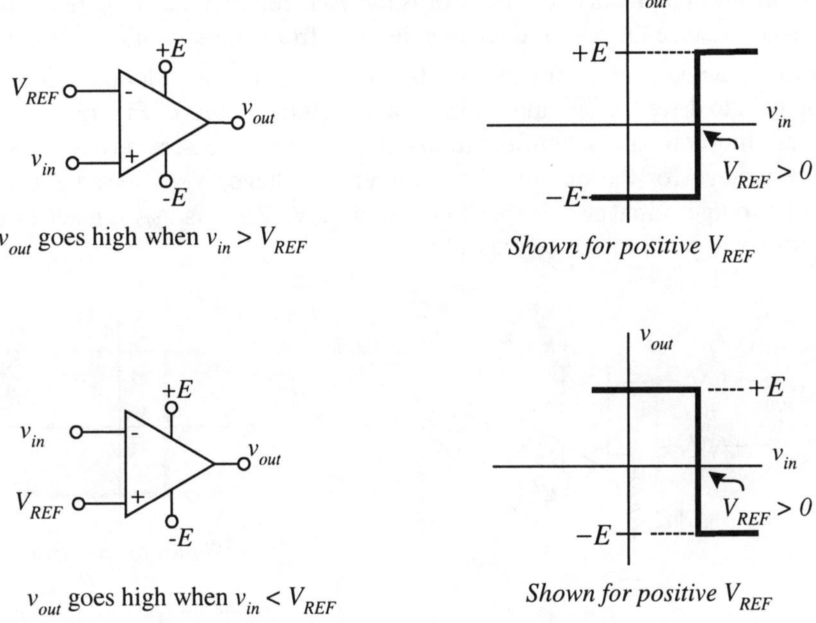

Figure 13.15 – Saturation Comparator

When the input is varying around V_{REF}, transitions occur in the output whenever v_{in} crosses the V_{REF} axis. That is, at one instant, v_{in} might be less than V_{REF} while at the next instant, the reverse is true. Ideally, the output should instantaneously jump from its positive saturation value to its negative value. In practice, a small amount of response time is required due to capacitive effects in the circuit. A typical value of this response time is a few microseconds. For example, the μA741 switches in about 40 μs.

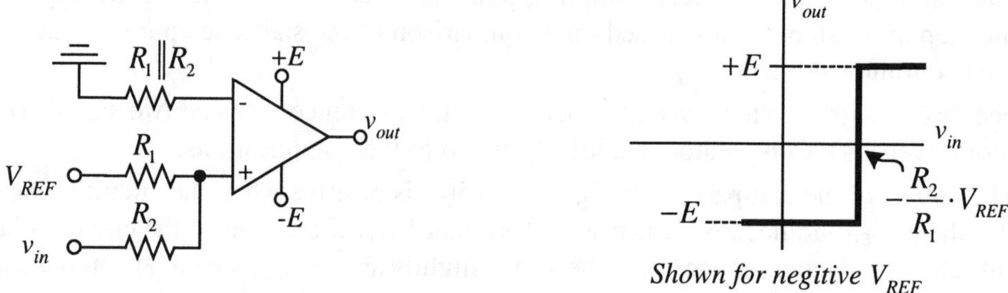

Figure 13.16 – Variable crossover comparator

The *accuracy* of a practical comparator is the voltage difference required between the input and reference to cause the output to change its state from one saturation value to the other.

Saturation comparators, which utilize the op-amp in the open-loop mode, depend on high open-loop gain to drive the op-amp into saturation. Both circuits of Figure 13.15 have op-amps used in saturating comparator configurations. In both of these cases, the op-amp saturates at $\pm E$, the supply voltage for the op-amp. The reference voltage, V_{REF}, may be either positive or negative. The output-input curves are shown for positive V_{REF}. As V_{REF} is made more positive, the $v_{out} = 0$ crossover point moves to the right.

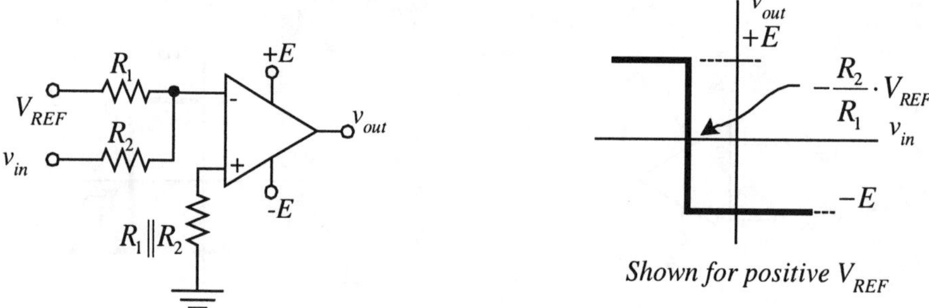

Figure 13.17 – Variable crossover comparator

Figures 13.16 and 13.17 show other comparator configurations that can be used to vary the *crossover* voltage, and the shape of the curves.

Again, either polarity of V_{REF} may be used. The output-input curve of Figure 13.16 is for $V_{REF} < 0$. v_{out} is high when

$$\frac{V_{REF}}{R_1} + \frac{v_{in}}{R_2} > 0 \tag{13.19}$$

or

$$v_{in} > -\frac{R_2}{R_1} \cdot V_{REF}$$

In Figure 13.17, $V_{REF} > 0$ and v_{out} is high when

$$\frac{V_{REF}}{R_1} + \frac{v_{in}}{R_2} < 0 \tag{13.20}$$

or

$$v_{in} < -\frac{R_2}{R_1} V_{REF}$$

A *limiting comparator* is formed with a diode as the feedback element, as shown in Figure 13.18(a). When the diode is open-circuited, the lack of feedback causes the op-amp to operate in the open-loop mode, and to saturate for negative input voltages.

$$v_{out} = E = V_{REF} \tag{13.21}$$

As v_{in} increases, the diode forward-biases (turns on). This happens when v_{in} exceeds (V_{REF} + V_{ON}).

To find the equation for the saturation curve when the diode is conducting, we refer to Section 13.2 where we use Equation (13.15) for a limiter. In this equation, we let R_F approach infinity, $R_f \ll R_1 \| R_2$, and $V_{ON} = 0$. This results in

$$v_{out} = -\frac{R_2}{R_A} \cdot v_{in} - \frac{R_2}{R_1} \cdot V_{REF} \tag{13.22}$$

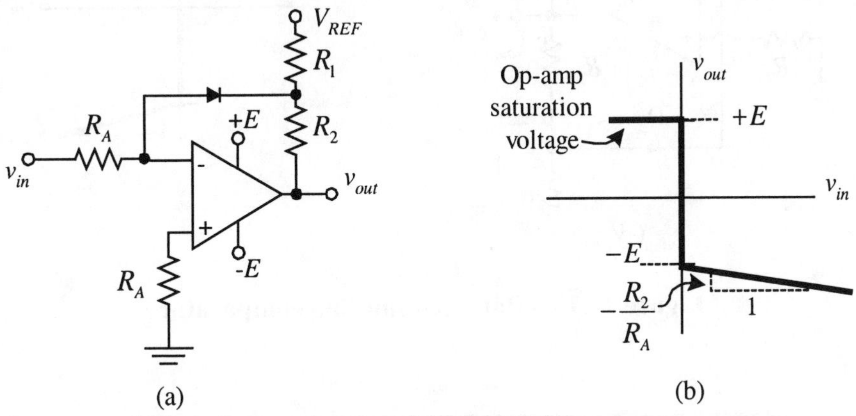

(a) (b)

Figure 13.18 – Limiting comparator

This is the output voltage, v_{out}, as a function of the input voltage and the reference voltage. The slope of the curve, for positive input voltage, is given by

$$\frac{v_{out}}{v_{in}} = -\frac{R_2}{R_A} \tag{13.23}$$

The transfer characteristics for Equation (13.22) are shown in Figure 13.18(b).

Note that the output voltage for an input of $v_{in} = V_{REF}$ is found from Equation (13.22) to be

$$-R_2 \cdot V_{REF} \cdot \left(\frac{1}{R_A} + \frac{1}{R_1} \right) \tag{13.24}$$

The limiter described here is not *balanced* since the switching transfer characteristics are not symmetrical. We can modify the circuit to provide for balanced operation. The transfer characteristic for the resulting balanced positive and negative limiter is shown in Figure 13.19. The analysis is performed in a manner similar to that used for the unbalanced limiter. The circuit is a special case of entry 2 in Table 13.4.

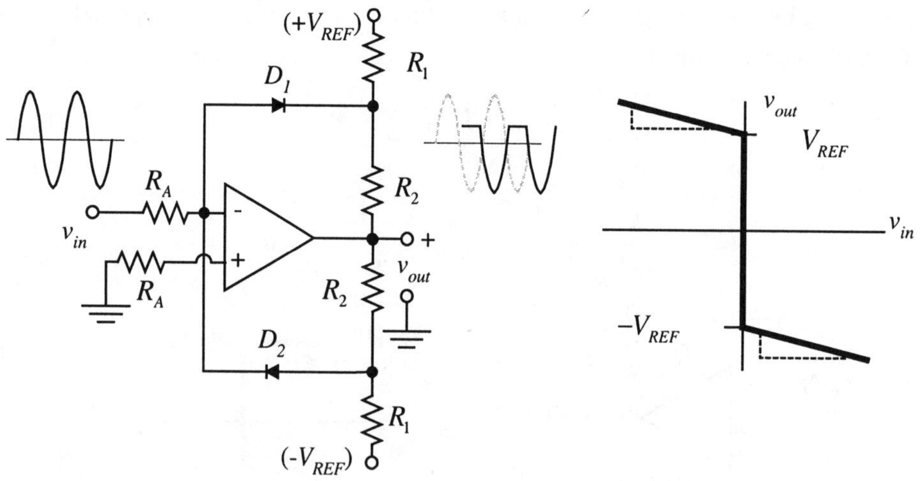

Figure 13.19 – Balanced limiting comparator

EXAMPLE 13.6:

Design a balanced limiting comparator of the type shown in Figure 13.19 with limiting required at 8 V and the slope of the limited part of the characteristic to be -1/20. Assume that $V_{REF} = \pm 10$ V, $R_A = 50$ kΩ, $V_{ON} = 0.7$ V and $R_f = 100$ Ω. The gain in the non-limited region is -10.

Solution: We have one equation in two unknowns. The second equation comes from the given slope in the limited region (-1/20 in this example). From Equation (13.15), we solve for the two resistor values with the result

$$R_2 = 2.33\ \text{k}\Omega; \qquad R_1 = 3.42\ \text{k}\Omega$$

This completes the design.

13.4 SCHMITT TRIGGERS

One class of comparator, known as the *Schmitt trigger*, uses positive feedback to speed up the switching cycle. With positive feedback, a small change in the input is amplified and fed back in phase. This reinforces the input signal, thereby leading to larger and more rapid changes. The feedback increases the gain and steepens the transition between the two output levels. Positive feedback holds a comparator in one of the two saturation states unless a sufficiently large input is applied to overcome the feedback.

Figure 13.20(a) illustrates one form of Schmitt trigger where a reference voltage of zero volts is implied (since $v_- = 0$). We now develop the characteristic curves. We start with v_{in} as a large positive voltage. This causes the output voltage, v_{out}, to be at $+E$, the op-amp saturation voltage. The non-inverting voltage, v_+, is found by writing a node equation at the v_+ node as follows:

$$\frac{v_+ - v_{in}}{R_1} + \frac{v_+ - v_{out}}{R_2} = 0 \qquad (13.25)$$

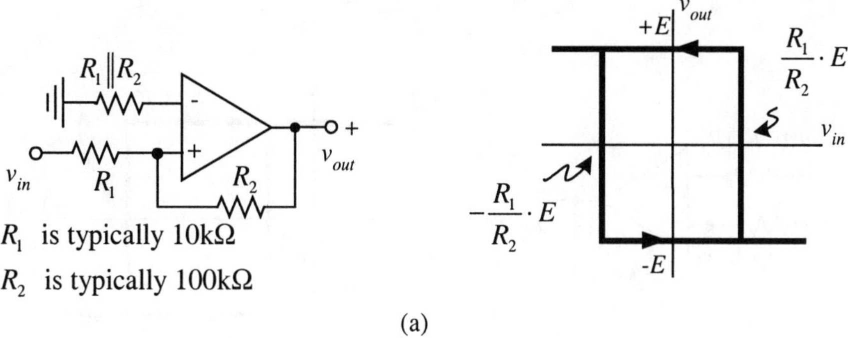

Figure 13.20 (part a) – Schmitt trigger

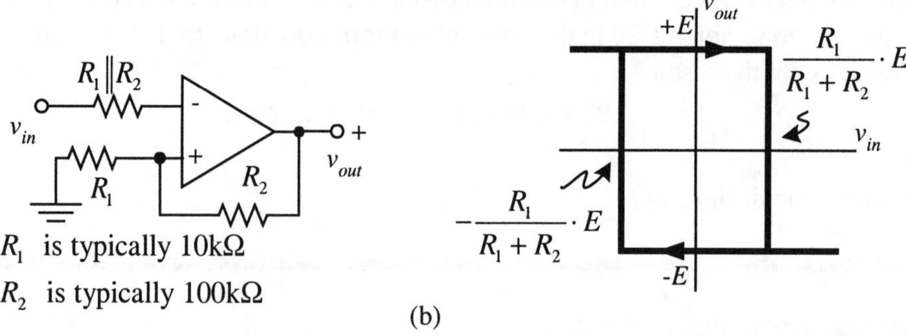

(b)

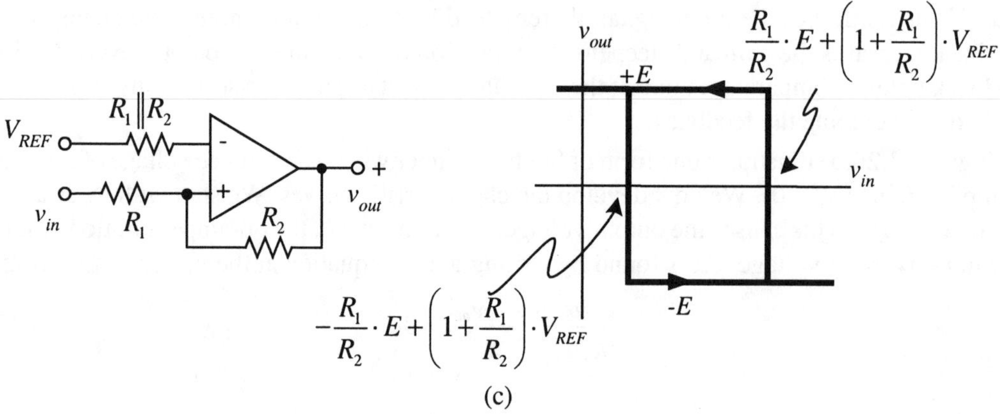

(c)

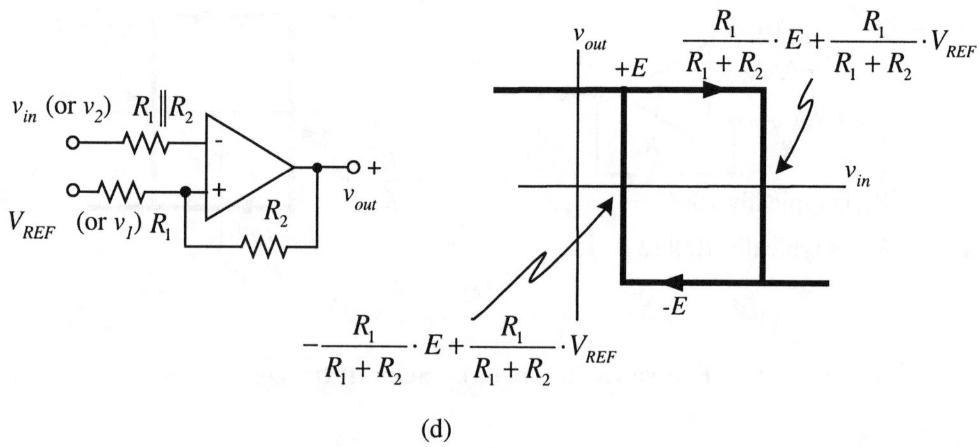

(d)

Figure 13.20 (parts b, c and d) – Schmitt trigger

Then

$$v_+ \cdot \left(\frac{1}{R_1} + \frac{1}{R_2} \right) = \frac{v_{in}}{R_1} + \frac{v_{out}}{R_2} \tag{13.26}$$

Now let's start reducing the magnitude of v_{in} to find the switching point. Since $v_- = 0$ and $v_+ = v_-$ (once the op-amp comes out of saturation), we set Equation (13.26) to zero to obtain

$$v_{in} = \frac{-R_1 v_{out}}{R_2} = \frac{-R_1 E}{R_2} \tag{13.27}$$

As v_{in} is further reduced, the output voltage, v_{out}, is switched from $+E$ to $-E$. Switching takes place at the point where v_+ goes to zero. This happens when v_{in} reaches $-R_1E/R_2$. As the input voltage, v_{in}, is reduced further, v_{out} remains at $-E$.

If we now increase the input voltage from a large negative value, the output voltage switches to $+E$ when $v_+ = 0 = v_-$. Hence the switching takes place at

$$v_{in} = \frac{-R_1 v_{out}}{R_2} = \frac{-R_1(-E)}{R_2} = \frac{R_1 E}{R_2} \tag{13.28}$$

v_{out} remains at $+E$ as v_{in} is further increased past $+R_1E/R_2$.

The loop shown in the characteristic curve of Figure 13.20(a) is a form of *hysteresis*. This word is used to describe a situation where the system has *memory*. That is, the output at any particular time does not depend only on the present value of the input, but also on past values. For example, there are two possible values of v_{out} for an input voltage of $v_{in} = 0$. Which value applies depends on the *direction* in which we approach $v_{in} = 0$.

This observation about hysteresis indicates one important application of the Schmitt trigger. This circuit can be used as a *binary memory device*. That is, since the output depends on past values of the input, we can apply a voltage to the input and then remove that voltage. The trigger circuit *remembers* whether the voltage was above or below the reference level. We can therefore *write* one of two possible values into this memory.

A second important application of the Schmitt trigger is as a square-wave generator. A continuous signal at the input (e.g., a sine wave) produces an output that rapidly jumps back and forth between two levels. The jump occurs as the input moves across the reference level. In this manner, a pulse-type waveform can be generated from a continuous sinusoidal input.

The inverting Schmitt trigger of Figure 13.20(b) interchanges the ground and the input voltages at the op-amp input. It is analyzed in a manner similar to that used above. The switching point is found from the equations,

$$v_- = v_{in}$$

$$v_+ = \frac{R_1 v_{out}}{R_1 + R_2} \tag{13.29}$$

The circuit switches state when the two voltages are equal, that is, when

$$v_{in} = \frac{R_1 v_{out}}{R_1 + R_2} \tag{13.30}$$

When $v_{out} = +E$ and v_{in} is increasing from a large negative voltage toward a positive voltage, the switching point occurs at

$$v_{in} = \frac{R_1 v_{out}}{R_1 + R_2} = \frac{R_1 E}{R_1 + R_2} \tag{13.31}$$

If $v_{out} = -E$ and v_{in} is decreasing from a large positive voltage toward a negative voltage, the switching point occurs at

$$v_{in} = \frac{-R_1 E}{R_1 + R_2} \tag{13.32}$$

The circuit of Figure 13.20(c) replaces the ground of the v_+ input of Figure 13.20(b) with a reference voltage, V_{REF}. The second voltage, v_{in}, is the input voltage. The equations are derived in the same manner as those above, and are included along with the hysteresis curve on the figure. Note that the entire characteristic is shifted to the right so it is no longer symmetrical about the origin. (We hope you will take the time to verify these results before continuing.)

The circuit of Figure 13.20(c) can be viewed in a different manner when v_{in} is the reference and V_{REF} is the input. This then represents a variation of the circuit of Figure 13.20(a) where the ground input to v_- is replaced by the v_{in} . The resulting curve is shown in Figure 13.20(d).

The algebraic sign of the following expression determines the switching for this Schmitt trigger.

$$\frac{R_2}{R_1 + R_2} \cdot v_1 + \frac{R_1}{R_1 + R_2} \cdot v_{out} - v_2 \tag{13.33}$$

This expression allows us to determine the $v_{out} = 0$ crossings shown on the output-input curves.

EXAMPLE 13.7:

Determine the output voltage for the Schmitt trigger of Figure 13.20(a) if the input voltage is

$$v_{in} = 20 \cdot \sin(200\pi t)$$

$$E = 5\text{ V},\ R_1 = 20\text{ k}\Omega \text{ and } R_2 = 100\text{ k}\Omega$$

Solution: The hysteresis curve for these values is plotted in Figure 13.21(a). When an input sinusoid, $v_{in} = 20\sin(200\pi t)$, is applied to the Schmitt trigger of Figure 13.20(a), a square wave results. Figure 13.21(b) shows the input sinusoid (shown as a solid line) and the output pulse train (shown as a dashed line). The peak-to-peak voltage is 10 V and the zero crossings of the square wave are offset slightly from the zero crossings of the sine wave because of the hysteresis loop of Figure 13.21(a).

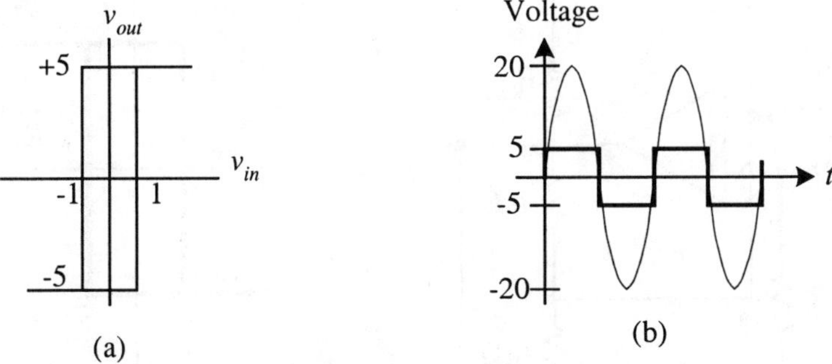

Figure 13.21 - Schmitt trigger output for Example 13.7

13.4.1 Schmitt Triggers with Limiters

The limiting comparator, which we studied in Section 13.3, can be used in conjunction with any of the Schmitt triggers of Figure 13.20. In so doing, the op-amp saturation voltage, E, (which is not very precise) is replaced with an accurate voltage, V_{REF}.

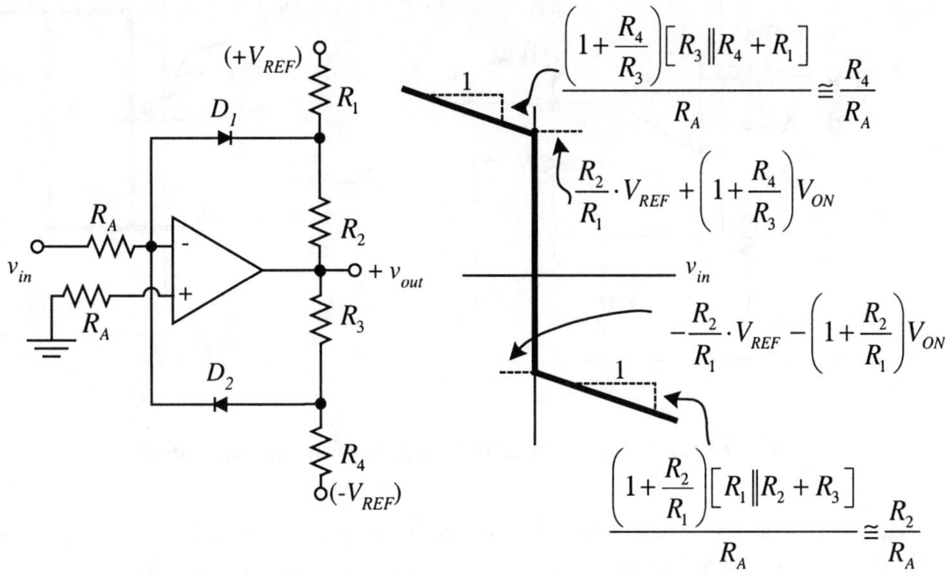

Figure 13.22 – Unbalanced limiting comparator

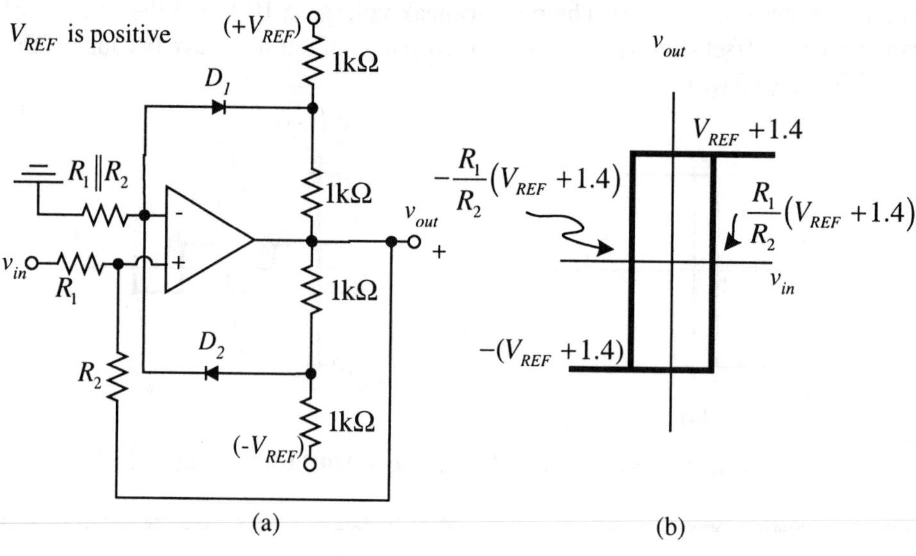

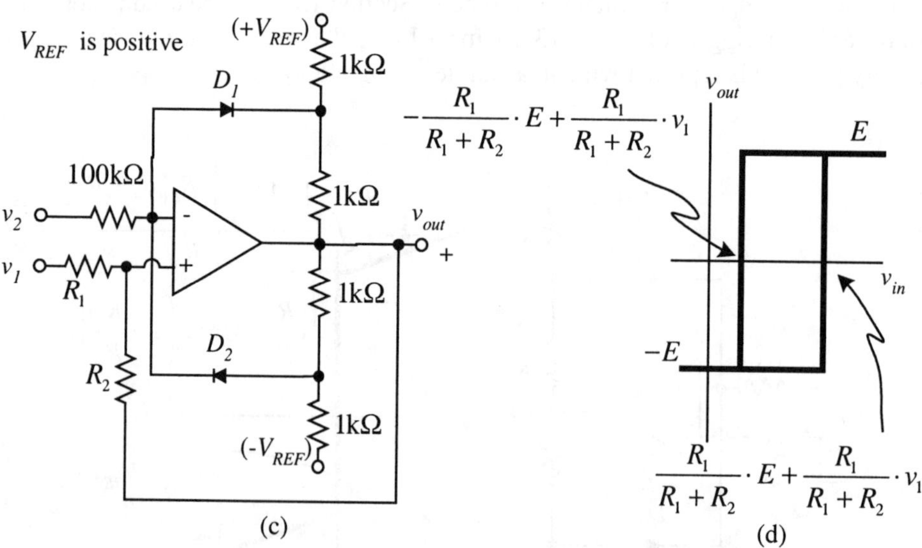

Figure 13.23 – Schmitt trigger with limited values

Figure 13.22(a) illustrates an unbalanced limiting comparator. This is the same as entry 2 of Table 13.4 with equal reference voltage magnitudes. The diode, D_1, controls the lower saturation point and D_2 controls the upper saturation point. The resulting characteristic curve is shown in Figure 13.22(b).

The saturation voltages, E, are replaced with the limiting voltages shown on the figure.

As an example of the use of a limiter with a Schmitt trigger, consider the circuit of Figure

13.23(a). We have combined the Schmitt trigger of Figure 13.20(a) with a balanced limiting comparator.

This circuit uses positive feedback to achieve the faster switching action. The operation follows the hysteresis loop for a Schmitt trigger, but with the limits of the voltage output curve determined by V_{REF}.

When a *dc* voltage is placed at one input of a Schmitt trigger, it causes the hysteresis loop to move along the v_{in} axis. This is shown in Figure 13.23(c) where we have used the circuit of Figure 13.20(c) for the Schmitt trigger. v_1 is usually a *dc* reference voltage (i.e., $v_1 = V_{dc}$) and $v_2 = v_{in}$.

The $v_{out} = 0$ intersections are found using Kirchhoff's laws to be [see the equations on Figure 13.20(c)]:

On the right:

$$v_{in} = \frac{R_2 V_{dc}}{R_1 + R_2} + \frac{R_1 E}{R_1 + R_2} \tag{13.34}$$

On the left:

$$v_2 = \frac{R_2 V_{dc}}{R_1 + R_2} - \frac{R_1 E}{R_1 + R_2} \tag{13.35}$$

EXAMPLE 13.8:

Design an unbalanced limiting comparator of the type shown in Figure 13.22. Limiting should occur at +6 V and -4 V with the slope of the limiting characteristic as -1/25. Assume $V_{REF} = 10$ V, $R_A = 50$ kΩ, $V_{ON} = 0.7$ V and $R_f = 100$ Ω.

Solution: We find V_{oc} from Equation (13.17) with $V_{oc} = +6$ V.

$$\frac{R_2}{R_1} = 0.495$$

The slope requirement provides us with the second equation in R_1 and R_2. From the *ac* gain Equation (13.15), we obtain

$$R_2 = 1.85\ \text{k}\Omega; \qquad R_1 = 3.74\ \text{k}\Omega$$

Note that this first part of the design parallels that of Example 13.4. We now solve for the remaining two resistors. Again, from Equation (13.17), we let $V_{oc} = -4$ V and find $R_4/R_3 = 0.308$. We equate the slope to -1/25 and, using Equation (13.15) solve for the resistors.

$$R_4 = 1.87\ \text{k}\Omega; \qquad R_3 = 6.07\ \text{k}\Omega$$

EXAMPLE 13.9

Design a Schmitt trigger that will operate according to the v_{out}/v_{in} characteristic curve that is shown in Figure 13.24. Assume that a ± 10 V precision reference voltage is available.

Solution: We first shift the hysteresis loop to have symmetrical voltage swings, as shown in Figure 13.25. We use the Schmitt trigger shown in Figure 13.20(d) with $v_1 = E$ and $v_2 = v_{in}$. The values of R'_1 and R'_2 are calculated as follows (see Figure 13.20(d)). Setting the left edge of the hysteresis loop at $v_{in} = 0$, we have

$$\frac{-R'_1}{R'_2} E + \left(1 + \frac{R'_1}{R'_2}\right) v_2 = 0$$

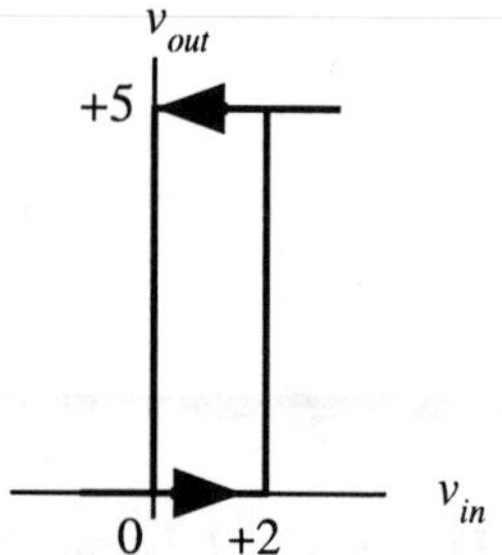

Figure 13.24 – Characteristic curve for Example 13.9

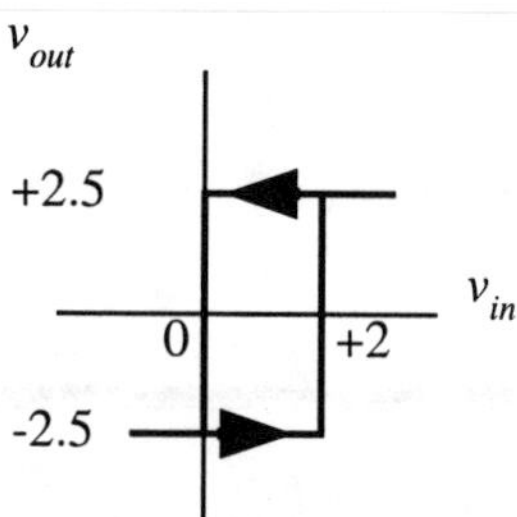

Figure 13.25 – Hysteresis loop for Example 13.9

The center of the hysteresis loop falls at $v_{in} = 1$, so from Figure 13.20(d), we have

$$\left(1 + \frac{R'_1}{R'_2}\right) \cdot v_2 = 1$$

Combining these equations and recognizing $E = 2.5$ V, we obtain

$$\frac{R'_1}{R'_2} E = 1 = \frac{R'_1}{R'_2}(2.5)$$

so

$$R'_2 = 2.5 \cdot R'_1$$

Now from the first equation we have

$$\left(1+\frac{R'_1}{R'_2}\right)v_2=\left(1+\frac{1}{2.5}\right)v_2=1$$

$$v_2=0.71 \text{ V}$$

If we set R'_1 to 100 kΩ, then $R'_2 = 250$ kΩ. The resulting design is shown in Figure 13.26.

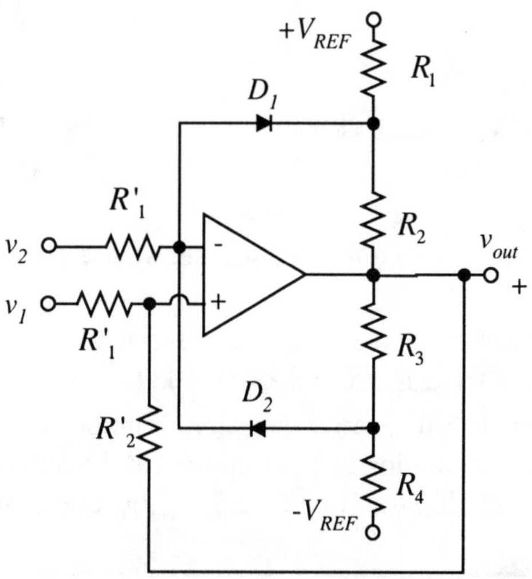

Figure 13.26 – Circuit for Schmitt trigger

We now design the limiter by referring to Figure 13.22. To establish the horizontal portions of the hysteresis loop, we set the slope, $R_4/R'_1 \approx 0$. Then $R_4 \ll R'_1$.

We find the value of V_{REF} from the equation,

$$\frac{R_4}{R_3}V_{REF}+\left(1+\frac{R_4}{R_3}\right)V_{ON}=2.5 \text{ V}$$

We have more unknowns than equations, so we are free to choose some of the unknown variables. Suppose we let $R_1 = R_2 = R_3 = R_4$. Let us choose 5 kΩ for these resistor values (we do not want to choose too high a value since this would require an excessively large R_1'). We then have,

$$V_{REF} = 2.5 - 1.4 = 1.1 \text{ V}$$

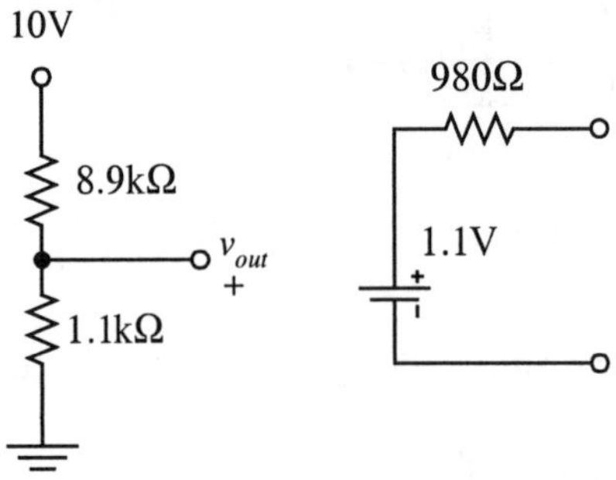

Figure 13.27 – Voltage divider

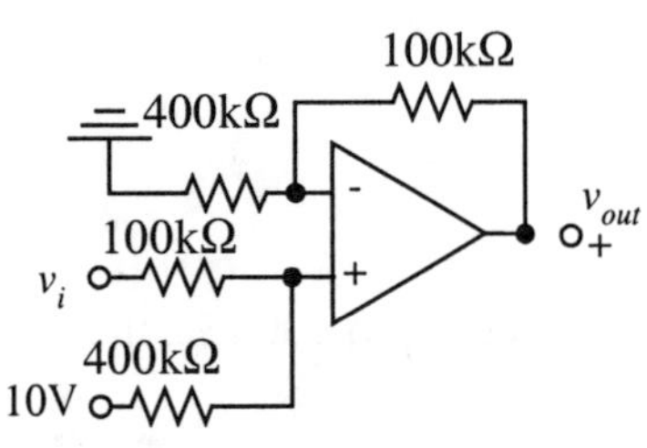

Figure 13.28 – Additional op-amp circuit for level shift

Since we have a ± 10 V precision reference source, we use a voltage divider to obtain V_{REF} as shown in Figure 13.27.

The equivalent resistor of the voltage divider is in series with the sources, so it adds to R_1 and R_3. Hence, we must reduce R_1 and R_3 from 5 kΩ to 5 kΩ - 980 Ω, so $R_1 = R_3 = 4020\ \Omega$.

Finally, we perform a level shift to move the v_{out}/v_{in} relationship up by +2.5 V, as specified in Figure 13.24. We can do this by adding another op-amp at the output, as shown in Figure 13.28. This sums v_{in} and 2.5 V to develop the final desired v_{out}/v_{in} curve of Figure 13.24.

EXERCISES

Design op-amp circuits with the approximate transfer characteristics shown in Figures E13.9 and E13.10. Reference supplies available are ± 10 V. Op-amp supply voltages are ± 15 V. The solutions are shown on the figures. Assume $V_{ON} = 0.7$ V and $R_f = 100\ \Omega$.

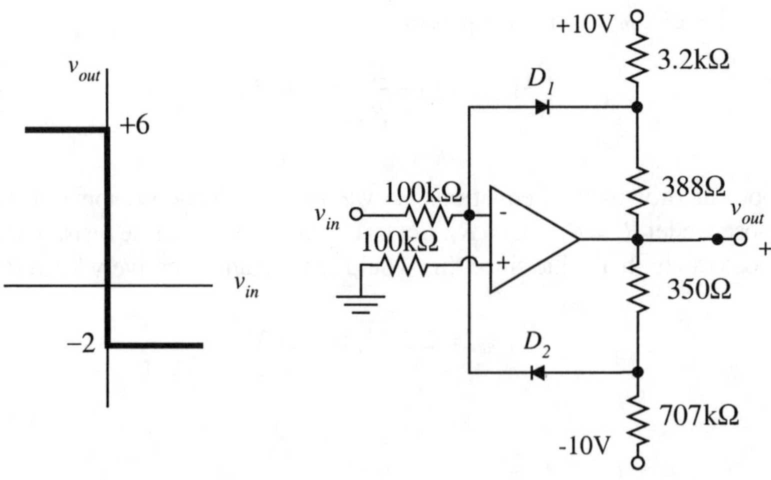

Figure E13.9

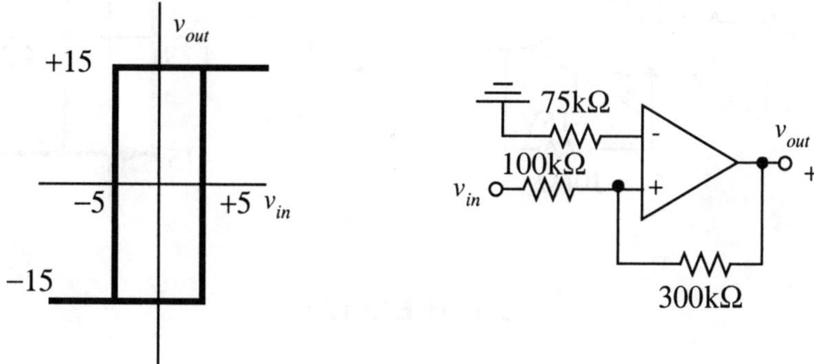

Figure E13.10

Find approximate relationships between the input voltage, v_{in} and the output voltage, v_{out}, in the circuits shown in Figures E13.11 and E13.12. Assume that $V_{ON} = 0.7$ V and $R_f = 100\ \Omega$. The solutions are shown on the figures.

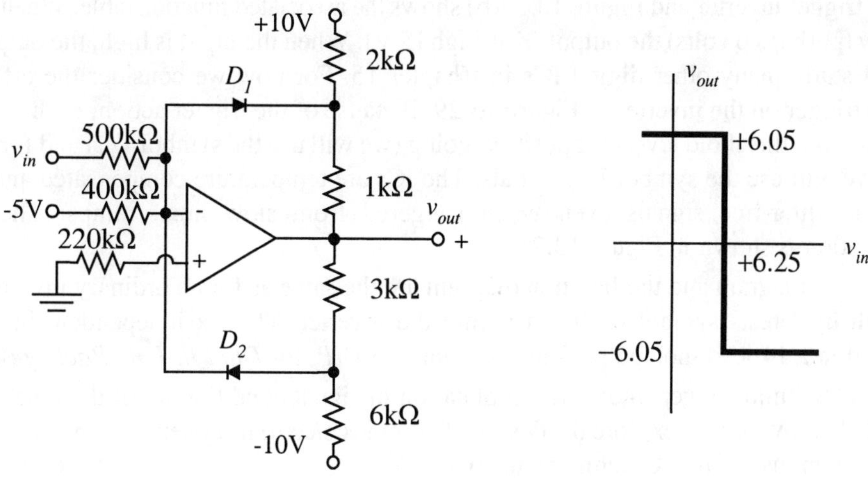

Figure E13.11

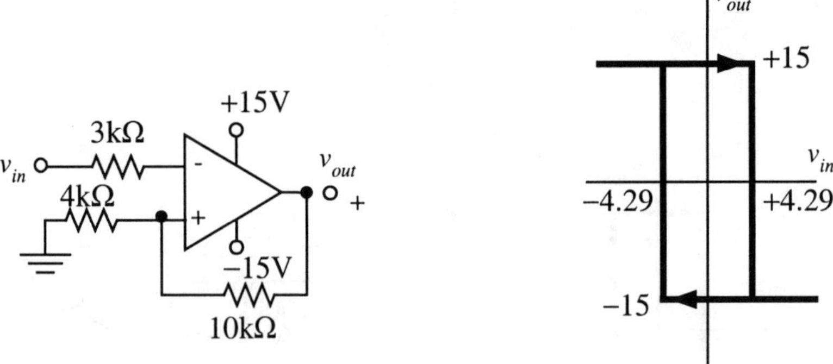

Figure E13.12

13.4.2 Integrated Circuit Schmitt Trigger

We will rarely find it necessary to *design* a Schmitt trigger. We will, however, need to *use* Schmitt triggers in a wide assortment of design applications. A variety of Schmitt triggers are available for our designs. The hysteresis loop of the Schmitt trigger is incorporated into several digital integrated circuits (ICs). In this section, we consider the 7414 Hex Schmitt trigger inverter, which contains six independent inverters. Figure 13.29(a) shows the symbol of a Schmitt trigger inverter and Figure 13.29(b) shows the associated function table. When the input, *A*, is low (perhaps 0 volts) the output, *Y*, is high [5 V]. When the input is high, the output is low. We will study many other digital ICs in Chapter 15. For now we consider the effect of the Schmitt trigger on the inverter of Figure 13.29. Because of the trigger action, each inverter has different input threshold levels for positive-going (we will use the symbol V_{T+}) and for negative-going (we will use the symbol V_{T-}) signals. The ICs are temperature compensated and produce clean and jitter-free signals even when triggered from slow input ramps. The package configuration is shown in Figure 13.29(c).

The logic diagram and the function diagram are the same as for an ordinary inverter, except the small hysteresis symbol is shown within the inverter. The six independent inverters are contained in a 14-lead molded package (known as a *DIP*, for *Dual In-Line Package*).

The IC Schmitt trigger finds wide application in signal conditioning of the type we saw in Example 13.7. When we explore the design of complex electronic systems in Chapter 17, we will make frequent use of the IC Schmitt trigger.

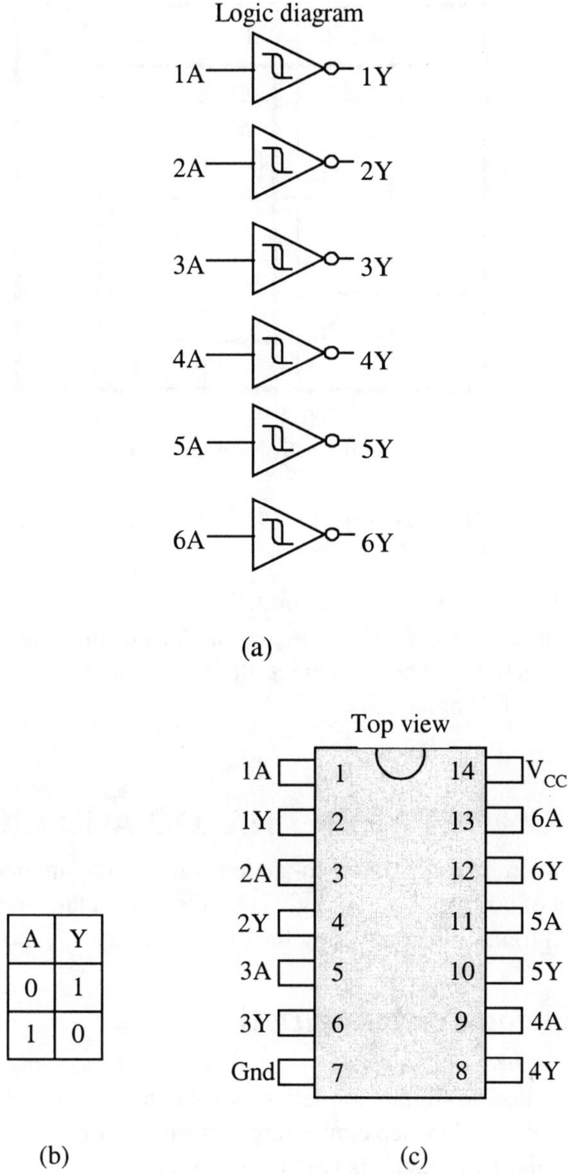

A	Y
0	1
1	0

(b)

Figure 13.29 – 7414 Hex Schmitt trigger inverter

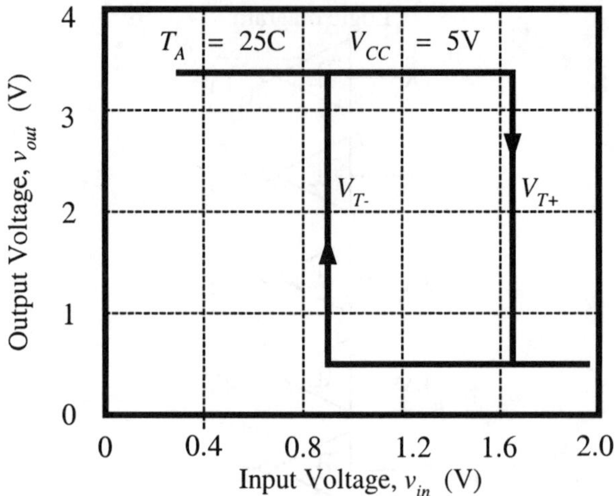

Figure 13.30 – Hysteresis loop for 7414 hex Schmitt trigger inverter

The hysteresis loop for the 7414 Hex Schmitt trigger inverter is shown in Figure 13.30. As you can see from this figure, $V_{T-} = 0.85$ V and $V_{T+} = 1.66$ V. The high state occurs at a voltage of 3.3 V and the low state is at 0.2 V. These voltages are the high and low values for the TTL logic family (as we will discuss in Chapter 15).

13.5 CONVERSION BETWEEN ANALOG AND DIGITAL

Analog-to-digital converters (and digital-to-analog converters), are not truly digital devices, but rather a combination of both analog and digital circuits. We include them in this chapter since they often form a critical transition connecting the two domains.

13.5.1 Digital to Analog Converter (D/A)

Digital-to-analog converters (D/A) change a digital word into an analog voltage or current. We cover these before analog-to-digital converters since some of the techniques we develop in D/A conversion will be applicable when converting in the other direction. Numerous techniques are used to accomplish this. Two methods are presented here.

The magnitude of the D/A output is generally proportional to the current flowing through weighted resistors, or inversely proportional to the resistor values. An example of an 8-bit binary D/A converter with a current to voltage converter operational amplifier is shown in Figure 13.31.

Each of the inputs is weighted according to the input summing resistors so that the proper power of 2 is developed. An 8-bit signal at the input yields an analog output. You should analyze the circuit of Figure 13.31 and verify that v_{out} is the analog equivalent to the digital input.

Another method is based on using a CMOS switch to change the resistors in a resistance ladder, as shown in Figure 13.32.

This method is called *current switching R-2R ladder* and uses a series of deposited silicon chromium resistors. These resistors, of value R or $2R$, are arranged in the ladder, and comprise the DAC 830 D/A converter. The circuit uses only two values of resistance, R and $2R$. Since the ladder network divides the current at each of the nodes, the accuracy of the ratio of the two resistors is more critical than their absolute values. Hence, the *R-2R ladder* is relatively easy to fabricate. The ladder also presents a relatively constant resistance load to the V_{REF} source.

The digital input code applied to the input of the D/A converter controls the position of the current switches. In this manner, the available ladder current is steered to either i_{OUT1} or i_{OUT2} as determined by the logic level (either 0 or 1 respectively). Since the CMOS switches are bilateral they can switch currents of either polarity with only a small voltage drop.

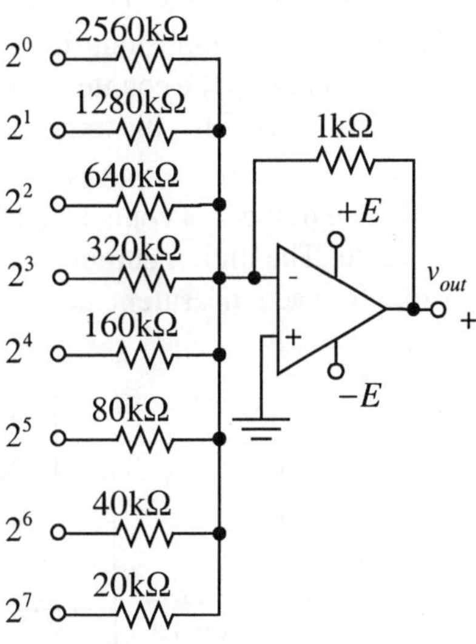

Figure 13.31 – D/A converter

With the use of the *R-2R ladder* network, this D/A converter can produce 0.05% of full-scale maximum linearity error. Typical conversion time is 1 µsec, and with an 8-bit input, this circuit is capable of generating 256 distinguishable output current levels. The resolution is 8-bit.

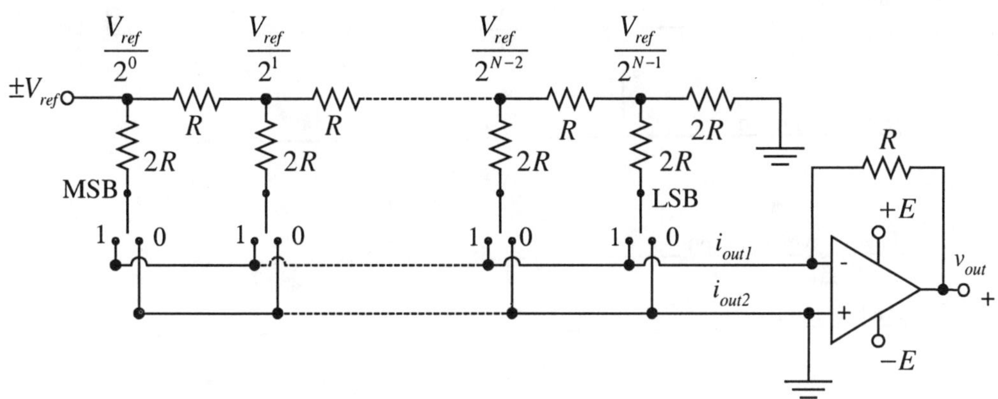

Figure 13.32 – Current switching R-2R ladder network

13.5.2 Analog to Digital Converter (A/D)

Analog to digital converters change an analog voltage level into a corresponding digital word. There are many ways of producing an A/D converter. We discuss several in this section.

One way of accomplishing the conversion is to increment a counter which feeds a D/A converter and to stop the counter when the D/A converter's output exceeds the analog voltage in question. This method is illustrated in Figure 13.33.

The D/A converter output is a staircase function. It can be thought of as a discrete ramp function. The number of counts it takes before the ramp crosses the analog value is proportional to that value. The digital output word is the counter output. An 8-bit counter resets and starts from zero for each measurement.

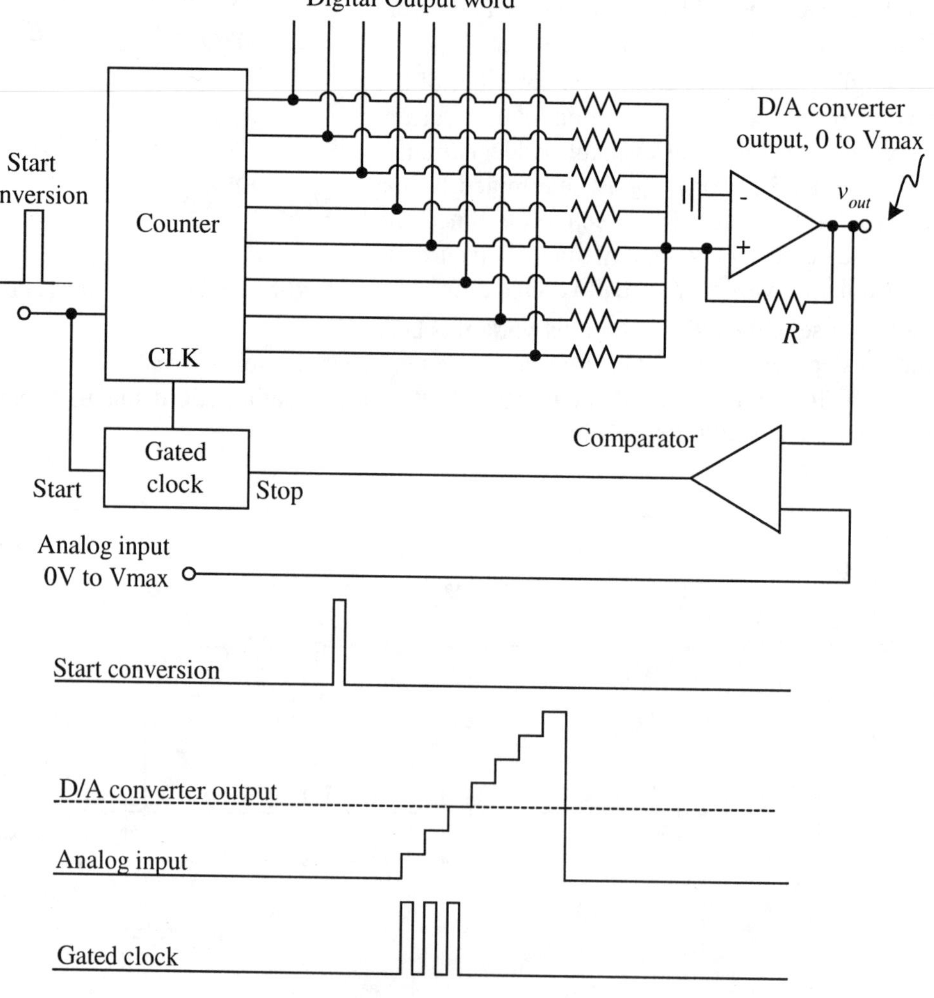

Figure 13.33 – A/D converter

A second method of generating a digital word from an analog voltage is to use successive approximations. When we assign binary numbers to various voltage levels starting with the lowest voltage (all 0's) and counting toward the highest (all 1's), we can use the basic properties of binary sequences to simplify the conversion. The *most significant bit* in the binary number indicates whether the voltage is in the upper of lower half of the range. The next bit subdivides this half-range in half, and so on. This is equivalent to the observation that in a binary counter, each bit is oscillating at half the frequency of the previous bit. The conversion is then accomplished by a series of comparisons with the regional dividing points.

A specific example of this type of A/D converter is the ADC0801 IC, which contains a high input impedance comparator, 256 series resistors and analog switches, control logic and output latches. Conversion is performed using a successive approximation technique where the unknown analog voltage is compared to the voltage at the resistor tie points using analog switches. When the appropriate tie point voltage matches the unknown voltage, conversion is complete. The digital outputs contain an 8-bit complementary binary word corresponding to the unknown voltage. You should refer to the manufacturers' data sheets for details. Many of these are available on the World Wide Web, and can be downloaded using appropriate viewing software.

The 3 1/2-Digit A/D Converter

The 3 ½-digit A/D converter is essentially a digital voltmeter. Incorporated into the design of this digital voltmeter IC is the *dual slope* method of analog to digital conversion. We present the ICL7106/7107 CMOS A/D converter as an example. The pin-out diagram for this IC is shown in Figure 13.34.

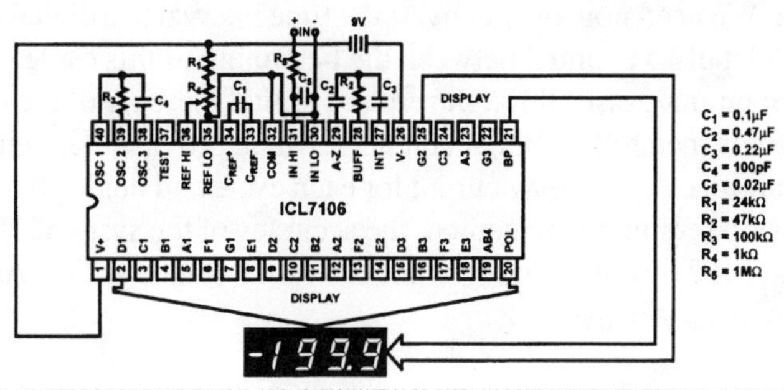

Figure 13.34 – ICL7106/7107 Digital voltmeter IC – ***Courtesy of Intersil Inc.***

The ICL7106 drives a liquid crystal display (LCD) and the ICL7107 drives a light emitting diode (LED) display. Included are 7-segment decoders, display drivers, references, and a clock. The IC operates in three phases: (1) auto-zero, (2) signal integrate, and (3) reference integrate. In Phase 1 of the dual slope conversion, the cycle is zeroed for a new start. This process is known as the *auto-zero phase*. The block diagram is shown in Figure 13.35.

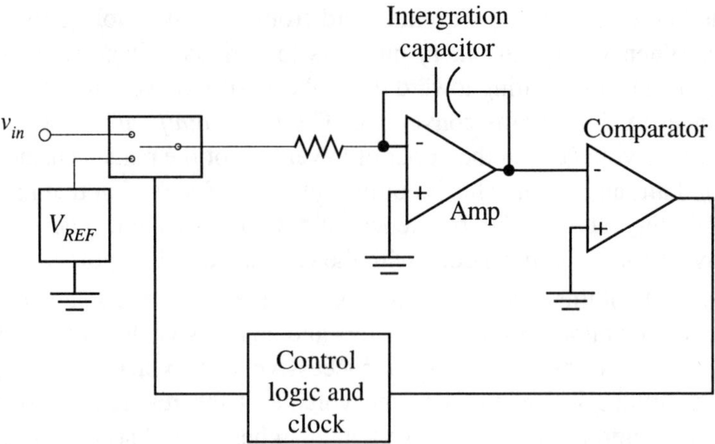

Figure 13.35 – Phases in dual-slope-conversion

In Phase 2 of the dual slope method, the signal is integrated for a fixed period of time with the slope depending upon the *RC* combination of the integrating op-amp. Since the time period is fixed, the value of the integral is proportional to the signal amplitude. In Phase 3, the integrator input is switched from v_{in} to V_{REF}. The polarity is determined during Phase 2 so that the integrator discharges back toward zero. Since the slope of the discharge function is fixed, the time required to return to zero is proportional to the starting amplitude. We have therefore succeeded in translating the sample amplitude value into a time interval whose length is proportional to the original amplitude. We need now only convert the time interval to a digital number using a clock. The number of clock pulses counted between the beginning of this cycle (Phase 3) and the time when the integrator output passes through zero is a digital measure of the magnitude of v_{in}. This digital measurement is then fed to digital counters, which provide the digital output. The digital control logic synchronizes the display output for each cycle and begins the A/D conversion cycle again. In the dual-slope comparison method, the accuracy of the system is limited by the number of bits of the counter and by the accuracy of the reference voltages. This A/D converter depends only upon the ratio of v_{in} to V_{REF}.

EXERCISE

E13.13 Analyze the input circuit for a thermometer that uses the 3 ½ digit DVM (ICL7106) of Figure 13.34 for the digital voltmeter.

Answer: The 1N4002 diode provides the basic sensor to measure temperature. The bridge circuit provides the signal to the op-amp and also the zero adjust. This is shown in Figure E13.13(a). On Figure E13.13(b), we show the full-scale adjustment.

The calibration is as follows:

(a) Let us first use the 3 ½ DVM as digital Centigrade thermometer. Calibration is achieved by placing the sensing diode in ice water and adjusting the zeroing potentiometer for a 000.0 reading. The sensor is then placed in boiling water and the scale factor potentiometer is adjusted for a reading of 100.

(b) Now we use the 3 ½ DVM as a digital Fahrenheit thermometer. The procedure is the same as that of the digital centigrade thermometer except that we adjust the zeroing potentiometer for a 032.0 reading, and adjust the scale factor potentiometer for a 212.0 reading.

SUMMARY

Quasi-linear circuits form the bridge between analog and digital electronics. We began this chapter with an examination of piecewise linear circuits, various forms of the rectifier. We saw how to produce arbitrary input-output relationships using one or more operational amplifiers.

We then explored a variety of types of limiters, including the important class of feedback limiters. Then we turned our attention to comparators which typically produce a binary output whose value depends on the relative size of two inputs.

Schmitt triggers form an important building block for many electronic circuits. These devices use positive feedback to speed up the rate at which switching occurs. We combined Schmitt triggers with limiters to increase accuracy.

The final section of this chapter explored both discrete an integrated circuits for converting between analog and digital. These circuits are extremely important in mixed analog and digital processing, where we need to smoothly go back and forth between the two domains.

PROBLEMS

Section 13.1

Find approximate relationships between the input voltages, v_1 (or v_{in}) and v_2, and the output voltage, v_{out}, in each of the circuits of Figures P13.1 to P13.5. Assume $V_{ON} = 0.7$ V and $R_f = 100$ Ω.

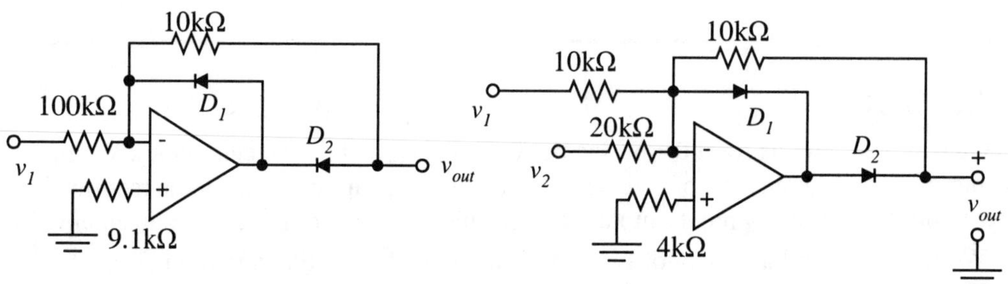

Figure P13.1

Figure P13.2

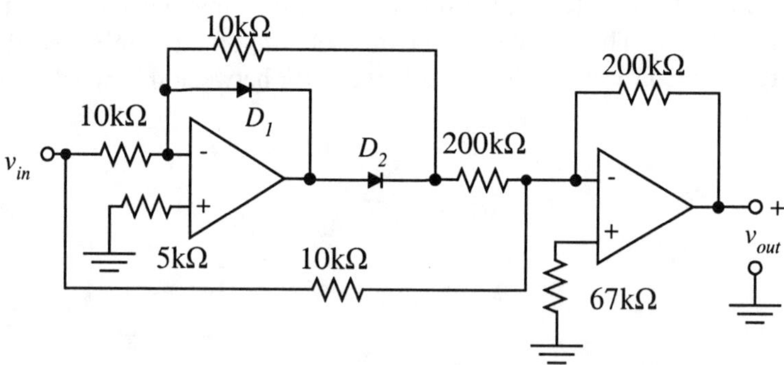

Figure P13.3

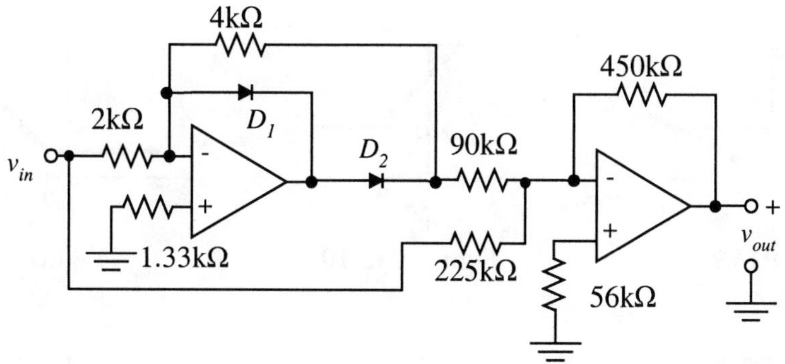

Figure P13.4

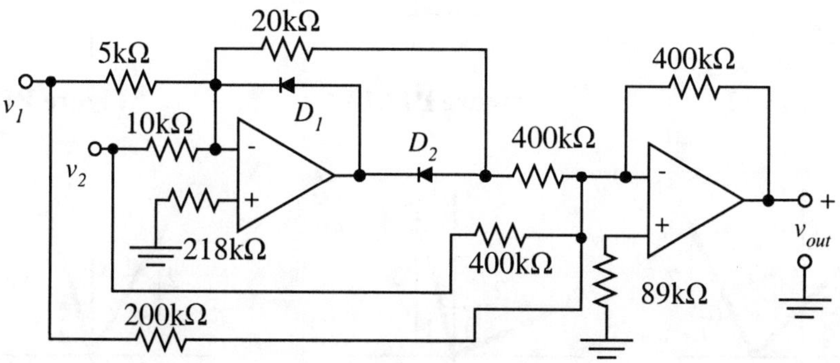

Figure P13.5

Section 13.2

Design 741 circuits with the approximate transfer characteristics shown in Figures P13.6 to P13.19. Use as few op-amps as possible. Reference supplies of +10 V and -10 V are available. Assume that $V_{ON} = 0.7$ V and $R_f = 100$ Ω.

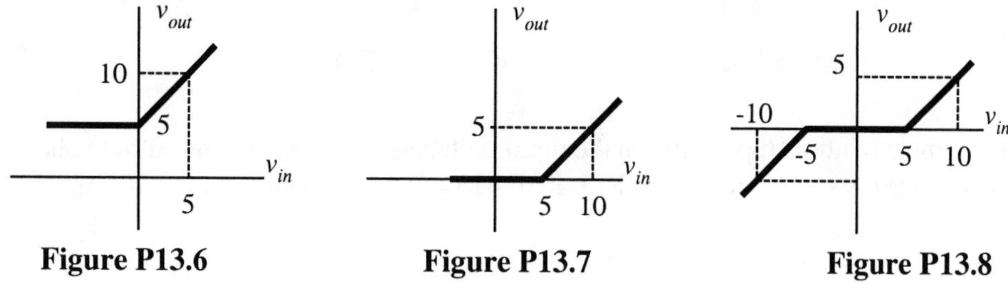

Figure P13.6 **Figure P13.7** **Figure P13.8**

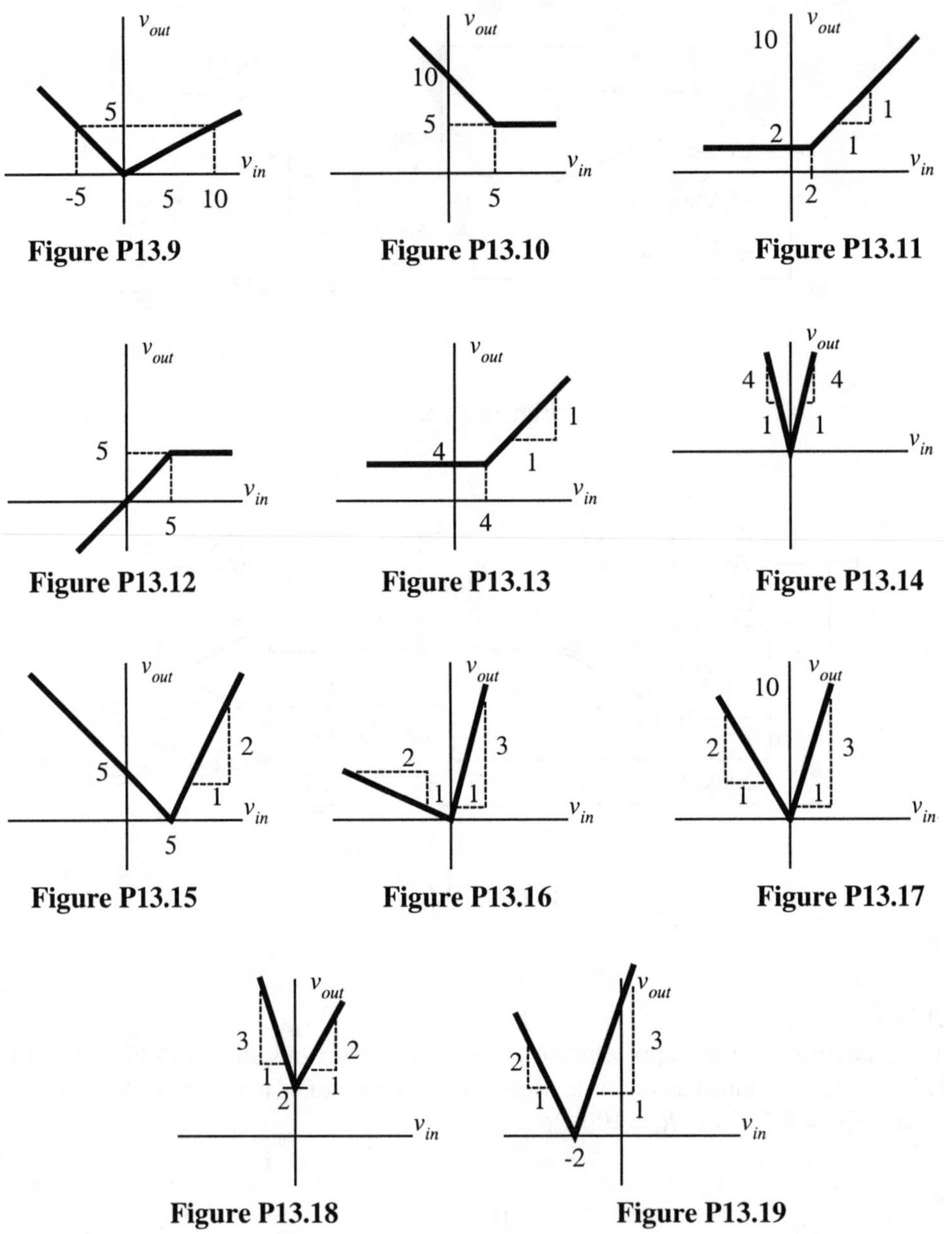

Figure P13.9

Figure P13.10

Figure P13.11

Figure P13.12

Figure P13.13

Figure P13.14

Figure P13.15

Figure P13.16

Figure P13.17

Figure P13.18

Figure P13.19

Find approximate relationships between the input voltages, v_1 and v_2, and the output voltage, v_{out}, in each of the circuits shown in Figures P13.20 to P13.24. Assume that $V_{ON} = 0.7$ V and $R_f = 100$ Ω.

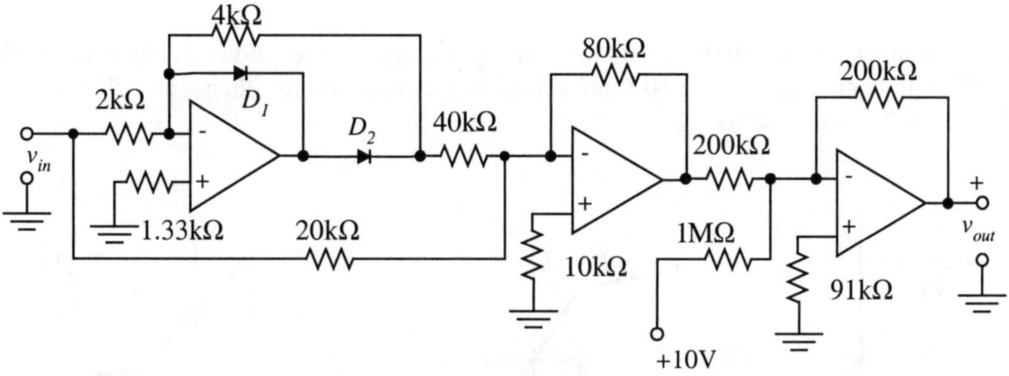

Figure P13.20

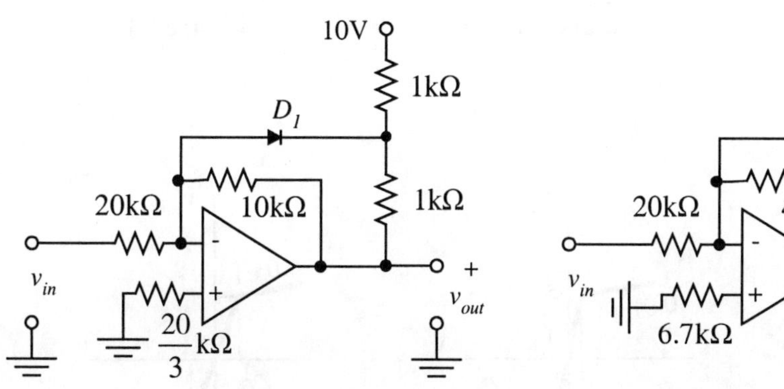

Figure P13.21 **Figure P13.22**

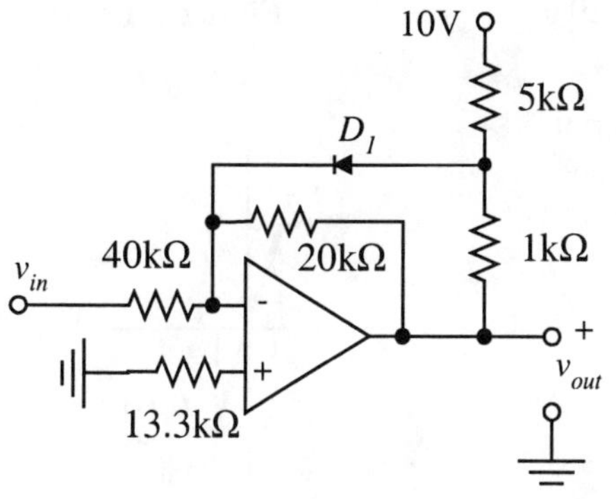

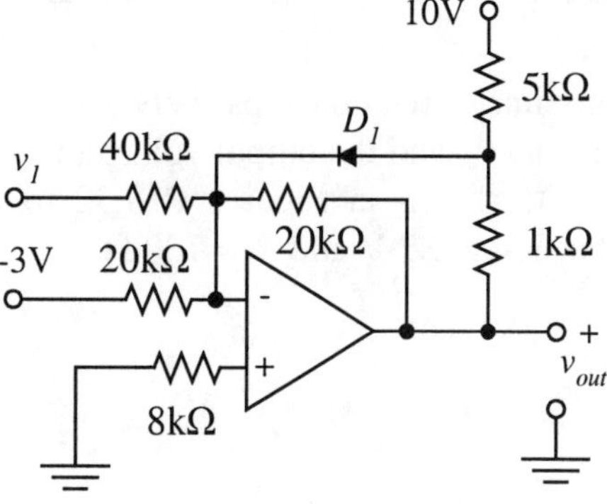

Figure P13.23 **Figure P13.24**

Design op-amp circuits with the approximate transfer characteristics shown in Figures P13.25 to P13.31. Reference supplies of ± 10 V are available. Op-amp supply voltages are 15 V. Assume that $V_{ON} = 0.7$ V and $R_f = 100\ \Omega$.

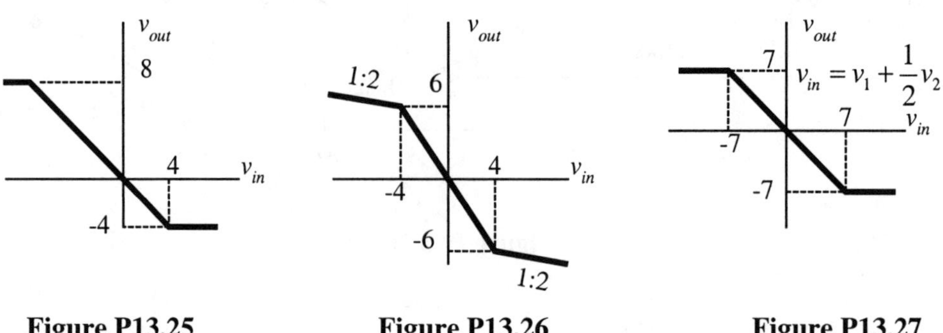

Figure P13.25 Figure P13.26 Figure P13.27

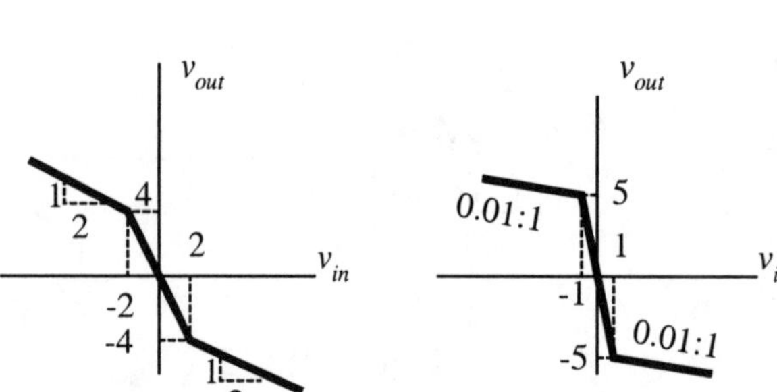

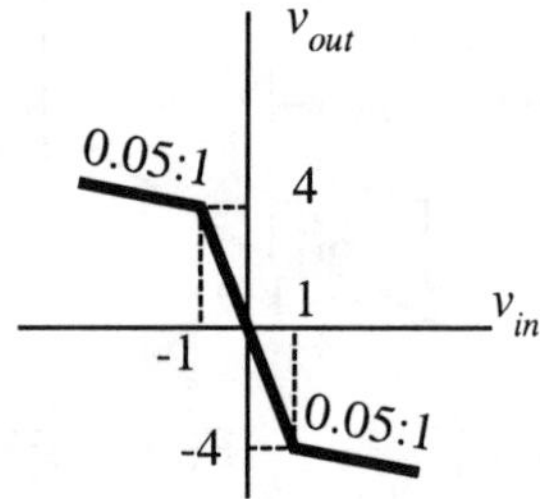

Figure P13.28 Figure P13.29 Figure P13.30

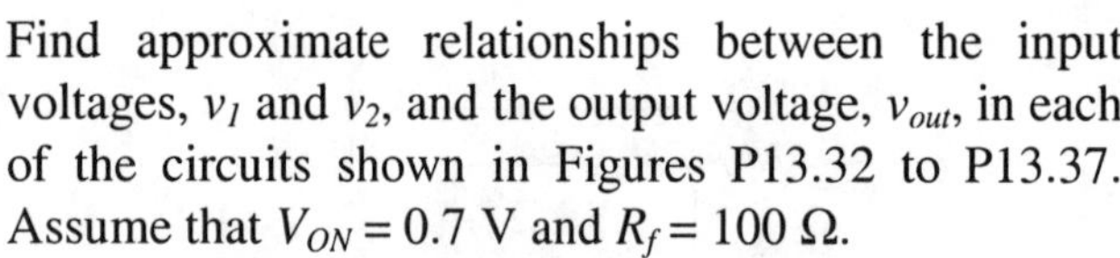

Find approximate relationships between the input voltages, v_1 and v_2, and the output voltage, v_{out}, in each of the circuits shown in Figures P13.32 to P13.37. Assume that $V_{ON} = 0.7$ V and $R_f = 100\ \Omega$.

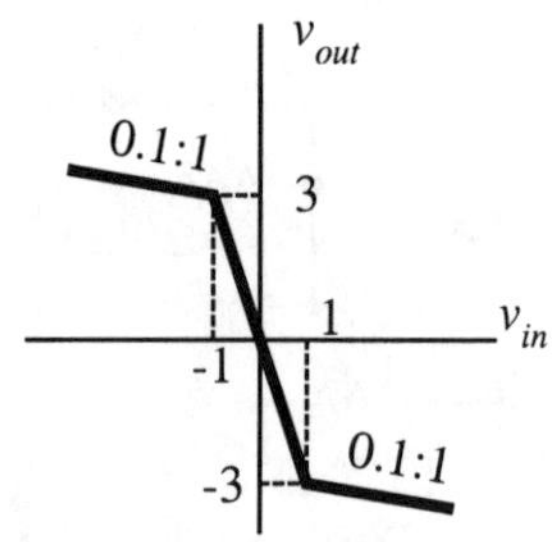

Figure P13.31

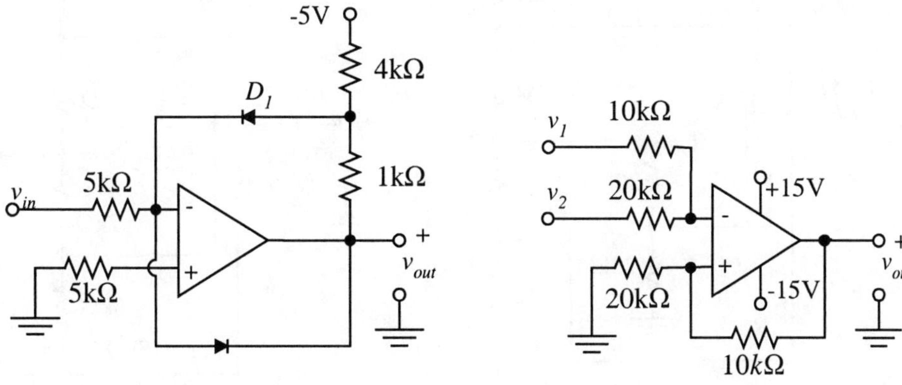

Figure P13.32 **Figure P13.33**

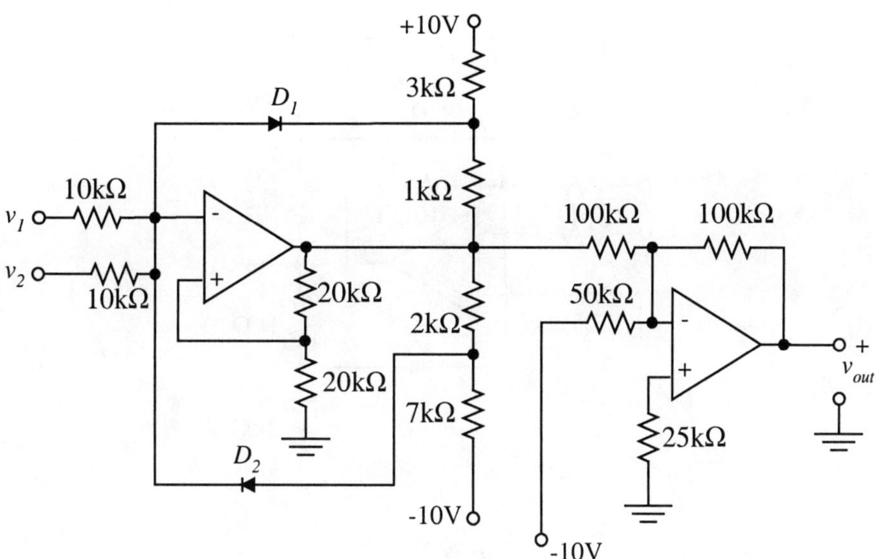

Figure P13.34

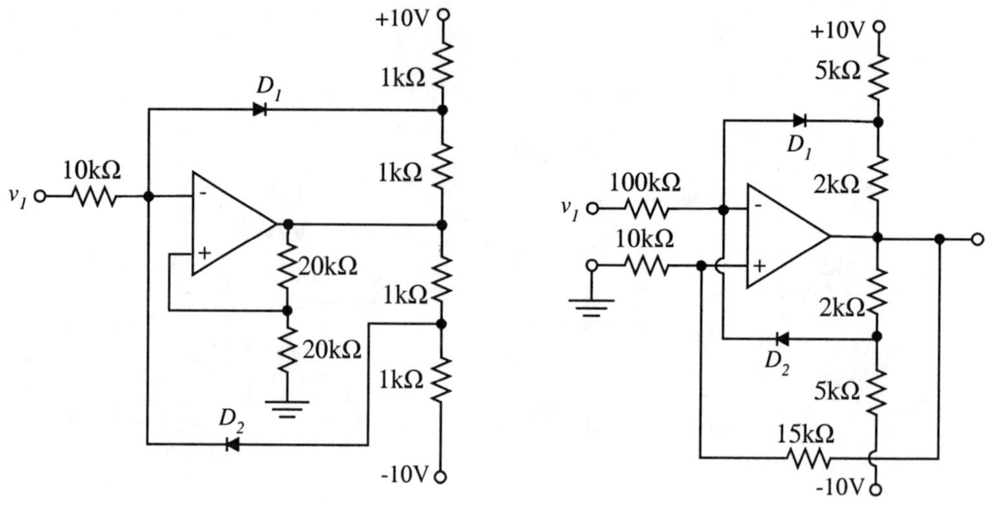

Figure P13.35 **Figure P13.36**

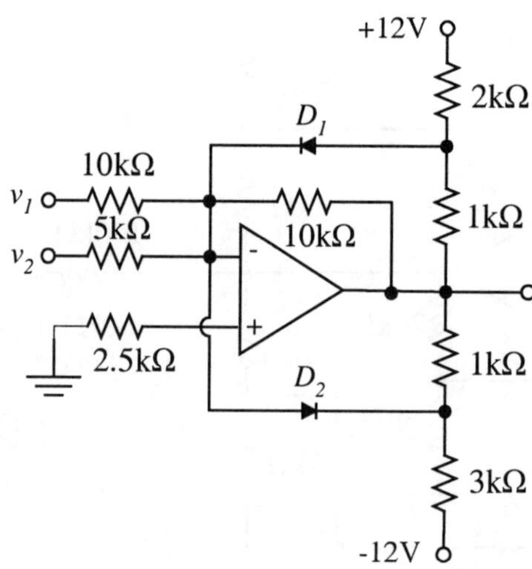

Figure P13.37

Sections 13.3 and 13.4

Design op-amp circuits with the approximate transfer characteristics shown in Figure P13.38 to P13.44. Reference supplies of $\pm$ 10 V are available. Op-amp supply voltages are $\pm$ 15 V. Assume $V_{ON} = 0.7$ V and $R_f = 100\ \Omega$.

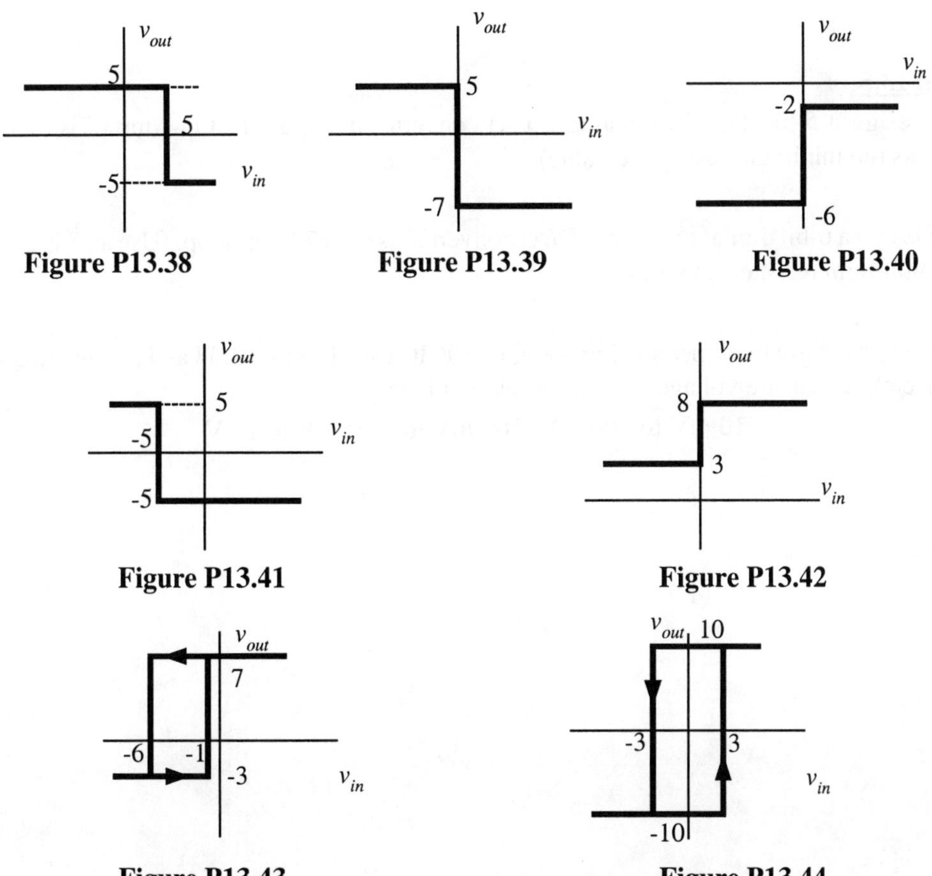

13.45 Analyze the precision absolute value circuit of Figure P13.45. The output, v_{out}, equals v_{in}. Because of the high gain of the op-amps, the ON voltage drop of the diode is effectively zero.

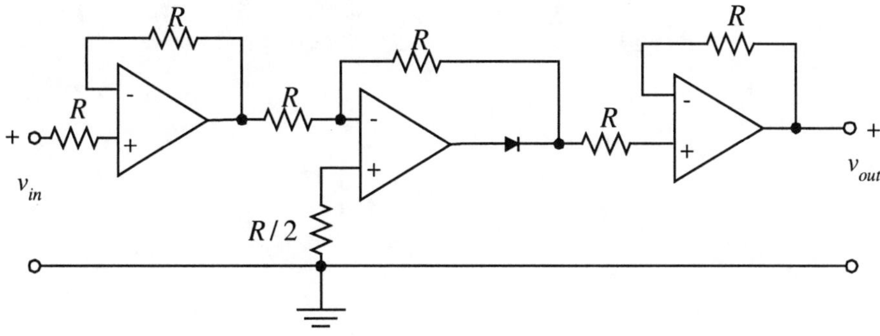

Figure P13.45

Section 13.5

13.46 Design a 5-bit digital to analog (D/A) converter using a 741 Op-Amp. (Use an 8 kΩ resistor as the minimum resistance value).

13.47 Design a 6-bit digital to analog (D/A) converter using a 741 op-amp. (Use an 8 kΩ resistor as the minimum resistance value).

13.48 Design a digital voltmeter using the ICL7106 IC (See Figure 13.34 and the manufacturers data sheets) to measure voltages in the following ranges:

10 mV to 100 mV; 100 mV to 1 V; 1 V to 10 V

Chapter 14

Pulsed Waveforms and Timing Circuits

14.0 INTRODUCTION

The topics covered throughout Chapters 2 through 13 of this text emphasize *analog* electronics. In such circuits, we are interested in voltage and current gain, maximum undistorted amplitude swings, and input and output resistance. Typical applications include the amplification of music or speech.

Beginning with this chapter, we concentrate our attention on *digital* electronics. There are very good reasons why digital processing has replaced analog in a wide variety of applications ranging from sound to instrumentation. You have probably learned some of these reasons in other courses. Others will reveal themselves in our current study. Digital signals have the potential of reducing errors, complexity and cost of electronic systems. They also often allow more flexible approaches toward signal processing.

After studying the material in this chapter, you will

- Be able to analyze systems with pulsed inputs.
- Understand the effects of diodes on pulsed signals.
- Be able to design trigger circuits.
- Understand the operation and applications of timers.
- Be able to design monostable and astable timing circuit.

Digital electronics deals with signals which take on one of only two values: *high* or *low*, *on* or *off*, 1 or 0. These signals are said to be *binary* and are the type found in many electronic digital systems. (Digital systems can be non-binary, and many of the circuits we discuss can be generalized to be non-binary). Any bipolar junction transistors in the circuit are either in the *cutoff* or *saturated* condition. We are no longer interested in the linear operating region of electronic devices. Instead, we are only concerned with whether the device is on or off, that is, whether the output voltage is near zero or near the supply voltage value. By reducing the range of possible voltages to one of two values, the circuit often becomes simpler and the chance of making errors is greatly reduced. This last point deserves more emphasis. In an *analog* system, the output can take on any value within a continuum of values. Therefore, any disturbance, whether in the form of additive noise or distortion, results in an error. In a *binary digital* system, we are dealing with only two possible signal values. A disturbance must be large enough to make one value look like the other to cause a change. If the disturbance is not that large, the error is zero.

The signals that are processed through digital systems are a series of lows and highs, that is, a series of discrete values. For example, we could use +5 V for the high value and 0 V for the low value. A representative series of values is shown in Figure 14.1 as a train of pulses.

Since digital systems respond to pulse trains such as that of Figure 14.1, we first study the behavior of these systems when a pulse train is applied.

Most systems found in nature are analog and not digital. For example, the velocity of an automobile can take on a continuum of values. The temperature of the human body is also an analog variable. For this reason, when we design digital systems we must first change the continuous variables into pulse trains that can be processed by the digital electronics. We must *digitize* or *quantize* the magnitude of the samples of the continuous variable using an *analog-to-digital* converter. The resulting signal is a pulse train or sequence of binary numbers that represents the magnitude of the samples of the analog signal.

An electronic system frequently measures the continuously varying input variable, such as the speed of a car. The signal is amplified and digitized to become a pulse train that is processed by the digital system. The output may be displayed on a digital readout (e.g., the digital speedometer in a car) or it may be used to drive an analog actuator (e.g., a speed-control system). The design engineer must be proficient in both analog and digital electronics.

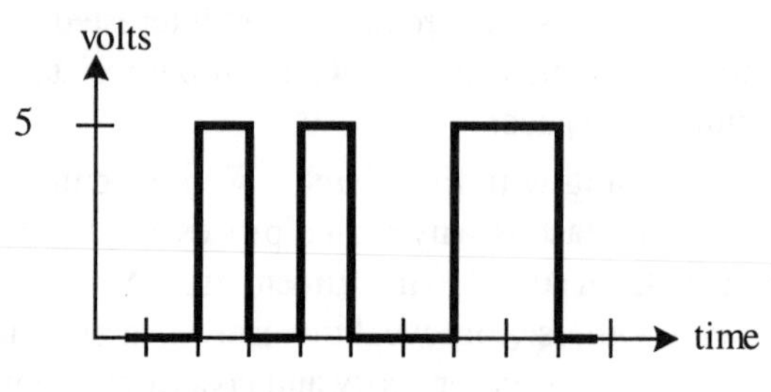

Figure 14.1 – Pulse train

The heart of most digital systems is the clock. The clock produces a steady stream of pulses which is used to synchronize the timing of the electronic system. We consider several clocks (square wave pulse generators) and spend time analyzing the 555 pulse generator (oscillator). We use the 555 in a variety of applications for both oscillators and monostables.

14.1 HIGH-PASS *RC* NETWORK

A series capacitor and a shunt resistor form a simple high-pass network. The input voltage is applied across the combination and the output voltage is taken across the resistor, as shown in Figure 14.2(a).

We analyzed the first order high-pass filter in Chapter 12, where we found the transfer function to be of the form,

$$\frac{V_{out}}{V_{in}} = \frac{RC \cdot s}{RC \cdot s + 1} = \frac{\tau s}{\tau s + 1} \tag{14.1}$$

The time constant, τ, is given by RC. The sinusoidal steady-state amplitude plot of this response is shown in Figure 14.2(b). Notice that the corner frequency is f_c which is equal to $1/(2\pi RC)$ in Hertz [or $\omega_c = (RC)^{-1}$ in radians per second].

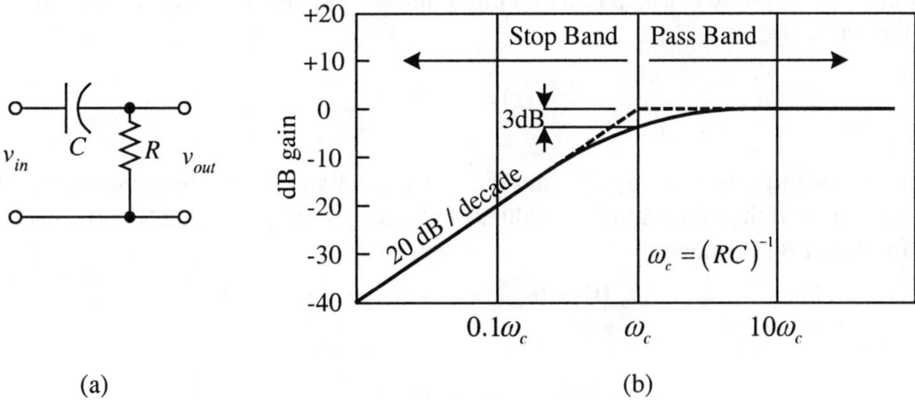

Figure 14.2 - High-pass *RC* network

Now suppose the input to this system is a step function of amplitude *E*. That is,

$$v_{in}(t) = E \cdot u(t) \tag{14.2}$$

where $u(t)$ is the unit step function. We can use Laplace transform analysis to find the output. The Laplace transform of the output is found by multiplying the transfer function by E/s, the Laplace transform of the step input. If the initial conditions are zero, this output is given by Equation (14.3). We have also given the corresponding time function.

$$V_{out} = \frac{\tau \cdot E}{\tau s + 1} \qquad v_{out}(t) = E \cdot e^{-t/\tau} \cdot u(t) \tag{14.3}$$

The input step function and the output exponential response are shown in Figure 14.3.

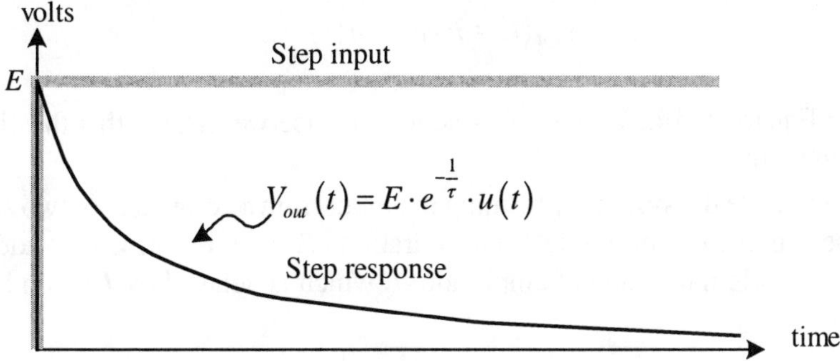

Figure 14.3 Step response of a high-pass network

Since the equations for a single *RC* network are governed by a first-order differential equation, the form of the response to a step function input must be exponential. The voltage functions must be of the form,

$$v(t) = A + Be^{-\frac{t}{\tau}} \tag{14.4}$$

The time constant, τ, is given by *RC*, and the constants *A* and *B*, are chosen to match the initial and final values. If the initial and final values of $v(t)$ are given by V_{inital} and V_{final} respectively, we solve for *A* and *B* as follows:

$$v_{out}(0) = V_{initial} = A + Be^{0} = A + B$$

$$v_{out}(\infty) = V_{final} = A + Be^{-\infty} = A \tag{14.5}$$

$$A = V_{final}$$

$$B = V_{initial} - V_{final}$$

The equation for the curve is then

$$v(t) = V_{final} + (V_{inital} - V_{final})e^{-t/\tau},\ t > 0 \tag{14.6}$$

Equation (14.6) provides the engineer with a simple method for developing time responses. As an example of the use of this equation, let us once again find the solution for the high-pass network of Figure 14.2 when the input is the step function shown in Figure 14.3.

The initial value of the output voltage is *E* since the capacitor voltage cannot change instantaneously when the input jumps from 0 to *E* volts. The final value is zero since the capacitor looks like an open circuit for a *dc* input. Therefore we have $V_{initial} = E$ and $V_{final} = 0$. Substituting these values into Equation (14.6) yields,

$$v_{out}(t) = E \cdot e^{-t/\tau} \cdot u(t) \tag{14.7}$$

as we found in Equation (14.3). The $u(t)$ is added in since we assume that the circuit is at rest prior to the step input.

We now complicate the system by forming the input from a composite of two steps. Consider the input to be a pulse of amplitude *E* and duration, *T*. This is formed by adding a step of amplitude *E* at the origin to a step of amplitude -*E* which is delayed by *T* seconds, as shown in Figure 14.4(a).

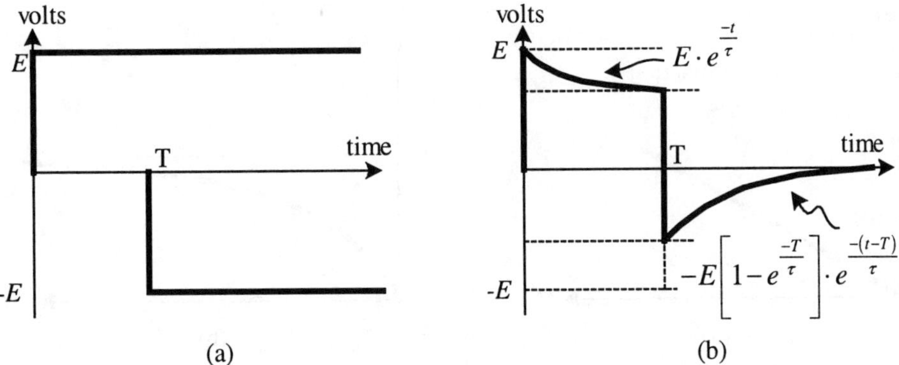

Figure 14.4 - Single pulse formed from two step functions

We solve for the output waveform in two parts. We find the output for times prior to $t = T$ as done previously. That is, since the system cannot see into the future (it is *causal*), it does not know that another step occurs at $t = T$ until the input reaches that point. Therefore, the output prior to time T is given by

$$v_{out}(t) = E \cdot e^{-t/\tau} \tag{14.8}$$

We use this equation to find the output just prior to time T, the time at which the second step is applied. We call this time T^-.

$$v_{out}(T^-) = E \cdot e^{-\frac{(T^-)}{\tau}} \tag{14.9}$$

The output voltage in the high-pass network of Figure 14.2 *can* jump instantaneously since the output voltage is measured across a resistor, R. Hence, we use the notation T^- to indicate the time just prior to the transition time. At time $t = T$, the input voltage jumps negatively by E volts. Since the capacitor voltage cannot change instantaneously and the sum of voltages around the loop is zero, the output must jump down by E volts to equal,

$$v_{out}(T^+) = v_{out}(T^-) - E = E\left(e^{-T/\tau} - 1\right) \tag{14.10}$$

This forms the initial value for the second portion of the output. The final value is zero. Therefore, we use Equation (14.6) to find the second portion of the output.

$$v_{out}(t) = -E\left(1 - e^{-\frac{T}{\tau}}\right) \cdot e^{-\frac{(t-T)}{\tau}} \tag{14.11}$$

The composite output is plotted as Figure 14.4(b).

Before extending this single-step result to apply to a pulse train input, we briefly consider the ramp input with slope α, as shown in Figure 14.5(a).

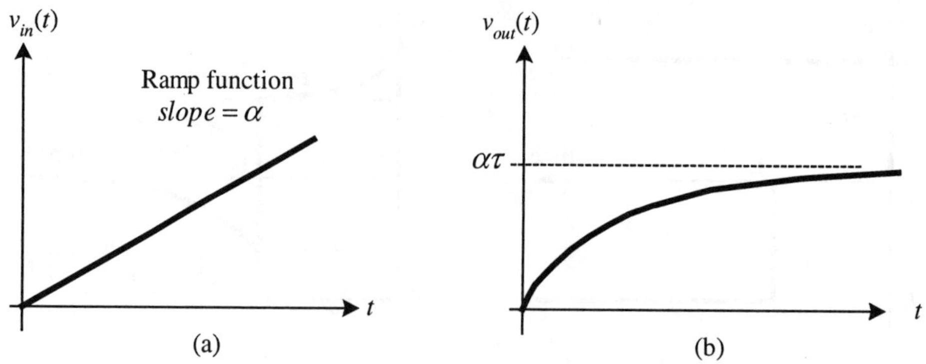

Figure 14.5 - Ramp response of high-pass *RC* network

We find the response of the *RC* network using Laplace transforms. The transform of the ramp is a/s^2. Therefore, the output transform and time function are given by

$$V_{out}(s) = \frac{\alpha}{s^2} \cdot \frac{s\tau}{s\tau + 1} = \alpha \cdot \frac{1}{s(s + 1/\tau)}$$

$$v_{out}(t) = \alpha \cdot \tau \left(1 - e^{-t/\tau}\right) \cdot u(t) \tag{14.12}$$

We could also have found this solution by noting that a ramp is the integral of a step. Therefore, the ramp response is the integral of the step response. This response is shown in Figure 14.5(b).

EXAMPLE 14.1

The ramp of Figure 14.5(a) forms the input to a high-pass *RC* filter with a lower 3-dB frequency of 10^4 radians/second. The slope of the input ramp is 10 volts/sec.

(a) Find the steady-state output voltage.

(b) How long does it take the output to reach 90% of its steady-state value?

(c) Sketch the output voltage waveform.

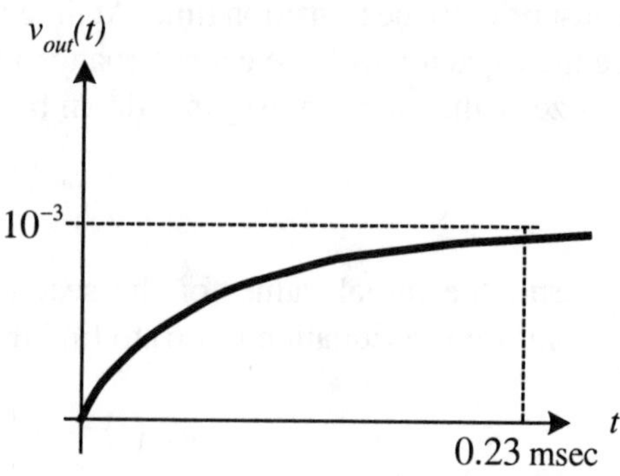

Figure 14.6 – Output for Example 14.1

Solution:

(a) Since the 3-dB frequency is the reciprocal of the time constant, $\tau = 10^{-4}$. The steady-state output is found from Equation (14.12) or Figure 14.5 to be $a\tau$. Therefore

$$v_{out}\big|_{t\to\infty} = \alpha\tau = (10 \text{ volts/sec})(10^{-4} \text{ sec}) = 10^{-3} \text{ V}$$

(b) The output voltage will reach 90% of its steady state value when

$$\alpha\tau\left(1 - e^{-t/\tau}\right) = 0.9\alpha\tau$$

$$t = -\tau \ln(0.1) = 0.23 \text{ ms}$$

Note that this result is independent of α.

(c) The output voltage waveform is shown in Figure 14.6.

14.1.1 Steady-State Response of High-Pass Network to Pulse Train

Now that we know the response to a single pulse, we a ready to consider the periodic pulse input as shown in Figure 14.7(a). We apply this square waveform to the high-pass network of Figure 14.2. Without making some logical assumptions, the solution of this circuit analysis problem is tedious. Without such assumptions, we would start with the first pulse and repeat the analysis of Figure 14.4. But then when the second pulse comes along, we have a new initial value for the voltage, and we must repeat the analysis for this second pulse. This analysis must be repeated for each input pulse. We would only know that steady state is reached if the initial values no longer change from those at the start of the previous cycle. That is, we must continue solving for the pulse response until the transient dies out. Of course the transient is exponential, so it may take a long time to die out. Surely we can find a better way to evaluate the steady-state response.

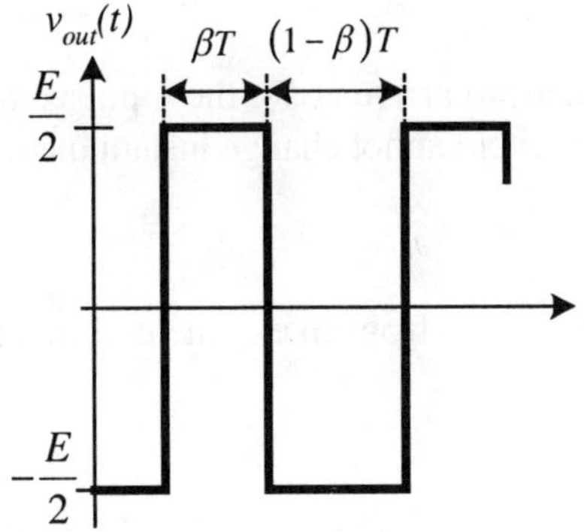

Figure 14.7(a) – Pulse input

We assume that the output resembles the waveform shown in Figure 14.7(b) (We will soon see the reason that three curves are shown, but for now, concentrate upon the center curve, labeled $\tau \approx T$). We can make this assumption since the input remains constant over periods of the time, and during these periods, the output must exponentially approach zero. We know that steady state has been reached when the values of the voltages repeat for each cycle. That is, we go from V_1 to V_2 then to V_3 and exponentially decay to V_4. We have completed a cycle when we go from V_4 back to the beginning. If the curve returns to V_1, we have reached steady state. This condition is used to develop the steady-state solution.

Let us examine the case where the time constant and the period of the input are of the same order of magnitude. This is represented by the middle sketch in Figure 14.7(b). The output decays by a noticeable amount, but does not reach zero between transitions. We need four equations to solve for the four unknown voltages.

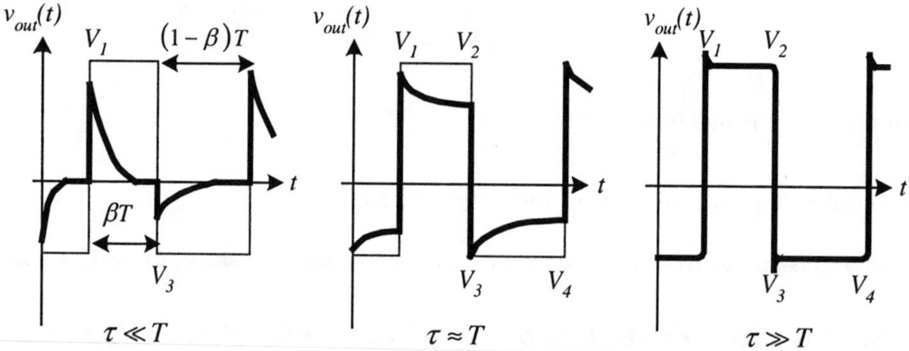

Figure 14.7(b) – Periodic input response of a high-pass *RC* filter

The relationship between V_1 and V_2 is found directly from Equation (14.6).

$$V_2 = V_1 e^{-\beta T/\tau} \tag{14.13}$$

When we arrive at V_2, the input voltage changes by $-E$ volts, and since the voltage across the capacitor cannot change instantaneously, V_2 and V_3 differ by V.

$$V_3 = V_2 - E \tag{14.14}$$

We find V_4 from an exponential that starts at V_3 and decays toward zero for $(1 - \beta)T$ seconds.

$$V_4 = V_3 e^{-\frac{(1-\beta)T}{\tau}} \tag{14.15}$$

When we reach V_4, the input voltage jumps by $+E$ volts, and again since the voltage across the capacitor cannot change instantaneously, the output voltage must also jump by $+E$ volts. If we assume steady state, V_4+E must equal V_1, the voltage where we started at the beginning of the cycle. Hence,

$$V_1 = V_4 + E \tag{14.16}$$

We now have four equations in four unknowns. These equations are solved for the four voltage values (please take the time to verify these results).

$$V_1 = E \cdot \frac{1 - e^{\frac{-(1-\beta)T}{\tau}}}{1 - e^{-T/\tau}}$$

$$V_2 = E \cdot \frac{e^{-\beta T/\tau} - e^{-T/\tau}}{1 - e^{-T/\tau}}$$

$$V_3 = E \cdot \frac{e^{-\beta T/\tau} - 1}{1 - e^{-T/\tau}} \qquad (14.17)$$

$$V_4 = E \cdot \frac{e^{-T/\tau}\left(1 - e^{\beta T/\tau}\right)}{1 - e^{-T/\tau}}$$

Let us now investigate the shape of the waveform when we change the relative size of τ with respect to T.

If the time constant is much less than the period of the input ($\tau \ll T$), the exponential has time to decay almost to zero between transitions, and the output resembles the first sketch in Figure 14.7(b). Let ($\tau \ll T$) in Equation (14.17) to obtain

$$\begin{aligned} V_1 &\to E \\ V_2 &\to 0 \\ V_3 &\to -E \\ V_4 &\to 0 \end{aligned} \qquad (14.18)$$

Note that the peak-to-peak output voltage is now twice E.

If $\tau \gg T$, the waveform doesn't have enough time to decay very much. Intuitively, we would expect V_1 to approximately equal V_2 and V_3 to approximately equal V_4. Indeed, examination of Equation (14.17) verifies this observation. The resulting waveform is shown in the right sketch on Figure 14.7(b). We could find the various voltage values by solving Equation (14.17) or (more quickly) by noting that the average value of the output voltage must be zero. This is true since the series capacitor cannot pass direct current. Because of this, the area of the output curve above zero volts must equal the area of the output curve below zero volts. For long time constants (i.e., $V_2 = V_1$ and $V_4 = V_3$) we then have

$$\begin{aligned} \beta T(V_1) &= -(1-\beta)TV_3 \\ V_3 + E &= V_1 \end{aligned} \qquad (14.19)$$

Finally,

$$V_1 = V_2 = E(1-\beta)$$
$$V_3 = V_4 = -E\beta \tag{14.20}$$

Note that for this case, the output waveform is similar to that of the input, but with a voltage shift.

In designing a system, the choice of time constant is often critical. If narrow pulses are required for a triggering operation, the output must look similar to the first sketch in Figure 14.7(b). We therefore design with a time constant much less than the period of the input. On the other hand, if we wish to reproduce the input at the output, we should choose a time constant much larger than the period of the input.

EXAMPLE 14.2

A symmetrical square wave with a peak-to-peak voltage of 10 V is applied to a high-pass *RC* filter with R = 1 kΩ and C = 1 μF. Sketch the output waveform and identify key voltages. Assume that the frequency of the square wave is

(a) 50 Hz

(b) 500 Hz

(c) 5 kHz

Solution: Note that since the input waveform is symmetrical, it spends an equal portion of the period at positive and at negative values. Therefore β = 1/2 and the previous equations are considerably simplified.

We first find the time constant,

$$\tau = RC = (1\ \text{k}\Omega)(1\ \mu\text{F}) = 1\ \text{ms}$$

and then compare this time constant to the period of the square wave.

(a) $T = 1/f = 20$ msec, which is much larger than the time constant, $\tau \ll T$. Therefore,

$$V_1 = E = 10$$
$$V_3 = -E = -10$$

The result is shown in Figure 14.8(a). Note that the peak-to-peak voltage is 20 volts.

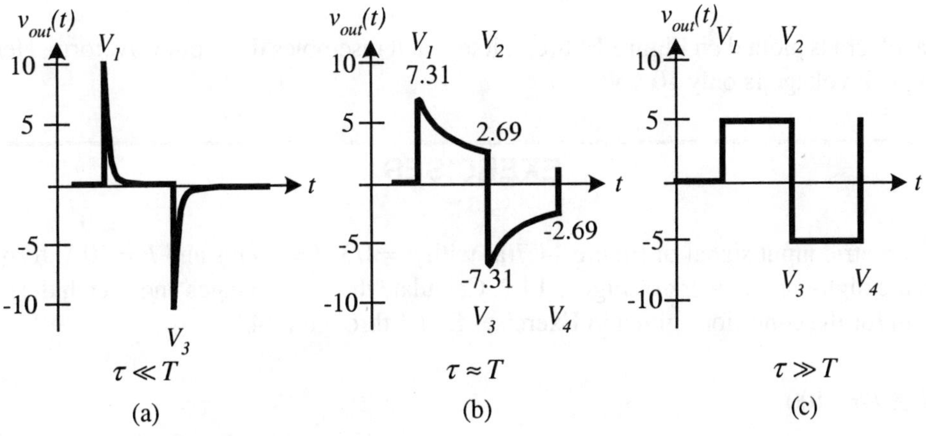

Figure 14.8 – Output waveforms for Example 14.2

(b) For the second input condition,

$$T = \frac{1}{f} = \frac{1}{500} = 2 \text{ ms}$$

For this case, the input period and the time constant are of the same order of magnitude. We solve for the four voltages from Equation (14.17) with $\beta = 0.5$ to find,

$$V_1 = -V_3 = \frac{E\left(1 - e^{-T/2\tau}\right)}{1 - e^{-T/\tau}} = 7.31 \text{ V}$$

$$V_2 = -V_4 = V_1 e^{-T/2\tau} = 2.69 \text{ V}$$

This waveform is shown in Figure 14.8(b). The peak-to-peak voltage is 14.62 volts for this case.

(c) For the third input condition,

$$T = \frac{1}{f} = \frac{1}{5000} = 0.2 \text{ ms}$$

This represents a case where the time constant is much larger than the period of the input. Therefore,

$$V_1 = V_2 = \frac{E}{2} = 5 \text{ V}$$

$$V_3 = V_4 = \frac{E}{2} = -5 \text{ V}$$

This waveform is plotted on Figure 14.8(c). Note that it resembles the input waveform. Here the peak-to-peak voltage is only 10 volts.

EXERCISES

The asymmetric input signal of Figure 14.7(a) with $\beta = 1/3$, $T = 10$ ms and $E = 10$ V forms the input to the high-pass network of Figure 14.2. Calculate the four voltages and sketch the output waveform for the conditions given in Exercises E14.1 through E14.3.

E14.1 Let $T/\tau = 100$

Answer: $V_1 = 10$ V; $V_2 = 0$; $V_3 = -10$ V; $V_4 = 0$

E14.2 Let $T/\tau = 1$

Answer: $V_1 = 7.7$ V; $V_2 = 5.52$ V; $V_3 = -4.48$ V; $V_4 = -2.3$ V

E14.3 Let $T/\tau = 0.01$

Answer: $V_1 = 6.68$ V; $V_2 = 6.66$ V; $V_3 = -3.35$ V; $V_4 = -3.32$ V

14.2 STEADY-STATE RESPONSE OF LOW-PASS *RC* NETWORK TO PULSE TRAIN

We now take the output of the *RC* circuit across the capacitor instead of the resistor. The result is the low-pass *RC* network shown in Figure 14.9.

This network passes low frequencies and attenuates high frequencies. The sinusoidal steady-state amplitude response is shown in Figure 14.10 where the solid line is the actual curve and the dashed line is the Bode plot asymptotic approximation.

The transfer function for the circuit of Figure 14.9 is given by

$$\frac{V_{out}}{V_{in}} = \frac{1}{1+s\tau} \qquad (14.21)$$

$$\tau = RC$$

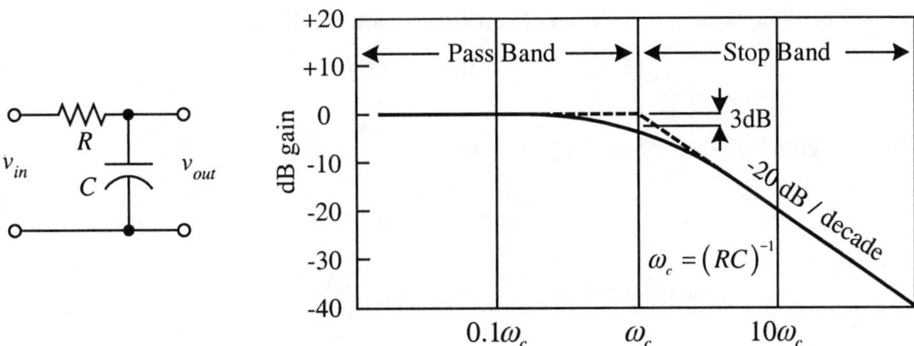

Figure 14.9 – Low-pass *RC* network

Figure 14.10 – Amplitude Response of low-pass network

Let us turn our attention to the square wave input shown in Figure 14.11(a). We will want the response for both a symmetrical and asymmetrical pulse train. We start with the asymmetrical since we will be able to consider the symmetrical to be a special case of this.

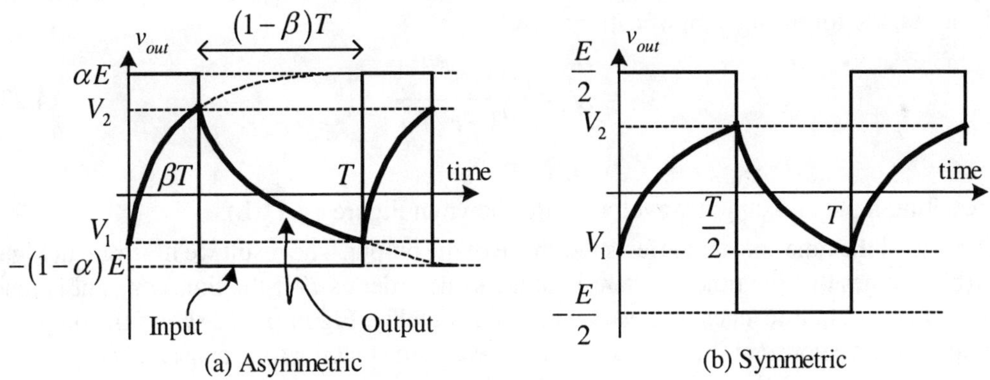

Figure 14.11 - Input and output of low-pass filter

Both the square wave input and the resulting output are shown on the same set of axes.

Since the output voltage is taken across the capacitor, it cannot change instantaneously. We first examine the region between $t = 0$ and $t = \beta T$. The initial value of this exponential waveform is V_1. The final value is the value the voltage would attain if given infinite time. Thus,

$$V_{initial} = V_1$$
$$V_{final} = \alpha E \qquad (14.22)$$

These two values are used in the general expression of Equation (14.6) to find the waveform in the first interval:

$$v_{out}(t)=\alpha E+(V_I-\alpha E)e^{-t/\tau} \tag{14.23}$$

Evaluating this expression at $t = \beta T$ yields an expression for V_2 as follows:

$$v_{out}(\beta T)=V_2=\alpha E+(V_I-\alpha E)e^{-\beta T/\tau} \tag{14.24}$$

For the next region between βT and T, we have

$$\begin{aligned} V_{final} &= -(1-\alpha)E \\ V_{initial} &= V_2 \\ v_{out}(t) &= -(1-\alpha)E+(V_2+E-\alpha E)e^{-(t-\beta T)/\tau} \end{aligned} \tag{14.25}$$

Evaluating this expression at $t = T$ yields the second equation in the two unknowns.

$$v_{out}(T)=V_I=-(1-\alpha)E+(V_2+E-\alpha E)e^{-(1-\beta)T/\tau} \tag{14.26}$$

We next solve these two equations to obtain expressions for V_I and V_2. We will see this solution in Example 14.3 (it is easier to solve these simultaneous equations when numbers are given for the parameters.)

If the input waveform voltage values are symmetrical, α is 1/2. If the input waveform spends an equal amount of time at both positive and negative values, then β is also 1/2. Substituting these values, the following simplifications result.

$$V_2=-V_I=\frac{E\left(1-e^{T/2\tau}\right)}{2\left(1+e^{T/2\tau}\right)} \tag{14.27}$$

The resulting input and output waveforms are shown in Figure 14.11(b).

The size of the time constant affects the shape of the output. The result we illustrate in Figure 14.11(b) assumes that the time constant is of the same order as T. If the time constant is much less than T, the output reaches its steady-state value quickly. Figure 14.12 shows the output for two values of time constant. In Figure 14.12(a) we assume that the time constant is of the same order as T. Note from Equation (14.27) that the larger the time constant, the smaller the amplitude of the output. Figure 14.12(b) shows the output for a time constant much less than the input period, T. For this case, the amplitude is approximately 1/2, and the output resembles the input.

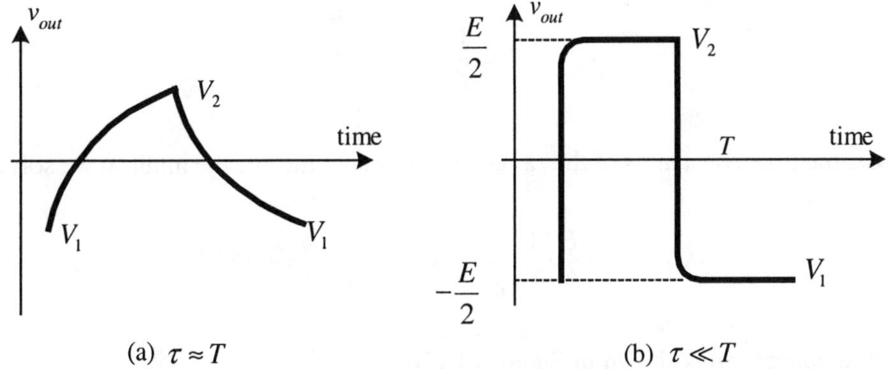

(a) $\tau \approx T$ (b) $\tau \ll T$

Figure 14.12 - Output of low-pass *RC* filter with symmetrical square wave input

If the input waveform is not symmetrical about the zero axis, α is not equal to 1/2. It is not necessary to re-derive all of the expressions. The results of Figure 14.12 are simply shifted in the vertical direction by the average value of the input wave.

EXAMPLE 14.3

A symmetric square wave, with a peak-to-peak voltage of 5 V, is applied to the low-pass *RC* filter of Figure 14.9 with $R = 10\ \text{k}\Omega$, $C = 0.1\ \mu\text{F}$. Sketch the output voltage waveform and identify key voltages for the following three values of the square wave frequency:

(a) 50 Hz
(b) 500 Hz
(c) 5 kHz

Solution: The time constant of the circuit is

$$\tau = RC = (10\,k\Omega)(0.1\,\mu F) = 1 \text{ ms}$$

(a) The period of the input is

$$T = \frac{1}{f} = 20 \text{ ms}$$

In this case, the time constant is much less than the period, so

$$-V_1 = +V_2 = \frac{E}{2} = 2.5 \text{ V}$$

The output is as shown in Figure 14.12(b).

(b) The period of the input is

$$T = \frac{1}{f} = 2 \text{ ms}$$

In this case, the time constant is of the same order of magnitude of the input so we solve for the two key voltages,

$$-V_1 = V_2 = \frac{E}{2} \cdot \frac{1 - e^{-T/2\tau}}{1 + e^{-T/2\tau}} = 2.5\, \frac{1 - e^{-1}}{1 + e^{-1}} = 1.155 \text{ V}$$

The resulting waveform is shown in Figure 14.12(a).

(c) The period is given by

$$T = \frac{1}{f} = 0.2 \text{ ms}$$

The time constant is much greater than the period and the output is close to zero. The values of the key voltages are found as in part (b) of this example.

$$-V_1 = V_2 = \frac{E}{2} \cdot \frac{1 - e^{-T/2\tau}}{1 + e^{-T/2\tau}} = 2.5 \cdot \frac{1 - e^{-0.1}}{1 + e^{-0.1}} = 0.125 \quad \text{V}$$

Now we will examine the response of the low-pass filter to the ramp input shown in Figure 14.13. The output is found is the same manner as is done for the high-pass filter, and is given by

$$v_{out}(t) = \left(-\alpha\tau + \alpha t + \alpha\tau e^{-t/\tau}\right) u(t) \tag{14.28}$$

This is shown as the solid line in the figure. Once again α is the slope of the input ramp in volts per second. The transient causes a slight rounding at the start of the output.

EXAMPLE 14.4

The ramp input of Figure 14.13 is applied to a low-pass *RC* filter with a corner frequency of 5000 rad/sec. The slope of the input ramp is 10 volts/second. Calculate and sketch the output voltage waveform.

Solution: The time constant is the inverse of the 3-dB frequency, so

$$\tau = \frac{1}{5000}\, s$$

The output waveform is written directly from Equation (14.28).

$$v_{out}(t) = \left(-\alpha\tau + \alpha t + \alpha\tau e^{-t/\tau}\right)u(t)$$

$$= (-0.002 + 10t + 0.002e^{-5000t})u(t)$$

This is plotted in Figure 14.14.

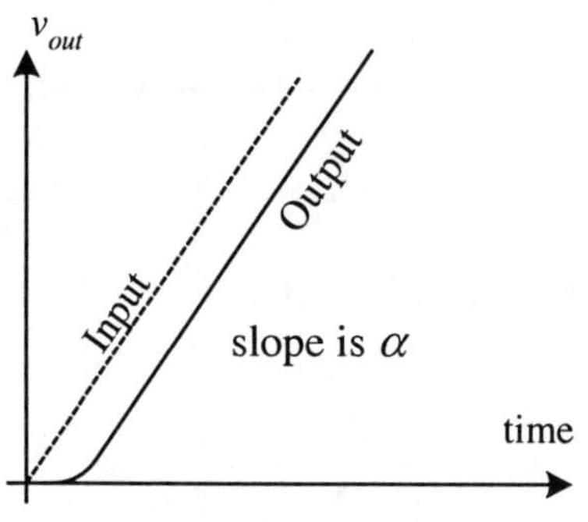

Figure 14.13 – Low-pass *RC* filter response

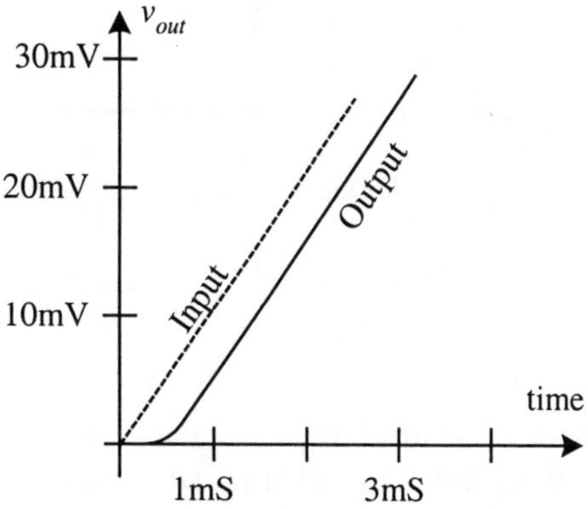

Figure 14.14 – Response for ramp Example 14.4

14.3 DIODES

Diodes are often coupled with *RC* networks to achieve desirable results. In performing an approximate analysis of such circuits, we use the piecewise linear diode model shown in Figure 14.15.

When the diode is forward biased and therefore conducting, it is represented by a small forward resistance, R_f. (We are neglecting the forward voltage, V_{ON}). When the diode is reverse-biased, it is represented by a large reverse resistance, R_r.

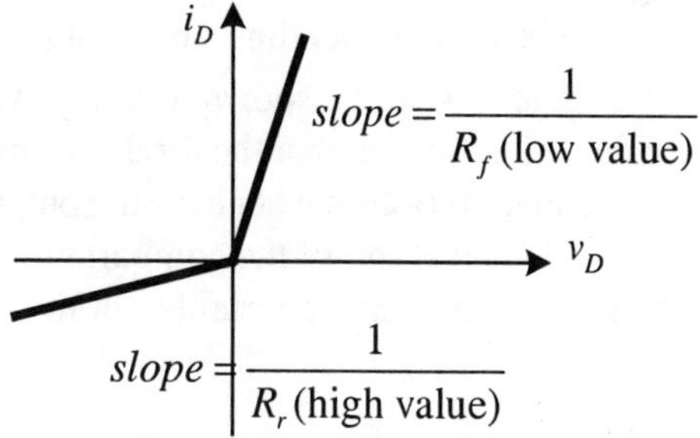

Figure 14.15 - Diode model

14.3.1 Steady-State Response of Diode Circuit to Pulse Train

Circuits used in digital applications often combine resistors, capacitors and diodes. One such configuration is shown in Figure 14.16(a).

In the following analysis, we will ignore the load resistance, R_{load}. That is, we will assume that it is large compared to the resistance of the diode. In fact, this is really not true when the diode is back biased. Ignoring the resistance will greatly simplify the equations. As you will see in

Example 14.5, modification of the results to account for R_{load} is quite simple. We simply replace the diode resistance by the parallel combination of that resistance with the load resistance.

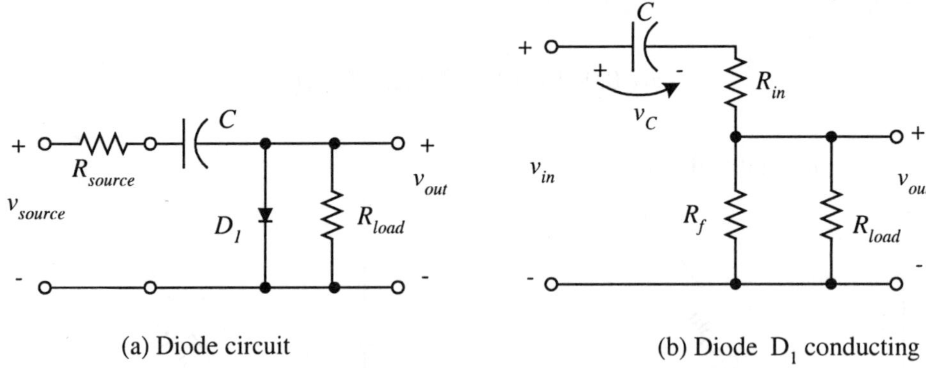

Figure 14.16 (parts a and b) – Circuit configuration

If the diode is ideal, the circuit acts as a *clamper*. The capacitor cannot discharge, so it charges to the peak value of the input. The output is therefore "clamped" to a zero voltage level since the capacitor voltage subtracts from the input.

If the pulse train in Figure 14.17(a) forms the input, the circuit behaves in a manner similar to that of the *RC* circuit analyzed earlier in this chapter.

The only difference is that two different time constants apply depending on the state of the diode.

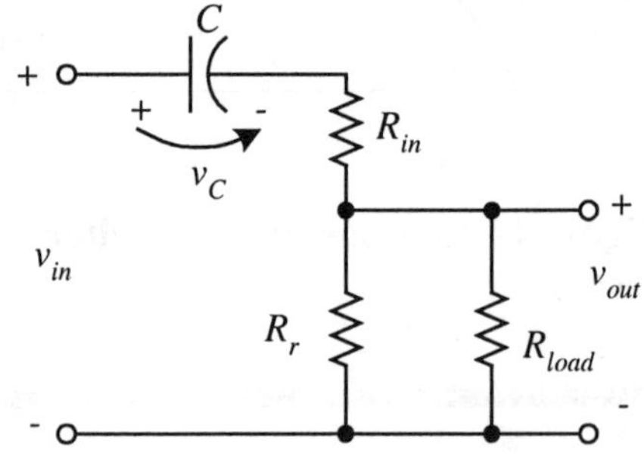

(c) Diode D_1 not conducting

Figure 14.16 (c) – Circuit configuration

Figure 14.16(b) shows the equivalent circuit under the condition that the diode is forward-biased. This situation occurs whenever the output is positive. Figure 14.16(c) shows the comparable situation for negative outputs, when the diode is reverse-biased. The two time constants, for the forward and reverse-biased condition, are therefore given by

$$\tau_f = (R_f + R_{in})C \qquad (14.29)$$
$$\tau_r = (R_r + R_{in})C$$

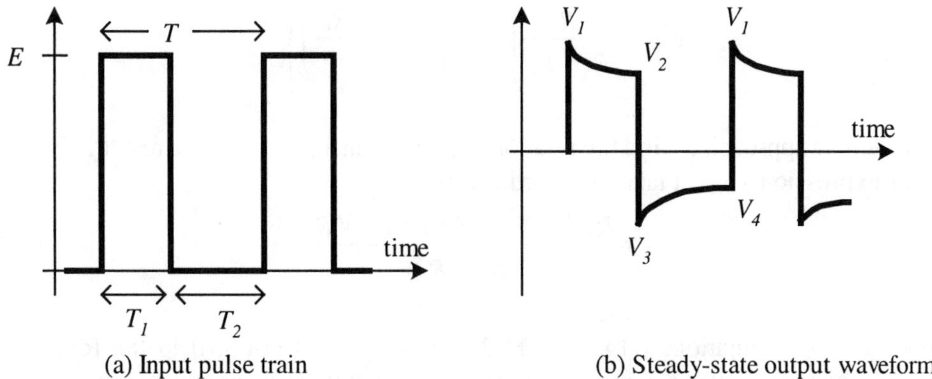

(a) Input pulse train (b) Steady-state output waveform

Figure 14.17 – Steady-state response of diode circuit

Note that since $R_r >> R_f$, $\tau_r >> \tau_f$. The steady-state output due to the pulse train of Figure 14.17(a) is shown in Figure 14.17(b). We are assuming that V_1 and V_2 are positive, and V_3 and V_4 are negative. This assumption is needed to be able to determine the state of the diode. After solving the equations, if we find the assumption is incorrect, we need to re-solve the problem. This "guess and check" technique is quite common for solving circuits with diodes.

We need four equations in order to find V_1, V_2, V_3 and V_4. As in the earlier circuit without the diode, two of these equations come from the exponential decay relationship and the other two come from the magnitude of the voltage transitions. The exponential decay relationships are

$$\begin{aligned} V_2 &= V_1 \cdot e^{-T_1/\tau_f} \\ V_4 &= V_3 \cdot e^{-T_2/\tau_r} \end{aligned} \tag{14.30}$$

At the instant before the input voltage drops by E volts, the output is at V_2. When the input drops, the capacitor voltage cannot change instantaneously. Therefore, the voltage across the series combination of R_{in} and R_f must drop by E volts. If the resistor value did not change from R_f to R_r during this transition, we could simply use a voltage divider formula to find the relationship between V_3 and V_2. Since the state of the diode does indeed change during this transition, we must find the new output by examining the capacitor voltage (since that cannot jump). The capacitor voltage just prior to this transition is found by writing a loop equation for the circuit of Figure 14.16(b). The loop equation yields a capacitor voltage of

$$v_C = E - V_2 - \frac{R_{in}}{R_f} V_2 = E - \frac{V_2(R_f + R_{in})}{R_f} \tag{14.31}$$

At the instant after the input voltage drops to zero, the capacitor voltage is still at this value. The new value of the output is found by writing a loop equation for the circuit in Figure 14.16(c). This equivalent is used since the diode is now reverse-biased. The result is:

$$V_3 = -\frac{R_r}{R_r + R_{in}}\left[E - V_2\left(\frac{R_f + R_{in}}{R_f}\right)\right] \qquad (14.32)$$

We use a similar approach to find the relationship between V_1 and V_4. The result is (you should verify this expression - don't take our word for it)

$$V_1 = \frac{R_f E + V_4 R_f (R_r + R_{in})/R_r}{R_f + R_{in}} \qquad (14.33)$$

We now have four equations [(14.30), (14.31), (14.32), and (14.33)] in the four unknown voltages. Rather than give a general solution (which will look complex due to the many parameters), we will defer solution of the four equations until the examples where numbers substitute for the various parameter symbols.

EXAMPLE 14.5

You are given the circuit of Figure 14.16(a) with $R_{in} = 100\ \Omega$; $R_f = 100\ \Omega$; $R_r = 1\ \text{M}\Omega$; $R_{load} = 10\ \text{k}\Omega$; $C = 1\ \mu\text{F}$. Find the critical voltages of the output waveform if the input is as shown in Figure 14.18.

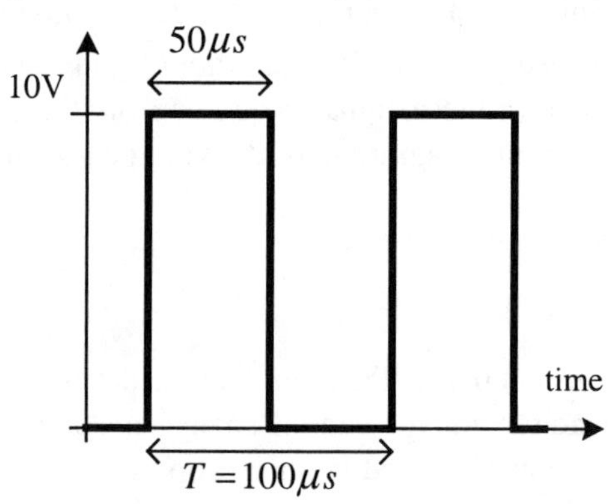

Solution: Since $R_{load} >> R_f$ and $R_r >> R_{load}$, the parallel combination of the diode and the load resistance simply looks like the diode for forward bias and like the load resistor for back bias. That is,

$$R_{load} \| R_f \approx R_f$$

$$R_{load} \| R_r \approx R_{load}$$

Figure 14.18 – Input waveform for Example 14.5

We now evaluate the two time constants.

$$\tau_f = (R_f + R_{in})C = 200\ \mu\text{s}$$

$$\tau_r = (R_{load} + R_{in})C = 10\ \text{ms}$$

The four equations derived above then yield,

$$10 = 2V_1 - 1.0001V_4$$

$$10 = 2V_2 - 1.0001V_3$$

$$V_2 = V_1 e^{-1/4} = 0.78V_1$$

$$V_4 = V_3 e^{-0.005} = 0.995V_3$$

Solving these four equations for the four unknown voltages yields,

$V_1 = 0.11$ V $\qquad V_2 = 0.09$ V

$V_3 = -9.73$ V $\qquad V_4 = -9.68$ V

The input waveform is repeated in Figure 14.19(a) for comparison to the resulting output waveform plotted in Figure 14.19(b).

Note that both time constants are large compared to the period of the input, so the exponentials do not decay appreciably between transitions. Further note that the derivation of this section neglected the diode forward voltage, V_{ON}. Since V_1 and V_2 turned out to be of the same order of magnitude as V_{ON}, the model used in this section is less accurate for this example. When we include the effect of V_{ON}, we have the same wave shape shown in Figure 14.19, but the curve is shifted by the V_{ON} voltage.

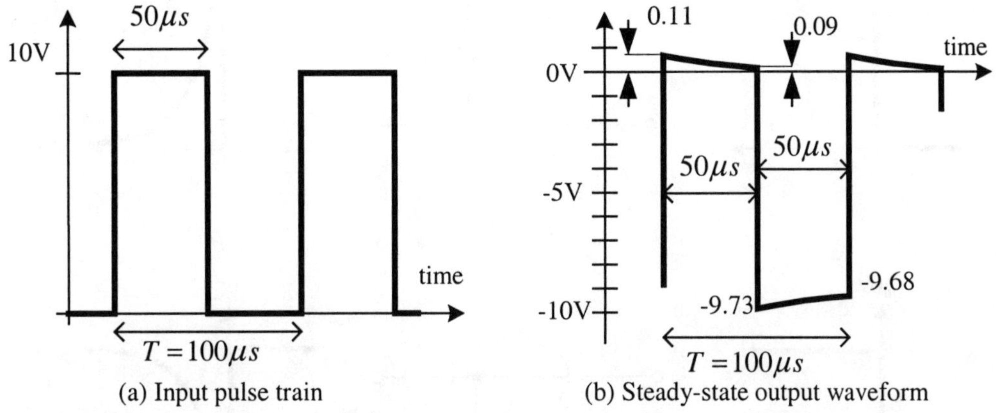

(a) Input pulse train

(b) Steady-state output waveform

Figure 14.19 – Solution for Example 14.5

14.4 TRIGGER CIRCUITS

Binary digital systems operate with discrete time signals. That is, since the information is contained in sequences of binary digits, each of these bits occurs at a specific time. *Timing* is therefore extremely important and transitions must occur at carefully controlled points in time. Many digital circuits require a trigger pulse to be generated and this trigger pulse is used to control the timing.

Trigger pulses are usually generated at either the leading or trailing edge of a pulse train. As one example, consider the *positive edge trigger* of Figure 14.20(a).

The input to the circuit is a pulse which has a transition between 0 and E volts. This step function is applied to the high-pass RC network. Equation (14.6) can be used to find the output for $t > 0$.

$$v_{out}(t) = Ee^{-t/\tau}u(t) \tag{14.34}$$

In this case, $\tau = RC$ resulting in a positive going trigger pulse. The trigger pulse is narrow, with the width dependent on the RC time constant. It can be used for accurate timing purposes.

The *negative edge trigger* is shown in Figure 14.20(b). The output is also shown in the diagram. For $t > 0$, the output is found from Equation (14.6) to be

$$v_{out}(t) = E\left(1 - e^{-t/\tau}\right) \tag{14.35}$$

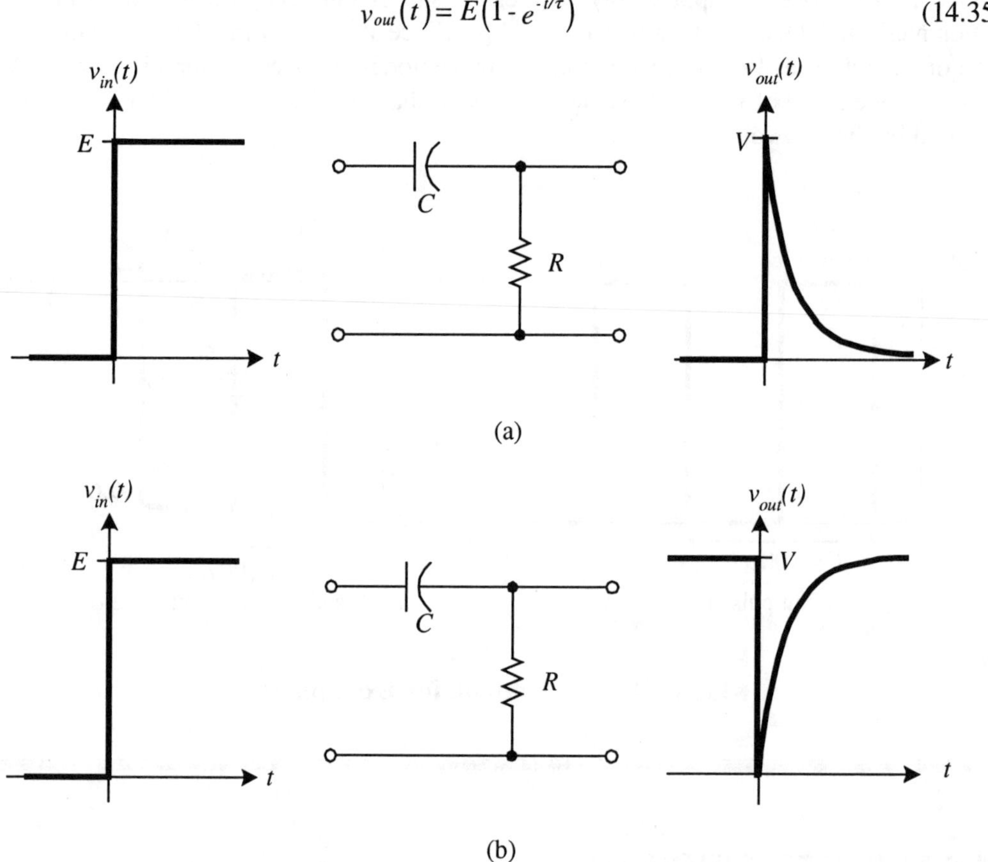

Figure 14.20 – Trigger circuits

The exponential decay of both of these outputs can be shortened by reducing the time constant. In the next chapter, we shall explore methods of making the output pulse even sharper.

14.4.1 Pulse Train Response

The networks of the previous section detected both a positive and negative edge of a single step function. We now study a pulse train as the input to an RC circuit. The input and corresponding output are shown in Figure 14.21(a).

The output is comprised of a series of positive and negative going pulses of amplitude E volts.

Recall from the discussion of Figure 14.7(b) that sharp pulses of this type occur if the time constant is much smaller than the period of the input. Therefore, the RC product must be

$$\tau = RC \ll T \tag{14.36}$$

We often require only a negative going pulse to act as a trigger, so a diode can be used to remove the positive going pulses. This is shown in Figure 14.21(b). If the diode is reversed, the negative going pulses are removed and the positive going pulses remain.

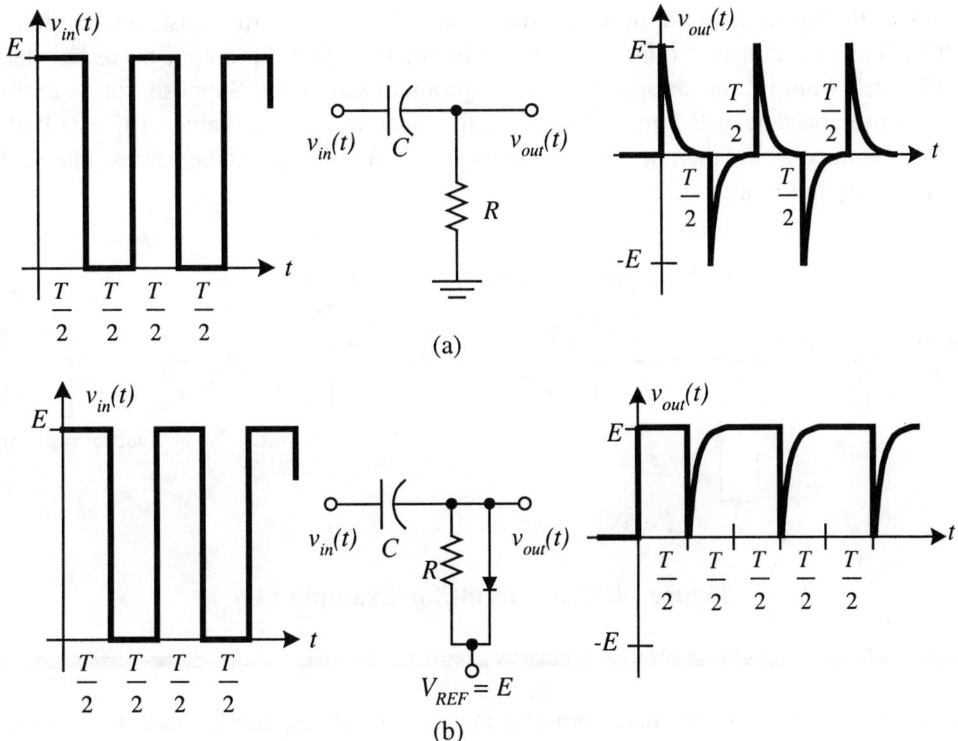

Figure 14.21 – Response to a pulse train

EXAMPLE 14.6

A symmetrical 60 Hz rectangular pulse train forms the input to the system shown in Figure 14.22(a). Design a circuit to develop a trigger pulse which must be less than 2 ms wide, and exists only on the negative-going edges of the input clock pulse train.

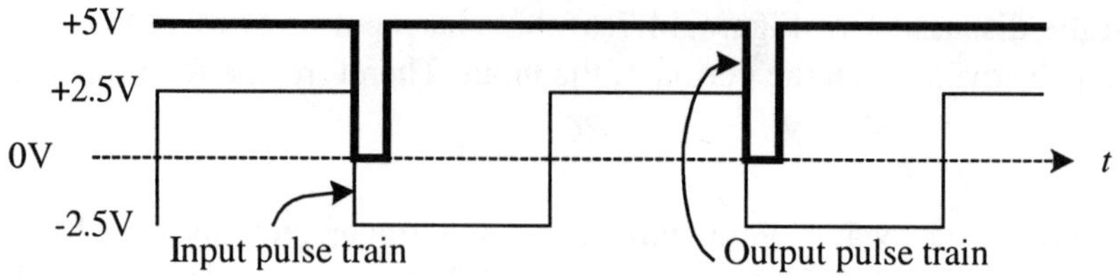

Figure 14.22(a)

Solution: The period of the input is 16.7 ms, so we want the RC time constant to be much less than this. The time constant must be sufficiently small so that the output pulse has decayed almost to zero within 2 ms, as specified in the problem statement. Suppose, for example, we choose a time constant of 0.5 ms. If we were to select a capacitor value of $C = 0.1\ \mu F$, the required resistance would then be 5 kΩ to force the RC time constant to be 0.5 ms. The resulting circuit is shown in Figure 14.22(b).

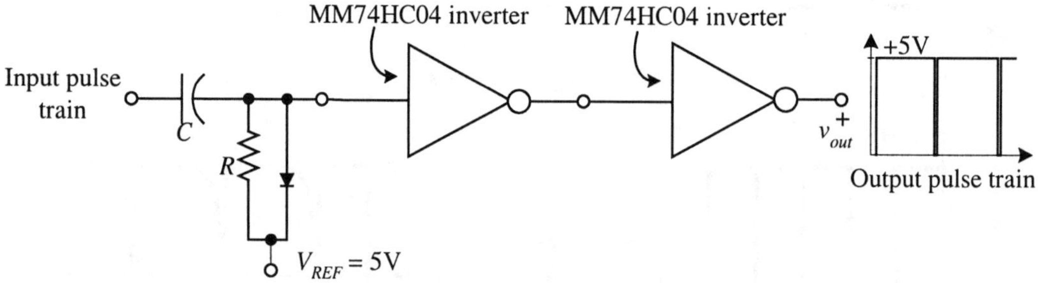

Figure 14.22(b) Circuit for Example 14.6

A *buffer*, which can be formed from two inverters in series, can be used at the output of Figure 14.22(b). The buffer changes this exponential signal to a rectangular pulse and provides a low output impedance. We discuss this in more detail later.

14.5 THE 555 TIMER

Although this chapter is intended to introduce *digital* electronics, the circuits and signals we have been discussing so far are analog. They are operating upon, and producing waveforms that take on a continuum of values rather than simply responding to one of two levels.

There exists a class of devices that possess the characteristics of both analog and digital circuits. Within this class are *timers* and *waveform generators.* The major characteristic of these circuits is that the time (period) may be set either by an external voltage or by a resistor-capacitor combination. These devices often have external control lines so that the frequency or the pulse width may be easily controlled by an external source.

In this section we present two useful types of relaxation oscillator. Other types can be found in the IC data books supplied by the manufacturers (in hard copy or on the Internet).

14.5.1 The Relaxation Oscillator

We ease our way into timing circuits by first analyzing the op-amp *relaxation oscillator* as shown in Figure 14.23(a).

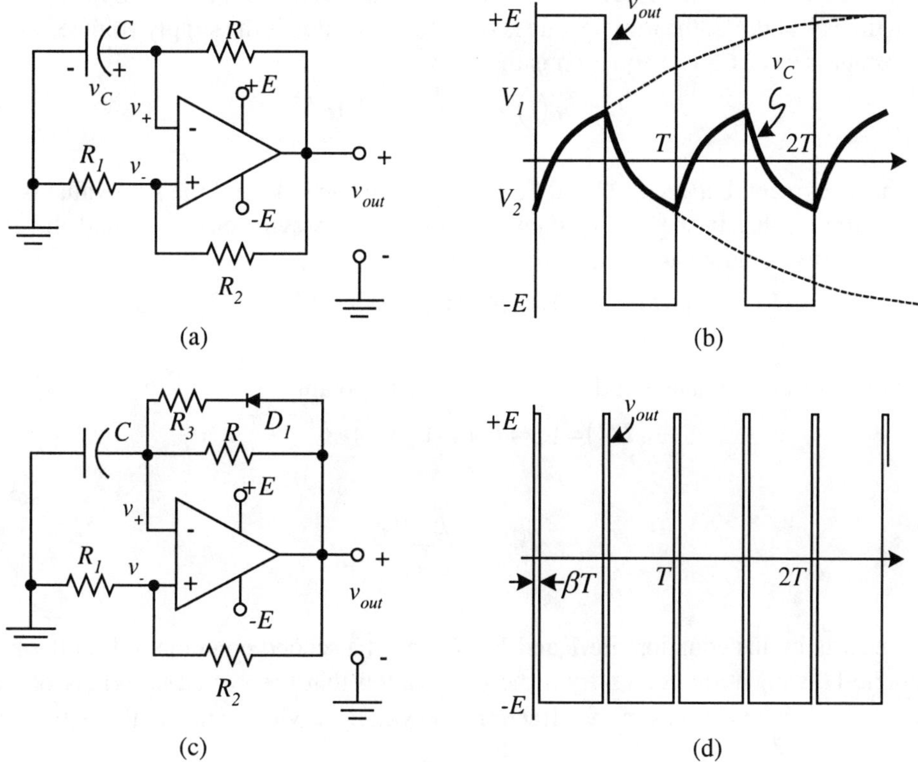

Figure 14.23 – Relaxation oscillator

The voltage at the non-inverting input of the op-amp is obtained by feeding the output voltage back through a resistor divider composed of R_1 and R_2. The voltage at the inverting input is developed across the capacitor as part of an RC combination. This is *positive feedback* so the amplifier has only two possible outputs: $+E$ or $-E$. This is true since the gain is very high. If the differential input ($v_+ - v_-$) is positive, the op-amp output saturates at a value near the positive supply voltage. If the differential input is negative, the output saturates at a value near the negative of the supply voltage.

The following analysis assumes that zero current flows into the op-amp. Let's first suppose the output is positive. The non-inverting input stays constant at a fraction $[R_1/(R_1+R_2)]$ of the output voltage. The inverting input voltage is equal to the voltage across the capacitor, and the capacitor exponentially charges toward the output voltage with time constant, RC. At some point, this increasing inverting input voltage causes the op-amp to switch to the other state and the output voltage goes negative. Once the output switches to the negative supply voltage, the capacitor starts discharging toward this negative value. The non-inverting input is at a fraction of the negative output voltage. The circuit stays in this state until the differential input once again becomes positive.

From the above discussion, we see the output is a square wave as shown in Figure 14.23(b). The capacitor voltage, v_C, is also shown in this figure. We find the equation for the exponential curve by using the initial and final values and the time constant. For the first segment of the curve between times 0 and $T/2$, the initial value is $-V_I$, the final value is the supply voltage, $+E$, and the time constant is $\tau = RC$. The equation is therefore

$$v_-(t) = v_C(t) = E + (-V_I - E)e^{-t/RC} \tag{14.37}$$

For the next segment, between $T/2$ and T, the starting value is V_I and the final value is $-E$. Note we are assuming that in the steady state, the waveform is symmetrical around the zero axis (otherwise there would be an additional unknown voltage).

$$v_-(t) = v_C(t) = -E + (V_I + E)e^{-(t-T/2)/(RC)} \tag{14.38}$$

These equations are evaluated at the transition time to obtain[1]

$$v_-(T/2) = V_I = E + (-V_I - E)e^{-T/(2RC)}$$

$$e^{-T/(2RC)} = \frac{E - V_I}{E + V_I} \tag{14.39}$$

The unknowns in this equation are T and V_I. We need a second equation to find the period of oscillation. This equation comes from the observation that the switching points occur when $v_+ = v_-$. In both states, v_+ is simply a fraction (the voltage divider ratio) of the output. Thus,

$$V_I = \frac{R_I \cdot E}{R_I + R_2} \tag{14.40}$$

and we have enough equations to solve for the unknowns (given the resistor values and the source voltages). As an example suppose the two divider resistors are equal, $R_I = R_2$. We then have

[1]In formulating these equations, we can simplify the expressions by shifting any of the exponential segments to the origin. In this manner, we don't need to carry delay factors such as $(t - T/2)$, and the final equations are identical to those found in this section.

$$e^{-T/2RC} = \frac{1}{3}$$

$$\frac{-T}{2RC} = \ln\left(\frac{1}{3}\right) = -1.1$$

$$T = 2.2RC \tag{14.41}$$

$$f = \frac{1}{T} = \frac{0.455}{RC} \quad \text{Hz}$$

This results assumes the op-amp is ideal. As we learned in Chapter 9, the op-amp gain reduces with increasing frequency. Therefore, if the oscillation frequency is too high, the equations must be modified.

Suppose now that we desire an *asymmetrical* pulse train at the output of the oscillator. The circuit of Figure 14.23(c) is used to produce the waveform of Figure 14.23(d). Note that a diode is added in order to permit two different time constants to exist. When the diode is ON, the charging path for the capacitor is through a resistance made up of R in parallel with R_3 (we are neglecting the forward resistance of the diode). When the diode is OFF, the discharge path is through a resistor of value R.

EXAMPLE 14.7

Find the output of the circuit of Figure 14.23(c) if

$C = 0.1\ \mu\text{F}$; $R = 20\ \text{k}\Omega$; $R_1 = R_2$; $R_3 = 1\ \text{k}\Omega$

Solution: We first find the two time constants for charging and discharging the capacitor.

$$\tau_c = C\left(R \| R_3\right) = 0.095 \text{ ms}$$

$$\tau_d = RC = 2 \text{ ms}$$

The equation for the first portion of the waveform is

$$v_-(t) = E + \left(-V_1 - E\right)e^{-t/0.095 \text{ ms}}$$

Since $R_1 = R_2$, the transition occurs when this voltage reaches $E/2$ since. Thus,

$$v_-(\beta T) = E + \left(-V_1 - E\right)e^{-\beta T/0.095 \text{ ms}} = \frac{E}{2}$$

but setting $V_1 = E/2$ yields

$$\exp\left(\frac{-\beta T}{\tau_c}\right) = \frac{1}{3}$$

$$\beta T = 0.1 \text{ ms}$$

For the discharge region,

$$v_-(t) = -E + (V_1 + E)\exp\left(\frac{-(t - \beta T)}{\tau_d}\right)$$

Setting $t = T$ for the second transition yields

$$v_-(T) = -\frac{E}{2} = -E + \left(\frac{E}{2} + E\right)\exp\left(\frac{-(T - \beta T)}{\tau_d}\right)$$

$$(1 - \beta)T = 2.2 \text{ ms}$$

$$T = \beta T + (1 - \beta)T = 2.3 \text{ ms}$$

14.5.2 The 555 as an Oscillator

We now focus our attention on the very useful *555 timer*. This unique, inexpensive, and accurate device can operate in two modes:

(1) As a free-running oscillator producing a continuous square wave of variable frequency and duty cycle (time high/period). We term this mode the *astable mode* since the 555 is operating as a free-running oscillator.

(2) As a single-pulse generator to generate an accurate pulse output. This mode is termed the *monostable mode*. In this mode, the circuit is not free running but produces a single pulse of predetermined duration each time a trigger pulse is applied at the input.

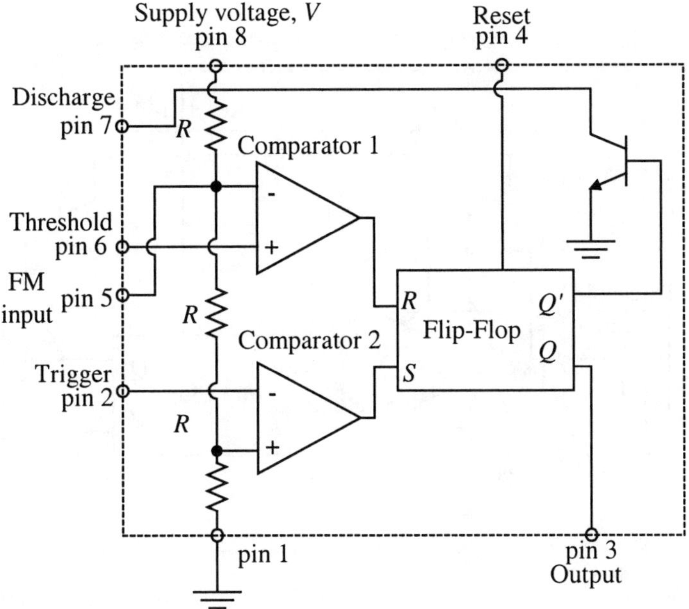

Figure 14.24 – Block diagram of the 555 timer

The 555 consists of a mixture of digital and analog circuitry. Figure 14.24 illustrates a block diagram of the 555.

The circuit contains analog comparators, amplifiers, buffers, and a flip-flop. Although we cover flip-flops in Chapter 16, a basic knowledge is sufficient for now (the kind of things you learn in a basic digital logic course). You can think of the *set-reset flip-flop* as an electrically operated switch. *Setting* the switch causes the output, Q, to go high (approximately to the supply voltage) and *resetting* the flip-flop causes the output to go low (almost to zero). The basic flip-flop also has two outputs, Q and its inverse, Q'. In reality, one output can easily be derived from the other using an inverter.

The three resistors, R, are used as a voltage divider to provide 2/3 and 1/3 of the supply voltage levels to the analog comparators.

Pin 2 (trigger) and pin 6 (threshold) control the output of the 555 circuit. When the voltage at pin 6 goes above the 2/3 supply level, the output of comparator 1 goes to the positive supply voltage, and the flip-flop *resets*. This causes the output (pin 3) to go low, and the complementary output, Q', goes high. This complementary output biases the discharge transistor ON (i.e., the transistor is saturated), causing its output (pin 7) to go low.

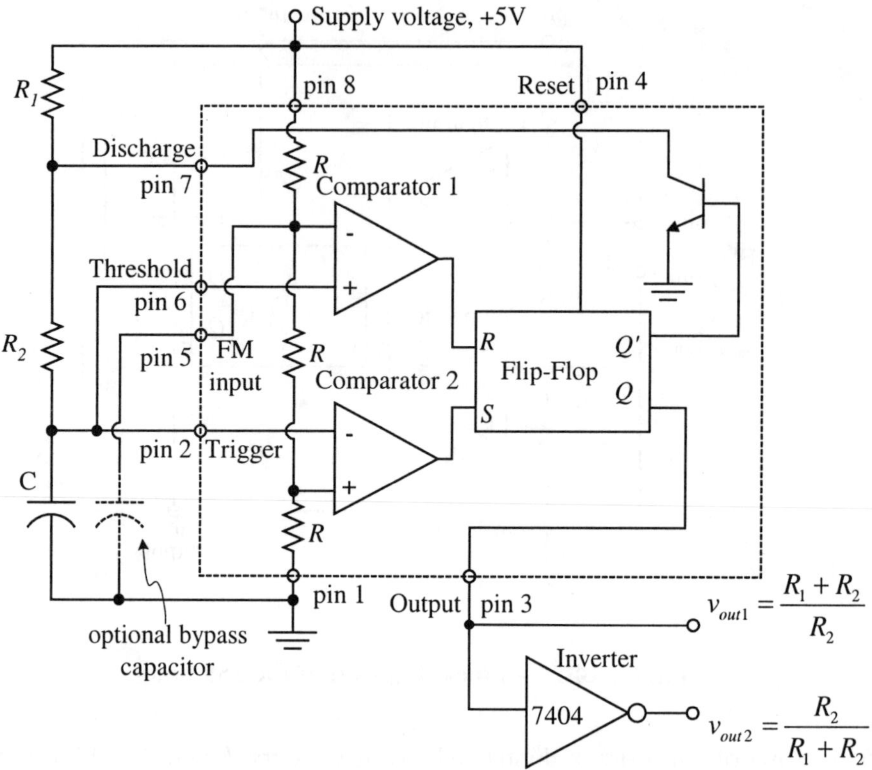

Figure 14.25(a) – The 555 as a pulse generator

When the voltage at pin 2 is less than the 1/3 supply level, comparator 2 has a positive output, and the flip-flop *sets*. This causes the output to go high, and the complementary output is low. The discharge transistor is then cut off, and the discharge pin 7 is allowed to float.

Pin 4 is used to reset the flip-flop. By connecting pin 4 to ground, the flip-flop resets to low. When not in use, this pin is connected to the positive supply. Pin 4 is used to disable the 555 since the output is zero when pin 4 is set to 0 volts. The output oscillates normally when pin 4 is positive [typically +5 V].

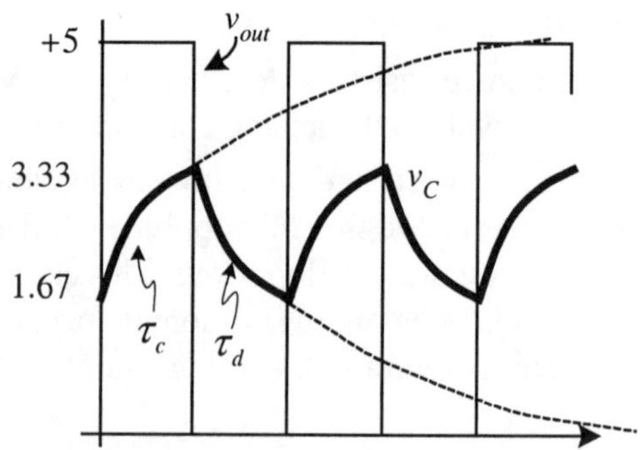

Figure 14.25(b) – Waveforms for pulse generator

The 555 can be used as a pulse generator (astable mode) if configured as shown in Figure 14.25(a).

Let us first assume that the output is high (i.e., the complementary output is low), so the flip-flop is *set*. The discharge, pin 7, is floating (i.e., the transistor is cut off). The external circuitry is really simply a series combination of two resistors and a capacitor between the positive supply and ground (the op-amps draw no current). The capacitor then starts to charge through R_1 and R_2, as shown in Figure 14.25(b). At some point, the capacitor voltage reaches 2/3 of the supply voltage [10/3 V for the +5 V shown]. This forces the output of comparator 1 to go high, thus *resetting* the flip-flop. The flip-flop output goes low, and the complementary output goes high. This saturates the transistor, and pin 7 goes low.

With pin 7 low, the capacitor starts to discharge through R_2 (i.e., R_1 is no longer a consideration since it is connected between the positive source and ground). When the capacitor has discharged to a value of 1/3 of the supply, the comparator pin 2 goes high, and the flip-flop *sets*. The cycle then repeats.

The capacitor voltage therefore goes exponentially between 1/3 and 2/3 of the supply voltage. The charging and discharging time constants are given by

$$\begin{aligned} \tau_c &= (R_1 + R_2)C \\ \tau_d &= R_2 C \end{aligned} \tag{14.42}$$

During charging, the capacitor voltage starts at 1/3 of the supply and exponentially charges toward the supply. Switching takes place when the voltage reaches 2/3 of the supply. The reverse is true during discharge where the capacitor voltages starts at 2/3 of the supply, and exponentially discharges toward zero.

We can find the critical times without writing extensive equations. During both charging and discharging, switching occurs when the capacitor has gone half-way between its initial and final value. An exponential reaches 50% of its total value after 0.693 of a time constant. Therefore, the charging and discharging times are given by

$$\begin{aligned} T_c &= 0.693(R_1 + R_2)C \\ T_d &= 0.693 R_2 C \end{aligned} \tag{14.43}$$

The output is high during charge and low during discharge. The total period of the square wave output is given by the sum of the two times.

$$T = 0.693(R_1 + 2R_2)C \tag{14.44}$$

The *frequency* is the reciprocal of this, as follows:

$$f = \frac{1}{T} = \frac{1.44}{(R_1 + 2R_2)C} \tag{14.45}$$

When the 555 is connected to +5 V, the output pulse train goes from 0 to +5 V. As we will see in Chapter 15, this is compatible with TTL circuits. The circuit can operate with supply voltages in the range of 4 V to 15 V. The output is capable of supplying more than 100 mA if required. Therefore, it can directly drive a small loudspeaker.

The *duty cycle* is found as the ratio of the time high to the period (i.e., the *fraction* of time high). Then

$$Duty\ cycle = \frac{time\ high}{T} = \frac{T_c}{T_c + T_d} = \frac{R_1 + R_2}{R_1 + 2R_2} \tag{14.46}$$

Note that the duty cycle ranges from 1/2 (when $R_2 >> R_1$) to 1 (when $R_1 >> R_2$). If we desire a duty cycle less than 1/2, we can use an inverter to invert the output of the 555.

EXAMPLE 14.8

Design an astable 555 square wave generator to deliver a 1 kHz output signal with a duty cycle of approximately 50%

Solution: We take this opportunity to give some practical limitations of the 555 timer. The capacitance should be kept larger than 500 pF (5×10^{-10} F) to swamp out stray capacitance. Since one end of the capacitor is connected to ground, we can use *electrolytics* of high capacitance to produce low frequencies. Each of the resistors, R_1 and R_2, should be larger than 1 kΩ to limit the current. The sum, $R_1 + R_2$ should be no larger than 3.3 MΩ. It should be noted that with these constraints, we cannot achieve a frequency of greater than about 1 MHz using the circuit of Figure 14.25.

As in all design problems, there are more unknowns than there are equations. We are free to choose some of the components based on unstated criteria, or on component availability. Let us select $C = 0.01$ μF. We wish to have a duty cycle of nearly 50% That is, we desire the waveform to spend about as much time at the positive value as at the zero value. The discharge time should then be the same as the charging time. Equation (14.43) indicates that these times cannot be exactly equal. If we choose R_2 to be much greater than R_1, the times are close to being equal. Let us assume that this is the case. The frequency is then approximately given by

$$f = 1\,\text{kHz} \approx \frac{1.44}{2R_2C}$$

Using the assumed value of C, this yields,

$$R_2 = 72\ \text{k}\Omega$$

We can choose R_1 to be about 1 kΩ and still be within the design guidelines given above. The design is then complete.

The 555 is relatively insensitive to supply voltage variation because the comparator values are determined by the three equal resistors (R). Since the external C, R_1 and R_2 are driven from the same supply voltage as are the internal resistors, changes in power supply voltage have little effect on the frequency of the output. If high accuracy (e.g., frequencies within 1.0% of specifications) is required, a multi-turn potentiometer should be used for R_1 and R_2 to adjust the frequency. If extremely high accuracy (0.1%) is required, then it may be necessary to use the *ac* power line, or a crystal controlled oscillator.

EXAMPLE 14.9

Find the frequency and the duty cycle for the 555 circuit shown in Figure 14.26(a). Note that the 555 is driven from a +5 V power source while the timing resistors and capacitors are driven from a +10 V power source. Let $R_1 = 10\ \text{k}\Omega$, $R_2 = 66.7\ \text{k}\Omega$ and $C = 0.01\ \mu\text{F}$.

Solution: Refer to Figure 14.26(b) during this discussion.

During charging (i.e., flip-flop set and pin 7 floating) the capacitor charges from 5/3 V toward 10 V with a time constant of τ_c as given below.

$$v_C(t) = 10 + (1.67 - 10)e^{-t/\tau_c} = 10 - 8.33e^{-t/\tau_c}$$

$$\tau_c = (10^{-8})(76.7 \times 10^3) = 7.67 \times 10^{-4}$$

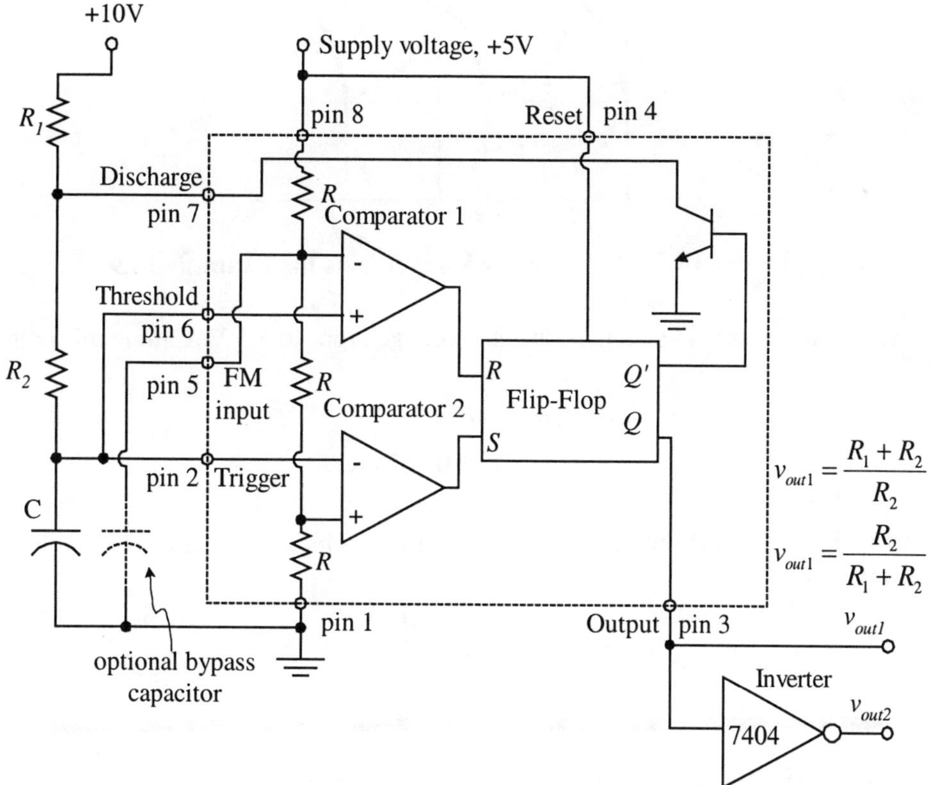

Figure 14.26(a) – 555 driven from two power sources

The capacitor continues to charge until the voltage reaches 10/3 V at which point the flip-flop resets. The time, T_1, required to charge C to 3.33 V is found from

$$3.33 = v_C(T_1) = 10 - 8.33e^{-T_1/\tau_C}$$

$$T_1 = 0.17 \text{ ms}$$

Pin 7 is now brought to ground, and the capacitor discharges toward zero with a discharge time constant of τ_d. The capacitor voltage is given by

$$v_C(t) = 3.33e^{-(t-T_1)/\tau_d}$$

$$\tau_d = (10^{-8})(66.7 \times 10^3) = 6.67 \times 10^{-4}$$

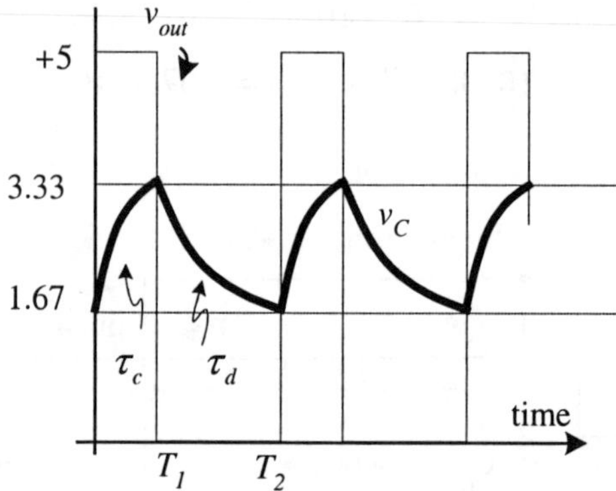

Figure 14.26(b) – Expected waveforms for Example 14.9

The next transition occurs when the capacitor voltage drops to 5/3 V. Calling this point T_2, we have

$$v_C(T_2) = 1.667 = 3.33e^{-(T_2-T_1)/\tau_d}$$

$$T_2 - T_1 = 0.462 \text{ ms}$$

The total period is then 0.63 ms, so the frequency is the reciprocal of this or 1.587 kHz. The duty cycle is given by

$$duty\ cycle = \frac{T_1}{T} = \frac{0.17}{0.63} = 27\%$$

Although the 555 is a *user-friendly* device, a few practical considerations must be observed. The supply voltage must be held constant with a regulated power supply and a decoupling capacitor from pin 8 to ground. This prevents power supply variations and associated timing errors. If large resistors are used, *ac* hum can be introduced into the output. To reduce this effect, timing resistors and capacitors should be physically located as close to the 555 IC as possible.

The voltage on pin 5 (the *FM input*) is normally 2/3 of the supply voltage and it forms the inverting input to comparator 1. This FM input can be used to *frequency modulate* the output of the 555. Figure 14.27 plots the relative frequency, f/f_n, as a function of applied voltage on pin 5.

To develop this curve, the 555 was operated with V_{CC} = +8 V, and with nominal frequencies of 10 Hz, 100 Hz, 1 kHz, and 10 kHz. For each pin 5 voltage, the relative frequency, f/f_n, was measured and plotted. Note that for a pin 5 voltage of 2/3 of 8, the relative frequency is unity. Although the curve is relatively linear, it must be modified with operational amplifiers to change its slope. Figure 14.27 shows that as we increase pin 5 voltage, relative frequency reduces. If we are to use the 555 for a *voltage-controlled oscillator*, we typically want the frequency to *increase* for increasing voltages. We use op-amps to provide the necessary inversion. This feature has some limited uses in electronic music systems. For other timing applications, it is good practice to bypass pin 5 to ground through a 0.1 μF capacitor.

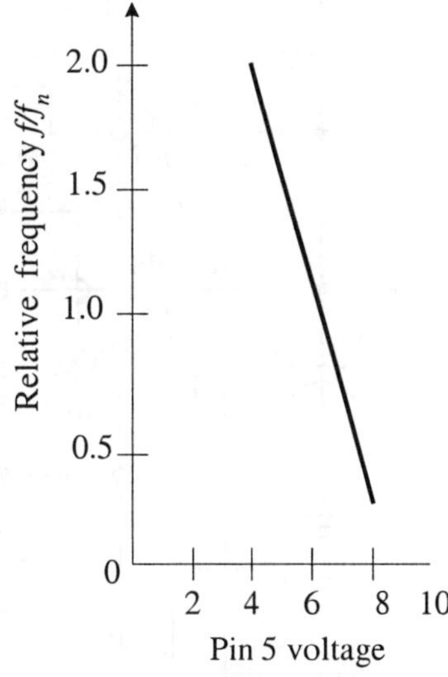

Figure 14.27 – 555 astable frequency variation

14.5.3 The 555 as a Monostable Circuit

The 555 can be used to produce a single pulse, with an accurate pulse width. This is the *monostable mode*. The circuit is also known as a *one shot*. It requires eliminating R_2 and connecting C between pins 6 and 7 and ground, as shown in Figure 14.28.

In the monostable mode, the circuit output consists of a single pulse with a specified duration. This pulse occurs each time a specially configured trigger pulse is delivered to pin 2, driving the comparator below 5/3 V. When pin 2 goes low, the flip-flop *sets* and the output (pin 3) goes high. Since the discharge transistor is turned off, pin 7 is allowed to float, and the capacitor starts to charge from its initial value of zero volts. When it has charged to 10/3 V the flip-flop *resets* and the output goes low. The trigger pulse, several of which are shown in Figure 14.21, must start at +5 V and drop to zero, then return to +5V, as shown in Figure 14.28. The trigger pulse must be of shorter duration than the desired output pulse. (A design rule of thumb is to make the trigger pulse about 1/5 as wide as the duration of the desired output pulse). The *on-time* is the amount of time the output pulse is high. This is the time it takes the exponential charging voltage to go from 0 to 2/3 of its final value. This will be 1.1 time constants since

$$1 - e^{-1.1} = \frac{2}{3} \tag{14.47}$$

The ON time is therefore

$$T = 1.1RC \tag{14.48}$$

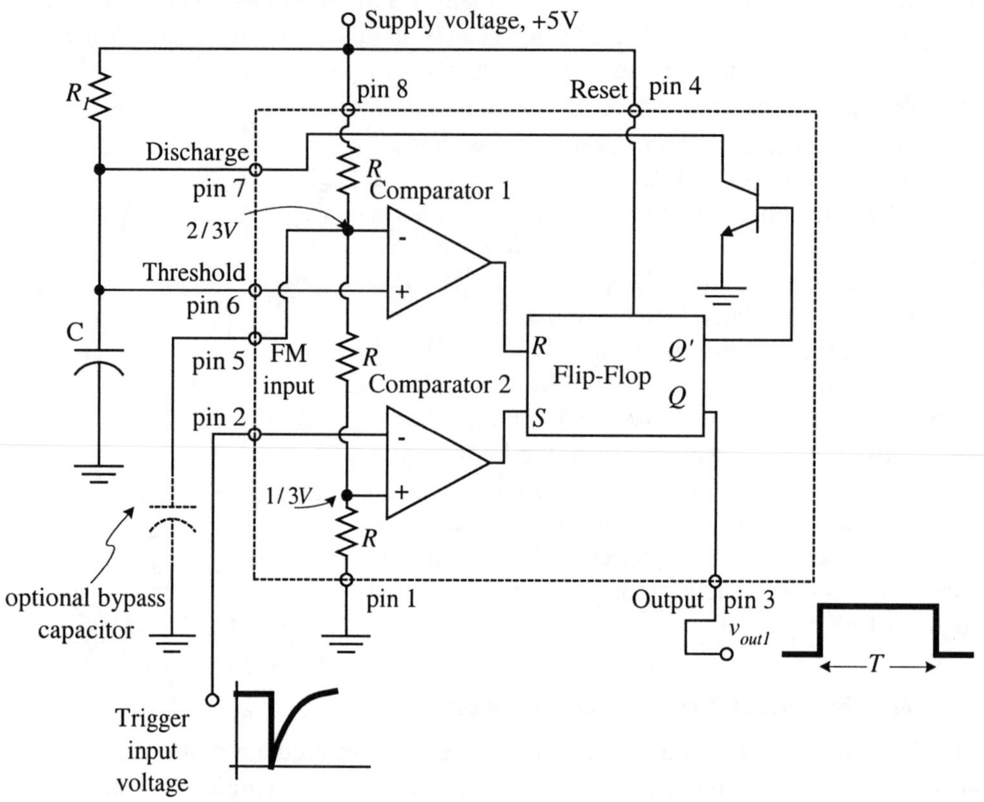

Figure 14.28 – The 555 in a monostable mode

EXAMPLE 14.10

Design a 555 in the monostable mode to provide a 100 ms pulse each time an input trigger is applied.

Solution: Since we only have one equation in two unknowns, let us choose a capacitor of 1 μF. Equation (14.48) then yields the value of R:

$$R = \frac{T}{1.1C} = \frac{100 \times 10^{-3}}{1.1 \times 10^{-6}} = 91\text{k}\Omega$$

The form of the trigger pulse necessary to initiate the 555 monostable is most important. As shown on Figure 14.28, the trigger pulse, applied to pin 2, is at +5 V. This voltage is briefly dropped to zero to initiate the timing sequence. At the instant that the trigger is brought to zero, an output pulse of duration, $1.1RC$, is generated. In contrast to the astable mode of operation, the cycle does not repeat. Another trigger pulse is required to initiate another output pulse.

The method of obtaining these trigger pulses for the 555 in the monostable mode was discussed earlier (see Figure 14.21(b)). It may be desirable to use a non-inverting buffer at the output of the circuit of Figure 14.21(b) to "square up" the trigger pulse and also to reduce the loading effect on the source.

The reset pin (pin 4) can be used to disable or stop the timing cycle after it begins. When the reset pin is brought to ground, the operation is inhibited. When not required, pin 4 should be tied to the positive supply, as shown in Figure 14.28.

The FM input pin (pin 5) can be used to vary the charging time by applying a modulation voltage. We can produce a *pulse-width-modulated* (PWM) signal by changing the charging time using a voltage applied to pin 5. We drive the monostable 555 with a continuous pulse train of fixed frequency and with short duration +5 V to 0 to +5 V pulses. The pulse width of the constant frequency pulse train output is modulated with the voltage applied to pin 5.

SUMMARY

This important chapter has formed a transition between the analog and digital portions of this text. You have learned how to design several types of timing and pulsed circuits. These will become important building blocks of complex digital electronic designs.

The trigger pulses you have generated will supply critical synchronization signals necessary to make digital systems operate in the correct sequence. The accurate timed pulses will serve as an interface between the analog world and control circuitry. We will find these necessary in a variety of systems ranging from frequency counters to traffic light control systems.

Finally the periodic timing waveforms that you now know how to produce are necessary in virtually every digital design. The designs of the following chapters will normally be driven by a clock signal, and the circuits of the current chapter generate that signal.

PROBLEMS

Section 14.1

14.1 A 10 Hz symmetrical square wave has a peak-to-peak voltage of 5 V. It forms the input to a high-pass circuit with lower corner frequency of 5 Hz [$f_c = 1/(2\pi RC)$]. Sketch the output waveform. What is the peak-to-peak output amplitude?

14.2 A 10-Hz square wave forms the input to an amplifier which acts as a high-pass circuit. The peak-to-peak voltage is V. Plot the output waveform if the lower corner frequency is

(a) 0.3 Hz

(b) 3 Hz

(c) 30 Hz

14.3 A square wave extends ± 2 V with respect to ground. The duration of the positive section is 0.1 second and that of the negative section is 0.2 second. The waveform is applied to a high-pass network with time constant, $RC = 0.2$ s. Plot the steady-state output waveform and calculate the important maximum and minimum voltages.

14.4 The limited ramp of Figure P14.4 is applied to a high-pass network. Let $V_m = 1$ V. Draw the output waveform for each value of T.

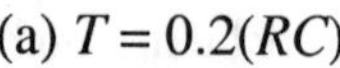

(a) $T = 0.2(RC)$

(b) $T = RC$

(c) $T = 5(RC)$

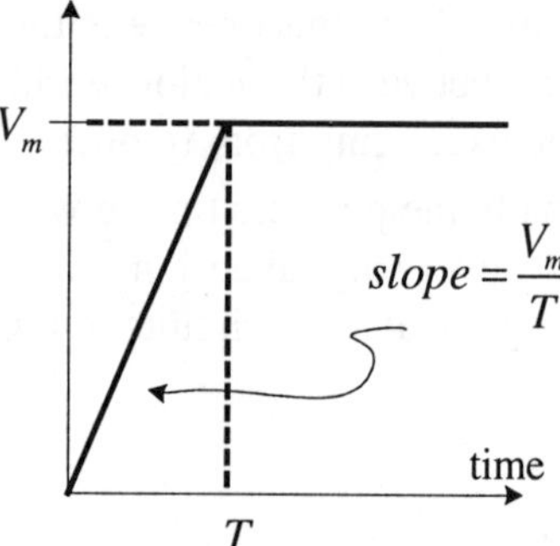

Figure P14.4

Section 14.2

14.5 A symmetrical square wave with an average value of zero has a peak-to-peak voltage of 10 V and a period of 2 μs. This waveform is the input to a low-pass circuit with corner frequency of 0.16 MHz. Calculate and sketch the steady-state output wave form. What is the peak-to-peak output voltage?

Section 14.3

14.6 The pulse train shown in Figure P14.6 is applied to the input of a diode-capacitor network. Plot the steady-state output voltage, $v_{out}(t)$, and calculate the four important voltages in the output. Assume that the diode voltage is zero when forward biased (i.e., $V_{ON} = 0$), $R_f = 100\ \Omega$, $R_r = 100$ kΩ, T_1 =1ms and T_2=4 ms.

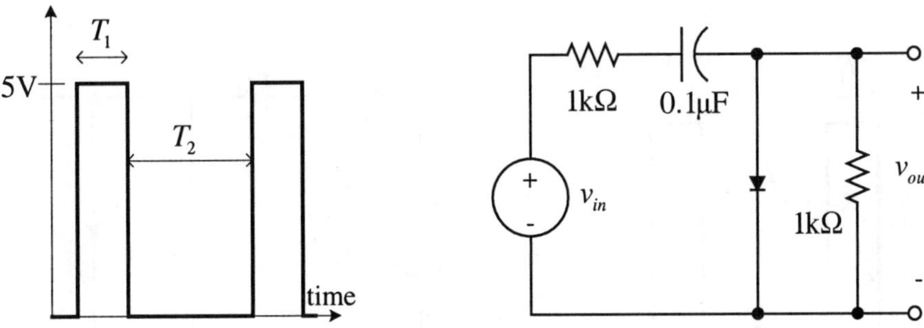

Figure P14.6

14.7 The limited ramp of Figure P14.4 is applied to a low-pass network with $V_m = 1$ V. Draw the output waveform for

(a) $T = 0.2(RC)$

(b) $T = RC$

(c) $T = 5(RC)$

14.8 A 10 kHz pulse train with peak value, $V_{peak} = 10$ V with respect to ground is applied to the diode clamping circuit of Figure P14.8(b). The parameter values are $R = 10$ kΩ, $C = 1$ μF. The diode has $R_r, \rightarrow \infty$, $R_f = 0$, $V_{ON} = 0$, and the source impedance is zero.

(a) Sketch the output waveform.

(b) If the diode forward resistance is 1 kΩ, sketch the output waveform. Calculate the maximum and minimum voltage with respect to ground.

(c) Repeat part (b) if the source impedance is 1 kΩ.

14.9 The pulse train shown in Figure P14.8(a) with $T = 50$ μs is applied to the circuit of Figure P14.8(b). The circuit has $R_{in} = 1$ kΩ, $R = 10$ kΩ, $C = 0.1$ μF, $R_f = 100$ Ω, $R_r = 100$ kΩ and $V_{ON} = 0$. Find the steady-state output waveform, $v_{out}(t)$ if $V_{peak} = 10$ V.

<u>**Section 14.5**</u>

14.10 Design a signal generator using a 555 circuit in the astable mode to provide pulse rates of 100 kHz, 10 kHz, and 1 kHz. Keep the duty cycle constant.

14.11 Design a trigger circuit and a monostable 555 to produce a train of 100 ms pulses. Assume that you have a zero to 5 V, 1-Hz pulse train input to this circuit.

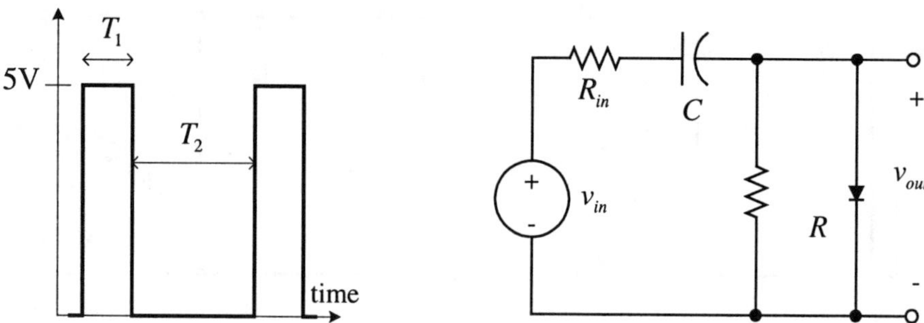

Figure P14.8

14.12 Use a 555 in the astable mode and an inverter (needed to obtain a duty cycle less than 1/2) to produce a pulse generator for the following continuously variable frequency ranges. Switch three capacitors into the circuit, one for each frequency range, and use a potentiometer to vary the frequency in each range.

(a) 10 Hz to 100 Hz

(b) 100 Hz to 1 kHz

(c) 1 kHz to 10 kHz

The duty cycle must be no greater than 0.167. Select all resistor and capacitor values, and select the chip number for the inverter. Assume that you have available any power you need. Draw the circuit diagram for the design.

14.13 Develop a 60-Hz pulse train using the 60-Hz, 110 V power line voltage with the system shown in Figure P14.13. The output is a pulse train with a 50% duty cycle. Select all resistor and capacitor values. Draw the circuit diagram for your complete design.

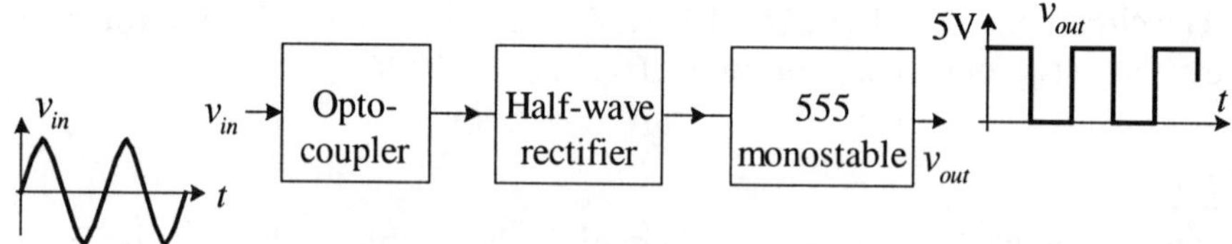

Figure P14.13

14.14 Design a pulse generator that will have the following continuously variable ranges:

(a) 0.1 kHz to 1 kHz

(b) 1 kHz to 10 kHz

(c) 10 kHz to 100 kHz

A duty cycle of 0.5 is required. Assume you have available any power needed in the design.

14.15 Design a traffic light control system using digital circuitry. The traffic light is to be used at a four-way intersection, and each direction will have three lights: red, yellow, and green. Your circuit must provide an output of +5 V for each lamp that is to be turned on. If the output to a certain lamp circuit is zero, that lamp will be off. The required times and a map of the intersection are shown in Figure P14.15.

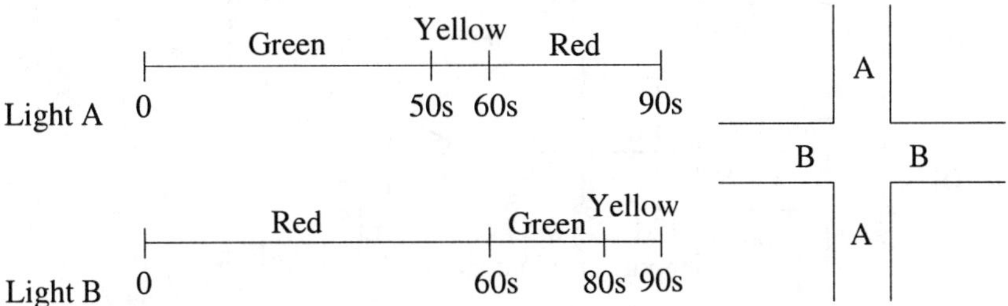

Figure P14.15

14.16 Design a pulse delay network to provide a 15 millisecond delay for a pulse input whose duration is 1 milliseconds as shown in Figure P14.16.

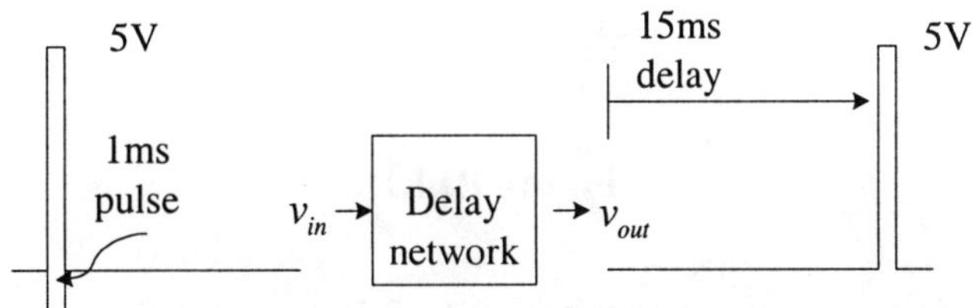

Figure P14.16

14.17 Design a pulse generator to provide the clock pulse for an electronic system. Use the 110 V 60 Hz power line as the basic drive for the pulse generator. The duty cycle of the clock pulse output is 0.33. Calculate all resistor and capacitor values and specify the type number of the ICs used.

14.18 Analyze the circuit shown in Figure P14.18. Sketch the output signal as a function of time. Calculate all important frequencies and pulse widths. Switch SW is normally closed. You are to plot the output signal after the time that the switch is open.

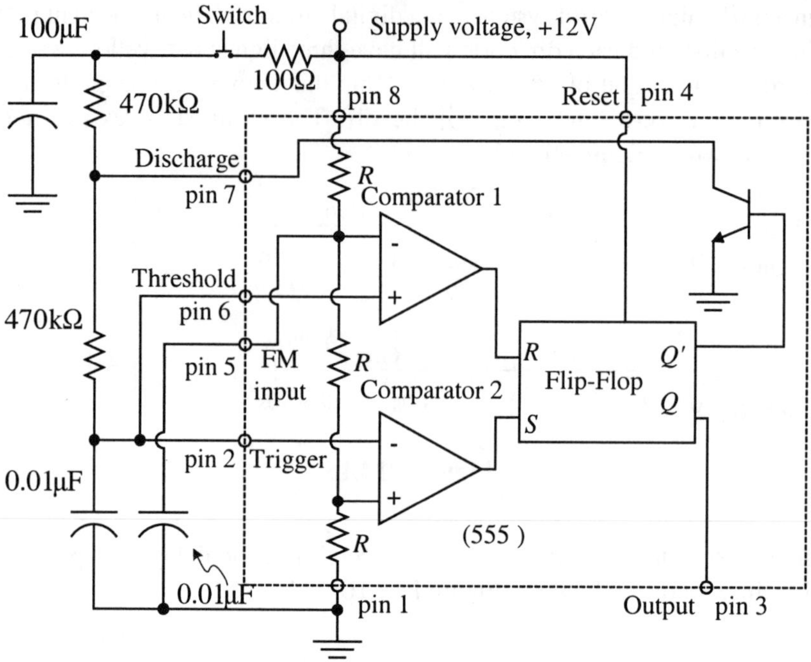

Figure P14.18

14.19 Design a 1 kHz pulse generator with a 0 to 5 V output, using an astable 555 timer to provide the 1 kHz pulse train. The duty cycle of the output clock pulses must be variable from 0.167 to 0.91. Use one potentiometer and one monostable 555 to generate the duty cycle. Calculate all resistor and capacitor values and specify the type numbers for the ICs used in the design.

14.20 Use op-amps and a 555 monostable in the design of a signal conditioning system. The input for the system is obtained from the ignition system for an engine. One hundred turns of wire are wrapped around the supply line to one of the spark plugs. This produces a voltage pulse once for each two revolutions of the engine. The signal has the form shown in Figure P14.20(a). The transients are large and do not die out for 10 msec.

Design an electronic system to condition this input signal so it will be suitable to drive a TTL system. The suitable signal will have only one output pulse for each firing of the spark plug. That is, the signal conditioning system should ignore the transients and only produce ONE pulse for each burst of energy. The pulse train should look like that shown in Figure P14.20(b). Each pulse of the output pulse train corresponds to two revolutions of the engine and the maximum engine speed is 6000 rpm.

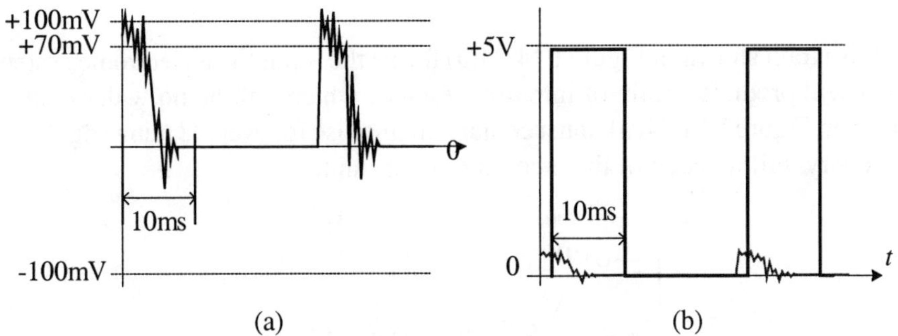

Figure P14.20

14.21 Design a warning alarm signal that has the form shown in Figure P14.21. The desired alarm signal is a 2-kHz square wave (developed by one 555 astable) that is turned on and off 30 times each minute (by another 555 astable). The time on is approximately equal to the time off.

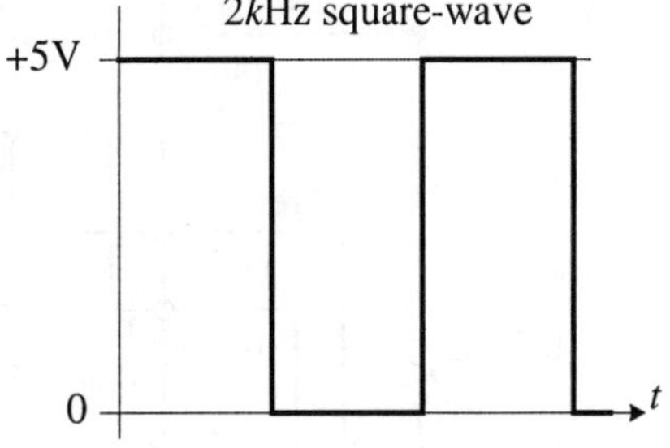

Figure P14.21

14.22 An input clock signal has a variable pulse width, as shown in Figure P14.22. The pulse width varies from 1 ms to 3 ms, and the frequency is constant at 200 Hz. Use a monostable 555 and a trigger circuit in the design of an electronic system to process this input signal. The output pulse train must have a frequency of 200 Hz with a constant duty cycle of 0.167.

14.23 The circuit shown in Figure P14.23 produces a frequency from the astable mode 555 that varies as the voltage applied to the timing resistors and capacitors changes. We refer to such a circuit as a *voltage controlled oscillator*. Calculate the output frequency (v_{out}) for each of the three settings of the top switch. Calculate the frequency as was done in Example 14.7 [use Equation (14.6)]. Plot the output frequency as a function of the applied voltage.

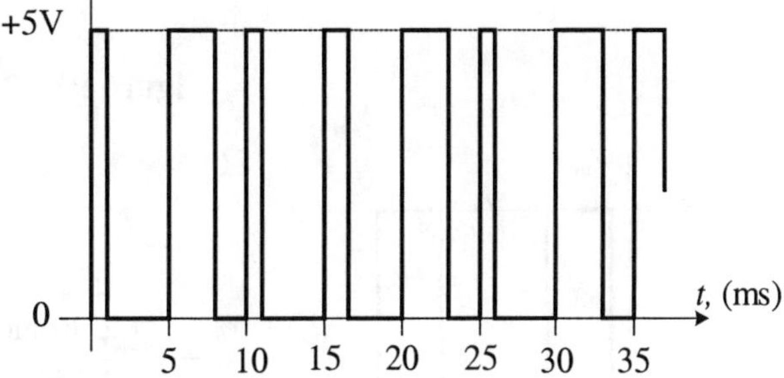

Figure P14.22

14.24 The pulse train shown in Figure P14.24(a) forms the input to an electronic system. Design a system that will produce a train of impulses, each of which will be no wider than 2 ms. The output, shown in Figure P14.24(b), must contain an impulse for every leading edge, and a second impulse for every trailing edge of the incoming pulse train.

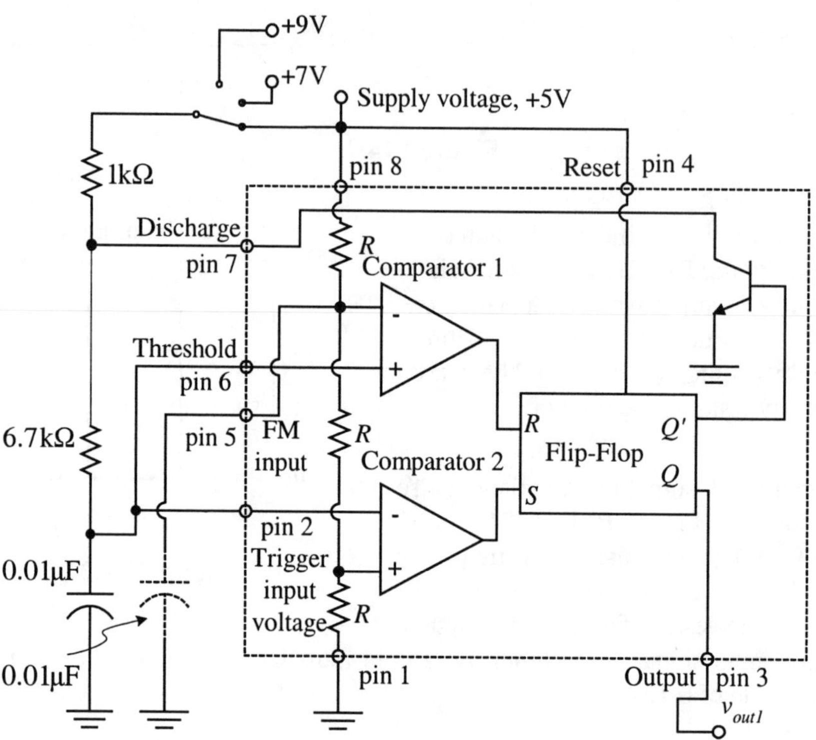

Figure P14.23

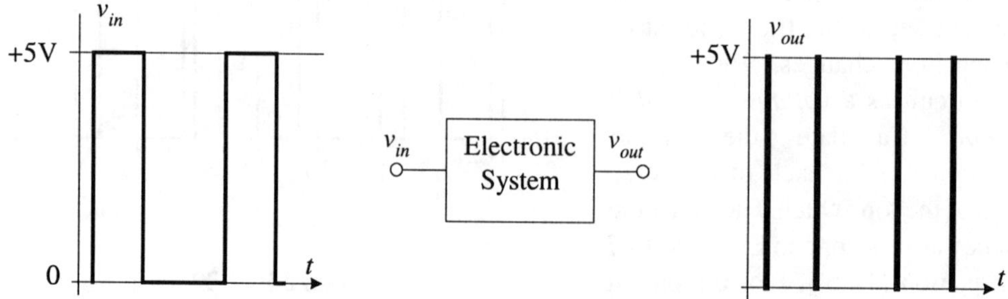

Figure P14.24

14.25 Use the output of the system of Problem 14.24 [Figure P14.24(b)] to produce a train of pulses with 50% duty cycle, but with twice the frequency of the input signal [Figure P14.24(a)]. The results of Problems 14.24 and 14.25 constitute a frequency doubler circuit.

14.26 Design a 1-kHz clock that has a variable duty cycle. One potentiometer should be used to vary the duty cycle from 0.167 to 0.91. The frequency must not change from 1 kHz. Use a 555 in the astable mode to set the frequency. A 555 in the monostable mode is triggered from the astable 555 to provide the variable duty cycle.

14.27 Design an electronic circuit to accomplish the following operation. A 3-ms wide pulse forms the input. Your circuit must reproduce this pulse and send it on to another circuit. In addition to repeating the input pulse, your design must produce an "echo" pulse which starts 10 ms after the start of the initial pulse, as shown in Figure P14.27.

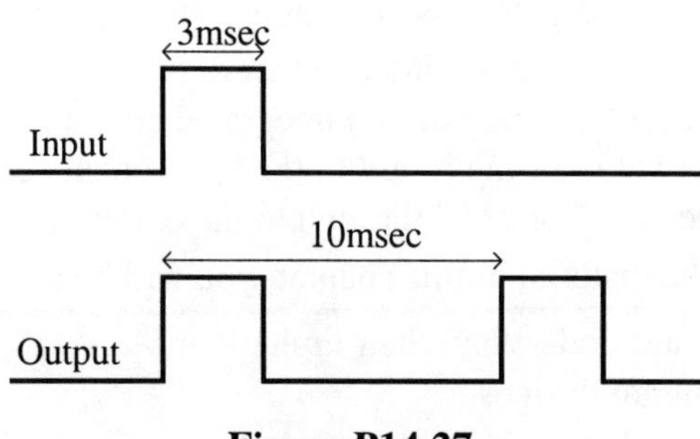

Figure P14.27

Chapter 15

Digital Logic Families

15.0 INTRODUCTION

Digital electronics forms a subset of the broader field of digital engineering. A typical study of digital engineering includes Boolean functions. A particular function is specified and then, prior to considering implementation, the function is reduced to its simplest form. It is only following that reduction that we consider filling in the blocks on the system diagram with electronic circuitry. In this text, we concentrate upon the circuitry, while presenting a brief summary of some digital engineering results in Section 15.1. It is assumed that you either have had a course in digital engineering, or will accept the specifications as being the result of logic operations.

Binary digital ICs accept inputs consisting of either of two logic levels, usually denoted by 0 and 1. Since each component of a binary digital integrated circuit produces a logic 0 or 1 at the output depending upon the value of the input(s), the components can be thought of as "logic gates". A *gate* will let either a "1" or a "0" through to the output.

Once you understand the material in this chapter, you will be able to:

- Analyze digital circuits and understand their limitations.
- Incorporate BJTs into digital designs.
- Understand the differences between the various logic families.
- Utilize the FET in various digital designs.
- Analyze and design CMOS circuits.

15.1 BASIC CONCEPTS OF DIGITAL LOGIC

Logic has been a field of study since the days of the Greek philosophers. Many of the concepts that are used in digital logic were derived from earlier sources. Several of the basic functions were used by philosophers to prove statements and solve puzzles.

Two of these operations, known as AND and OR, form the basic building blocks of a logic system. These can be considered as analogous to addition and multiplication in the basic algebra system. We start with these two, and then expand to more complex functions.

Prior to defining the functions, we need to explore ways to express a digital relationship. In algebra, a *function* is usually expressed in one of three ways. First, we can give an *equation* for the function where that equation contains basic operations such as addition and multiplication. Alternatively, we can present a *graph* of the function in two dimensions, with one variable (independent) on the abscissa, and the other (dependent) on the ordinate of the graph. A third technique for specifying the function is to give the value of the function for *every* possible value of the independent variable. In the analog continuous case, this would involve a table with an infinite number of entries.

Two of these analog functional representation techniques lend themselves nicely to describing digital functions. We can write an *equation* once we define some notation for the basic logic operations. Alternatively, we can present a *table* which specifies the value of the function for every possible input. In contrast with the analog case, this table only has a finite number of entries. It is known as a *function table*, or *truth table*, and we use it to define the various functions.

15.1.1 State Definitions - Positive and Negative Logic

Since binary digital signals can take on only one of two possible values, the inputs to the system must each be one of these values. Although these parameters are represented as voltages in a circuit, they are usually referred to as 0 and 1. The values of the two voltages used depend on the type of circuitry. For example, we will see that TTL circuits use one voltage close to zero and the other close to 5 V. We refer to these as LOW (0 or OFF) and HIGH (1 or ON), respectively.

In order to convey digital information, two distinct signals are needed. There is nothing magic about 0 and 1. For example, the digital number 10110, when appearing in this text, could just as well be represented by XYXXY. As long as two distinct signals are used, the information is conveyed. We therefore have two choices in assigning the binary numbers, 0 and 1, to the two voltages present in a circuit.

Positive logic: Associate HIGH voltage with 1 and LOW voltage with 0.

Negative logic: Associate HIGH voltage with 0 and LOW voltage with 1.

The manufacturer's data sheets define the logic levels in terms of H (high-voltage level) and L (low-voltage level). The selection of H equal to 1 and L equal to 0 results in *positive logic*. If we were to select H equal to 0 and L equal to 1, we would obtain *negative logic*.

Logic gates are usually named using positive logic. However, we can change the type of gate, and also its name, by changing from positive to negative logic. For example, as we will show soon, a positive logic AND gate is the same circuit as a negative logic OR gate. Since the logic itself is independent of whether we choose positive or negative logic, we may find it possible to economize on parts (and hence power consumption) by using a combination of positive and negative logic in the same electronic system. If your design results in several unused portions of logic packages, a change from positive to negative logic may simplify the parts requirements.

15.1.2 Time-Independent or Un-clocked Logic

A *time-independent logic function* is one which has no memory. This form of logic responds only to the *present* inputs that are applied, previous inputs have no effect upon the present output. In essence, the circuit forgets any previous logic conditions. Function tables for such circuits are easy to construct since there are no clock signals or previous conditions to be considered. Time-independent logic is also known as *un-clocked*, or *asynchronous logic*.

15.1.3 Time-Dependent or Clocked Logic

A *time-dependent logic function* is one which has a *memory*. This form of logic responds not only to the present inputs that are applied to it, but the output also depends upon previous input and/or output conditions (i.e., the *state* of the system). A dependency on the previous output state represents a form of feedback in digital circuits. Time-dependent logic functions often have inputs with labels such as *clock*, *strobe*, *enable*, *set* or *reset*. We encounter these terms in the following chapter. The output may change state at the rising or falling edge of an input, or it may be a function of a high or low logic level of a critical input or combination of inputs. Time-dependent logic is also known as *clocked* or *synchronous logic*.

15.1.4 Elementary Logic Functions

The first digital ICs produced were simple gates and inverters containing one to six devices in a package. The variety of gates has increased dramatically. The levels of digital IC complexity and size are as follows.

- *Small-scale integration (SSI)* includes simple devices such as gates and flip-flops. Devices within this classification contain between one and ten equivalent gates.
- *Medium-scale integration (MSI)* consists of more complex devices such as counters, shift registers, encoders, decoders, and small memories. MSI devices contain from 10 to 100 equivalent gates.
- *Large-scale integration (LSI)* includes larger memories and microprocessors. LSI devices consist of between 100 and 1000 equivalent gates.
- *Very large-scale integration (VLSI)* includes the largest memories and microprocessors. VLSI devices have more than 1000 equivalent gates.
- *Ultra large-scale integration (ULSI)* devices have more than 10,000 equivalent gates.

Figure 15.1 illustrates eight logic functions. We briefly describe each operation in the following.

A *buffer* has a single input and a single output. The output is always in the same logic state as the input. The purpose of a buffer is to provide additional power to drive other logic inputs.

The *inverter* is a device for which the output is the *opposite* of the input. If the input is 0, the output is 1 and vice versa. The output is always the *complement* of the input. The truth table for the function is simple since there are only two possible inputs. We therefore enter each possible input value and write the corresponding output next to this value. The truth table is shown in the figure. The equation is given in the form,

$$Y = \overline{A} = A' \tag{15.1}$$

We have illustrated two popular notation forms for the complement – a bar over the variable or a prime. The notation used in the block diagram to denote inversion is a small circle at the output of the logic symbol. The inversion operation is sometimes referred to as a *NOT gate*. Thus, the output of the inverter with A as input is sometimes known as "NOT A". If two inverters are cascaded, the result is a buffer. That is, taking the inverse twice returns us to the original value.

An AND gate has two (or more) inputs and one output. The output is at logic level 1 only when *all* of the inputs are in the logic 1 state. Note that the notation of the AND operation used in the formula is to write the two variables next to each other as if we were talking about algebraic multiplication. We also sometimes use a dot between the variables. Thus we denote the AND operation as

$$Y = AB = A \cdot B \tag{15.2}$$

where both notations are shown. Since this gate has two inputs, the truth table has three columns, one for each input and one for the output. Since each of the two inputs can take on either of two values, there are four possible input combinations. These form the four rows of the table. In general, the truth table will have 2^n rows, where n is the number of inputs.

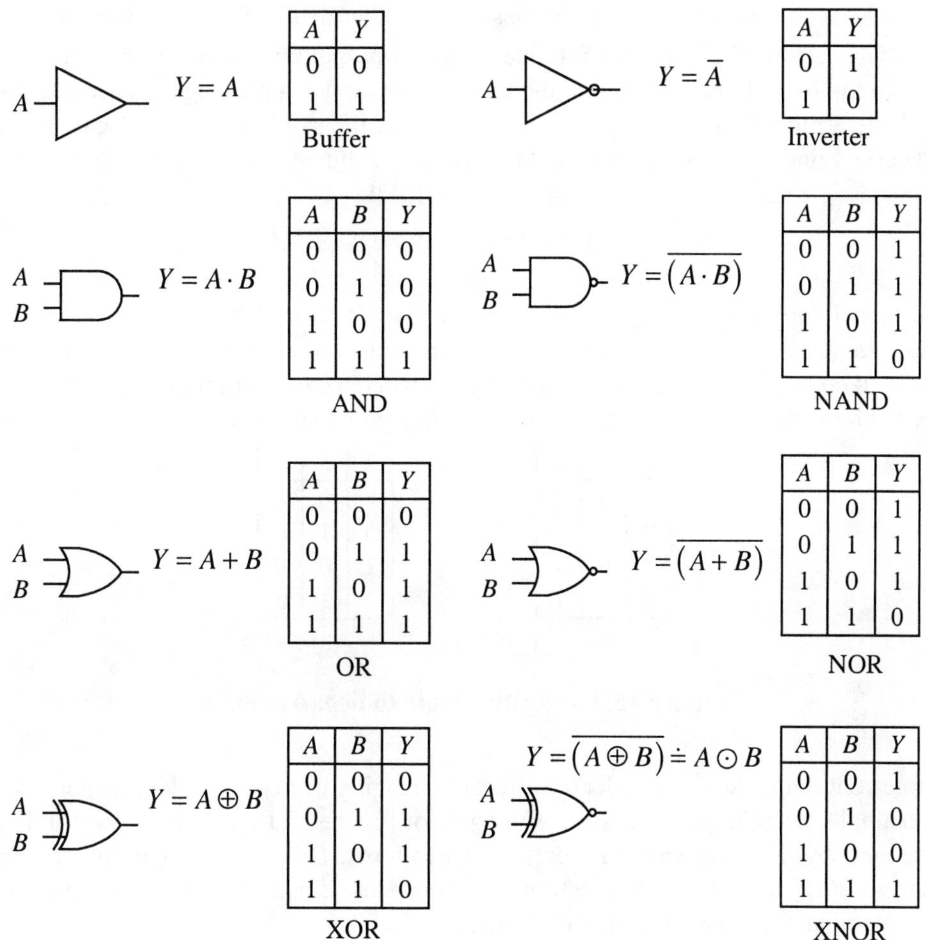

A	Y
0	0
1	1

A	Y
0	1
1	0

A	B	Y
0	0	0
0	1	0
1	0	0
1	1	1

A	B	Y
0	0	1
0	1	1
1	0	1
1	1	0

A	B	Y
0	0	0
0	1	1
1	0	1
1	1	1

A	B	Y
0	0	1
0	1	1
1	0	1
1	1	0

A	B	Y
0	0	0
0	1	1
1	0	1
1	1	0

A	B	Y
0	0	1
0	1	0
1	0	0
1	1	1

Figure 15.1 - Elementary gate summary

The NAND gate provides a logic 0 at the output only when *all* of the inputs are in the logic 1 state. The NAND gate can be viewed as an AND gate followed by an inverter. In words, the operation is NOT AND. Note that the equation and the circuit diagram are both developed by combining the notation for the AND with that of the inversion operation. *Any* zero at the input produces a one at the output.

The *OR* gate has two (or more) inputs. The gate provides a logic 1 at the output when *any one or more* of the inputs is in the logic 1 state. That is, the output, Y, is 1 if A and/or B are equal to 1. The formula notation for the operation of OR is the plus sign. The circuit symbol contains a curved line at the left edge, as shown in the figure.

A NOR gate provides a logic 0 output when *any one or more* of the inputs is in the logic 1 state. Note that the NOR gate can be viewed as an OR gate followed by an inverter. Both the equation and the circuit diagram are developed by combining the two individual representations.

The NAND and NOR gates are internally simpler than the AND and OR. They therefore require less power, so we attempt to use these gates rather than AND and OR gates.

The XOR gate, or *Exclusive* OR provides a logic 1 output when *any one, but only one* of its inputs is in the logic 1 state. Note that the formula notation is a plus sign (as used for the OR) with a circle around it. The circuit notation starts with the symbol for an OR gate and adds a second curved line at the input. This could be viewed as binary (modulo 2) addition where

$$\begin{aligned} 0 \oplus 0 = 1 \oplus 1 = 0 \\ 1 \oplus 0 = 0 \oplus 1 = 1 \end{aligned} \tag{15.3}$$

The final logic operation shown is the *Exclusive NOR* or *XNOR* gate. The XNOR gate provides a logic 0 output when *any one, but only one* of its inputs is in the logic 1 state. This gate is also called *equivalence* since the output is logic 1 when the two inputs are equal. Note that the XNOR can be viewed as an exclusive OR gate followed by an inverter.

A	*B*	*Y*
0	0	0
0	1	1
1	0	1
1	1	1

(a)

A	*B*	*Y*
0	0	1
0	1	0
1	0	0
1	1	0

(b)

Figure 15.2 – Positive logic to negative logic

Before continuing, let us consider the effect of changing from positive logic to negative logic. As an example, take the positive-logic AND gate of Figure 15.1 and change the truth table to negative logic by changing zeros to ones and ones to zeros. This results in the truth table shown in Figure 15.2(a). Hence the same electronic hardware that is named an AND gate with positive logic is named an OR gate with negative logic.

EXAMPLE 15.1

What is the function of the positive logic NAND gate of Figure 15.1 when we use negative logic.

Solution: We start with the truth table of Figure 15.1 and reverse the assignment of 0 and 1 by changing 0 to 1 and 1 to 0. This results in the truth table of Figure 15.2(b). If we look at the function tables of Figure 15.1, we see that this is now the function table for a NOR gate. Hence the same electronic hardware for a positive-logic NAND gate becomes a negative-logic NOR gate.

15.1.5 Boolean Algebra

Whenever binary variables are manipulated, equations result. We need rules for working with these equations. Boolean algebra gives us the necessary set of rules. In Boolean algebra, the two elementary algebraic operations of addition and multiplication are replaced by the elementary logic operations of OR and AND. Functions are defined either through an equation, or by giving the value of the function for every possible input. This latter approach gives rise to the truth (or function) table, as discussed in the previous section.

The Boolean equation is a shorthand way of writing the truth table. *Boolean identities* can be proven by referring to the function tables for the gates as shown in Figure 15.1. The following exercises present an overview of several important Boolean identities.

EXERCISES

Prove each of the relationships given in Exercises E15.1 through E15.16.

E15.1 $A + (B + C) = (A + B) + C$ (Associative Law for Addition)

E15.2 $A(BC) = (AB)C$ (Associative Law for Multiplication)

E15.3 $\overline{A+B}=\overline{A}\,\overline{B}$ (DeMorgan's Theorem for Addition)

E15.4 $\overline{ABC}=\overline{A}+\overline{B}+\overline{C}$ (DeMorgan's Theorem for Multiplication)

E15.5 $A + 0 = A$

E15.6 $A + A = 0$

E15.7 $A + \overline{A} = 1$

E15.8 $A \cdot 0 = 0$

E15.9 $A \cdot 1 = A$

E15.10 $A \cdot A = A$

E15.11 $A \cdot \overline{A} = 0$

E15.12 $A + AB = A$

E15.13 $AB + A\overline{B} = A$

E15.14 $(\overline{\overline{A}})= A$

E15.15 $\overline{(A+B)}\,\overline{(\overline{A}+B)}=0$

E15.16 $B + A\overline{B} = A + B$

DeMorgan's Theorem (See Exercises E15.3 and E15.4) can be used to develop alternate forms for implementing the NOR and NAND operation. These alternate forms are sometimes preferable for reasons related to practical considerations, as we shall see later.

Starting with the NOR and NAND operations, we can use the theorem to show

$$\begin{gathered} \overline{A+B}=\overline{A}\,\overline{B} \\ \overline{A+B+C}=\overline{A}\,\overline{B}\,\overline{C} \\ \overline{AB}=\overline{A}+\overline{B} \\ \overline{ABC}=\overline{A}+\overline{B}+\overline{C} \end{gathered} \tag{15.4}$$

The resulting alternate forms of the basic gates are shown in Figure 15.3.

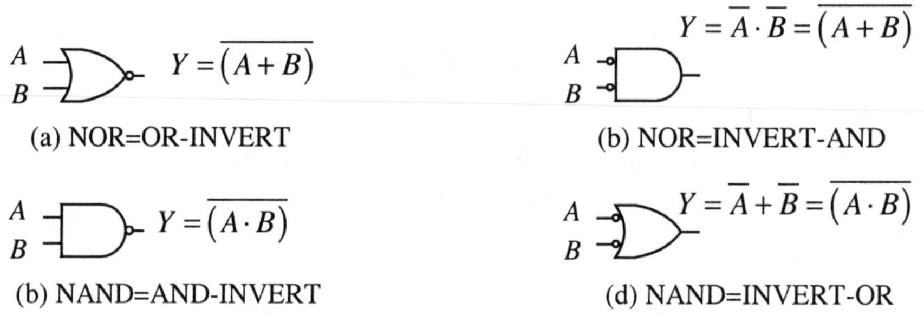

A, B — $Y=\overline{(A+B)}$

(a) NOR=OR-INVERT

A, B — $Y=\overline{A}\cdot\overline{B}=\overline{(A+B)}$

(b) NOR=INVERT-AND

A, B — $Y=\overline{(A\cdot B)}$

(b) NAND=AND-INVERT

A, B — $Y=\overline{A}+\overline{B}=\overline{(A\cdot B)}$

(d) NAND=INVERT-OR

Figure 15.3 - Alternate forms for NOR and NAND gates

15.2 IC CONSTRUCTION AND PACKAGING

Integrated circuits are fabricated using a sequence of processing steps which includes growing, slicing, and etching silicon wafers, masking and doping them with *n*- and *p*-type impurities, and depositing conductor patterns. This complex processing sequence produces complete functional circuits containing patterns of resistors, capacitors, diodes and transistors.

A functional circuit pattern is repeated numerous times to fill the useable area of a wafer. Upon completing the processing steps, the wafer is sliced into small rectangles or *chips*, each containing one or more functional circuits. Each chip is tested and mounted in a package. A typical package is the 14-pin *dual in-line package* (known as a *DIP*). The package provides structural support, an arrangement of pins for external connections, and a sealed cover to keep out moisture and contamination. The complexity of VLSI chips, with their large numbers of inputs and outputs, has caused some decline in the use of the DIP. Newer package configurations provide for additional external connections and faster (therefore less expensive) manufacturing techniques. This is particularly true when these chips are part of larger system modules. Several of the popular packages are shown in Figure 15.4.

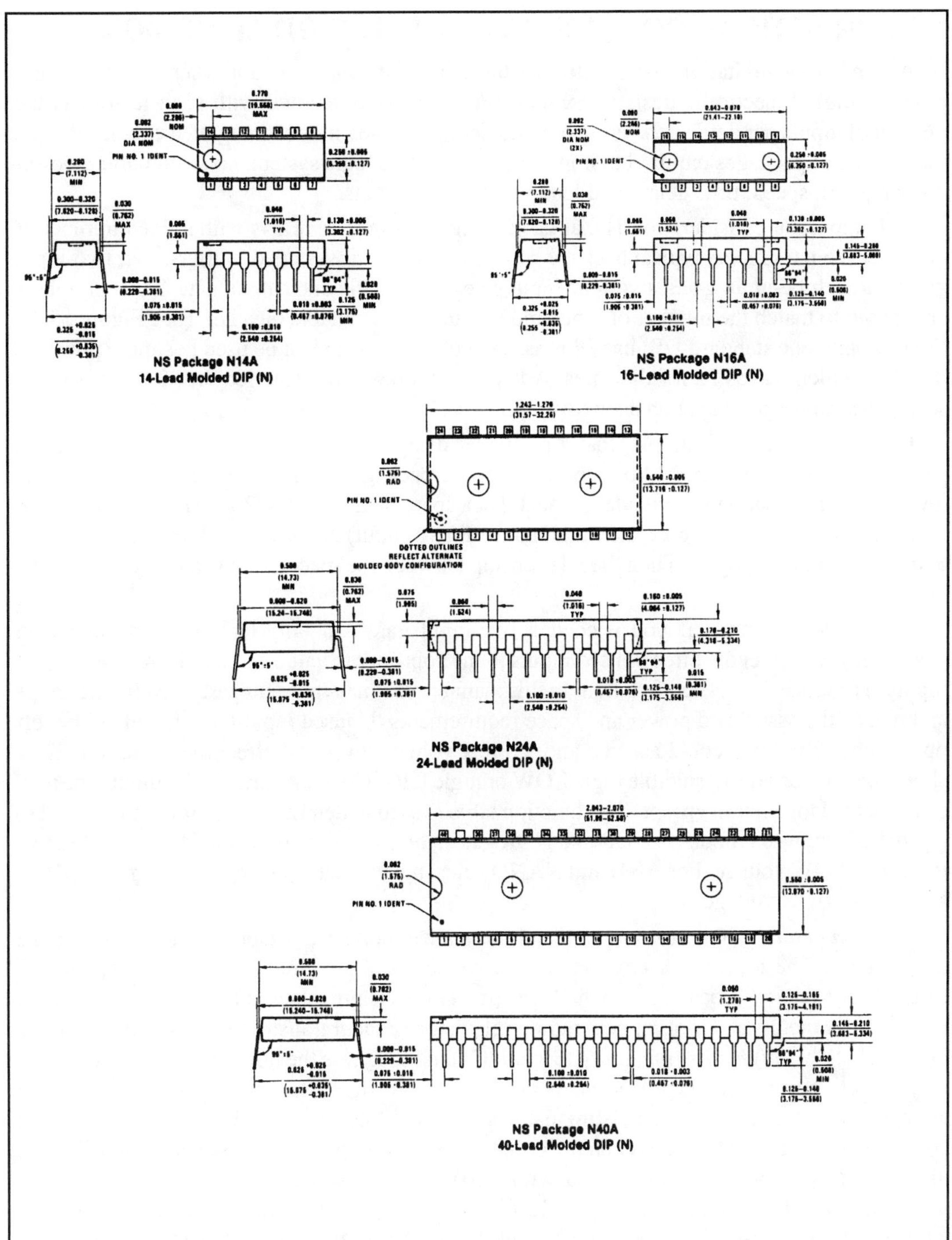

Figure 15.4 – IC package configurations *(Courtesy of National Semiconductor)*

15.3 PRACTICAL CONSIDERATIONS IN DIGITAL DESIGN

A number of limitations or constraints must be taken into account when approaching a practical digital electronic design problem. We must be concerned with such factors as the number of inputs per device, the number of devices contained in each integrated circuit package, the number of packages required to implement a complete logic system, noise immunity, power consumption, speed, time delay, and loading of logic outputs.

One important consideration is that gates come packaged in arrays with a fixed number of gates in each package. A typical package contains either six inverters or buffers, four two-input gates, three three-input gates, two four-input gates, or a single eight-input gate. These numbers are chosen to match the number of input and output leads available on a DIP (See Figure 15.4). For example, one standard DIP has 14 pins. Two of these pins must be used to supply power to the chip, which leaves 12 for the gates. A two-input, one-output gate requires 3 leads, so four such gates can be packaged on a single chip.

Let us suppose, for example, that a particular design required 7 inverters. Since a typical package contains 6 inverters, you would need two packages, and this would leave 5 devices unused. On the other hand, consider the fact that a spare NAND or NOR gate may be used as an inverter. For example, suppose the first input to a (two-input) NAND gate is set equal to 1 (tied to the HIGH of the supply). Then the relationship between the second input and the output is that of the inverter.

As another example, if you needed a five-input gate and only had an eight-input gate available, you can set the three unused inputs to the appropriate value and use the remaining five inputs to produce the desired function. In this manner, you may save purchase of additional chips and reduce the associated power and space requirements. Unused input pins should not be left open. Otherwise, they could assume an incorrect voltage level and affect the operation. They should be connected to a suitable logic LOW or logic HIGH level. Alternatively, input pins may be connected together in groups. The function table is used to determine the proper logic level to be applied to unused inputs. For OR and NOR gates, the unused inputs should be connected to a logic 0, or LOW voltage. For AND and NAND gates, the unused inputs should be connected to a logic 1, or HIGH voltage.

Noise immunity, power consumption and *speed* are important considerations in the design of a logic circuit. The location or environment in which the logic circuit will operate should be carefully considered. Locations in which electrical noise is prevalent (such as in factories with large electric motors and tools or near radios, television or radar transmitters) may require a logic family which has *high noise immunity*. Digital ICs tend to ignore the noise inputs into the system more effectively than do linear ICs, where noise that enters the system propagates throughout the entire system. If a digital IC can distinguish between a HIGH and a LOW input and interpret it correctly, the noise has little effect on the proper operation of the circuit. Because digital families differ in the voltage values associated with LOW and HIGH, noise immunity is one of the parameters that determines which digital IC family we choose. High noise immunity means that the logic family is insensitive to noise voltages that are radiated or conducted into the electronic system. That is, the probability of noise making one logic level look like the other is very small. If noise is still a problem, then it may be necessary to use shielded enclosures, filtered power and shielded logic wiring.

Power consumption, which is the power that must be supplied by the power supply, is usually of little consequence for equipment which is connected to a 110 V *ac* outlet. On the other hand, portable battery powered equipment requires a logic family that consumes low power. Operating speed requirements also affect the choice of logic families.

Output loading should be carefully checked to make sure that each logic output is not being asked to drive an excessive number of logic inputs. This consideration also applies to any other type of loads which exceed the manufacturer's rating for the device.

The number of logic inputs that a single IC can drive is defined as *fan out*. Suppose, for example that all ICs require the same input current. The fan out would then be equal to the amount of load current that the IC can drive divided by the current required into each logic input.

Another performance characteristic of logic circuits is *time delay*, or *propagation delay*. This is the time between the application of a logic input and the appearance of the corresponding logic output. We will now show that time delay can sometimes cause serious problems such as undesired transients, or *glitches*.

Consider the example shown in Figure 15.5(a).

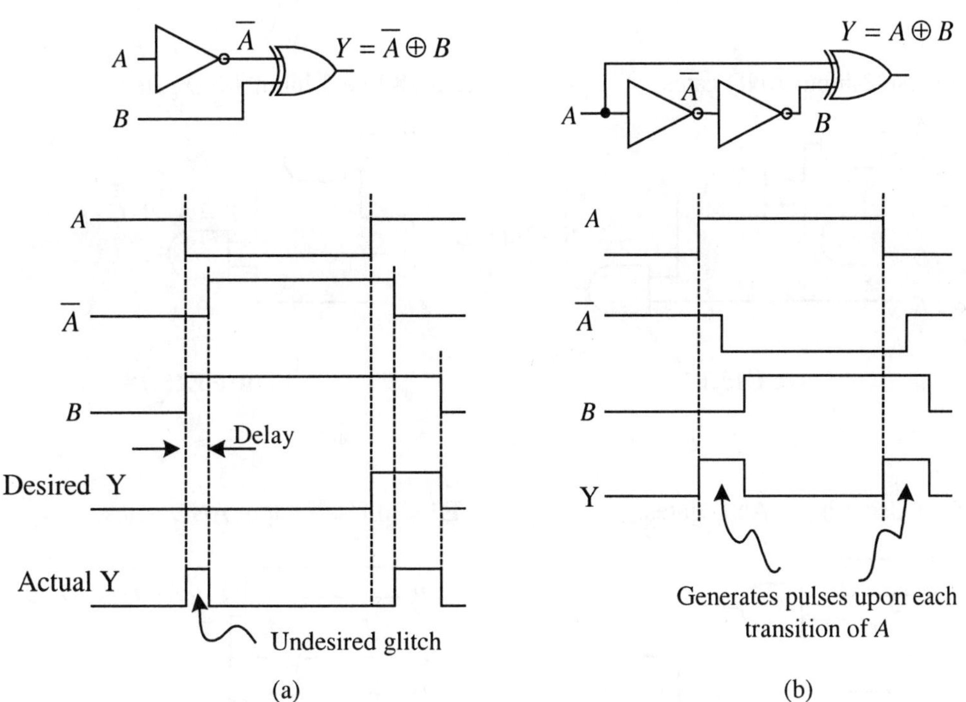

Figure 15.5 – Generation of undesired glitch

Underneath the circuit diagram is a series of five sketches which comprise what is known as a *timing diagram*. We start by drawing assumed shapes for inputs A and B. These shapes are piecewise constant waveforms, and are chosen to produce various combinations of transitions and input levels. In Figure 15.5(a), we let A start HIGH, then go LOW, and finally, back to HIGH.

The second input, B, starts LOW. It goes from LOW to HIGH at the same time that input A is changing from HIGH to LOW. Then B returns to LOW following the second transition in A.

The circuit performs an exclusive OR operation between B and the inverse of A. Thus the output, Y, should be HIGH if either A is low or B is high, but not both. The desired output is shown as *Desired Y*. However, now suppose that the inverter introduces a delay. The resulting output is as shown as *Actual Y*. Note that a narrow pulse has been generated at the first transition time. This undesired pulse is known as a *glitch*.

Sometimes glitches can be useful, as shown in the example of Figure 15.5(b). This demonstrates how two inverters (or any even number) may be used with an exclusive OR to generate a narrow pulse whenever a logic input changes from one logic state to the other (i.e., at both the rising transition and the falling transition).

EXERCISES

In Exercise E15.17 through E15.20, form a 5-input AND gate using only the specified gates. Answers are shown in the figures.

E15.17 Use 2-input AND gates.

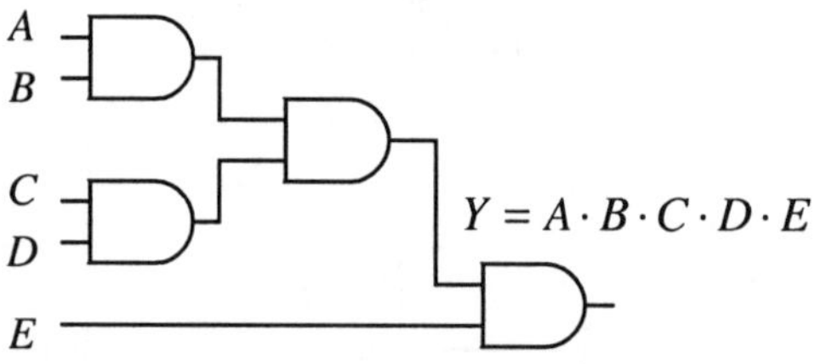

Figure E15.17

E15.18 Use 3-input AND gates.

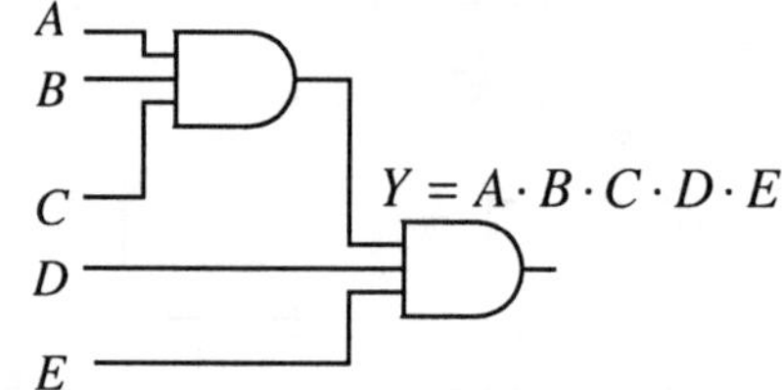

Figure E15.18

E15.19 Use 4-input AND gates.

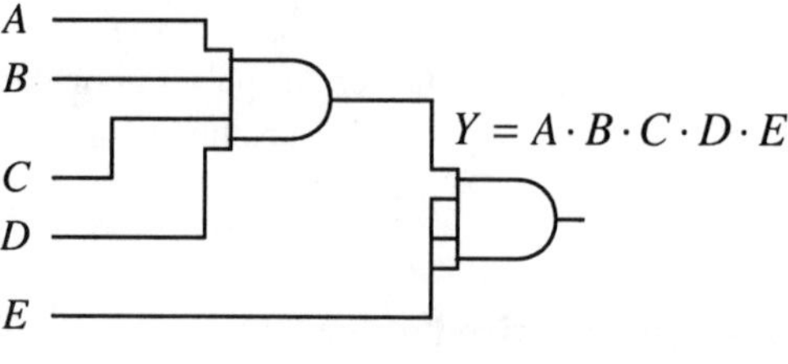

Figure E15.19

E15.20 Use 8-input AND gates.

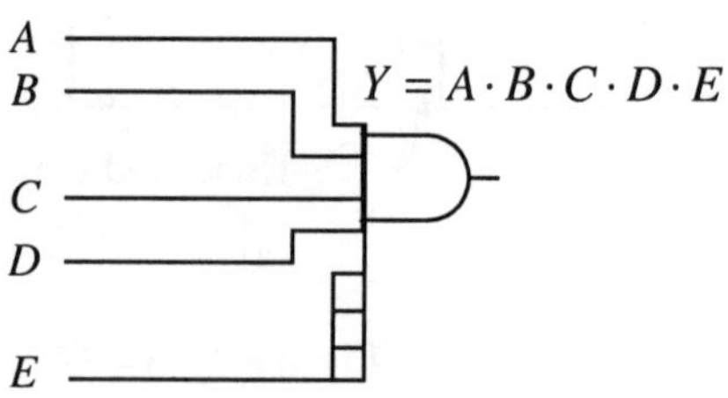

Figure E15.20

15.4 DIGITAL CIRCUIT CHARACTERISTICS OF BJTs

When we design an analog circuit with BJTs, we concentrate on assuring operation in the linear or active region of the characteristic curves. In the case of digital circuits, we require that the transistor be either ON (usually in the saturated condition) or OFF (in the cut-off condition). In effect, we operate at either of the two extremes of the transistor characteristic curves, as shown in Figure 15.6(a).

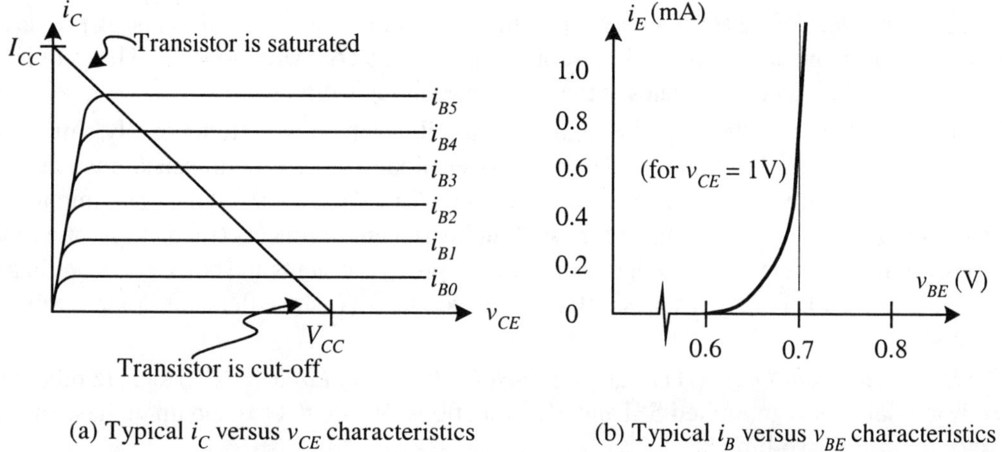

(a) Typical i_C versus v_{CE} characteristics

(b) Typical i_B versus v_{BE} characteristics

Figure 15.6 – *npn* Silicon transistor characteristics

When the transistor is saturated, the voltage from the collector to emitter, v_{CE}, is approximately 0.2 V. When the transistor is cut off, an open circuit exists between collector and emitter.

The i_B vs. v_{BE} characteristic curve is shown in Figure 15.6(b). When v_{BE} is less than about 0.6 V, the transistor is cut off and the base and all other currents are zero. As v_{BE} increases, i_B and i_C increase rapidly. When the transistor is in saturation, the voltage between base and emitter, V_{BESAT}, is approximately 0.7 to 0.8 V.

The first step in the analysis of the BJT family of ICs is to prepare a function table that shows the status of each transistor (either ON or OFF) for all possible combinations of high and low levels of each of the inputs. The next step is to determine the numerical value of v_{BE} for each transistor. If v_{BE} is less than 0.6 V, the transistor is cut off. If v_{BE} is greater than 0.6 V, the transistor could be in the active region or it could be saturated. Which of these two states occurs depends on the transistor characteristics (e.g., β) and the various resistor values in the circuit. With some types of digital ICs, we avoid the active region and we cause the transistors to be either cut off or saturated.

15.5 BIPOLAR LOGIC FAMILIES

There are six important families of bipolar logic. These are known as TTL, ECL, RTL, DTL, HTL and HNIL. The first two of these are discussed in detail in Sections 15.6 and 15.7. The last four are of less current importance, and are included in this section only to provide historical perspective.

Resistor-Transistor Logic (RTL) was the earliest integrated circuit family. It utilizes only transistors and resistors, and provides logic gating by placing transistor collectors in parallel. The RTL family has disappeared since other families dissipate less power and show improved noise immunity.

Diode-Transistor Logic (DTL) was a popular logic family for several years. It provided improvements in noise immunity and fan-out capabilities as compared to RTL. The gating of DTL is performed by diode OR gates at the input to each logic circuit.

Several manufacturers developed digital logic families which were functionally similar to DTL, but with some of the diodes replaced by zener diodes so that the transistors would not conduct until the input voltages reached a level of about 6 V. This improved the noise immunity, making this logic family more suitable for use in industrial environments (such as factories and refineries where heavy electrical equipment produces spikes, transients and other variations in the power line voltage). DTL has been essentially replaced by TTL since the latter logic family is faster.

The *High-Threshold Logic* (HTL) and *High-Noise Immunity Logic* (HNIL) logic families are currently available only in limited SSI and MSI functions. We do not expand upon these in this text since their use is so limited.

15.6 TRANSISTOR-TRANSISTOR LOGIC (TTL)

Transistor-transistor logic (TTL) began as a single, unique logic family. As it grew, various requirements for higher speed, lower power, or higher output drive led to the development of several subgroups as discussed below.

The original logic family is still in use, although most new logic functions are being implemented in newer subgroups of the family. TTL utilizes BJTs and provides moderate speed and power consumption. The speed of TTL circuits is limited by the following conditions:

- In digital ICs, we operate the transistors in the saturated mode; i.e., turned ON. For a saturated transistor to turn from ON to OFF, charge must be removed from the base.
- The wiring capacitance and the transistor capacitance must discharge through the circuit resistances.

The following subgroups deal with these two limitations to achieve an improved result. We can speed up the operation by:

- preventing the transistor from fully saturating when in the ON mode.
- reducing the resistor values in the circuit to decrease the time required to discharge the capacitors (i.e., make the RC time constant smaller). This method increases the amount of power consumed by the IC.

High Power TTL (*H-TTL*) was developed for driver circuits and other applications requiring a high fan out (number of circuits which the output must drive) and high speed. The H-TTL family consumes more power than other TTL subgroups. It is not widely used, and is available only in a few logic functions. It utilizes smaller resistor values than those used in TTL. This leads to lower time constants and higher operating speeds.

Low Power TTL (*LP-TTL*) was developed for applications requiring lower power consumption, and where reduced operating speed can be tolerated. It utilizes saturating transistors, and attains lower power consumption by using larger resistors than those used in TTL. It has essentially been replaced by LS-TTL.

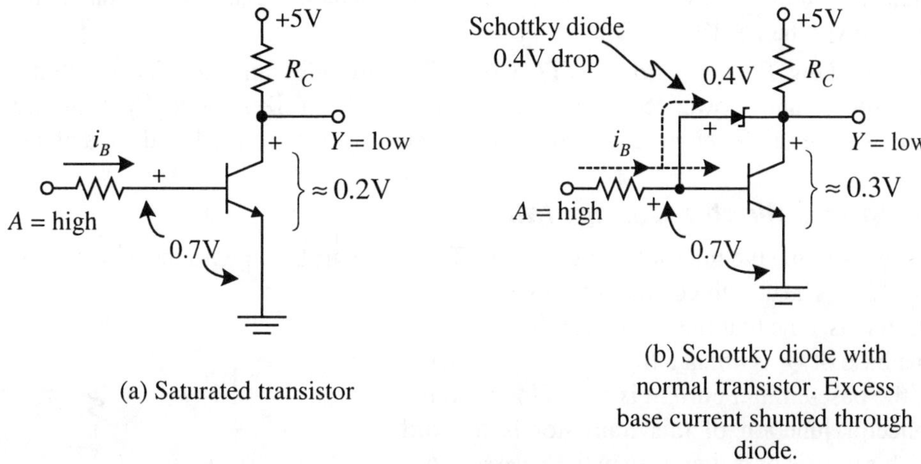

Figure 15.7 (Parts a and b) – Evolution of Schottky transistor

Schottky TTL (*S-TTL*) was developed for high speed applications. It attains high speed operation by both preventing transistor saturation and by reducing resistor values. We prevent transistor saturation by connecting a Schottky diode from base to collector for each saturated transistor in the IC. The resulting transistor shunted with a Schottky diode is called a *Schottky transistor*. The Schottky diode diverts some of the base driving current away from the base, thereby preventing the transistor from saturating. This technique of increasing speed is preferred to reducing resistor values since it does not increase the required power. By reducing resistor values we can speed up the IC, however, this does increase the power. Figure 15.7 shows a comparison between Schottky transistors and the standard BJT.

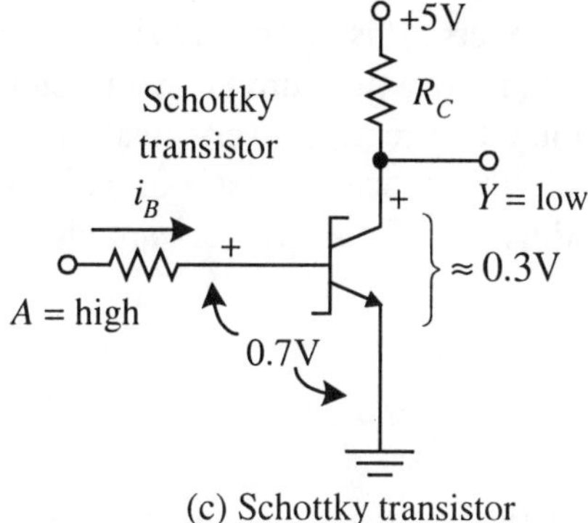

Figure 15.7 (Part c) – Evolution of Schottky transistor

The base-to-emitter voltage is typically 0.7 V, and the diode forward voltage drop is typically 0.4 V. Thus, when the collector voltage drops to 0.3 V, the excess base current is shunted through the diode to the collector, and the transistor is prevented from saturating. Since the transistor does not saturate, it does not suffer from the delay required to remove the excess base charge and turn the transistor OFF. Propagation delay is approximately 30% lower than that of standard TTL circuitry.

Low Power Schottky TTL (LS-TTL) is a subgroup which provides the speed of the original TTL family but with substantially reduced power consumption. It can be described as low power TTL using Schottky transistors instead of saturating transistors. It has been one of the most popular subgroups for many years, and most logic functions are available in LS-TTL.

Advanced Schottky TTL (AS-TTL) is a TTL subgroup which provides somewhat higher speed and lower power than S-TTL.

Advanced Low Power Schottky TTL (ALS-TTL) provides an excellent combination of desirable speed and power consumption properties. It utilizes Schottky transistors but incorporates material developments and smaller circuit layouts with reduced capacitance.

15.6.1 Open Collector Configurations

We now examine the internal circuitry of a TTL IC. Let us begin with the inverter, as shown in Figure 15.8. The circuit consists of two transistors. We will first assume that the input is HIGH, or +5 V. Since the base of Q_1 is *not* at a higher voltage than the emitter, the base-emitter current is zero. However, the base-collector junction of this transistor is forward biased. This transistor is therefore in the *reverse active* configuration. For some transistors, this would mean that the device follows normal transistor operation except that the collector and emitter are interchanged. However, in this case the transistor is constructed so that the reverse β is extremely small (perhaps 0.02). This means that the current in the emitter (i.e., the circuit input current) is a very small fraction of that in the collector. Since the base-to-collector voltage is approximately 0.7 V, Q_2 is forward biased. The base-to-collector current, I, then approximately equals

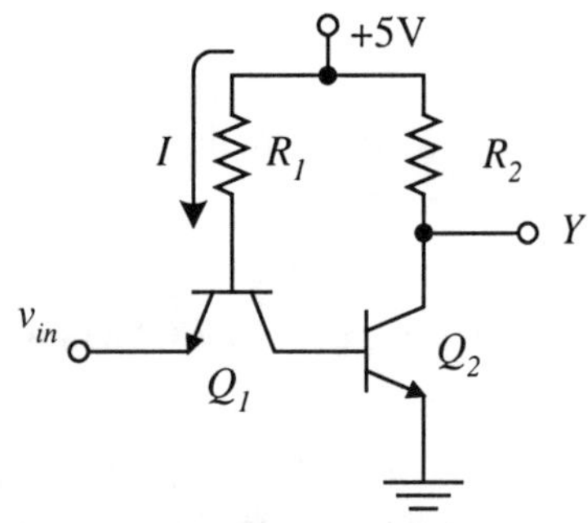

Figure 15.8 - Inverter

$$I = \frac{5 - 0.7 - 0.7}{R_1} \qquad (15.5)$$

Q_2 is either in the active mode, or saturated. In designing the chip, the collector resistor, R_2, is designed to saturate the transistor, so the output, Y, is approximately 0.2 V. We have therefore shown the first part of the inverter relationship – when the input is high, the output is low. We now look at the other case.

When the input, v_{in}, is low [0.2 V], Q_1 has a forward-biased base-emitter junction, and the base voltage is approximately 0.9 V. The base current is then

$$I = \frac{5 - 0.9}{R_1} \tag{15.6}$$

The collector current will be β times this. This large current will only exist until charge is pulled from the base of Q_2. After the charge is removed, this second transistor switches OFF since the base cannot sustain a negative current. This raises the output to +5 V, verifying the second half of the inverter relationship.

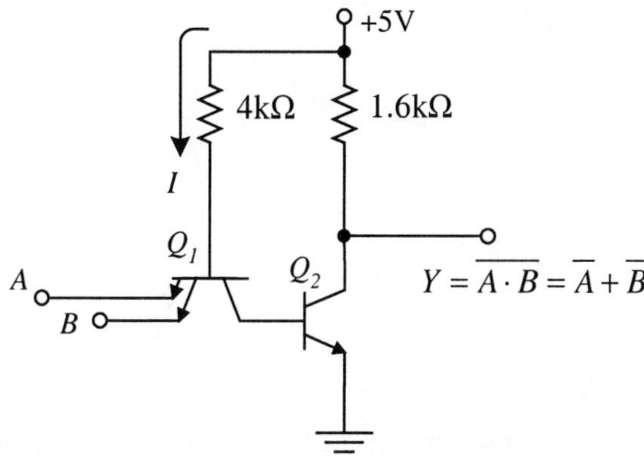

Figure 15.9 – Multiple-input NAND gate

We can modify the TTL circuit of Figure 15.8 to make this into a multiple input NAND gate. We do this by substituting a multiple emitter transistor for Q_1. Such a transistor is formed by depositing more than one *n*-doped emitter section. Figure 15.9 shows the structure of a two-emitter *npn* transistor. The collector current of this transistor will depend on the *sum* of the two emitter currents.

We now substitute the multi-emitter transistor for Q_1 to produce Figure 15.10(a), the schematic diagram for a two-input TTL NAND gate with open collector.

Note that we have added a third transistor to the circuit of Figure 15.9. We will see that this transistor speeds up the switching process. The operation of this basic TTL gate depends upon the dual emitter transistor, Q_1. The two inputs, *A* and *B*, are connected to the emitters.

The output of this open collector gate is taken from the collector of Q_3. A "pull up" resistor is externally inserted between the IC output and a voltage of level *V*, frequently 5 V. This pull up resistor causes the output of the IC to "pull up" to *V* when Q_3 is OFF. Since the logic block is a NAND gate, the output should be 1 when either or both of the inputs is 0.

The diodes, D_1 and D_2, are present to protect the IC. If either input, *A* or *B*, accidentally became negative, a high current could flow in Q_1 thus destroying the transistor. The diodes prevent this.

When either or both of the emitters of Q_1 is low, I_{C1} is large and positive (+ on the function table) and Q_2 turns OFF. When Q_2 is OFF, Q_3 is also OFF since there is no positive voltage between its base and emitter. When Q_3 is OFF, its collector goes HIGH (it goes to +5 V without any load, and to a lesser amount when load current is drawn because of the voltage drop across the pull-up resistor). This verifies the first three rows of the function table in Figure 15.10(b).

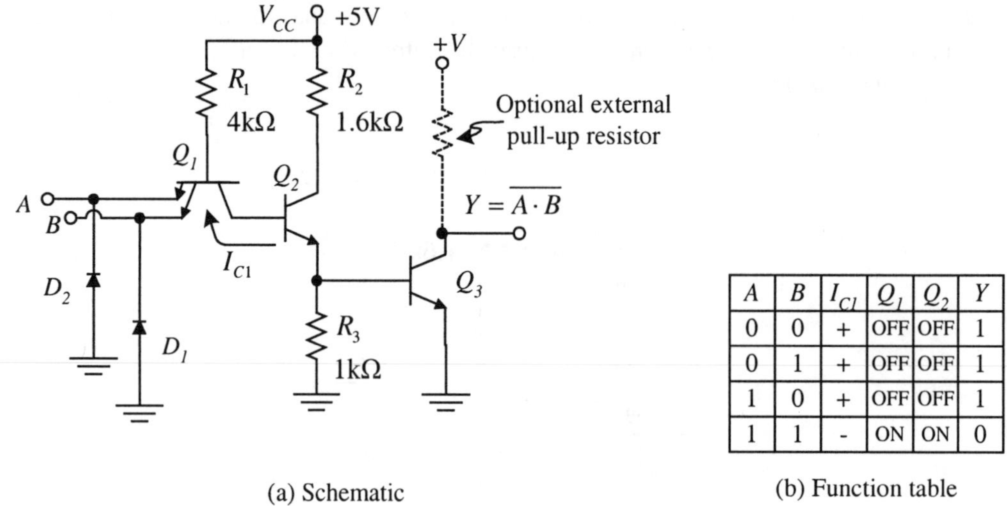

A	B	I_{C1}	Q_1	Q_2	Y
0	0	+	OFF	OFF	1
0	1	+	OFF	OFF	1
1	0	+	OFF	OFF	1
1	1	-	ON	ON	0

(a) Schematic (b) Function table

Figure 15.10 - Two-input TTL NAND gate (open collector)

Now let's examine the case of both emitters of Q_1 high. As in the previous analysis of the inverter (Figure 15.8), Q_1 is in the reverse active mode. The collector-base junction of Q_1 is forward biased, and Q_2 turns on. When Q_2 is saturated, the voltage at the base of Q_3 is approximately given by equation (15.7).

$$\frac{(5 - V_{CE})R_3}{R_2 + R_3} = \frac{4800}{2600} = 1.85 \text{ V} \qquad (15.7)$$

We have set $V_{CE} = 0.2$ V. This is sufficient to drive Q_3 into saturation (ON).

With Q_3 saturated, the output, *Y*, is brought to LOW [0.2 V]. This verifies the final row of the function table of Figure 15.10(b).

Let us now examine some of the major applications for the open collector gate. The gate can be used as a means of interfacing the TTL logic family to another logic family. For example, in a system that includes both TTL and CMOS ICs (discussed later in this chapter), the HIGH and LOW voltage levels may be different. In particular, the HIGH level for TTL is between 2.4 V and 5 V while for CMOS, it can be 10 V. If the pull up resistor of Figure 15.10(a) is connected to 10 V, then the open collector gate acts as an interface between the TTL portion of the system and the CMOS portion.

A second application of the open-collector gate occurs when several gates are attached to a common *bus*. In the operation of this common bus, each gate can only control the logic level of the bus by bringing it LOW, but not HIGH. With the collector left open, each gate that has Q_3

OFF exerts no control upon the bus. Only when the output transistor is ON does the gate bring the bus to logic level 0.

A third application for the open collector occurs when a lamp or relay is driven from the output of a gate. The lamp or relay is placed between the output terminal of the open collector IC and the voltage source through an appropriate limiting resistor. When Q_3 is saturated, a path to ground exists and the lamp or relay is ON. When Q_3 is OFF, there is no path to ground so the lamp or relay is OFF.

15.6.2 Active Pull Up

Figure 15.11(a) shows a two-input TTL NAND gate with active pull up on the output. This circuit configuration is known as a *totem-pole* output. The circuit is similar to that of Figure 15.10(a) except for the addition of D_3, Q_4 and R_4. This type of gate is used when increased operating speed is required. The *propagation delay* for an open collector gate is approximately 35 ns. The propagation delay for the active pull up gate is only about 8 ns. The clear advantage is in increasing the speed of this totem-pole compared to that of the open collector

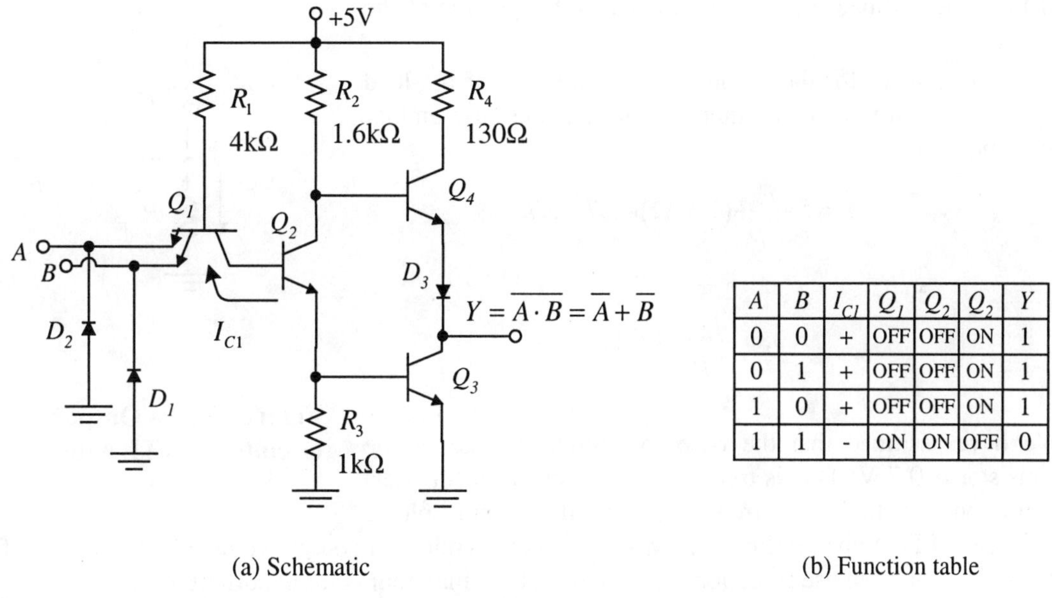

A	B	I_{C1}	Q_1	Q_2	Q_2	Y
0	0	+	OFF	OFF	ON	1
0	1	+	OFF	OFF	ON	1
1	0	+	OFF	OFF	ON	1
1	1	-	ON	ON	OFF	0

(a) Schematic (b) Function table

Figure 15.11 - Two-input TTL NAND gate (active pull up)

output gate. One potential problem in the use of these totem-pole output TTL devices is that during the transition from ON to OFF and OFF to ON, large current spikes are drawn from the power supply which can interfere with other ICs. The effects of this problem can be reduced by physically placing a bypass capacitor next to the IC and connected between the V_{CC} terminal of the IC and ground.

As we will see in the following analysis, when Q_3 is ON, Q_4 is OFF, and vice versa. Therefore, the output is either pulled toward ground (when Q_3 saturates) or pulled toward the supply voltage (when Q_4 saturates). We will see that the diode, D_3, is required to assure that both output transistors do not turn ON simultaneously.

Suppose first that Q_2 and Q_3 are ON [the bottom entry in the table of Figures 15.10(b) and 15.11(b)]. The voltage at the base of Q_4 is then given by

$$V_B(Q_4) = V_{CE}(Q_2) + V_{BE}(Q_3) = 0.2 + 0.7 = 0.9\text{ V} \tag{15.8}$$

The voltage necessary to turn Q_4 ON must be greater than 1.6 V. That is,

$$V_{BE}(Q_4) + V(D_3) + V_{CE}(Q_3) = 0.7 + 0.7 + 0.2 = 1.6\text{ V} \tag{15.9}$$

Since the base voltage of Q_4 is only 0.9 V, Q_4 is OFF, as shown in the bottom entry of Figure 15.11(b). When Q_2 and Q_3 are OFF, the base-emitter junction of Q_4 is forward biased and the output goes to logic 1. In order to determine the state of transistor Q_4 (i.e., active or saturated), we must know the nature of the attached load. Figure 15.12 isolates this portion of the circuit.

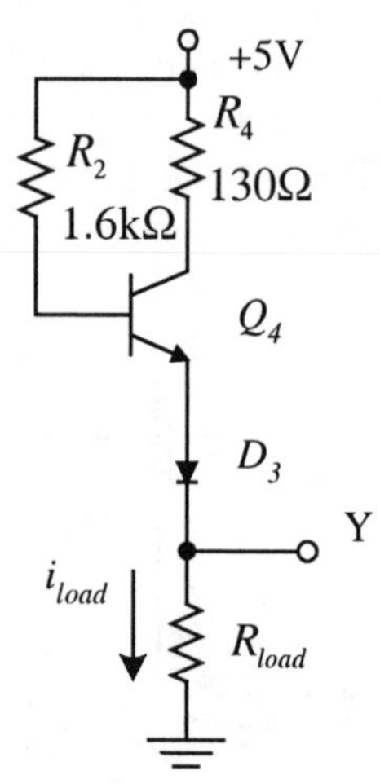

Figure 15.12 – Output circuitry of TTL gate

We can solve for the output voltage in terms of the load current by writing a loop equation through the base-emitter junction. This yields

$$Y = 5 - \frac{i_{load}}{\beta}(1.6\text{k}\Omega) - 0.7 - 0.7$$

$$= 3.6 - \frac{i_{load}}{\beta}(1.6\text{ k}\Omega) \tag{15.10}$$

We have assumed that the base to emitter voltage of the transistor is 0.7 V. This is true if the transistor is at (or near) saturation. As the load current increases, the output voltage decreases. TTL chip specifications typically specify a minimum output voltage (for a logic 1) of 2.4 V. We can then use Equation (15.10) to find the maximum output current to be

$$i_{load}(\max) = \frac{1.2\beta}{1600} \tag{15.11}$$

Finally, this maximum can be used to determine the maximum number of gates this TTL circuit can drive (i.e., the *fan out*). Another way to state this is that we can use the maximum load current to find the minimum value of load resistance, R_{load}.

Since the load capacitance can now discharge through a resistor of about 150 Ω (130 Ω plus the resistances of Q_4 and D_3) the time to change from 1 to 0 is faster than for the open collector gate, which must discharge through a larger value pull up resistor.

The totem-pole output gate cannot be used in the applications of the previous section. For example, suppose we tried to connect two totem-pole outputs to a common bus. If the output of one gate is HIGH and the output of the other is LOW, an excessive amount of current results and this could overheat and damage the ICs.

EXAMPLE 15.2

Determine the status of each transistor in the circuit of Figure 15.13.

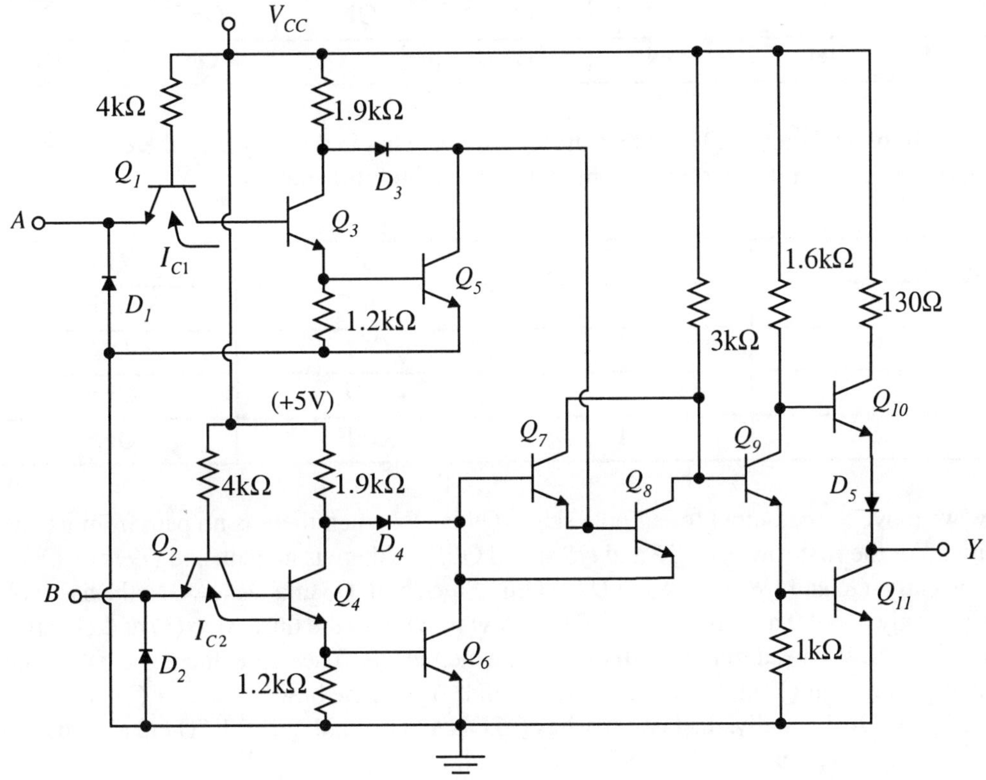

Figure 15.13 – Circuit for Example 15.2

Solution: First note that the three-transistor sections, *Q1*, *Q3*, *Q5* and *Q2*, *Q4*, *Q6* are in the same configuration as the basic TTL gate of Figure 15.8. Additionally, *Q9*, *Q10* and *Q11* are in the totem-pole configuration, just like *Q2*, *Q3* and *Q4* of Figure 15.11.

We can start the table by using these observations to find the first six transistor states. Just as in Figure 15.8, *Q3* matches *Q5* and *Q4* matches *Q6*. Note in the following table that *RA* means Reverse Active.

Now let's look at *Q7* and *Q8*. In order for *Q7* to be ON, the first requirement is that *Q4* be OFF. If *Q4* is ON, the collector voltage at *Q4* is too low to provide a positive base-emitter voltage for *Q7*. Now suppose *Q4* is OFF. There is then a path to the base of *Q7* from the source through to 1.9 kΩ resistor and then through the diode. Since *Q6* is OFF when *Q4* is OFF, the only possible path for the base-emitter current of *Q7* is up through *Q5* to ground. Thus, *Q7* will be on only if *Q4* is OFF and *Q5* is ON. This establishes the *Q7* column of the table.

A	B	Q1	Q3	Q5	Q2	Q4	Q6
0	0	ON	OFF	OFF	ON	OFF	OFF
0	1	ON	OFF	OFF	RA	ON	ON
1	0	RA	ON	ON	ON	OFF	OFF
1	1	RA	ON	ON	RA	ON	ON

Q8 will be ON only if *Q3* is OFF and *Q6* is ON. That is the only way there will be a path through the base-emitter to ground. This establishes the following:

A	B	Q7	Q8
0	0	OFF	OFF
0	1	OFF	ON
1	0	ON	OFF
1	1	OFF	OFF

Now we move to the output totem pole stage. *Q9* is ON when there is no path from its base to ground. For the first row, *Q6*, *Q7* and *Q8* are all OFF, so there is no path and *Q9* is ON. For the second entry, *Q6* and *Q8* are ON and *Q7* is OFF. Since both *Q8* and *Q6* are ON, the base voltage of *Q9* is only about 0.4 volts, so *Q9* is OFF. Now moving to the third row, *Q6* and *Q8* are OFF and *Q7* is ON. We need to look further to *Q5*, which is ON. Therefore, there is a path from the base of *Q9* through *Q7* and through *Q5* to ground. Again, the base voltage of *Q9* is only at 0.4 volts, so it is OFF. Finally, the last entry has *Q6* ON and *Q7* and *Q8* OFF. There is no path from the base of *Q9* to ground, so it is ON.

We can read the states of *Q10* and *Q11* from the table in Figure 15.9 (note that the order is reversed - in that table the bottom transistor in the totem-pole precedes the top. This leads to the final portion of the table.

A	B	Q9	Q10	Q11	Y
0	0	ON	OFF	ON	0
0	1	OFF	ON	OFF	1
1	0	OFF	ON	OFF	1
1	1	ON	OFF	ON	0

15.6.3 H-TTL and LP-TTL Gates

The two input NAND gate for the H-TTL circuit is shown in Figure 15.14(a) and the function table is presented as Figure 15.14(b).

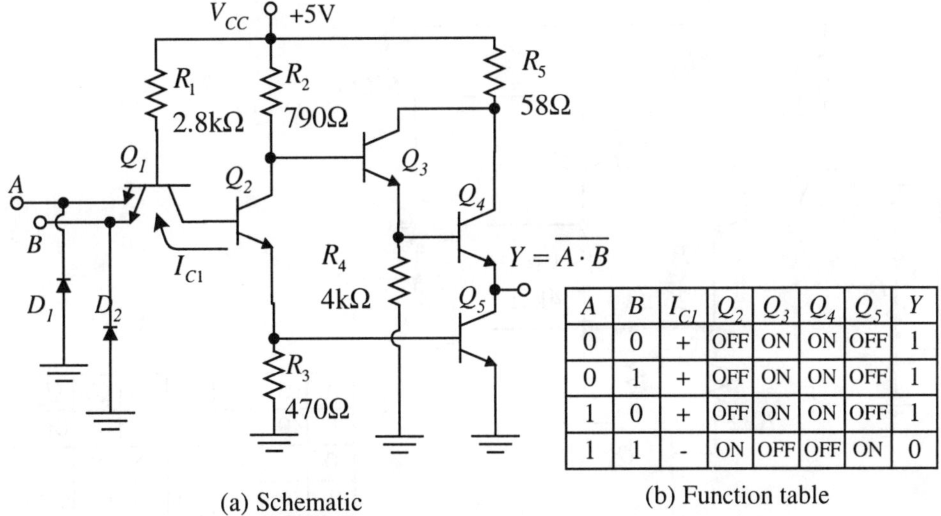

A	B	I_{CI}	Q_2	Q_3	Q_4	Q_5	Y
0	0	+	OFF	ON	ON	OFF	1
0	1	+	OFF	ON	ON	OFF	1
1	0	+	OFF	ON	ON	OFF	1
1	1	-	ON	OFF	OFF	ON	0

(a) Schematic (b) Function table

Figure 15.14 - Two-input H-TTL NAND gate

Note that H-TTL NAND gate has one more transistor than does the TTL NAND gate with active pull up. The function tables are identical through the column for Q_2. Starting with the next column, the state of Q_3 for the H-TTL gate is opposite that of Q_2. In the H-TTL gate, transistors Q_3 and Q_5 are fed by the collector and emitter of Q_2. In the TTL NAND gate of Figure 15.11(a), transistors Q_4 and Q_3 are fed by the collector and emitter of Q_2. The results are therefore comparable [i.e., Columns Q_3 and Q_5 of Figure 15.14(b) match columns Q_4 and Q_3 of Figure 15.11(b)].

15.6.4 Schottky TTL Gates

The Schottky subgroup of the TTL family is designed to reduce the propagation delay time of the standard TTL gates. The time needed for a transistor to switch from ON to OFF can be greatly reduced if the transistor is not permitted to go into saturation. In the circuit of Figure 15.7(b) we placed a Schottky diode between base and collector. Some of the base current shunts through the diode. This reduces current in the base, thereby preventing the transistor from going into saturation. A Schottky diode differs from a conventional diode in that the Schottky diode is formed with a connection of a *metal* and a semiconductor, rather than a junction of a *p*- and *n*-type semiconductor material. The voltage across a conducting Schottky diode is approximately 0.4 V. The Schottky diode and the transistor are combined to form a Schottky transistor as in Figure 15.7(c).

The circuit schematic and the function diagram for the two input NAND gate is shown in Figure 15.15. The transistors in the gate are of the Schottky type except for Q_5, which is of the standard type. The protection diodes are also Schottky. In this circuit, Q_5 and Q_4 form a

Darlington pair, providing a high current gain and low output resistance (See Section 8.4 for a discussion of Darlington pair transistor configurations). The resistor values in Figure 15.15(a) are approximately one-half the value of those in the standard TTL circuit of Figure 15.9.

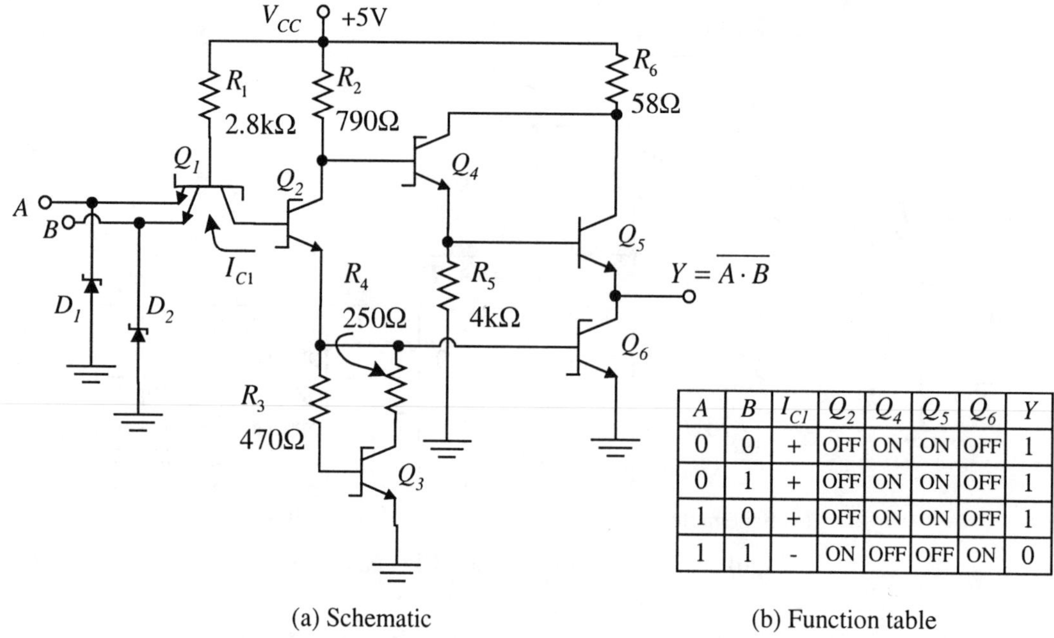

A	B	I_{C1}	Q_2	Q_4	Q_5	Q_6	Y
0	0	+	OFF	ON	ON	OFF	1
0	1	+	OFF	ON	ON	OFF	1
1	0	+	OFF	ON	ON	OFF	1
1	1	-	ON	OFF	OFF	ON	0

(a) Schematic (b) Function table

Figure 15.15 – Two-input S-TTL NAND gate

This increases the speed of the gate, however, the power dissipation is approximately doubled.

The schematic for the S-TTL gate [Figure 15.15(a)] has an additional sixth transistor, Q_3, which does not appear in the H-TTL gate. The state of this sixth transistor is not carried in the table since it has no direct effect upon the states of the other transistors. In performance, Q_3 is analogous to the Q_4 transistor of the active pull up (totem-pole) discussed in Section 15.6.2. The fixed resistor of Figure 15.14(a) is replaced with an active circuit comprising R_3, R_4, and Q_3. Just as the totem-pole speeds up the turn on and turn off time of the output stage, this active circuit speeds up the turn on and turn off time of Q_6. Hence the propagation delay of the gate is reduced. The verification of the entries in the function table follows the procedure of the previous sections.

15.6.5 Tri-State Gates

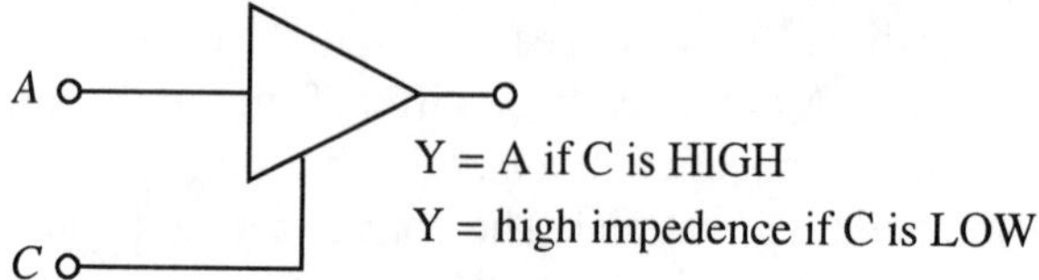

Figure 15.16 – Tri-state bus driver

The *tri-state* family of gates combines the high speed advantage of the totem-pole output with the advantages of an open collector output. The tri-state gate has a totem-pole output, with the associated speed advantage. However, because of its design, it can be connected to a bus system (as an open collector gate can). The output transistors; i.e., Q_3 and Q_4 of Figure 15.15, can assume three states (hence the name tri-state) as follows:

1. $Y = 1$ when Q_3 is ON and Q_4 is OFF
2. $Y = 0$ when Q_3 is OFF and Q_4 is ON
3. Y is an open circuit when Q_3 is OFF and Q_4 is OFF.

The tri-state bus driver is shown in the schematic of Figure 15.16. The tri-state operation is achieved with a control line, C, which permits the gate to operate normally if C is HIGH. The gate exhibits a high impedance when C is LOW. A high input impedance occurs when C is LOW. This permits several of these gates to be attached to a common bus as with the open collector gate.

EXERCISES

Determine the state of each transistor and the output in the circuits shown in Exercises E15.21 and E15.22. The solution is shown on the figure.

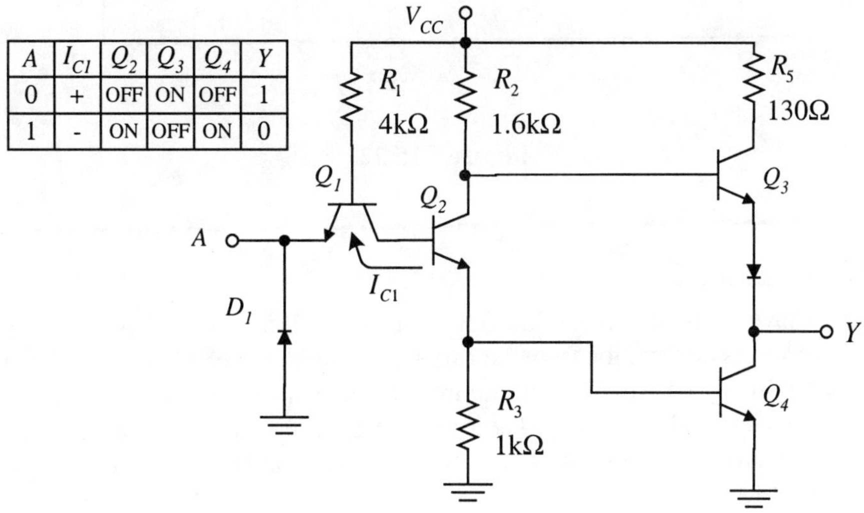

A	I_{C1}	Q_2	Q_3	Q_4	Y
0	+	OFF	ON	OFF	1
1	-	ON	OFF	ON	0

Figure E15.21

A	B	I_{C1}	I_{C2}	Q_3	Q_4	Q_5	Q_6	Q_7	Q_8	Y
0	0	+	+	OFF	OFF	OFF	ON	OFF	ON	0
0	1	+	-	OFF	ON	ON	OFF	ON	OFF	1
1	0	-	+	ON	OFF	ON	OFF	ON	OFF	1
1	1	-	-	ON	ON	ON	OFF	ON	OFF	1

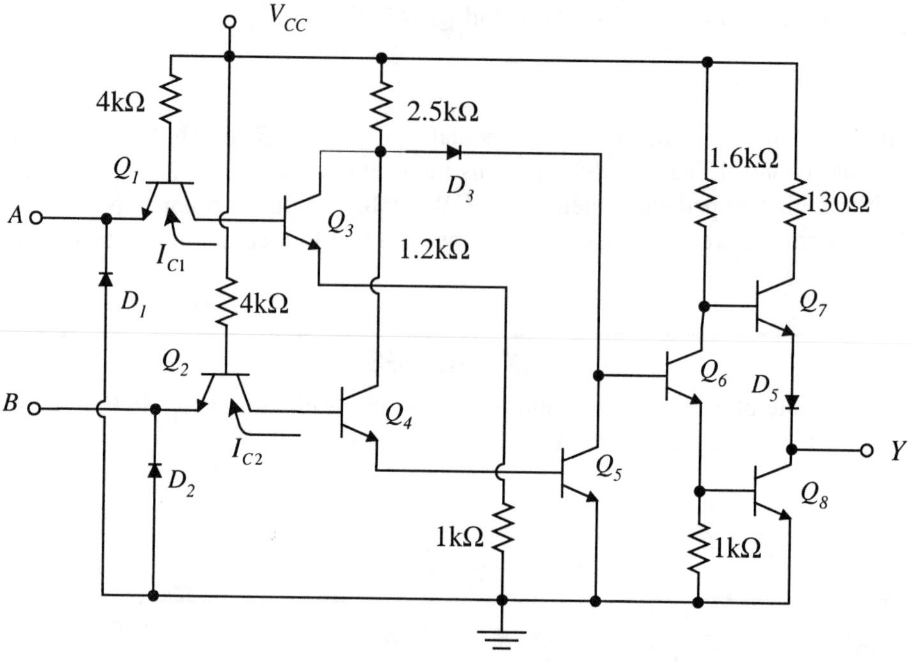

Figure E15.22

15.6.6 Device Listings

Table 15.1 shows a partial listing of the devices in the TTL family. At this point, we suggest that you learn to access information from the various IC manufacturers. In some cases, this takes the form of a hard-copy data book from the manufacturer. In other cases, the information is accessed through the World Wide Web. These resources are listed in the references at the end of this text. It is virtually impossible to successfully complete digital electronic designs without access to this information.

Type Number	Description
7400	Quad 2-input NAND
7401	Quad 2-input NAND, open collector
7402	Quad 2-input NOR
7403	Quad 2-input NOR, open collector

7404	Hex inverter
7405	Hex inverter, open collector
7406	Hex inverter, open collector to 30 V
7407	Hex buffer/driver, open collector to 30 V
7408	Quad 2-input AND
7409	Quad 2-input AND, open collector
7410	Triple 3-input NAND
7411	Triple 3-input AND
7414	Hex Schmitt-trigger inverters
7420	Dual 4-input NAND
7421	Dual 4-input AND
7427	Triple 3-input NOR
7430	8-input NAND
7432	Quad 2-input OR
7486	Quad 2-input XOR

Table 15.1 - TTL device listing

15.7 EMITTER-COUPLED LOGIC (ECL)

The ECL family operates at the highest speed of all of the logic families studied in this text. This happens because none of the transistors are operated in saturation. Since propagation delays of 1 to 2 ns are achievable, ECL is useful in high-speed applications such as radar signal processors, computers, and data transmission. There are fewer chips in the ECL family than in TTL.

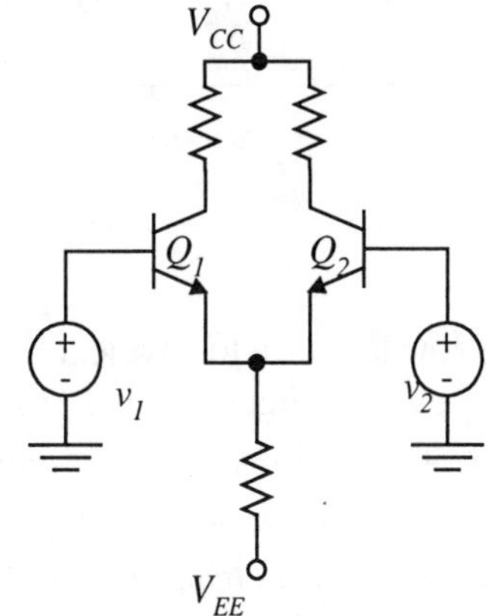

Figure 15.17 – Differential amplifier

Before we analyze an ECL gate, we will look at the *differential amplifier* of Figure 15.17.

In an analog differential amplifier, the output is taken between the two collectors. For digital applications, we really only need to verify one observation, as follows. *When one source voltage is larger than the other, the transistor associated with that higher voltage will be ON and the other transistor will be OFF.*

Let us first assume that *Q1* is ON. The emitter voltage of *Q1* is then equal to

$$V_E(Q1) = v_1 - V_{BE}(Q1) \tag{15.12}$$

Since the emitters of the two transistors are connected together, this is also the emitter voltage of *Q2*. The second source must be greater than this for *Q2* to conduct current. A similar conclusion would have resulted if we had started with an assumption that *Q2* is ON. The important result is that as long as one input voltage exceeds the other by at least V_{BE}, the transistor associated with the smaller input voltage is OFF. While we have been using a value of V_{BE} equal to 0.7 V, it is important to note that this value applies to a saturated transistor. Since transistors are not saturated in ECL gates, the actual base-to-emitter voltage is less than 0.7 V. This simple observation will prove sufficient to make analysis of the ECL gate very straightforward.

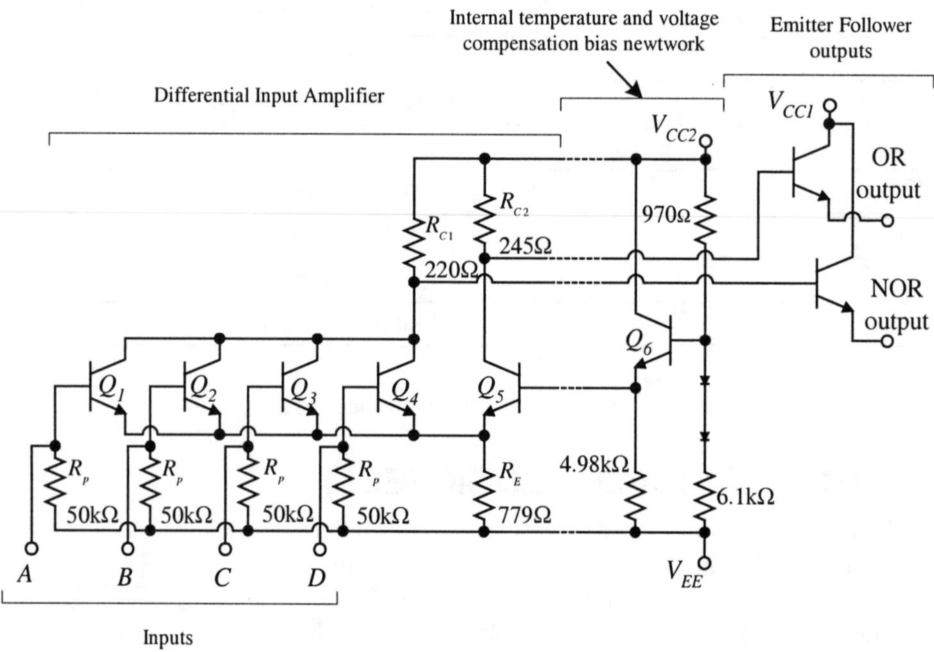

Figure 15.18 – MECL 10,000 basic gates

Now let's turn to a typical ECL gate. We illustrate the MECL 10,000, one of several types of ECL gate, in Figure 15.18. This basic gate can be divided into three sections:

1. The *differential input amplifier section* which contains the differential amplifiers. This section provides the logic gating and voltage gain for the circuit.
2. An *internal temperature and voltage-compensated bias network* which supplies a reference voltage for the differential amplifier. The bias voltage, V_{BB} is shown in Figure 15.18 and is set at -1.3 V. We shall see that this voltage is the midpoint between the voltages used for a logic 1 and a logic 0. V_{CC1} and V_{CC2} are set to zero and V_{EE} is -5.2 V. The two diodes and Q_6 provide the required temperature compensation.
3. The *emitter-follower output devices* provide level shifting from the differential amplifier to the ECL output levels. The emitter followers also provide a low impedance output for driving transmission lines.

The ECL family utilizes voltages of -1.8 V and -0.8 V to represent a 0 and a 1 respectively. The differential amplifier circuit allows current to flow in only one of the transistors at a time. This is known as *current steering*. Suppose, for example, that one or more of the inputs is at -0.8 V. This is 0.5 V above the reference, V_{BB}. From what we just learned about the differential amplifier (see Figure 15.16), we know that the associated transistor(s) will be active and *Q5* will be OFF. Alternatively, if all inputs are at -1.8 V, the reference is 0.5 V above this. *Q5* is active and all input transistors are OFF. The transistor voltages and currents are controlled to prevent transistor saturation without requiring special Schottky transistors.

Emitter-coupled logic uses a negative supply voltage and consumes a large amount of power. The devices are more susceptible to noise than are most other logic families. The fast rise and fall times of the output waveform often require use of special wiring techniques to prevent overshoot, ringing or reflections of the wave returning from the other end of a cable.

Figure 15.19 shows an example of an ECL gate that provides both an OR and a NOR function. The *Y* output provides the OR, and *Z* provides NOR. The function table is shown in Figure 15.19(b). You should take the time to verify the entries in this table.

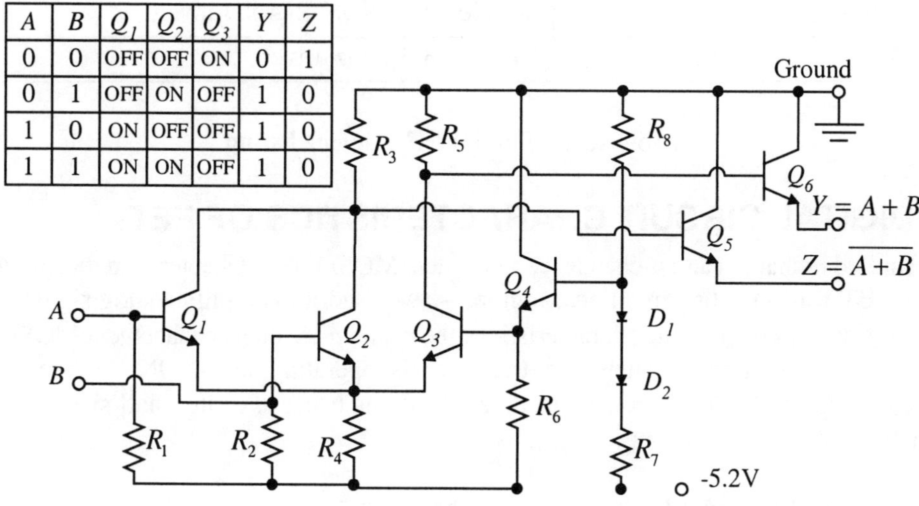

A	B	Q_1	Q_2	Q_3	Y	Z
0	0	OFF	OFF	ON	0	1
0	1	OFF	ON	OFF	1	0
1	0	ON	OFF	OFF	1	0
1	1	ON	ON	OFF	1	0

Figure 15.19 - Two-input ECL OR/NOR gate

15.7.1 Device Listings

Table 15.2 presents a partial listing of devices in the ECL family.

Type Number	Description
10100/10500	Quad 2-input NOR with strobe
10101/10501	Quad OR/NOR
10102/10502	Quad 2-input NOR

10103/10503	Quad 2-input OR
10104/10504	Quad 2-input AND
10105/10505	Triple 2-3-2-input OR/NOR
10106/10506	Triple 4-3-3-input NOR
10107/10507	Triple 2-input exclusive OR/exclusive NOR
10109/10509	Dual 4-5 input OR/NOR
10110	Dual 3-input 3-output OR
10111	Dual 3-input 3-output NOR
10113/10513	Quad exclusive OR
10117/10517	Dual 2-wise 2-3-input OR-AMD/OR-AND-invert
10118/10518	Dual 2-wide 3-input OR-AND
10119/10519	4-wide 4-3-3-input OR-AND
10121/10521	4-wide OR-AND/OR-AND-invert
10123	Triple 4-3-3-i bus driver

Table 15.2 - Partial ECL device listing

15.8 DIGITAL CIRCUIT CHARACTERISTICS OF FETs

We studied *n*-channel and *p*-channel enhancement MOSFETs in Chapter 6. In that discussion, the MOSFET was operating in a linear region – we used it to amplify analog signals. In the current section, we consider the characteristic of the *n*- and *p*-channel enhancement MOSFET for use in digital applications, where the transistor is operating in an ON-OFF mode. The enhancement MOSFET is often used in IC applications because of its small size and simple construction.

15.8.1 The n-Channel Enhancement MOSFET

The *n*-channel enhancement MOSFET has no channel between source and drain (a broken line is shown in the symbol). However, as the gate-to-source voltage, v_{GS}, becomes more positive, an *n*-channel region forms that extends from source to drain. This region provides a low resistance between source and drain. In order to turn the transistor ON, we apply a v_{GS} that is greater than the threshold voltage, V_T. This voltage, V_T, can vary upward from 1 V depending on the device. To turn the transistor OFF, we simply let $v_{GS}<V_T$ (we usually say $v_{GS} = 0$) so no channel is formed. With the gate grounded, the resistance between source and ground is high, and the transistor is OFF.

It is important to note that the input gate is an open circuit and resembles a small capacitor. No input current is required, except for the brief period when we charge or discharge this small input gate capacitor. When $v_{GS} = 0$, the resistance between source and drain is high and we can model this as an open switch. When v_{GS} is greater than V_T, the transistor turns ON and the channel between source and drain becomes equivalent to a low value resistor (i.e., a closed switch). The only voltage drop is a small one from source to drain across this resistance.

15.8.2 The p-Channel Enhancement MOSFET

The *p*-channel enhancement MOSFET is the mirror image of the *n*-channel device. With a negative voltage applied to v_{GS} (i.e., when $v_{GS} < V_T$), the channel is formed and the transistor turns ON. When v_{GS} is zero, the transistor is an open circuit.

15.9 FET TRANSISTOR FAMILIES

In this section we consider the *n*-channel and *p*-channel MOS integrated circuit. These are considered separately to aid in understanding the operation of the more useful CMOS devices. Since the gate of an FET leads only to an equivalent capacitor, no input current is required except for that needed to charge and discharge the small gate capacitor. This means that we are not concerned with the number of gates that can be driven from a single gate (fan out).

15.9.1 n-Channel MOS

The *n*-channel MOS (NMOS) ICs are constructed using *n*-channel MOS transistors. An example of an NMOS inverter and its function table is shown in Figure 15.20.

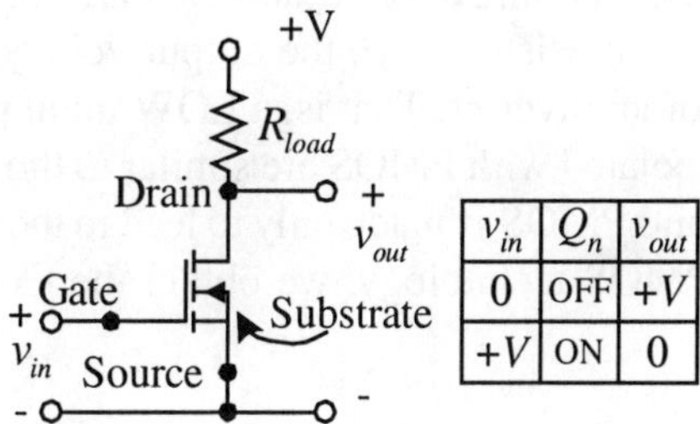

v_{in}	Q_n	v_{out}
0	OFF	$+V$
$+V$	ON	0

Figure 15.20 – NMOS Inverter

We analyze the *n*-channel FET by noting that if the gate voltage and the substrate voltage are the same, the transistor is OFF. When the gate voltage is greater than the substrate voltage (by an amount equal to V_T), the transistor is ON. With the transistor ON, the output voltage is near zero depending upon the value of R_{load} and the FET characteristics. We show it as zero in the function table. With the transistor OFF, the output is raised to $+V$ volts. Note that if current is drawn into the load, the output drops below $+V$ volts. The function table of Figure 15.20 shows that with the input HIGH, the output is LOW, and vice-versa. This function table defines an inverter.

Although NMOS has some good qualities, it suffers from the need for large current from the power supply during the ON state. A large power supply is therefore needed to drive a system composed of multiple NMOS ICs.

15.9.2 p-Channel MOS

The *p*-channel MOS (PMOS) ICs are constructed with *p*-channel MOS transistors. These were the first types of memory circuits to be developed. An example of a PMOS inverter and its function table is shown in Figure 15.21.

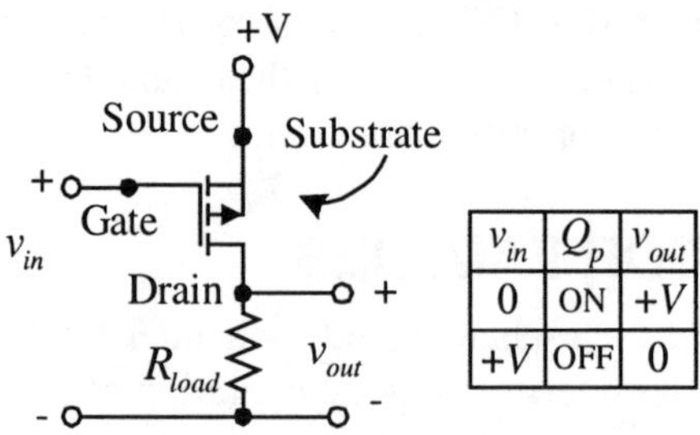

v_{in}	Q_p	v_{out}
0	ON	$+V$
$+V$	OFF	0

Figure 15.21 – PMOS inverter

We analyze this circuit by noting that if the voltage on the gate (the input voltage) is the same as the voltage on the substrate, the transistor is OFF. If the voltage on the gate is less than that on the substrate (by an amount equal to V_T), the transistor is ON. With the transistor ON, the output voltage is raised to nearly $+V$, depending upon R_L and the FET characteristics. We show it as $+V$ in the function table. With the transistor OFF, the output voltage is zero. Again, the function table of Figure 15.21 is that of an inverter. That is, a LOW input produces a HIGH output, and vice-versa. The problems associated with PMOS are similar to those of NMOS. In fact, this brief presentation of both NMOS and PMOS is made only to lead to the exciting CMOS family of ICs. By combining NMOS and PMOS technology, we obtain the Complementary MOS (CMOS) family.

15.10 Complementary MOS (CMOS)

Complementary MOS (CMOS) integrated circuits are constructed with complementary pairs, or sets, of *p*-channel and *n*-channel MOS transistors. A CMOS inverter is formed from one *p*-channel and one *n*-channel MOSFET, as shown in Figure 15.22(a).

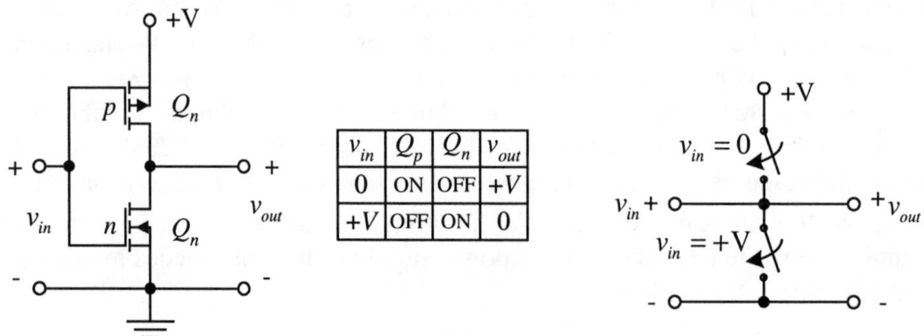

v_{in}	Q_p	Q_n	v_{out}
0	ON	OFF	$+V$
$+V$	OFF	ON	0

Figure 15.22 – CMOS inverter

Notice that no resistor (such as R_{load} in Figure 15.20 and 15.21) is needed in this circuit. The load for the *p*-channel MOSFET is the *n*-channel MOSFET, and the load for the *n*-channel MOSFET is the *p*-channel MOSFET. Figure 15.22(b) shows a simplified equivalent of this circuit where we have replaced the transistors with voltage-controlled switches.

When v_{in} is zero, Q_p is ON and Q_n is OFF, so the output is connected to $+V$ through the on-resistance of Q_p. With no load resistor on the output, $v_{out} = +V$ as shown in the first line of the function table. When v_{in} is $+V$ volts, Q_p is OFF and Q_n is ON. Now the output is connected to ground through the ON-resistance of Q_n. With no load resistor on the output, $v_{out} = 0$ V. Notice that the small supply power is needed only when the gate changes state. It takes a little energy to charge and discharge the gate capacitor, and to supply the source-drain energy while the transistors are briefly on during transitions between states.

Before moving on to more complex CMOS circuitry, we will take a closer look at the transition between the two logic states. Let's begin with an input voltage of zero. For this input, Q_n is OFF and Q_p is in the triode region. As we start to raise the input voltage, once it reaches V_T, Q_n moves into the saturation region and a channel is created. Thus the open circuit that did represent Q_n is replaced with a voltage that decreases as the input voltage increases. If the transistors are matched[1], the input-output curve displays a symmetry as shown in Figure 15.23. The important thing to note about this curve is that it closely resembles an ideal switching curve (which would be an ideal square pulse).

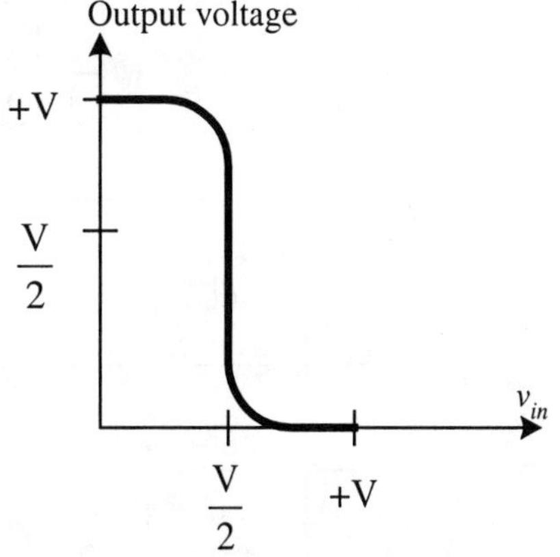

Figure 15.23 – CMOS input-output transfer curve

The output voltage changes state at an input voltage of approximately *V*/2. Thus, noise must be of sufficient magnitude to break this threshold voltage in order for an error to occur. This gives CMOS excellent noise immunity. In addition, the CMOS family allows for large swings in voltage from the HIGH to LOW logic states.

We now turn our attention to multiple-input logic gates. Figure 15.24 shows a CMOS two-input NAND gate.

In viewing Figure 15.24, you should note an important change from all of our previous MOS transistor applications. If you focus on transistor Q_3, you will note that the substrate is *not* connected to the source (as was the case in all previous circuits). In fabricating the integrated circuit, the substrates of all of the NMOS devices are connected together and then to the ground (or to a negative supply if one is present). The substrates of all of the PMOS devices are

[1]Matching the transistors means that they have the same threshold voltage (magnitude) and the values of K are also the same. To achieve this matching, the devices will have different widths.

connected together and then to the positive supply. We did not address this situation in Chapter 6 since none of our other applications required such an analysis.

In transistor Q_3, a positive voltage exists across the source-substrate terminals. This voltage represents a reverse bias between the source and body (substrate) of the transistor. This *body effect* (see Section 6.5.2) raises the threshold voltage. When the transistor is used as a switch, the switching characteristic is not as sharp as that shown in Figure 15.23.

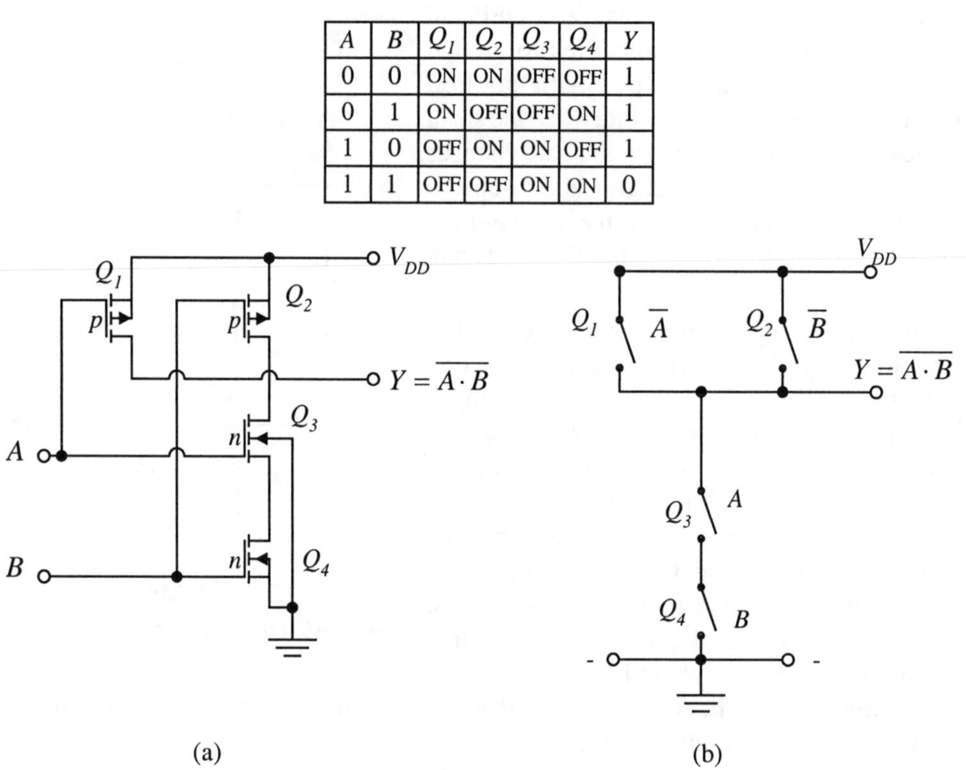

A	B	Q_1	Q_2	Q_3	Q_4	Y
0	0	ON	ON	OFF	OFF	1
0	1	ON	OFF	OFF	ON	1
1	0	OFF	ON	ON	OFF	1
1	1	OFF	OFF	ON	ON	0

Figure 15.24 – Two-input CMOS NAND gate

Now returning to Figure 15.24, we see that the circuit behaves like four switches as shown in Figure 15.24(b). Two of the switches are connected in parallel to V_{DD} and are controlled by $\overline{A}$ and $\overline{B}$. Two are connected in series to ground, and are controlled by A and B. When A is LOW, Q_1 is ON and Q_3 is OFF. When A is HIGH, Q_1 is OFF and Q_3 is ON. Likewise, when B is LOW, Q_2 is ON and Q_4 is OFF. When B is HIGH, Q_2 is OFF and Q_4 is ON. The function table is shown in Figure 15.24(c). Notice that in this table we use a 0 to indicate a low voltage near 0 and a 1 to indicate a voltage near V_{DD} (depending on the load on the gate output).

We now examine the CMOS two-input NOR gate, as shown in Figure 15.25. This circuit can be represented by two switches in series with V_{DD} and two switches in parallel to ground, as shown in Figure 15.25(b). The two switches in series are controlled by $\overline{A}$ and $\overline{B}$. The two switches in parallel are driven by A and B. We use the rule that if the voltage on the gate and on the substrate are the same, the transistor is OFF. If the gate voltage is different from the substrate voltage, the transistor is ON. We obtain the function table of Figure 15.25(c) by applying these conditions.

CMOS logic can operate over a wide range of supply voltages, typically 3 V to 18 V. Special circuits, such as digital watches, can operate at lower supply voltages. The primary form of power consumption for CMOS logic involves the charging and discharging of wiring and load capacitance as logic levels switch between ground and the supply voltage. As a result, CMOS operates with low power supply drain (especially at low frequencies where capacitive impedance is high). CMOS is ideally suited for battery-powered portable devices.

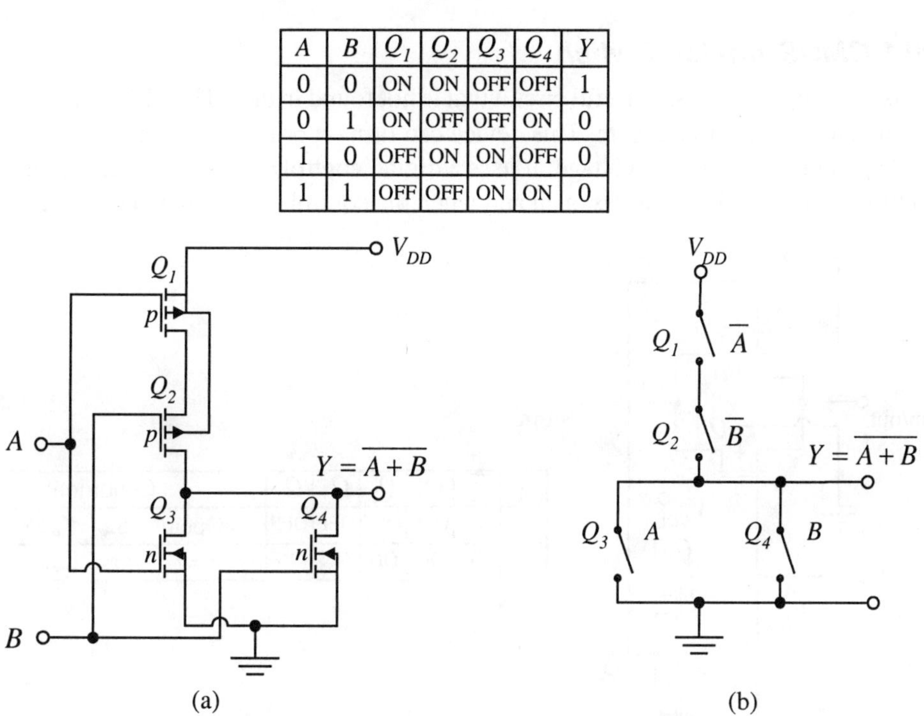

A	B	Q_1	Q_2	Q_3	Q_4	Y
0	0	ON	ON	OFF	OFF	1
0	1	ON	OFF	OFF	ON	0
1	0	OFF	ON	ON	OFF	0
1	1	OFF	OFF	ON	ON	0

Figure 15.25 – Two-input CMOS NOR gate

CMOS is slower than most of the bipolar logic families. However, as the manufacturers succeed in reducing the physical size of the devices, the capacitance is reduced, and the speed of operation is increased. CMOS ICs cannot drive as much power into output devices as other types of ICs. However, since the input to a CMOS gate is essentially an open circuit, a large number of CMOS inputs can be driven by one CMOS output, so a high-powered output is not so important. In addition, a buffered series of CMOS is available for supplying a larger output power.

We summarize the advantages and characteristics of the CMOS logic family as follows:

- The gate input is an open circuit, so it is easy to drive.
- Power-supply current is low, so CMOS is ideal for battery-powered devices.
- Good noise immunity exists since the logic changes from LOW to HIGH at V/2.
- CMOS can operate over a wide range of power supply voltage.
- CMOS creates little noise of its own.

15.10.1 CMOS Analog Switch

In this section, we discuss a useful circuit that is not found in the TTL or ECL families – the analog switch or transmission gate. This device can turn on or turn off an analog signal with a peak voltage below the supply voltage. It uses a digital control signal in the same range. When the control line is low, the switch is open and when the control line is high, the switch is closed.

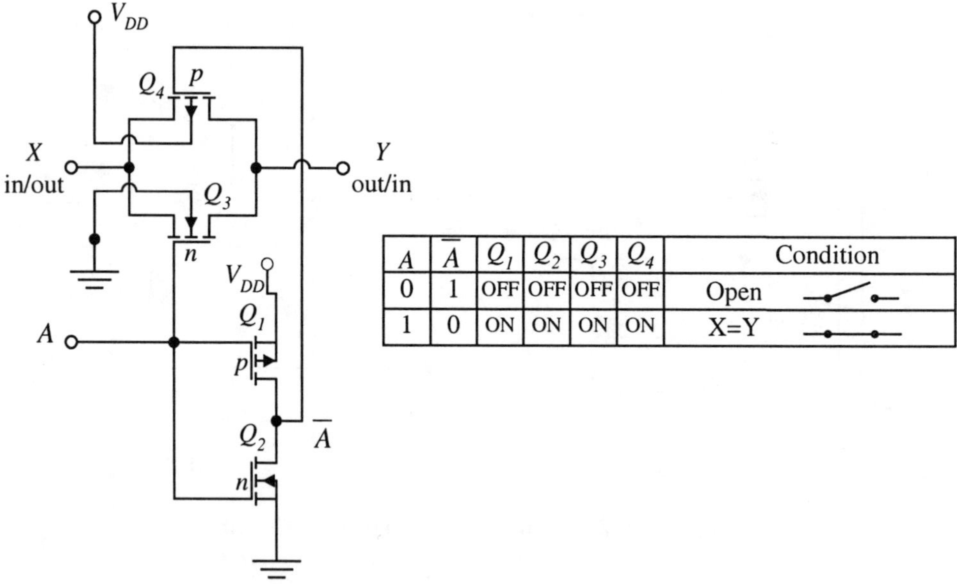

A	$\overline{A}$	Q_1	Q_2	Q_3	Q_4	Condition
0	1	OFF	OFF	OFF	OFF	Open
1	0	ON	ON	ON	ON	X=Y

Figure 15.26 – MM74HC4016 CMOS analog switch

A circuit diagram for the MM74HC4016 (CD 4016) analog switch is shown in Figure 15.26. The switch is comprised of two sections. Q_1 and Q_2 form a CMOS inverter identical to that shown in Figure 15.22. The second section is composed of two parallel transistors, Q_3 (an *n*-channel FET) and Q_4 (a *p*-channel FET). The gate of Q_3 is driven with *A* and the gate of Q_4 is driven with $\overline{A}$. As a result, when $A = 0$ ($\overline{A}=1$) the switch is open. When $A = 1$ ($\overline{A}=0$) the switch is closed. The supply voltage should be between 3 V and 15 V, and the maximum input/output voltage is limited to the supply voltage.

The switch is enabled in 20 ns, with an input voltage in the range of 0 to 12 V. At room temperature, the switch typically has 50 Ω on-resistance and low leakage current (+0.1 nA) when off. The switches are bilateral-any analog input may be substituted as an input, and vice-versa. All analog inputs and outputs and the control lines are protected from electrostatic damage by diodes connected to V_{CC} and ground.

The analog switch provides the engineer with a versatile tool to use in a number of design applications, including:

- Analog signal switching and multiplexing
- Modulation/demodulation
- Commutation/chopping
- Sampling for analog to digital conversion
- Digital control of frequency, phase and gain
- Switching regulation
- Switched capacitor design

EXERCISES

Determine the status of each transistor and the output in the circuits shown in Exercises E15.23 and E15.24.

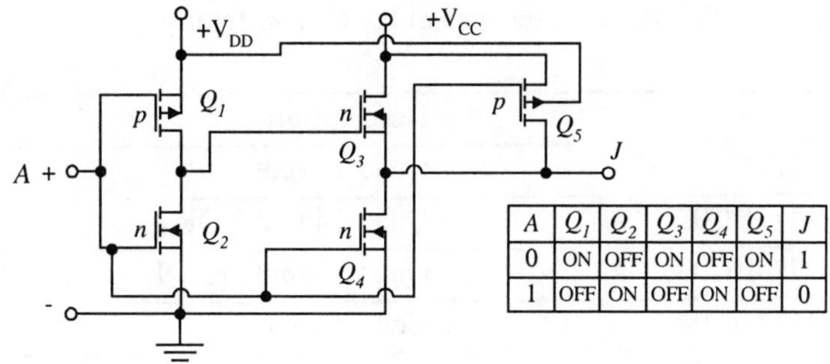

A	Q_1	Q_2	Q_3	Q_4	Q_5	J
0	ON	OFF	ON	OFF	ON	1
1	OFF	ON	OFF	ON	OFF	0

E15.23

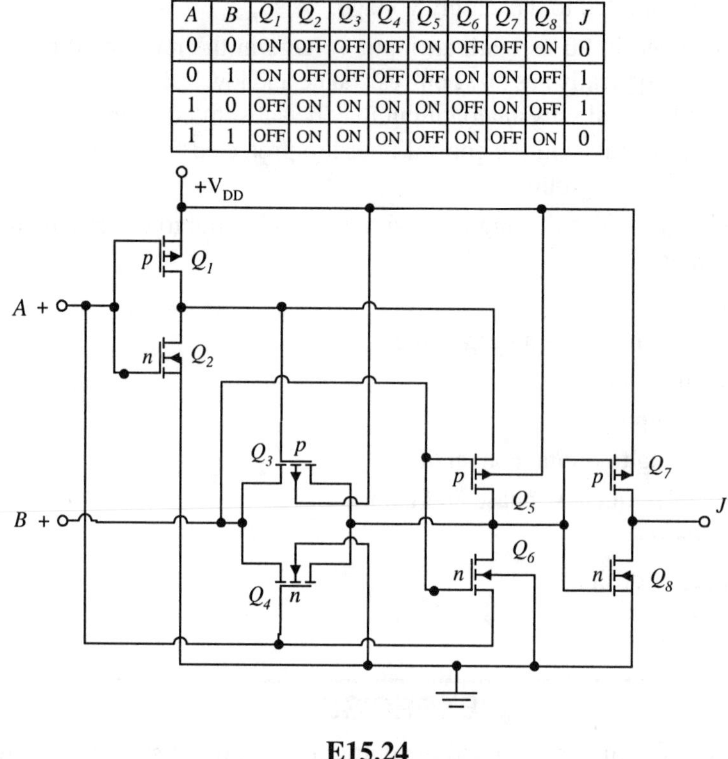

A	B	Q_1	Q_2	Q_3	Q_4	Q_5	Q_6	Q_7	Q_8	J
0	0	ON	OFF	OFF	OFF	ON	OFF	OFF	ON	0
0	1	ON	OFF	OFF	OFF	OFF	ON	ON	OFF	1
1	0	OFF	ON	ON	ON	ON	OFF	ON	OFF	1
1	1	OFF	ON	ON	ON	OFF	ON	OFF	ON	0

E15.24

15.10.2 CMOS Device Listings and Usage Rules

Table 15.3 shows a partial listing of devices of the CMOS family.

Type Number	Description
MM54HC00/MM74HC00	Quad 2-input NAND gate
MM54HC02/MM74HC02	Quad 2-input NOR gate
MM54HC03/MM74HC03	Quad 2-input open drain NAND gate
MM54HC04/MM74HC04	Hex inverter
MM54HC08/MM74HC08	Quad 2-input AND gate
MM54HC10/MM74HC10	Triple 3-input NAND gate
MM54HC11/MM74HC11	Triple 3-input AND gate
MM54HC14/MM74HC14	Hex inverting Schmitt trigger
MM54HC20/MM74HC20	Dual 4-input NAND gate
MM54HC27/MM74HC27	Triple 3-input NOR gate
MM54HC30/MM74HC30	8-input NAND gate

MM54HC32/MM74HC32	Quad 2-input OR gate
MM54HC51/MM74HC51	Dual AND-OR-invert gate
MM54HC58/MM74HC58	Dual AND-OR gate
MM54HC86/MM74HC86	Quad 2-input exclusive OR gate
MM54HC132/MM74HC132	Quad 2-input NAND Schmitt trigger
MM54HC133/MM74HC133	13-input NAND gate
MM54HC266/MM74HC266	Quad 2-input exclusive NOR gate
MM54HC4002/MM74HC4002	Dual 4-input NOR gate
MM54HC04049/MM74HC4049	Hex inverting logic level down converter
MM54HC4050/MM74HC4050	Hex logic level down converter
MM54HC4075/MM74HC4075	Triple 3-input OR gate
MM54HC4078/MM74HC4078	8-input NOR/OR gate
MM54HCT00/MM74HCToo	Quad 2-input NAND gate
MM54HCT04/MM74HCT04	Hex inverter
MM54HCT05/MM74HCT05	Hex inverter (open drain)
MM54HCT34/MM74HCT34	Noninverter gate (TTL input)
MM54HCU04/MM74HCU04	Hex inverter

Table 15.3 - Partial CMOS device listing

We conclude with the following important rules that are important when using the CMOS family:

1. Attach every terminal to $+V$, ground, or to an input signal.
2. Avoid exceeding the limits of the IC, thereby preventing the input diodes from conducting.
3. Avoid static electricity by storing CMOS devices on conductive foam or foil.
4. De-bounce all mechanical switches or contacts.

15.11 COMPARISON OF LOGIC FAMILIES

Table 15.4 summarizes the parameters of the various logic families. It is presented to provide comparisons among the various groups. This makes it useful as an aid in selecting the proper family of circuit for a particular application. The most important families are TTL, ECL and CMOS.

Logic Family	Supply voltage (V)	Power per Gate (mW)	Propa-gation Delay per Gate (nsec)	Max Clock Freq (MHz)	Max Logic Zero Input (V)	Min Logic One Input (V)	Max Logic Zero Output (V)	Min Logic One Output (V)
RTL	3.6	20	10		0.5	0.88	0.3	
DTL	5	8	30	5				
HTL	15	40	110	0.5	6.5	8.5	1	14.4
TTL	5	10	10	35	0.8	2	0.4	2.4
HTTL	5	22	6	50	0.8	2	0.4	2.4
LPTTL	5	1	33	3	0.8	2	0.4	2.4
STTL	5	16	4	75	0.8	2	0.5	2.7
LSTTL	5	2	10	40	0.8	2	0.5	2.7
ASLTTL	5	1	4	50	0.8	2	0.5	2.5
ASTTL	5	8	2.5	100	0.8	2	0.5	3
ECL	-5.2	25	2	150	-1.48	-1.13	-1.6	-0.98
PMOS	-9 -5	1	4	100	-4	-1.2	-8.5	-1
NMOS	+5 +12	0.1	100	3	0.8	2.4	0.4	2.4
CMOS	3-15	0.5	100	3	1.5	3.5	0.5	4.5
HCMOS	5	0.5	10	30	1	3.5	0.05	4.95

Table 15.4 - Logic family comparison

EXAMPLE 15.3

Design a theft alarm system for an automobile. Use two 555 timers, one operating in the monostable mode and one operating in the astable mode.

Solution: [2]A block diagram for the alarm is shown in Figure 15.27.

Either a motion sensor, which we attach to the automobile, or a door-open detector, which turns the dome light on and off, will trigger the 555 monostable, and develop a 60 second pulse.

---

[2]This project was designed and built by James Mao, and presented at the 1989 IEEE Design Competition at California State University, Los Angeles.

The motion detector momentarily closes a switch when the car is moved, and the door-open detector is the switch on any car door that turns the dome light on when the door is opened.

The alarm is activated by a lock switch located on the front fender of the car. When the alarm is on, an indicator LED starts to blink continuously. This LED alerts anyone approaching the car that the alarm is set.

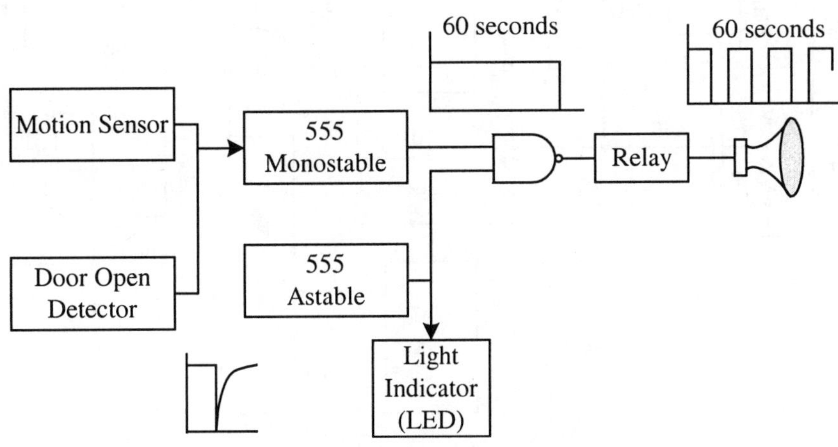

Figure 15.27 – Block diagram for Example 15.3

When the lock switch is on, the astable 555 generates a continuous pulse train for the LED to continuously blink and provides the signal for car horn. We desire the horn "on period" to be longer than the "off period".

The duty cycle, $(R_1+R_2)/(R_1+2R_2)$, is variable. In this design, we set it to 0.87. The frequency of this astable 555 oscillator, $1.44/[(R_1+2R_2)C_1]$, can be adjusted with the selection of R_1, R_2, and C_1. In this design, we select $C_1 = 4.7$ μF and $f = 0.69$ Hz. The wiring diagram is shown in Figure 15.28.

When the motion sensor or the door-open detector triggers the 555 monostable, it develops a pulse. The pulse duration time, $1.1R_3C_2$, is set here to 53.2 seconds. If the value of C_2 were changed to 470 μF, the pulse duration time would increase to approximately 2 minutes.

The alarm uses the 12 V car battery, and the ICs are supplied with power from a voltage divider which produces 5.14 V. We decide to use the TTL family since we have so much available power. We use a 7410 NAND gate, discussed in this chapter, instead of an AND gate because of lower cost and also since it can be used as an inverter. An *npn* transistor is used for the relay driver. A diode is connected in parallel with the relay coil to protect the transistor from relay inductance transients.

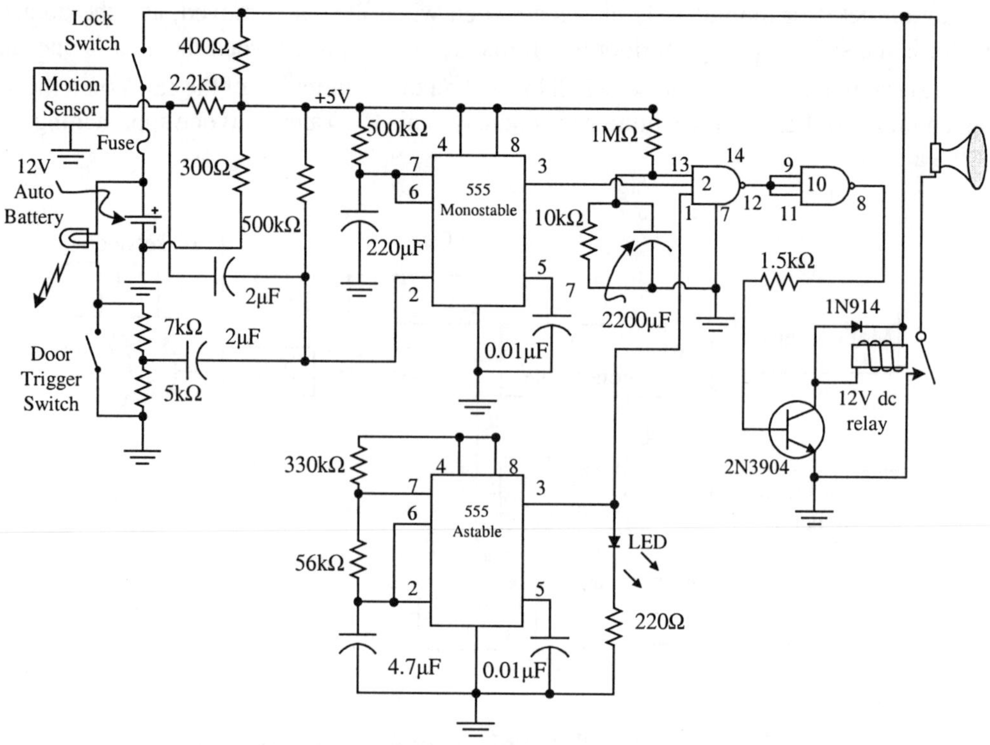

Figure 15.28 – Wiring diagram for Example 15.3

The motion sensor is readily available as is the lock switch. The alarm can be further improved by using a remote control system, as developed for a home garage door opener, to replace the lock switch located on the fender.

15.12 SUMMARY

You have been introduced to the topic of digital electronics and gained some familiarity with the basic time independent logic families. Now you are in a position to execute the first level of digital electronic design, and to formulate some useful circuits.

Let us now return to the auto safety control box described in the introduction to this chapter. This device can be effectively designed using the basic blocks presented in this chapter. The change from analog to digital electronics goes a long way toward reducing the effects of ignition noise. You could choose the CMOS family for your design since it provides excellent noise immunity, and the operating frequencies in your system are low. However since power is not of critical concern (an automotive battery looks like a virtually unlimited source of power when compared to the power required by ICs!), TTL could also be used. In Example 15.3 and in the problems at the back of this chapter, we ask you to design the burglar alarm portion of the system.

PROBLEMS

Section 15.1

Construct logic diagrams and function tables for the Boolean algebraic expressions given in 15.1 through 15.7 below.

15.1 $Y = \overline{A} \cdot B \cdot \overline{C} \cdot C$

15.2 $Y = \overline{A} \cdot B \cdot \overline{C} + A \cdot B \cdot \overline{C}$

15.3 $Y = A \cdot B + A \cdot \overline{B}$

15.4 $Y = A \cdot \overline{B} + B$

15.5 $Y = A + B$

15.6 $Y = \overline{A + B + C}$

15.7 $Y = \overline{A \cdot B \cdot C}$

15.8 Develop a logic circuit such that the output is HIGH if inputs A, B, and C are all HIGH or if inputs D, E, and F are all HIGH.

15.9 Develop a logic circuit such that the output is HIGH if inputs A and B are HIGH or if inputs C and B are HIGH.

15.10 Design a four-passenger auto seat belt warning system that will sound an alarm if the ignition is on and there is a passenger with an unfastened seat belt. Normally-open switches with one contact grounded are available to sense the presence of passengers and to sense the connection of each seat belt. This is shown in Figure P15.10(a). A normally-open switch with one contact grounded senses whether the engine ignition is on. This circuit is shown in Figure P15.10(b). A 2 kHz signal should sound for any unsafe condition.

(a) Switch is closed when a passenger is sitting. Same for seatbelt

(b) When the ignition is turned ON, the switch is closed

Figure P15.10

15.11 Design a safety reminder system for your automobile to sound a 2 kHz tone when the headlights are left on and the key is left in the ignition switch. This system uses the following normally-open switches:

a. Headlight switch which is closed when lights are on and open when lights are off.

b. Ignition key switch which is closed when key is in the lock and open when key is removed from the lock.

c. Door switch which is closed when the door is open and open when the door is closed.

The alarm should sound only when the door is open and the headlights are on and/or the key is in the ignition switch and the door opens.

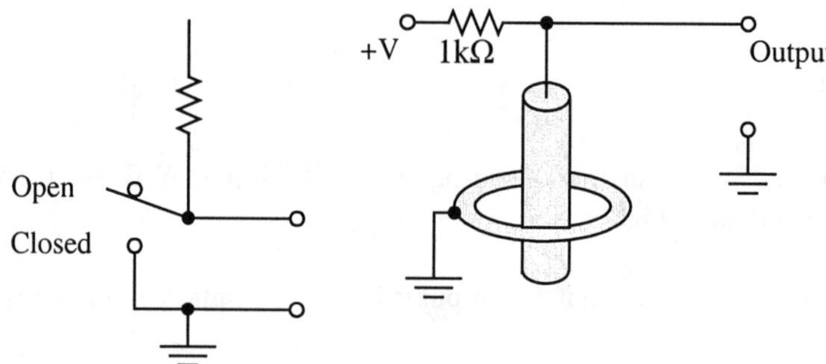

Figure P15.12

15.12 Design an automobile burglar alarm system that will sound a 500 Hz, 5-W sound. A normally-open alarm switch is built into the left front fender. When the key is turned to the "armed" position, the switch is closed. A motion switch is mounted in the automobile such that when any motion occurs, a momentary contact is made. This is shown in Figure P15.12. When any disturbance to the automobile occurs, the output signal momentarily drops to zero (ground). The burglar alarm should sound the (500 $\pm 10\%$ Hz) signal *only* if the fender switch was previously armed. The alarm should sound for 2 minutes and then shut off.

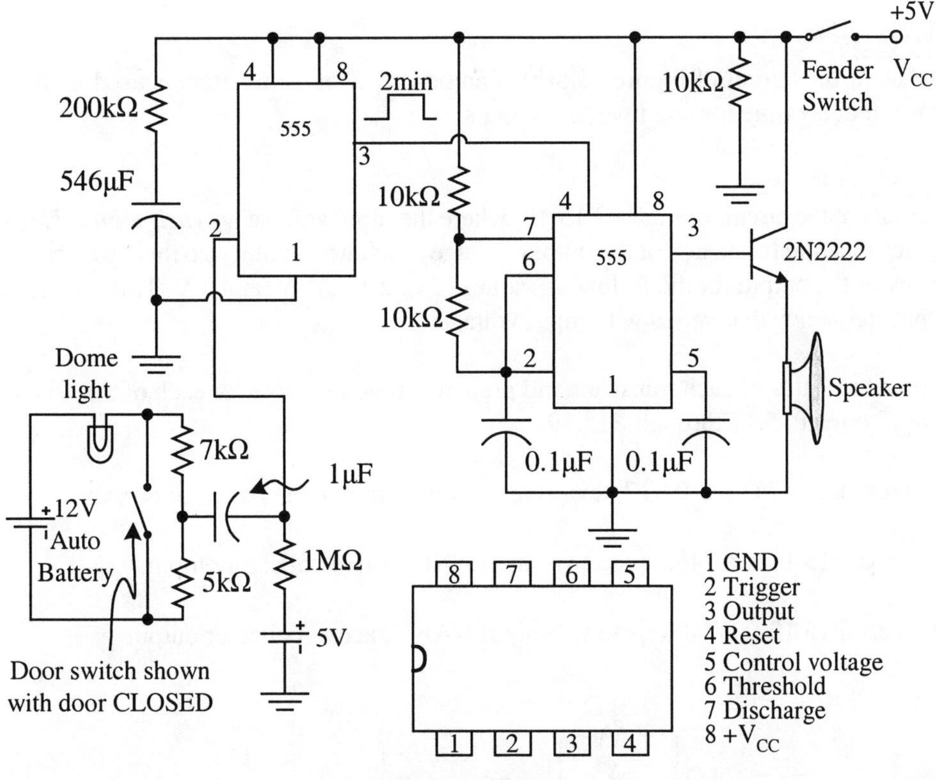

Figure P15.13

15.13 Analyze the auto burglar alarm system illustrated in Figure P15.13. Describe the operation of this electronic system.

15.14 Design a digital lock that operates in two steps. First, the code is set by activating 3 of the 6 two-position push-button switches. For this example, set the code to: *b d e*. Second, the toggle switch connected to the output is thrown. If the correct code is selected, the output will go LOW and the lock will be released with a solenoid (a solenoid is an electromechanical device that produces a mechanical motion when a signal is applied to the solenoid coil). If the incorrect code is selected, a 1 kHz tone will sound for 1 minute. See Figure P15.14 for details.

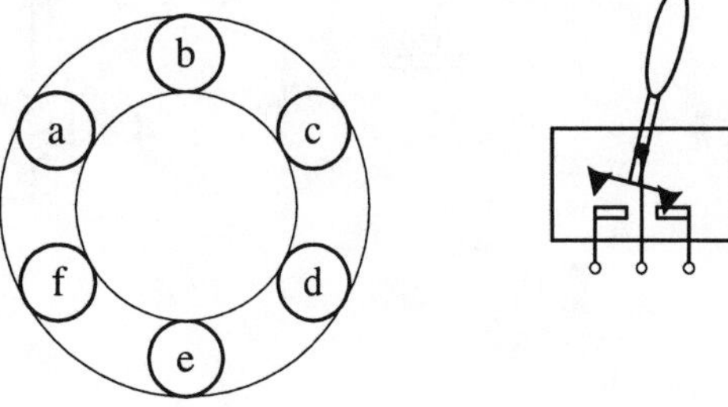

Figure P15.14

Section 15.3

15.15 Sketch the output of Figure 15.5(b) if an odd number of inverters is used in the circuit. Assume the delay time for one inverter is 35 ns.

Section 15.6

15.16 Analyze the circuit of Figure P15.16, where the input voltage, v_i, *varies linearly* from 2 to 3 V. Determine the frequency of the output voltage as a function of v_i. Do this by calculating the frequency of the output for the following values of v_i: 2 V, 2.5 V, and 3 V. This circuit exhibits an output frequency that varies with input voltage.

Determine the status of each transistor and prepare a function table for each of the TTL circuits given in Figures P15.17 through P15.19.

15.17 Figure P15.17 C a 7407/17 hex drive, non-inverting, open collector output.

15.18 Figure P15.18 C a 7408 quad two-input AND, active collector output.

15.19 Figure P15.19 C a 7400 quad two-input NAND, active collector output.

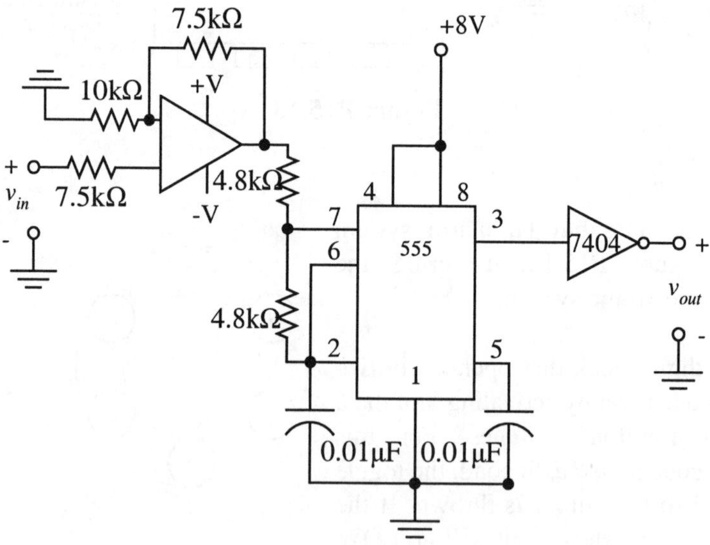

Figure P15.16

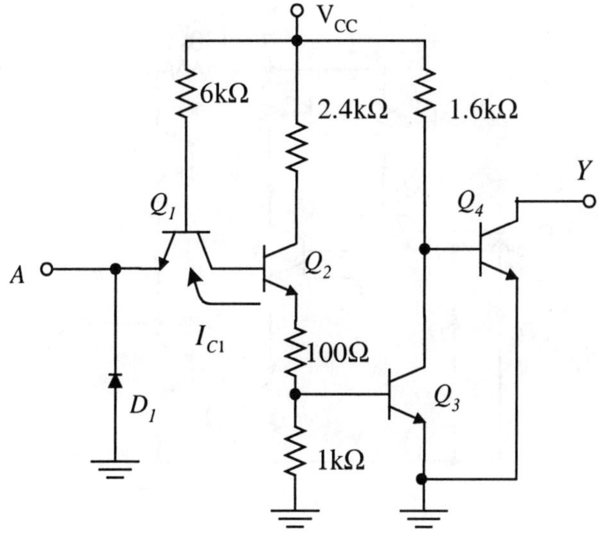

Figure P15.17

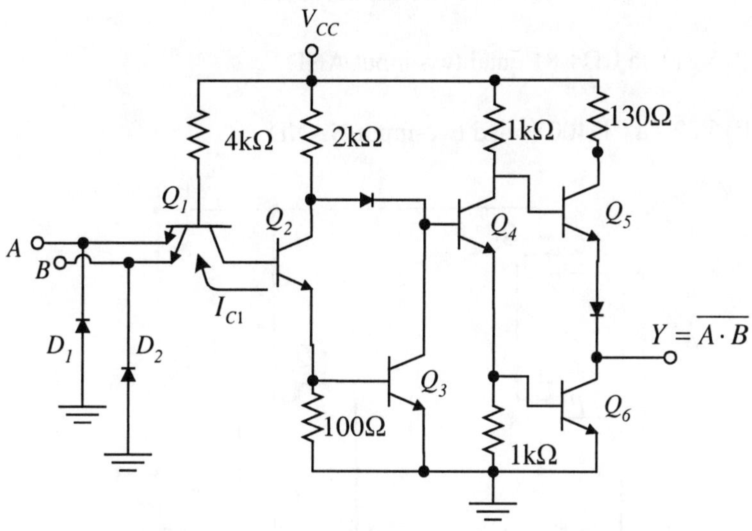

Figure P15.18

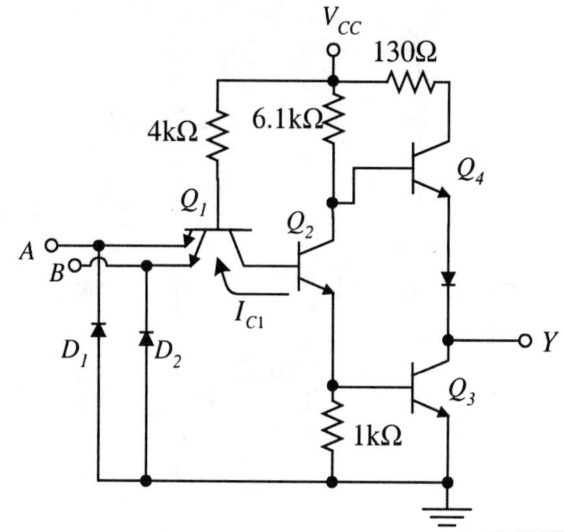

Figure P15.19

Section 15.9

Determine the status of each FET and prepare a function table for the CMOS circuits of Problems 15.20 through 15.22.

15.20 Figure P15.20 – a CD 4001 quad two-input NOR.

15.21 Figure P15.21 – a CD4-81 quad two-input AND.

15.22 Figure P15.22 - a CD4001 quad two-input NAND.

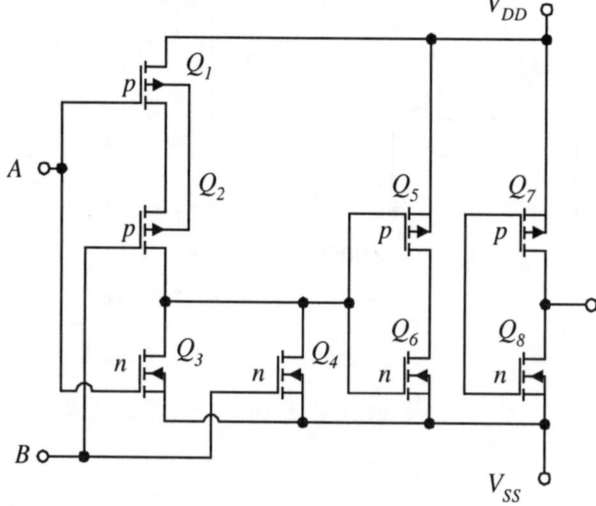

Figure P15.20

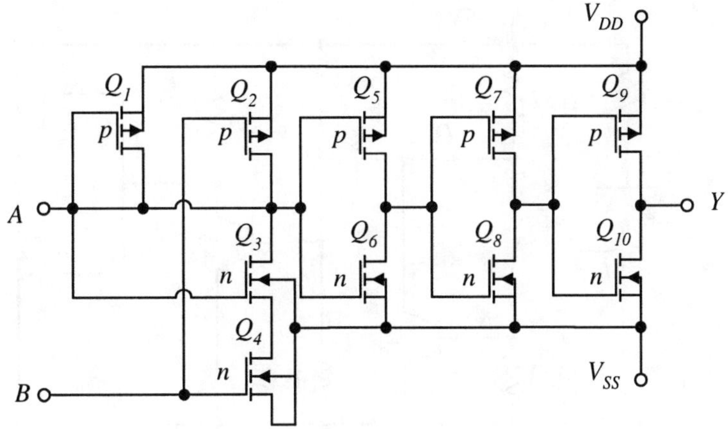

Figure P15.21

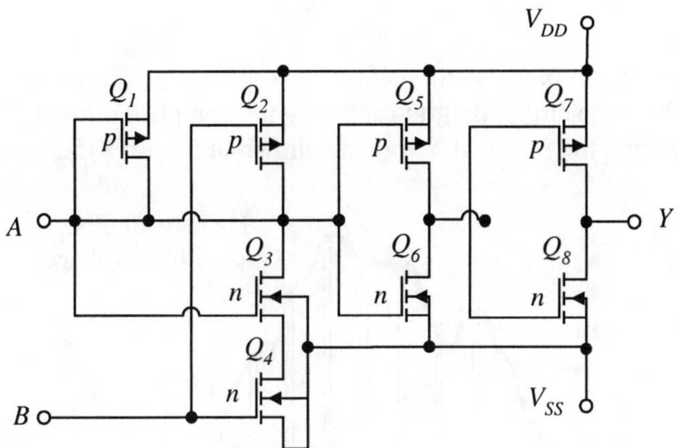

Figure P15.22

Section 15.10

15.23 Complete the function table to the right for the TTL CMOS circuit shown in Figure P15.23.

A	B	I_{C1}	Q_2	Q_3	Q_4	Q_5	Q_6	Q_7	Y
0	0								
0	1								
1	0								
1	1								

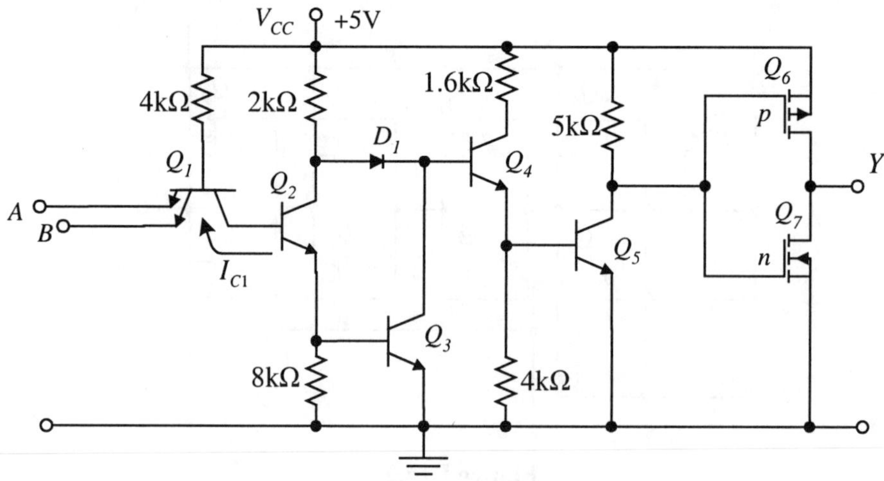

Figure P15.23

15.24 Design a circuit to sample a function of time every 100 ms. The sampling time must be no greater than 5 ms. Draw the circuit diagram showing the complete pin-out of each IC used. The function of time, *f(t),* and the sampled output are shown in Figure P15.24.

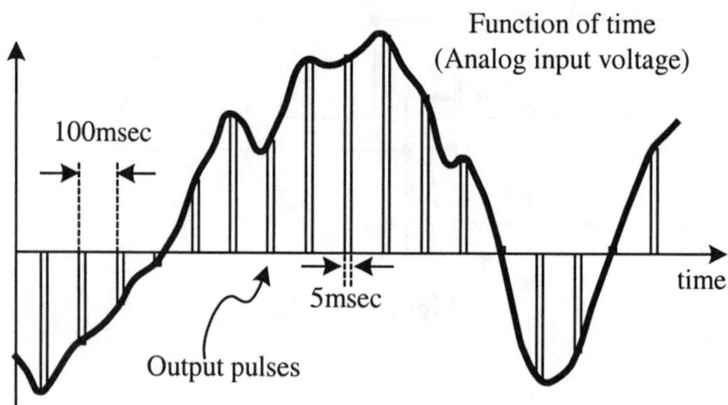

Figure P15.24

15.25 Design a system to provide an emergency warning signal. Use a 555 and a CMOS switch to provide a signal of the form shown in Figure P15.25. The signal consists of a 3-kHz sinusoid with ±5 V amplitude that is turned on and off 30 times each minute. The time on is approximately equal to the time off. The 3-kHz sinusoidal voltage is provided to you from a sine wave generator.

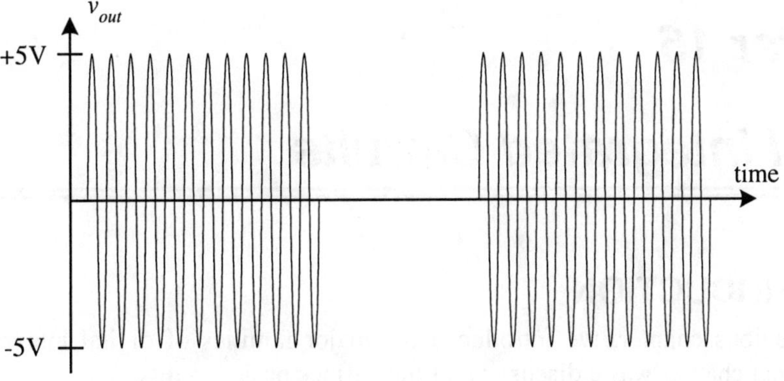

Figure P15.25

Chapter 16

Digital Integrated Circuits

16.0 INTRODUCTION

In the previous chapter, we introduced the major families of digital integrated circuits. Included in that chapter was a discussion of the various basic circuits.

The intent of the present chapter is to expand this catalog of integrated circuits so that you have the necessary tools to perform a wide variety of designs. After studying this chapter, you will

- Understand decoders and encoders.
- Be able to display numbers on seven-segment displays.
- Understand the applications of flip-flops, latches, and other simple memory devices.
- Understand the operation of more advanced memory devices such as RAMs, ROMs, and EPROMs.
- Be able to read data sheets for a variety of advanced devices.

There are a large number of different circuits on the market. These can be divided into several major categories. These categories form the major sections of this chapter. Application examples are presented throughout.

The figures in the text often contain excerpts from data sheets. You can obtain these data sheets in several ways. Some of the manufacturers issue data books, and you can find these in the library or purchase them from the manufacturer. Most of the major suppliers of integrated circuits provide data sheets and other information via the World Wide Web. Some have completely replaced printed copies with downloadable versions. In some cases, you need special software to download the data sheets (e.g., Adobe Acrobat7). In virtually all cases, the appropriate software can be downloaded.

Following are some of the home page addresses of the major suppliers of integrated circuits. Others can be obtained from index sources and browsers.

Texas Instruments: http://www.ti.com
National Semiconductor: http://www.national.com
Motorola: http://www.mot.com
Fairchild Semiconductor: http://www.fairchildsemi.com
Analog Devices: http://www.analog.com

Throughout this chapter, we present a "systems approach". None of the circuit diagrams show transistors. Indeed, the basic building blocks are the integrated circuits of the previous chapters.

16.1 DECODERS AND ENCODERS

A wide variety of multiple-input/multiple-output devices are lumped under the term decoder. Devices that fit into this category are given more specific names that accurately describe their function. Examples include multiplexers and de-multiplexers. Whatever the specific name, decoders share a common trait with the elementary gates: these ICs have no memory. Regardless of the values of previous inputs and outputs, the device's present output depends only upon its present input.

The first example we present is a 1-of-8 decoder/de-multiplexer as shown in Figure 16.1.

Connection Diagrams

DM74LS138

DATA OUTPUTS

VCC 16, Y0 15, Y1 14, Y2 13, Y3 12, Y4 11, Y5 10, Y6 9

1 A, 2 B, 3 C, 4 G2A, 5 G2B, 6 G1, 7 Y7, 8 GND

SELECT ENABLE OUTPUT

Function Tables

DM74LS138

Inputs					Outputs							
Enable		Select										
G1	G2 (Note 1)	C	B	A	Y0	Y1	Y2	Y3	Y4	Y5	Y6	Y7
X	H	X	X	X	H	H	H	H	H	H	H	H
L	X	X	X	X	H	H	H	H	H	H	H	H
H	L	L	L	L	L	H	H	H	H	H	H	H
H	L	L	L	H	H	L	H	H	H	H	H	H
H	L	L	H	L	H	H	L	H	H	H	H	H
H	L	L	H	H	H	H	H	L	H	H	H	H
H	L	H	L	L	H	H	H	H	L	H	H	H
H	L	H	L	H	H	H	H	H	H	L	H	H
H	L	H	H	L	H	H	H	H	H	H	L	H
H	L	H	H	H	H	H	H	H	H	H	H	L

Logic Diagrams

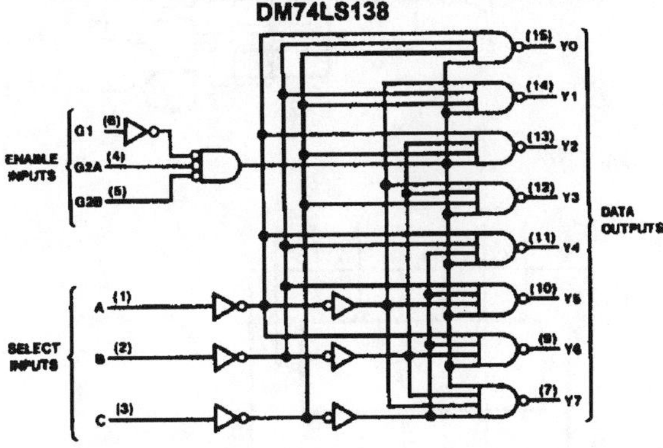

Figure 16.1 - DM74LS138 1-of-8 decoder (*Courtesy of Fairchild Semiconductor*)

Function Table

No.	BCD Input				Decimal Output									
	D	C	B	A	0	1	2	3	4	5	6	7	8	9
0	L	L	L	L	L	H	H	H	H	H	H	H	H	H
1	L	L	L	H	H	L	H	H	H	H	H	H	H	H
2	L	L	H	L	H	H	L	H	H	H	H	H	H	H
3	L	L	H	H	H	H	H	L	H	H	H	H	H	H
4	L	H	L	L	H	H	H	H	L	H	H	H	H	H
5	L	H	L	H	H	H	H	H	H	L	H	H	H	H
6	L	H	H	L	H	H	H	H	H	H	L	H	H	H
7	L	H	H	H	H	H	H	H	H	H	H	L	H	H
8	H	L	L	L	H	H	H	H	H	H	H	H	L	H
9	H	L	L	H	H	H	H	H	H	H	H	H	H	L
I	H	L	H	L	H	H	H	H	H	H	H	H	H	H
N	H	L	H	H	H	H	H	H	H	H	H	H	H	H
V	H	H	L	L	H	H	H	H	H	H	H	H	H	H
A	H	H	L	H	H	H	H	H	H	H	H	H	H	H
L	H	H	H	L	H	H	H	H	H	H	H	H	H	H
I	H	H	H	H	H	H	H	H	H	H	H	H	H	H
D														

H = HIGH Level
L = LOW Level

Logic Diagram

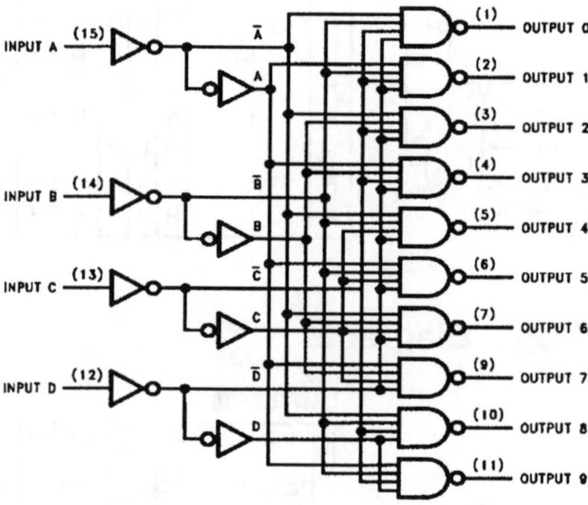

Connection Diagram

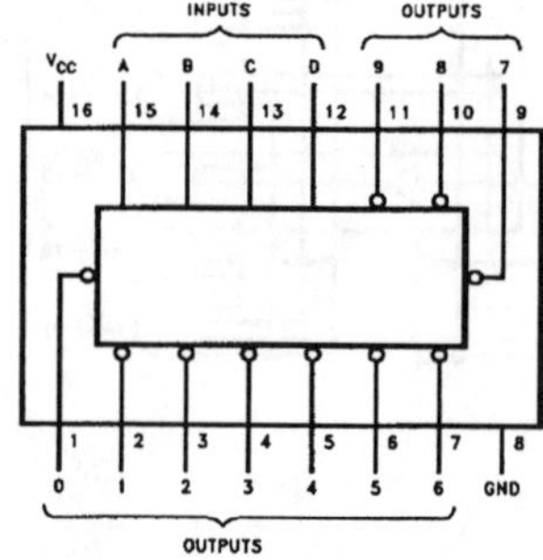

Figure 16.2 - The DM7442A BCD to decimal decoder (*Courtesy of Fairchild Semiconductor*)

We have selected a DM74LS138 circuit for purposes of illustration. The 1-of-8 decoder/de-multiplexer is used to enable (i.e., turn on) one among eight possible outputs. It is comprised of a series of gates as shown in Figure 16.1. The 1-of-8 decoder accepts 3-bit binary inputs representing a binary number between 000 and 111. These correspond to the decimal numbers 0 through 7. Of the 8 output lines, only one is LOW at any one time, as shown in the function table of Figure 16.1. The output that is LOW is the one numbered to match the binary input. The input appears on pins A, B and C, and is referred to as the SELECT. For example, if the binary number 010 (LHL) forms the input, the second output (Y2) is LOW and all the others are HIGH. If we desire the selected output to be HIGH instead of LOW, we can feed the various outputs into an inverter.

The circuit diagram and the function table contain several enable lines. In order to operate the system as a decoder, input *G1* must be HIGH and input *G2*must be LOW. Note that *G2*=*G2A*+*G2B*, which means that if *either G2A* or *G2B* is HIGH, *G2* is HIGH and the operation is disabled. At this point, it may seem strange that there are three separate enable inputs. However, you will see later that this provides additional flexibility in digital design. We will often want the selecting process to occur only when a combination of other conditions apply.

The 1-of-8 decoder illustrates the concept that 3 bits of input data can control 2^3 lines of output. In more general terms, an *n*-of-*m* decoder converts *n* input lines into a maximum of $m = 2^n$ output lines.

Before going on to the next topic, you should take the time to verify some of the entries in the function table. Do this by applying the appropriate logic HIGH and LOW inputs and tracing these through the logic block diagram.

In its most general form, the decoder accepts one binary word as input, and produces a second binary word as output. This leads to a large number of possible decoder configurations. We now examine six of these configurations used in many applications. While we introduce these here, some of them are covered in greater detail later in the chapter.

1. **Binary-to-Single Output** - An n-bit binary word selects a single output from one of 2^n possible outputs. The circuit of Figure 16.1 is an example of this configuration with n = 3.

2. **BCD-to-7-Segment Display** - This decoder accepts a binary input and produces a 7-bit binary code as the output. The input is a 4-bit BCD number between 0000 and 1001, representing the decimal digits between 0 and 9. This is known as the binary-coded decimal (BCD) code. The output is matched to a seven-segment display. Seven straight-line segments (3 horizontal and 4 vertical) are used to display any digit between 0 and 9. The decoder yields the appropriate output to light the necessary segments thereby producing the decimal digit.

3. **Multiple-Input to Multiple-Output** - There are many devices used to convert numbers for one form to another. These devices are often used to perform simple mathematical operations or to multiplex several signals together.

An important example of a multiple-input to multiple-output device is the BCD to Binary Converter. The BCD code represents each decimal digit between 0 and 9 by a 4-bit binary number. Thus, for example, the decimal number 64 would become 01100100 in BCD. Note that this differs from a simple conversion of 64 to binary. Such a conversion would result in the binary number, 1000000, which is only 7 bits in length instead of 8 bits as in the BCD code.

The DM7442A BCD-to-decimal decoder is illustrated in Figure 16.2

The input to this device is a four-bit BCD code of a single decimal digit. There are 10 separate outputs, and only one of these is LOW for any valid input combination. The one that is LOW represents the decimal equivalent of the input BCD number. The BCD code uses only 10 of the 16 possible 4-bit combinations. Therefore six input combinations are invalid and should not exist in the BCD code. If the input matches any of these invalid combinations, an error had to have occurred prior to that point in the circuitry. The IC is designed to respond to these invalid inputs by not allowing any of the 10 outputs to go LOW.

4. **Testers** - This group of devices performs tests upon coded information and produces an output containing information regarding the outcome of the test. The comparator is an example of a tester. It accepts two binary codes as the input, and the output indicates which of the two inputs is larger. Parity checkers represent another important application of testing ICs.

5. **Arithmetic** - These devices perform simple mathematical operations such as addition and subtraction. A full adder is one example of such a device. This adder accepts three input bits. Two of these are the bits to be added together, and the third is a carry bit from a previous, or lower weight, column. Thus, the full adder is suited to applications where multiple bit binary numbers must be added together. There are two outputs from a full adder. One of these is the sum, and the second is the carry bit. For example, the binary sum of 1+0+0 is 1 with a carry of 0. The sum of 1+1+1 is 1 with a carry of 1.

6. **Multiplexers** - The multiplexer selects one of many inputs to be transferred to one output. This is the reverse of the de-multiplexer, which routes one input to one of many outputs.

   Multiplexers are used to interleave data from several sources. For example, if only one transmission line were available to send four different signals, the bits would have to be interleaved (commutated) to form a time-division multiplexed signal. The first bit of the first signal is followed by the first bit of the second, and so on. Finally, the first bit of the fourth signal is followed by the second bit of the first signal, and the cycle continues until the four signals are sent in their entirety. At the receiving end, a de-multiplexer (de-commutator) is used to separate the various signals and sort them out onto different transmission paths.

16.1.1 Data Selector/Multiplexer

The data selector/multiplexer selects one input from many possibilities and transfers this input to the output. Figure 16.3 shows the DM74150 data selector/multiplexer.

There are four data select inputs, labeled A, B, C, and D (pins 15, 14, 13 and 11 respectively). Depending upon the value of these select inputs, the corresponding data input is transferred to the output. This particular IC yields an output (W) which is the complement of the selected input. Thus, for example, if the data select inputs are LLHL representing the binary number 0010 (the decimal number 2), the output is equal to the complement of input 2, that is, $\overline{E_2}$. This can be seen from the fourth line of the truth table. Note that the symbol, X, in the truth table indicates a "don't care" condition - the value of that variable has no effect on the output. This particular unit has a strobe input which must be LOW for the circuit to operate as a multiplexer.

It is often important to supply proper timing to avoid transients in the output. The data select, which is a four-bit binary number, changes whenever it is desired to transfer a different input to the output. If, for example, the select is changing from 1010 to 0101, we desire that input 10 be transferred to the output prior to the change, and that input 5 be transferred after the change. However the three binary select inputs may not change at the exact same moment, so there may be intermediate select configurations prior to arrival at 0101. Without clocking, the output will reflect each of these intermediate input values. The appropriate timing control can be incorporated into later circuits (e.g., the multiplexer output is only read at specific times), or it can be part of the multiplexer chip.

Connection Diagram

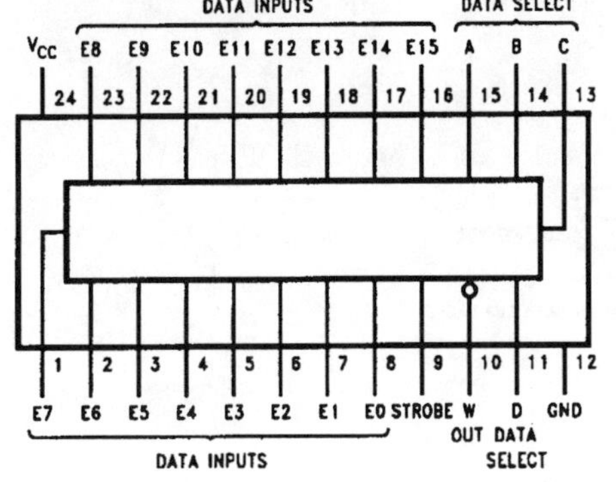

Function Table

Inputs					Outputs
Select				Strobe	W
D	C	B	A	S	
X	X	X	X	H	H
L	L	L	L	L	$\overline{E0}$
L	L	L	H	L	$\overline{E1}$
L	L	H	L	L	$\overline{E2}$
L	L	H	H	L	$\overline{E3}$
L	H	L	L	L	$\overline{E4}$
L	H	L	H	L	$\overline{E5}$
L	H	H	L	L	$\overline{E6}$
L	H	H	H	L	$\overline{E7}$
H	L	L	L	L	$\overline{E8}$
H	L	L	H	L	$\overline{E9}$
H	L	H	L	L	$\overline{E10}$
H	L	H	H	L	$\overline{E11}$
H	H	L	L	L	$\overline{E12}$
H	H	L	H	L	$\overline{E13}$
H	H	H	L	L	$\overline{E14}$
H	H	H	H	L	$\overline{E15}$

H = HIGH Level
L = LOW Level
X = Don't Care
$\overline{E0}$, $\overline{E1}$ ...$\overline{E15}$ = the complement of the level of the respective E input

Figure 16.3 - DM74150 Data Selector/Multiplexer (*Courtesy of Fairchild Semiconductor*)

16.1.2 Keyboard Encoders/Decoders

A keyboard consists of a series of switches activated by keys. The keyboard can be in any of a wide variety of configurations, including that of a typewriter or of a numeric keypad. Prior to the development of digital electronics, each key was connected to the appropriate printing mechanism, often through a series of mechanical linkages. With the advent of digital electronics, it became possible to code the input into a binary code.

The purpose of the encoder is to produce a binary output which contains information regarding which of the keys is being depressed. As a specific example, we consider the MM74C922 16-key encoder, as illustrated in Figure 16.4. This is a 16-key to 4-bit encoder intended for use with manual data entry devices such as calculators or typewriter keyboards. Any 4-bit output code can be implemented. Note that the input is in the form of a row and a column. This is called a *switch matrix*, and they are available in various configurations (e.g., a 20 key matrix has 5 rows and 4 columns). Thus, four rows and four columns can be used to identify one of 16 keys reducing the number of input lines from 16 to 8.

Inputs are normally wired through the keyboard switches to the +5 V power supply. The sixteen possible outputs represent all possible combinations of four bits. The outputs can be configured to yield the binary equivalent of the particular input which is HIGH. Thus, for example, if input 9 is HIGH, the output is LHHH. Note that depressing the 9 key activates column X2 and row Y3.

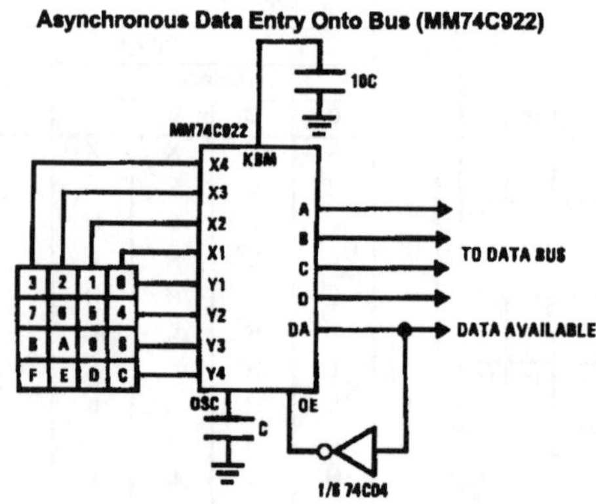

Figure 16.4 – Keyboard encoder (*Courtesy of Fairchild Semiconductor*)

As the mechanical switch is depressed or released, a bounce effect some times occurs. The mechanical switch makes momentary contact, then momentarily breaks contact, and finally makes a solid connection. The oscillator capacitor in the figure is used to de-bounce the switch, thus eliminating this effect.

16.1.3 Parity Generators/Checkers

The parity of a binary number indicates whether the total number of 1's is odd or even. Thus, for example the binary number 101 has even parity while the number 100 has odd parity. By adding one additional bit to a number, it is possible to force the enlarged number to have either even or odd parity. To create even parity, the added bit is a 1 if the original number had odd parity, while it is a 0 if the original number had even parity.

If a single bit in a word changes, the parity of the word changes. Therefore, addition of a parity bit allows detection of single bit errors. Suppose, for example, that a parity bit is added to each word to force the parity of the enlarged word to always be even. The system could then check parity at critical test points. If odd parity is detected, it knows a bit error occurred. In actuality, any odd number of bit errors causes a parity change and any even number of errors causes no change. The single parity bit is thus effective when we can rarely expect more than one bit error per word.

The problem associated with detecting multiple bit errors can prove serious in applications where errors frequently occur, such as in a high noise environment. (i.e., bit error rates much higher than that assumed above. In very high noise environments, the bit error rate can approach 0.5.) In such cases, undetected multiple errors can be expected. Improvement is possible by using additional parity bits.

16.2 DRIVERS AND ASSOCIATED SYSTEMS

Driver ICs are used to power displays and other special purpose devices. The driver circuits in this family are designed to operate over a wide range of voltages and currents since the display devices often use nonstandard voltages and currents. Figure 16.5 illustrates a DM7447A BCD to Seven Segment Decoder/Driver.

The function table for this device is shown in the figure. Four of the inputs represent a 4-bit binary number between 0 and 15. The 4-bit binary numbers between 0 and 9 generate a display which is the decimal digit corresponding to the number. By convention, the seven lines that make up the display are labeled *a* through *g*, with *a* for the top segment, and the remaining segments labeled in order moving clockwise around the perimeter. The center segment is labeled *g*.

The remaining 6 input combinations generate symbols which may be used to convey various types of information (e.g., overload). Suppose, for example, the 4-bit input is HLLH representing the binary number 1001 and the decimal digit, 9. Reference to the 7-segment LED display shows that we wish to light segments a, b, c, f, and g of the display to show the integer 9. The function table verifies that it is these specific five outputs that will be LOW. The 7447 delivers active low outputs designed for driving common-anode LEDs or incandescent lamps. The driver portion of the circuit provides an open-collector output.

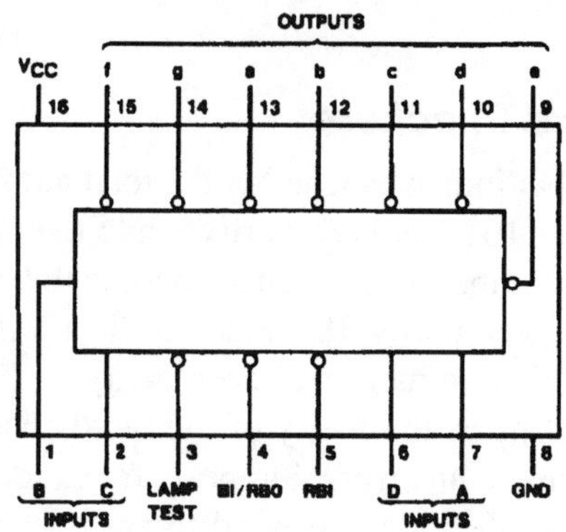

Function Table

Decimal or Function	Inputs						BI/RBO	Outputs							Note
	LT	RBI	D	C	B	A	(Note 1)	a	b	c	d	e	f	g	
0	H	H	L	L	L	L	H	L	L	L	L	L	L	H	(Note 2)
1	H	X	L	L	L	H	H	H	L	L	H	H	H	H	
2	H	X	L	L	H	L	H	L	L	H	L	L	H	L	
3	H	X	L	L	H	H	H	L	L	L	L	H	H	L	
4	H	X	L	H	L	L	H	H	L	L	H	H	L	L	
5	H	X	L	H	L	H	H	L	H	L	L	H	L	L	
6	H	X	L	H	H	L	H	H	H	L	L	L	L	L	
7	H	X	L	H	H	H	H	L	L	L	H	H	H	H	
8	H	X	H	L	L	L	H	L	L	L	L	L	L	L	
9	H	X	H	L	L	H	H	L	L	L	H	H	L	L	
10	H	X	H	L	H	L	H	H	H	H	L	L	H	L	
11	H	X	H	L	H	H	H	H	H	L	L	H	H	L	
12	H	X	H	H	L	L	H	H	L	H	H	H	L	L	
13	H	X	H	H	L	H	H	L	H	H	L	H	L	L	
14	H	X	H	H	H	L	H	H	H	H	L	L	L	L	
15	H	X	H	H	H	H	H	H	H	H	H	H	H	H	
BI	X	X	X	X	X	X	L	H	H	H	H	H	H	H	(Note 3)
RBI	H	L	L	L	L	L	L	H	H	H	H	H	H	H	(Note 4)
LT	L	X	X	X	X	X	H	L	L	L	L	L	L	L	(Note 5)

H = HIGH level, L = LOW level, X = Don't Care

Note 1: BI/RBO is a wire-AND logic serving as blanking input (BI) and/or ripple-blanking output (RBO).

Note 2: The blanking input (BI) must be OPEN or held at a HIGH logic level when output functions 0 through 15 are desired. The ripple-blanking input (RBI) must be OPEN or HIGH if blanking of a decimal zero is not desired.

Note 3: When a LOW logic level is applied directly to the blanking input (BI), all segment outputs are HIGH regardless of the level of any other input.

Note 4: When ripple-blanking input (RBI) and inputs A, B, C, and D are at a LOW level with the lamp test input HIGH, all segment outputs go H and the ripple-blanking output (RBO) goes to a LOW level (response condition).

Note 5: When the blanking input/ripple-blanking output (BI/RBO) is OPEN or held HIGH and a LOW is applied to the lamp-test input, all segment outputs are L.

Figure 16.5 - DM7447A BCD to Seven Segment Decoder/Driver (*Courtesy of Fairchild Semiconductor*)

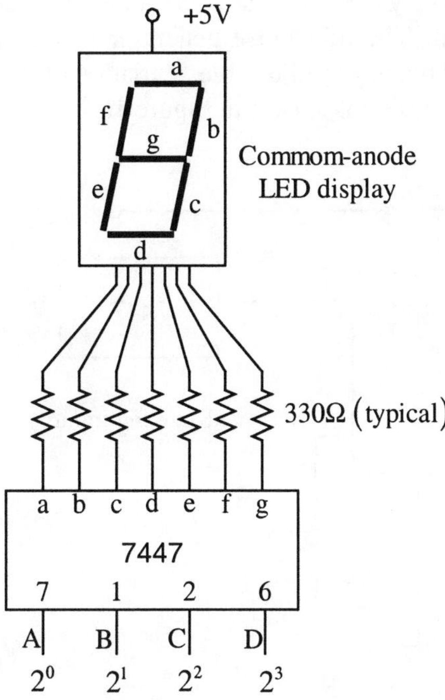

Figure 16.6 – 7447 BCD decoder and display

In addition to the 4-bit binary word, two additional binary inputs are provided. These are designated lamp test (LT) and blanking (RBI). The last line of the table shows that a LOW input on the lamp test pin causes every display segment to light[1]. This is used to test the circuit and the display. The display is turned completely off if the binary number 1111 forms the input, or if the blanking signal is LOW. This is used both to turn off the display, and to modulate it. By modulating the display, or turning it on and off periodically, the perceived brightness can be adjusted.

The 7447 is easily combined with a common-anode LED display, as shown in Figure 16.6. The typical forward voltage of the LED is 1.7 V with a current of 10 mA. We have used 330-Ω resistors to connect the open collector outputs of the 7447 to the $V_{CC} = +5$ V source through each segment of the LED. These resistors are necessary to limit the current through each LED segment.

EXAMPLE 16.1

Design a circuit using a 555 oscillator to control the brightness of the 7-segment display.

Solution: With the BCD to seven-segment decoder, we place a LOW signal on the blanking

1 Notice, in this, and most other pin diagrams that some of the inputs are shown in inverted form (with a bar above them). Thus, for example, the lamp test input has a bar. This can lead to confusion when reading a data book. To be precise, we would have to observe that when the lamp *signal* is HIGH, the lamp test *input* is LOW and vice-versa. In reading the data books, you may need to be careful observing when an input is inverted.

input in order to turn the display OFF. We use a 555 timer to construct a pulse generator to drive the decoder blanking input. The 555 pulse generator modulates the blanking input so the brightness of the 7-segment display is adjustable. Variation of the duty cycle of the 555 changes the display brightness. The design is shown in Figure 16.7.

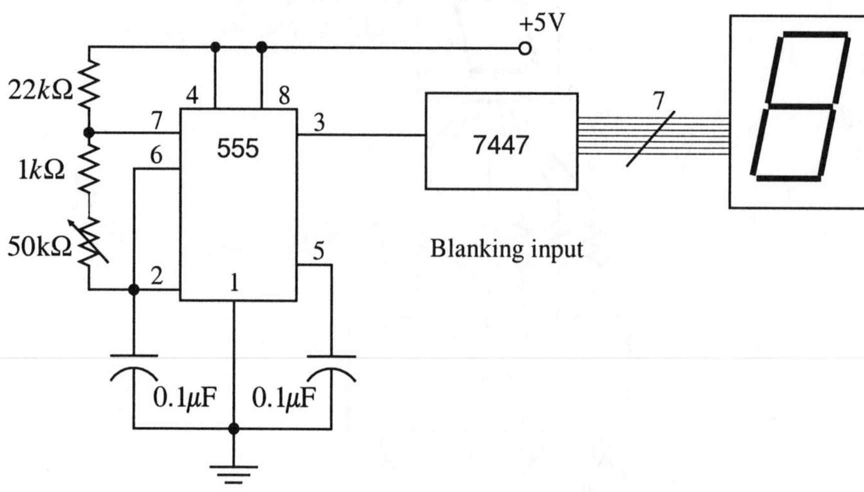

Figure 16.7 – Variable brightness control for 7-segment display

The duty cycle is varied by adjusting the setting of the 50 kΩ potentiometer. The frequency must be at least 100 Hz to eliminate flicker in the display. A higher frequency is recommended.

16.2.1 Liquid Crystal Display (LCD)

The liquid crystal display (LCD) requires very low power and is ideally suited for battery operated devices, such as digital watches. Liquid crystal displays are driven by applying a symmetrical square wave to the back-plane (BP). To turn on a segment, a waveform 180° out of phase with BP (and of equal amplitude) is applied to that segment. Excessive dc voltages (>50 mV) will permanently damage the display if applied for more than a few minutes. A schematic diagram for a liquid crystal cell is shown in Figure 16.8.

As can be seen in Figure 16.8, when the cell is activated, the light is scattered so the display shows black. When the cell is un-activated, the cell shows white.

The segments of the 7-segment LCD display are driven to form the numbers from 0 to 9 as is done for the 7-segment LED display.

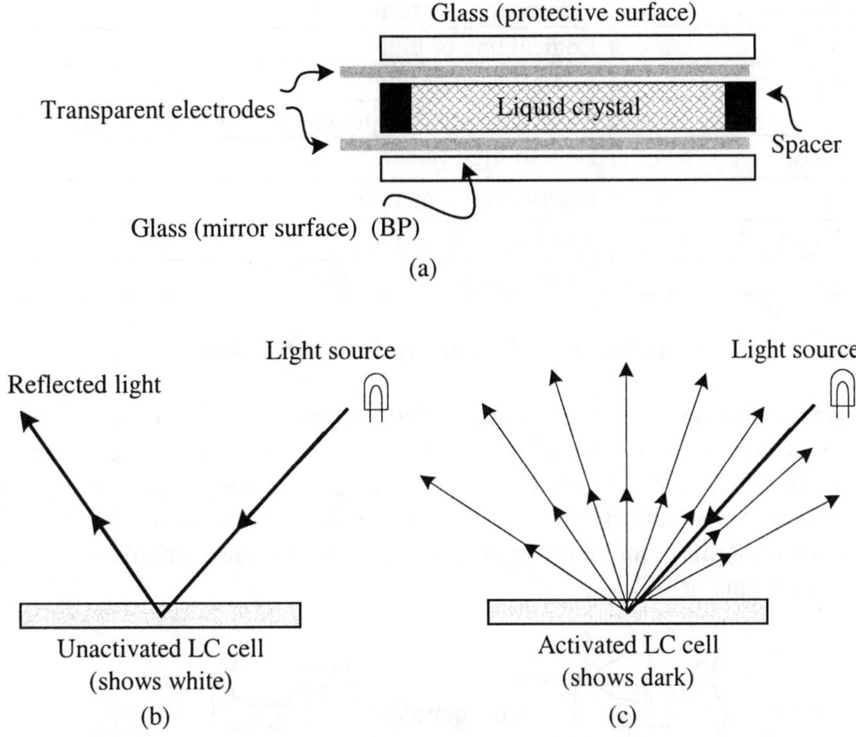

Figure 16.8 – Liquid crystal display

16.3 FLIP-FLOPS, LATCHES, and SHIFT REGISTERS

We are now ready to study circuits with memory. The outputs not only depend on the current value of the inputs, but also upon the past values. This is known as clocked logic, synchronous logic, or time dependent logic.

The function tables considered so far contain only two symbols, 0 and 1 or L and H. We now expand our vocabulary of function table symbols, by introducing some new symbols in Table 16.1.

The first three entries in the table represent symbols with which you are already familiar. The first entry is the data HIGH, or 1. The second is the data LOW, or 0. The third symbol, X, is used in function tables to represent values that do not matter–that is, they have no effect upon the output. These are referred to as don't care conditions.

In some cases, the transitions are important in determining system output. A particular effect could occur on the leading (or trailing) edge of a clock input. In such a case, the transitions are important, and we use the fourth and fifth entries in Table 16.1 to specify the direction of transition. The symbol, NC, is used to designate no change in an output.

Symbols	Common function table
1, H	Logical one or high
0, L	Logical zero or low
X	Don't care input; input can be any level or waveform
$\uparrow$ or	Low-to-high transition
$\downarrow$ or	High-to-low transition
NC	No change in output
Q_{n+1}	Output after a given event

Table 16.1 - List of Equivalent Symbols

More than one function table is often used to indicate the values of outputs and inputs before and after a clock pulse or transition. It is possible to combine these tables, and to apply a name to variables before and after the change. In such cases, a variable Q is designated as Q_n and Q_{n+1} to represent the value before and after a given event respectively. Some authors and data books have adopted variations of this terminology such as Q(t) and Q(t+1). The particular choice of symbols is usually self-explanatory.

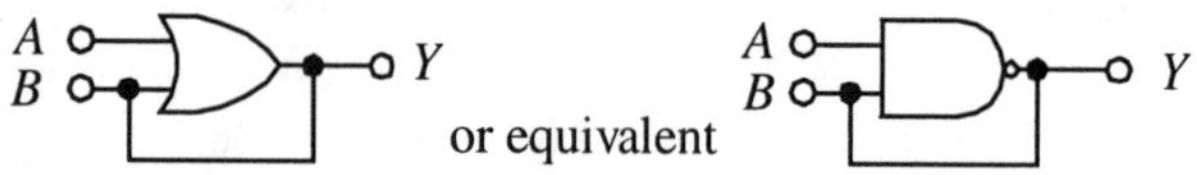

Figure 16.9 – Always gate

We can change circuits with no memory into circuits with memory by feeding the output back to the input. A simple example is shown in Figure 16.9. The output of an OR gate is fed back to the input. The equivalent form uses a NAND gate with feedback. This configuration is known as an always gate for reasons that will shortly become clear.

Suppose we start with input and output equal to 0 (LOW). If we now apply a HIGH to input A, the output will go HIGH. If input A is now made LOW again, the output remains HIGH because the B input is now HIGH. Once A goes HIGH, the output will always be HIGH regardless of subsequent changes in A (the analog equivalent is the peak detector).

The always gate is an exceedingly simple circuit with limited applications. Nonetheless, it illustrates the fact that feedback can be used to create a circuit with memory from one that previously had none.

16.3.1 Flip-Flops

***SR* Flip-Flop**: We can combine two always gates in the manner shown in Figure 16.10 to arrive at an extremely useful configuration. This is known as the set-reset, or *SR* flip-flop. It has two inputs (S and R) and two usually complementary outputs, Q and $\overline{Q}$.

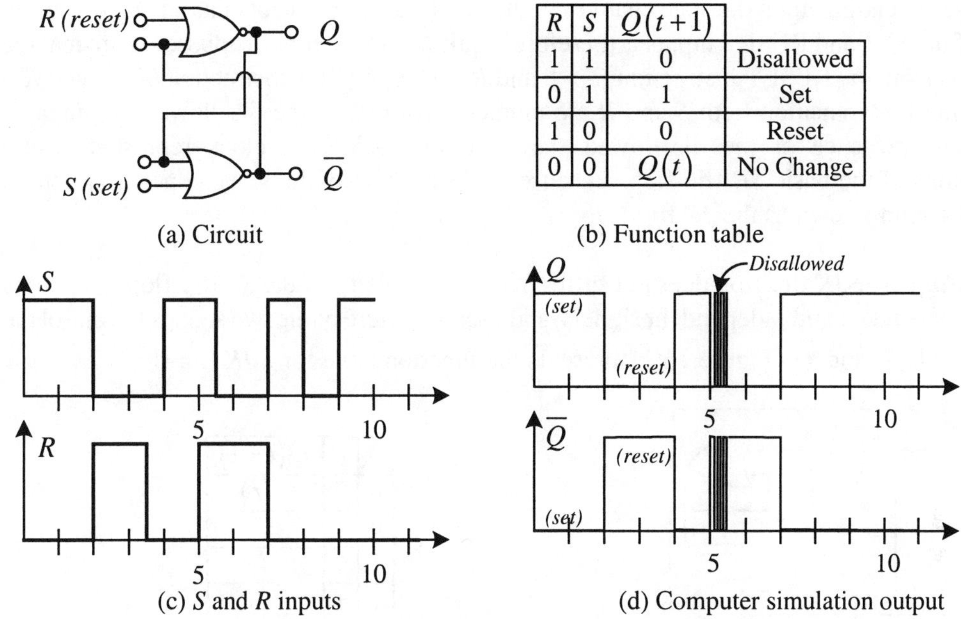

R	S	Q(t+1)	
1	1	0	Disallowed
0	1	1	Set
1	0	0	Reset
0	0	Q(t)	No Change

Figure 16.10 – Set-Reset flip-flop

The two inputs are S, for set, and R, for reset. The flip-flop is set when Q is 1 and $\overline{Q}$ is 0, and it is reset when Q is 0 and $\overline{Q}$ is 1. The function diagram of this flip-flop is shown in Figure 16.10(b). Q(t) is the logic value of Q before a change of R or S, and Q(t+1) is the value after a change of R or S.

As we describe the following operation, refer to Figure 16.10(c). First assume both inputs, R and S, are 0. In this case, no change occurs from the previous state. You can verify this easily by considering the two separate cases ($Q = 0$ and $\overline{Q} = 1$). Now suppose that S is brought to 1. In that case, $\overline{Q}$ becomes 0 and Q becomes 1. This is the set condition. Now we again start with $R = S = 0$, but bring R to 1. Then Q becomes 0 and $\overline{Q}$ is 1. This is the reset condition. The output remains in either of these two stable states until the SET or RESET lines are changes.

There are four possible combinations of inputs, and we have already dealt with three of these. The fourth occurs when both R and S are set to 1. The NOR gates would then force both Q and $\overline{Q}$ to be 0, so they are no longer a complementary pair. In fact, if the R and S inputs are not exactly synchronized, or if the two NOR gates are not identical (i.e., have different propagation delays), the output can oscillate (see the computer simulation of Figure 16.10(d)). This condition, where we are instructing the flip-flop to both set and reset at the same time, is a disallowed state. The *SR* flip-flop acts like a memory since the outputs remain the same until a momentary change occurs at the input.

The *SR* flip-flop has several significant shortcomings. The first is the disallowed state that we have already discussed. A second shortcoming of this simple circuit is that transitions can occur at any time depending upon the state changes of the inputs. The circuit contains no clock. Careful control of the SET and RESET inputs is therefore required. For example, suppose we are making a transition from the RESET instruction ($S = 0$ and $R = 1$) to the SET instruction ($S = 1$ and $R = 0$). If during this transition both S and R are momentarily 1, then the disallowed output state occurs. The presence of the disallowed state and the lack of a clock represent severe shortcomings of the basic *SR* flip-flop. Because of these shortcomings, we concentrate on an improved circuit known as the *JK* flip-flop.

JK Flip-Flop: The *JK* flip-flop does not suffer from the problems of the *SR* flip-flop. It features both time dependent and independent signals, and uses a mixture of the two signals to control the output signals, Q and $\overline{Q}$. Figure 16.11 presents the function table for a *JK* flip-flop.

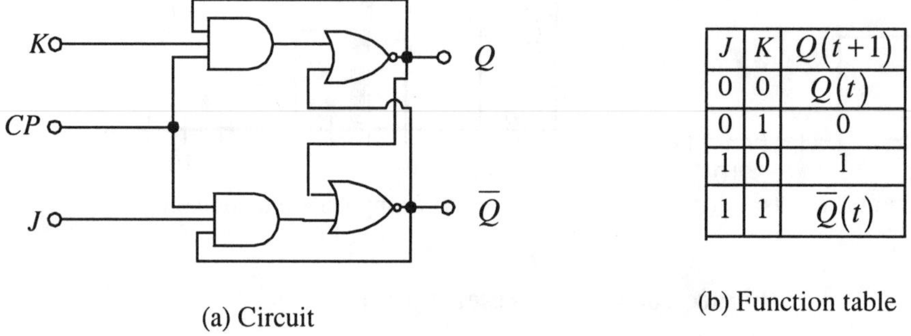

J	K	$Q(t+1)$
0	0	$Q(t)$
0	1	0
1	0	1
1	1	$\overline{Q}(t)$

(a) Circuit

(b) Function table

Figure 16.11 - *JK* flip-flop

In this table, the letter J is for set and the letter K is for reset. The clock is omitted to simplify the table.

By adding two gates to the input of the *SR* flip-flop, we obtain the circuit of Figure 16.10(a). The flip-flop output responds to changes in the input only when the clock pulse appears at the *CP* input. The output of this clocked flip-flop responds to changes in the input only when the clock pulse is equal to 1.

Since Q is ANDed with the K and *CP* inputs, the flip-flop is reset (cleared) when $K = Q = 1$ and the clock pulse occurs. Similarly, since $\overline{Q}$ is ANDed with the J and *CP* inputs, the flip-flop is set when $\overline{Q} = J = 1$ and the clock pulse occurs.

Q(t) is the logic value of Q before the application of the clock pulse, and Q(t+1) is the value of Q after the application of the clock pulse. The table of Figure 16.11 should be compared with that of Figure 16.9 to see the differences between the *SR* and *JK* flip-flops. Note that if the J is considered as the SET input and the K as the RESET, three of the entries in the tables match. Thus a 0 on the J and a 1 on the K input RESETS the flip-flop regardless of what state it was in before the application of these signals. The opposite conditions, $J = 1$ and $K = 0$, SETS the flip-flop. If both inputs are 0, the *RS* flip-flop goes into a disallowed state with both outputs at 1. The *JK* flip-flop, with 0 as both inputs, remains in its current state. That is, Q(t+1) = Q(t).

Now, if both inputs are 1, then the *SR* flip-flop does not change output while the *JK* flip-flop changes state. That is, the output of the *JK* flip-flop under the condition of $J = 1$ and $K = 1$ is given as $Q(t+1) = \overline{Q}(t)$, which means that the new output is the inverse of the old. We say that the flip-flop toggles. For example, if the flip-flop is set (i.e., $Q = 1$) and both J and K are 1 when the clock pulse occurs, only the K signal gets through the associated AND gate. The J signal is ANDed with $\overline{Q}$, which is equal to 0. The flip-flop resets.

Clocked Flip-Flops: Clocked flip-flops can only change state when the clock signal appears at the input. No matter how many changes occur in *J* or *K* between clock signals, the state of the circuit will not change. This form of logic can hold an output constant while some of the inputs are changing. A clocked logic device can therefore be used as a memory device to store an output so that it can be referred to again and again. Another advantage of clocked logic is that all changes in a complex circuit can be forced to occur at exactly the same time. This restriction is used to prevent potentially severe problems.

There are two basic types of clocking–level and edge. With level clocking, the input data cannot be changed except immediately after a clock pulse arrives. It is important that the input change only once during the period that the clock pulse is present. The state of the clock (either 0 to 1) determines whether changes in the output can occur. Alternatively, with edge clocking the input data can change at any time. Changes in the output only occur during transitions of the clock signal, so it is the value of the inputs at these times that matters.

Figure 16.12 illustrates the 74107 dual *JK* flip-flop connection diagram and logic symbol. We have discussed each of the labels except *CD*. This additional input is for direct clear. A LOW signal on the *CD* input overrides all other inputs and forces *Q* to go LOW. This flip-flop changes state on the HIGH-to-LOW transition of the clock (*CP*) input.

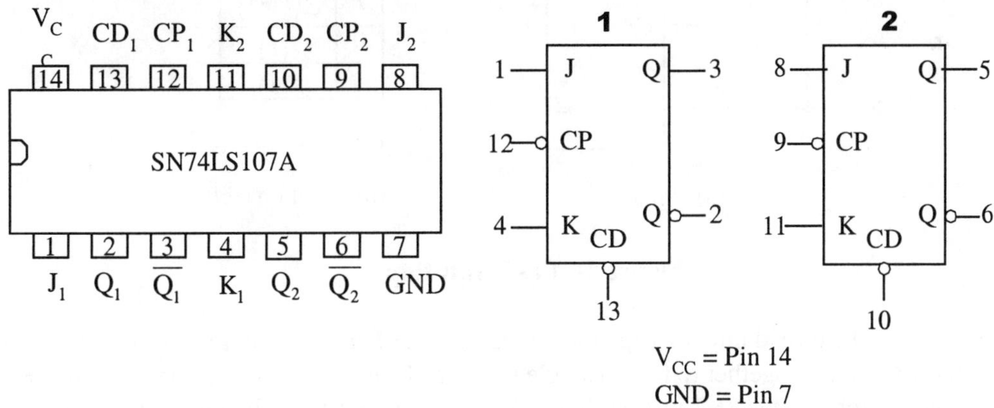

Figure 16.12 – SN74LS107A Dual *JK* negative edge triggered flip-flop

D and T Flip-Flops: There are two other major categories of flip-flops in addition to the *JK* flip-flop, these being the *D* and the *T* flip-flop. The *D*, or Data, flip-flop has only one input instead of two (as is the case with the *SR* and *JK* flip-flop). Regardless of the input level, the *D* input is transferred to the output. Figure 16.13 illustrates the circuit and the function table for this type of flip-flop.

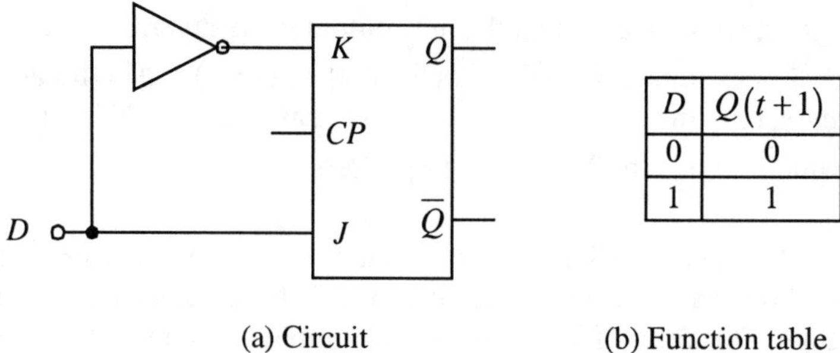

D	$Q(t+1)$
0	0
1	1

(a) Circuit (b) Function table

Figure 16.13 - D flip-flop

Notice that the next state of the output is given by the current value of the input. A 1 at the input SETS the flip-flop while a 0 at the input RESETS the flip-flop.

The *D* flip-flop can be constructed from a *JK* flip-flop by setting J equal to the *D* input and *K* equal to the complement of the *D* input. Thus, if $D = 1$ for the *D* flip-flop, this is the same as $J = 1$, $K = 0$ for the *JK* flip-flop, and this SETS the device. The reverse is true for an input of $D = 0$. By forcing *K* to be the complement of *J*, we have eliminated two rows from the *JK* function table.

The *T*, or Toggle, flip-flop also has only one input. If the input, *T*, is equal to 1, then the flip-flop changes state. If the input is 0, the flip-flop remains in its current state. This is shown in the function table of Figure 16.14.

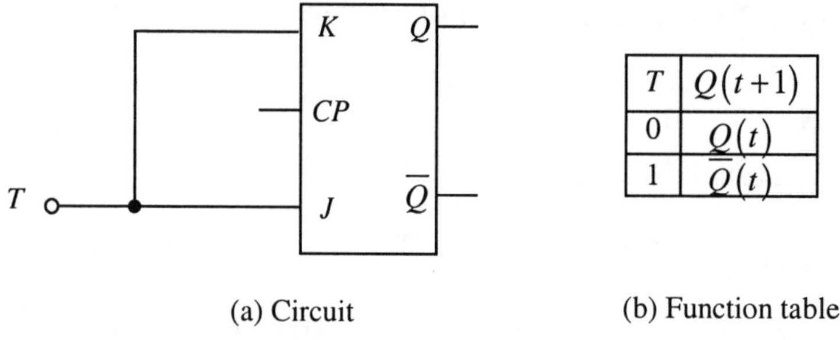

T	$Q(t+1)$
0	$Q(t)$
1	$\overline{Q}(t)$

(a) Circuit (b) Function table

Figure 16.14 - T flip-flop

A *JK* flip-flop can be turned into a *T* flip-flop by setting both *J* and *K* equal to *T*. That is, the two inputs to the *JK* are tied together to form a single input, *T*. Thus, if $T = 1$ this is the same as $J = 1$ and $K = 1$, which toggles the *JK* flip-flop. If $T = 0$, then $J = 0$ and $K = 0$ so the *JK* flip-flop does not change state.

16.3.2 Latches and Memories

The latch memory is a form of flip-flop that has the ability to remember a previous input and store it until the device is either cleared or the data are called up to be read by another IC. Latch ICs come in sizes ranging from devices that store one bit to those that store thousands of bits of information.

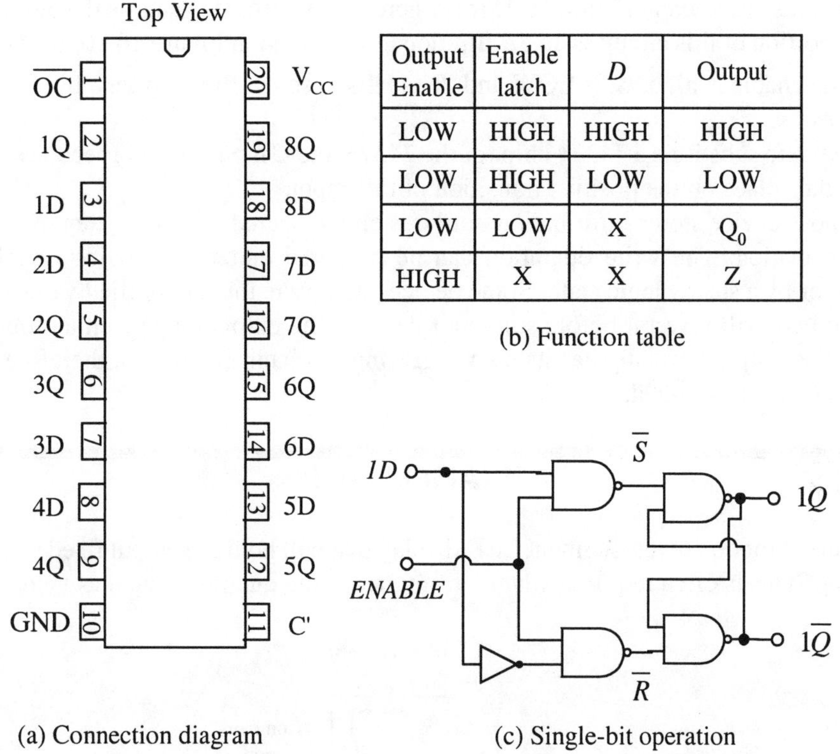

Output Enable	Enable latch	*D*	Output
LOW	HIGH	HIGH	HIGH
LOW	HIGH	LOW	LOW
LOW	LOW	X	Q_0
HIGH	X	X	Z

(b) Function table

Figure 16.15 – 74C373 Tri-state octal D-type latch

Figure 16.15 illustrates the pin diagram and function table for the 74C373 tri-state octal *D*-type latch. This is an 8-bit storage element.

There are eight data input lines, labeled D1 through D8, and eight output lines labeled Q1 through Q8. The device is assembled in a 20 pin dual in line (DIP) package. Eight of the pins are used for data input, eight for data output, two for power. This leaves room for two additional inputs as described below. The outputs are specially designed to drive high capacitive loads such as those found in a system bus. An additional input is labeled ENABLE LATCH on the function table and *C*, for clock, on the connection diagram. When this is HIGH, the *Q* outputs follow the *D* inputs just as in the case of the *D* type flip-flop. In this state the latch is said to be "transparent" since the outputs follow the input. When the ENABLE LATCH input is LOW, the outputs do not change. This is indicated in the manufacturer's function table by showing *Q* to equal Q_0. In this state, the data are latched at the level that existed when *C* was brought LOW.

An additional input is labeled OUTPUT ENABLE ($\overline{OC}$ on the connection diagram). When this input is HIGH (which really means the enable is LOW due to the bar over *OC*), all of the outputs go to a high impedance state regardless of the status of the other inputs. The *Z* in the last entry of the function table of Figure 16.15(b) signifies the high-impedance state. This is equivalent to disconnecting the pins.

The operation of the latch IC can be appreciated by viewing the circuit diagram of a single bit operation. This is shown in Figure 16.15(c), where we use NAND gates as the building blocks. The right portion of this circuit is an *SR* flip flop as presented in Figure 16.10. If *1D* is HIGH at the time the enable is high, $\overline{S}$ is LOW and $\overline{R}$ is HIGH, so the flip-flop sets. If *1D* is LOW, the flip-flop resets.

If we were to substitute a 74374 chip for the 74373, the *C* input (pin 11) becomes a clock, and latching takes place on the positive transition of this input.

A memory device stores information until it is either cleared, set, or written over by another bit of information. The write operation can be triggered either by a rising or falling clock transition, or by a steady logic state. Some devices will write the unmodified value of the input data and others will invert it before storage. Likewise, the output may be either unmodified or inverted. The output normally has its own triggering mechanism, and can therefore be read by means of an enabling signal.

EXAMPLE 16.2

Design a drive for one seven-segment LED display that will hold the output fixed while the input is changing. This is often required when we are measuring quantities such as velocity.

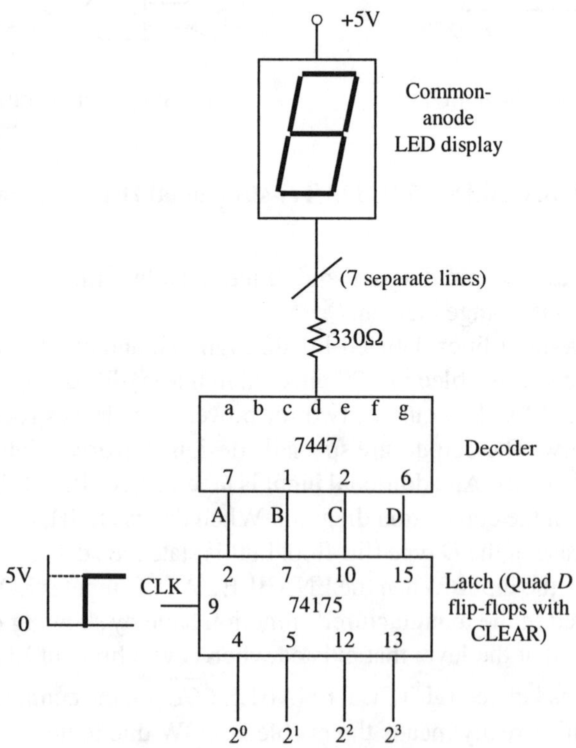

Figure 16.16 – LED display with latch

Solution: A possible solution for this design problem is shown in Figure 16.16. Since only four data lines are required, we have chosen a 74175 latch to hold the data on the display while the inputs are changing. Information on the four input lines (Pins 4, 5, 12 and 13) is transferred to the output lines (Pins 2, 7, 10 and 15) on the positive-going edge of the clock pulse on Pin 9. When the clock input is at either the HIGH or LOW level, the data input has no effect upon the output. The latch output feeds the 7447 BCD to 7-segment decoder/driver, which in turn, feeds the seven inputs of the LED display through 330 resistors. We have introduced the notation of a connection with a slash through it. This is shown in the figure as a slash with a "7" next to it. The slash-7 is a shorthand notation which avoids drawing 7 separate lines, and represents seven wires with seven resistors connecting the 7447 to the common anode LED display.

16.3.3 Shift Registers

A shift register is comprised of a number of *JK* or *D* flip-flops cascaded in a string so that on clocking, the contents contained in each stage are moved, or shifted, either one stage to the left or to the right. A simple shift register is shown in Figure 16.17.

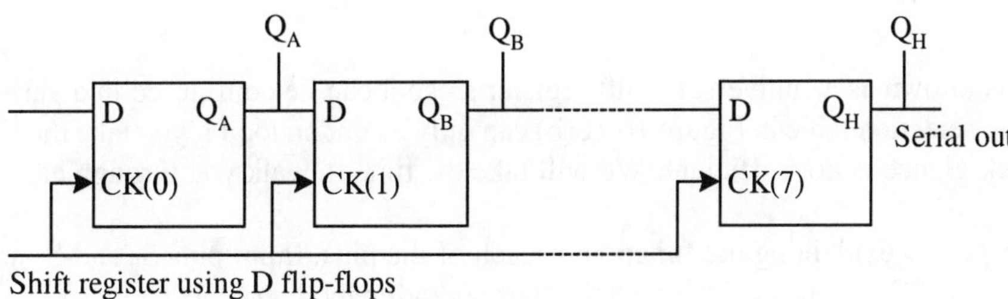

Figure 16.17 – Shift register

We illustrate eight stages, Q_A through Q_H. The bits of data, either 0 or 1, are passed on in order so the first bit in is the first bit out. The shifting usually takes place upon the rising edge of the clock signal. As a result, the eight-stage register of Figure 16.17 will delay the input data for eight clock pulses.

A shift register can be thought of as a memory device that consists of N memory elements connected together in a chain. Each cell in the chain is capable of remembering one bit of in formation. That bit can be transferred to the adjacent cell, left or right, upon a proper control instruction.

Figure 16.18 illustrates one particular class of 4-bit shift register, the 74194.

Mode Select Table

Operating Mode	Inputs						Outputs			
	$\overline{MR}$	S_1	S_0	D_{SR}	D_{SL}	P_n	Q_0	Q_1	Q_2	Q_3
Reset	L	X	X	X	X	X	L	L	L	L
Hold	H	l	l	X	X	X	q_0	q_1	q_2	q_3
Shift Left	H	h	l	X	l	X	q_1	q_2	q_3	L
	H	h	l	X	h	X	q_1	q_2	q_3	H
Shift Right	H	l	h	l	X	X	L	q_0	q_1	q_2
	H	l	h	h	X	X	H	q_0	q_1	q_2
Parallel Load	H	h	h	X	X	P_n	p_0	p_1	p_2	p_3

H (h) = HIGH Voltage Level
L (l) = LOW Voltage Level
P_n (q_n) = Lower case letters indicate the state of the referenced input (or output) one setup time prior to the LOW-to-HIGH clock transition.
X = Immaterial

(a)

Connection Diagram

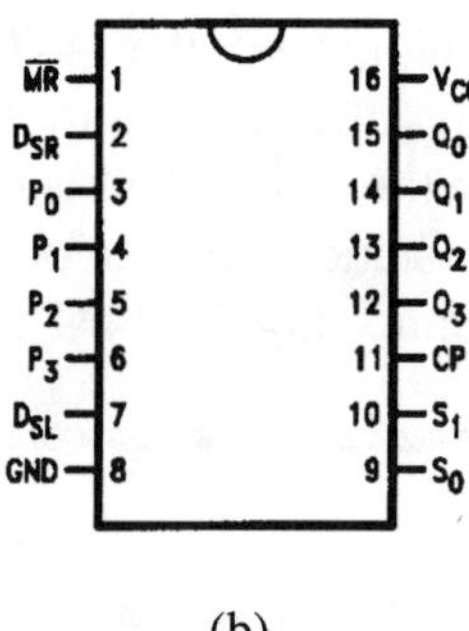

(b)

Figure 16.18 – 74F194 4-bit bi-directional universal shift register (*Courtesy of Fairchild Semiconductor*)

This is known as a "universal" shift register since it can be configured in a variety of ways. The mode selection table in Figure 16.18(b) can only be understood if you take the time to study it–a quick glance is not sufficient. We will take the time to walk you through each row in this table.

We begin by explaining the function of each of the pins. Input pins S_0 and S_1 are the mode control inputs. These are used to select the four operating modes of the IC. Pins P_0 through P_3 are the four parallel data input pins. D_{SR} is the serial data input for a shift to the right, while D_{SL} is the input for a shift to the left. *CP* is the clock input, and transitions occur on the HIGH going edge of this input. *MR* is the master reset. Q_0 to Q_3 are the four parallel output pins.

Starting with the top row of the truth table, we see that a LOW input into the master reset pin causes the shift register to clear. All four outputs go LOW regardless of the state of the other inputs. Note that all other rows of the table have the *MR* input as HIGH. This represents the case of not telling the register to clear.

The second row of the table indicates that when the two mode control inputs are LOW, the outputs do not change, independent of the other inputs. The notation of lower case q indicates the value of the respective output just before shifting occurs. Thus, for example, $Q_0 = q_0$ means that the first output does not change.

If we now set the mode controls to S_1 HIGH and S_0 LOW, the data shift to the left on the rising edge of the clock pulse (study the function table to convince yourself that the fourth and fifth rows are confirming this observation). Note that when the data shift left, the rightmost cell is loaded with the serial data input, D_{SL}.

Alternatively, a LOW input to mode control S_1 and a HIGH on S_0 causes a shift to the right upon the rising edge of the clock pulse. The sixth and seventh rows of the table confirm this.

The shift register can be loaded in a parallel fashion by setting both MODE controls, S_0 and S_1, HIGH. This is shown in the final row of the table. Then the parallel data inputs, P_0 through P_3 are loaded into the associated flip-flops. The output is read in parallel as Q_0 through Q_3. The "X" in the SERIAL columns of the table indicate that, during the parallel loading mode, serial data flow is inhibited.

Although there exist numerous shift register configurations, they can be divided into the following four broad categories, depending on whether inputs and outputs are handled serially (one after another) or in parallel.

(a) Serial-In Serial-Out (SISO): Input data enter the shift register serially and the data are taken from the output lead in a serial fashion delayed by a number of clock pulses equal to the number of storage cells. Figure 16.18 is an example of a SISO shift register.

(b) Serial-In Parallel-Out (SIPO): Input data enter the shift register serially but the data are taken from the output leads in a parallel fashion. This requires more than one output lead since the bits are read in groups of multiple bits. For example, if the bits represent a BCD code, the output bits are read in groupings of four to represent one BCD word.

(c) Parallel-In Serial-Out (PISO): This type of shift register has the capability of loading the data in parallel and shifting the data out serially. This register uses NAND gates and inverters with the flip-flops to properly sequence the input data.

(d) Parallel-In Parallel-Out (PIPO): This type of parallel access shift register is considerably more complex because of the additional gates that must be added. It can be thought of as a parallel combination of SISO shift registers.

16.4 COUNTERS

Counters can be either asynchronous (ripple) or synchronous. Figure 16.19 illustrates an asynchronous counter. Each of the blocks in this diagram is a *JK* flip-flop configured as a *T* flip-flop (i.e., the *J* and *K* inputs are tied together). Since the *J* and *K* of each flip-flop is tied to the +5 V supply, each flip-flop will toggle whenever it sees a clock input.

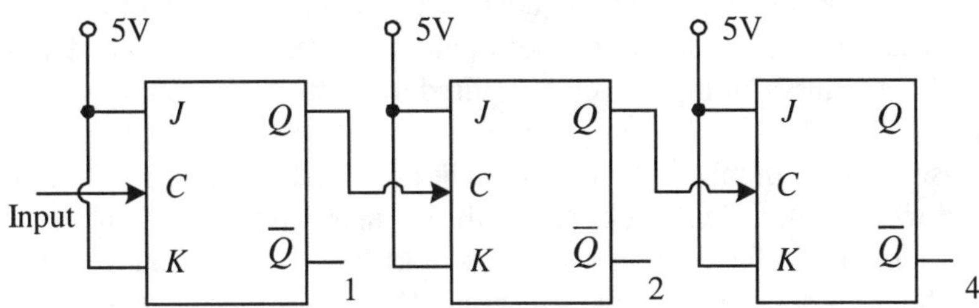

Figure 16.19 – Ansynchronous counter

Suppose we feed a pulse train into the first flip-flop. The first time the input goes HIGH, the flip-flop will SET. The second time the input goes HIGH, the flip-flop will CLEAR, and so on. Thus, the output of the first flip-flop, labeled "1", is a pulse waveform at one half of the frequency of the input. The second flip-flop toggles whenever the first output goes from LOW to HIGH. As we move to the right, each device toggles once for every two toggles of the device to its left. The outputs are labeled according to the weight in a binary number. Thus, the third output corresponds to 2^2 or 4. The counter generates a 3-bit number which cycles as follows:

000, 001, 010, 011, 100, 101, 110, 111, 000, ...

Note that the frequency of each bit changing from 0 to 1 is one half of that of the bit to its left. Thus, the circuit counts between 000 through 111 and back to 000 as the input is pulsed eight times. The counter is asynchronous since counts occur whenever input transitions take place.

The circuit of Figure 16.20 is a synchronous counter since the clock input feeds into all three flip-flops simultaneously.

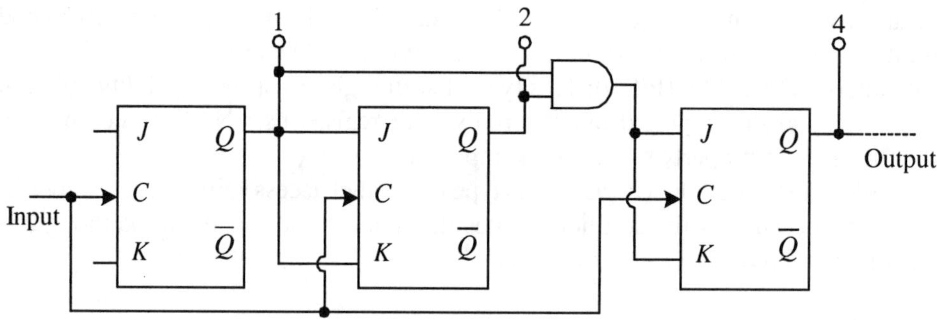

Figure 16.20 – Synchronous counter

The second flip-flop toggles upon a clock pulse only if the output of the first flip-flop is a 1. This represents a carry condition in the operation of adding 1 to the previous output. The third flip-flop toggles on a clock pulse only if both the first and second outputs are 1.

Since the output of each flip-flop is at a frequency which is one half that of its input, the flip-flop is often known as a divide-by-2 circuit. The counter is therefore often called a divide-by-n counter, where n is the number of input cycles required to produce one output cycle.

The majority of TTL and CMOS counters are up-only counters, that is, they count only in a direction of increasing binary numbers. Inverters can be used on the outputs in order to change an up-counter into a down-counter. This works only if the counter counts to a binary length that is a power of two. That is, if a 3-bit counter counts from 000 to 111 (2^3 counts), the inversion operation changes from up-counting to down-counting. However, if the counter is used to count only between 000 and 101, then inversion does have the desired effect.

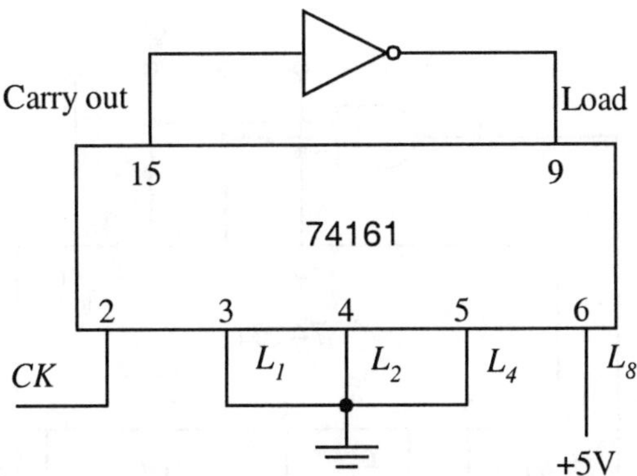

Figure 16.21 – Connection diagram to count from 8 to 14

An up/down counter either adds to, ignores, or subtracts from the current count at any time. Examples are the TTL 74190 and 74192 and the CMOS 74C192, 74HC160, 161 and 162. While these are the most flexible and versatile of counters, they are usually more expensive and consume more power than the up-only counters.

Counters can be connected in sequence with the output of the first forming the input to the second, and in this manner, the count is lengthened. It is possible to shorten the count sequence of a particular counter by presetting it to a non-zero number. An example is shown in Figure 16.21. This circuit uses a 74161 synchronous pre-settable counter configured to count from 8 to 14. The load inputs, L_1, L_2, L_4 and L_8, are used to preset the counter to any desired value. In this example, the connections preset the counter to 1000 or in decimal, 8. These bits are loaded into the counter whenever the LOAD pin, 9, goes LOW. The CARRY OUT lead (also known as carry look-ahead), pin 15, goes high when the count reaches 15 (1111). This is fed through the inverter so that the LOAD input goes LOW, thus resetting the counter to 1000.

Figure 16.22 shows another example of a truncated count sequence. In this case, we set the load input to 0000, so the counter will start counting at 0000. When the count output reaches 0111, or 7, all three inputs to the NAND gate are HIGH, and the NAND out put goes LOW. This clears the counter to 0000. Alternative, we could have fed the NAND output to the LOAD input. We see that the counter can be configured to start at any value and to end at any other value.

We now take a more detailed look at the 74161 IC which is used in the previous two examples. Figure 16.23 presents some information regarding the 74160 series of synchronous 4-bit counters. This figure is abstracted from the data sheets, and represents only one piece of information available to the design engineer. The 74160 and 74162 are decade counters (i.e., they count from 0000 to 1001), while the 74161 and 74163 are 4-bit binary counters (i.e., they count from 0000 to 1111).

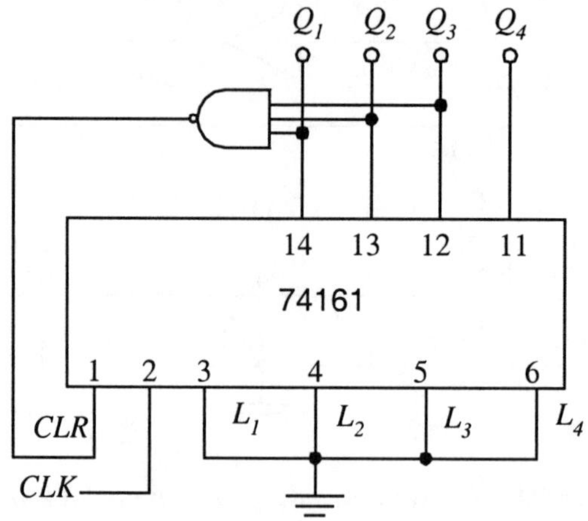

Figure 16.22 – Connection diagram to cause counter to clear

The ICs are composed of flip-flops that are all clocked from the same signal. This class of counters is programmable, that is, the output can be preset to any desired combination. When signals are placed into the load inputs and the LOAD is enabled, the counter presets, regardless of the values of the other inputs.

We examine the decade counter (74160 and 74162) timing diagram in the second part of Figure 16.23. Moving from left to right (increasing time), the first action is that the CLEAR input goes low. Both asynchronous clear (in the 74160) and synchronous clear (in the 74162) are available. Note that in the asynchronous clear case, the outputs, Q_A through Q_D, clear as soon as the $\overline{CLR}$ input goes LOW. In the synchronous clear case, clearing occurs at the first positive clock transition following the $\overline{CLR}$ input.

Top view

$\overline{\text{CLR}}$	1	14	V_{CC}
CLK	2	13	RCO
A	3	12	Q_A
B	4	11	Q_B
C	5	10	Q_C
D	6	9	Q_D
ENP	7	8	ENT
GND	7	8	$\overline{\text{LOAD}}$

Figure 16.23(a) – 74161 and 74163 series synchronous 4-bit counter

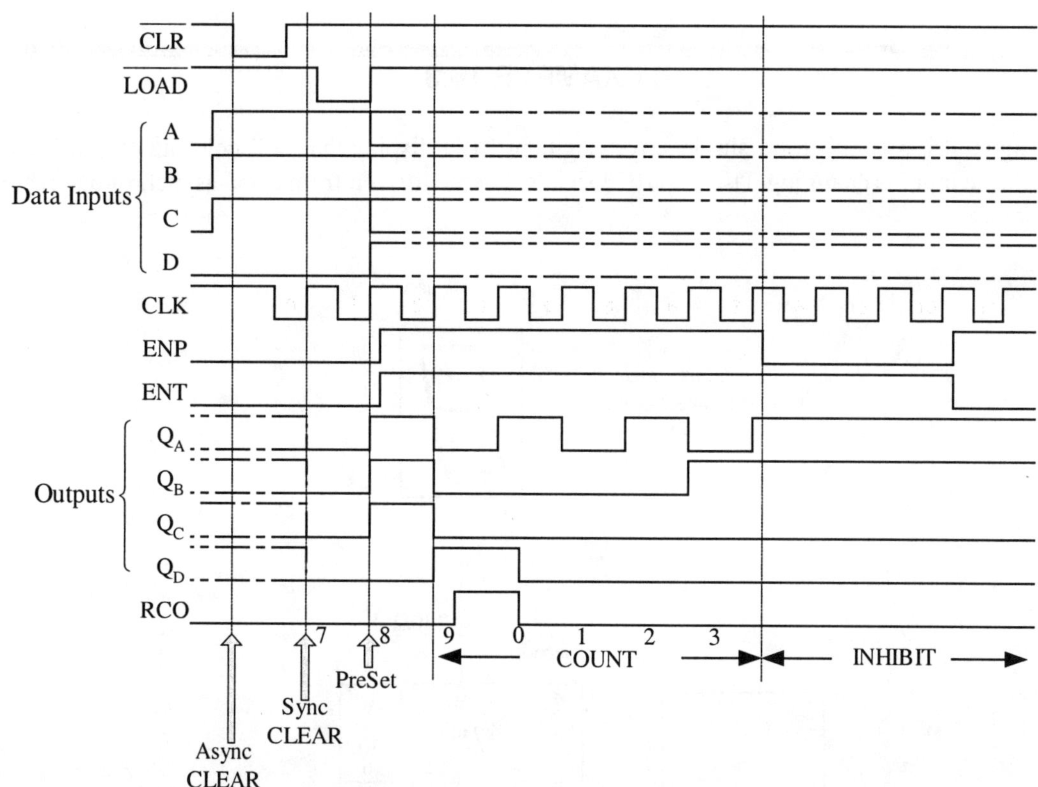

Figure 16.23(b) 74161 and 74163 series synchronous 4-bit counter timing diagram

The next action shown in the diagram is the $\overline{LOAD}$ input going LOW. This causes the data input to be loaded at the next clock transition. Note that the example shows 0111, or 7, as the load sequence (D is the most significant bit and A is the least significant). The count is then enabled with the enable inputs going HIGH. The reason there are two enable inputs (ENP and ENT) is that this gives maximum flexibility when counters are cascaded. Referring back to Figure 16.19, we had to include an AND gate to make sure the rightmost flip-flop toggled only when both of the other flip-flops were set. This represents the carry condition for a counter. The use of two separate enables permits a more efficient approach toward controlling a sequence of cascaded counters for high-speed applications. Counters with this feature are known as look-ahead-carry counters.

The counter is shown incrementing through 0111, 1000, 1001, 0000, 0001, 0010. At that point, the ENABLE P goes LOW and the counter holds the last value.

EXAMPLE 16.3

Design a drive circuit for a single seven-segment LED display that will hold the output fixed while the input is changing. Use a 74162 Decade Counter driven from a 555 asynchronous pulse generator.

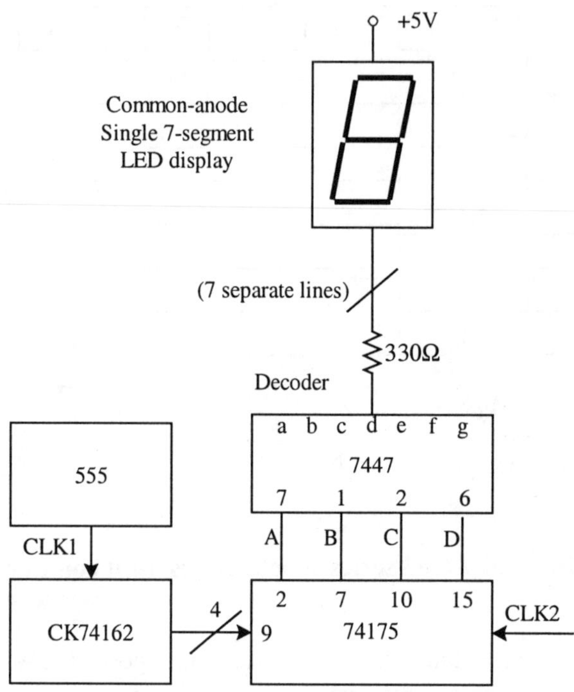

Figure 16.24 – Solution for Example 16.3

Solution: Refer to Figure 16.24 for a solution to this problem. The 555 clock (CK1) drives the 74162 synchronous 4-bit counter providing a signal to the 74175 latch. Whenever the second clock signal (CK2) goes from LOW to HIGH, the data at the input of the latch are transferred to the output and then to the 7-segment display.

EXAMPLE 16.4

Repeat Example 16.3 using a 74143 4-bit counter/latch, 7-segment LED Driver.

Solution: As can be seen from the block diagram of Figure 16.25, the single IC will solve the complete design, since contained within the IC are a BCD counter, 4-bit latch, and decoder/driver.
An important difference in using the 74143 is that we latch the count into the display with a LEVEL latch strobe voltage. We must hold CK2 (pin 21) high to latch the data into the display. This is shown in Figure 16.26 as CK2.

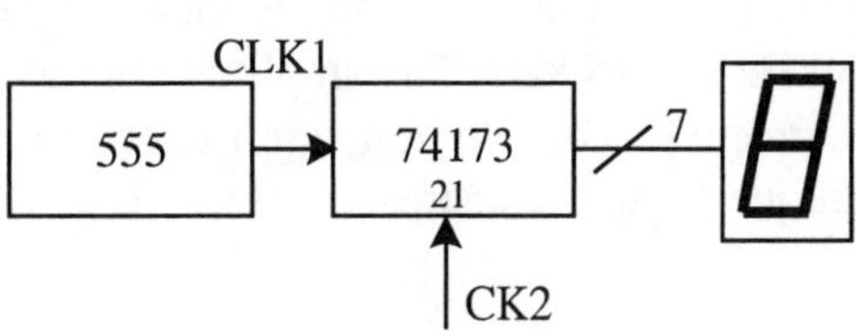

Figure 16.25 – Solution for Example 16.4

16.4.1 Frequency Measurement

An important application of counters is in frequency measurement. A counter can be combined with a pulse generator to form a frequency counter. This is shown in Figure 16.26.

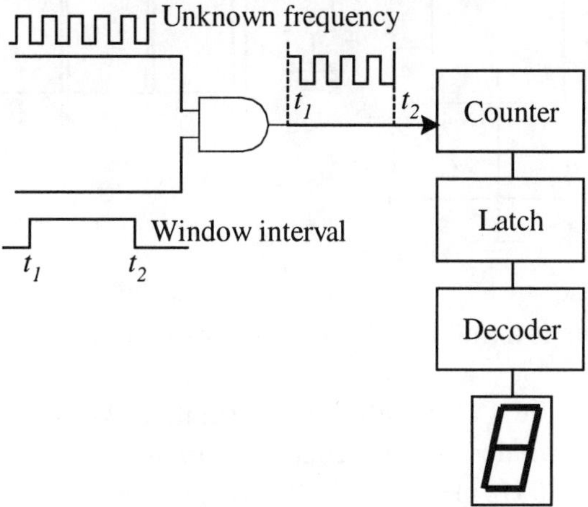

Figure 16.26 – Frequency counter

The counter counts the number of pulses (or cycles) that occur during the time that the "window" pulse is HIGH. Since the width of the window pulse is known, the frequency of the input can be calculated. For example, if the window is exactly one second long, the counter yields an output in Hertz.

EXAMPLE 16.5:

Design a frequency counter to measure the frequency of a sinusoidal signal in the range between 5 kHz and 15 kHz. The amplitude of the input signal is 10 V rms. Display the output on four 7-segment LEDs with four significant digits (i.e., XX.XX kHz). This means we are displaying the frequency to the nearest 10 Hz.

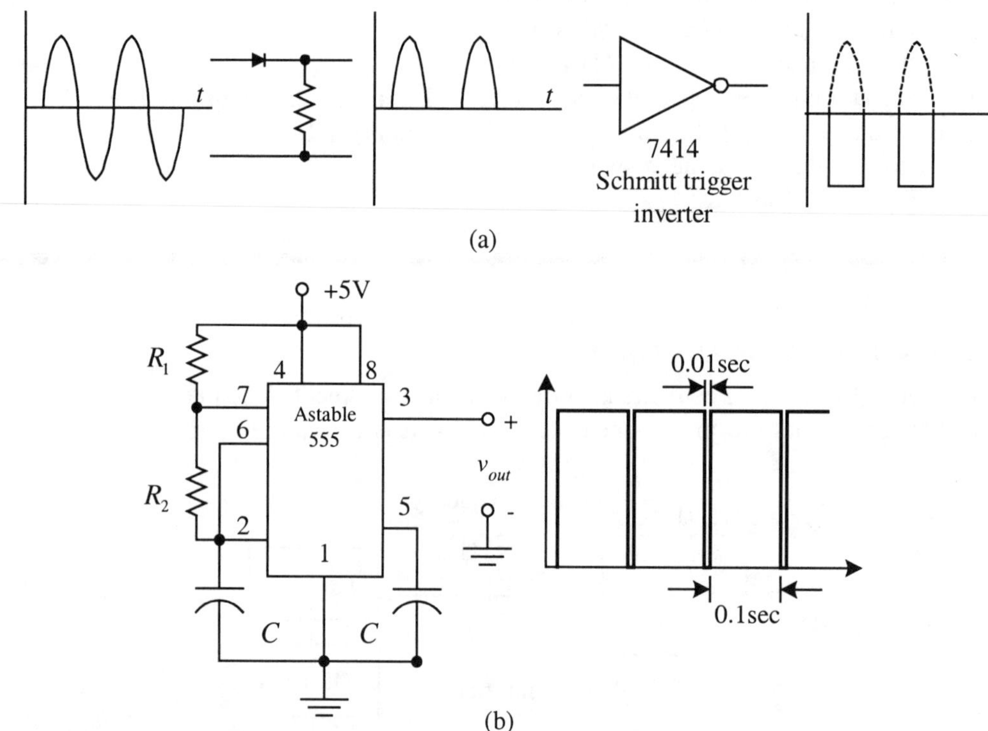

Figure 16.27 (parts a and b) – Frequency measurement for Example 16.5

Solution: Let us choose the TTL family for this solution. We refer to the system shown in Figure 16.26. If we set the window to 0.1 second, each multiple of 10 Hz would result in a single pulse in the window (e.g., 10 Hz means one cycle every 0.1 sec, 20 Hz means two cycles, and so on). We need simply gate the input over 0.1 seconds and count the number of cycles using a four-digit counter.

The sinusoidal signal is first conditioned to create pulses, as shown in Figure 16.27(a).

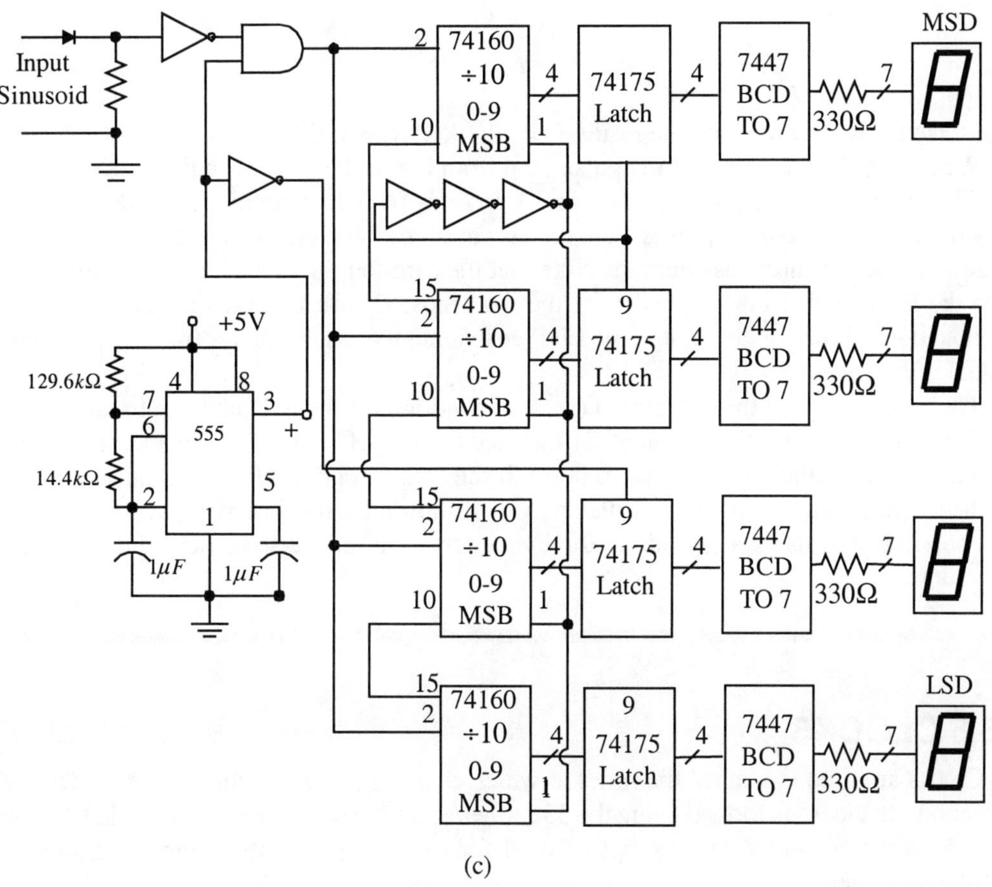

(c)

Figure 16.27(c) - Frequency measurement for Example 16.5

The window is developed with an astable 555. We want the time LOW to be short so that little time is wasted before the window goes high and counting repeats. Let us set the LOW time to 0.01 second, yielding a duty cycle of 91% The period of the astable 555 is 0.11 second so the frequency is f = 1/T = 9.09 Hz.

We then use the techniques of Chapter 14 to design the timer, as follows: Select C = 1 μF and obtain

$$9.09 = \frac{1.44}{C(R_1 + 2R_2)}$$

$$R_1 + 2R_2 = \frac{1.44}{9.09 \times 10^{-6}} = 158 \text{ k}\Omega$$

Since the duty cycle is 91%, we have

$$\frac{R_1 + R_2}{R_2} = 10$$

We solve for R_2 and R_1, with the result $R_2 = 14.4\ \text{k}\Omega$; $R_1 = 130\ \text{k}\Omega$

We now AND the output of the pulse train from Figure 16.27(a) with the window of Figure 16.27(b) to yield the number of pulses in 0.1 second. The complete block diagram is shown in Figure 16.27(c), where the pulses from the output of the 7408 AND gate are counted with four 74160 decade synchronous counters. Note that the carry output of each counter (pin 15) is fed into the ENT enable input (pin 10) of the next most significant counter (the one above it). Although not shown on the figure, the ENP enable input of each counter (pin 7) must be tied to HIGH.

The trailing edge of the 555 output (i.e., the window) is used to latch the ultimate count into the LED display. Thus, the output of INV1 is fed to pin 9 of the latches. This same transition is also used to clear the counter back to 0000. If the counters clear while their outputs are being latched, errors could occur. The display may well show all zeros for any input count. We avoid this possibility by using a cascade of three inverters to introduce some delay prior to the clear operation.

16.5 CLOCKS

Clocks are used to control the times at which changes occur in a digital circuit. One of the most popular clocks is formed using the 555 timer/oscillator which we discussed in Chapter 14. A wide variety of other devices can be used for clocks, such as multi-vibrators, timers and oscillator/dividers.

16.5.1 Voltage Controlled Oscillator (VCO)

The output frequency of most oscillators depends upon the setting of an RC time constant. We sometimes require a frequency that varies with an input voltage. Examples of such situations include frequency modulators (FM), tone generators, analog-to-digital converters, and digital voltmeters. Oscillators of this type are termed voltage-controlled-oscillators (VCO), or voltage-to-frequency converters (V/F).

The frequency of oscillation of a relaxation oscillator, such as the 555 in the astable mode, depends on both the RC time constant and upon the voltage to which the capacitor charges. In most of the applications of the 555 discussed in Chapter 14, we drive the external charging circuit and the internal voltage dividers with the same voltage. We will now permit different voltages.

Figure 16.28(a) repeats the circuit diagram for a 555 in the astable mode.

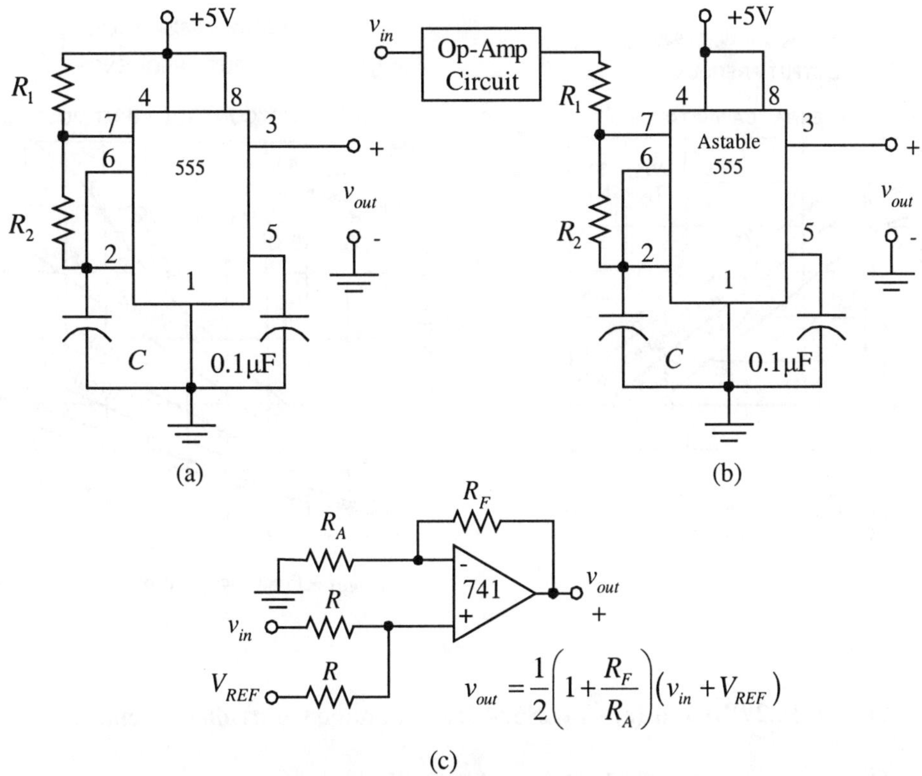

Figure 16.28 - VCO

In this configuration, we use the same voltage drivers for both external and internal circuitry to assure that the output frequency is independent of the supply voltage variations.

We now configure the 555 as shown in Figure 16.28(b), with the external charging circuit driven by an input voltage, v_{in}. The op-amp circuit shown as a box is expanded in Figure 16.28(c). The internal voltage dividers are driven by a fixed reference voltage, V_{REF}. If we vary the input voltage the output frequency changes as a function of this voltage. We saw this effect in Example 14.9. The result is a simplified VCO, with limitations of linearity and frequency range. These limitations cause us to consider a more sophisticated circuit.

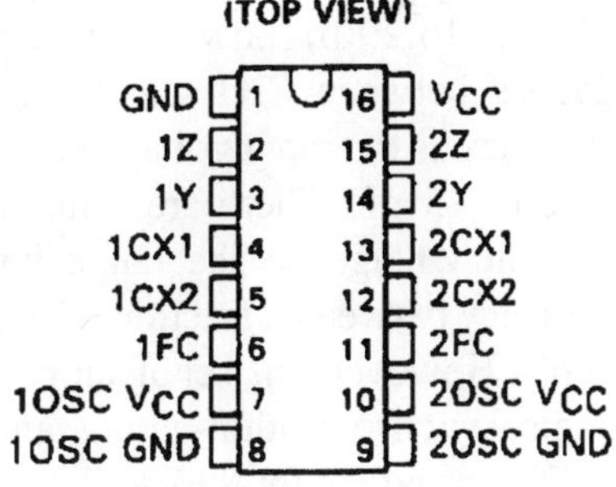

Figure 16.29(a) – 74LS624 Dual voltage controlled oscillator

Figure 16.29 shows the pin diagram and the typical characteristic curves for the 74LS624-629 series Dual Voltage Controlled Oscillator. This IC features two independent voltage controlled oscillators in a single package.

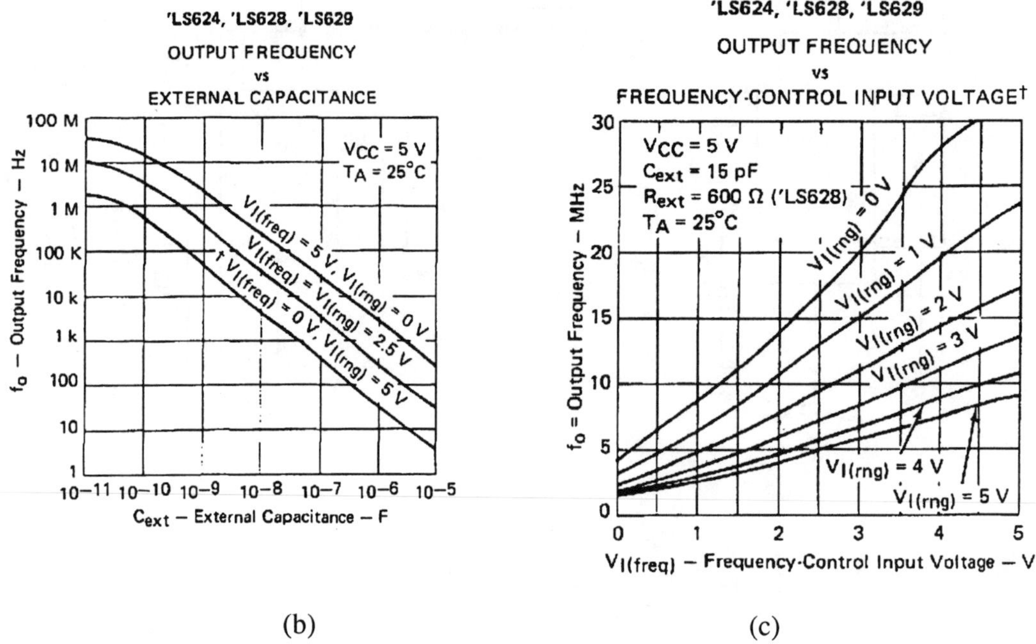

(b) (c)

Figure 16.29(b) and (c) - 74LS624 Dual Voltage Controlled Oscillator

The output frequency of each VCO is established by a single external component, either a capacitor or a crystal, in combination with two voltage sensitive inputs. One of the inputs controls the frequency range and the other controls the specific frequency value within that range. The relationship of these inputs to output frequency is shown in the curves of Figure 16.29. The curve of Figure 16.29(b) shows the center frequency as a function of the external capacitance which is attached between CX1 and CX2. The curves of Figure 16.29(c) show the range of output frequency as the input voltage varies. The particular curves shown in the figure are for a capacitor value of 15 pF. There are a number of parametric curves on this graph. Each represents a different voltage on the range input. These stable oscillators can be set to operate at any frequency between a fraction of a hertz and about 85 MHz. They can operate from a single 5 V supply. However, one set of supply voltage and ground pins (V_{CC} and GND) is provided for the enable, synchronization-gating, and + output sections while a separate set (OSC V_{CC} and OSC GND) is provided for the oscillator and associated frequency control circuits. This is done so that effective isolation can be accomplished in the system.

EXAMPLE 16.6

Use the 74S625 VCO to convert the voltage output of a temperature-sensitive bridge circuit to a frequency which is proportional to temperature. The center frequency should be 10 MHz. The temperature sensor provides the following outputs:

When the temperature is 110° F, the output is 4 V.
When the temperature is 90° F, the output is 2 V.

Solution: The design consists of selecting the 74S625 and assuring appropriate voltage inputs. We first set the center frequency using the frequency curves of Figure 16.29(b). To achieve a frequency of 10 MHz, the capacitance is approximately 1.5×10^{-12} F or 15 pF (we are interpolating between curves for an average range voltage of 3 volts. We can refine this following the next part of the design).

We must next decide what voltage value to use for the RANGE input. The set of curves in Figure 16.29(c) provides the necessary information (we need to select the proper family of curves for the selected capacitor value). The input voltage ranges from 2 to 4 V, and this is read on the abscissa. We wish to choose a $V_{1(rng)}$ that will allow this voltage variation to cause a symmetrical swing around a frequency of 10 MHz. For example, if we choose a RANGE voltage of 4 V, the input of 2 V would create an output frequency of about 5MHz and 4 V would create about 9 MHz. These values are read from the $V_{1(rng)} = 4$ V curve in Figure 16.29(c). This is a poor choice of range voltage for this particular input voltage variation since the frequencies are not symmetrical around 10 MHz. A better choice would be a range input of approximately 2.5 V.

Repeating the analysis for a range input of 2.5 V, we see that an input of 4 V yields an output frequency of about 12.5 MHz. For an input of 2 V, the curve yields a frequency of approximately 7.5 MHz. This is close to symmetrical.

In the previous example, the voltage range at the output of the temperature sensor conveniently matched the range of voltages required by the 74LS625 VCO chip. Suppose instead that the input voltages ranged from V_{min} to V_{max}, where these can take on any value (including negative). We would then have to use the op-amp circuit of Figure 16.28(c) to change this range. The input-output relationship of the op-amp is given by

$$v_{out} = \left(\frac{1}{2} + \frac{R_F}{2R_A}\right)\cdot v_{in} + \left(\frac{1}{2} + \frac{R_F}{2R_A}\right)\cdot V_{REF} \tag{16.1}$$

We can establish the limits on v_{out} by plugging in V_{min} and V_{max} for v_{in} in Equation (16.1). We can set this limit on v_{out} to whatever values we wish. For the 74LS624, we may want to have v_{out} range from 2 V to 4 V. This yields

$$\begin{aligned} 2 &= \left(\frac{1}{2} + \frac{R_F}{2R_A}\right)\cdot V_{min} + \left(\frac{1}{2} + \frac{R_F}{2R_A}\right)\cdot V_{REF} \\ 4 &= \left(\frac{1}{2} + \frac{R_F}{2R_A}\right)\cdot V_{max} + \left(\frac{1}{2} + \frac{R_F}{2R_A}\right)\cdot V_{REF} \end{aligned} \tag{16.2}$$

Equations (16.2) represent two equations in three unknowns, R_F, R_A, and V_{REF}. We can select one of these based on available values, and then solve for the other two.

16.6 MEMORIES

We consider various types of memory devices, which are summarized in the block diagram of Figure 16.30.

16.6.1 Serial Memories

Data entered into the storage of serial memory devices are not immediately available for reading. Typically each stored bit is transferred sequentially through 64 or more storage locations between the time it is written into memory and the time it first becomes available for reading.

In Section 16.3.2 we studied the use of latches to hold the output lines (which drive the LED display) fixed while the inputs are being updated. This is a form of memory, since the latch remembers the most recent value and holds this value on the display while the data are being updated. With the 74175 latch, we transfer the most recent information to the display with the rising edge of the clock pulse. The D flip-flop in the 74175 remembers this number until another rising edge of a clock pulse is applied.

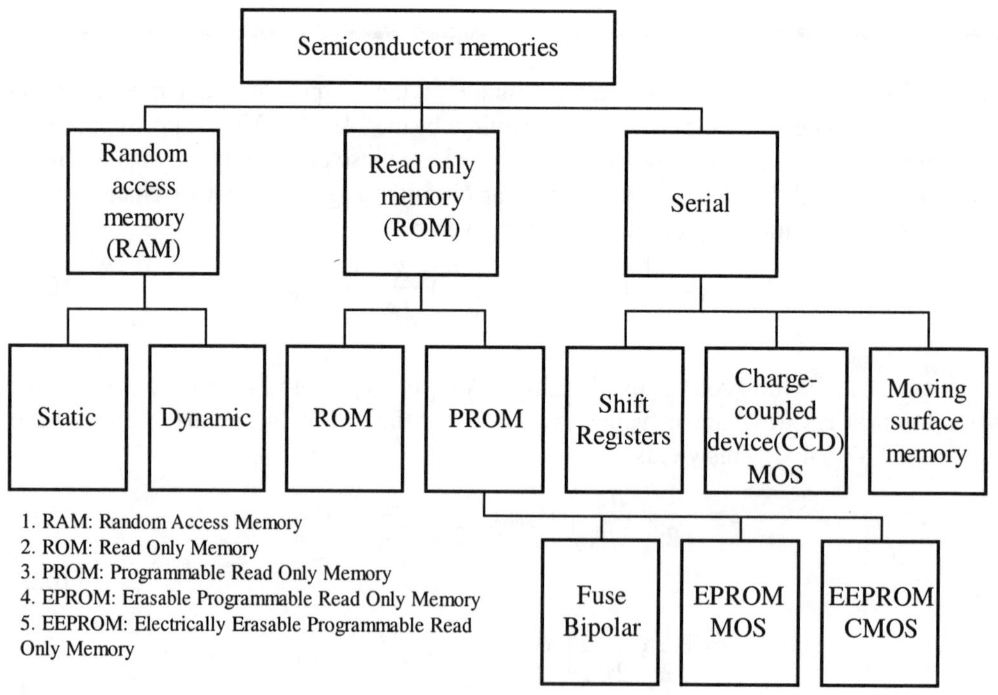

Figure 16.30 – Memory overview

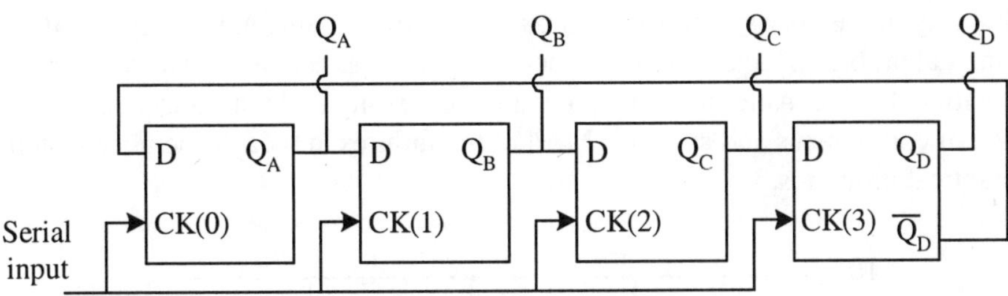

Figure 16.31(a) – Circuit diagram of switch-tail ring counter

A shift register (see Section 16.3.3) is another form of memory, where the data are transferred from flip-flop to flip-flop. These stored data can be shifted right or left or manipulated in a parallel manner. Throughout these operations, the shift register remembers the data. Frequently, data at the output flip-flop can be fed back to the input flip-flop. In this manner, the data in the register are held unchanged but circulate in what is termed a ring counter. A variation of this is the switch-tail ring counter (or Johnson counter), in which we use a circular shift register. This form of shift register is shown in Figure 16.31(a).

Clock Pulse	Q_A	Q_B	Q_C	Q_D
0	0	0	0	0
1	1	0	0	0
2	1	1	0	0
3	1	1	1	0
4	1	1	1	1
5	0	1	1	1
6	0	0	1	1
7	0	0	0	1
0	0	0	0	0

Figure 16.31(b) – Function table

We take the complement of the output flip-flop and feed that back to the input flip-flop. When a 1 is injected into the input D flip-flop, at each clock pulse we generate the function as shown in Figure 16.31(b).

Moving-surface memories are the slowest form of serial memory. The moving magnetic tape player is an example of this type. This form of memory is cheaper than electronic memories because there is no need to define individual physical patterns or structures for each individual storage cell. However, precision mechanical components may be needed to transport the magnetic storage medium, leading to a high initial cost.

Bubble memories are serial in organization, so access time depends on the number of storage locations in a serial path and on the maximum shifting rate. Serial paths range in length from about 10 locations to over 1000 locations. Shifting rates range from a fraction of a microsecond to several microseconds. The most attractive potential application of bubble memories is the replacement of tape and disk memories with a capacity of between one million and ten million bits. A key feature of bubble memories is that stored information is retained even when external power is interrupted.

When selecting a particular memory, it is important to consider the price per bit of storage capacity. Price depends strongly on access time. We have intentionally avoided units on Figure 16.32 since these are rapidly changing. The cost per bit varies over a very wide range. For bipolar memories, it is of the order of one cent per bit, while for tape, it is a fraction of 10^{-5} cents per bit.

The relationship between price per bit and access time is approximately logarithmic over a wide range of prices per bit. This relationship is shown in Figure 16.32.

The reliability of memory systems is a function of both fundamental and practical problems. The fundamental problems have to do with phenomena such as corrosion. The practical problems have to do with defective manufacturing, packaging or testing and with mistakes in the use and maintenance of components and systems. Most of the failures in today's memory systems result from the practical problems.

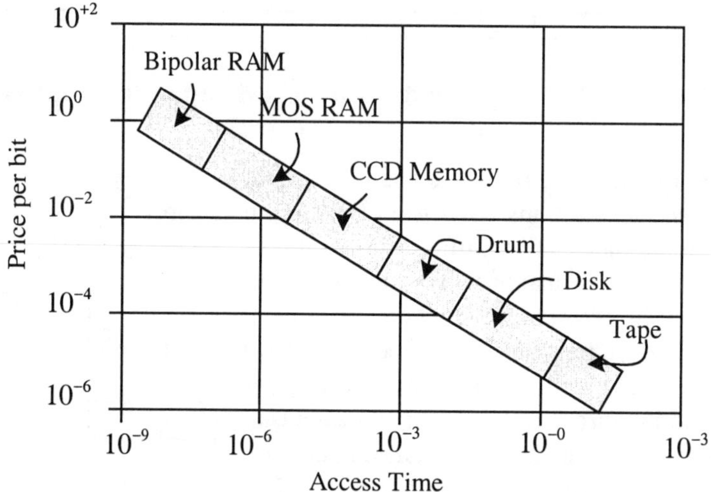

Figure 16.32 - Access time versus price

16.6.2 Random Access Memory (RAM)

Dynamic memories store their data in the form of a charge on a small capacitor. A dynamic memory cell cannot store data indefinitely. The capacitor storage cell can lose stored information in two ways. First the capacitor itself has an associated leakage current. Second, when the cell is selected for a read operation, the charge stored is shared between the cell capacitor and the large capacitance of the data line.

For the dynamic memory to retain valid data, the capacitor charge must be periodically restored. This restoration must occur at least once every 2 msec. Rewriting is accomplished internally without the need to reapply the original external data. This rewriting operation is called refresh.

Memories that do not require refresh operations are termed static memories. In spite of their higher cost per bit of storage, they are favored for small memory systems because they require a minimum of external support circuitry. At a further premium in cost, the power consumption of static memories can be significantly reduced. These memories are found in pocket calculators where small batteries must provide sufficient power for operating over days and weeks.

A static RAM is an array of latches with a common addressing structure for both reading and writing. In the WRITE mode, the information at the data input is written into the latch selected by the ADDRESS. In the READ mode, the content of the selected latch is fed to the data output.

Semiconductor memories have non-destructive readout. That is, the memory can be read without destroying the data stored therein. Semiconductor read/write memories are volatile. That is, data can be stored only as long as the power is uninterrupted.

Memories are generally identified by specifying the number of words, number of bits per word and function. For example, a 1024 × 16 RAM is a random access read/write memory containing 1024 words of 16 bits each.

High-density RAM memories are usually organized into arrays of n words of one bit each. Only one input/output lead is needed in addition to the address leads, thus optimizing lead usage.

Addressing (word selection) in a semiconductor memory consists of two operations. First, a given device or group of devices must be selected; Second, a given location in a device or group of devices must be specified. The selection of the device can be done by supplying an input to the CHIP SELECT function of each device. The input is LOW for all but the desired device. The input can be derived from a binary-to-n decoder. The binary address of the device is fed in, and only the select output for that device is HIGH.

Figure 16.33 shows the block and connection diagrams for the 74F189 16-word by 4-bit RAM.

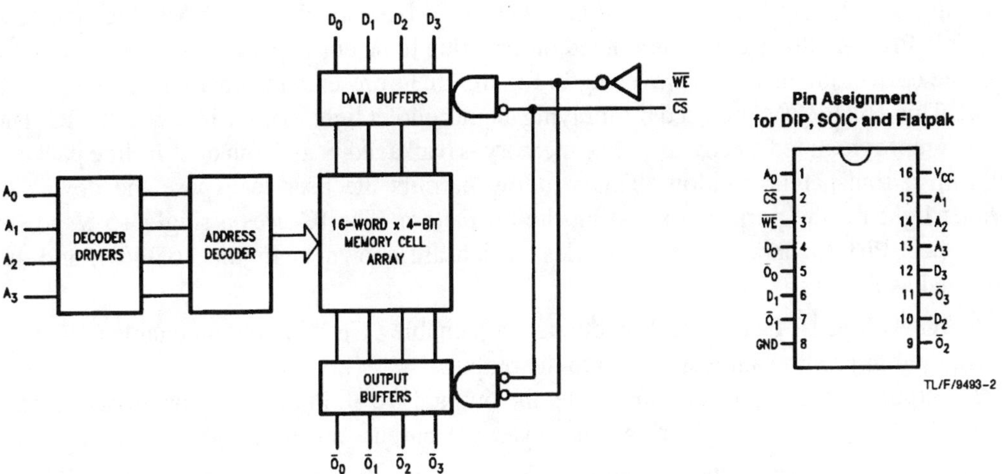

Figure 16. 33 – 74F189 64-bit RAM (*Courtesy of National Semiconductor*)

This is a high-speed 64-bit RAM organized as a 16-word by 4-bit array. The memory address is specified by a four-bit number, inputs A_0 through A_3 (on larger memories, we specify a row and a column number).

The actual 4-bit word is fed into inputs D_0 through D_3, and the inverted outputs are read out from pins 5, 7, 9, and 11. Data can be read when the write enable ($\overline{WE}$) and chip select $\overline{CS}$ inputs are LOW.

16.6.3 ROMs and PROMs

A read-only memory (ROM) is a random access memory in which the stored information is fixed and non-volatile. A semiconductor ROM is a circuit whose stored information is fixed during manufacture, while a programmable ROM (PROM) is a memory that can be programmed after manufacture. A ROM is best suited for systems produced in large volume. Here the tooling charge for a unique mask is relatively small on a per-unit basis and is often counterbalanced by the economies of batch processing. PROMs are the best choice in low-volume production or in systems having limited useful life, in short procurement cycle situations for applications where some degree of system tailoring is required for each installation, and where there is a high probability that the stored information will be changed at some future date.

16.6.4 EPROMs

PROMs can be programmed with any desired array of binary numbers. The process of programming is sometimes known as burning the PROM since the programming can be thought of as burning out appropriate fuses. Once this process is performed, the PROM can never be reprogrammed, although it is possible to make additional outputs high by burning additional fuses. That is, none of the output 1's can be changed to 0's, but the reverse is possible.

A class of PROMs exists where the programmed data can be cleared and the PROM reprogrammed with new data. Erasable PROMs (EPROM) are available with MOS technology. An erasable PROM allows the programmed information to be erased by exposure to ultraviolet light of the correct intensity and wavelength. Figure 16.34 presents information for a 16k × 8 EPROM. This 16k PROM is erased by applying an ultraviolet light to the window in the IC. The memory is reprogrammed electrically. The memory is packaged in a 28 pin dual-in-line package (DIP) with a transparent window. This window permits the user to expose the device to ultraviolet light for the purpose of erasing the bit pattern. The IC uses a single +5 V power supply. The EPROM operates in six modes, which are shown in Figure 16.34(b), and are summarized as follows:

1. READ mode - Two control functions: chip enable ($\overline{CE}$) and output enable ($\overline{OE}$) are required to gate the addressed data to the output.
2. Output Disable mode - In this mode, the outputs are all in the high impedance state.
3. STANDBY mode - When in this mode, the outputs are in a high impedance state, independent of $\overline{OE}$. In this standby mode, the power dissipation is reduced by 99%.
4. PROGRAMMING mode - After erasure, all bits in the memory are in the logic 1 state. Data are introduced by selectively programming logic 0 into the desired bit locations. To change a 0 to a 1, however, we must use ultraviolet light erasure. The memory is in a programming mode when the V_{PP} power supply is at 12.75 V and $\overline{OE}$ is at a high input voltage (V_{IH}).
5. PROGRAM VERIFY mode - To be certain that the bit pattern is correctly programmed, we can use this mode. We verify the program with $V_{PP} = 12.75$ V.
6. PROGRAM INHIBIT mode - When programming multiple memories in parallel, it is necessary to inhibit the memories that are not being programmed. A low level $\overline{CE}$/PGM input inhibits the other parallel memories from being programmed.

An electrically erasable PROM (EEPROM) is useful when we wish to alter stored data. Erasing and programming are accomplished by applying electrical signals to the appropriate inputs of the IC.

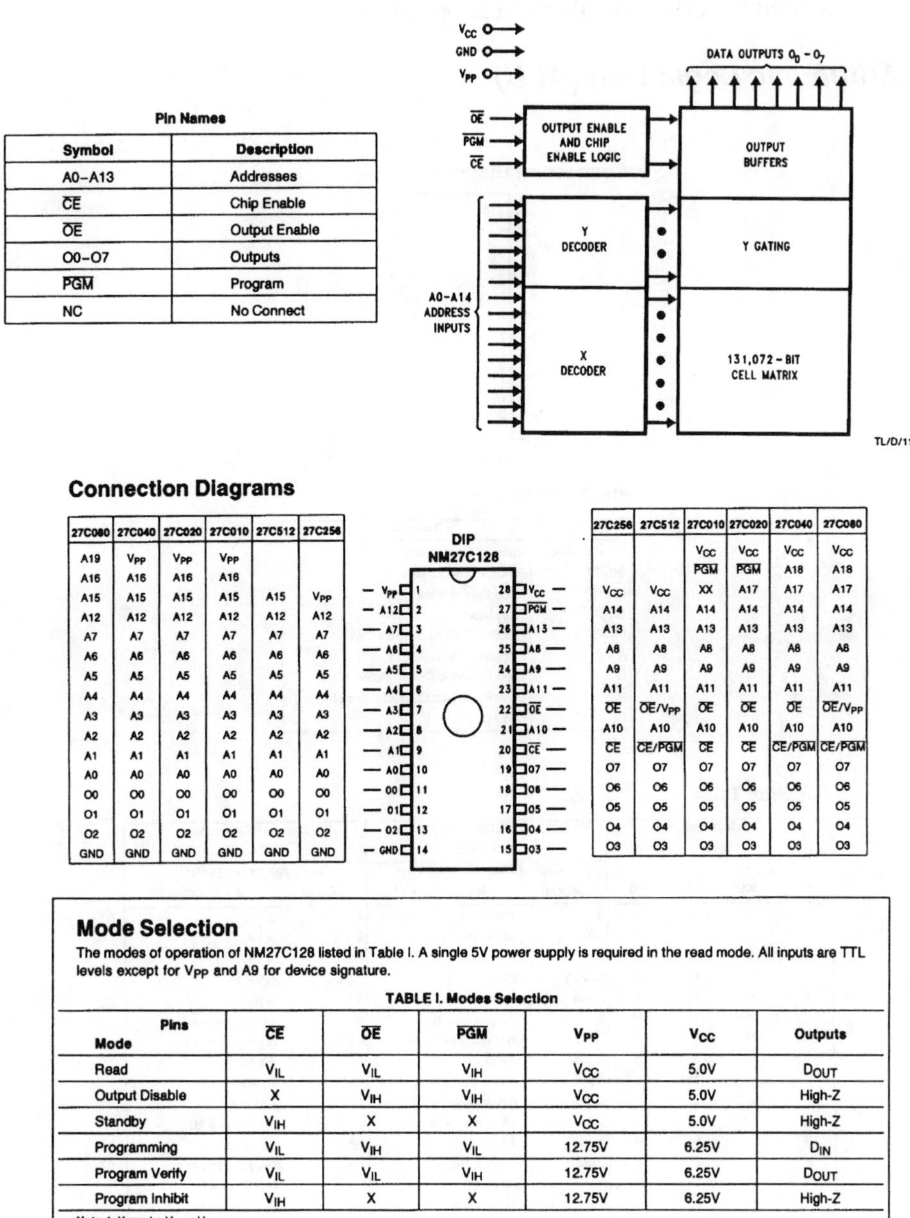

Pin Names

Symbol	Description
A0–A13	Addresses
$\overline{CE}$	Chip Enable
$\overline{OE}$	Output Enable
O0–O7	Outputs
$\overline{PGM}$	Program
NC	No Connect

Connection Diagrams

27C080	27C040	27C020	27C010	27C512	27C256
A19	V_{PP}	V_{PP}	V_{PP}		
A16	A16	A16	A16		
A15	A15	A15	A15	A15	V_{PP}
A12	A12	A12	A12	A12	A12
A7	A7	A7	A7	A7	A7
A6	A6	A6	A6	A6	A6
A5	A5	A5	A5	A5	A5
A4	A4	A4	A4	A4	A4
A3	A3	A3	A3	A3	A3
A2	A2	A2	A2	A2	A2
A1	A1	A1	A1	A1	A1
A0	A0	A0	A0	A0	A0
O0	O0	O0	O0	O0	O0
O1	O1	O1	O1	O1	O1
O2	O2	O2	O2	O2	O2
GND	GND	GND	GND	GND	GND

DIP NM27C128

Pin	Signal	Pin	Signal
1	V_{PP}	28	V_{CC}
2	A12	27	$\overline{PGM}$
3	A7	26	A13
4	A6	25	A8
5	A5	24	A9
6	A4	23	A11
7	A3	22	$\overline{OE}$
8	A2	21	A10
9	A1	20	$\overline{CE}$
10	A0	19	O7
11	O0	18	O6
12	O1	17	O5
13	O2	16	O4
14	GND	15	O3

27C256	27C512	27C010	27C020	27C040	27C080
		V_{CC}	V_{CC}	V_{CC}	V_{CC}
		$\overline{PGM}$	$\overline{PGM}$	A18	A18
V_{CC}	V_{CC}	XX	A17	A17	A17
A14	A14	A14	A14	A14	A14
A13	A13	A13	A13	A13	A13
A8	A8	A8	A8	A8	A8
A9	A9	A9	A9	A9	A9
A11	A11	A11	A11	A11	A11
$\overline{OE}$	$\overline{OE}/V_{PP}$	$\overline{OE}$	$\overline{OE}$	$\overline{OE}$	$\overline{OE}/V_{PP}$
A10	A10	A10	A10	A10	A10
$\overline{CE}$	$\overline{CE}/\overline{PGM}$	$\overline{CE}$	$\overline{CE}$	$\overline{CE}/\overline{PGM}$	$\overline{CE}/\overline{PGM}$
O7	O7	O7	O7	O7	O7
O6	O6	O6	O6	O6	O6
O5	O5	O5	O5	O5	O5
O4	O4	O4	O4	O4	O4
O3	O3	O3	O3	O3	O3

Mode Selection

The modes of operation of NM27C128 listed in Table I. A single 5V power supply is required in the read mode. All inputs are TTL levels except for V_{PP} and A9 for device signature.

TABLE I. Modes Selection

Mode \ Pins	$\overline{CE}$	$\overline{OE}$	$\overline{PGM}$	V_{PP}	V_{CC}	Outputs
Read	V_{IL}	V_{IL}	V_{IH}	V_{CC}	5.0V	D_{OUT}
Output Disable	X	V_{IH}	V_{IH}	V_{CC}	5.0V	High-Z
Standby	V_{IH}	X	X	V_{CC}	5.0V	High-Z
Programming	V_{IL}	V_{IH}	V_{IL}	12.75V	6.25V	D_{IN}
Program Verify	V_{IL}	V_{IL}	V_{IH}	12.75V	6.25V	D_{OUT}
Program Inhibit	V_{IH}	X	X	12.75V	6.25V	High-Z

Note 1: X can be V_{IL} or V_{IH}.

Figure 16.34 – NM27C128Q200 (16k×8) UV erasable CMOS PROM (*Courtesy of National Semiconductor*)

16.7 MORE COMPLEX CIRCUITS

We now briefly present some of the more complex digital integrated circuits. We concentrate on those that are used to perform mathematical operations.

16.7.1 Arithmetic Logic Unit (ALU)

Connection Diagram

Pin name	Pin	Pin	Pin name
$\overline{B0}$	1	24	V_{CC}
$\overline{A0}$	2	23	$\overline{A1}$
S3	3	22	$\overline{B1}$
S2	4	21	$\overline{A2}$
S1	5	20	$\overline{B2}$
S0	6	19	$\overline{A3}$
Cn	7	18	$\overline{B3}$
M	8	17	$\overline{G}$
$\overline{F0}$	9	16	Cn+4
$\overline{F1}$	10	15	$\overline{P}$
$\overline{F2}$	11	14	A=B
GND	12	13	$\overline{F3}$

Pin Descriptions

Pin Name	Description
$\overline{A0}$–$\overline{A3}$, $\overline{B0}$–$\overline{B3}$	Operand Inputs (Active LOW)
S0–S3	Function Select Inputs
M	Mode Control Input
Cn	Carry Input
$\overline{F0}$–$\overline{F3}$	Function Outputs (Active LOW)
A = B	Comparator Output
$\overline{G}$	Carry Generate Output (Active LOW)
$\overline{P}$	Carry Propagate Output (Active LOW)
C_{n+4}	Carry Output

Function Table

Mode Select Inputs				Active LOW Inputs & Outputs		Active HIGH Inputs & Outputs	
				Logic	Arithmetic (Note 2)	Logic	Arithmetic (Note 2)
S3	S2	S1	S0	(M = H)	(M = L) (C_n = L)	(M = H)	(M = L) (C_n = H)
L	L	L	L	$\overline{A}$	A minus 1	$\overline{A}$	A
L	L	L	H	$\overline{AB}$	AB minus 1	$\overline{A}+\overline{B}$	A + B
L	L	H	L	$\overline{A}+\overline{B}$	A$\overline{B}$ minus 1	$\overline{A}$B	A + $\overline{B}$
L	L	H	H	Logic 1	minus 1	Logic 0	minus 1
L	H	L	L	$\overline{A}+\overline{B}$	A plus (A + $\overline{B}$)	$\overline{AB}$	A plus A$\overline{B}$
L	H	L	H	$\overline{B}$	AB plus (A + $\overline{B}$)	$\overline{B}$	(A +B) plus A$\overline{B}$
L	H	H	L	$\overline{A}\oplus\overline{B}$	A minus B minus 1	A ⊕ B	A minus B minus 1
L	H	H	H	A + $\overline{B}$	A + $\overline{B}$	A$\overline{B}$	A$\overline{B}$ minus 1
H	L	L	L	$\overline{A}$B	A plus (A + B)	$\overline{A}$ + B	A plus AB
H	L	L	H	A ⊕ B	A plus B	A ⊕ B	A plus B
H	L	H	L	B	A$\overline{B}$ plus (A + B)	B	(A + $\overline{B}$) plus AB
H	L	H	H	A + B	A + B	AB	AB minus 1
H	H	L	L	Logic 0	A plus A (Note 1)	Logic 1	A plus A (Note 1)
H	H	L	H	A$\overline{B}$	AB plus A	A + $\overline{B}$	(A + B) plus A
H	H	H	L	AB	A$\overline{B}$ minus A	A + B	(A + $\overline{B}$) plus A
H	H	H	H	A	A	A	A minus 1

H = HIGH Voltage Level
L = LOW Voltage Level

Note 1: Each bit is shifted to the next more significant position

Note 2: Arithmetic operations expressed in 2s complement notation

Figure 16.35 – Arithmetic logic unit (*Courtesy of Fairchild Semiconductor*)

The Arithmetic Logic Unit (ALU) performs logic or arithmetic operations. We examine the DM93S41 as a typical example. The pin diagram and function table for this IC is shown in Figure 16.35.

Circuits of this type perform 16 binary arithmetic operations on two 4-bit words as shown in the table of Figure 16.35. These operations are selected by the three function-select lines (S0, S1 and S2). The 16 possible configurations of the select lines each lead to a form of addition, subtraction, exclusive OR and multiplication (AND). These functions are provided in various combinations, with and without carry bits.

In addition to its utility as an arithmetic processor, the ALU can also be used as a digital comparator. This is done by placing the ALU in the subtract mode so one input is subtracted from the other. The IC is then configured to test whether this difference is positive, negative, or zero.

This circuit has been designed to incorporate most of the requirements that a design engineer may desire for arithmetic operations, and also to provide 8 possible functions of two Boolean variables without the need for external circuitry. The Boolean logic functions are selected by use of the four function-select inputs, and with the mode-control input (M) at HIGH to disable the internal carry operation. The logic functions include AND, OR and exclusive-OR, as shown in the table of Figure 16.35.

16.7.2 Full Adders

A full adder is a circuit that forms the arithmetic sum of three input bits, as shown in the circuit of Figure 16.36. This circuit has three inputs and two outputs. Two of the input variables, denoted A_i and B_i, represent the two significant bits to be added. The third input, C_i, represents the carry from the previous lower significant position addition operation. Two outputs are necessary because the arithmetic sum of three binary digits ranges in value from 0 to 3, thus requiring two bits. The two outputs are designated S (for sum) and C (for carry).

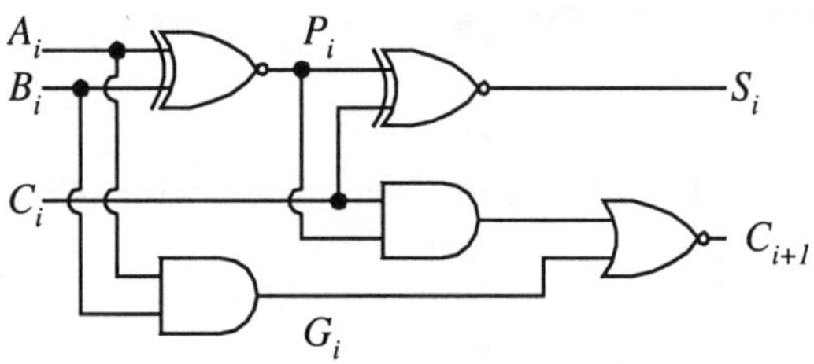

Figure 16.36 – Full-adder

16.7.3 Look-Ahead Carry Generators

When two numbers are added together, we assume that the numbers are immediately available for computation at the same time. However, with digital circuits the signals must propagate through gates before the correct level is available at the output terminals. Rather than wait for the signals to propagate through a group of adders, we consider two new variables defined as follows. The carry generate, G_i, is defined by,

$$G_i = A_i B_i \tag{16.3}$$

The carry propagate, P_i, is defined by,

$$P_i = A_i \oplus B_i \tag{16.4}$$

The sum, S_i and the carry, C_{i+1}, can be written as

$$S_i = A_i \oplus B_i \oplus C_i = P_i \oplus C_i$$

(16.5)

$$C_{i+1} = G_i + P_i C_i$$

Look-ahead carry generator circuits are used to speed up the operation of a group of adders. The DM74S182 look-ahead carry generator IC is illustrated in Figure 16.37.

Connection Diagram

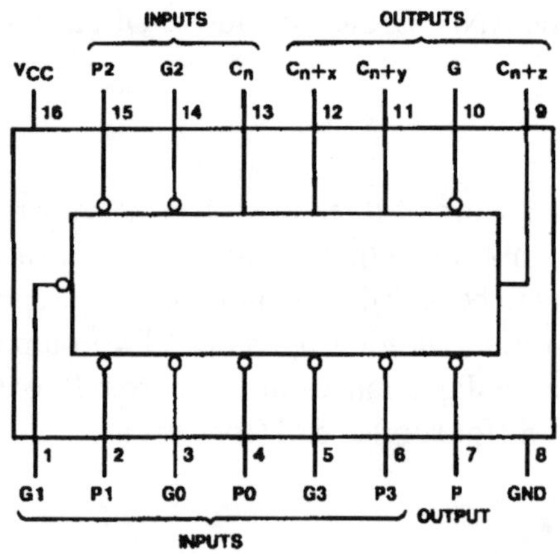

Pin Designations

Designation	Pin Nos.	Function
G0, G1, G2, G3	3, 1, 14, 5	Active LOW Carry Generate Inputs
P0, P1, P2, P3	4, 2, 15, 6	Active LOW Carry Propagate Inputs
C_n	13	Carry Input
C_{n+x}, C_{n+y}, C_{n+z}	12, 11, 9	Carry Outputs
G	10	Active LOW Carry Generate Output
P	7	Active LOW Carry Propagate Output
V_{CC}	16	Supply Voltage
GND	8	Ground

Figure 16.37 – 74S182 Look-ahead Carry Generator (*Courtesy of Fairchild Semiconductor*)

This is a high speed look-ahead carry generator capable of anticipating a carry across four binary adders or a group of adders. The IC looks across all four individual binary summation operations and generates an overall carry generate, *G*, and carry propagate, *P*. That is, rather than wait for the four individual binary operations to be completed before passing information on to the next IC in an arithmetic operation, the IC examines the four individual operations and develops the resulting carry information before the arithmetic is completed.

16.7.4 Magnitude Comparator

The comparison of two numbers is an operation that determines if one number is greater than, less than, or equal to the other number. A magnitude comparator is a circuit that compares two numbers, A and B, to determine their relative magnitudes. The outcome of the comparison is specified by three binary variables that indicate whether A > B, A = B, or A < B.

The comparator follows a bit-by-bit procedure to compare the two numbers. Suppose we are dealing with two 4-bit numbers, designated $A_3A_2A_1A_0$ and $B_3B_2B_1B_0$. The two numbers are equal if A_i=B_i for all i between 0 and 3. To see if A > B, we first examine the most significant bits, A_3 and B_3. If these are unequal (one is 1 and the other is 0), the comparator need look no further. If they are equal, the comparator must look at the next set of bits. The 74LS85 is an example of a magnitude comparator, and the truth table is illustrated in Figure 16.38.

Function Table

Comparing Inputs				Cascading Inputs			Outputs		
A3, B3	A2, B2	A1, B1	A0, B0	A > B	A < B	A = B	A > B	A < B	A = B
A3 > B3	X	X	X	X	X	X	H	L	L
A3 < B3	X	X	X	X	X	X	L	H	L
A3 = B3	A2 > B2	X	X	X	X	X	H	L	L
A3 = B3	A2 < B2	X	X	X	X	X	L	H	L
A3 = B3	A2 = B2	A1 > B1	X	X	X	X	H	L	L
A3 = B3	A2 = B2	A1 < B1	X	X	X	X	L	H	L
A3 = B3	A2 = B2	A1 = B1	A0 > B0	X	X	X	H	L	L
A3 = B3	A2 = B2	A1 = B1	A0 < B0	X	X	X	L	H	L
A3 = B3	A2 = B2	A1 = B1	A0 = B0	H	L	L	H	L	L
A3 = B3	A2 = B2	A1 = B1	A0 = B0	L	H	L	L	H	L
A3 = B3	A2 = B2	A1 = B1	A0 = B0	L	L	H	L	L	H
A3 = B3	A2 = B2	A1 = B1	A0 = B0	X	X	H	L	L	H
A3 = B3	A2 = B2	A1 = B1	A0 = B0	H	H	L	L	L	L
A3 = B3	A2 = B2	A1 = B1	A0 = B0	L	L	L	H	H	L

H = HIGH Level, L = LOW Level, X = Don't Care

Figure 16.38 – 74LS85 4-bit magnitude comparator (*Courtesy of Fairchild Semiconductor*)

The function table in the figure expands on the discussion above. For example, the first row in the table indicates that if $A_3 > B_3$, we need look no further. The A > B output goes high, and the other two go low.

If we wish to compare words of length greater than 4 bits, we can cascade these ICs together. For example for 8-bit comparisons, we cascade two ICs together. The inputs to the second (most significant) IC include the two 4-bit numbers plus the three outputs from the first IC. This is included in the function table. Note that as long as the four most significant bits are not the same (the first 8 rows in the table), there is no need to even look at the outputs from the previous IC. Therefore, the cascading inputs are marked as "X" for don't care or irrelevant inputs.

16.8 PROGRAMMABLE ARRAY LOGIC (PAL)

A basic knowledge of digital engineering combined with the practical material presented so far in this chapter should be sufficient to design digital systems using the basic logic packages. It is not unusual for a design to require several hundred logic circuits. For example, the video games of the early 1980s required about 150 ICs to control a simple simulated sport such as tennis. Although the cost of individual ICs is quite low, these systems become expensive both due to manufacturing costs associated with wiring all of the ICs together and because the large number of circuits requires an unreasonably large amount of space.

As integrated circuit technology developed, circuits became smaller and versatility increased until the ultimate goal of full programmability was reached. The microprocessor represents a major breakthrough in versatility and reduction of manufacturing complexity.

A user-programmable array of logic gates can be used to replace a number of separate packages with a single IC. The array is known as programmable array logic (PAL). It uses Schottky components so it operates at high speed. With this IC, we can implement registers, flip-flops and basic logic. The PAL typically is packaged in a single 20-pin DIP and it can be used to replace between 4 and 12 SSI and MSI packages.

The basic logic structure of a PAL includes a programmable AND array that feeds a fixed OR array. The ICs are available in sizes ranging from 10×8 (10 input, 8 output) to 16×2. The wide variety of input/output formats allows the PAL to replace many different-sized blocks of combinational logic with a single package.

16.9 INTRODUCTION TO PROBLEMS

The problems that conclude this chapter are generally quite challenging, and each has no single correct solution. In fact, as time goes on and new and better devices are developed, the possible solutions to these problems will improve.

In formulating these problems, we have tried to pick situations for which you now have the necessary tools to at least make an attempt at the solution. There are, however, just a few loose ends we would like to tie up now to enlarge your repertoire of available tools.

In this section, we present several techniques that you will find useful in designing the systems specified in the problems. In particular, we consider the following:

- Methods of generating random numbers
- Measurement of mechanical angle or velocity
- The Hall-effect switch
- Use of timing windows.

16.9.1 Generating Random Numbers

In game-related situations, you will find it necessary to generate random numbers. Fortunately, this is a simple task with a number of possible approaches. One of the simplest ways to generate a random number is as shown in Figure 16.39.

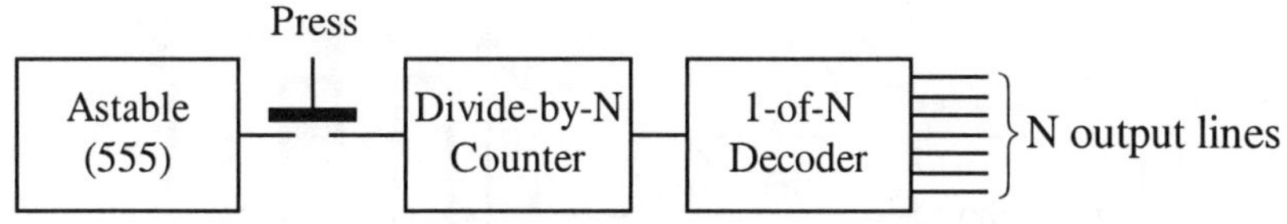

Figure 16.39 – Random number generator

A 555 astable clock is run at a high frequency. The output of the 555 is used to select one output line of a decoder. When the signal from the 555 to the decoder is interrupted, the decoder stops and one output line is high. All output lines of the decoder have an equal probability of going high. Since the frequency of the 555 is high compared to the other frequencies in the system (e.g., your reaction time if you are pushing a button), the instant at which the timer stops is random.

16.9.2 Measurement of Mechanical Angle or Velocity

You will often need ways of providing inputs to digital systems from mechanical devices, such as shaft angle or velocity. A variable reluctance pickup is a device for providing such a signal to a digital system. Figure 16.40 illustrates one example of the use of this pickup device in conjunction with a rotating gear.

As the gear tooth, which is made of magnetic material, moves past the magnet, a voltage is generated at the output of the coils wrapped about the magnetic circuit. The resulting output pulse train is noisy and the voltage levels are generally incompatible with digital circuits because it is so small. The signal must therefore be conditioned.

The conditioning of the signal consists of amplifying it to a level compatible with the particular digital logic being used, and then applying it to a Schmitt trigger, as shown in Figure 16.41. The output is then a zero to +5 V (in the case of TTL) signal that is compatible with the digital circuitry.

An optoelectronic detector used in an interrupted reflector module can count the number of revolutions of a shaft. Such a device is discussed in Section 5.7.4.

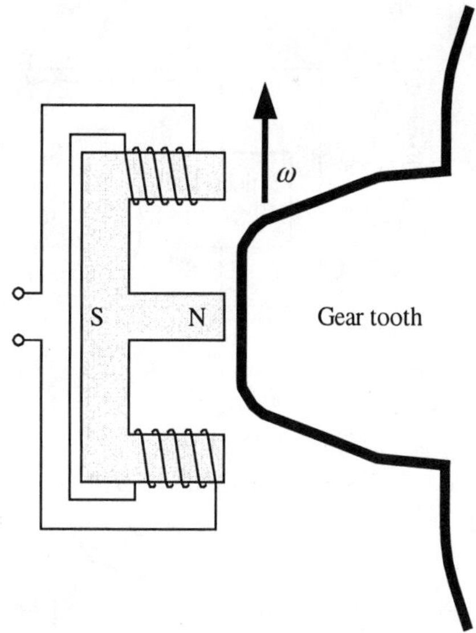

Figure 16.40 – Variable reluctance pickup

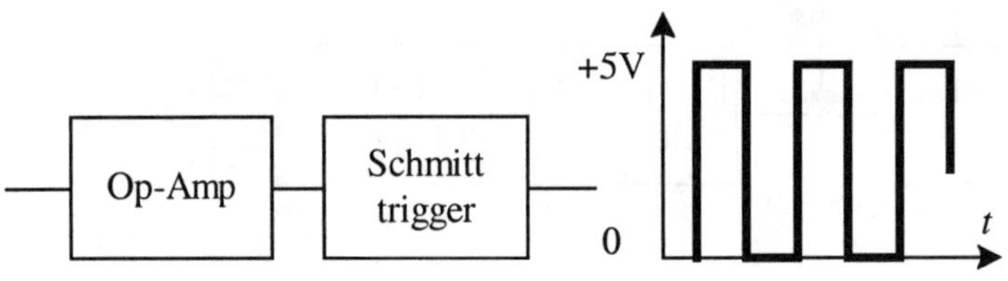

Figure 16.41 – Signal conditioning

16.9.3 The Hall-Effect Switch

Electronic design for instrumentation systems requires measurement of numerous physical properties. We often deal with magnets in the process of position sensing, thickness determination, weight measurement, speed control and pressure monitoring. We must be able to sense a magnetic field. This can be done with a Silicon Hall-effect switch. The TL170C, as shown in Figure 16.42, is one example of such a switch.

This is a low-cost magnetically operated switch which is composed of a Hall-effect sensor, signal conditioning and hysteresis functions, and an output transistor. The outputs of these circuits are usually compatible with the digital ICs, so little, if any, signal conditioning is required.

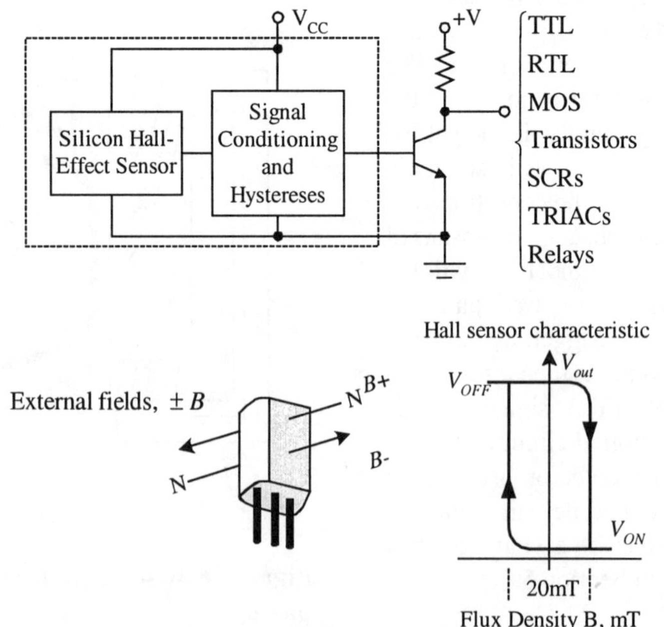

Figure 16.42 - Hall-effect generator

Hall-effect switches are used in security systems. For example, we can use a normally-off Hall-effect switch as an open door sensor. The switch is installed in the door frame and a permanent magnet is positioned in the door. While the door is closed, the magnet keeps the Hall-effect switch ON, and there is current in the door-sensing circuit. When the door is opened, the magnet moves away from the sensor, and the Hall- effect switch returns to the OFF condition, thus triggering an alarm. Wires are connected only to the door frame, and not in the door. As an additional security feature, the alarm sounds if any connecting wire is cut open.

16.9.4 Use of Timing Windows

We have used a window in the solution of several design problems. Before moving to the design problems at the end of this chapter, we present three uses of a window for various electronic system applications.

1. Use of a window to measure frequency or velocity - If we hold a window high for a fixed time, t_w, we will count the number of pulses in a signal with unknown frequency. We accomplish this by ANDing the window with the pulse train of unknown frequency, as shown in Figure 16.43(a).

   The output of the AND gate yields the number of pulses (of the signal with unknown frequency) that occur in the time period, t_w. As shown in Figure 16.43(a), the ideal window is high for the time, t_w, and low for a short time, $0.1t_w$. The trailing edge of the window is used to set the latch and then clear the counter in anticipation of the next time the window goes high.

2. Use of a window to measure wavelength or 1/f - This mode, which is shown in Figure 16.43(b), uses the signal with unknown wavelength as the window, and a higher fixed frequency signal as the input. These are ANDed with the result that the number of pulses of fixed frequency is proportional to the length of time that the window is held open. Hence, the number of output pulses is proportional to the wavelength.

3. Use of a window to produce a multiplication of input pulses - In applications where the number of pulses coming from the sensor is insufficient to drive the counter, we must multiply the number of pulses by a constant. Suppose, for example, we require 10 pulses each time we receive one pulse from the instrumentation. We set up a window so that with one pulse as input to the system, ten pulses are generated at the output. This is accomplished by letting the input pulses trigger the 555 monostable of Figure 16.43(c), to provide a window of duration T. We design a 555 astable in such a manner that during the time T, precisely 10 pulses are produced at the output. The window of period T is ANDed with the pulse train of the 555 astable to produce the 10 desired pulses for each input pulse.

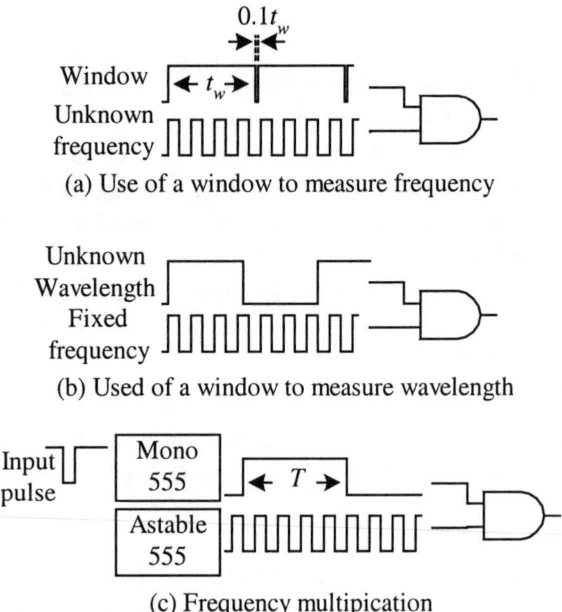

(a) Use of a window to measure frequency

(b) Used of a window to measure wavelength

(c) Frequency multipication

Figure 16.43 – Use of windows

16.10 CONCLUDING REMARKS

The design process probably appears overwhelming if this is your first exposure to it. It is important to realize that this is an area where practice is extremely important. You should also know that help is available in the form of data books and application notes (available on the Web), other engineers who may be working in the same company with you, your professors, books, magazines and technical publications. While your skill is an important asset in effective design, it is also critical that you be knowledgeable regarding new developments in the field. This requires extensive reading and attendance at meetings of professional societies. By being organized in methods, willing to research information, and by writing down the steps followed to produce a working prototype, you can solve many difficult problems.

With this assortment of tools combined with what you have learned in this book, you are now ready to approach the wide array of challenging electronic system design problems. After solving some of these problems, we hope you will be motivated to invent your own problems. You need only examine your daily environment to formulate a virtually unlimited list of projects.

Good luck in this exciting undertaking! Don't become discouraged, no matter how difficult the task appears. And always strive to produce results that help make life better and improve humankind.

PROBLEMS

Section 16.1:

16.1 Compare the 4028 and the 7442 decoders.

16.2 Contrast the 74150 TTL and 74C150 CMOS Data Selector/Multiplexer.

Section 16.2:

16.3 Draw a diagram showing the connection of a CD4511 to drive a 7-segment LED display.

16.4 Design a system to drive four 7-segment LED displays with 74143 drivers.

Section 16.4:

16.5 Use a CD4047 as an astable multivibrator to operate at 50 kHz.

16.6 Design an instrument to measure the frequency of a sinusoidal signal over the range of 1.0 Hz to 9.0 kHz. The voltage level of the input signal is 10 V rms. Display the output on two 7-segment LED displays, as shown in Figure P16.6.

Figure P16.6

16.7 Use the circuit of Figure 16.27 in the design of a device to measure the frequency of the ac power line. Select $t_2 - t_1$ to be 10 seconds and use the 74160 decade counter.

16.8 Convert the 74161 binary counter to a decade counter.

Section 16.5:

16.9 Design a VCO to operate at a base output frequency of 10 kHz. Use a 74LS124 and calculate the maximum obtainable output frequency variation.

16.10 Design a 0-5 V pulse train generator to develop the following continuously variable frequency ranges:
 (a) 100 Hz to 1 kHz
 (b) 1 kHz to 10 kHz
 (c) 10 kHz to 100 kHz
Use a *JK* flip-flop to produce an output that is symmetrical; that is, the time high is the same as the time low.

Comprehensive Design Problems:

Use TTL or CMOS integrated circuits and/or discrete elements in each of the following problems. Your final design should include a written explanation of how the system operates and a schematic diagram. Include the component values used and the type numbers of the integrated circuits and discrete elements. Assume that any power supply voltages you need are available, so do not design the power supply for these problems. Use as few components as possible.

16.11 Design a keychain equipped with an electronic system that will help locate your keys if they are lost. The device is to emit a 1 kHz tone for 30 seconds whenever you loudly clap your hands together. Use a duty cycle of 0.33 for the 1 kHz oscillator, and provide 0.25 W into the speaker. The crystal microphone produces a 300 mV peak-to-peak signal when you clap your hands together within 20 feet of the key chain. Calculate all resistor and capacitor values and specify the type numbers for the ICs used in the design.

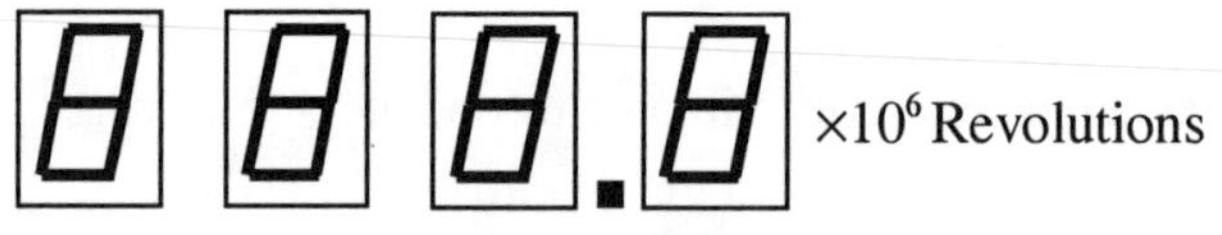

Figure P16.12

16.12 Design an electronic system to measure the total number of revolutions of an engine. This electronic system uses the conditioned pulse train from Problem 14.20 as the input, which is shown in Figure P14.20. The output of this electronic system is displayed on four 7-segment LED displays. This display is illustrated in Figure P16.12 and shows total revolutions in 10^6 revolutions. Remember that each pulse corresponds to 2 revolutions of the engine. Be sure to provide battery power to the critical parts of this system so that the total number of revolutions displayed is not lost during a power failure.

16.13 Design a pair of digital dice that uses the LED pattern shown in Figure P16.13. The dice are "rolled" by pressing a button, and the digital dice box displays a random number between 1 and 6, as shown in the figure.

Figure P16.13

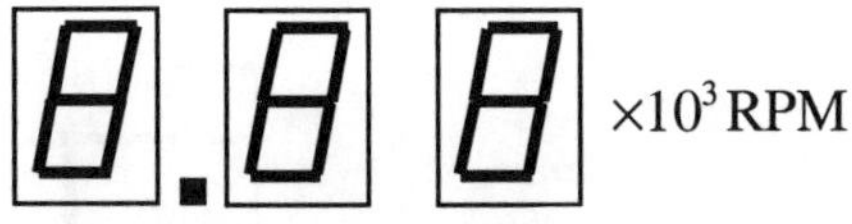

Figure P16.14

16.14 Design an rpm meter to display engine speed, which ranges in value from 0 to 6000 rpm. The input to this system is a pulse train from Problem 14.20, which is shown in Figure P14.20(b). This conditioned pulse train is TTL compatible, and each pulse corresponds to two revolutions of the engine. The output is shown on three 7-segment LED displays, as shown in Figure P16.14.

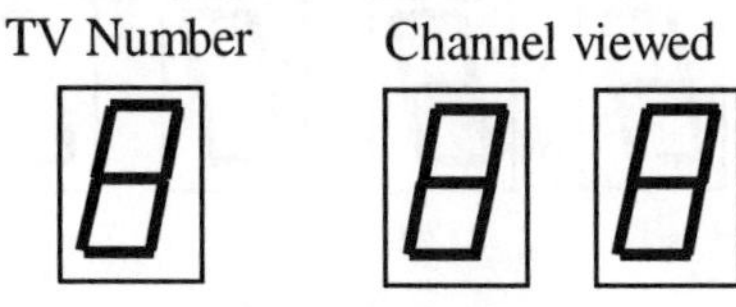

Figure P16.15

16.15 Design a system to measure the audience viewing interest in the various TV channels. To sample which channels the audience is viewing, the TV channel selector is instrumented. Eight families are selected to have their TV receivers fitted with potentiometers. The signals from the eight instrumented TV receivers are sent to a central station. The voltage on each of the lines is identical to the channel being viewed. For example, if Channel 4 is being viewed, the voltage on that line is 4 V. If the set is off, the voltage is 0 V. Each of the eight TV receivers is continuously sampled for 8 seconds each. While the receiver is being sampled, a display, consisting of three 7-segment LED displays, reads the TV family number and the channel being viewed. The display is shown in Figure P16.15. Use a CD4051 single 8 channel analog multiplexer.

16.16 Design a system that will count the number of cars in a parking lot. The maximum capacity of the lot is 99 cars. Each time a car enters the parking lot, an entrance gate opens. When the gate opens, a pulse appears on the "IN" line, as shown in Figure P16.16(a). Each time a car leaves, an exit gate opens and a pulse appears on the "OUT" line, as shown in Figure P16.16(b). These are two separate lines. Use two 7-segment LEDs to continuously show the number of cars in the parking lot. When the lot is full (99 cars in the lot) light 4 LEDs displaying the word "FULL".

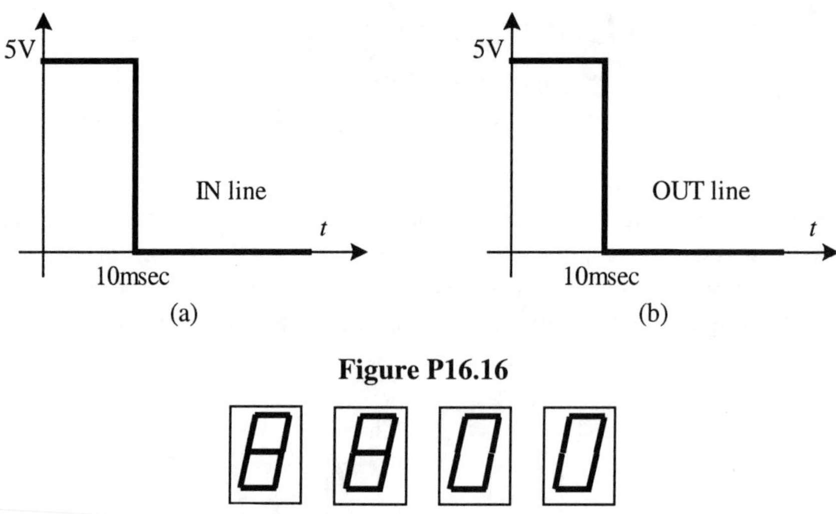

Figure P16.16

Figure P16.17

16.17 Design a tachometer for your automobile engine which operates in the range of 0 to 5000 RPM. A Hall-effect generator provides 10 pulses for each revolution of the engine. The pulses are 100 mv in magnitude so they must be signal conditioned. The output of this tachometer is displayed on two 7-segment LEDs with only the first two digits significant, as shown in Figure P17.20. Divide the design into three parts, as follows:

(a) Design an electronic circuit to produce 10 pulses per engine revolution, where each pulse is 0 to 5 V in magnitude.

(b) Design a window that will scale the tachometer so that when the engine is rotating at 5000 RPM, the two 7-segment LEDs will read 50. The LEDs are shown in Figure P16.17.

(c) Design a counter and display for the tachometer. Do this by ANDing the input pulse train of part (a) with the window of part (b) and using the appropriate counters, latches, and decoders to display the RPM to 2 significant digits, as shown in Figure P16.17.

16.18 Design an electronic system to measure the frequency of a 0-5 V pulse generator which operates between 10 and 99 Hz. The output of this instrument is displayed on two 7-segment LEDs that read the pulse generator frequency to two significant digits. Conduct this design in two parts. In part (a), you will design the window to obtain the scaling and division by time necessary to measure Hz (cycles per second). In part (b), you will design the counter and the display.

(a) Design a window circuit, the output will be ANDed with the input signal (frequency of 10 to 99 Hz) to be delivered to the counter and display system of part (b). You must scale the window time so that when the input frequency is 25 Hz, the display shows the number 25. You must also deliver the appropriate CLEAR and LATCH signals to the circuit of part (b).

(b) Design a counter and a display system to display the frequency, as provided from part (a), on two 7-segment LEDs. Be sure to include all CLEAR and LATCH signals.

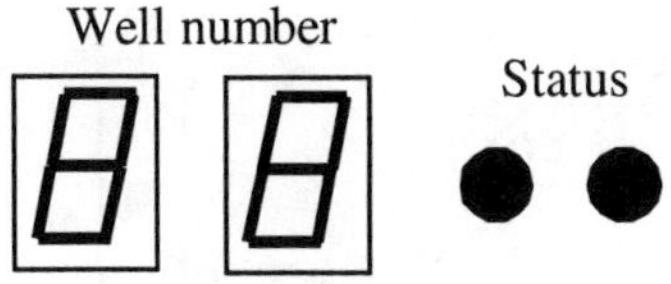

Figure P16.19

16.19 Design an oil well monitoring system to measure the output of a field of 16 oil wells. The output of each well is measured with a flow meter that outputs a binary digital number corresponding to one of the following four flow conditions. Logic 1 corresponds to 5V.

00 - no flow
01 - 33.3% flow
10 - 66.6% flow
11 - 100% flow

The information from all 16 wells is transmitted to a control center where two LEDs and two 7-segment LED displays are used in the format shown in Figure P16.19. The two 7-segment LED displays identify the oil well number (0 to 15) being measured. The two single LEDs indicate the flow information (status). Each oil well is to be sampled and read for 0.1 minutes, once every 1.6 minutes. In addition, when the flow is 00 for any oil well, a 1 kHz tone is sounded when that oil well number is displayed.

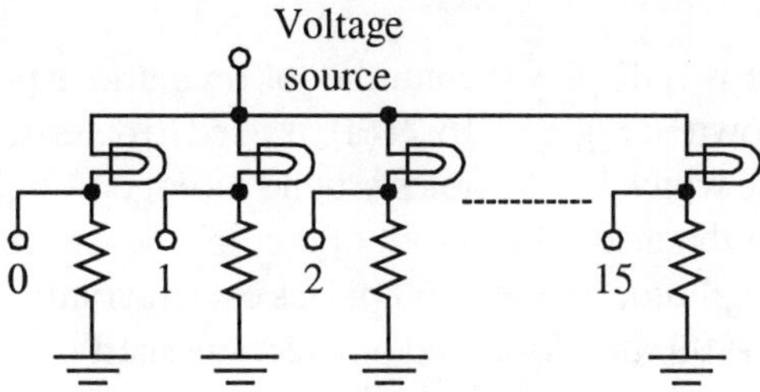

Figure P16.20

16.20 Design a lamp test indicator for a commercial aircraft to test 16 important running and landing lights about the aircraft. Each lamp has a small resistor between the light and ground, as shown in Figure P16.20. When the lamp is operational, the voltage across the resistor is 5 V. When the lamp is not operational, the voltage across the resistor drops to zero. Test each of the lamps for a period of 5 seconds and display the lamp number (0 to 15) on two 7-segment LED displays. Each time a lamp is faulty, sound a 1-kHz tone for the 5 seconds that the faulty lamp is being tested. Power of 1/4 W is sufficient to drive the 8-Ω speaker.

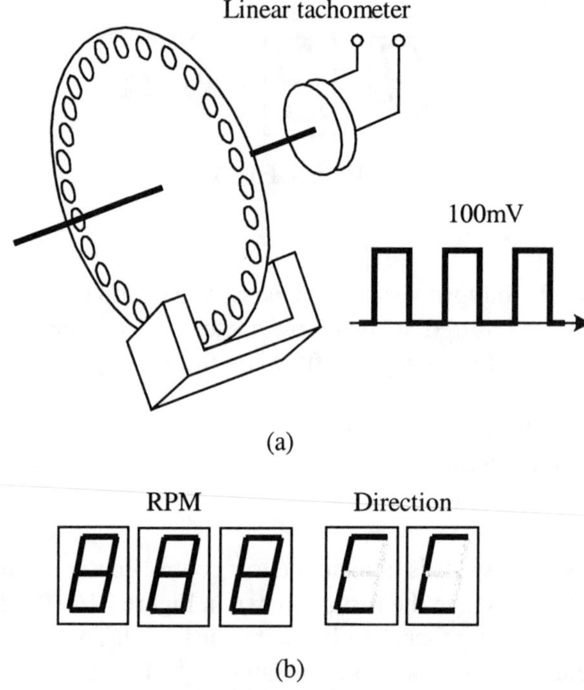

Figure P16.21

16.21 Design a counter that will display the number of revolutions per minute (rpm) of a shaft. The mechanical system, shown in Figure P16.21(a), is used to determine the shaft rpm. Mounted on the shaft is a circular disc which has 60 holes around its edge. A light sensor is interrupted 60 times for each revolution of the disc. The output of the light sensor is a pulse train, as shown in the figure with a 100 mV amplitude and with 60 pulses each revolution. The speed of the shaft is in the range of -999 rpm to +999 rpm. Mounted on the same shaft is an analog tachometer which produces a +5 V signal for clockwise rotation and a -5 V signal for counter-clockwise rotation. The output display comprises five 7-segment LEDs, as shown in Figure P16.21(b). The first three 7-segment LEDs show the value of rpm and the second two 7-segment LEDs show the letter C if the shaft is going clockwise, and CC if the shaft is going counter-clockwise.

(a) Design an electronic system to count the rpm and display the speed in the range of -999 to +999 rpm with the first three 7-segment LEDs, as shown in the figure. Be sure to condition the 100 mV input.

(b) Use the analog tachometer to drive the two 7-segment LEDs which show the direction of rotation.

16.22 Use two 7-segment LEDs in the design of a circuit that shows the most significant digit (MSD) on one 7-segment display, and the "$\times 10^n$" range on another 7-segment display. The input signal is between 1 Hz and 9000 Hz. The reading on this "n-display" would be as follows:

If frequency is 1 to 9, display 0, since the frequency is H10^0.
If frequency is 10 to 99, display 1, since the frequency is H10^1.
If frequency is 100 to 999, display 2, since the frequency is H10^2.
If frequency is 1000 to 9000, display 3, since the frequency is H10^3.

For example, if the frequency is 857, the MSD display would indicate 8 and the H10^n display would show 2.

16.23 Design an electronic circuit that displays the amount of liquid in a large storage tank on one 7-segment display. The display shows the amount of liquid in the tank in percent full from 10% to 90% in 10% increments. Sound a 1 kHz alarm if the liquid level falls below 10% full or exceeds 90% full. The level is measured with a sonar device that provides pulses as shown in Figure P16.23.

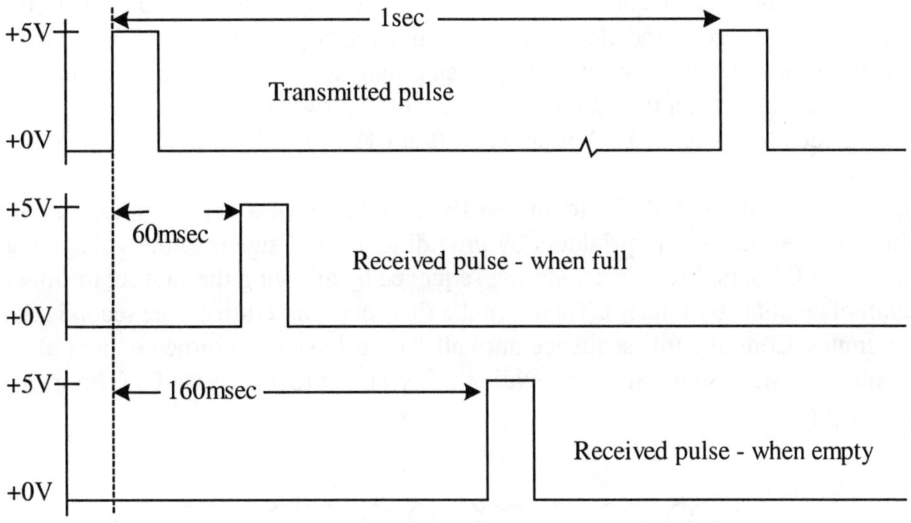

Figure P16.23

16.24 Design a countdown sequencer to time the firing of a sounding rocket. The sequencer should count down from 10 minutes before firing and then keep track of the time after the launch of the rocket according to the following schedule:

10.0 minutes - Start Countdown
7.0 minutes - Transfer to rocket power supply
6.0 minutes - Activate the on-board cooling
4.0 minutes - Transfer to on-board computer
3.0 minutes - Activate firing sequencer
2.0 minutes - Remove external cable
0.0 minutes - Fire

Figure P16.24

After firing, the counter will count up for at least 20 min. Use three 7-segment LED displays to show the time before and after firing to tenths of minutes, and use a digital CMOS switch (such as the 74HC4066) to activate each of the important times in the countdown. The three LED displays are to be arranged as shown in Figure P16.24. Preload a 74190 UP/DOWN decade counter with 10.0 and in the DOWN mode, go through the pre-fire events. When the count reaches 00.0, change the counter to count UP to record time. As a suggestion, use three 74190 decade up/down counters. (A zero on pin 5 makes the counter count up and a makes it count down). An astable 555 operating at 100 Hz can be used for the clock.

16.25 Design a 24-hour clock and a system to control the turn-on and turn-off functions needed in an apartment complex. If the clock reads 14.3 this means 2:18 PM since 3/10 of an hour is 3/10 of 60 minutes which is 18 minutes. For clock timing accuracy, use the 60-Hz line frequency and an opto-isolator. Design the system to activate the following:

1. Turn garden lights on at 18.0 hours and off at 01.1 hours by providing a 5 V signal to a relay.
2. Use a data distributor (74154) to turn on 10 possible sets of water sprinklers (one at a time). Turn on the first set of sprinklers by providing a +5 V signal to the voltage-controlled valve at 4.0 hours. Provide a watering sequence by allowing the first set to flow for one-tenth of an hour (6 minutes). Then turn the first set off and turn on the second set, also for 6 minutes. Continue this sequence until all 10 sets have been turned on and off.
3. Turn the music system on (by providing a 5 V signal to a relay) at 09.0 hours and off at 21.0 hours.

Figure P16.26

16.26 Design a controller to activate a large incandescent advertising sign as shown in Figure P16.26. There are 64 lights around the circumference of the sign, and they are lighted 4 at a time in a sequence rotating as follows:

	Lights ON
1st second	0, 16, 32, 48
2nd second	1, 17, 33, 49
3rd second	2, 18, 34, 50

Each light is to remain on for 1 second. The letters are formed by an array of lights and are lighted in sequence as follows:

	Letter ON
1st interval	C
2nd interval	CA
3rd interval	CAS
4th interval	CASI
5th interval	CASIN
6th interval	CASINO
7th interval	--------
1st interval	Repeat sequence

Each interval is to be 4 second long. In this design, do not concern yourself with the output power requirements, but only with the electronic design. The output of the electronic design is sufficient to drive one LED for each of the peripheral lights and only one LED to drive each letter C, A, S, I, N, and O.

16.27 Design a pressure altitude hold system for a small commercial aircraft. The system is to operate over the range of 0 to 50,000 ft with a 200 ft resolution. The actual pressure altitude, A, which is measured in feet, is obtained from a digital pressure transducer which outputs an 8-bit binary signal with each binary number equivalent to 200 ft. For example, if the pressure transducer outputs 01101101, the pressure altitude is 109×200 ft = 21,800 ft. The pilot sets the desired altitude, B, in feet, with a three-position switch on the control stick, as shown in Figure P16.27. This three-position switch allows the pilot to increase, by pushing the switch forward, or decrease, by pushing the switch back, the set altitude. The set altitude will remain the same if the pilot's finger is removed from the switch.

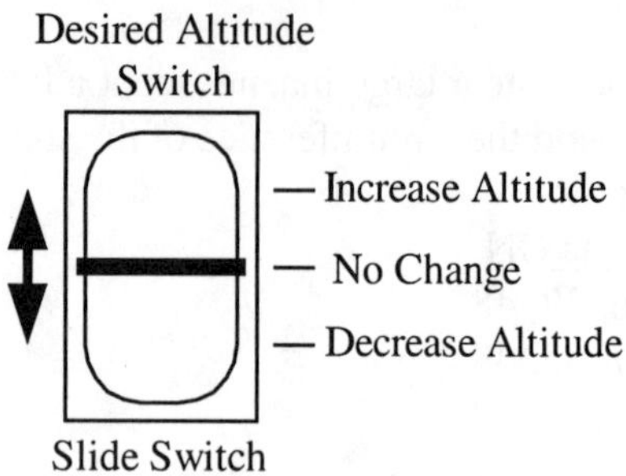

Figure P16.27

Three 7-segment LED displays indicate the set altitude (desired altitude) where the least significant digit corresponds to 200 ft. Compare the actual altitude with the set altitude, and provide a 5 V signal according to the following schedule:

Terminal	A > B	A = B	A < B
Altitude decreases	1	0	0
No change	0	1	0
Altitude increases	0	0	1

16.28 Design a temperature monitoring system for an aircraft engine. Your device must monitor 8 points throughout the engine with the circuit shown in Figure P16.28(a). The voltage, V_{ON}, across the diode is 0.7 V at 25°C = T_1, and this voltage reduces as the temperature increases, as follows:

$\Delta V_{ON} = -2(T_2 - T_1)$ mV with T_1 and T_2 in degrees centigrade. The output is displayed on three 7-segment LEDs as shown in Figure P16.28(b).

A single LED identifies the diode being read and the three 7-segment LEDs read the temperature at the point in question. Each temperature is sampled sequentially and read for 6 sec. An analog multiplexer (74HC4051) is used to sample each of the eight values of voltage. The analog signal from the diode must be conditioned with the op-amp circuit of Figure P16.28(c).

The voltage V_{ON} is

$$V_{ON} = 700 - 2(T - 25) = (750 - 2T) \text{ mV}$$

where T is expressed in degrees Centigrade. The voltage, V_c is

$$V_c = \frac{50}{r + 10} \quad \text{V}$$

where r is in kΩ. The output voltage, V_o from the op- amp is

$$V_{out} = \frac{R}{175\,k\Omega} \cdot \left(V_c - V_{ON}\right)$$

and substituting, we obtain,

$$V_{out} = \frac{-R}{175\,k\Omega}\left(750 - 2T - \frac{50 \times 10^3}{r + 10}\right) \quad \text{mV}$$

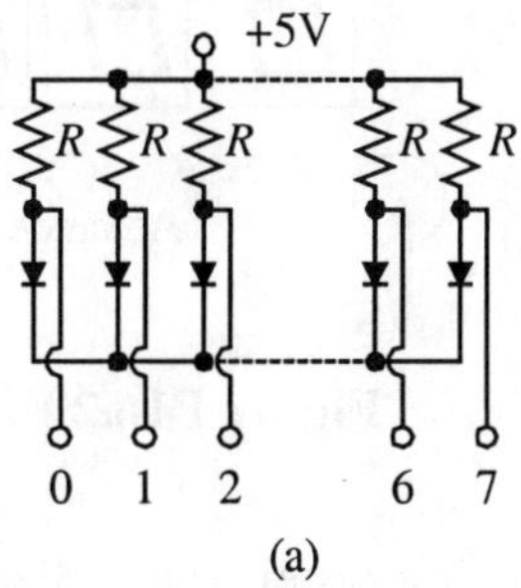

(a)

Temperature location point

Temperature C

(b)

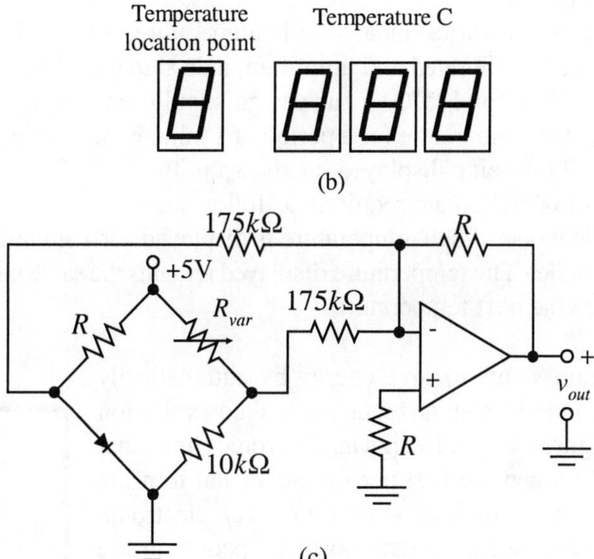

(c)

Figure P16.28

We choose r by letting

$$\frac{50 \times 10^3}{r + 10} - 750 = 0$$

We set the gain by selecting R from the equation,

$$V_{out} = \frac{2R}{100\,k\Omega} \cdot T \quad \text{mV}$$

Use a 3-1/2 digit DVM to output the signal to the LED display.

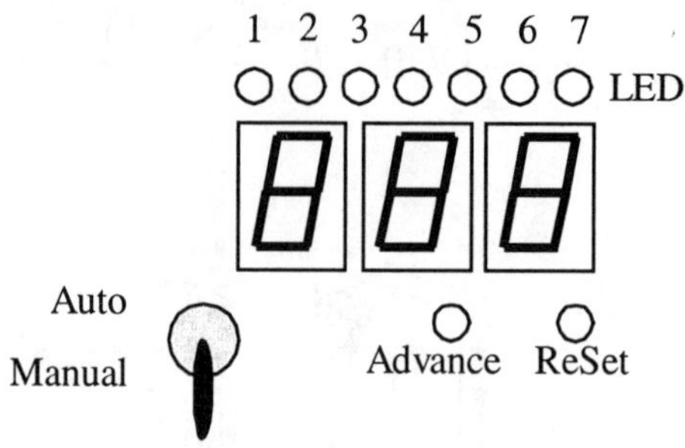

Figure P16.29

16.29 Design a temperature monitoring system that will display seven different temperatures on three 7-segment displays. Seven diodes are used to measure the seven temperatures. The output voltage of each diode, which varies linearly with temperature, is fed into an op-amp. When the op-amp output is properly calibrated and amplified, a dc signal is obtained which ranges from 0.25 V for 25°C to 1.25 V for 125°C. Your design should monitor each of these outputs, in sequence, and display the temperature for a period of 1 minute. Seven single LEDs will indicate which temperature point is being displayed, as shown in Figure P16.29.

Two modes of operation are required, as follows:

(a) Automatic mode - Each temperature is displayed for 1 minute.

(b) Manual mode - The temperature displayed remains the same until the user presses the advance button, to see the next temperature.

16.30 A large museum wants to save energy by automatically turning the lights on and off in an infrequently visited exhibition room, as shown in Figure P16.30. Design an electronic circuit that will turn the lights on when the first person enters and turn the lights off when the last person leaves the room. The electronic system should be able to accommodate up to 99 people in the room at any time. The entrance sensor (and the exit sensor) each consists of a parallel light beam. Assume these sensors normally provide a 0 V output which changes to 5 V when the beam is broken. Provide a reset switch to set the count to 0. Assume that the entrance is narrow enough to allow only one person to enter at a time and that the light beams break only once per person.

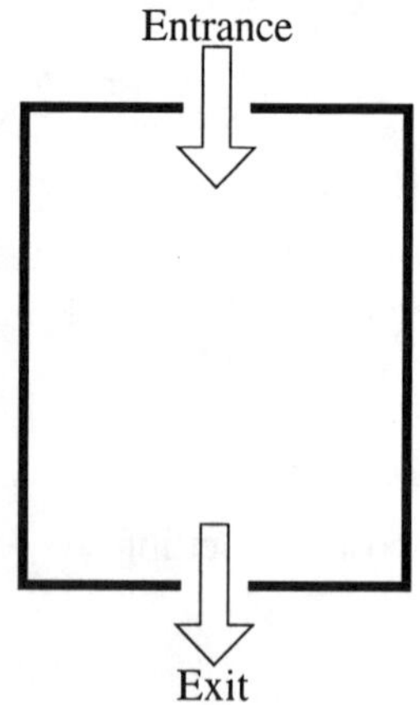

Figure P16.30

16.31 Design a television monitor for a hotel with 14 rooms on each floor. Design the electronic system (for one floor only) to detect when any TV receiver is ON. When the TV is ON, a 5 V signal is delivered to the office from a switch installed on each TV. When the TV is OFF, the signal delivered to the office is 0 V. Each TV is monitored for one minute before passing to the next TV on the floor, and the process continues with each TV being monitored once every 14 minutes. Use the 60-Hz power line for timing.

The readout is comprised of two 7-segment LED displays which indicate the room numbers from 0 to 13, and a single LED which is ON when the TV in that room is ON and OFF when the TV is OFF.

16.32 Design an electronic voting system to be used for Parliament, which consists of 250 members. Each member has two switches, as shown in Figure P16.32(a). The first switch is used to indicate that the member is present at the session. Each member in attendance turns this switch ON, thus sending a 5 V signal to the podium. When the member is absent, the signal at the podium is 0 V. A YES vote, as recorded by throwing the second switch, sends 5 V on the line to the podium, and a NO vote puts 0 V on the line at the podium.

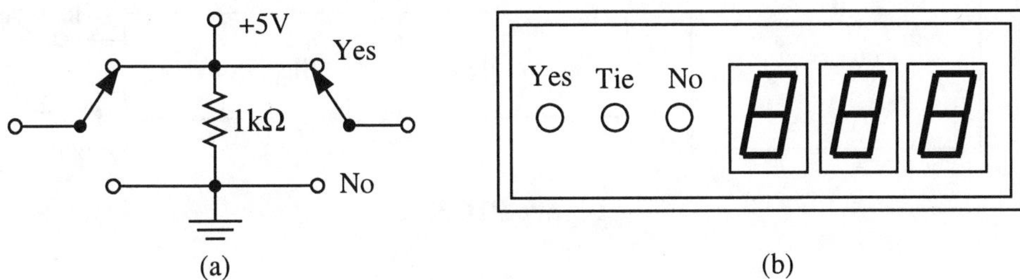

Figure P16.32

The output is composed of three single LEDs, which indicate the result of the vote; i.e., either YES, TIE, or NO. In addition, three 7-segment LED displays indicate the number of members voting. This display is shown in Figure P16.32(b).

The head of Parliament, who stays at the podium, has one switch which is used to disable the circuit. When all members have voted, either YES or NO, the head of Parliament throws the podium switch to ON which latches the results into the display. Once the switch is thrown ON, further vote changes do not change the results that have been latched into the display.

16.33 Design a digital control system to control the angular velocity of the main rotor of a helicopter. The system is shown in Figure P16.33. The rotor speed is displayed on two 7-segment LED displays. The desired rotor speed, which is displayed on two other 7-segment LEDs, is set on the control panel for the range of 500 to 700 rpm. The rotor, which rotates at a speed between 500 and 700 RPM, is connected through a gear train to the turbine engine which rotates at 5,000 to 7000 RPM. The difference between desired velocity, f_d, and the actual velocity, f_a, (in RPM) is used to change the setting of the throttle. Increasing the throttle will increase the speed of the turbine which increases the speed of the rotor. Each pulse into the stepper motor advances (or retards) the throttle setting and hence increases (or decreases) the angular velocity of the rotor.

The actual velocity, f_a, is generated with a 500 tooth iron gear attached to the engine shaft. This gear is used with a variable reluctance pick off, which produces a 100 mV peak-to-peak pulse train. Each time the rotor rotates one revolution, 5000 pulses are generated at the output.

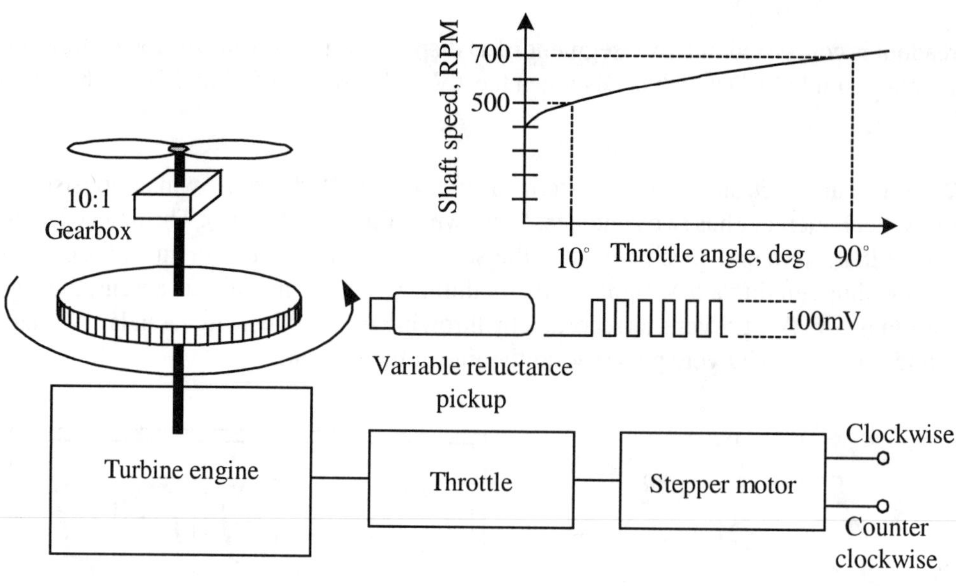

Figure P16.33

16.34 An experimental windmill must have its blade RPM monitored and displayed. The expected operating range is 60 to 240 RPM. A 100-tooth iron gear is attached to the blade shaft and is sensed by a variable-reluctance pickup, which provides a +100 mV pulse as each tooth passes the sensor.

(a) The circuit should process the signal from the sensor and display the speed of the windmill in RPM using three 7-segment LED displays.

(b) The circuit should energize a 400 Hz alarm if the RPM exceeds 240 RPM. Assume that the IC output can directly drive a small speaker.

16.35 Design a digital control system to precisely measure the error in angular velocity of a large centrifuge. This large centrifuge rotates at a precise angular velocity and is used to apply acceleration to large objects. This is an A-V-E (angular-velocity-error) indicator. The output comprises five 7-segment LED displays to yield the error velocity, ω_E (in rpm) to three decimal places. The A-V-E indicator is used to detect the error in angular velocity of the centrifuge. The large arm is to rotate at 60 RPM, and the motor rotates at 6000 rpm. An accurate reference velocity, ω_R, is obtained from a crystal oscillator (temperature controlled) that produces a 1 MHz pulse train. The actual velocity, ω_a is generated with a 500 tooth iron gear that is attached to the motor shaft and is sensed with a variable reluctance pick up. This produces a 100 mV pulse train with a frequency of ω_a. Use an UP-DOWN counter and two identical windows. First, up-count ω_R during a window period, then down-count ω_a during an identical window period. Assuming that $\omega_R > \omega_a$, the count left after the end of the second window is the error in revolutions per minute.

16.36 Use a comparator in the design of a speed control system for your automobile. The throttle is positioned with a stepper motor that operates as shown in Figure P16.36. The desired speed is set by depressing a switch on the steering wheel. This switch causes two 7-segment LED displays to advance and to indicate the set speed. When the switch is released, a latch holds this speed as the desired speed of your automobile. When the display reaches 80 mph, it resets to zero. The actual speed is taken from the engine distributor which outputs 8 pulses for each 2 revolutions of the engine. In DRIVE gear, the ratio of engine speed to forward velocity is given by the following equation:

$$\text{Ratio} = \frac{1000 \text{ rpm}}{25 \text{ mph}} = 40 \text{ rpm/mph}$$

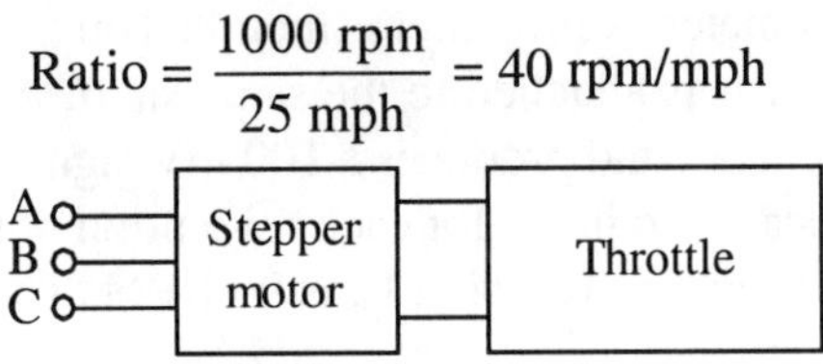

Terminal	A	B	C	
	1	0	0	Engine speed increases
	0	1	0	No change in engine speed
	0	0	1	Engine speed decreases

Figure P16.36

In the design, include a disable capability when the brake pedal is depressed, and provide an ON/OFF switch.

16.37 Design an electronic system to measure the rate at which your heart beats. The system is mounted on a stationary bicycle, so you are able to use the 60-Hz power line rather than battery for timing purposes. The device must read the heart rate from 150 to 250 beats per minute.

The heart rate is measured with an infrared sensor that produces a 100 mV pulse each time that the heart beats. This sensor is attached to the index finger of your hand. These pulses are not clean pulses, so they must be signal conditioned. The readout is comprised of three 7-segment LED displays which read the heart rate in beats per minute.

16.38 Design a miles-per-gallon indicator to be used on an automobile. Two inputs are available as follows:
(a) Odometer Signal - This produces a 5 V pulse for every tenth of a mile traveled.
(b) Fuel Tank Signal - The fuel tank is instrumented so that a 5 V pulse is produced each time the fuel reduces by 0.1 gallon.

The output comprises two 7-segment LED displays which display miles per gallon to the nearest mile per gallon.

16.39 Design a wind velocity meter. A propeller is mounted on a ball bearing shaft so it will turn freely, and a 100 tooth iron gear is attached to the same shaft. A variable-reluctance sensor is used to sense the teeth on the gear, and produces a 100 mV signal each time a gear tooth passes the sensor. Hence 100 pulses are produced for each revolution of the propeller. When the wind velocity, V_w, is 20 mph, the propeller velocity, f_p, is 90 RPM. The relation is linear as follows:

$$f_p = 4.5\ V_p\ \text{RPM}$$

where V_w is the wind velocity in mph. The output display is composed of two 7-segment LEDs to read the wind velocity to the nearest digit.

16.40 Design a warning tachometer for a gas turbine engine which operates in the range of 8000 to 9000 RPM. A 100 tooth iron gear is mounted on the engine shaft. A variable reluctance pickup mounted near the gear and it produces 100 pulses for each revolution of the engine. The pulses are only 100 mV in magnitude, so they must be conditioned. The display is comprised of two 7-segment LED displays, which display the word "LO" when the speed is 8000 RPM or less, and the word "HI" when the speed is 9000 RPM or more. In the range between 8000 and 9000 RPM, the LED displays are blank. When LO is displayed, a 500-Hz tone is sounded and when HI is displayed, a 1-kHz tone is sounded. One quarter watt of power is needed for each tone.

16.41 Design a system to monitor the doors on the eight cars of a subway train. Each car has a door that must be closed before the train can proceed. Eight wires, one from the Hall-effect switch mounted on each of the 8 car doors, are brought to the train operator's compartment. When the car door is open, the voltage on the wire is 0 V. When the car door is closed, the voltage on the wire is +5 V.

Energize a green LED when all doors are closed. Energize a red LED for one second when a door is open. Indicate, with one 7-segment LED, the number of the car that has the door open. The car doors are continuously being checked, for one second each, and the numbers, 1, 2, 3, 4, 5, 6, 7, and 8 are being continuously displayed on the 7-segment LED. If any door is open, the red LED will light for one second while the number of the car is displayed. When all doors are closed, the green LED will light, but the car numbers will still be displayed as the doors are checked.

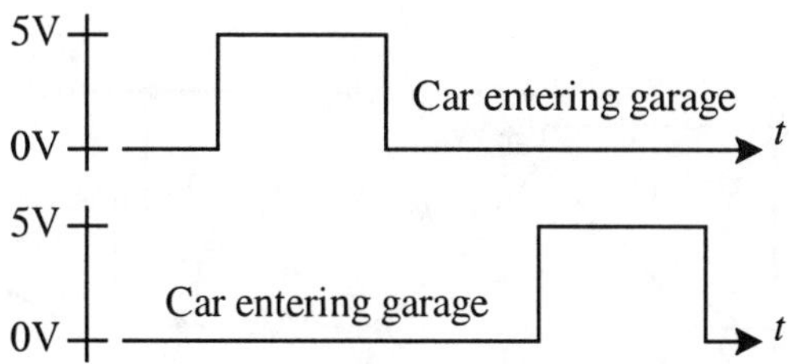

Figure P16.42

16.42 Design an electronic system to determine the number of cars in a parking garage containing 300 spaces. Each time a car enters the garage, the entrance gate lifts and a pulse of variable width is generated. The pulse is of variable width because of the difference in time required for the gate to drop after each car of different length and different speed passes through. Each time a car leaves the garage, the exit gate, at another location, lifts and another pulse of variable width is generated. These pulses are shown in Figure P16.42. Provide a CLEAR for the system so that the counter can be reset to zero. The visual display is composed of the following:

1. Three 7-segment LED displays which show the number of cars in the garage at any time.
2. Four 7-segment LED displays which show the word "FULL" when the garage contains 300 cars.

16.43 Design a digital thermometer using a thermistor bridge as the temperature sensor and a voltage-controlled oscillator (VCO). The output of the thermistor bridge is as follows:

With 110°F, the output is 50 mV
With 90°F the output is 34.4 mV.

The readout is to be three 7-segment LED displays yielding the temperature in degrees Fahrenheit to the nearest whole number. Compute the scale factor showing that your system will yield accurate temperature readings in the 90° to 110° range.

16.44 Repeat Problem 16.43 using a 3 1/2 digit A/D Converter, (ICL7106).

16.45 Design a digital bathroom scale using a strain gauge load cell as the weight sensor. The load cell produces an output voltage that is proportional to weight. The system is shown on Figure P16.45(a), where we write the equation for V_1 and V_2 as follows:

$$V_1 = \frac{(R - \Delta R)V}{R - \Delta R + R + \Delta R} = \frac{V(R - \Delta R)}{2R}$$

$$V_2 = \frac{R}{2R}V = \frac{V}{2}$$

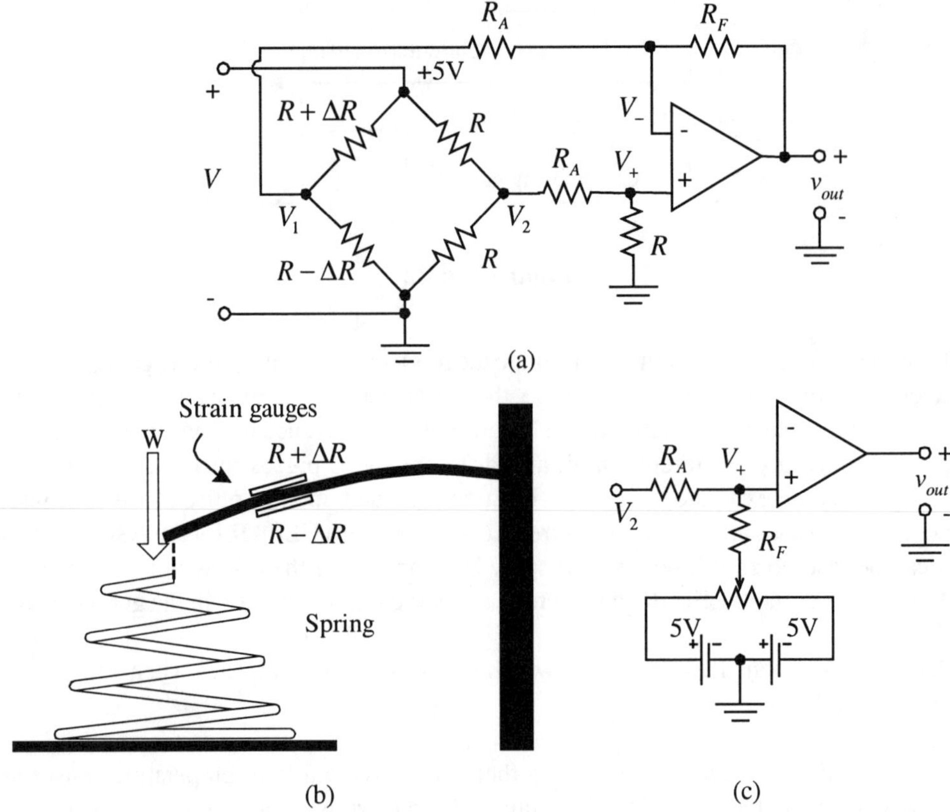

Figure P16.45

The equation for the output of the op-amp is

$$v_{out} = \frac{R_F}{R_A}(V_2 - V_1) = \frac{R_F}{R_A} \cdot \left[\frac{V}{2} - \frac{V(R - \Delta R)}{2R} \right] = \frac{R_F V}{2R_A R} \cdot \Delta R$$

Select $R = 5\ \text{k}\Omega$, $R_A = 100\ \text{k}\Omega$, and V = 9 V. The change in resistance, ΔR, is proportional to the weight.

Figure P16.45(b) shows a schematic of the mechanical system. A strain gauge is attached to the top and bottom of the beam. The beam bends down because of the application of the weight on the scale. As a result, the resistance of the upper strain gauge increase ($R + \Delta R$) and the resistance of the lower gauge decreases (R - ΔR). This provides the input to the bridge system of Figure P16.45(a). Two additional strain gauges, not shown on the diagram of Figure P16.45(b), are attached to the beam in a direction that causes no change in resistance, R, as the weight is applied. These two gauges form the other two legs of the bridge and are shown as R in Figure P16.45(a). Since resistance is a function of temperature, the bridge will remain balanced as the temperature changes, and will yield a voltage output only for a change in weight.

The scale is to respond to changes in weight from 0 to 399 lbs. The load cell is linear, and when the weight is 399 lbs,

$$V_{out} = \frac{R_F}{R_A} \cdot (34\ \text{mV})$$

Hence, over the range of 0 to 399 pounds, the output voltage of the system of Figure P16.45(a) varies from 0 to $R_F/R_A \times (34\ \text{mV})$. When someone steps on the scale, a normally-open switch closes and hence applies power to the device. Three 7-segment LED displays read the weight in pounds. Calculate the scale factor, R_F/R_A, and provide a zero adjustment which can be accomplished with the circuit shown in Figure P16.45(c). The resistance of the potentiometer should be approximately 10% of the value of R_F.

16.46 Design an odometer to be used on a bicycle. A Hall-effect switch is mounted near the rear wheel. A magnet is mounted on one of the spokes of the rear wheel. As the magnet passes the generator, a 5 V pulse is generated. Hence, each time the wheel revolves once, the Hall-effect switch generates a 5 V pulse. With a nominal 26 wheel (including the effect of the tire), the bicycle travels 7 ft each time the wheel turns through one revolution. Thus, each pulse corresponds to 7 ft of travel by the bicycle. Since there are so few pulses generated by the Hall-effect generator, use pulse multiplication as discussed in Section 16.9.4.

The readout is comprised of three 7-segment LED displays connected so that the least significant digit reads 100 ft increments, and the most significant digit reads 10,000 ft increments.

Consider the changes to the design required for the following improvements:

(a) Change the output to read from 00.0 to 99.9 miles rather than feet.

(b) Change the odometer to operate with variable bicycle wheel diameters.

16.47 Design a run-in-place odometer to help you exercise by running in one place inside your home. A normally-open switch closes each time either of your feet strikes the pad. The switch within the pad is a mechanical device, so it must be de-bounced. The controls consist of a reset button to activate the device and a potentiometer to set the length of each individual's stride in feet. The output is shown on three 7-segment LED displays with the MSD equal to 10^4 ft and the LSD equal to 10^2 ft. Use a monostable 555 to de-bounce the switch, and use the pulse multiplication technique as discussed in Sect. 16.9.4 to increase the number of pulses. The number of pulses we generate for each pulse from the mechanical switch should be related to the stride. The stride potentiometer sets the frequency of the astable 555.

For example, if a person, when running, travels 2.8 ft every time either foot hits the ground, the stride is 2.8 ft. In this case, the frequency of the astable 555, in the pulse multiplication circuit, should be set for 28. Hence each time either foot strikes the pad, 28 pulses are generated for the counter.

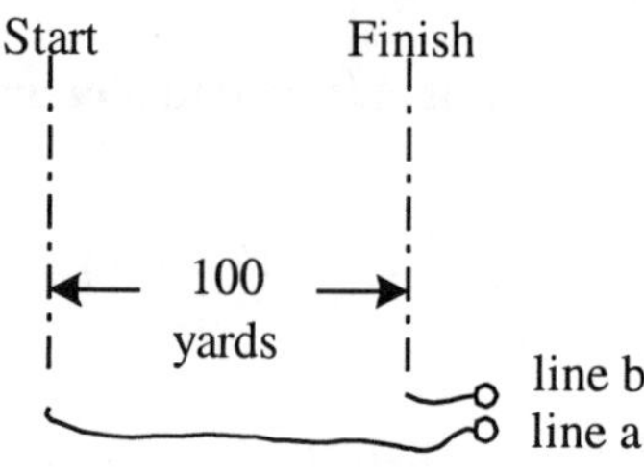

Figure P16.48

16.48 Design a timing system to measure the time for athletes to run the 100 yard dash. As the athletes leave the starting line, they break a beam of light, and when the first runner reaches the 100 yard mark at the end of the race, another beam of light is broken. The system is shown in Figure P16.48. Two wires are brought to the timing circuit: line (a) from the starting point and line (b) from the finish line. The voltage on each line is normally +5 V. When the beam is broken, the voltage drops to 0 V. Display the time on three 7-segment LEDs with the least significant digit representing 0.1 seconds.

16.49 Design a pulse generator to operate in the range of 0 to 99 Hz. The generated pulses must have a duty cycle of approximately 0.5. Provide two 7-segment LEDs to display the frequency of the pulse generator output.

16.50 Design a temperature control system for a home air conditioner. The control system turns ON the refrigeration unit when the actual temperature, T_a, is greater than the desired temperature, T_d. The refrigeration unit is turned OFF when $T_a < T_d$. The control system must operate from 0° to 60° C. A temperature sensor, which you are not required to design, provides the actual temperature on two 4-line BCD outputs for the MSD and the LSD digits, as shown in Figure P16.50(a). The desired temperature is set by use of a three position switch, which is shown in Figure P16.50(b). To increase the desired temperature, a 1-Hz pulse train is switched to the UP position, and to decrease the desired temperature, the 1 Hz pulse is switched to the DOWN position. (The 1-Hz pulse train has a duty cycle of approximately 0.5.) The desired temperature is displayed on two 7-segment LEDs. The required output is a control voltage delivered to the refrigeration system. The refrigeration system is turned ON when a +5 V signal is delivered to it, and OFF when 0 V is delivered to it.

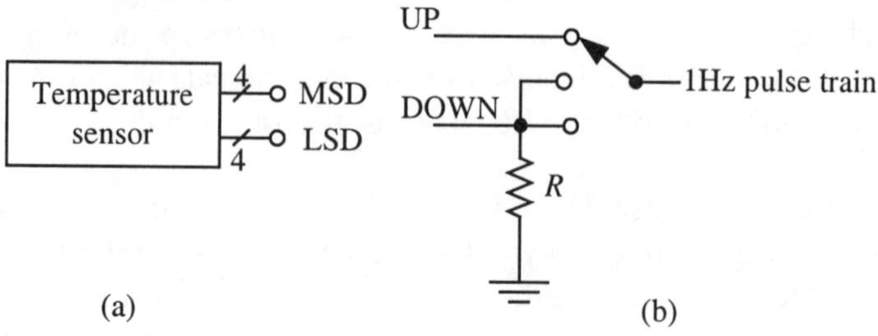

Figure P16.50

Appendix A
Standard Component Values

Introduction

This appendix presents standard component values to aid in the selection of resistor and capacitor values when designing an electronic system. There is some variation in these tabulated values from one manufacturer to another. Therefore, the tables should be considered as typical.

It is important to be aware of the practical constraints represented by component availability. It would be a waste of time to design a circuit with precise component values if financial constraints required the use of components with relatively high tolerances. For example, if you design a precise electronic circuit that requires a resistor of value 213.04Ω, you might be wasting time and effort. If your budget required use of 5% resistors, the closest you could come to this with "off-the-shelf" components is a 220Ω resistor which the manufacturer guarantees to have a resistance between 209Ω and 231Ω.

Similarly, it would not make much sense to design an oscillator that required a 3 farad capacitor. This value is not practical (a baked potato with two nails stuck into it might approximate such a capacitor if you carefully controlled the size and degree of baking).

Resistors

Five percent tolerance carbon composition resistors are available in the following power ratings: 1/4, 1/2, 1, and 2 watt. These resistors are manufactured in the sizes shown in the table below. Thus, for example, if your design called for a 675Ω resistor, you would actually choose a 680Ω resistor. If this is a 5% tolerance resistance, the manufacturer is guaranteeing the actual value to be between 646Ω and 714Ω. It would not make sense for the manufacturer to offer a resistor of nominal value 700Ω since this is already within the tolerance range of the 675Ω resistor.

Each of the values in the following table are multiplied by 10^n, where n is an integer. Thus, for example, the 2.2 entry in the table could be a resistor of 2.2Ω, 22Ω, 220Ω, 2.2 kΩ, 22 kΩ, 220 kΩ or 2.2 MΩ.

2.2	2.4	2.7	3.0	3.3	3.6	3.9	4.3
4.7	5.1	5.6	6.2	6.8	7.5	8.2	9.1
10	11	12	13	15	16	18	20

Capacitors

In the table below, we present typical capacitor values from one manufacturer. These are 10% tolerance capacitors, and the values in the table are in μF.

3.3	5	6	6.8	7.5	8	10	12
15	18	20	22	24	25	27	30
39	47	50	51	56	68	75	82
91	100	120	130	150	180	200	220
240	250	270	300	330	350	360	390
400	470	500	510	560	600	680	750
800	820	910	1000	1200	1300	1500	1600
1800	2000	2200	2500	2700	3000	3300	3900
4000	4300	4700	5000	5600	6800	7500	8200

Tantalum Capacitors

Tantalum capacitors are available in the following sizes. Each of the values in the following table are multiplied by 10^n, where n is an integer. A typical maximum capacitance value is 330 μF.

0.0047	0.0056	0.0068	0.0082	0.010	0.012
0.015	0.018	0.022	0.027	0.033	0.019

Appendix B
Manufacturers' Data Sheets

This appendix contains copies of representative data sheets for diodes, transistors, voltage regulators and op-amps. The information is extracted from the manufacturers' data books. In some cases, only selected information is presented in order to give a sampling of the available data.

The appendix is not meant as a substitute for obtaining the appropriate data information from books or from the World Wide Web. We present only a very brief assortment of those sheets you will need to solve the problems within this text.

GENERAL SEMICONDUCTOR®

1N4001 THRU 1N4007

General Purpose Plastic Rectifier

Reverse Voltage 50 to 1000 V
Forward Current 1.0 A

DO-204AL (DO-41)

1.0 (25.4) MIN.

0.107 (2.7) / 0.080 (2.0) DIA.

0.205 (5.2) / 0.160 (4.1)

1.0 (25.4) MIN.

0.034 (0.86) / 0.028 (0.71) DIA.

NOTE: Lead diameter is 0.026 (0.66) / 0.023 (0.58) for suffix "E" part numbers

Dimensions in inches and (millimeters)

Features

- Plastic package has Underwriters Laboratories Flammability Classification 94V-0
- Construction utilizes void-free molded plastic technique
- Low reverse leakage
- High forward surge capability
- High temperature soldering guaranteed: 250°C/10 seconds, 0.375" (9.5mm) lead length, 5 lbs. (2.3kg) tension

Mechanical Data

Case: JEDEC DO-204AL, molded plastic body
Terminals: Plated axial leads, solderable per MIL-STD-750, Method 2026
Polarity: Color band denotes cathode end
Mounting Position: Any
Weight: 0.012 ounce, 0.3 gram

Maximum Ratings & Thermal Characteristics

Ratings at 25°C ambient temperature unless otherwise specified.

	SYMBOLS	1N 4001	1N 4002	1N 4003	1N 4004	1N 4005	1N 4006	1N 4007	UNITS
*Maximum repetitive peak reverse voltage	V_{RRM}	50	100	200	400	600	800	1000	V
*Maximum RMS voltage	V_{RMS}	35	70	140	280	420	560	700	V
*Maximum DC blocking voltage	V_{DC}	50	100	200	400	600	800	1000	V
*Maximum average forward rectified current 0.375" (9.5mm) lead length at T_A=75°C	$I_{F(AV)}$	1.0							A
*Peak forward surge current 8.3 ms single half sine-wave superimposed on rated load (JEDEC Method) T_A=75°C	I_{FSM}	30							A
*Maximum full load reverse current full cycle average 0.375" (9.5mm) lead length at T_L=75°C	$I_{R(AV)}$	30							µA
Typical thermal resistance (NOTE 1)	$R_{\theta JA}$ $R_{\theta JL}$	50 25							°C/W
Maximum DC blocking voltage temperature	T_A	+150							°C
*Operating junction and storage temperature range	T_J, T_{STG}	-50 to +175							°C

Electrical Characteristics

Ratings at 25°C ambient temperature unless otherwise specified.

	SYMBOLS	1N 4001	1N 4002	1N 4003	1N 4004	1N 4005	1N 4006	1N 4007	UNITS
*Maximum instantaneous forward voltage at 1.0A	V_F	1.1							V
*Maximum DC reverse current at rated DC blocking voltage T_A= 25°C / T_A=100°C	I_R	5.0 50							µA
Typical reverse recovery time at I_{FM}=20mA, I_{RM}=1mA (NOTE 2)	t_{rr}	30							µs
Typical junction capacitance at 4.0V, 1MHz	C_J	15							pF

NOTES:
(1) Thermal resistance from junction to ambient, and from junction to lead at 0.375" (9.5mm) lead length, P.C.B. mounted
(2) Measured on Tektronix type "S" recovery plug-in. Tektronix 545 scope or equivalent.
*JEDEC registered values

11/29/99

1N4001 THRU 1N4007

Ratings and Characteristic Curves (TA = 25°C unless otherwise noted)

FIG.1 - FORWARD CURRENT DERATING CURVE

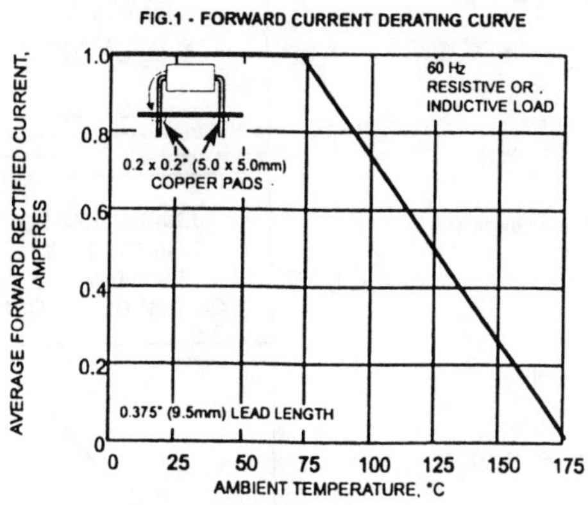

FIG. 2 - MAXIMUM NON-REPETITIVE PEAK FORWARD SURGE CURRENT

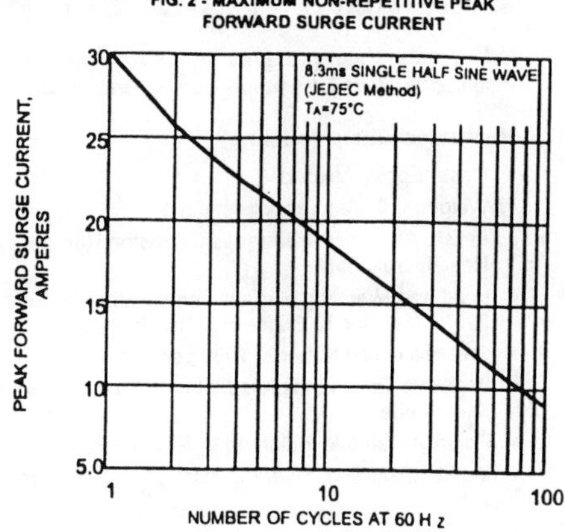

FIG. 3 - TYPICAL INSTANTANEOUS FORWARD CHARACTERISTICS

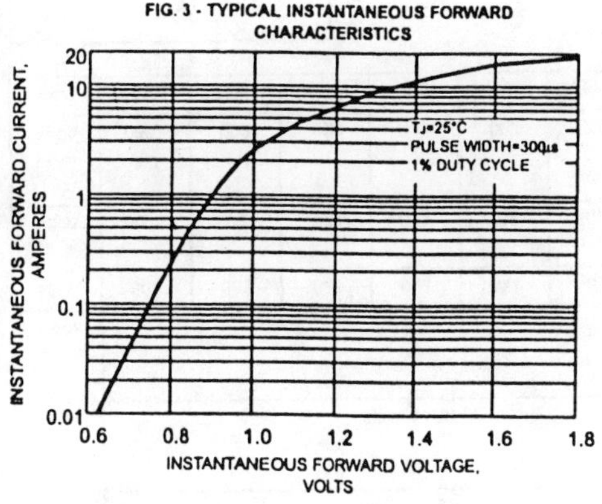

FIG. 4 - TYPICAL REVERSE CHARACTERISTICS

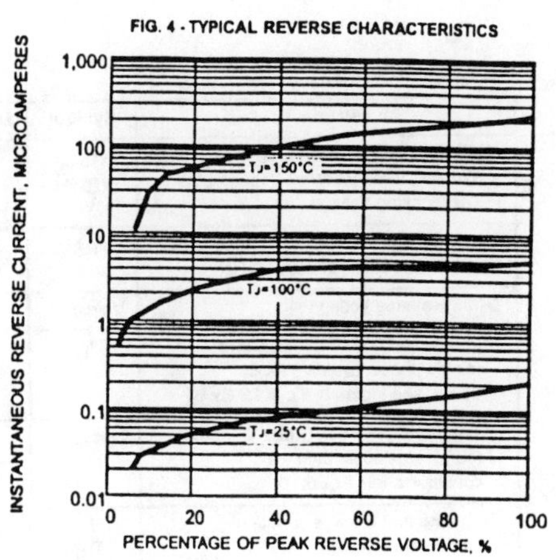

FIG. 5 - TYPICAL JUNCTION CAPACITANCE

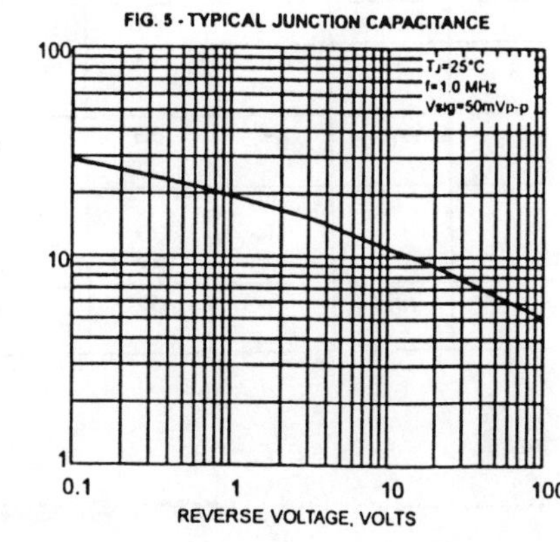

FIG. 6 - TYPICAL TRANSIENT THERMAL IMPEDANCE

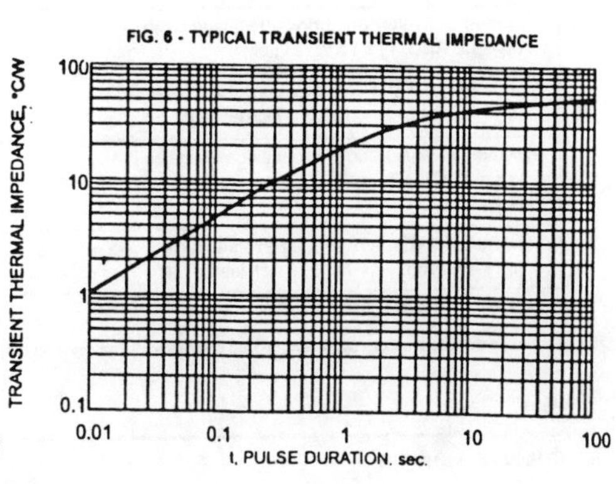

MOTOROLA
SEMICONDUCTOR TECHNICAL DATA

Order this document by 1N4001/D

Axial Lead Standard Recovery Rectifiers

1N4001 thru 1N4007

1N4004 and 1N4007 are Motorola Preferred Devices

This data sheet provides information on subminiature size, axial lead mounted rectifiers for general–purpose low–power applications.

Mechanical Characteristics

- Case: Epoxy, Molded
- Weight: 0.4 gram (approximately)
- Finish: All External Surfaces Corrosion Resistant and Terminal Leads are Readily Solderable
- Lead and Mounting Surface Temperature for Soldering Purposes: 220°C Max. for 10 Seconds, 1/16″ from case
- Shipped in plastic bags, 1000 per bag.
- Available Tape and Reeled, 5000 per reel, by adding a "RL" suffix to the part number
- Polarity: Cathode Indicated by Polarity Band
- Marking: 1N4001, 1N4002, 1N4003, 1N4004, 1N4005, 1N4006, 1N4007

LEAD MOUNTED RECTIFIERS
50–1000 VOLTS
DIFFUSED JUNCTION

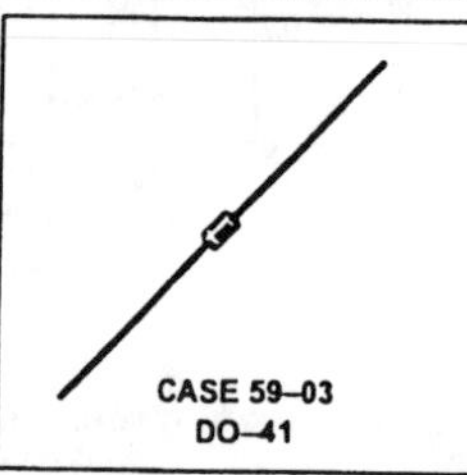

CASE 59–03
DO–41

MAXIMUM RATINGS

Rating	Symbol	1N4001	1N4002	1N4003	1N4004	1N4005	1N4006	1N4007	Unit
*Peak Repetitive Reverse Voltage Working Peak Reverse Voltage DC Blocking Voltage	V_{RRM} V_{RWM} V_R	50	100	200	400	600	800	1000	Volts
*Non–Repetitive Peak Reverse Voltage (halfwave, single phase, 60 Hz)	V_{RSM}	60	120	240	480	720	1000	1200	Volts
*RMS Reverse Voltage	$V_{R(RMS)}$	35	70	140	280	420	560	700	Volts
*Average Rectified Forward Current (single phase, resistive load, 60 Hz, see Figure 8, $T_A = 75°C$)	I_O	1.0							Amp
*Non–Repetitive Peak Surge Current (surge applied at rated load conditions, see Figure 2)	I_{FSM}	30 (for 1 cycle)							Amp
Operating and Storage Junction Temperature Range	T_J T_{stg}	– 65 to +175							°C

ELECTRICAL CHARACTERISTICS*

Rating	Symbol	Typ	Max	Unit
Maximum Instantaneous Forward Voltage Drop ($i_F = 1.0$ Amp, $T_J = 25°C$) Figure 1	v_F	0.93	1.1	Volts
Maximum Full–Cycle Average Forward Voltage Drop ($I_O = 1.0$ Amp, $T_L = 75°C$, 1 inch leads)	$V_{F(AV)}$	—	0.8	Volts
Maximum Reverse Current (rated dc voltage) ($T_J = 25°C$) ($T_J = 100°C$)	I_R	 0.05 1.0	 10 50	µA
Maximum Full–Cycle Average Reverse Current ($I_O = 1.0$ Amp, $T_L = 75°C$, 1 inch leads)	$I_{R(AV)}$	—	30	µA

*Indicates JEDEC Registered Data

Preferred devices are Motorola recommended choices for future use and best overall value.

Rev 5

MOTOROLA

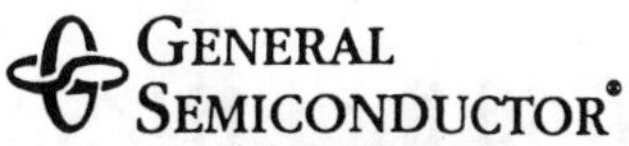

1N746 thru 1N759

Zener Diodes

Vz Range 3.3 to 12V
Power Dissipation 500mW

DO-204AH (DO-35 Glass)

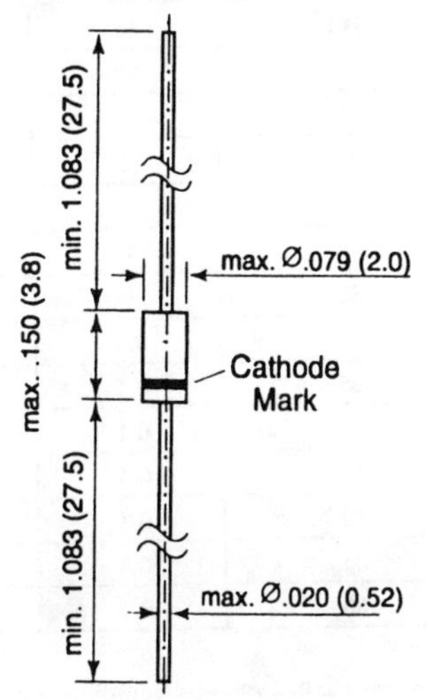

Dimensions in inches and (millimeters)

Features

- Silicon Planar Power Zener Diodes.
- Standard Zener voltage tolerance is ±5% for "A" suffix. Other tolerances are available upon request.

Mechanical Data

Case: DO-35 Glass Case
Weight: approx. 0.13 grams
Packaging codes/options:
D7/10K per 13" reel, (52mm tape), 20K/box
D8/10K per Ammo tape (52mm tape), 20K/box

Maximum Ratings and Thermal Characteristics (T_A = 25°C unless otherwise noted)

Parameter	Symbol	Value	Unit
Zener Current (see Table "Characteristics")			
Power Dissipation at T_L = 75°C	P_{tot}	500(1)	mW
Thermal Resistance Junction to Ambient Air	$R_{\theta JA}$	300(2)	°C/W
Maximum Junction Temperature	T_j	175	°C
Storage Temperature Range	T_S	–65 to +175	°C

Notes:
(1) T_L is measured 3/8" from body.
(2) Valid provided that leads at a distance of 3/8" from case are kept at ambient temperature.

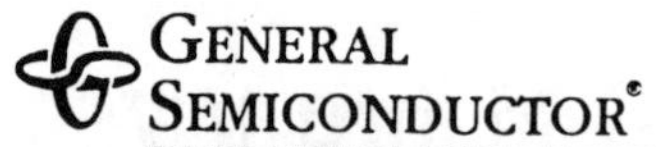

1N746 thru 1N759

Zener Diodes

Electrical Characteristics (T_A = 25°C unless otherwise noted) Maximum V_F = 1.5V at I_F = 200mA

Type Number	Nominal Zener Voltage V_Z @ I_{ZT}[3] (Volts)	Test Current I_{ZT} (mA)	Maximum Zener Impedance Z_{ZT} @ I_{ZT}[1] (Ω)	Maximum Regulator Current I_{ZM}[2] (mA)	Maximum Reverse Leakage Current T_A = 25°C I_R @ V_R = 1V (μA)	T_A = 150°C I_R @ V_R = 1V (μA)
1N746A	3.3	20	28	110	10	30
1N747A	3.6	20	24	100	10	30
1N748A	3.9	20	23	95	10	30
1N749A	4.3	20	22	85	2	30
1N750A	4.7	20	19	75	2	30
1N751A	5.1	20	17	70	1	20
1N752A	5.6	20	11	65	1	20
1N753A	6.2	20	7	60	0.1	20
1N754A	6.8	20	5	55	0.1	20
1N755A	7.5	20	6	50	0.1	20
1N756A	8.2	20	8	45	0.1	20
1N757A	9.1	20	10	40	0.1	20
1N758A	10	20	17	35	0.1	20
1N759A	12	20	30	30	0.1	20

Notes:

(1) The Zener impedance is derived from the 1 kHz AC voltage which results when an AC current having an RMS value equal to 10% of the Zener current (I_{ZT}) is superimposed on I_{ZT}. Zener impedance is measured at two points to insure a sharp knee on the breakdown curve and to eliminate unstable units.

(2) Valid provided that leads at a distance of 3/8" from case are kept at ambient temperature.

(3) Measured with device junction in thermal equilibrium.

MOTOROLA
SEMICONDUCTOR TECHNICAL DATA

Order this document
by 2N3903/D

General Purpose Transistors
NPN Silicon

2N3903
2N3904*

*Motorola Preferred Device

COLLECTOR
3

2
BASE

1
EMITTER

CASE 29–04, STYLE 1
TO–92 (TO–226AA)

MAXIMUM RATINGS

Rating	Symbol	Value	Unit
Collector–Emitter Voltage	V_{CEO}	40	Vdc
Collector–Base Voltage	V_{CBO}	60	Vdc
Emitter–Base Voltage	V_{EBO}	6.0	Vdc
Collector Current — Continuous	I_C	200	mAdc
Total Device Dissipation @ T_A = 25°C Derate above 25°C	P_D	625 5.0	mW mW/°C
Total Device Dissipation @ T_C = 25°C Derate above 25°C	P_D	1.5 12	Watts mW/°C
Operating and Storage Junction Temperature Range	T_J, T_{stg}	–55 to +150	°C

THERMAL CHARACTERISTICS(1)

Characteristic	Symbol	Max	Unit
Thermal Resistance, Junction to Ambient	$R_{\theta JA}$	200	°C/W
Thermal Resistance, Junction to Case	$R_{\theta JC}$	83.3	°C/W

ELECTRICAL CHARACTERISTICS (T_A = 25°C unless otherwise noted)

Characteristic	Symbol	Min	Max	Unit
OFF CHARACTERISTICS				
Collector–Emitter Breakdown Voltage (2) (I_C = 1.0 mAdc, I_B = 0)	$V_{(BR)CEO}$	40	—	Vdc
Collector–Base Breakdown Voltage (I_C = 10 μAdc, I_E = 0)	$V_{(BR)CBO}$	60	—	Vdc
Emitter–Base Breakdown Voltage (I_E = 10 μAdc, I_C = 0)	$V_{(BR)EBO}$	6.0	—	Vdc
Base Cutoff Current (V_{CE} = 30 Vdc, V_{EB} = 3.0 Vdc)	I_{BL}	—	50	nAdc
Collector Cutoff Current (V_{CE} = 30 Vdc, V_{EB} = 3.0 Vdc)	I_{CEX}	—	50	nAdc

1. Indicates Data in addition to JEDEC Requirements.
2. Pulse Test: Pulse Width ≤ 300 μs; Duty Cycle ≤ 2.0%.

Preferred devices are Motorola recommended choices for future use and best overall value

REV 2

2N3903 2N3904

ELECTRICAL CHARACTERISTICS (T_A = 25°C unless otherwise noted) (Continued)

Characteristic		Symbol	Min	Max	Unit
ON CHARACTERISTICS					
DC Current Gain(1)		h_{FE}			—
(I_C = 0.1 mAdc, V_{CE} = 1.0 Vdc)	2N3903		20	—	
	2N3904		40	—	
(I_C = 1.0 mAdc, V_{CE} = 1.0 Vdc)	2N3903		35	—	
	2N3904		70	—	
(I_C = 10 mAdc, V_{CE} = 1.0 Vdc)	2N3903		50	150	
	2N3904		100	300	
(I_C = 50 mAdc, V_{CE} = 1.0 Vdc)	2N3903		30	—	
	2N3904		60	—	
(I_C = 100 mAdc, V_{CE} = 1.0 Vdc)	2N3903		15	—	
	2N3904		30	—	
Collector–Emitter Saturation Voltage(1)		$V_{CE(sat)}$			Vdc
(I_C = 10 mAdc, I_B = 1.0 mAdc)			—	0.2	
(I_C = 50 mAdc, I_B = 5.0 mAdc			—	0.3	
Base–Emitter Saturation Voltage(1)		$V_{BE(sat)}$			Vdc
(I_C = 10 mAdc, I_B = 1.0 mAdc)			0.65	0.85	
(I_C = 50 mAdc, I_B = 5.0 mAdc)			—	0.95	
SMALL–SIGNAL CHARACTERISTICS					
Current–Gain — Bandwidth Product		f_T			MHz
(I_C = 10 mAdc, V_{CE} = 20 Vdc, f = 100 MHz)	2N3903		250	—	
	2N3904		300	—	
Output Capacitance (V_{CB} = 5.0 Vdc, I_E = 0, f = 1.0 MHz)		C_{obo}	—	4.0	pF
Input Capacitance (V_{EB} = 0.5 Vdc, I_C = 0, f = 1.0 MHz)		C_{ibo}	—	8.0	pF
Input Impedance		h_{ie}			kΩ
(I_C = 1.0 mAdc, V_{CE} = 10 Vdc, f = 1.0 kHz)	2N3903		1.0	8.0	
	2N3904		1.0	10	
Voltage Feedback Ratio		h_{re}			X 10^{-4}
(I_C = 1.0 mAdc, V_{CE} = 10 Vdc, f = 1.0 kHz)	2N3903		0.1	5.0	
	2N3904		0.5	8.0	
Small–Signal Current Gain		h_{fe}			—
(I_C = 1.0 mAdc, V_{CE} = 10 Vdc, f = 1.0 kHz)	2N3903		50	200	
	2N3904		100	400	
Output Admittance (I_C = 1.0 mAdc, V_{CE} = 10 Vdc, f = 1.0 kHz)		h_{oe}	1.0	40	μmhos
Noise Figure		NF			dB
(I_C = 100 μAdc, V_{CE} = 5.0 Vdc, R_S = 1.0 kΩ, f = 1.0 kHz)	2N3903		—	6.0	
	2N3904		—	5.0	

SWITCHING CHARACTERISTICS

Characteristic	Conditions		Symbol	Min	Max	Unit
Delay Time	(V_{CC} = 3.0 Vdc, V_{BE} = 0.5 Vdc, I_C = 10 mAdc, I_{B1} = 1.0 mAdc)		t_d	—	35	ns
Rise Time			t_r	—	35	ns
Storage Time	(V_{CC} = 3.0 Vdc, I_C = 10 mAdc, I_{B1} = I_{B2} = 1.0 mAdc)	2N3903	t_s	—	175	ns
		2N3904		—	200	
Fall Time			t_f	—	50	ns

1. Pulse Test: Pulse Width ≤ 300 μs; Duty Cycle ≤ 2.0%.

2N3903 2N3904

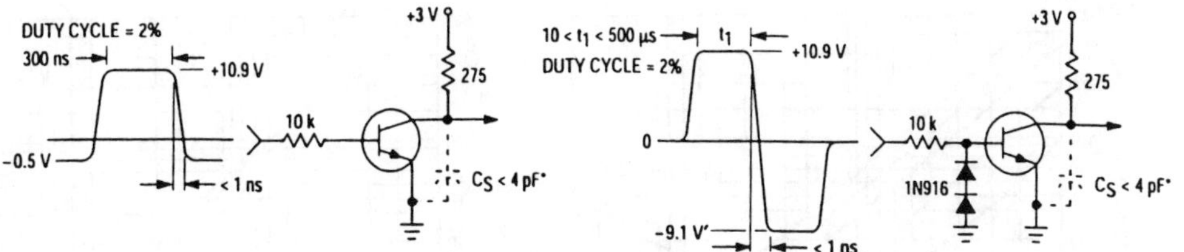

* Total shunt capacitance of test jig and connectors

Figure 1. Delay and Rise Time Equivalent Test Circuit

Figure 2. Storage and Fall Time Equivalent Test Circuit

TYPICAL TRANSIENT CHARACTERISTICS

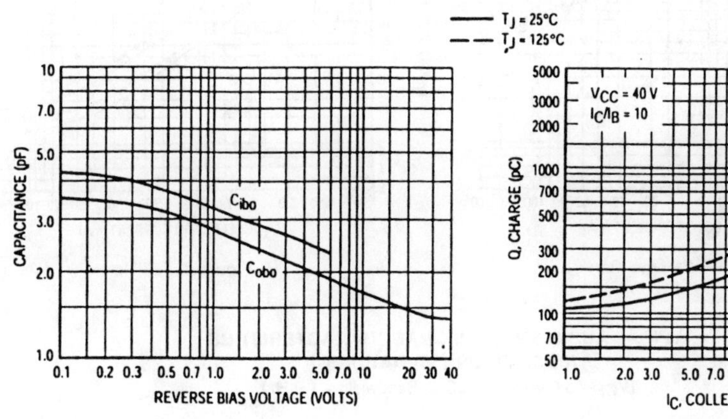

Figure 3. Capacitance

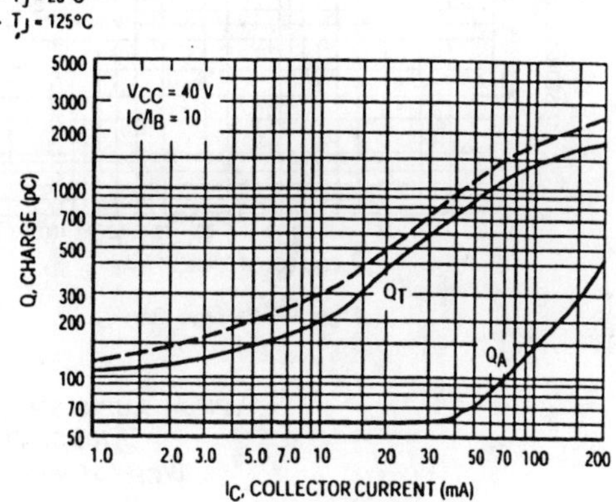

Figure 4. Charge Data

2N3903 2N3904

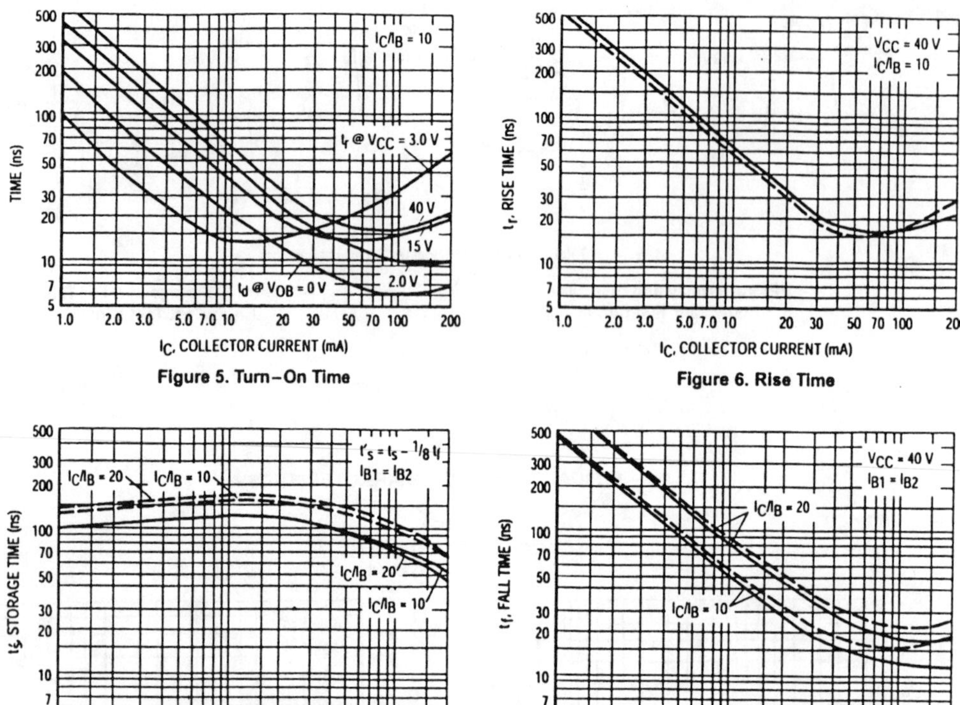

Figure 5. Turn–On Time

Figure 6. Rise Time

Figure 7. Storage Time

Figure 8. Fall Time

TYPICAL AUDIO SMALL–SIGNAL CHARACTERISTICS
NOISE FIGURE VARIATIONS
(V_{CE} = 5.0 Vdc, T_A = 25°C, Bandwidth = 1.0 Hz)

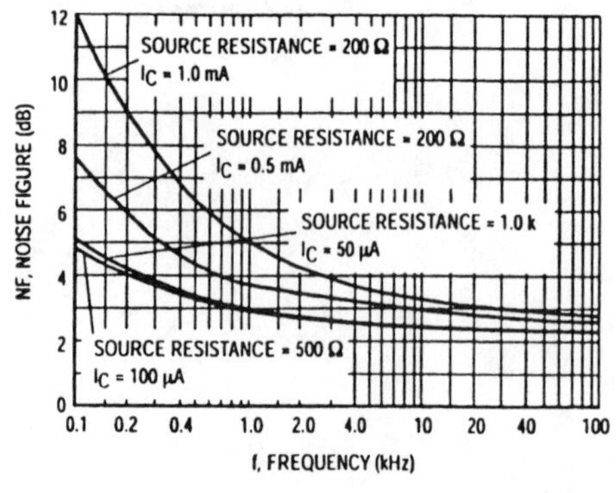

Figure 9.

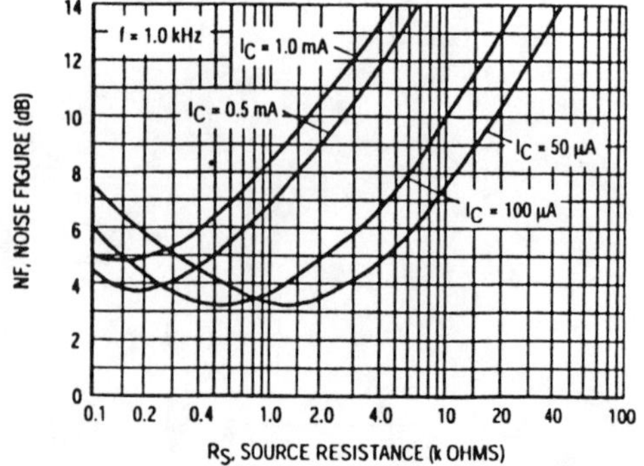

Figure 10.

2N3903 2N3904

h PARAMETERS

(V_{CE} = 10 Vdc, f = 1.0 kHz, T_A = 25°C)

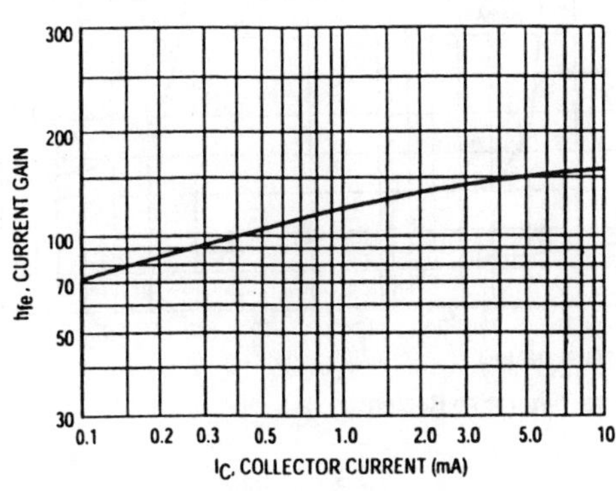

Figure 11. Current Gain

100
50
20
10
5
2
1
h_{oe}, OUTPUT ADMITTANCE (μ mhos)
0.1 0.2 0.3 0.5 1.0 2.0 3.0 5.0 10
I_C, COLLECTOR CURRENT (mA)

Figure 12. Output Admittance

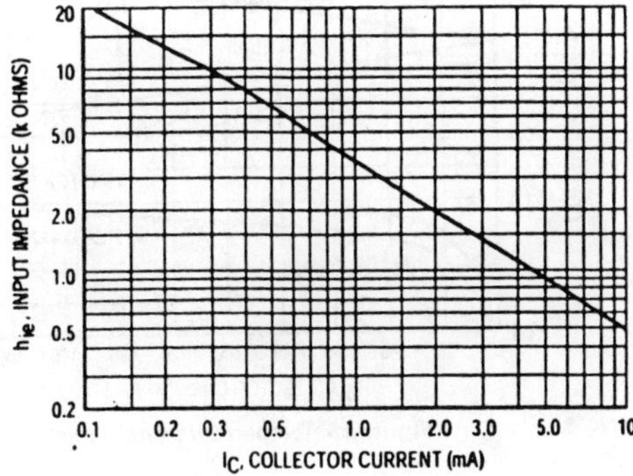

Figure 13. Input Impedance

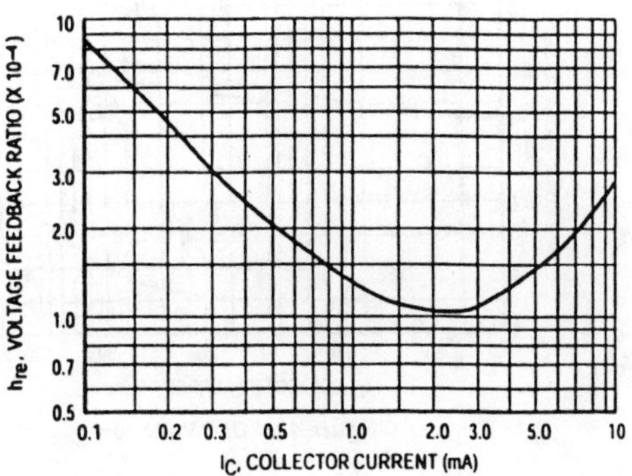

Figure 14. Voltage Feedback Ratio

TYPICAL STATIC CHARACTERISTICS

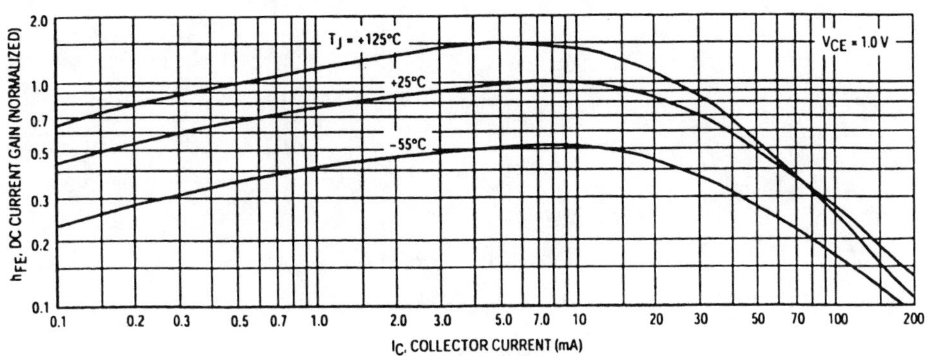

Figure 15. DC Current Gain

2N3903 2N3904

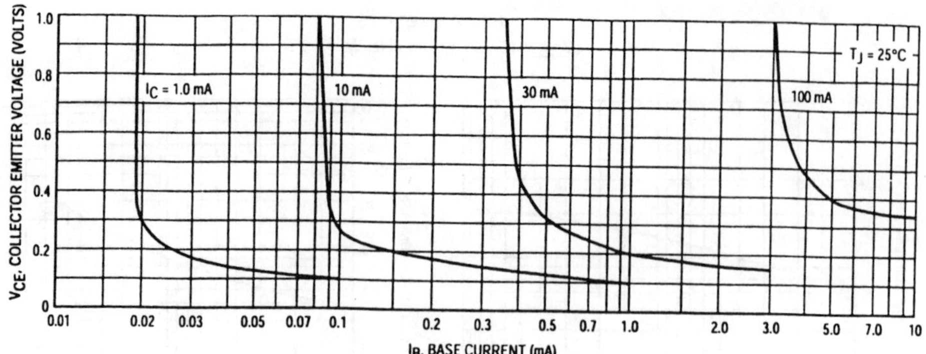

Figure 16. Collector Saturation Region

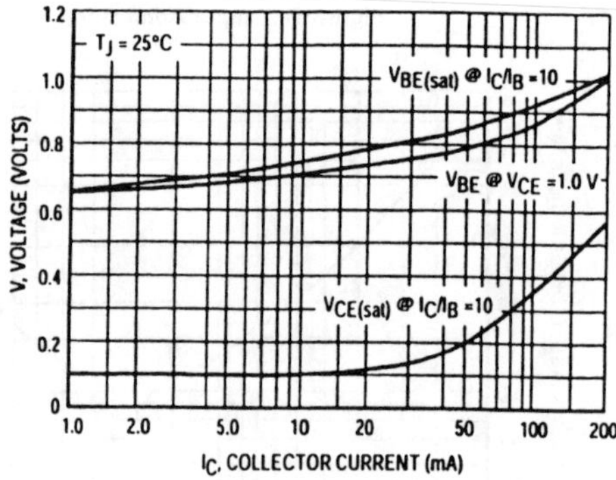

Figure 17. "ON" Voltages

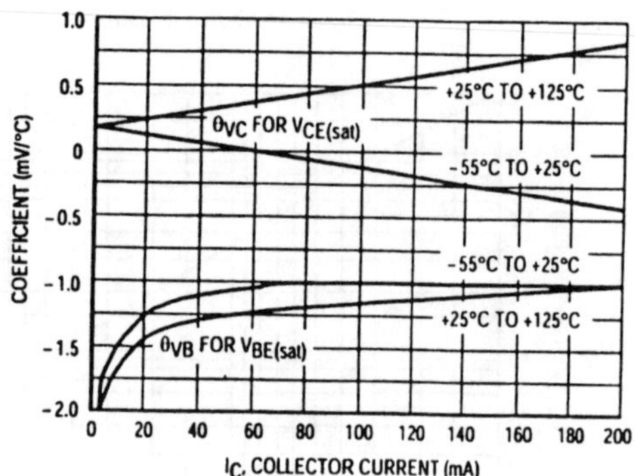

Figure 18. Temperature Coefficients

MOTOROLA
SEMICONDUCTOR TECHNICAL DATA

Order this document by 2N3905/D

General Purpose Transistors
PNP Silicon

2N3905
2N3906*

*Motorola Preferred Device

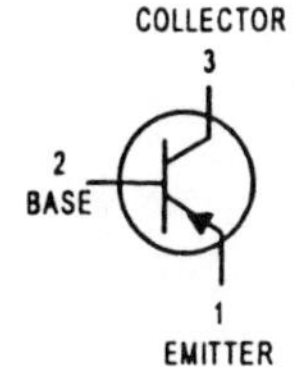

CASE 29–04, STYLE 1
TO–92 (TO–226AA)

MAXIMUM RATINGS

Rating	Symbol	Value	Unit
Collector–Emitter Voltage	V_{CEO}	40	Vdc
Collector–Base Voltage	V_{CBO}	40	Vdc
Emitter–Base Voltage	V_{EBO}	5.0	Vdc
Collector Current — Continuous	I_C	200	mAdc
Total Device Dissipation @ T_A = 25°C Derate above 25°C	P_D	625 5.0	mW mW/°C
Total Power Dissipation @ T_A = 60°C	P_D	250	mW
Total Device Dissipation @ T_C = 25°C Derate above 25°C	P_D	1.5 12	Watts mW/°C
Operating and Storage Junction Temperature Range	T_J, T_{stg}	–55 to +150	°C

THERMAL CHARACTERISTICS(1)

Characteristic	Symbol	Max	Unit
Thermal Resistance, Junction to Ambient	$R_{\theta JA}$	200	°C/W
Thermal Resistance, Junction to Case	$R_{\theta JC}$	83.3	°C/W

ELECTRICAL CHARACTERISTICS (T_A = 25°C unless otherwise noted)

Characteristic	Symbol	Min	Max	Unit
OFF CHARACTERISTICS				
Collector–Emitter Breakdown Voltage (2) (I_C = 1.0 mAdc, I_B = 0)	$V_{(BR)CEO}$	40	—	Vdc
Collector–Base Breakdown Voltage (I_C = 10 μAdc, I_E = 0)	$V_{(BR)CBO}$	40	—	Vdc
Emitter–Base Breakdown Voltage (I_E = 10 μAdc, I_C = 0)	$V_{(BR)EBO}$	5.0	—	Vdc
Base Cutoff Current (V_{CE} = 30 Vdc, V_{EB} = 3.0 Vdc)	I_{BL}	—	50	nAdc
Collector Cutoff Current (V_{CE} = 30 Vdc, V_{EB} = 3.0 Vdc)	I_{CEX}	—	50	nAdc

1. Indicates Data in addition to JEDEC Requirements.
2. Pulse Test: Pulse Width ≤ 300 μs; Duty Cycle ≤ 2.0%.

Preferred devices are Motorola recommended choices for future use and best overall value.

REV 2

2N3905 2N3906

ELECTRICAL CHARACTERISTICS (T_A = 25°C unless otherwise noted) (Continued)

Characteristic		Symbol	Min	Max	Unit
ON CHARACTERISTICS(1)					
DC Current Gain		h_{FE}			—
(I_C = 0.1 mAdc, V_{CE} = 1.0 Vdc)	2N3905		30	—	
	2N3906		60	—	
(I_C = 1.0 mAdc, V_{CE} = 1.0 Vdc)	2N3905		40	—	
	2N3906		80	—	
(I_C = 10 mAdc, V_{CE} = 1.0 Vdc)	2N3905		50	150	
	2N3906		100	300	
(I_C = 50 mAdc, V_{CE} = 1.0 Vdc)	2N3905		30	—	
	2N3906		60	—	
(I_C = 100 mAdc, V_{CE} = 1.0 Vdc)	2N3905		15	—	
	2N3906		30	—	
Collector–Emitter Saturation Voltage		$V_{CE(sat)}$			Vdc
(I_C = 10 mAdc, I_B = 1.0 mAdc)			—	0.25	
(I_C = 50 mAdc, I_B = 5.0 mAdc			—	0.4	
Base–Emitter Saturation Voltage		$V_{BE(sat)}$			Vdc
(I_C = 10 mAdc, I_B = 1.0 mAdc)			0.65	0.85	
(I_C = 50 mAdc, I_B = 5.0 mAdc)			—	0.95	
SMALL–SIGNAL CHARACTERISTICS					
Current–Gain — Bandwidth Product		f_T			MHz
(I_C = 10 mAdc, V_{CE} = 20 Vdc, f = 100 MHz)	2N3905		200	—	
	2N3906		250	—	
Output Capacitance (V_{CB} = 5.0 Vdc, I_E = 0, f = 1.0 MHz)		C_{obo}	—	4.5	pF
Input Capacitance (V_{EB} = 0.5 Vdc, I_C = 0, f = 1.0 MHz)		C_{ibo}	—	10.0	pF
Input Impedance		h_{ie}			k Ω
(I_C = 1.0 mAdc, V_{CE} = 10 Vdc, f = 1.0 kHz)	2N3905		0.5	8.0	
	2N3906		2.0	12	
Voltage Feedback Ratio		h_{re}			X 10^{-4}
(I_C = 1.0 mAdc, V_{CE} = 10 Vdc, f = 1.0 kHz)	2N3905		0.1	5.0	
	2N3906		0.1	10	
Small–Signal Current Gain		h_{fe}			—
(I_C = 1.0 mAdc, V_{CE} = 10 Vdc, f = 1.0 kHz)	2N3905		50	200	
	2N3906		100	400	
Output Admittance		h_{oe}			μmhos
(I_C = 1.0 mAdc, V_{CE} = 10 Vdc, f = 1.0 kHz)	2N3905		1.0	40	
	2N3906		3.0	60	
Noise Figure		NF			dB
(I_C = 100 μAdc, V_{CE} = 5.0 Vdc, R_S = 1.0 k Ω, f = 1.0 kHz)	2N3905		—	5.0	
	2N3906		—	4.0	

SWITCHING CHARACTERISTICS

Characteristic	Conditions		Symbol	Min	Max	Unit
Delay Time	(V_{CC} = 3.0 Vdc, V_{BE} = 0.5 Vdc, I_C = 10 mAdc, I_{B1} = 1.0 mAdc)		t_d	—	35	ns
Rise Time			t_r	—	35	ns
Storage Time	(V_{CC} = 3.0 Vdc, I_C = 10 mAdc, I_{B1} = I_{B2} = 1.0 mAd	2N3905	t_s	—	200	ns
		2N3906		—	225	
Fall Time		2N3905	t_f	—	60	ns
		2N3906		—	75	

1. Pulse Test: Pulse Width ≤ 300 μs; Duty Cycle ≤ 2.0%.

2N3905 2N3906

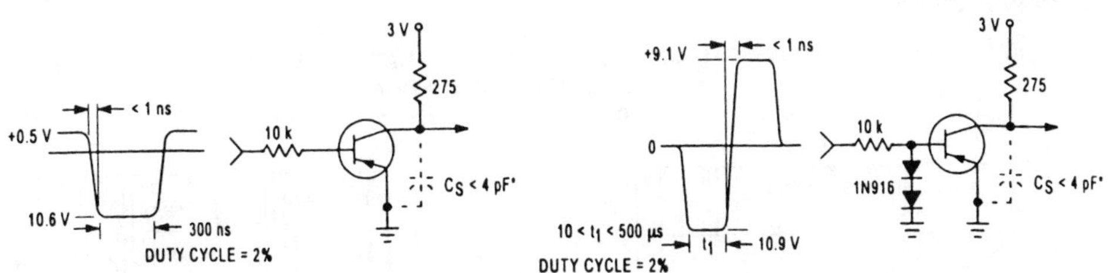

* Total shunt capacitance of test jig and connectors

Figure 1. Delay and Rise Time Equivalent Test Circuit

Figure 2. Storage and Fall Time Equivalent Test Circuit

TYPICAL TRANSIENT CHARACTERISTICS

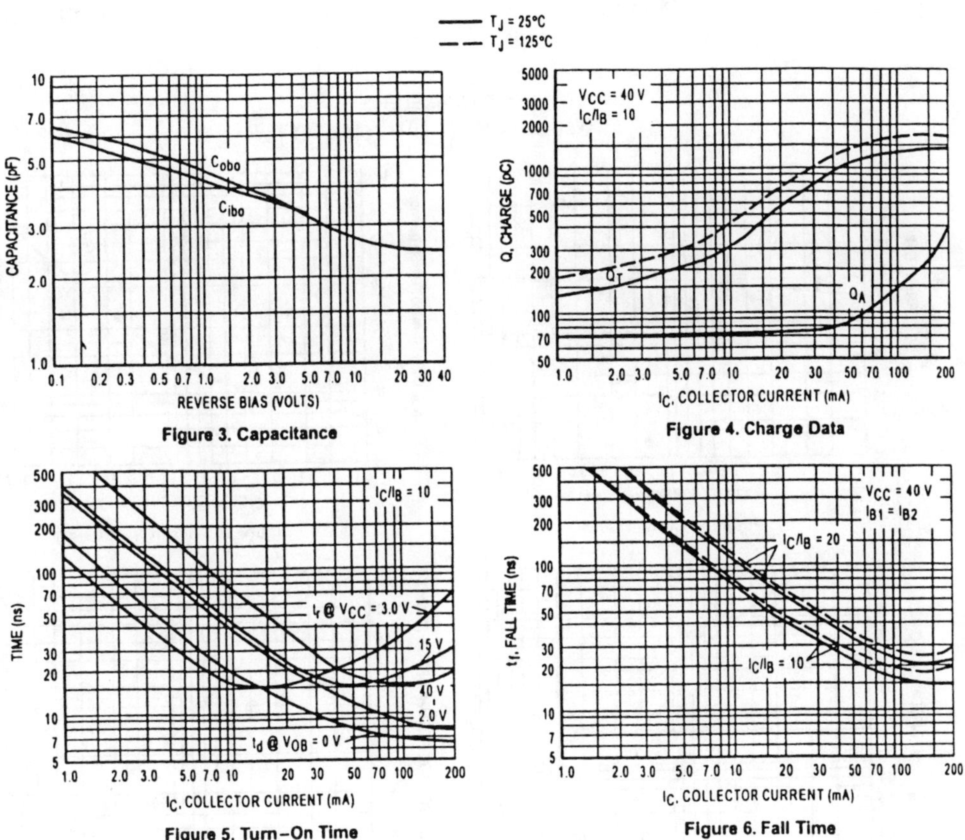

Figure 3. Capacitance

Figure 4. Charge Data

Figure 5. Turn–On Time

Figure 6. Fall Time

2N3905 2N3906

TYPICAL AUDIO SMALL–SIGNAL CHARACTERISTICS
NOISE FIGURE VARIATIONS

(V_{CE} = –5.0 Vdc, T_A = 25°C, Bandwidth = 1.0 Hz)

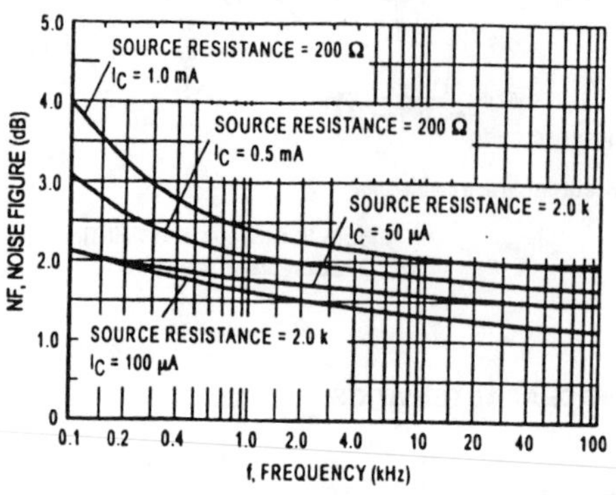

Figure 7.

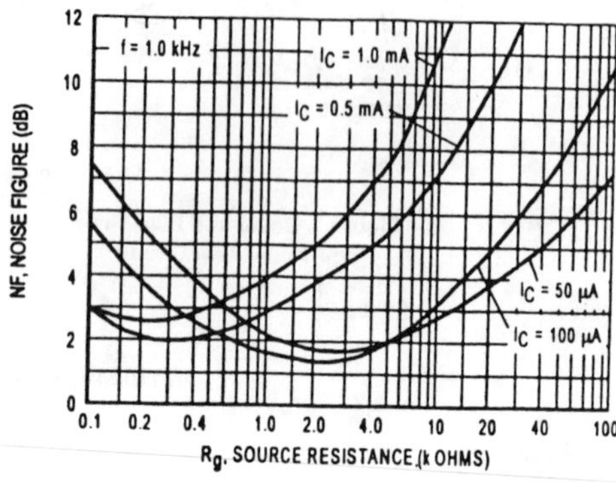

Figure 8.

h PARAMETERS

(V_{CE} = –10 Vdc, f = 1.0 kHz, T_A = 25°C)

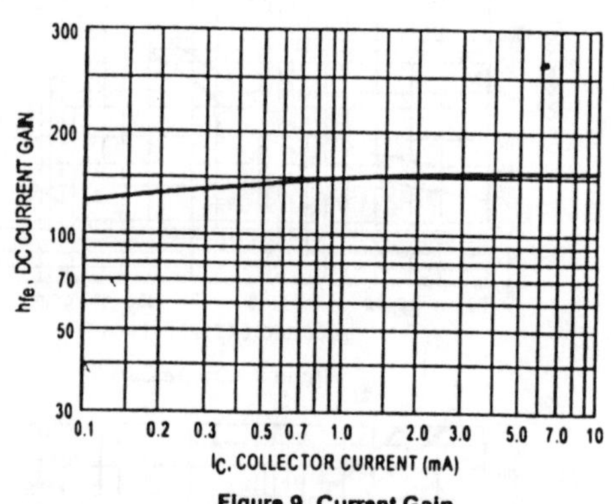

Figure 9. Current Gain

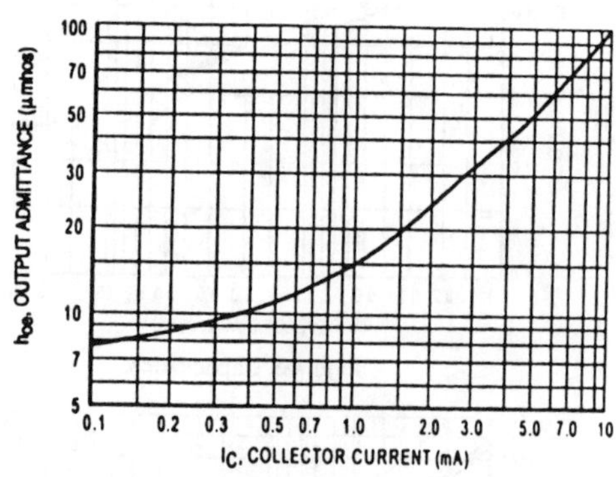

Figure 10. Output Admittance

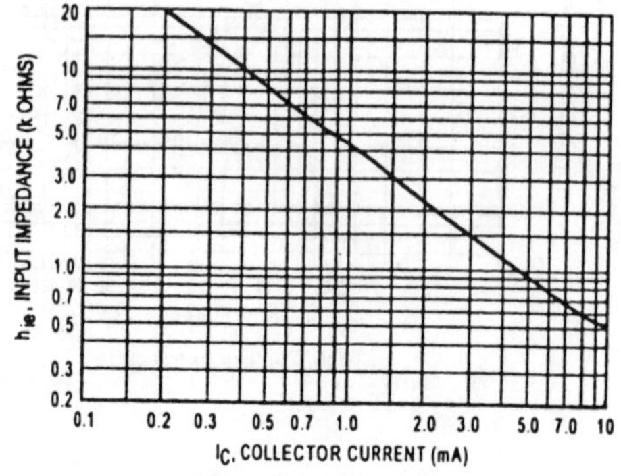

Figure 11. Input Impedance

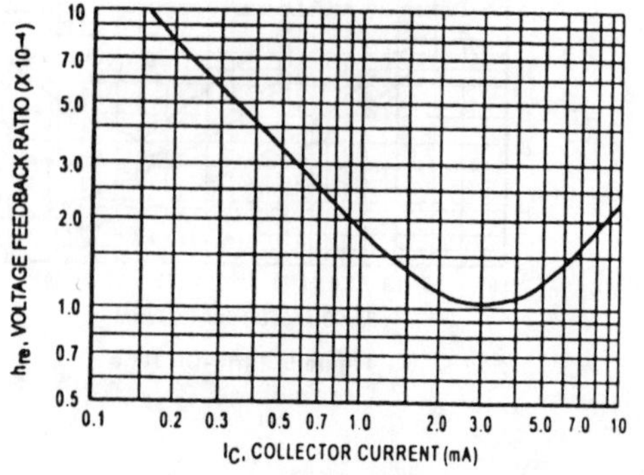

Figure 12. Voltage Feedback Ratio

TYPICAL STATIC CHARACTERISTICS

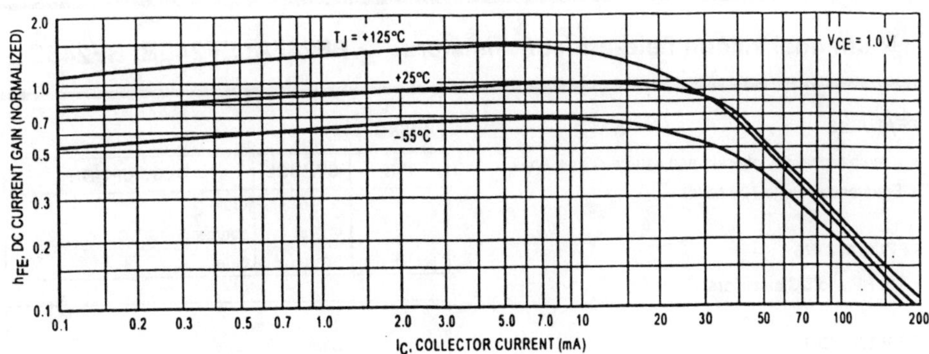

Figure 13. DC Current Gain

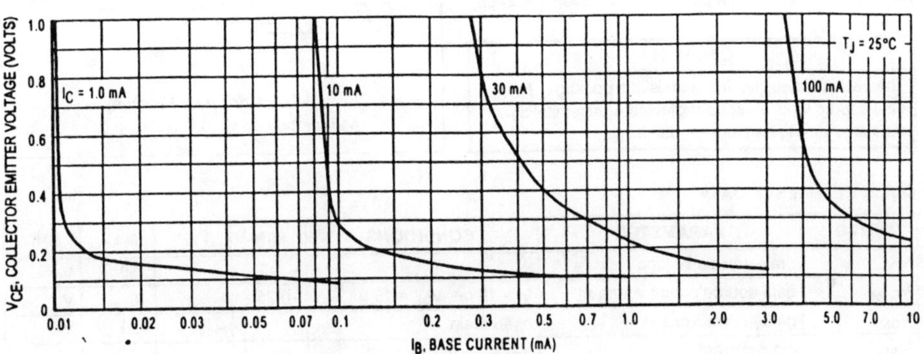

Figure 14. Collector Saturation Region

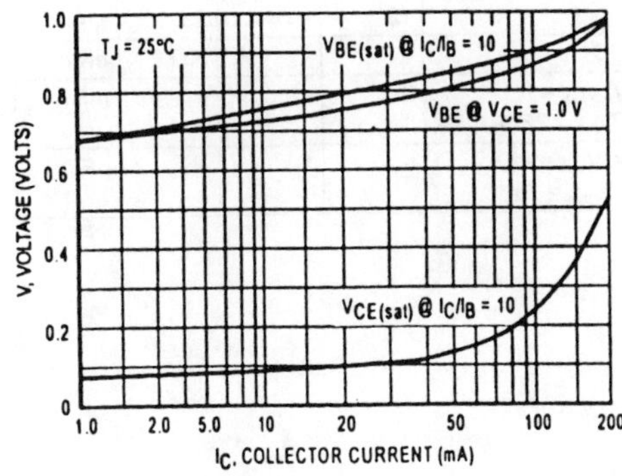

Figure 15. "ON" Voltages

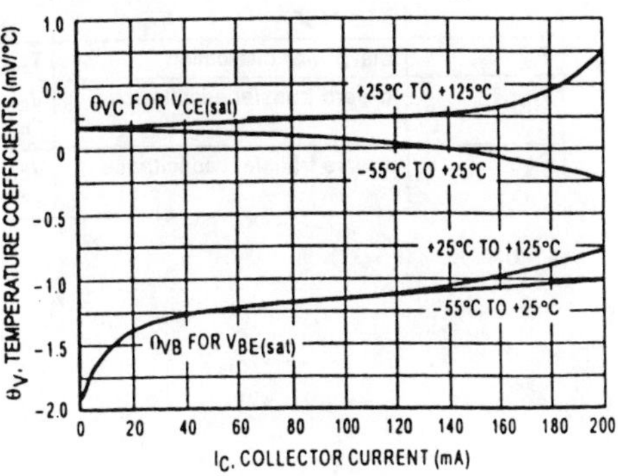

Figure 16. Temperature Coefficients

N-channel silicon field-effect transistors BF245A; BF245B; BF245C

FEATURES

- Interchangeability of drain and source connections
- Frequencies up to 700 MHz.

APPLICATIONS

- LF, HF and DC amplifiers.

DESCRIPTION

General purpose N-channel symmetrical junction field-effect transistors in a plastic TO-92 variant package.

CAUTION
The device is supplied in an antistatic package. The gate-source input must be protected against static discharge during transport or handling.

PINNING

PIN	SYMBOL	DESCRIPTION
1	d	drain
2	s	source
3	g	gate

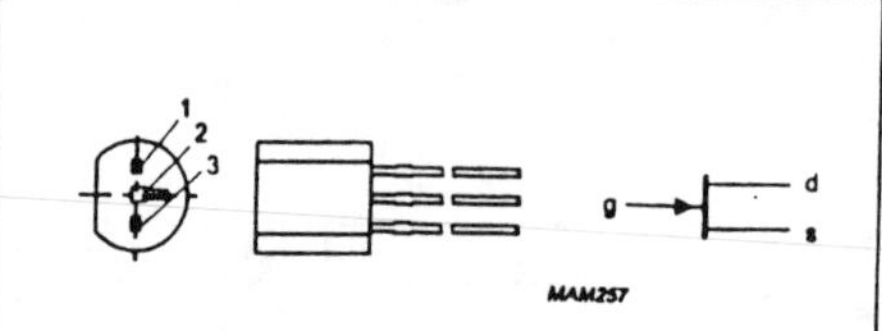

Fig.1 Simplified outline (TO-92 variant) and symbol.

QUICK REFERENCE DATA

SYMBOL	PARAMETER	CONDITIONS	MIN.	TYP.	MAX.	UNIT
V_{DS}	drain-source voltage		–	–	±30	V
V_{GSoff}	gate-source cut-off voltage	I_D = 10 nA; V_{DS} = 15 V	−0.25	–	−8	V
V_{GSO}	gate-source voltage	open drain	–	–	−30	V
I_{DSS}	drain current	V_{DS} = 15 V; V_{GS} = 0				
	BF245A		2	–	6.5	mA
	BF245B		6	–	15	mA
	BF245C		12	–	25	mA
P_{tot}	total power dissipation	T_{amb} = 75 °C	–	–	300	mW
$\|y_{fs}\|$	forward transfer admittance	V_{DS} = 15 V; V_{GS} = 0; f = 1 kHz; T_{amb} = 25 °C	3	–	6.5	mS
C_{rs}	reverse transfer capacitance	V_{DS} = 20 V; V_{GS} = −1 V; f = 1 MHz; T_{amb} = 25 °C	–	1.1	–	pF

N-channel silicon field-effect transistors BF245A; BF245B; BF245C

LIMITING VALUES

In accordance with the Absolute Maximum Rating System (IEC 134).

SYMBOL	PARAMETER	CONDITIONS	MIN.	MAX.	UNIT
V_{DS}	drain-source voltage		–	±30	V
V_{GDO}	gate-drain voltage	open source	–	−30	V
V_{GSO}	gate-source voltage	open drain	–	−30	V
I_D	drain current		–	25	mA
I_G	gate current		–	10	mA
P_{tot}	total power dissipation	up to T_{amb} = 75 °C;	–	300	mW
		up to T_{amb} = 90 °C; note 1	–	300	mW
T_{stg}	storage temperature		−65	+150	°C
T_j	operating junction temperature		–	150	°C

Note

1. Device mounted on a printed-circuit board, minimum lead length 3 mm, mounting pad for drain lead minimum 10 mm × 10 mm.

THERMAL CHARACTERISTICS

SYMBOL	PARAMETER	CONDITIONS	VALUE	UNIT
$R_{th\ j\text{-}a}$	thermal resistance from junction to ambient	in free air	250	K/W
	thermal resistance from junction to ambient		200	K/W

STATIC CHARACTERISTICS

T_j = 25 °C; unless otherwise specified.

SYMBOL	PARAMETER	CONDITIONS	MIN.	MAX.	UNIT
$V_{(BR)GSS}$	gate-source breakdown voltage	I_G = −1 μA; V_{DS} = 0	−30	–	V
V_{GSoff}	gate-source cut-off voltage	I_D = 10 nA; V_{DS} = 15 V	−0.25	−8.0	V
V_{GS}	gate-source voltage	I_D = 200 μA; V_{DS} = 15 V			
	BF245A		−0.4	−2.2	V
	BF245B		−1.6	−3.8	V
	BF245C		−3.2	−7.5	V
I_{DSS}	drain current	V_{DS} = 15 V; V_{GS} = 0; note 1			
	BF245A		2	6.5	mA
	BF245B		6	15	mA
	BF245C		12	25	mA
I_{GSS}	gate cut-off current	V_{GS} = −20 V; V_{DS} = 0	–	−5	nA
		V_{GS} = −20 V; V_{DS} = 0; T_j = 125 °C	–	−0.5	μA

Note

1. Measured under pulse conditions: t_p = 300 μs; δ ≤ 0.02.

N-channel silicon field-effect transistors BF245A; BF245B; BF245C

DYNAMIC CHARACTERISTICS

Common source; T_{amb} = 25 °C; unless otherwise specified.

SYMBOL	PARAMETER	CONDITIONS	MIN.	TYP.	MAX.	UNIT
C_{is}	input capacitance	V_{DS} = 20 V; V_{GS} = −1 V; f = 1 MHz	–	4	–	pF
C_{rs}	reverse transfer capacitance	V_{DS} = 20 V; V_{GS} = −1 V; f = 1 MHz	–	1.1	–	pF
C_{os}	output capacitance	V_{DS} = 20 V; V_{GS} = −1 V; f = 1 MHz	–	1.6	–	pF
g_{is}	input conductance	V_{DS} = 15 V; V_{GS} = 0; f = 200 MHz	–	250	–	μS
g_{os}	output conductance	V_{DS} = 15 V; V_{GS} = 0; f = 200 MHz	–	40	–	μS
$\lvert y_{fs} \rvert$	forward transfer admittance	V_{DS} = 15 V; V_{GS} = 0; f = 1 kHz	3	–	6.5	mS
		V_{DS} = 15 V; V_{GS} = 0; f = 200 MHz	–	6	–	mS
$\lvert y_{rs} \rvert$	reverse transfer admittance	V_{DS} = 15 V; V_{GS} = 0; f = 200 MHz	–	1.4	–	mS
$\lvert y_{os} \rvert$	output admittance	V_{DS} = 15 V; V_{GS} = 0; f = 1 kHz	–	25	–	μS
f_{gfs}	cut-off frequency	V_{DS} = 15 V; V_{GS} = 0; g_{fs} = 0.7 of its value at 1 kHz	–	700	–	MHz
F	noise figure	V_{DS} = 15 V; V_{GS} = 0; f = 100 MHz; R_G = 1 kΩ (common source); input tuned to minimum noise	–	1.5	–	dB

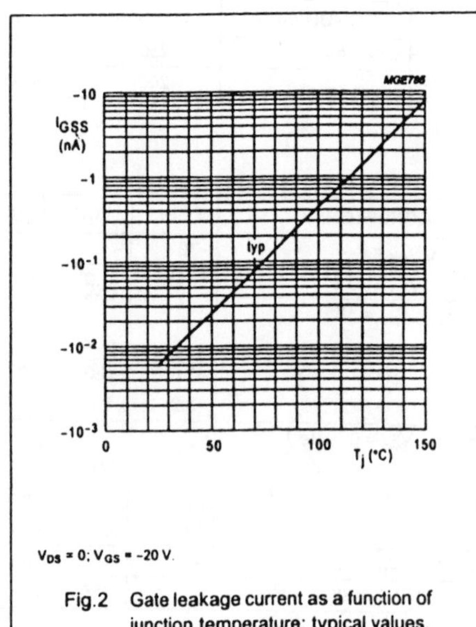

Fig.2 Gate leakage current as a function of junction temperature; typical values.

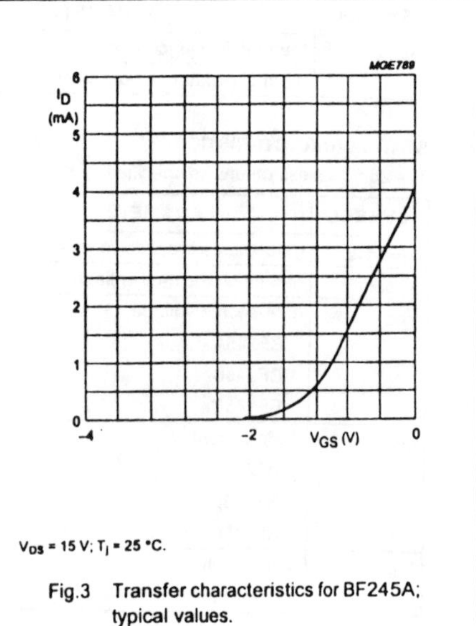

Fig.3 Transfer characteristics for BF245A; typical values.

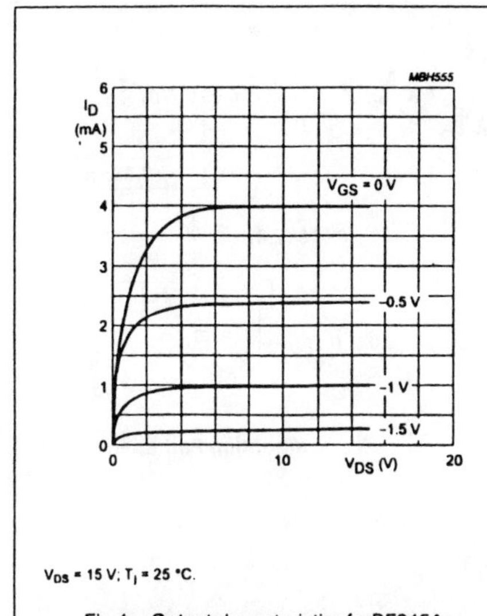

V_{DS} = 15 V; T_j = 25 °C.

Fig.4 Output characteristics for BF245A; typical values.

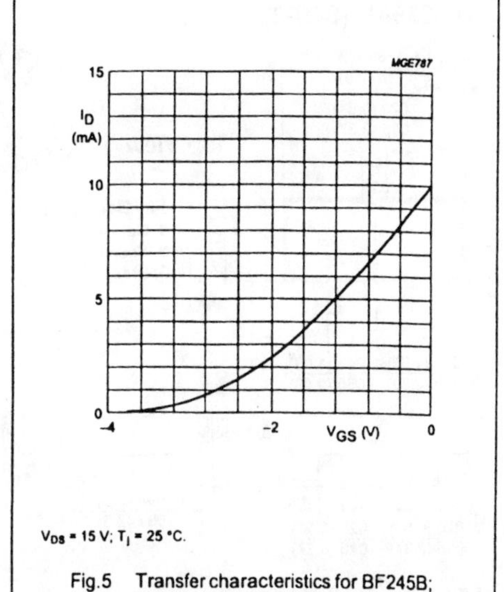

V_{DS} = 15 V; T_j = 25 °C.

Fig.5 Transfer characteristics for BF245B; typical values.

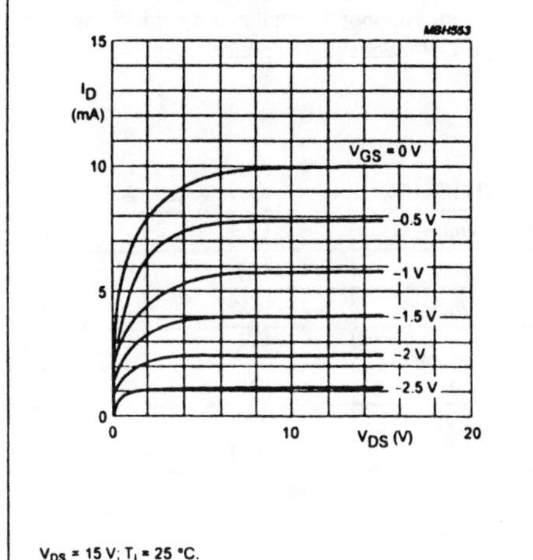

V_{DS} = 15 V; T_j = 25 °C.

Fig.6 Output characteristics for BF245B; typical values.

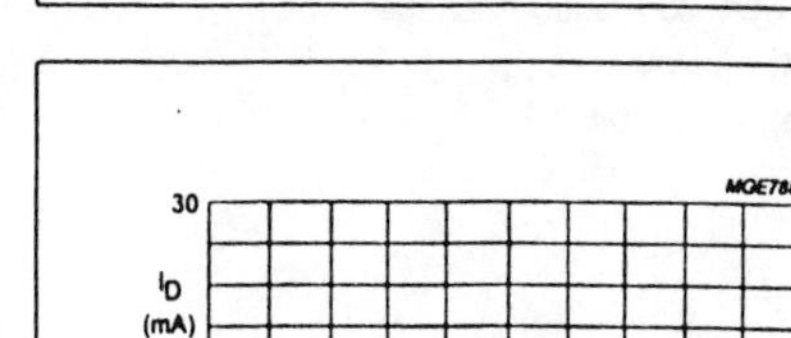

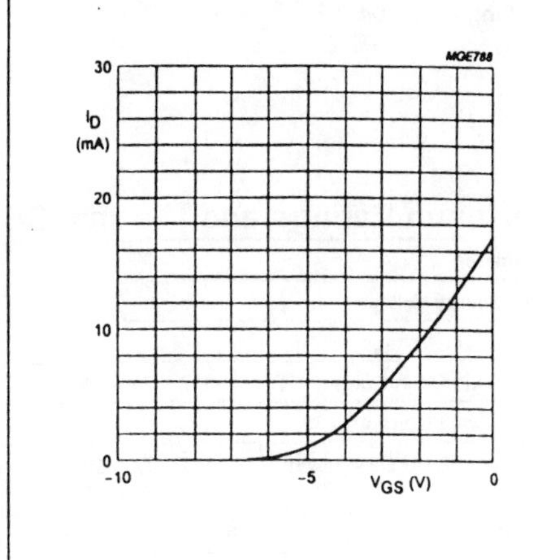

V_{DS} = 15 V; T_j = 25 °C.

Fig.7 Transfer characteristics for BF245C; typical values.

GF2304

N-Channel Enhancement-Mode MOSFET

V_{DS} 30V $R_{DS(ON)}$ 0.117Ω I_D 2.5A

TO-236AB (SOT-23)

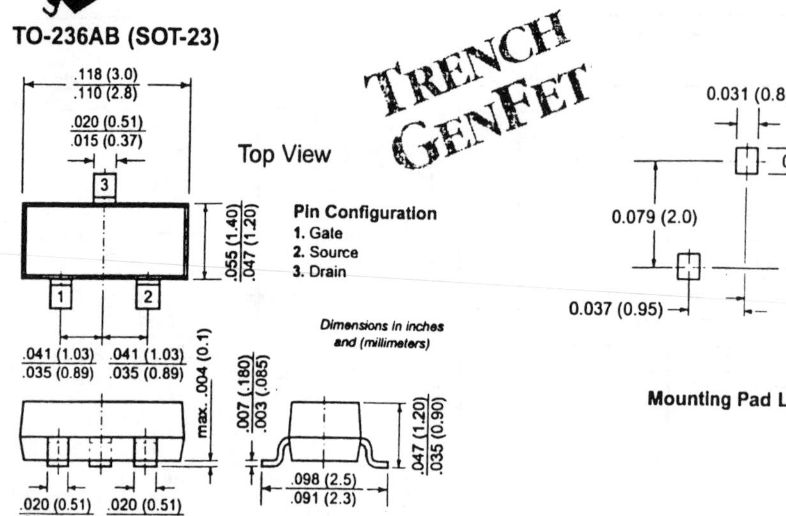

Mechanical Data

Case: SOT-23 Plastic Package
Weight: approx. 0.008g
Marking Code: 04

Features

- Advanced trench process technology
- High density cell design for ultra-low on-resistance
- Popular SOT-23 package with copper lead-frame for superior thermal and electrical capabilities
- Compact and low profile

Maximum Ratings and Thermal Characteristics (T_A = 25°C unless otherwise noted)

Parameter	Symbol	Limit	Unit
Drain-Source Voltage	V_{DS}	30	V
Gate-Source-Voltage	V_{GS}	±20	V
Continuous Drain Current T_J = 150°C T_A = 25°C	I_D	2.5	A
Pulsed Drain Current[1]	I_{DM}	10	A
Maximum Power Dissipation[2] T_A = 25°C T_A = 70°C	P_D	1.25 0.80	W
Operating Junction and Storage Temperature Range	T_J, T_{stg}	–55 to +150	°C
Maximum Junction-to-Ambient Thermal Resistance[2]	$R_{\theta JA}$	100	°C/W

Notes:
(1) Pulse width limited by maximum junction temperature.
(2) Surface mounted on FR4 board, (1" x 1", 2oz. Cu)

5/3/01

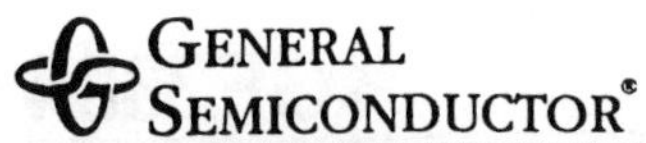

GF2304

N-Channel Enhancement-Mode MOSFET

V_{DS} 30V $R_{DS(ON)}$ 0.117Ω I_D 2.5A

Electrical Characteristics (T_J = 25°C unless otherwise noted)

Parameter	Symbol	Test Condition	Min	Typ	Max	Unit
Static						
Drain-Source Breakdown Voltage	BV_{DSS}	V_{GS} = 0V, I_D = 250μA	30	–	–	V
Gate Threshold Voltage	$V_{GS(th)}$	V_{DS} = V_{GS}, I_D = 250μA	1.0	–	—	V
Gate-Body Leakage	I_{GSS}	V_{DS} = 0V, V_{GS} = ±20V	–	–	±100	nA
Zero Gate Voltage Drain Current	I_{DSS}	V_{DS} = 30V, V_{GS} = 0V	–	–	0.5	μA
		V_{DS}=30V, V_{GS}=0V, T_J=55°C	–	–	10	
On-State Drain Current[1]	$I_{D(on)}$	V_{DS} ≥ 4.5V, V_{GS} = 10V	6	–	–	A
		V_{DS} ≥ 4.5V, V_{GS} = 4.5V	4	–	–	
Drain-Source On-State Resistance[1]	$R_{DS(on)}$	V_{GS} = 10V, I_D = 2.5A	–	0.096	0.117	Ω
		V_{GS} = 4.5V, I_D = 2.0A	–	0.135	0.190	
Forward Transconductance[1]	g_{fs}	V_{DS} = 4.5V, I_D = 2.5A	–	4.6	–	S
Dynamic						
Total Gate Charge	Q_g	V_{DS} = 15V, V_{GS} = 10V I_D = 2.5A	–	3.7	10	nC
Gate-Source Charge	Q_{gs}		–	0.5	-	
Gate-Drain Charge	Q_{gd}		–	0.6	-	
Turn-On Delay Time	$t_{d(on)}$	V_{DD} = 15V, R_L = 15Ω I_D ≈ 1A, V_{GEN} = 10V R_G = 6Ω	–	6	20	ns
Rise Time	t_r		–	8.8	30	
Turn-Off Delay Time	$t_{d(off)}$		–	26	35	
Fall Time	t_f		–	2.4	20	
Input Capacitance	C_{iss}	V_{GS} = 0V V_{DS} = 15V f = 1.0MHz	–	163	-	pF
Output Capacitance	C_{oss}		–	27	-	
Reverse Transfer Capacitance	C_{rss}		–	9	-	
Source-Drain Diode						
Maximum Diode Forward Current	I_S	—	—	—	2.1	A
Diode Forward Voltage	V_{SD}	I_S = 1.25A, V_{GS} = 0V	–	0.82	1.2	V

Note: (1) Pulse test; pulse width ≤ 300 μs, duty cycle ≤ 2%

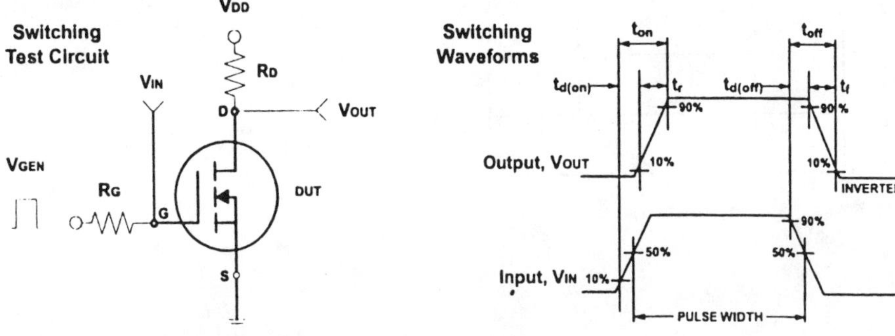

GF2304

N-Channel Enhancement-Mode MOSFET

Ratings and Characteristic Curves (T_A = 25°C unless otherwise noted)

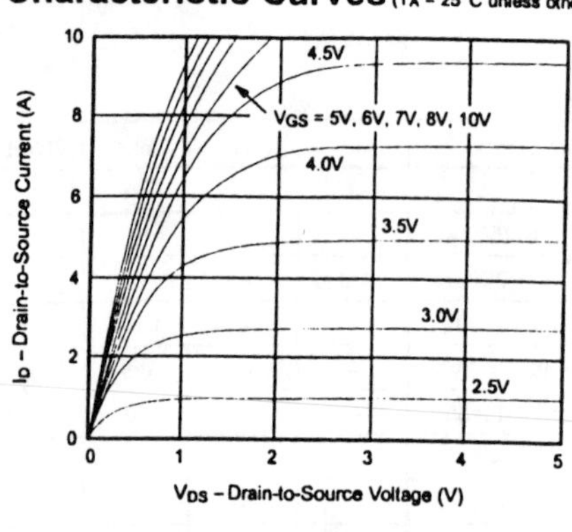

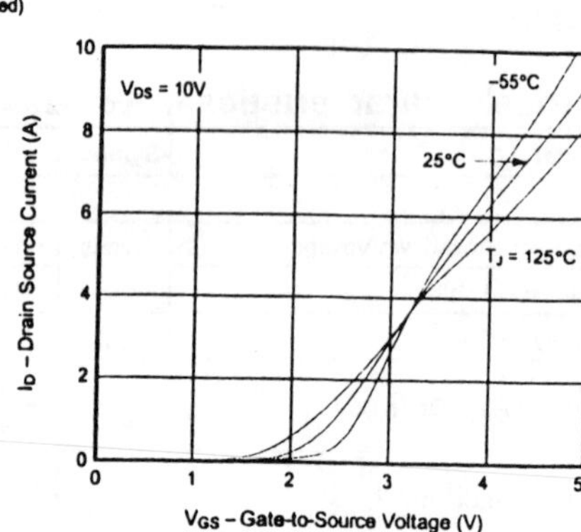

Fig. 3 – Capacitance

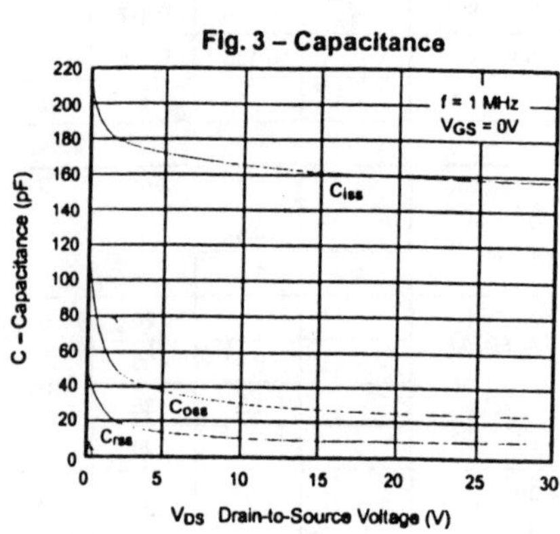

Fig. 4 – On-Resistance vs. Drain Current

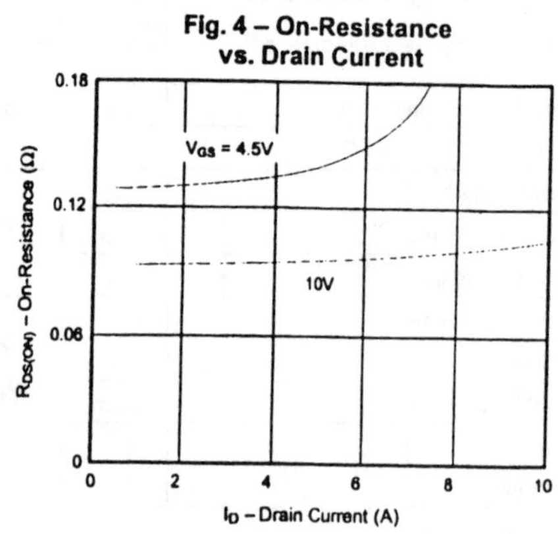

Fig. 5 – Gate Charge

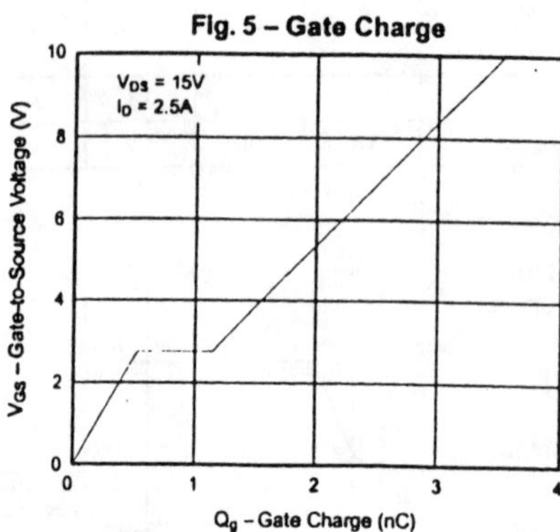

GF2304

N-Channel Enhancement-Mode MOSFET

Ratings and Characteristic Curves (TA = 25°C unless otherwise noted)

Fig. 6 – On-Resistance vs. Gate-to-Source Voltage

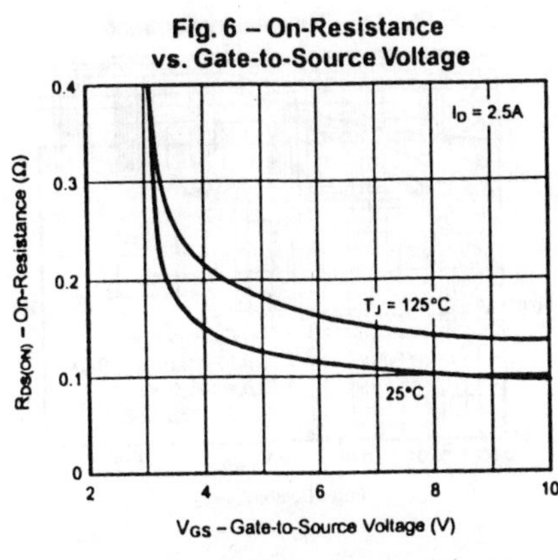

Fig. 7 – Source-Drain Diode Forward Voltage

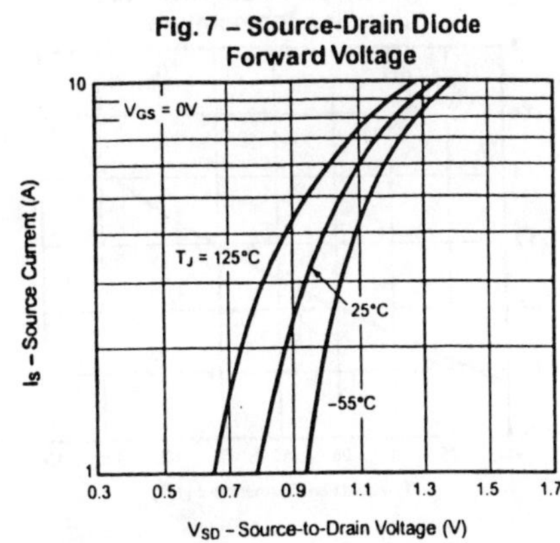

Fig. 8 – Breakdown Voltage vs. Junction Temperature

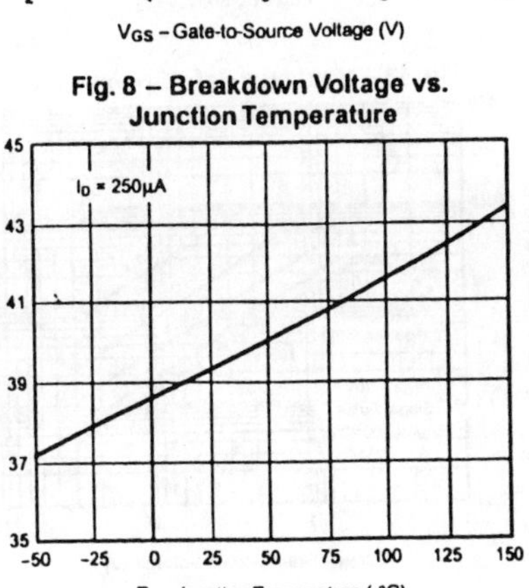

Fig. 9 – Threshold Voltage

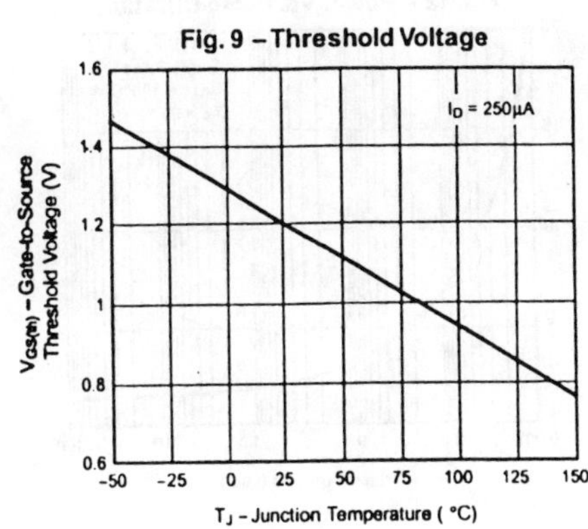

GF2304

N-Channel Enhancement-Mode MOSFET

Ratings and Characteristic Curves (T_A = 25°C unless otherwise noted)

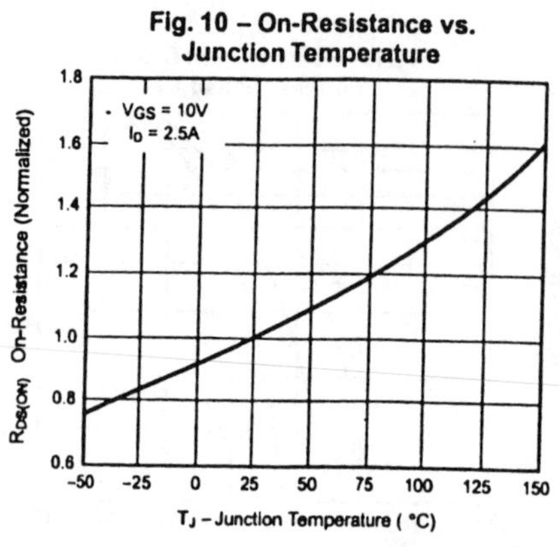

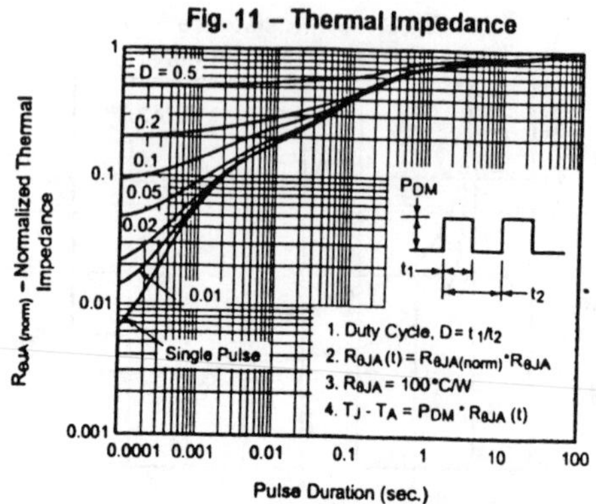

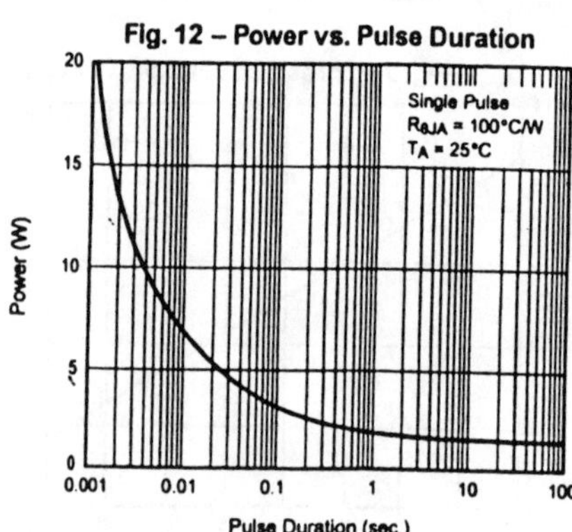

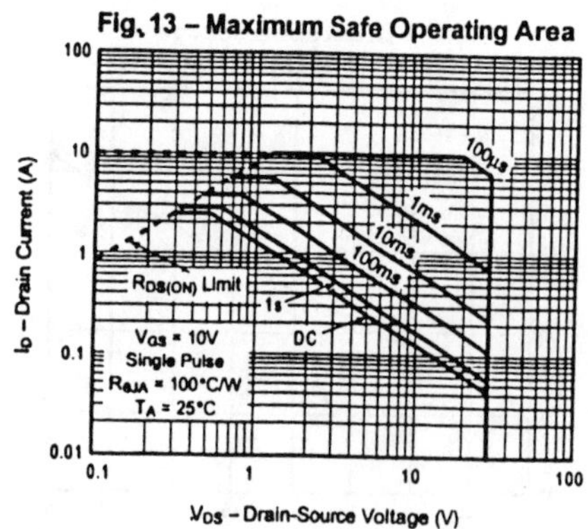

MC7800, MC7800A, LM340, LM340A Series

Three-Terminal Positive Voltage Regulators

These voltage regulators are monolithic integrated circuits designed as fixed-voltage regulators for a wide variety of applications including local, on-card regulation. These regulators employ internal current limiting, thermal shutdown, and safe-area compensation. With adequate heatsinking they can deliver output currents in excess of 1.0 A. Although designed primarily as a fixed voltage regulator, these devices can be used with external components to obtain adjustable voltages and currents.

- Output Current in Excess of 1.0 A
- No External Components Required
- Internal Thermal Overload Protection
- Internal Short Circuit Current Limiting
- Output Transistor Safe-Area Compensation
- Output Voltage Offered in 2% and 4% Tolerance
- Available in Surface Mount D ²PAK, DPAK and Standard 3-Lead Transistor Packages

MAXIMUM RATINGS (T_A = 25°C, unless otherwise noted.)

Rating	Symbol	Value	Unit
Input Voltage (5.0 – 18 V)	V_I	35	Vdc
(24 V)		40	
Power Dissipation			
Case 221A (TO-220)			
T_A = 25°C	P_D	Internally Limited	W
Thermal Resistance, Junction-to-Ambient	$R_{\theta JA}$	65	°C/W
Thermal Resistance, Junction-to-Case	$R_{\theta JC}$	5.0	°C/W
Case 936 (D^2PAK)			
T_A = 25°C	P_D	Internally Limited	W
Thermal Resistance, Junction-to-Ambient	$R_{\theta JA}$	See Figure 14	°C/W
Thermal Resistance, Junction-to-Case	$R_{\theta JA}$	5.0	°C/W
Case 369A (DPAK)			
T_A = 25°C	P_D	Internally Limited	W
Thermal Resistance, Junction-to-Ambient	$R_{\theta JA}$	92	°C/W
Thermal Resistance, Junction-to-Case	$R_{\theta JC}$	5.0	°C/W
Storage Junction Temperature Range	T_{stg}	–65 to +150	°C
Operating Junction Temperature	T_J	+150	°C

NOTE: ESD data available upon request.

ON Semiconductor™

http://onsemi.com

TO-220
T SUFFIX
CASE 221A

Heatsink surface connected to Pin 2.

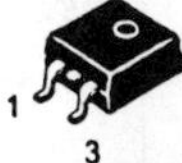

D^2PAK
D2T SUFFIX
CASE 936

Pin 1. Input
2. Ground
3. Output

Heatsink surface (shown as terminal 4 in case outline drawing) is connected to Pin 2.

DPAK
DT SUFFIX
CASE 369A

STANDARD APPLICATION

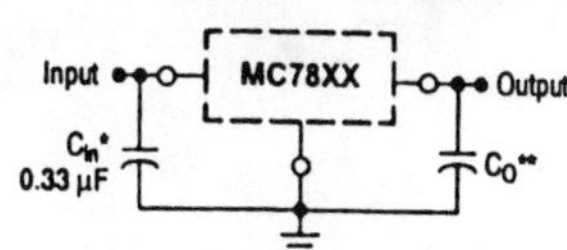

A common ground is required between the input and the output voltages. The input voltage must remain typically 2.0 V above the output voltage even during the low point on the input ripple voltage.

XX, These two digits of the type number indicate nominal voltage.

* C_{in} is required if regulator is located an appreciable distance from power supply filter.

** C_O is not needed for stability; however, it does improve transient response. Values of less than 0.1 μF could cause instability.

ORDERING INFORMATION

See detailed ordering and shipping information in the package dimensions section on page 16 of this data sheet.

DEVICE MARKING INFORMATION

See general marking information in the device marking section on page 18 of this data sheet.

MC7800, MC7800A, LM340, LM340A Series

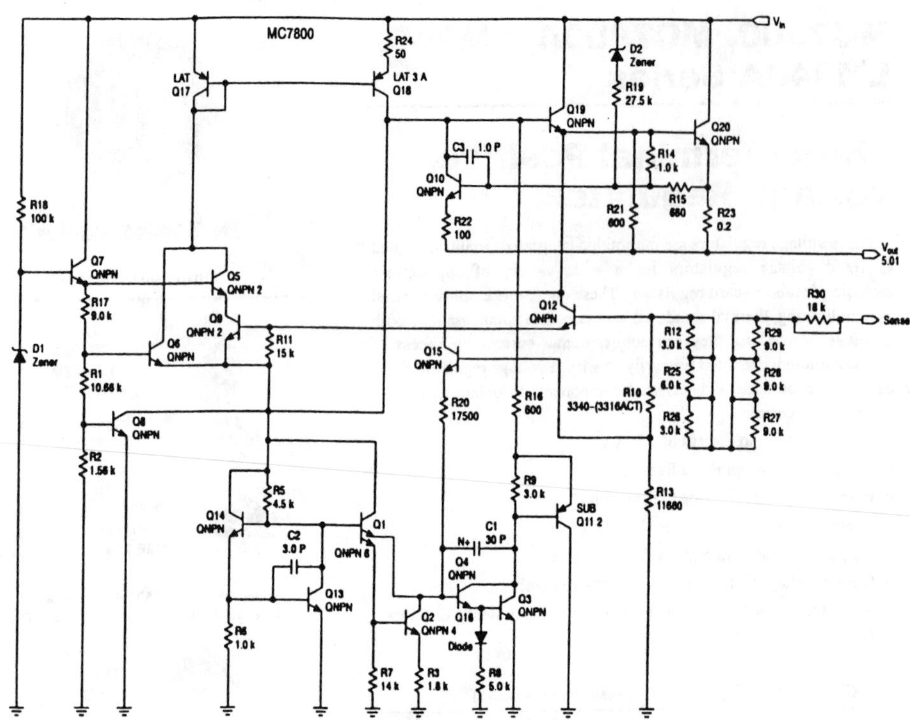

This device contains 22 active transistors.

Figure 1. Representative Schematic Diagram

MC7800, MC7800A, LM340, LM340A Series

ELECTRICAL CHARACTERISTICS (V_{in} = 10 V, I_O = 500 mA, T_J = T_{low} to T_{high} [Note 1], unless otherwise noted.)

Characteristic	Symbol	MC7805B Min	MC7805B Typ	MC7805B Max	MC7805C/LM340T-5 Min	MC7805C/LM340T-5 Typ	MC7805C/LM340T-5 Max	Unit
Output Voltage (T_J = 25°C)	V_O	4.8	5.0	5.2	4.8	5.0	5.2	Vdc
Output Voltage (5.0 mA ≤ I_O ≤ 1.0 A, P_D ≤ 15 W)	V_O							Vdc
7.0 Vdc ≤ V_{in} ≤ 20 Vdc		–	–	–	4.75	5.0	5.25	
8.0 Vdc ≤ V_{in} ≤ 20 Vdc		4.75	5.0	5.25	–	–	–	
Line Regulation (Note 2)	Reg_{line}							mV
7.5 Vdc ≤ V_{in} ≤ 20 Vdc, 1.0 A		–	5.0	100	–	0.5	20	
8.0 Vdc ≤ V_{in} ≤ 12 Vdc		–	1.3	50	–	0.8	10	
Load Regulation (Note 2)	Reg_{load}							mV
5.0 mA ≤ I_O ≤ 1.0 A		–	1.3	100	–	1.3	25	
5.0 mA ≤ I_O ≤ 1.5 A (T_A = 25°C)		–	0.15	50	–	1.3	25	
Quiescent Current	I_B	–	3.2	8.0	–	3.2	6.5	mA
Quiescent Current Change	ΔI_B							mA
7.0 Vdc ≤ V_{in} ≤ 25 Vdc		–	–	–	–	0.3	1.0	
5.0 mA ≤ I_O ≤ 1.0 A (T_A = 25°C)		–	–	0.5	–	0.08	0.8	
Ripple Rejection 8.0 Vdc ≤ V_{in} ≤ 18 Vdc, f = 120 Hz	RR	–	68	–	62	83	–	dB
Dropout Voltage (I_O = 1.0 A, T_J = 25°C)	$V_I - V_O$	–	2.0	–	–	2.0	–	Vdc
Output Noise Voltage (T_A = 25°C) 10 Hz ≤ f ≤ 100 kHz	V_n	–	10	–	–	10	–	µV/V_O
Output Resistance f = 1.0 kHz	r_O	–	0.9	–	–	0.9	–	mΩ
Short Circuit Current Limit (T_A = 25°C) V_{in} = 35 Vdc	I_{SC}	–	0.2	–	–	0.6	–	A
Peak Output Current (T_J = 25°C)	I_{max}	–	2.2	–	–	2.2	–	A
Average Temperature Coefficient of Output Voltage	TCV_O	–	–0.3	–	–	–0.3	–	mV/°C

ELECTRICAL CHARACTERISTICS (V_{in} = 10 V, I_O = 1.0 A, T_J = T_{low} to T_{high} [Note 1], unless otherwise noted.)

Characteristic	Symbol	MC7805AB/MC7805AC/LM340AT-5 Min	Typ	Max	Unit
Output Voltage (T_J = 25°C)	V_O	4.9	5.0	5.1	Vdc
Output Voltage (5.0 mA ≤ I_O ≤ 1.0 A, P_D ≤ 15 W) 7.5 Vdc ≤ V_{in} ≤ 20 Vdc	V_O	4.8	5.0	5.2	Vdc
Line Regulation (Note 2)	Reg_{line}				mV
7.5 Vdc ≤ V_{in} ≤ 25 Vdc, I_O = 500 mA		–	0.5	10	
8.0 Vdc ≤ V_{in} ≤ 12 Vdc, I_O = 1.0 A		–	0.8	12	
8.0 Vdc ≤ V_{in} ≤ 12 Vdc, I_O = 1.0 A, T_J = 25°C		–	1.3	4.0	
7.3 Vdc ≤ V_{in} ≤ 20 Vdc, I_O = 1.0 A, T_J = 25°C		–	4.5	10	
Load Regulation (Note 2)	Reg_{load}				mV
5.0 mA ≤ I_O ≤ 1.5 A, T_J = 25°C		–	1.3	25	
5.0 mA ≤ I_O ≤ 1.0 A		–	0.8	25	
250 mA ≤ I_O ≤ 750 mA		–	0.53	15	
Quiescent Current	I_B	–	3.2	6.0	mA
Quiescent Current Change	ΔI_B				mA
8.0 Vdc ≤ V_{in} ≤ 25 Vdc, I_O = 500 mA		–	0.3	0.8	
7.5 Vdc ≤ V_{in} ≤ 20 Vdc, T_J = 25°C		–	–	0.8	
5.0 mA ≤ I_O ≤ 1.0 A		–	0.08	0.5	

1. T_{low} = 0°C for MC78XXAC, C, LM340AT–XX, LM340T–XX T_{high} = +125°C for MC78XXAC, C, LM340AT–XX, LM340T–XX
   = –40°C for MC78XXB, MC78XXAB
2. Load and line regulation are specified at constant junction temperature. Changes in V_O due to heating effects must be taken into account separately. Pulse testing with low duty cycle is used.

MC7800, MC7800A, LM340, LM340A Series

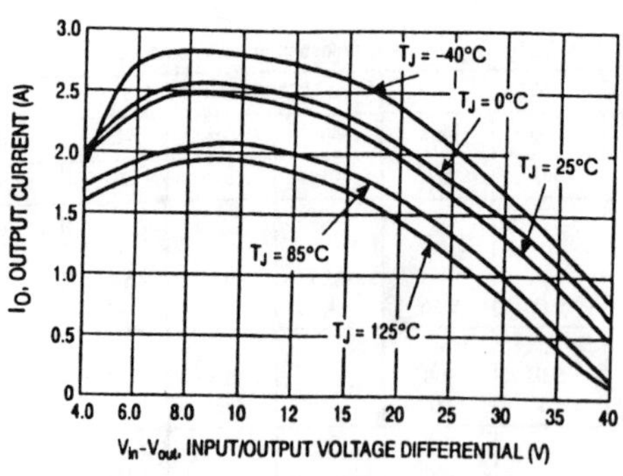

Figure 2. Peak Output Current as a Function of Input/Output Differential Voltage (MC78XXC, AC, B)

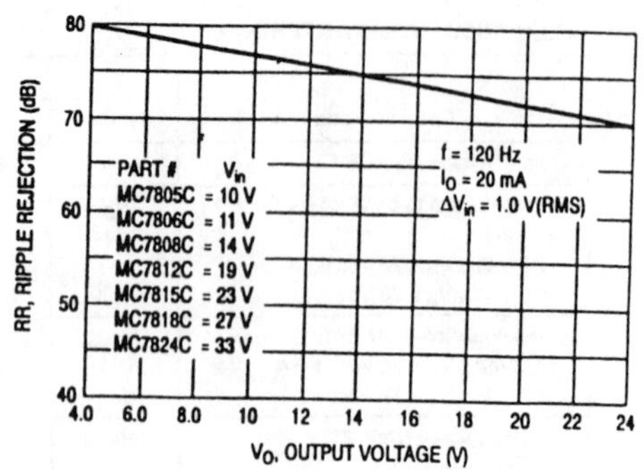

Figure 3. Ripple Rejection as a Function of Output Voltages (MC78XXC, AC, B)

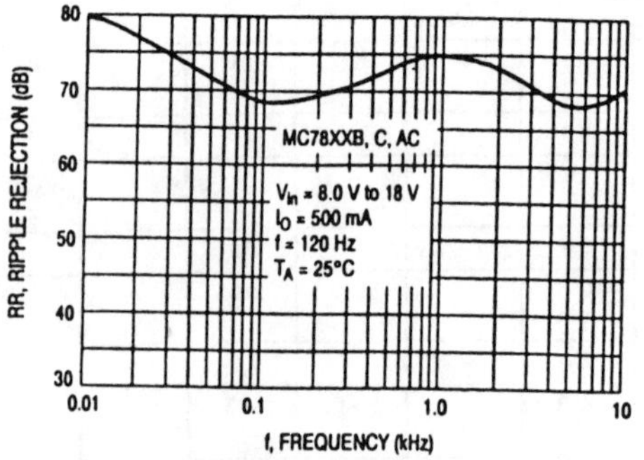

Figure 4. Ripple Rejection as a Function of Frequency (MC78XXC, AC, B)

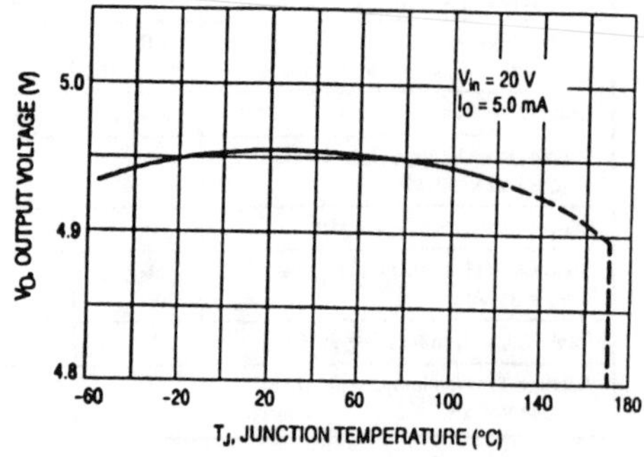

Figure 5. Output Voltage as a Function of Junction Temperature (MC7805C, AC, B)

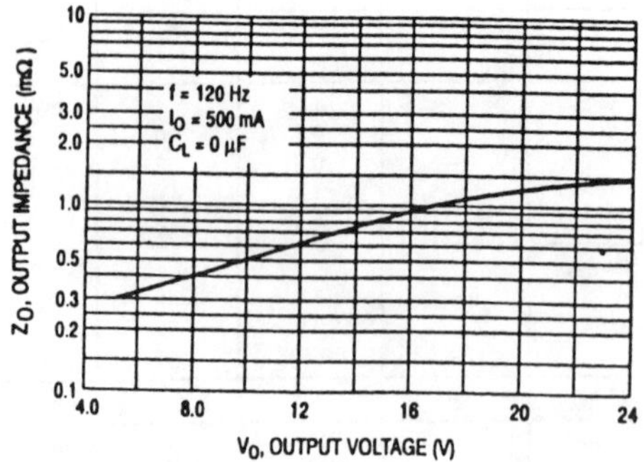

Figure 6. Output Impedance as a Function of Output Voltage (MC78XXC, AC, B)

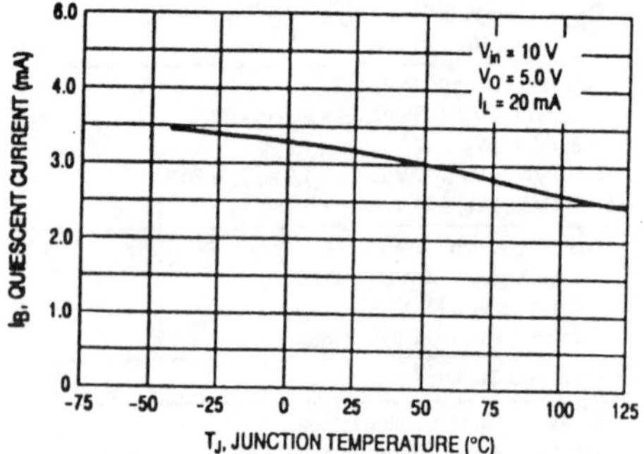

Figure 7. Quiescent Current as a Function of Temperature (MC78XXC, AC, B)

MC7800, MC7800A, LM340, LM340A Series

APPLICATIONS INFORMATION

Design Considerations

The MC7800 Series of fixed voltage regulators are designed with Thermal Overload Protection that shuts down the circuit when subjected to an excessive power overload condition, Internal Short Circuit Protection that limits the maximum current the circuit will pass, and Output Transistor Safe–Area Compensation that reduces the output short circuit current as the voltage across the pass transistor is increased.

In many low current applications, compensation capacitors are not required. However, it is recommended that the regulator input be bypassed with a capacitor if the regulator is connected to the power supply filter with long wire lengths, or if the output load capacitance is large. An input bypass capacitor should be selected to provide good high–frequency characteristics to insure stable operation under all load conditions. A 0.33 μF or larger tantalum, mylar, or other capacitor having low internal impedance at high frequencies should be chosen. The bypass capacitor should be mounted with the shortest possible leads directly across the regulators input terminals. Normally good construction techniques should be used to minimize ground loops and lead resistance drops since the regulator has no external sense lead.

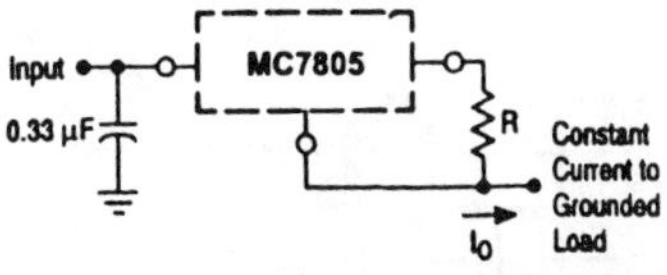

The MC7800 regulators can also be used as a current source when connected as above. In order to minimize dissipation the MC7805C is chosen in this application. Resistor R determines the current as follows:

$$I_O = \frac{5.0\ V}{R} + I_B$$

I_B ≅ 3.2 mA over line and load changes.

For example, a 1.0 A current source would require R to be a 5.0 Ω, 10 W resistor and the output voltage compliance would be the input voltage less 7.0 V.

Figure 8. Current Regulator

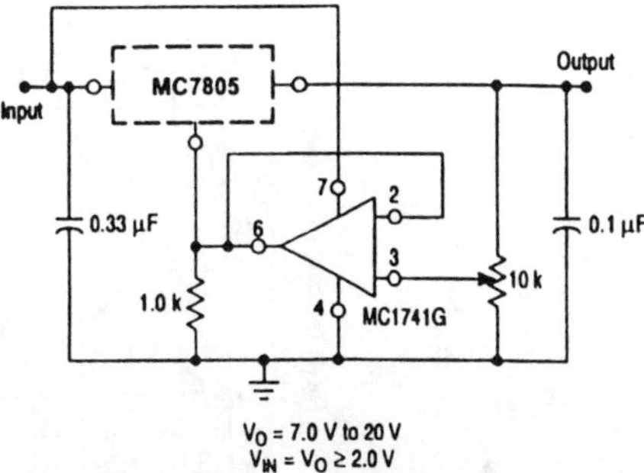

The addition of an operational amplifier allows adjustment to higher or intermediate values while retaining regulation characteristics. The minimum voltage obtainable with this arrangement is 2.0 V greater than the regulator voltage.

Figure 9. Adjustable Output Regulator

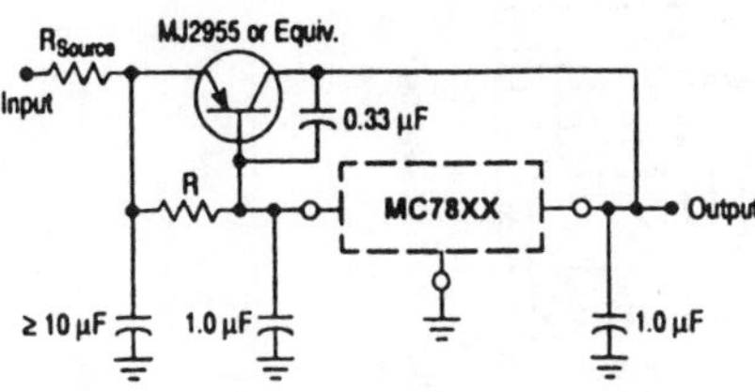

XX = 2 digits of type number indicating voltage.

The MC7800 series can be current boosted with a PNP transistor. The MJ2955 provides current to 5.0 A. Resistor R in conjunction with the V_{BE} of the PNP determines when the pass transistor begins conducting; this circuit is not short circuit proof. Input/output differential voltage minimum is increased by V_{BE} of the pass transistor.

Figure 10. Current Boost Regulator

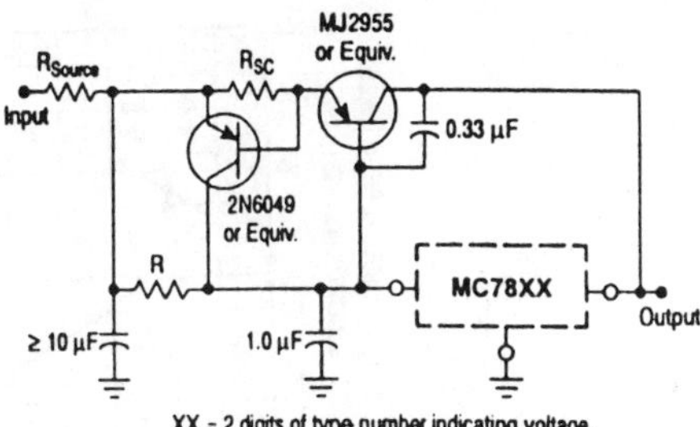

XX = 2 digits of type number indicating voltage.

The circuit of Figure 10 can be modified to provide supply protection against short circuits by adding a short circuit sense resistor, R_{SC}, and an additional PNP transistor. The current sensing PNP must be able to handle the short circuit current of the three–terminal regulator. Therefore, a four–ampere plastic power transistor is specified.

Figure 11. Short Circuit Protection

MC7800, MC7800A, LM340, LM340A Series

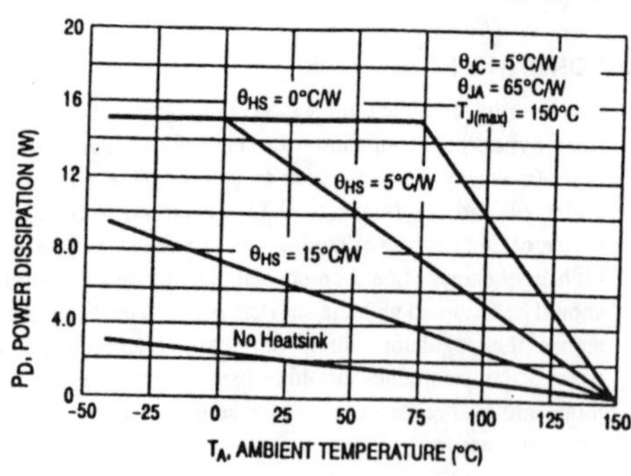

Figure 12. Worst Case Power Dissipation versus Ambient Temperature (Case 221A)

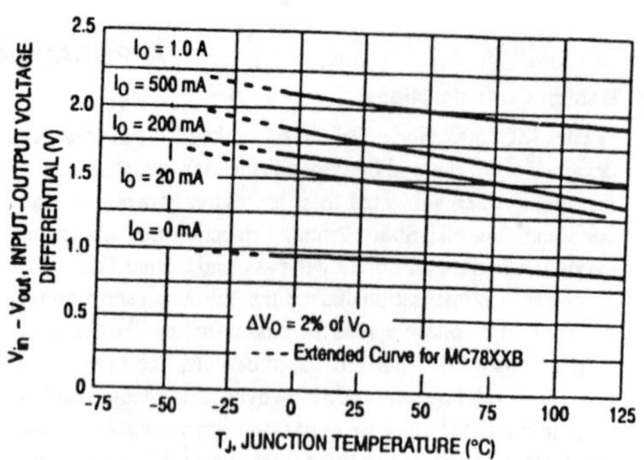

Figure 13. Input Output Differential as a Function of Junction Temperature (MC78XXC, AC, B)

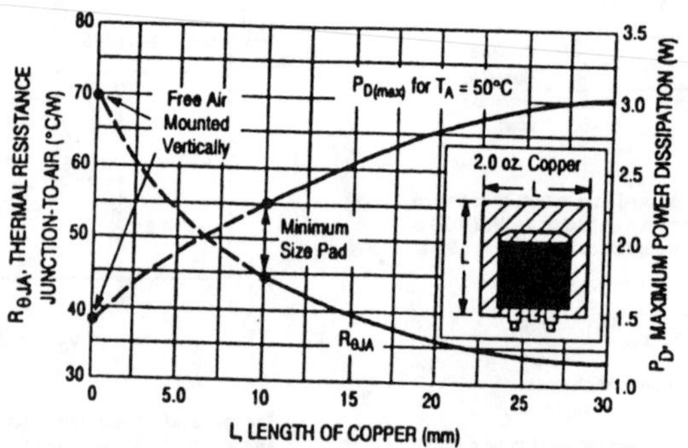

Figure 14. D²PAK Thermal Resistance and Maximum Power Dissipation versus P.C.B. Copper Length

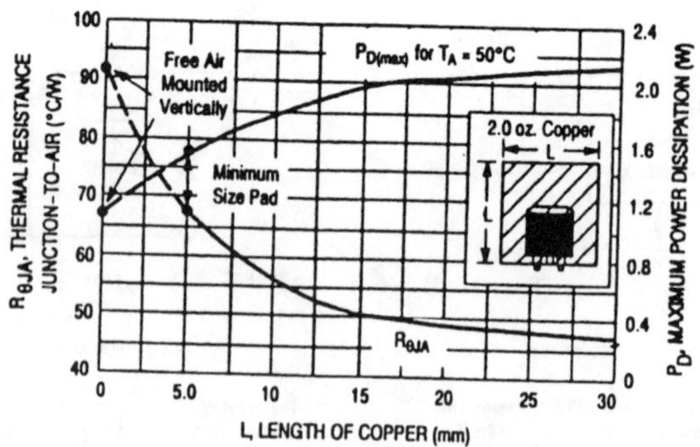

Figure 15. DPAK Thermal Resistance and Maximum Power Dissipation versus P.C.B. Copper Length

National Semiconductor

August 2000

LM741
Operational Amplifier

General Description

The LM741 series are general purpose operational amplifiers which feature improved performance over industry standards like the LM709. They are direct, plug-in replacements for the 709C, LM201, MC1439 and 748 in most applications.

The amplifiers offer many features which make their application nearly foolproof: overload protection on the input and output, no latch-up when the common mode range is exceeded, as well as freedom from oscillations.

The LM741C is identical to the LM741/LM741A except that the LM741C has their performance guaranteed over a 0°C to +70°C temperature range, instead of −55°C to +125°C.

Connection Diagrams

Metal Can Package

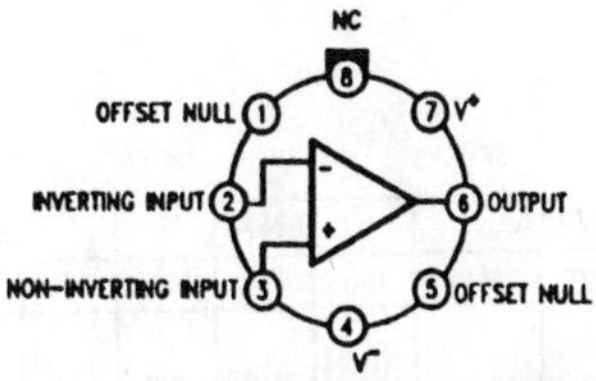

Note 1: LM741H is available per JM38510/10101

Order Number LM741H, LM741H/883 (Note 1), LM741AH/883 or LM741CH
See NS Package Number H08C

Dual-In-Line or S.O. Package

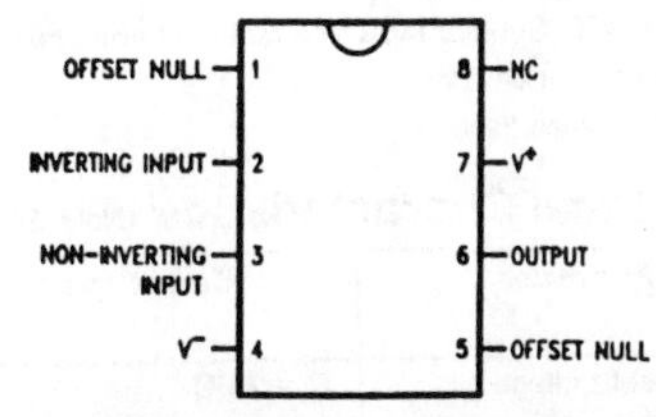

Order Number LM741J, LM741J/883, LM741CN
See NS Package Number J08A, M08A or N08E

Ceramic Flatpak

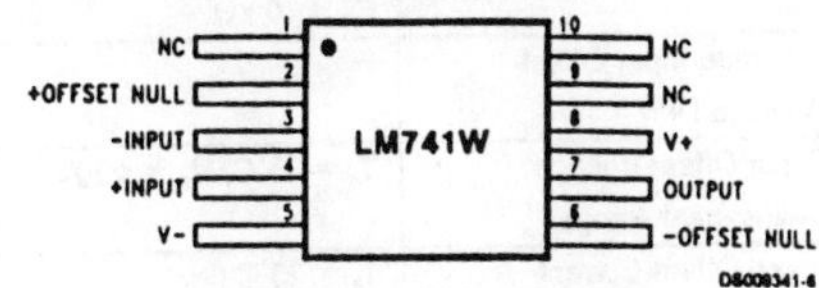

Order Number LM741W/883
See NS Package Number W10A

Typical Application

Offset Nulling Circuit

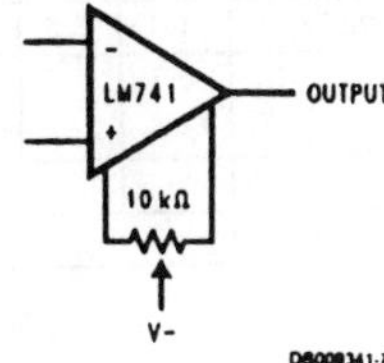

Absolute Maximum Ratings (Note 2)

If Military/Aerospace specified devices are required, please contact the National Semiconductor Sales Office/ Distributors for availability and specifications.

(Note 7)

	LM741A	LM741	LM741C
Supply Voltage	±22V	±22V	±18V
Power Dissipation (Note 3)	500 mW	500 mW	500 mW
Differential Input Voltage	±30V	±30V	±30V
Input Voltage (Note 4)	±15V	±15V	±15V
Output Short Circuit Duration	Continuous	Continuous	Continuous
Operating Temperature Range	−55°C to +125°C	−55°C to +125°C	0°C to +70°C
Storage Temperature Range	−65°C to +150°C	−65°C to +150°C	−65°C to +150°C
Junction Temperature	150°C	150°C	100°C
Soldering Information			
N-Package (10 seconds)	260°C	260°C	260°C
J- or H-Package (10 seconds)	300°C	300°C	300°C
M-Package			
Vapor Phase (60 seconds)	215°C	215°C	215°C
Infrared (15 seconds)	215°C	215°C	215°C

See AN-450 "Surface Mounting Methods and Their Effect on Product Reliability" for other methods of soldering surface mount devices.

	LM741A	LM741	LM741C
ESD Tolerance (Note 8)	400V	400V	400V

Electrical Characteristics (Note 5)

Parameter	Conditions	LM741A			LM741			LM741C			Units
		Min	Typ	Max	Min	Typ	Max	Min	Typ	Max	
Input Offset Voltage	$T_A = 25°C$										
	$R_S \leq 10\ k\Omega$					1.0	5.0		2.0	6.0	mV
	$R_S \leq 50\Omega$		0.8	3.0							mV
	$T_{AMIN} \leq T_A \leq T_{AMAX}$										
	$R_S \leq 50\Omega$			4.0							mV
	$R_S \leq 10\ k\Omega$						6.0			7.5	mV
Average Input Offset Voltage Drift				15							μV/°C
Input Offset Voltage Adjustment Range	$T_A = 25°C$, $V_S = \pm 20V$	±10				±15			±15		mV
Input Offset Current	$T_A = 25°C$		3.0	30		20	200		20	200	nA
	$T_{AMIN} \leq T_A \leq T_{AMAX}$			70		85	500			300	nA
Average Input Offset Current Drift				0.5							nA/°C
Input Bias Current	$T_A = 25°C$		30	80		80	500		80	500	nA
	$T_{AMIN} \leq T_A \leq T_{AMAX}$			0.210			1.5			0.8	μA
Input Resistance	$T_A = 25°C$, $V_S = \pm 20V$	1.0	6.0		0.3	2.0		0.3	2.0		MΩ
	$T_{AMIN} \leq T_A \leq T_{AMAX}$, $V_S = \pm 20V$	0.5									MΩ
Input Voltage Range	$T_A = 25°C$							±12	±13		V
	$T_{AMIN} \leq T_A \leq T_{AMAX}$				±12	±13					V

Electrical Characteristics (Note 5) (Continued)

Parameter	Conditions	LM741A			LM741			LM741C			Units
		Min	Typ	Max	Min	Typ	Max	Min	Typ	Max	
Large Signal Voltage Gain	T_A = 25°C, $R_L \geq 2$ kΩ										
	V_S = ±20V, V_O = ±15V	50									V/mV
	V_S = ±15V, V_O = ±10V				50	200		20	200		V/mV
	$T_{AMIN} \leq T_A \leq T_{AMAX}$,										
	$R_L \geq 2$ kΩ,										
	V_S = ±20V, V_O = ±15V	32									V/mV
	V_S = ±15V, V_O = ±10V				25			15			V/mV
	V_S = ±5V, V_O = ±2V	10									V/mV
Output Voltage Swing	V_S = ±20V										
	$R_L \geq 10$ kΩ	±16									V
	$R_L \geq 2$ kΩ	±15									V
	V_S = ±15V										
	$R_L \geq 10$ kΩ				±12	±14		±12	±14		V
	$R_L \geq 2$ kΩ				±10	±13		±10	±13		V
Output Short Circuit	T_A = 25°C	10	25	35		25			25		mA
Current	$T_{AMIN} \leq T_A \leq T_{AMAX}$	10		40							mA
Common-Mode	$T_{AMIN} \leq T_A \leq T_{AMAX}$										
Rejection Ratio	$R_S \leq 10$ kΩ, V_{CM} = ±12V				70	90		70	90		dB
	$R_S \leq 50\Omega$, V_{CM} = ±12V	80	95								dB
Supply Voltage Rejection	$T_{AMIN} \leq T_A \leq T_{AMAX}$,										
Ratio	V_S = ±20V to V_S = ±5V										
	$R_S \leq 50\Omega$	86	96								dB
	$R_S \leq 10$ kΩ				77	96		77	96		dB
Transient Response	T_A = 25°C, Unity Gain										
Rise Time			0.25	0.8		0.3			0.3		μs
Overshoot			6.0	20		5			5		%
Bandwidth (Note 6)	T_A = 25°C	0.437	1.5								MHz
Slew Rate	T_A = 25°C, Unity Gain	0.3	0.7			0.5			0.5		V/μs
Supply Current	T_A = 25°C					1.7	2.8		1.7	2.8	mA
Power Consumption	T_A = 25°C										
	V_S = ±20V		80	150							mW
	V_S = ±15V					50	85		50	85	mW
LM741A	V_S = ±20V										
	$T_A = T_{AMIN}$			165							mW
	$T_A = T_{AMAX}$			135							mW
LM741	V_S = ±15V										
	$T_A = T_{AMIN}$					60	100				mW
	$T_A = T_{AMAX}$					45	75				mW

Note 2: "Absolute Maximum Ratings" indicate limits beyond which damage to the device may occur. Operating Ratings indicate conditions for which the device is functional, but do not guarantee specific performance limits.

Electrical Characteristics (Note 5) (Continued)

Note 3: For operation at elevated temperatures, these devices must be derated based on thermal resistance, and T_j max. (listed under "Absolute Maximum Ratings"). $T_j = T_A + (\theta_{jA} P_D)$.

Thermal Resistance	Cerdip (J)	DIP (N)	HO8 (H)	SO-8 (M)
θ_{jA} (Junction to Ambient)	100°C/W	100°C/W	170°C/W	195°C/W
θ_{jC} (Junction to Case)	N/A	N/A	25°C/W	N/A

Note 4: For supply voltages less than ±15V, the absolute maximum input voltage is equal to the supply voltage.

Note 5: Unless otherwise specified, these specifications apply for V_S = ±15V, −55°C ≤ T_A ≤ +125°C (LM741/LM741A). For the LM741C/LM741E, these specifications are limited to 0°C ≤ T_A ≤ +70°C.

Note 6: Calculated value from: BW (MHz) = 0.35/Rise Time(μs).

Note 7: For military specifications see RETS741X for LM741 and RETS741AX for LM741A.

Note 8: Human body model, 1.5 kΩ in series with 100 pF.

Schematic Diagram

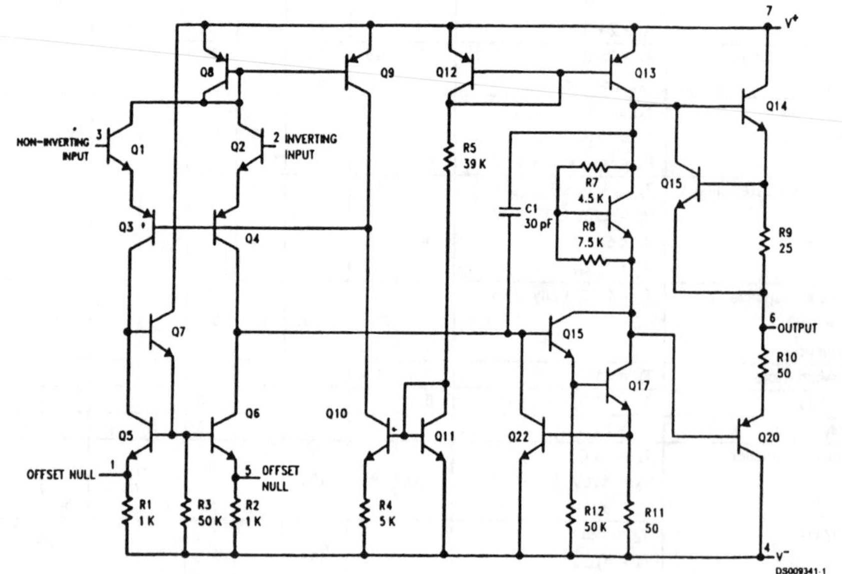

Appendix C
Answers to Selected Problems

In this appendix, we present answers to selected end-of-chapter problems. The more complex the problem, the less likely you will find the answer here. For example, the design problems in the later text chapters are intended to be *projects* involving many trade-off decisions. In most cases, there is more than one correct answer. To give one solution, and imply that you have achieved success if your answer agrees with ours, would be counterproductive.

The solutions to problems have been calculated out to three significant digits. As such, rounding has occurred during complex mathematical operations.

2.1 $v_o = v_1/2 + v_2$ **2.4** $v_o = -v_1/5 + v_2$ **2.7** $v_o = 22/7\ v_1 + 11/7\ v_2$ **2.10** $v_o = -v_1 + v_2$ **2.13** Using Example 2.4 – $R_F = 600$ kΩ, $R_1 = 600$ kΩ, $R_2 = 60$ kΩ, $R_a = 30$ kΩ, $R_b = 12$ kΩ, $R_x = 10$ kΩ; Using Example 2.5 – $R_F = 710$ kΩ, $R_1 = 710$ kΩ, $R_2 = 71$ kΩ, $R_a = 35.5$ kΩ, R_b =14.2 kΩ, $R_x = 11.8$ kΩ **2.16** Using Example 2.4 – $R_F = 60$ kΩ, $R_1 = 20$ kΩ, $R_2 = 60$ kΩ, $R_3 = 10$ kΩ, $R_a = 15$ kΩ, $R_b = 12$ kΩ Using Example 2.5 – $R_F = 100$ kΩ, $R_1 = 33.3$ kΩ, $R_2 = 100$ kΩ, $R_3 = 16.7$ kΩ, $R_a = 25$ kΩ, $R_b = 20$ kΩ **2.19** $R_F = 90$ kΩ, $R_1 = 22.5$ kΩ, $R_2 = 10$ kΩ, $R_3 = 18$ kΩ, $R_4 = 15$ kΩ, $R_5 = 18$ kΩ **2.22** $v_2 = 207$ mV, v_L = .125 mA **2.25** $v_o = 2v_1 - 10v_2 + 5v_3 + 4v_4$ **2.28** $R = 100$ kΩ **2.31** $i_o = .63$ sin1000t mA **2.35** $v_o/v_i = 0$ **2.37** $v_o/v_{in} = -(j\omega C_1R_1)/[(\omega^2C_1C_2R_1R_2 + R_2/R_3) - j\omega C_1R_1]$ **2.40** (a) $v_o = -v_i$ (b) $v_o = .952\ v_i$ **2.43** $v_o = 20/21\ v_i$ **2.46** $v_o/v_i = 1/[(R_1R_2C_1C_2)s^2 + (R_1 + R_2)C_2s + 1]$

3.3 $V_{on} = +0.56$ (V) **3.6** Full-wave Rectification with positive peaks up to 22.7 (V) **3.9** Half-wave rectification with positive peaks up to 5.6 (V) **3.12** D_1 shorted, D_2 and D_3 open circuited **3.15** (a) $I_3 = 47.1$ mA (b) $I_3 = 35.7$ mA **3.18** $C = 33.4$ μF **3.27** (a) $I = 5$ mA (b) $V_{olow} = 9.112$ (V), $V_{ohigh} = 10.2$ (V) **3.30** (a) $R_i = 9.87$ Ω (b) $P_Z = 10.1$ W (c) $V_{Llow} = 9.112$ (V), $V_{Lhigh} = 10.12$ (V) **3.33** (a) $I_{ZMax} = 125$ mA (b) $R_i = 93.6$ Ω (c) C = 142 μF (d) % Reg = 2.81% **3.36** $R_i = 29.3$ Ω, C =1230 μF **3.39** (a) Positive peak goes to 13.3 (V) while negative peak goes to -20 (V) (b) Positive 10 (V) except where peaks exceed 10 (V) and then they go to 19.7 instead of 20 (V) **3.42** (a) Negative peak only and goes to -4 (V) and then peak is flattened to -7.33 (V) instead of going on to -9 (V) – no wave form above zero (b) Positive peak goes to 5 (V) and then is flattened to peak of 7 (V) instead of the 9 (V). Same thing for negative peak except it goes to -6 (V) and then flattened to -8 (V) rather than going to -9 (V) **3.45** C = .125 μF for five time constants **3.48** (a) Acts like standard clamper (b) Capacitor discharges too fast so result is negative half-wave rectifier **3.51** Square wave with top at +1 (V) and bottom at -5.5 (V) **3.55** $R_C = 630\ \Omega$.

4.1 (a) 14.9 mA Saturation (b) 2.81 mA Saturation (c) $I_C = 0$ cutoff **4.4** $I_C = -4.65$ mA, $V_{CE} = -6.05$ (V), $V_C = -5.35$ (V) **4.7** (a) $I_C = 2.77$ mA, $V_{CE} = 4.18$ (V) (b) $I_C = 4.76$ mA, $V_{CE} = 10$ (V) (c) $R_1 = 9.25$ kΩ **4.10** (a) $R_1 = 2.34$ kΩ, $R_2 = 13.8$ kΩ (b) $V_o = 6$ (V) P-P (c) $V_{CE} = 15$ (V), $V_{CC}' = 18$ (V), $I_{CMax} = 60$ mA **4.13** From 0 to 2.42 mA with $I_C = 1.21$ mA **4.16** (a) $R_1 = 4.75$ kΩ, $R_2 = 34.5$ kΩ (b) $V_{CE} = 12$ (V), $V_{CC}' = 18$ (V), $I_{CMax} = 18$ mA (c) $V_o = 12$ (V) P-P **4.19** (a) $I_C = 4.17$ mA, $V_{CE} = 15.8$ (V) (b) $V_o = 5.56$ (V) P-P **4.22** (a) $P_{VCC} = 19.9$ mW (b) $P_{R1} = .212$ mW, $P_{RE} = .657$ mW, $P_{RC} = 11.0$ mW (c) $P_{Trans} = 6.13$ mW **4.25**(a) $R_1 = 2.17$ kΩ, $R_2 = 25.3$ kΩ (b) $V_o = 8$ (V) (c) $V_{CE} = 11.2$ (V), $V_{CC}' = 15.2$ (V), $I_{CMax} = 15.2$ mA **4.28** $R_1 = 6.70$ kΩ, $R_2 = 57.7$ kΩ, $V_o = 12.5$ (V) P-P **4.31** (a) $R_1 = 14.2$ kΩ, $R_2 = 77.8$ kΩ (b) $V_o = 6.96$ (V) P-P (c) $P_o = 1.51$ mW, $P_{Trans} = 6.96$ mW **4.34** $R_B = 34$ kΩ **4.37** (a) $I_C = -4.04$ mA, $V_{CE} = -3.10$ (V) (b) $R_1 = 4.57$ kΩ, $R_2 = 32.2$ kΩ (c) $V_o = 5.39$ (V) P-P (d) $P_{Trans} = 12.5$ mW (e) $P_o = 3.62$ mW **4.40** $R_1 = 38.1$ kΩ, $R_2 = 27.6$ kΩ, $P_L = 9.76$ mW, $P_{Trans} = 39.1$ mW **4.43** $R_B = 9.47$ kΩ, $I_C = -2.43$ mA, $V_{CE} = -4.71$ (V) **4.46** $R_E = 787\ \Omega$ **4.49** (a) $\beta_{sat} = 55.5$ (b) $\beta_{sat} = 5.55$

5.1 $A_v = -400$ **5.4** (a) $A_v = -4.81$, $A_i = -4.73$, $R_{in} = 4.85$ kΩ, (b) $A_v = -9.26$, $A_i = -8.98$, $R_{in} = 4.85$ kΩ (c) $A_v = -35.7$, $A_i = -3.19$, $R_{in} = 4.47$ kΩ (d) $A_v = -125$, $A_i = -88.2$, $R_{in} = 3.53$ kΩ **5.10** $R_E = 140\ \Omega$, $R_1 = 3.67$ kΩ, $R_2 = 36.6$ kΩ, $V_o = 6.75$ (V) P-P, $R_{in} = 3$ kΩ **5.13** $R_E = 425\ \Omega$, $R_1 = 10.9$ kΩ, $R_2 = 126$ kΩ, $V_o = 8.42$ (V) P-P, $R_{in} = 9.0$ kΩ **5.17** $R_E = 117\ \Omega$, $R_1 = 5.02$ kΩ, $R_2 = 76.2$ kΩ, $V_o = 8.75$ (V) P-P, $A_i = -15$ **5.20** $R_E = 160\ \Omega$, $R_1 = 6.13$ kΩ, $R_2 = 83.1$ kΩ, $I_{CQ} = .656$ mA **5.23** $R_1 = 1.45$ kΩ, $V_o = 4.29$ (V) P-P **5.26** (a) $R_{in} = 2$ kΩ, $I_C = 80$ mA, $V_o = 14.4$ (V) P-P (b) $R_{in} = 2$ kΩ, $I_C = 32$ mA, $V_o = 19.4$ (V) P-P (c) $R_{in} = 2$ kΩ, $I_{CQ} = 20.6$ mA, $V_o = 6.19$ (V) P-P **5.29** (a) $I_{CQ} = 465$ mA, $R_{in} = 667\ \Omega$ (b) $A_i = 66.7$ (c) $V_{CE} = 15.4$ (V), $V_{CC}' = 17.7$ (V), $V_o = 2.9$ (V) P-P **5.32** $I_{CQ} = 1.6$ A, $R_1 = 410\ \Omega$, $R_2 = 152\ \Omega$, $A_i = 10$, $V_o = 14.4$ (V) P-P **5.35** $I_{CQ} = 2.57$ mA, $R_1 = 22.0$ kΩ, $R_2 = 138$ kΩ, $V_o = 9.25$ (V) P-P, $A_v = 198$ **5.38** $I_{CQ} = .938$ mA, $R_1 = 23.4$ kΩ, $R_2 = 216$ kΩ, $A_v = 30$, $V_o = 6.75$ (V) P-P **5.41** $I_{CQ} = 1.33$ mA, $R_1 = 116$ kΩ, $R_2 = 124$ kΩ, $V_o = 3.59$ (V) P-P **5.44** (a) 1st Amp $I_{CQ} = 1.45$ mA, $R_L \approx 400$ kΩ; 2nd Amp $V_{CQ} = 7.75$ (V), $V_{CEQ} = 7.86$ (V) (b) $V_o = 13.3$ (V) P-P (d) $v_o/v_{in} = -136$ **5.47** $v_{in} = 0.70$ (V) P-P **5.50** $A_i = 1070$, $R_{in} = 102\ \Omega$, $A_v = 20{,}980$ **5.53** $I_{CQ} = 1.56$ mA, $R_E = 83\ \Omega$, $R_1 = 4.96$ kΩ, $R_2 = 64.9$ kΩ, $V_o = 7.02$ (V) P-P, $A_i = -20$ **5.56** Q_2 shutoff, $I_{CQ1} = 2.15$ mA, $I_{CQ2} = 0$, $V_{C1} = -0.7$ (V), $V_{C2} = -5$ (V) **5.59** $R_{ref} = 19.3$ kΩ, $R_2 = 599\ \Omega$ **5.62** From Spec Sheet – $r_o = 233$ kΩ, $R_{Th} = 11.6$ MΩ **5.65** $R_1 = 9.65\Omega$, $R_3 = 5.99$ kΩ, $R_3 = 205\Omega$, $R_4 = 31.2$kΩ

6.1 (a) $V_{GS} = -.84$ (V) (b) $V_D = 10$ (V) (c) $V_{DS} = 7.5$ (V) (d) $R_1 = 109$ kΩ, $R_2 = 1.2$ MΩ **6.4** (a) $I_{DQ} = 4$ mA (b) $V_{GG} = .535$ (V) (c) $V_{GSQ} = -1.47$ (V) (d) $A_v = -1.34$ (e) $A_i = -6.73$ **6.7** $I_{DQ} = 4$ mA, $V_{GSQ} = -1.46$ (V), $A_v = .693$, $A_i = 23.1$ **6.10** $R_S(dc) = 500\Omega$, $R_D = 9.5$ kΩ, $R_S(ac) = 338\ \Omega$, $A_i = -21.1$ **6.13** $V_P = -3.01$, $I_{DSS} = 9.6$ mA **6.16** $R_S(dc) = 420$, $R_D = 2.91$ kΩ, $R_S(ac) = 70\ \Omega$, $A_i = -37.5$ **6.19** (a) $I_{DQ} = 4.18$ mA, $V_{GSQ} = -.836$ (V) (b) $g_m = 3.85$ mΩ^{-1} (c) $v_o/v_{in} = -4.63$ (d) $A_i = -232$ **6.22** $R_D = 2.64$ kΩ, $R_S = 27\ \Omega$ **6.25** R_{S1}

$= 2.5\ k\Omega$, $R_{S2} = 1.5\ k\Omega$, $R_G = 20.2\ k\Omega$, $A_i = -31$, $A_v = -1.24$ **6.28** $V_{GS} = -.94$ (V), $I_{DQ} = 4.7$ mA, $A_v = -3.67$, $A_i = -612$ **6.31** $V_{GSQ} = -.729$ (V), $I_{DQ} = 7.29$ mA, $g_m = 3.42\ m\Omega^{-1}$, $A_v = -3.82$, $A_i = -636$, $R_{in} = 1\ M\Omega$ **6.34** $R_D = 4.81\ k\Omega$, $R_S = 187\ \Omega$, $R_1 = 10.2\ k\Omega$, $R_2 = 36.5\ k\Omega$ **6.37** $R_D = 2.5\ k\Omega$, $R_S(dc) = 500\ \Omega$, $R_S(ac) = 167\ \Omega$, $A_i = -80$ **6.40** $R_S = 10.5\ k\Omega$, $R_1 = 37.8\ k\Omega$, $R_2 = 42.4\ k\Omega$ **6.43** $V_{GS} = -1.76$ (V), $g_m = 4.71 m\Omega^{-1}$, $R_S(dc) = 600\ \Omega$, $R_S(ac) = 113\ \Omega$, $A_v = .2$ **6.47** (a) $R_S(dc) = 2.34\ k\Omega$, $R_S(ac) = 701\ \Omega$ (b) $R_1 = 668\ k\Omega$, $R_2 = 997\ k\Omega$ (c) $A_v = 0.45$ **6.50** $R_S(dc) = 400\ \Omega$, $R_1 = 556\ k\Omega$, $R_2 = 5\ M\Omega$, $R_S(ac) = 182\ \Omega$ **6.53** $R_{S1} = 131\ \Omega$, $R_{S2} = 852\ \Omega$, $A_v = 623$, $A_i = 623$.

7.2 $I_{CQ} = 6.15$ mA, $R_B = 217\ k\Omega$ **7.5** (a) $R_E = 465\ \Omega$, $R_F = 460\ k\Omega$ (b) $V_o = 6.75$ (V) P-P (c) $V_o = 2.54$ (V) P-P **7.8** $\Delta I_C = 20.8$ mA, $V_o = 0$ (V) P-P at 85° C **7.11** $\Delta I_C = 206$ mA, $V_o = 11.1$ (V) P-P **7.14** $R_E = 318\ \Omega$ **7.17** Worst Case High Side $\Delta I_C = 2.64$ mA, $V_o = 8.66$ (V) P-P **7.20** $T_j = 167$°C, Yes.

8.1 $R_1 = 713\ \Omega$, $R_2 = 3.79\ k\Omega$, $P_{VCC} = 163$ mW, $V_o = 19.6$ (V) P-P **8.4** (a) $R_1 = 3.64\ k\Omega$, $R_2 = 38.4\ k\Omega$, (b) $V_o = 32.7$ (V) P-P (c) $A_i = -30$, $P_o = 66.9$ mW (d) $V_{CEQ} = 19.1$ (V), $I_{CQ} = 9.09$ mA **8.7** $R_1 = 18.1\ k\Omega$, $R_2 = 40.5\ k\Omega$, $P_{Trans} = 144$ mW, $P_L = 58.3$ mW **8.10** (a) $R_1 = 43.6\ k\Omega$, $R_2 = 231\ k\Omega$ (b) $V_o = 2.71$ (V) P-P (c) $P_{VCC} = .305$ W (d) $P_o = .115$ W **8.13** (a) $I_{CQ} = 10.5$ mA, $V_{CEQ} = 33.9$ (V) (b) $A_i = 26.4$ (c) $R_{in} = 3.71\ k\Omega$ (d) $V_o(Trans) = 2.87$ (V) P-P, **8.16** (a) $A_i = 40$ (b) $V_o = 21.4$ (V) P-P (c) $P_{VCC} = 10.6$ W (d) $P_{Trans} = 1.82$ W, $P_o = 7.18$ W **8.19** (a) $I_{CM} = 1.12$ A (b) $P_{VCC} = 10.2$ W (c) $R_2 = 167\ \Omega$, $A_i = 9.26$, $R_{in} = 76\ \Omega$ **8.22** (a) $R_2 = 168\ \Omega$, $R_{in} = 99.8\ \Omega$ (b) $A_i = 39.8$ (c) $P_{Trans} = 13$ W (d) $P_{VCC} = 82.0$ W **8.25** (a) $R_2 = 283\ \Omega$, $R_{in} = 125\ \Omega$ (b) $P_{Trans} = 45.6$ W (c) $A_i = 15.0$ **8.28** $R_2 = 1860\ \Omega$, $R_{in} = 861\ \Omega$, $A_i = 8.5$, $P_o = 12.5$ W **8.31** $I_{C2} = .101$ A, $R_{in} = 86.2\ k\Omega$, $A_i = 862$, $V_o = 6.42$ (V) P-P **8.34** $R_E = 40\ \Omega$, $R_{in} = 53.5\ k\Omega$, $A_v = -75$, $V_{in} = 93.6$ (V) P-P **8.37** (a) $R_E = 23.6\ \Omega$, $R_1 = 8.76\ k\Omega$, $R_2 = 96.4\ k\Omega$, $R_{in} = 8.0\ k\Omega$ (b) $P_o = 1.96$ mW (c) $V_o = 8.87$ (V) P-P (d) $P_{VCC} = 31.7$ mW **8.40** (a) $C_1 = 1720\ \mu F$, $R_i = 1.3\ k\Omega$ (b) $P_Z = 86.6$ mW (c) $V_{Variation} = 7.8$ mV **8.43** I_{ZMax} from Spec Sheet = 85 mA, $R_i = 106\ \Omega$, $V_{SMin} = 7.74$ V, $C = 1280\ \mu F$ **8.46** $a = 3.8{:}1$, $C = 1320\ \mu F$ **8.49** If $R_A = 5\ k\Omega$, then $R_F = 15\ k\Omega$

9.1 $I_{EE} = 1.43$ mA, $A_d = \pm 275$, $A_c = -.5$ **9.4** $V_{o1} = -200.2$ mV, $V_{o2} = 199.8$ mW **9.7** $V_{o3} = -1990\ V_1 + 2010\ V_2$ **9.10** $A_c = -.05$, $A_d = 116$, CMRR = 67.3 dB **9.14** $I_{EE} = 2.33$ mA, $A_c = 35.2$, $A_d = 6278$, $V_{do} = 3.14$ (V), $V_{cM} = .018$ (V) **9.17** CMRR = 63.7 dB, $R_1 = 4\ k\Omega$ **9.20** From 80.5 dB to 59.7 dB, $R_{Ref} = 4\ k\Omega$ **9.23** $R_C = 10.6\ k\Omega$, $R_1 = 7.15\ k\Omega$ (b) $A_C = .0525$, $A_d = 101$, CMRR = 65.7 dB (c) $v_o = 6.75$ (V) P-P (d) $v_{in} = .46$ mV (e) $v_o(CM) = 15.1$ mV **9.26** $R_1 = 143\ \Omega$, $R_2 = 51\ \Omega$, CMRR = 79.4 dB **9.29** $R_{Ref} = 3.7\ k\Omega$, CMRR = 90 dB **9.32** $V_o = 3.9$ (V) **9.35** $R_E = 2.38\ k\Omega$, $R_{E1} = 2.73\ k\Omega$, $R_3 = 130\ k\Omega$, $R_4 = 94\ k\Omega$ **9.38** (a) $I_C = .633$ mA, $I_{C1} = .94$ mA (b) $A_d = 24.6$, $A_c = .0214$, CMRR = 61.2 dB (c) $V_o = 4.19$ (V) P-P (d) $V_{in} = .591$ mV P-P (e) $R_{in}(Diff) = 3.28\ M\Omega$ **9.41** (a) $v_o = 2.75$ mV (b) $v_o = -0.6$ mV (c) $v_o = 2.15$ mV **9.44** $R_F = 160\ k\Omega$, V_1 and V_2 to positive terminal with $R_1 = 16\ k\Omega$ and $R_2 = 26.7\ k\Omega$, V_3 and V_4 to negative terminal and R_y from negative terminal to ground with $R_3 = 53.3$ kΩ, $R_4 = 40$ kΩ, and $R_y = 20$ kΩ, $R_{in}(V_1) = R_{in}(V_2) = 42.7$ kΩ, $R_{in}(V_3) = 53.3$ kΩ, $R_{in}(V_4) = 40$ kΩ, $R_{out} = .012$ Ω **9.47** $R_F = 240$ kΩ, V_1 and V_4 to positive terminal with $R_1 = 30$ kΩ and $R_4 = 60$ kΩ, V_2 and V_3 to negative terminal with $R_2 = 34.3$ kΩ and $R_3 = 60$ kΩ, $R_{in}(V_1) = R_{in}(V_4) = 90$ kΩ, $R_{in}(V_2) = 34.3$ kΩ, $R_{in}(V_3) = 60$ kΩ, $R_{Out} = .009$ Ω **9.50** $R_F = 120$ kΩ, V_1 and V_2 into positive terminal with $R_1 = 40$ kΩ, $R_2 = 24$ kΩ and R_x to ground = 17.1 kΩ, V_3 and V_4 into negative terminal with $R_3 = 15$ kΩ and $R_4 = 20$ kΩ, $R_{in}(V_1) = 50$ kΩ, $R_{in}(V_2) = 36$ kΩ, $R_{in}(V_3) = 15$ kΩ, $R_{in}(V_4) = 20$ kΩ, $R_{Out} = .0113$ Ω **9.55** $V_{in}(low) = .075$ (V), $V_{in}(high) = .125$ (V), V_1 into negative terminal of op-amp with $R_F = 10$ kΩ and $R_A = 10$ kΩ; That output into negative side of the 2nd op-amp using a 10 kΩ resistor; A second input into that negative terminal through a 10 kΩ resistor provides the negative output with the $R_F = 100$ kΩ, $V_{CC} = 15.6$ (V) Min.

10.3 $C_1 = 3.98$ μF, $C_2 = 19$ μF **10.6** (a) $R_E = 237$ Ω, $R_1 = 4.71$ kΩ, $R_2 = 57.0$ **kΩ** (b) $C_1 = 3.98$ μF, $C_2 = .796$ μF (c) $C_1 = .617$ μF, $C_2 = 1.23$ μF (d) $C = 0.89$ μF **10.9** $f_1 = 66.3$ Hz, $f_2 = 133$ Hz, $f_{Low} = 149$ Hz **10.12** (a) $R_1 = 57.2$ kΩ, $R_2 = 398$ kΩ (b) $C_1 = .25$ μF, C_2 not required, $C_3 = 1.59$ μF **10.16** $f_{Low} = 1040$ Hz **10.19** BW = 20.9 to 2 MHz **10.22** BW = 152 to 886 kHz **10.25** $f_{High} = 2.17$ MHz **10.28** $C_1 = .137$ μF, $C_2 = .249$ μF, $f_{High} = 110$ kHz **10.31** $C_{gd} = .28$ μF, $r_{ds} = 2$ kΩ, $C_{gs} = 6.72$ pF, $g_m = 5$ mΩ^{-1} **10.34** 39.5 Hz to 492 kHz Frequency Response **10.37** 110 Hz to 598 kHz Frequency Response **10.40** 83.3 Hz to 93.6 kHz Frequency Response **10.43** $f_{High} = 337$ MHz **10.47** 87.8 Hz to 644 kHz Frequency Response **10.50** 0 to 727 kHz Frequency Response **10.53** 2 op-amps in series with 1st one into negative terminals of 2nd; 1st op-amp - Input into + terminal $R_1 = 9.7$ kΩ, $R_A = 10$ kΩ, $R_F = 340$ kΩ; 2nd op-amp – $R_A = 10$ kΩ, $R_F = 200$ kΩ, $R_X = 9.5$ kΩ **10.56** 2 op-amp – V_1 input into positive terminal of output op-amp through a 10 kΩ resistor and 2nd op-amp (unity gain buffer) into negative terminal of output op-amp through a resistor of 100 kΩ with an $R_F = 100$ kΩ and an R_y of 12.5 kΩ. **10.59** 3 0p-amps – V_1 through a unity gain buffer through a 220 kΩ resistor into – terminal of output op-amp; V_2 into + terminal of the 3rd op-amp which has an $R_1 = 9.7$ kΩ, $R_A = 10$ kΩ and $R_F = 340$ kΩ, it is then also connected to - terminal of output op-amp through a 11 kΩ resistor which has an $R_F = 220$ kΩ **10.63** 3 op-amps - 2 op-amps feeding into the - terminal of output op-amp; V_1 feeds directly into + terminal of output op-amp through 9 kΩ resistor; V_2 feeds into + terminal of 2nd op-amp with $R_1 = 9$ kΩ, $R_A = 10$ kΩ and $R_F = 90$ kΩ and this op-amp feeds into - terminal of the output op-amp through a 21 kΩ resistor; V_3 feeds into + terminal of third op-amp through a 9.5 kΩ resistor and the op-amp has an $R_F = 190$ kΩ and an $R_A = 10$ kΩ; This op-amp feeds into the output op-amp through a 20 kΩ resistor and the $R_F = 400$ kΩ **10.67** 2 0p-amps with V_1 feeding into the positive terminal of the output op-amp through a 10 kΩ resistor; V_2 feeding the + terminal of the 2nd op-amp through a 9.4 kΩ resistor which has an $R_F = 157$ kΩ and $R_A = 10$ kΩ and it feeds into the - terminal of the output op-amp through a 10.4 kΩ; output op-amp has $R_F = 250$ kΩ **10.70** Need 4 op-amps; 2 op-amps for V_1 feeding into + terminal of third op-amp(output); Op-amps have gains of 2.5 and 20 respectively while the gain of the output op-amp for + terminal is 20; V_2 feeds into the other op-amp which has a gain of 15.8 which goes into negative terminal of the output op-amp which has gain of 19. **10.76** Need four op-amps with gains of 15, 6, 10, 10 respectively; V_{in} goes into + terminal and each op-amp feeds into + terminal of next one. **10.79** Need four op-amps; can be be broken down to gains of 25, 30, 40, & 20. V_{in} goes into + terminal of 1st op-amp and each succeeding op-amp. **10.82** Use 3 pF since gain needed is greater than 10; R_1 = 24.5 kΩ, R_2 = 16.3 kΩ, $R_A = R_y$ = 10 kΩ, R_{out} = .05 Ω, $R_{in}(V_1)$ = $R_{in}(V_2)$ = 40.8 kΩ, BW = 200 kHz.

11.1 A_v = -500, A_i = -9.26 **11.4** 0.3 **11.7** A_{vo} = -83.3, A_v = -8.93 **11.11** 0.04% **11.14** Amplitude starts at -40 dB/dec until 1 rad/sec then change to -20 dB/dec until 10 rad/sec then go back to -40 dB/dec; Phase starts at -180°, then rises at 45°/dec at .1 rad/sec until 1 rad/sec then flat until 10 rad/sec, then drops at 45°/dec until 100 rad/sec and then flat at -180°; Amplifier always stable as never passes 180° phase shift. **11.18** Amplitude starts at -20 dB/dec until 10 rad/sec, then drops at -40 dB/dec until 80 then drops further at -60 dB/dec; Phase Plot flat until 1 rad/sec then drops at -45°/dec until 8 rad/sec then drops at -90°/dec until 80 rad/sec then drops at -45°/dec until 800 rad/sec then becomes flat at -270°; Amplifier crosses 180° at 28.5 rad/sec and has 97.3 dB gain margin. **11.27** Open loop response: $GH(s)$ = s/62.8 × 1/(1 + s/62.8)^3 **11.39** Amplitude starts at -20 dB/dec until 8 rad/sec where it levels off until 10 rad/sec, then drops at -40 dB/dec; Phase starts at -90° until 0.8 rad/sec, then goes up at +45°/dec until 1 rad/sec, then drops at 45°/dec until 80 rad/sec, then drops at 90°/dec until 100 rad/sec, where it levels off at a phase of -180°; System is always stable since phase never crosses -180°. **11.42** $GH(s)$ = G_o/[(s/4 + 1)(s/40 + 10] **11.44** C = 4500 pF **11.48** R_D = 12.5 kΩ **11.51** C = .203 μF.

12.1 If C = 1 μF, then R = 100 kΩ. **12.4** Using Table 12.1(e), if C = 1 μF then R_1 = 1 MΩ, R_A = 100 kΩ, R_2 = 111 kΩ, R_x = 92 kΩ. **12.7** Inverting op-amp. If C = 10 μF, then R_1 = 100 kΩ, R_2 = 10 kΩ, R_3 = 189 kΩ. **12.10** Use a standard integrator when in one position of switch. Select an amplifier with negative fixed voltage for other position of switch. Then let C = 1 μF and R_A = 1 MΩ. When not integrating, R_F = 1 MΩ and V = -10 (V). **12.13** Figure 12.11(c): select C = 1 μF, R_2 = 400 kΩ. Then R_1 = 400 Ω and $R_1 \| R_2$ = 400 Ω **12.17** Figure 12.15(a): let C = 0.01 μF, then R = 79.6 kΩ, R_A = 88.4 kΩ, R_F = 796 kΩ. **12.20** High-pass filter. If C = 1 μF, then R_1 = 75 kΩ and R_2 = 250 kΩ. Low-pass filter. If C = 0.1 μF, then R_1 = 1 MΩ, R_2 = 750 kΩ, R_x = 429 kΩ. Combine in summing amplifier with all resistors = 20 kΩ. **12.23** Figure 12.11(a): If C = 0.01 μF, then R_1 = 15.9 kΩ, R_A = 16.8 kΩ, R_F = 320 kΩ. **12.26** Figure 12.18: if C = 0.01 μF, then R_1 = 79.6 kΩ, R_2 = 159 kΩ, $R_3 = R_4$ = 26.5 kΩ. **12.29** Figure 12.18: if C = 0.01 μF, then R_2 = 159 kΩ, R_1 = 159 kΩ, R_3 = 20 kΩ, R_4 = 40 kΩ, R_F = 386 kΩ. **12.32** Circuit shown in Figure P2.35. If C_1 = 0.1 μF and C_2 = 0.1 μF then R_2 = 800 kΩ and R_1 = 50 kΩ. **12.38** Figure 12.29: with ratio of 3.33 and -45 dB, n = 4. If C = 0.01 μF, then R_1 = 7.17 kΩ, R_2 = 12.4 kΩ, R_3 = 2.97 kΩ, R_4 = 76.4 kΩ. **12.41** n_B = 4.98 so use 5. If R = 10 kΩ, scale factor is 3.98 x 10^{-9}, C_1 = 0.007 μF, C_2 = 0.0054 μF, C_3 = 0.0017 μF, C_4 = 0.013 μF, C_5 = 0.0012 μF. High pass filter. Order 5. If C = 0.05 μF, then scale factor is 5305 and R_1 = 3.03 kΩ, R_2 = 3.92 kΩ, R_3 = 12.6

kΩ, R_4 = 1.64 kΩ, and R_5 = 17.2 kΩ. **12.44** If R = 10 kΩ, capacitor scale factor is 3.183 x 10^{-9}. If C = 0.005 μF, resistor scale factor is 10.61k. Low pass filter: C_1 = 0.0156 μF, C_2 = .00635 μF, C_3 = 0.0377 μF, C_4 = 745 μF. High pass filter: R_1 = 3.40 kΩ, R_2 = 8.36 kΩ, R_3 = 1.41 kΩ, R_4 = 71.3 kΩ.

13.1 Half-wave rectifier with v_o/v_1 = -0.1 in right half plane **13.4** Full-wave rectifier only for negative v_o with v_o/v_i = +8 n left half plane and v_o/v_i = -2 in right half plane. **13.7** Use circuit of basic negative output inverting in Table 13.1 and inverter. R_F/R_A = 1, R_A = R_F = 10 kΩ. Axis shift at input needs resistor of 20 kΩ to reduce -10 (V) to -5 (V). **13.10** Need half-wave rectifier with axis shift, then amplifier with level shift and finally an inverter. **13.13** Need level and axis shifing on half-wave rectifier. **13.16** Need half-wave rectifier and then an invertor. **13.20** First amplifier rectifies signal, second amplifier combines rectified signal and input and third amplifer inverts and level shifts. **13.26** If R_A = 10 kΩ, then R_F = 15 kΩ, R_1 = 9.8 kΩ, R_2 = 4.85 kΩ. **13.29** If R_A = 100 kΩ, then R_F = 500 kΩ, R_1 = R_3 =2.14 kΩ, R_2 = R_4 = 860 Ω, and R_x = 83.3 kΩ **13.34** $V_o(high)$ = 3.76 (V), $V_o(low)$ = -4.27 (V), Left V_{in} = -2.13 (V), Right V_{in}= 1.88 (V). **13.40** Limiting comparator first op-amp. Second op-amp is an inverter and level shifter. R_1 = R_3 = 3.18 kΩ, R_2 = R_4 = 388 Ω when R_A = 10 kΩ. **13.43** Schmitt trigger with limiter and axis shift with second op-amp as level shifter. If R_1 = 20 kΩ, then R_2 = 40 kΩ. If R_3 = 2 kΩ, then R_4 = 804 Ω. Need voltage dividers for both axis shift and level shift to provide proper voltages.

14.1 V_1 = 4.15 (V), V_2 = 0.85 (V). **14.6** V_1 = 0.459 (V). V_2 = 0 (V), V_3 = -4.51 (V), V_4 = -0.0855 (V). **14.9** V_1 = 0.0989 (V), V_2 = 0.0788 (V), V_3 = -8.221 (V), V_4 = -8.019 (V). **14.10** R_1 = 1 kΩ, R_2 = 6.7 kΩ, and the capacitor between pin 2 and ground is switchable among 0.001 μF, 0.01 μF, and 0.1 μF. **14.18** Result is a pulse train with the widths of the pulses increasing with time. The highest frequency is 102 Hz. **14.26** A 555 astable is set to operate at 1 kHz so the output at pin 3 is suitable to trigger the 555 monostable. It is good design practice to use a fixed resistor for R_1 and a 10-kΩ ten turn potentiometer for R_2 so that the frequency can be adjusted to 1 kHz. The variable duty cycle is achieved with a 555 monostable.

15.2

A	$\overline{A}$	B	C	$\overline{C}$	$\overline{A}\cdot B\cdot\overline{C}$	$A\cdot B\cdot\overline{C}$	Y
0	1	0	0	1	0	0	0
0	1	0	1	0	0	0	0
0	1	1	0	1	1	0	1
0	1	1	1	0	0	0	0
1	0	0	0	1	0	0	0
1	0	0	1	0	0	0	0
1	0	1	0	1	0	1	1
1	0	1	1	0	0	0	0

15.6

A	B	C	$A+B+C$	Y
0	0	0	0	1
0	0	1	1	0
0	1	0	1	0
0	1	1	1	0
1	0	0	1	0
1	0	1	1	0
1	1	0	1	0
1	1	1	1	0

15.9 $Y = A \cdot B + B \cdot A$

15.11

D	H	K	$ALARM$
0	0	0	0
0	0	1	0
0	1	0	0
0	1	1	0
1	0	0	0
1	0	1	1
1	1	0	1
1	1	1	1

15.19

A	B	I_{C1}	Q_2	Q_3	Q_4	Y
0	0	+	F	F	N	1
0	1	+	F	F	N	1
1	0	+	F	F	N	1
1	1	-	N	N	F	0

15.13 Alarm is armed with a key-operated switch located in the fender. Once the alarm is armed and the burglar opens the door, a trigger pulse activates the 555 monostable. This provides a 10-min pulse. The pulse enables the astable 555 for 10 min, with the output amplified by 2N2222 transistor driving the speaker located under the hood. Astable 555 frequency is 686 Hz.

15.22

A	B	1	2	3	4	5	6	7	8	Y
0	0	N	N	F	F	F	N	N	F	1
0	1	N	F	F	N	F	N	N	F	1
1	0	F	N	N	F	F	N	N	F	1
1	1	F	F	N	N	N	F	F	N	0

15.24 Use a 555 to a 7416 to a 4016. Use open collector to drive the 4016. If the C of the 555 is 1 μF, then $R_1 = 7.2\ \text{k}\Omega$ and $R_2 = 130\ \text{k}\Omega$.

16.2

	CMOS 74C150	TTL 74150
Supply V	3-15 (V)	7 (V)
Speed	120-250 ns	8-15 ns
Power dissipated	20 mW	200 mW

16.8 Output Q_1 is connected to the clock B input and the counter is reset when the count reaches 10. When the outputs are 1010, the output of the AND gate is high and the zero set inputs are high. This clears the counter. **16.9** For a base frequency f_o of 10 kHz, $C_{ext} = 0.05$ μF. Output frequency range is 5.7 to 11.3 kHz. **16.10** Use the 555 astable to develop a frequency that is twice the required frequency. This signal passes through a JK flip-flop that toggles on the rising edge of the pulse thus the JK divides the frequency by 2. **16.13** A 1-kHz 555 astable is used to clock a ÷N counter. The counter is enabled by pressing a button signifying a roll of the dice. The start signal is debounced before enabling the counter. A decoder circuit is designed using logic gates. The decoder outputs are fed into an LED display that resembles the face of the dice as shown in Fig P16.13. **16.14** The rpm meter accepts the TTL-compatible pulses and ANDs them with the window from a 555 astable. The output of the AND gate is the input to three decade counters(74160), three decoders(7447), and the three 7-segment displays. The clear signal is delayed with inverters so that the data is latched into the display before the counters are cleared. **16.20** A 555 astable IC is designed to output pulses at a frequency of 1 kHZ. These pulses are divided down until the output is one pulse per 5 sec. This output clocks a 7493 binary counter. The outputs of the counter are used as select lines to a 16-to-1 multiplexer. The output of a 74150 MUX is active low. If a lamp is good, the output of the MUX is low, and if a lamp is faulty, the MUX output is HIGH. The MUX output is ANDed with the 1-

kHz signal for the speaker. **16.23** We want to use a down-counter, since 9 represents full and 0 represents empty. Preset a 74193 Up/DOWN binary counter to 15 by connecting the transmitted pulse to the load of the counter. Also use the transmitted pulse to trigger a one-shot 555 IC to output a window pulse of 170 ms. This window pulse is ANDed with a 10-ms pulse train from a 555 astable IC. This gate, when enabled, begins the counter, which counts down from 15. After 6 counts the display will read 9, and after 16 counts will read 0. The received pulse latches the display and clears the counters, If the countdown does not reach 9 or goes past 0, the tank is either 90% full or under 10% empty, and the alarm sounds. **16.31** Use a 555 astable IC, designed to output one pulse per minute, as the circuit clock. Two cascaded 7490 decade counters are clocked by the 555 IC. To output the room number simultaneously, a 7493 binary counter is clocked and used to address a 16-to-1, 74150 multiplexer. After counting to 14, each counting system is cleared. Each room's TV set is monitored by the multiplexer for 1 minute every 14 minutes to determine whether it is on or off. The output of the multiplexer is connected through a resistor to an LED to display whether a TV is on or off. **16.42** The design requires an UP/DOWN counter to keep track of the number of cars in the garage. Initially (at the beginning of a workday), the counters must be cleared to zero. Every time a car enters, the counter counts up, and every time a car leaves the counter counts down. Since the pulse output from the entrance and exit gates is held high until a car passes through, the 74193 UP/DOWN BCD counters are ideally suited. Pins 4 and 5 of these counters are used to count down and up. The count can occur only if the pin not being clocked is held high, thus fitting the design specifications. The gate pulses need to be conditioned with an *RC* circuit to trigger the counters. Let the *RC* time constant equal 0.1 s. When the most significant counter reaches 3 (300 is the full count for the garage), display the word "FULL" in the four segment LED displays.

Index